Geologic Time Scale 2020

Volume 1

Geologic Time Scale 2020

Volume 1

Edited by

Felix M. Gradstein

James G. Ogg

Mark D. Schmitz

Gabi M. Ogg

ELSEVIER

Elsevier
Radarweg 29, PO Box 211, 1000 AE Amsterdam, Netherlands
The Boulevard, Langford Lane, Kidlington, Oxford OX5 1GB, United Kingdom
50 Hampshire Street, 5th Floor, Cambridge, MA 02139, United States

British Library Cataloguing-in-Publication Data
A catalogue record for this book is available from the British Library

Library of Congress Cataloging-in-Publication Data
A catalog record for this book is available from the Library of Congress

This Volume (1) ISBN: 978-0-12-824362-6
Volume 2 ISBN: 978-0-12-824363-3
Set ISBN: 978-0-12-824360-2

For Information on all Elsevier publications
visit our website at https://www.elsevier.com/books-and-journals

Front cover of Volume 1: Toarcian boundary stratotype section, Peniche, Portugal. Photograph by F.M. Gradstein.

Publisher: Candice Janco
Acquisitions Editor: Amy Shapiro
Editorial Project Manager: Susan Ikeda
Production Project Manager: Kiruthika Govindaraju
Cover Designer: Mark Rogers

Typeset by MPS Limited, Chennai, India
Printed in Great Britain
Last digit is the print number: 10 9 8 7 6 5 4

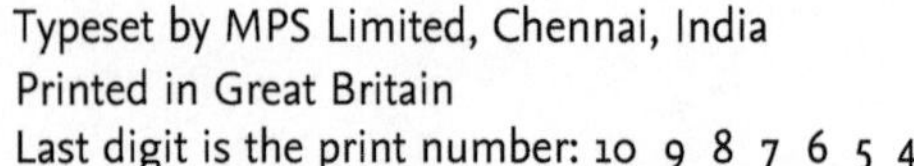

Quotes

To place all the scattered pages of Earth history in their proper chronological order is by no means an easy task.

Arthur Holmes

The fascination in creating a new geologic time scale is that it evokes images of creating a beautiful carpet by many skilled hands. All stitches must conform to a pre-determined pattern, in this case the pattern of physical, chemical and biological events on Earth aligned along the arrow of time.

This book—Foreword

Contents

Volume 2

Contributors

Senior authors

Felix M. Gradstein, Geological Museum, University of Oslo, P.O. Box 1172 Blindern, N-0318 Oslo, Norway, *felix.gradstein@gmail.com*

James G. Ogg, State Key Laboratory of Oil and Gas Reservoir Geology and Exploitation, Institute of Sedimentary Geology, Chengdu University of Technology, Chengdu, 610059, China, *jogg@purdue.edu*

Mark D. Schmitz, Department of Geosciences, Boise State University, 1910 University Drive, Boise, Idaho, 83725-1535, USA, *markschmitz@boisestate.edu*

Gabi M. Ogg, Geologic TimeScale Foundation, 1224 N. Salisbury St., West Lafayette, Indiana, 47906, USA, *gabiogg@hotmail.com*

Frits P. Agterberg, Geological Survey of Canada, 601 Booth Street, Ottawa, Ontario, K1A OE8, Canada, *Frits.Agterberg@NRCan-RNCan.gc.ca*

Markus Aretz, Laboratoire Géosciences Environnement, Université de Toulouse, CNRS, IRD, UPS, 31400 Toulouse, France, *markus.aretz@get.omp.eu*

Thomas R. Becker, Geologisch-Paläeontogisches Institut, Westfalische Wilhelm-Universität, Correnstrasse 24, D-48149 Münster, Germany, *rbecker@uni-muenster.de*

Anthony Butcher, School of the Environment, Geography and Geosciences, University of Portsmouth, Portsmouth, PO1 3QL, UK, *anthony.butcher@port.ac.uk*

Bradley D. Cramer, Earth and Environmental Sciences, University of Iowa, Iowa City, Iowa, 52242, USA, *bradley-cramer@uiowa.edu*

Richard E. Ernst, Department of Earth Sciences, Carleton University, Ottawa, Ontario, K1S 5B6, Canada, *richard.ernst@ernstgeosciences.com*

Selen Esmeray-Senlet, Chevron Energy and Technology Company, 1500 Louisiana St., Houston, Texas, 77002, USA, *selenesmeray@chevron.com*

Rob A. Fensome, Geological Survey of Canada (Atlantic), Natural Resources Canada, Dartmouth, Nova Scotia, B2Y 4A2, Canada, *rob.fensome@canada.ca*

Andrew S. Gale, School of the Environment, Geography and Geosciences, University of Portsmouth, Portsmouth, PO1 3QL, UK, *andy.gale@port.ac.uk*

Philip L. Gibbard, Department of Geography, University of Cambridge, Cambridge, CB2 3EN, UK, *plg1@cam.ac.uk*

Daniel Goldman, Department of Geology, University of Dayton, Dayton, Ohio, 45469, USA, *dgoldman1@u-dayton.edu*

Ethan L. Grossman, Department of Geology & Geophysics, Texas A&M University, College Station, Texas, 77843-3115, USA, *e-grossman@ta-mu.edu*

Galen P. Halverson, Department of Earth and Planetary Sciences, McGill University, Montréal, Québec, H3A 0E8, Canada, *galen.halverson@mcgill.ca*

Charles M. Henderson, Department of Geoscience, University of Calgary, Calgary, Alberta, T2N 1N4, Canada, *cmhender@ucalgary.ca*

Stephen P. Hesselbo, Camborne School of Mines, University of Exeter, Penryn, TR10 9FE, UK, *S.P.Hesselbo@exeter.ac.uk*

Harald Hiesinger, Institut für Planetologie, Westfälische Wilhelms-Universität Münster, D-48149 Münster, Germany, *hhies_01@uni-muenster.de*

Hans Kerp, Institut für Geologie und Paläontologie, Westfälische Wilhelms-Universität, D-48143 Münster, Germany, *kerp@uni-muenster.de*

Jacques Laskar, IMCCE, Observatoire de Paris, 77 Av. Denfert-Rochereau, 75014 Paris, France, *jacques.laskar@obspm.fr*

John M. McArthur, [Chemostratigraphy coordinator for GTS2020], Department of Earth Sciences, University College London, Gower Street, London, WC1E 6BT, UK, *j.mcarthur@ucl.ac.uk*

Michael J. Melchin, Department of Earth Sciences, St. Francis Xavier University, Antigonish, Nova Scotia, B2G 2W5, Canada, *mmelchin@stfx.ca*

Adina Paytan, Department of Earth and Planetary Sciences, University of California Santa Cruz, 1156 High St, Santa Cruz, California, 95064, USA, *apaytan@ucsc.edu*

Shanchi Peng, Nanjing Institute of Geology and Palaeontology, The Chinese Academy of Sciences, 39 East Beijing Road, Nanjing, 210008, China, *scpeng@nigpas.ac.cn*

Maria Rose Petrizzo, Department of Earth Sciences "Ardito Desio", Universitá degli Studi di Milano, Via Mangiagalli, 34 20133 Milano, Italy, *mrose.petrizzo@unimi.it*

Bernhard Peucker-Ehrenbrink, Woods Hole Oceanographic Institution, Woods Hole, Massachusetts, 02543-1541, USA, *behrenbrink@whoi.edu*

Isabella Raffi, Dipartimento di Ingegneria e Geologia, Università "G. d'Annunzio" di Chieti-Pescara, I-66013 Chieti Scalo, Italy, *raffi@unich.it*

Peter M. Sadler, Department of Earth Sciences, University of California, Riverside, Riverside, California, 92521, USA, *peter.sadler@ucr.edu*

Matthew R. Saltzman, School of Earth Sciences, Ohio State University, Columbus, Ohio, 43210-1398, USA, *saltzman.11@osu.edu*

Graham A. Shields, Department of Earth Sciences, University College London, London, WC1E 6BT, UK, *g.shields@ucl.ac.uk*

Michael D. Simmons, Halliburton, 97 Milton Park, Abingdon, OX14 4RY, UK, *mike.simmons@halliburton.com*

Robert P. Speijer, Department of Earth and Environmental Sciences, K.U. Leuven, B-3001 Leuven, Belgium, *Robert.Speijer@ees.kuleuven.be*

Rob Strachan, School of the Environment, Geography and Geosciences, University of Portsmouth, Portsmouth, PO1 3QL, UK, *rob.strachan@port.ac.uk*

David K. Watkins, Department of Earth & Atmospheric Sciences, University of Nebraska, Lincoln, Nebraska, 68588-0340, USA, *dwatkins1@unl.edu*

Shuhai Xiao, Department of Geosciences, Virginia Polytechnic Institute and State University, 4044 Derring Hall, Blacksburg, Virginia, 24061-0420, USA, *xiao@vt.edu*

Jan Zalasiewicz, Department of Geology, University of Leicester, Leicester, LE1 7RH, UK, *jazl@leicester.ac.uk*

Co-authors

Per Ahlberg, Department of Geology, Sölvegatan 12, SE-223 62 Lund, Sweden, *per.ahlberg@geol.lu.se*

Loren E. Babcock, School of Earth Sciences, Ohio State University, Columbus, Ohio, 43210, USA, *babcock.5@osu.edu*

Sietske J. Batenburg, Geosciences Rennes, Université de Rennes, UMR 6118, 35000 Rennes, France, *sbatenburg@gmail.com*

David P.G. Bond, Department of Geography, Environment and Earth Sciences, University of Hull, Hull, HU6 7RX, UK, *d.bond@hull.ac.uk*

Zhong-Qiang Chen, State Key Laboratory of Biogeology and Environmental Geology, School of Earth Sciences, China University of Geosciences, Wuhan, 430074, China, *zhong.qiang.chen@cug.edu.cn*

John Cope, Department of Natural Sciences, National Museum Wales, Cardiff CF10 3NP, UK, *john.cope@nmgw.ac.uk*

Anne-Christine Da Silva, Pétrologie sédimentaire, B20, Géologie, Université de Liège, B-4000 Liège, Belgium, *ac.dasilva@uliege.be*

James Darling, School of the Environment, Geography and Geosciences, University of Portsmouth, Portsmouth PO1 3QL, UK, *james.darling@port.ac.uk*

Andrew Davies, Halliburton, Milton Park, Abingdon, OX14 4RW, UK, *andrew.davies@halliburton.com*

Kristina L. Faul, Chemistry Department, Mills College, 5000 MacArthur Blvd, Oakland, California, 94613, USA, *kfaul@mills.edu*

Stephan R. Gradstein, Muséum National d'Histoire Naturelle, Department Systématique et Evolution, 57 rue Cuvier, 75231 Paris cedex 05, France, *gradstein@mnhn.fr*

Ellen T. Gray, Earth and Planetary Science, University of California Santa Cruz, Santa Cruz, California, 95064, USA, *eltgray@gmail.com*

Benjamin Gréselle, Halliburton, Milton Park, Abingdon, OX14 4RW, UK, *benjamin.greselle@halliburton.com*

Martin J. Head, Department of Earth Sciences, Brock University, St. Catharines, Ontario L2S 3A1, Canada, *mjhead@brocku.ca*

Hans-Georg Herbig, Universität zu Köln, Institut für Geologie und Mineralogie, 50674 Köln, Germany, *herbig.paleont@uni-koeln.de*

Andrew C. Hill, Centro de Astrobiología (INTA-CSIC), Instituto Nacional de Técnica Aeroespacial, 28850 Torrejón de Ardoz, Madrid, Spain, *andrew.hill@cliffsnr.com*

Christopher J. Hollis, GNS Science, Lower Hutt, 5040, New Zealand, *c.hollis@gns.cri.nz*

Jerry J. Hooker, Department of Palaeontology, Natural History Museum, London, SW7 5BD, UK, *j.hooker@nhm.ac.uk*

Richard J. Howarth, Department of Earth Sciences, University College London, London, WC1E 6BT, UK, *r.howarth@ucl.ac.uk*

Christina Ifrim, Institut für Geowissenschaften, Ruprecht-Karls-Universität Heidelberg, Im Nuenheimer Feld 234, 69120 Heidelberg, Germany, *christina.ifrim@geow.uni-heidelberg.de*

Ian Jarvis, Department of Geography, Geology and the Environment, Kingston University London, Kingston upon Thames KT1 2EE, UK, *I.Jarvis@kingston.ac.uk*

Michael M. Joachimski, GeoZentrum Nordbayern, Lithosphere Dynamics, Friedrich-Alexander-Universität Erlangen-Nürnberg, 91054 Erlangen, Germany, *michael.joachimski@fau.de*

Clark M. Johnson, Department of Geoscience, University of Wisconsin-Madison, 1215 W Dayton St., Madison, Wisconsin, 53706, USA, *clarkj@geology.wisc.edu*

Dieter Korn, Leibniz Institute for Research on Evolution and Biodiversity, Humboldt University Berlin, 10115 Berlin, Germany, *dieter.korn@mfn-berlin.de*

Stephen A. Leslie, Department of Geology and Environmental Science, James Madison University, MSC 6903, Harrisonburg, Virginia, 22807, USA, *lesliesa@jmu.edu*

Breandán A. MacGabhann, Earth and Ocean Sciences, National University of Ireland, Galway, Galway, Ireland, *b.macgabhann1@nuigalway.ie*

Gunn Mangerud, Department of Earth Science, University of Bergen, N-5020 Bergen, Norway, *Gunn.Mangerud@uib.no*

John E. Marshall, National Oceanography Centre Southampton, Southampton SO14 3ZH, UK, *jeam@soton.ac.uk*

Alistair J. McGowan, BioGeoD, 23 Glendinning Crescent, Edinburgh, Scotland, EH16 6DR, UK, *biogeod@gmail.com*

Ken G. Miller, Department of Earth & Planetary Sciences, Rutgers University, Piscataway, New Jersey, 08854, USA, *kgm@rutgers.edu*

Dirk K. Munsterman, T.N.O. Princetonlaan 6, 3508 TA Utrecht, The Netherlands, *Dirk.munsterman@tno.nl*

Brendan J. Murphy, Department of Earth Sciences, St Francis Xavier University, Antigonish, Nova Scotia, B2G 2W5, Canada, *bjmurphy@stfx.ca*

Joerg Mutterlose, Institut fuer Geologie, Mineralogie und Geophysik, 44801 Bochum, Germany, *joerg.mutterlose@rub.de*

Guy M. Narbonne, Department of Geological Sciences & Geological Engineering, Queen's University, Kingston, Ontario, K7L 3N6, Canada, *narbonne@geol.queensu.ca*

Heiko Pälike, MARUM Center for Marine Environmental Science, Universität Bremen, D-28359 Bremen, Germany, *hpaelike@marum.de*

Susannah M. Porter, Department of Earth Science, University of California Santa Barbara, Santa Barbara, California, 93106-9630, USA, *porter@geol.ucsb.edu*

Gregory E. Ravizza, Department of Geology & Geophysics, University of Hawaii at Manoa, Honolulu, Hawaii, 96822, USA, *ravizza@hawaii.edu*

David C. Ray, Halliburton, 97 Milton Park, Abingdon, OX14 4RY, UK, *david.ray@halliburton.com*

Alan D. Rooney, Department of Geology and Geophysics, Yale University, New Haven, Connecticut, 06520-8109, USA, *alan.rooney@yale.edu*

Micha Ruhl, Department of Geology, Trinity College, Dublin 2, Ireland, *Micha.Ruhl@tcd.ie*

Adrian Rushton, Department of Earth Sciences, The Natural History Museum, London, SW7 5BD, UK, *awarparadox@waitrose.com*

Shu-Zhong Shen, Nanjing Institute of Geology and Palaeontology, 39 East Beijing Road, Nanjing, 210008, China, *szshen@nigpas.ac.cn*

Brad S. Singer, The Department of Geoscience, University of Wisconsin-Madison, Madison, Wisconsin, 53706-1692, USA, *bsinger@geology.wisc.edu*

Craig Storey, School of the Environment, Geography and Geosciences, University of Portsmouth, Portsmouth PO1 3QL, UK, *craig.storey@port.ac.uk*

Ken Tanaka, 4214 N Fanning Dr., Flagstaff, Arizona, 86004, USA, *tanaka@npgcable.com*

Frans S. Van Buchem, Halliburton, Milton Park, Abingdon, OX14 4RW, UK, *frans.vanbuchem@halliburton.com*

Bridget S. Wade, Department of Earth Sciences, University College London, London, WC1E 6BT, UK, *b.wade@ucl.ac.uk*

Xiangdong Wang, Nanjing University, School of Earth Sciences and Engineering, Nanjing, 210023, China, *xdwang@nju.edu.cn*

Colin N. Waters, Department of Geology, University of Leicester, Leicester, LE1 7RH, UK, *cw398@leicester.ac.uk*

Mark Williams, School of Geography, Geology and the Environment, University of Leicester, Leicester, LE1 7RH, UK, *mri@leicester.ac.uk*

Weiqi Yao, Department of Earth Sciences, University of Toronto, Toronto, Ontario, Canada, *mri@leicester.ac.uk*

Shuan-Hong Zhang, Institute of Geomechanics, Chinese Academy of Geological Sciences, No. 11 South Minzudaxue Road, Beijing, 100081, China, *tozhang-shuanhong@163.com*

Ying Zhou, London Geochemistry and Isotope Centre, Institute of Earth and Planetary Sciences, University College London and Birkbeck, Gower Street, London, WC1E 6BT, UK, *y.shields-zhou@ucl.ac.uk*

With contributions by:

Alan G. Beu, GNS Science, Lower Hutt 5040, New Zealand, *a.beu@gns.cri.nz*

Martin Crundwell, GNS Science, Lower Hutt 5040, New Zealand, *m.crundwell@gns.cri.nz*

Linda A. Hinnov, Department of Atmospheric, Oceanic, and Earth Sciences, George Mason University, Fairfax, Virginia, 22030, USA, *lhinnov@gmu.edu*

Chunju Huang, School of Earth Sciences, China University of Geosciences, Wuhan, 430074, China, *huangcj@cug.edu.cn*

Haishui Jiang, State Key Laboratory of Biogeology and Environmental Geology, School of Earth Sciences, China University of Geosciences, Wuhan, 430074, China, *jiangliuis@163.com*

Wouter Krijgsman, Department of Earth Sciences, Utrecht University, Budapestlaan 17, 3584 CD Utrecht, The Netherlands, *W.Krijgsman@uu.nl*

Theodore Moore, Department of Earth and Environmental Sciences, University of Michigan, Ann Arbor, Michigan, 48109, USA, *tedmoore@umich.edu*

Michael Orchard, Geological Survey of Canada, 101-605 Robson Street, Vancouver, British Columbia, V6B 5J3, Canada, *morchard@nrcan.gc.ca*

J. Ian Raine, GNS Science, Lower Hutt, 5040, New Zealand, *i.raine@gns.cri.nz*

Raffaele Sardella, Dipartimento di Scienze della Terra, "la Sapienza" Università di Roma, 00185 Roma, Italy, *raffaele.sadella@uniroma1.it*

Yuliia Vernyhorova, Institute of Geological Sciences, National Academy of Sciences of Ukraine, Kyiv 01601, Ukraine, *juliy.vern@gmail.com*

Editors' Biographies

Felix M. Gradstein is Professor Emeritus at Oslo University, Norway, and visiting Research Fellow at the University of Portsmouth, United Kingdom. From 2000 to 2008, he was chair of the International Commission on Stratigraphy. Under his leadership, major progress was made with the formal definition of chronostratigraphic units from Precambrian through Quaternary. For his fundamental work concerning the Geologic Time Scale, geochronology in general, quantitative stratigraphy, and micropaleontology, the European Geosciences Union awarded him the Jean Baptiste Lamarck Medal in 2010. He is Chair of the Geologic TimeScale Foundation and teaches courses in quantitative stratigraphy and the geologic time scale. Now that he has free time again, after completing this book with his outstanding coeditors and coauthors, he studies the early evolution of planktonic foraminifera.

James G. Ogg is Professor at Purdue University, Indiana, United States, now retired/adjunct. He is also currently a visiting distinguished professor at Chengdu University of Technology and at China University of Geoscience (Wuhan). He served as Secretary General of the International Commission on Stratigraphy (2000–08) and currently is executive director of the Geologic TimeScale Foundation and coordinator of *TimeScale Creator* service (https://timescalecreator.org/). His Mesozoic Stratigraphy Lab group has worked on aspects of climate cycles, magnetic polarity correlations, and integration of stratigraphic information. Their *TimeScale Creator* array of visualization tools and extensive databases in global and regional Earth history was used to generate many of the diagrams in this book.

Mark D. Schmitz is Professor of Geochemistry at Boise State University, Idaho, United States. He has extensive research interests in the development and application of radiogenic isotope geochemistry and high-precision U–Pb geochronology to problems of Earth systems evolution. He has been an active member of the Earth Time community and was coeditor and author for the *Geologic Time Scale 2012*. He seeks to enrich the radioisotopic calibration of the time scale through targeted dating of stratigraphically important volcanic event beds and the construction of robust chronostratigraphic models through geologic time. His extensive database with over 300 standardized radiogenic isotope ages (mainly U/Pb and Ar/Ar) is vital to this book.

Gabi M. Ogg applied micropaleontology to Jurassic–Cretaceous correlations before concentrating on public outreach in geosciences. She coordinated the extensive array of graphics in this book and is the webmaster for the Geologic TimeScale Foundation (https://timescalefoundation.org) and for the *TimeScale Creator* visualization and database suites (https://timescalecreator.org). In addition to coauthoring the *Concise Geologic Time Scale* (GTS2016) and *The Geologic Time Scale* (GTS2012) books, she has produced numerous posters and time scale cards for public audiences.

Preface

This study presents the academic science community, industry, and schools with the new geologic time scale for c. 4 billion years of Earth history. A chapter also is devoted to time scales for our Moon and neighboring planets. This book details many recent advances in stratigraphy, the science of the layering of strata and its content, in evolution and biostratigraphy, in astrochronology, in geomagnetics, in radiogenic and stable isotope chronology, and in age and duration calculations using orbital tuning and geostatistics. The new scale closely links radioisotopic and orbitally tuned age dates and tries to provide comprehensive error analysis on the ages of a majority of boundaries for the geologic divisions of time. Much benefit is derived from the steady increase in formal definition of geologic stage boundaries such that we have more stability in their definition than in 2012. This book thus presents Geologic Time Scale 2020 (GTS2020), as the successor of GTS2012.

Besides being utilized as a scholarly and convenient standard, GTS2012 also provided fruit and gave impetus to a large body of new research in the fields of radiometrics, chronostratigraphy, orbital tuning, and other Earth Science specialties. One of the most rewarding aspects of science is always to see result becoming the springboard for exciting new developments, and unexpected new answers.

As a fruit of these intense developments, we now proudly present "The Geologic Time Scale 2020" building on a tremendous amount of new information, much of it generously assembled and contributed by the large team of specialists.

The fascination in creating a new geologic time scale is that it evokes images of creating a beautiful carpet by many skilled hands. All stitches must conform to a predetermined pattern, in this case the pattern of physical, chemical, and biological events on the Earth aligned along the arrow of time. It is thus, that this, new scale is a tribute to the truly close cooperation achieved by this new slate of outstanding coauthors. We also consider the new time scale a tribute to the scientific competence harbored and fostered by the global geoscience community.

We are deeply grateful to all coauthors and contributors, who without reservation accepted the challenge to be part of this dedicated team, slowly (!) stitching and weaving this carpet of time and its events that portray Earth's unique and splendid history.

The Norwegian Arctic explorer, scientist, and statesman Fridtjof Nansen is quoted as once saying "The difficult is what takes a little time; the impossible is what takes a little longer." To be frank, there were times when we encountered seemingly impossible obstacles in what otherwise seemed to be fairly smooth long-distance sailing from one specialty island to the next one, and staying in touch through a dense network of emails. To says it simple: the challenge with the construction of a detailed geologic time scale spanning almost 4 billion years of Earth history is that it should not have glaring gaps in time coverage.

Looking back at the 8 years it took to complete GTS2020, it is almost funny to consider that chapters of this book covering the oldest rocks and "some time before," that is, Precambrian and Planetary were completed first, followed by Late Proterozoic and Precambrian, whereas Mesozoic and particularly Paleogene and Neogene book chapters were last. We might consider that the younger record on the Earth is more complete, more easily accessible, and more easily decipherable but also creates high-resolution data swamping.

Whatever the timing and delays in bringing some chapters to market, we are grateful that all authors, without exception, have strived to keep to the final deadline agreed upon by Elsevier Publishing. To achieve clarity and uniformity in scientific and artistic presentation, Gabi M. Ogg drafted most of the figures. Christopher Scotese kindly provided paleogeographic map reconstructions with the chapters. The Elsevier Production Manager, Kiruthika Govindaraju, was very patient in shepherding the new GTS book through a seemingly endless type-setting and proofing process.

Felix M. Gradstein, James G. Ogg,
Mark D. Schmitz and Gabi M. Ogg

Oslo, Norway; W. Lafayette, IN, USA; and
Boise, ID, USA. 8 September 2020

ORGANIZATIONS

CGMW Commission for the Geological Map of the World
DNAG Decade of North American Geology
DSDP Deep Sea Drilling Project
GSC Geological Survey of Canada
ICS International Commission of Stratigraphy
IODP International Ocean Drilling Project
IGC International Geological Congress
IGCP International Geological Correlation Project
INQUA International Quaternary Association
IUGS International Union of Geological Sciences
IUPAC International Union of Pure and Applied Chemistry
ODP Ocean Drilling Project
SNS Subcommission (of ICS) on Neogene Stratigraphy
PGS Subcommission (of ICS) on Paleogene Stratigraphy
SQS Subcommission (of ICS) on Quaternary Stratigraphy
STS Subcommission (of ICS) on Triassic Stratigraphy
SOS Subcommission (of ICS) on Ordovician Stratigraphy
SCS Subcommission (of ICS) on Cambrian Stratigraphy
UNESCO United Nations Education, Scientific, and Cultural Organization
USGS United States Geological Survey

TIME SCALE PUBLICATIONS

NDS82 *Numerical Dating in Stratigraphy* (Odin et al., 1982)
GTS82 *A Geologic Time Scale* (Harland et al., 1982)
DNAG83 *Geologic Time Scale, Decade of North American Geology* (Palmer, 1983)
KG85 Kent and Gradstein (1985)
EX88 Exxon 1988 (Haq et al., 1988)
GTS89 *A Geologic Time Scale 1989* (Harland et al., 1990)
OB93 Obradovich (1993)
JGR94 *Journal of Geophysical Research* 1994 (Gradstein et al., 1994)
SEPM95 Society for Sedimentary Geology 1995 (Gradstein et al., 1995)
GO96 Gradstein and Ogg (1996)
GTS2004 Gradstein, Ogg and Smith (2004)
GTS2008 Ogg, Ogg and Gradstein (2008)
GTS2012 Gradstein, Ogg, Schmitz and Ogg (2012)
GTS2016 Ogg, Ogg and Gradstein (2016)

GEOSCIENTIFIC CONCEPTS

CA-TIMS Chemical abrasion—thermal ionization mass spectrometry (in U–Pb dating)
FAD First appearance datum
FOD First occurrence datum
FCT (FCs) Fish Canyon Tuff sanidine monitor standard (in Ar–Ar dating)
GPTS Geomagnetic polarity time scale
GSSP Global Boundary Stratotype Section and Point
GSSA Global Standard Stratigraphic Age (in Precambrian)
HO Highest occurrence level
HR–SIMS High-resolution secondary ion mass spectrometry (in U–Pb dating)
ID-TIMS Isotope dilution thermal ionization mass spectrometry (in U–Pb dating)
LAD Last appearance datum
LA-ICPMS Laser ablation-inductively coupled plasma-mass Spectrometry (in U–Pb dating)
LO Lowest occurrence level
LOD Last occurrence datum
LA2004 Laskar 2004 numerical solution of orbital periodicities
LA2010 Laskar 2010 numerical solution of orbital periodicities (Laskar et al., 2011)
MMhb-1 McClure Mountain hornblende monitor standard (in Ar–Ar dating)
SL13 Sri Lanka 13 monitor zircon standard (in HR–SIMS dating)
TCs Taylor Creek Rhyolite sanidine monitor standard (in Ar–Ar dating)

SYMBOLS

ka 10^3 years ago (kilo annum)
kyr 10^3 years duration
Ma 10^6 years ago (mega annum)
Myr 10^6 years duration
Ga 10^9 years ago (giga annum)
Gyr 10^9 years duration
SI Le Système Internationale d'Unités
a annus (year)
s second

Part I

Introduction

Introduction

Chapter outline

Abstract

The Geologic Time Scale (GTS) is the framework for deciphering and understanding the history of our planet. The steady increase in data, development of better methods and new procedures for actual dating and scaling of the rocks on Earth, and a refined relative scale with more defined units are stimulating the need for a comprehensive review of the GTS. This review is called GTS2020, of which GTS2012 is the ancestor. Relative to its ancestor, the scope of the GTS2020 study is considerably expanded, and stratigraphic resolution has further improved.

GTS2020 is laid out in two volumes. Volume 1 deals with principles and methods and Volume 2 with the stratigraphy and time scale units itself, for a total of 31 chapters, 14 Subchapters, and 2 Appendices. All information is clearly visualized in over 500 figures and tables.

1.1 The Geologic Time Scale

The Geologic Time Scale (GTS) is the framework for deciphering and understanding the long and complex history of our planet, Earth, the third planet in the constellation around the Sun and the fifth largest after Jupiter, Saturn, Uranus, and Neptune. As Arthur Holmes, the Father of the GTS once wrote (Holmes, 1965) "To place all the scattered pages of Earth history in their proper chronological order is by no means an easy task." Ordering these pages, and understanding the physical, chemical and biological processes that acted on them since Earth appeared and solidified, requires a detailed and accurate time scale. The time scale is the tool "par excellence" of the geological trade, and insight in its construction, strength, and limitations greatly enhances its function and its utility. All Earth scientists should understand how the time scale is constructed and how the myriad of physical and numerical data in it are calibrated, rather than merely using the numbers in them, plucked from a convenient wall chart or laminated wallet card. This calibration to linear time of the succession of events recorded in the rocks on Earth has three components:

1. the international stratigraphic divisions and their correlation in the global rock record,
2. the means of measuring linear time or elapsed durations from the rock record, and
3. the methods of joining the two scales, the stratigraphic one and the linear one.

For clarity and precision in international communication the rock record of Earth's history is subdivided into a "chronostratigraphic" scale of standardized global stratigraphic units, such as "Carboniferous," "Eocene," "*Zigzagiceras zigzag* ammonite zone," or "polarity Chron M19r." Unlike the continuous ticking clock of the "chronometric" scale (measured in years before the year CE 2000), the chronostratigraphic scale is based on relative time units in which global reference points at boundary stratotypes define the limits of the main formalized units, such as "Permian." The chronostratigraphic scale is an agreed convention, whereas its calibration to linear time is a matter for discovery or estimation (Fig. 1.1).

In contrast to the Phanerozoic that has an agreed-upon chronostratigraphic scale with formal stage boundary stratotypes, Precambrian stratigraphy is formally classified chronometrically, that is, the base of each Precambrian

Geologic Time Scale 2020. DOI: https://doi.org/10.1016/B978-0-12-824360-2.00001-2

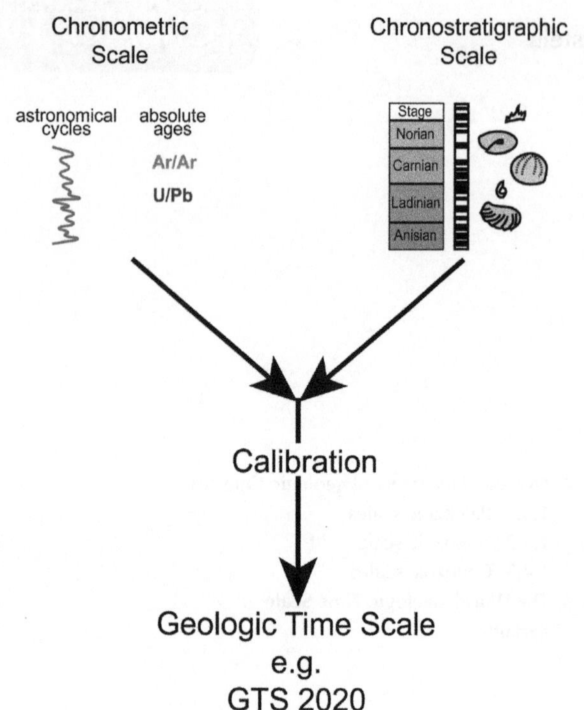

FIGURE 1.1 The construction of a geologic time scale is the merger of a chronometric scale (measured in years) and a chronostratigraphic scale (formalized definitions of geologic stages, biostratigraphic zonation units, magnetic polarity zones, and other subdivisions of the rock record).

eon, era, and period is assigned a numerical age (Table 1.1). In Chapter 16, Precambrian (4.56 Ga to 1 Ga), this Precambrian scale is outlined in some detail.

Moon, Earth's only satellite, the Sun, and the universe surrounding the Sun system play crucially important roles in geology (think of tidal movements, global climatic change, and Milankowić cyclicity, and meteorite impacts). Earth GTS is a component of a much broader and longer scale, the Astronomic Geologic Scale. Hence, this book also devotes an important planetary chapter to GTSs for our satellite Moon, our neighboring planets Venus and Mars, and the more distant planets. In the last decade, geologic research on these fascinating celestial bodies has much expanded and improved.

1.2 A Geologic Time Scale GTS2020

1.2.1 Recent developments

For the last few years, there have been several major developments that directly bear and have considerable impact on the international GTS.

1. Stratigraphic standardization through the work of the International Commission on Stratigraphy (ICS) is steadily refining the international chronostratigraphic scale. Of the 100 stage or series units in the Phanerozoic Eonothem a majority (75) now have ratified boundary definitions, versus fewer than 45 in 2004 and just over 30 in the year 2000. Details on the new and existing stage boundary definitions are presented in Chapter 2, The Chronostratigraphic Scale.
2. In many cases traditional European-based geologic stages have been replaced with new subdivisions that allow global correlation. The Tonian, Cryogenian, and Ediacaran Periods are "filling up" with stratigraphic information and the latter has a formal lower boundary definition (see Chapter 18: The Ediacaran Period). New stages have been introduced in Cambrian and Ordovician that allow global correlations, in contrast to British, American, Chinese, Russian, or Australian regional stages. Long ratified stage definitions in Silurian and Devonian are undergoing long overdue revision to better reflect the actually observed fossil

TABLE 1.1 Current framework for subdividing Earth stratigraphy.

Age in Ma	Eon	Era	Definition of base
To be discovered by correlation from GSSPs and dating. Base of Phanerozoic dated at 538.8 Ma.	Phanerozoic	Cenozoic Mesozoic Paleozoic	Boundaries defined in rock (chronostratigraphically) by GSSPs
Age of basal Proterozoic defined as 2500 Ma	Proterozoic	Neoproterozoic Mesoproterozoic Paleaoproterozoic	Boundaries defined in time (chronometrically) by arbitrary assignment of numerical age
Age of basal Archaen not defined	Archean	Neoarchean Mesoarchean Paleoarchean Eoarchean	Boundaries defined in time (chronometrically) by arbitrary assignment of numerical age

and rock record. The Cretaceous, for a long time the only period in the Phanerozoic without a formal definition for its base, has a realistic and practical biomagnetostratigraphic proposal for its lower boundary (see Chapter 27: The Cretaceous Period). Curiously, the largest formal stratigraphic knowledge gap is from Callovian to Aptian for which only one Global Boundary Stratotype Section and Point (GSSP) has been defined (Hauterivian). A similar, albeit slightly shorter GSSP gap exists in Pennsylvanian (Late Carboniferous) through Early Permian.

All Paleocene (Danian, Selandian, Thanetian), three Eocene (Ypresian, Lutetian, and Priabonian) and all Oligocene (Rupelian, Chattian) stages are now defined in the Cenozoic, and all but two Neogene Stages (Langhian and Burdigalian) have been defined and ratified. The Pleistocene and Holocene each are formally divided into several units, and the Anthropocene is eagerly working towards potential formal chronostratigraphic recognition.

3. New or enhanced methods of extracting linear time from the rock record have enabled age assignments with a precision of 0.1% or better, leading to improved age assignments of key geologic stage boundaries, and intrastage levels. A good protocol exists to assign uncertainty to age dates (see Chapter 6: Radioisotope Geochronology), and calibrate the two principal radiogenic isotope techniques using potassium–argon and uranium–lead isotopes. Improved analytical procedures for obtaining uranium–lead ages from single zircons have shifted published ages for some stratigraphic levels to older ages by more than 1 Myr (e.g., at the Permian/Triassic boundary). Similarly, an astronomically assigned age for the neutron irradiation monitor for the $^{40}Ar-^{39}Ar$ dating method makes earlier reported ages older by 0.64%. Also, the rhenium–osmium ($^{187}Re-^{187}Os$) shale geochronometer has a role to play for organic-rich strata with limited or no potential for ash bed dating with the uranium–lead isotopes. Details on the improved radiogenic isotope methods are in Chapter 6, Radioisotope Geochronology.
4. A welcome practice is that, instead of micro- and macrofossil events, also global geochemical excursions are defining criteria for chronostratigraphic boundaries, like the Corg positive anomaly at the Paleocene/Eocene boundary. Carbon isotope excursions are close proxies for base Cambrian, base Triassic, base Jurassic, base Aptian, and base Turonian. The famous iridium anomaly is at the Cretaceous/Paleogene boundary. More GSSPs should use global geochemical events.
5. Milanković orbital climate cyclicity tunes the Neogene GTS, scaling it in over 50 405-kyr Astrochrono Zones (see Chapter 29: The Neogene Period). For the first time the classical seafloor spreading and magnetochronology methods play only a minor role in scaling the Paleogene. It is now almost completely orbitally tuned (see Chapter 28: The Paleogene Period). Hence, magneto- and biochronology are refined and stage boundary ages strengthened. Parts of Jurassic and Cretaceous benefit from cycle scaling for sets of "floating" stages, providing detailed estimates of stage duration. Chapter 4, Astrochronology, provides an in-depth review of Astrochronology for the construction of an orbitally tuned GTS.
6. Improved scaling of stages is feasible with composite standard techniques on fossil zones, as a means of estimating relative zone durations. A good example is the Ordovician–Silurian interval with a refined graptolite composite standard with more and better age dates. Since radioisotopic dates often are now more accurate than zonal or fossil event assignments, the uneven spacing and fluctuating accuracy and precision of both radioisotopic dates and zonal composite scales demands special statistical and mathematical techniques to calculate the GTS. This is outlined in-depth in the important Chapter 14, Geomathematics, on time scale geomathematics and geostatistics.
7. The assignment of error bars to ages of stage boundaries, first advocated by Gradstein et al. (1994) attempts to combine the most up-to-date estimate of uncertainty in radioisotopic dating and in stratigraphic scaling into one number. Although stratigraphic reasoning to arrive at uncertainties plays a role, geosciences are no less than physics and chemistry when it comes to assigning realistic error bars to its vital numbers. The geomathematical and geostatistical methods employed to construct GTS2020 are outlined in Chapter 14, Geomathematics.

Continual improvements in data coverage, methodology, and standardization of chronostratigraphic units imply that no GTS can be final. The new GTS2020 provides detailed insight in the most up-to-date GTS and is the successor to GTS2012 (Gradstein et al., 2012), GTS2004 (Gradstein et al., 2004) and GTS1989 (Harland et al., 1990).

The set of chronostratigraphic units (stages, eras) and their computed ages that constitute the main framework for GTS2020 is shown in Fig. 1.2, with detailed descriptions and stratigraphic scales in appropriate chapters. About 30% of Phanerozoic stage boundary ages have a change of their lower boundary by more than 0.5 Myr, and in some cases much more (shown in red) (see Table 1.2).

The time scale project leading to GTS2020 commenced in 2016, and in total involved over 99 scientists.

GEOLOGIC TIME SCALE 2020

PHANEROZOIC

CENOZOIC

Period	Epoch	Age/Stage	Age
Quat.	Holocene	5 stages	
	Pleistocene		0.78
		Calabrian	1.81
		Gelasian	2.58
Neogene	Pliocene	Piacenzian	3.60
		Zanclean	5.33
	Miocene	Messinian	7.25
		Tortonian	11.63
		Serravallian	13.82
		Langhian	15.99
		Burdigalian	20.45
		Aquitanian	23.04
Paleogene	Oligocene	Chattian	27.3
		Rupelian	33.9
	Eocene	Priabonian	37.7
		Bartonian	41.0
		Lutetian	48.1
		Ypresian	56.0
	Paleocene	Thanetian	59.2
		Selandian	61.7
		Danian	66.0

MESOZOIC

Period	Epoch	Age/Stage	Age
Cretaceous	Late	Maastrichtian	72.2
		Campanian	83.7
		Santonian	85.7
		Coniacian	89.4
		Turonian	93.9
		Cenomanian	100.5
	Early	Albian	113.2
		Aptian	121.4
		Barremian	126.5
		Hauterivian	132.6
		Valanginian	137.7
		Berriasian	143.1
Jurassic	Late	Tithonian	149.2
		Kimmeridgian	154.8
		Oxfordian	161.5
	Middle	Callovian	165.3
		Bathonian	168.2
		Bajocian	170.9
		Aalenian	174.7
	Early	Toarcian	184.2
		Pliensbachian	192.9
		Sinemurian	199.5
		Hettangian	201.4
Triassic	Late	Rhaetian	205.7
		Norian	227.3
		Carnian	237.0
	Middle	Ladinian	241.5
		Anisian	246.7
	Early	Olenekian	249.9
		Induan	251.9

PALEOZOIC

Period	Epoch	Age/Stage	Age
Permian	Lopingian	Changhsingian	254.2
		Wuchiapingian	259.5
	Guadalupian	Capitanian	264.3
		Wordian	269.2
		Roadian	274.4
	Cisuralian	Kungurian	283.3
		Artinskian	290.5
		Sakmarian	293.5
		Asselian	298.9
Carboniferous	Pennsylvanian L	Gzhelian	303.7
		Kasimovian	307.0
	Pennsylvanian M	Moscovian	315.2
	Pennsylvanian E	Bashkirian	323.4
	Mississippian L	Serpukhovian	330.3
	Mississippian M	Visean	346.7
	Mississippian E	Tournaisian	359.3
Devonian	Late	Famennian	371.1
		Frasnian	378.9
	Middle	Givetian	385.3
		Eifelian	394.3
	Early	Emsian	410.5
		Pragian	412.4
		Lochkovian	419.0
Silurian	Pridoli		422.7
	Ludlow	Ludfordian	425.0
		Gorstian	426.7
	Wenlock	Homerian	430.6
		Sheinwoodian	432.9
	Llandovery	Telychian	438.6
		Aeronian	440.5
		Rhuddanian	443.1
Ordovician	Late	Hirnantian	445.2
		Katian	452.8
		Sandbian	458.2
	Middle	Darriwilian	469.4
		Dapingian	471.3
	Early	Floian	477.1
		Tremadocian	486.9
Cambrian	Furongian	Age 10	491.0
		Jiangshanian	494.2
		Paibian	497.0
	Miaolingian	Guzhangian	500.5
		Drumian	504.5
		Wuliuan	509.0
	Epoch 2	Age 4	514.5
		Age 3	521.0
	Terreneuvian	Age 2	529.0
		Fortunian	538.8

PRECAMBRIAN

Eon	Era	Period	Age
Proterozoic	Neoproterozoic	Ediacaran	635
		Cryogenian	720
		Tonian	1000
	Mesoproterozoic	Stenian	1200
		Ectasian	1400
		Calymmian	1600
	Paleoproterozoic	Statherian	1800
		Orosirian	2050
		Rhyacian	2300
		Siderian	2500
Archean	Neoarchean		2800
	Mesoarchean		3200
	Paleoarchean		3600
	Eoarchean		4000
Hadean (informal)			

Gradstein, Ogg, Schmitz, Ogg et al., GTS2020, Elsevier.

FIGURE 1.2 The new Geologic Time Scale.

TABLE 1.2 Modified ages of stage boundaries in this book relative to 'A Geologic Time 2012' (GTS2012). A majority of age changes involve a combination of better cycle stratigraphy, more radioisotopic dates, higher stratigraphic resolution, change in stage boundary definition and/or new composite standard and spline fits. Stages or series that changed boundary age by 0.5 Ma or more in GTS2020 are shown in red.

	Age/Stage	GTS2012	GTS2020	GTS2020 uncertainty in myr (95%)	Snapshot comments on selected levels
Quaternary	TOP	0 (2000)			
	Meghalayan		0.043		New Holocene stage
	Northgrippian		0.082		New Holocene stage
	Greenlandian	0.012	0.012		Base of Holocene Epoch
	Upper Pleistocene	0.126	0.126		
	Chibanian	0.78	0.78		
	Calabrian	1.81	1.81		
	Gelasian	2.59	2.58		Revised correlation of GSSP horizon to astronomical cycles
Neogene	Piacenzian	3.60	3.60		
	Zanclean	5.33	5.33		
	Messinian	7.25	7.25		
	Tortonian	11.63	11.63		
	Serravallian	13.82	13.82		
	Langhian	15.97	15.99		Enhanced magneto-cyclostratigraphic accuracy
	Burdigalian	20.43	20.45		" "
	Aquitanian	23.03	23.04		" "
Paleogene	Chattian	28.1	27.3		Ratified GSSP uses a higher marker and with revised magneto-cyclostratigraphic correlation
	Rupelian	33.9	33.9		
	Priabonian	37.8	37.7		Enhanced magneto-cyclostratigraphic accuracy
	Bartonian	41.2	41.0		" "
	Lutetian	47.8	48.1		" "
	Ypresian	56.0	56.0		
	Thanetian	59.2	59.2		
	Selandian	61.6	61.7		Enhanced magneto-cyclostratigraphic accuracy
	Danian	66.0	66.0	0.1	Precise lower stage boundary age date
Cretaceous	Maastrichtian	72.1	72.2	0.2	
	Campanian	83.6	83.7	0.5	
	Santonian	86.3	85.7	0.2	Revised marker and cyclostratigraphy
	Coniacian	89.8	89.4	0.2	Revised radioisotopic dating and cyclostratigraphy
	Turonian	93.9	93.9	0.2	Precise lower stage boundary age date
	Cenomanian	100.5	100.5	0.1	" "
	Albian	113.0	113.2	0.3	Ratified GSSP uses slightly older marker
	Aptian	126.3	121.4	0.6	New radioisotopic dating and magnetostratigraphy near base-Aptian boundary.

(*Continued*)

TABLE 1.2 (Continued)

	Age/Stage	GTS2012	GTS2020	GTS2020 uncertainty in myr (95%)	Snapshot comments on selected levels
	Barremian	130.8	126.5	0.7	Revised cyclostratigraphic duration of stage (ca. 5 myr) relative to base-Aptian and new radiometric date for upper Hauterivian
	Hauterivian	133.9	132.6	0.6	Early Cretaceous spline fit with Hauterivian stage duration set as 6.1 myr (French cyclostrat)
	Valanginian	140.2	137.7	0.5	Spline fit to radiometric dates with Valanginian stage duration set as 5.1 myr (French cyclostrat)
	Berriasian	145.0	143.1	0.6	Spline fit to new radiometric dates with Berriasian stage duration as ca. 5.4 myr. Base-Berriasian working definition uses new marker compared to GTS2012.
Jurassic	Tithonian	152.1	149.2	0.7	Tithonian through Bajocian from magnetostrat correlations to a spline-fit of M-sequence spreading rates as constrained by the base Berriasian age and stage durations from cyclostratigraphy.
	Kimmeridgian	157.3	154.8	0.8	See above, plus GSSP being voted (early 2020) uses a younger level.
	Oxfordian	163.5	161.5	1.0	See explanation for Tithonian; plus GSSP working definition uses a slightly younger level. No GSSP yet.
	Callovian	166.1	165.3	1.1	See explanation for Tithonian
	Bathonian	168.3	168.2	1.2	” ”
	Bajocian	170.3	170.9	0.8	Implied by revised Aalenian stage duration (3.8 myr) from cyclostratigraphy relative to base-Aalenian
	Aalenian	174.1	174.7	0.8	Implied by revised Toarcian stage duration (9.5 myr) from cyclostratigraphy relative to base-Toarcian
	Toarcian	182.7	184.2	0.3	Revised extrapolation of new radiometric dates to base-Toarcian
	Pliensbachian	190.8	192.9	0.3	Revised Pliensbachian stage duration (8.7 myr) from cyclostratigraphy relative to base-Toarcian
	Sinemurian	199.3	199.5	0.3	Implied by Hettangian stage duration (1.8 myr) from cyclostratigraphy relative to base-Hettangian
	Hettangian	201.3	201.4	0.2	Precise lower stage boundary radiometric date
Triassic	Rhaetian	209.5	205.7	0.4	Revised stage "working" boundary correlation to Newark cycle-scaled magnetostratigraphy. No GSSP; used proposed Italian candidate and marker instead of Austrian version in GTS2012
	Norian	228.4	227.3	0.4	Revised stage "working" boundary correlation to Newark cycle-scaled magnetostratigraphy. No GSSP
	Carnian	237.0	237.0	0.5	
	Ladinian	241.5	241.5	0.3	Precise lower stage boundary radiometric date
	Anisian	247.1	246.7	0.2	Cycle-duration (3.2 myr) relative to revised base-Induan date, plus radiometric dating of potential GSSP
	Olenekian	250.0	249.9	0.2	Cycle-duration (2.0 myr) relative to revised base-Induan date. No GSSP yet; used S.China candidate with conodont
	Induan	252.2	251.9	0.3	Revised precise radiometric dates on GSSP.
Permian	Changhsingian	254.2	254.2	0.4	
	Wuchiapingian	259.8	259.5	0.4	Revised spline fit
	Capitanian	265.1	264.3	0.4	” ”
	Wordian	268.8	269.2	0.4	New radioisotopic dating

(Continued)

TABLE 1.2 (Continued)

	Age/Stage	GTS2012	GTS2020	GTS2020 uncertainty in myr (95%)	Snapshot comments on selected levels
	Roadian	272.3	274.4	0.4	„ „
	Kungurian	279.3	283.3	0.4	Revised working definition uses an older marker and new spline fit
	Artinskian	290.1	290.5	0.4	Updated marker, revised spline fit
	Sakmarian	295.5	293.5	0.4	Ratified GSSP definition uses a younger marker, revised spline fit
	Asselian	298.9	298.9	0.4	Precise lower stage boundary age date
Carboniferous	Gzhelian	303.7	303.7	0.4	
	Kasimovian	307.0	307.0	0.4	
	Moscovian	315.2	315.2	0.4	
	Bashkirian	323.2	323.4	0.4	
	Serpukhovian	330.9	330.3	0.4	Revised spline fit
	Visean	346.7	346.7	0.4	„ „
	Tournaisian	358.9	359.3	0.3	„ „
Devonian	Famennian	372.2	371.1	1.1	Pragian through Famennian spline fit to new or updated correlation of radioisotopic dates
	Frasnian	382.7	378.9	1.2	„ „
	Givetian	387.7	385.3	1.2	„ „
	Eifelian	393.3	394.3	1.1	„ „
	Emsian	407.6	410.5	1.1	„ Future Emsian GSSP may give 407.3 Ma age
	Pragian	410.8	412.4	1.1	
	Lochkovian	419.2	419.0	1.8	
Silurian	Pridoli (*Epoch*)	423.0	422.7	1.6	Tremadocian through Pridoli with spline fit to new or updated correlation of radioisotopic dates and improved composite standard
	Ludfordian	425.6	425.0	1.5	„ „
	Gorstian	427.4	426.7	1.5	„ „
	Homerian	430.5	430.6	1.3	„ „
	Sheinwoodian	433.4	432.9	1.2	„ „
	Telychian	438.5	438.6	1.1	„ „
	Aeronian	440.8	440.5	1.0	„ „
	Rhuddanian	443.8	443.1	0.9	„ „
Ordovician	Hirnantian	445.2	445.2	0.9	„ „
	Katian	453.0	452.8	0.7	„ „
	Sandbian	458.4	458.2	0.7	„ „
	Darriwilian	467.3	469.4	0.9	„ „
	Dapingian	470.0	471.3	1.0	„ „
	Floian	477.7	477.1	1.2	„ „
	Tremadocian	485.4	486.9	1.5	New radioisotopic dating

(*Continued*)

TABLE 1.2 (Continued)

	Age/Stage	GTS2012	GTS2020	GTS2020 uncertainty in myr (95%)	Snapshot comments on selected levels
Cambrian	Age 10	489.5	491.0		" "
	Jiangshanian	494.0	494.2		
	Paibian	497.0	497.0		
	Guzhangian	500.5	500.5		
	Drumian	504.5	504.5		
	Wuliuan	509.0	509.0		
	Age 4	514.0	514.5		
	Age 3	521.0	521.0		
	Age 2	529.0	529.0		
	Fortunian	541.0	538.8	0.6	Revised radioisotopic dating
Ediacaran	Series 1	635.0	635.0		

The project includes contributions by past and present chairs and other officers of different subcommissions of ICS, geochemists, and physicists working with radiogenic and stable isotopes, stratigraphers using diverse tools from traditional animal and plant fossils to sequence stratigraphy to astronomical cycles to data programing, an astronomer and a geomathematician. GTS2020 is available both as two volumes paper book and in digital format.

1.2.2 Methods and ages

The methods used for the construction of GTS2020 integrate different techniques depending on the quality of data and methods available for different intervals and are shown schematically in Fig. 1.3.

GTS2020 construction may be summarized in five steps:

Step 1. Construct an updated global chronostratigraphic scale for the Earth's rock record.

Step 2. Scale the updated chronostratigraphic scale with magnetochronology (the mid-km C-and M-sequences tabled in Chapter 5: Geomagnetic Polarity Time Scale), or a composite standard technique. The latter commonly takes average zone thickness from many sections as directly proportional to zone duration. It is applied for Paleozoic periods.

Step 3. Identify key linear-age calibration levels for the chronostratigraphic scale using radioisotopic dates, and/or apply astronomical tuning to cyclic sediment, or scale and interpolate (near) linear segments of stable isotope sequences.

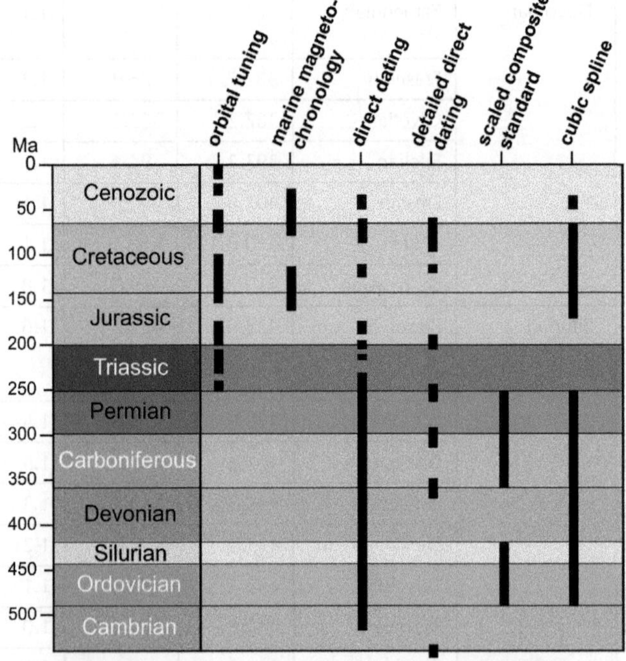

FIGURE 1.3 Methods used to construct GTS2020 integrate different techniques depending on the quality of data available within different intervals.

Step 4. Interpolate the combined chronostratigraphic and chronometric scale, for example with a cubic spline that fits closest to data points with the lowest possible error. Such splines effectively bridge gaps in data along the linear scale or along the chronostratigraphic scale.

Step 5. Calculate or estimate error bars on the combined chronostratigraphic and chronometric information to obtain a GTS with estimates of uncertainty on stage boundary ages.

The first step, integrating multiple types of stratigraphic information in order to construct the chronostratigraphic scale is the most time-consuming; it summarizes and synthesizes centuries of detailed geological research, while reconciling it with the most up-to-date information. The second step has progress wanting, with periods such as Cambrian, Devonian, Triassic, and part of Jurassic not yet having a composite standard of bio- and other events. The third step, identifying which radiogenic isotope and cycle-stratigraphic studies are to be used as the primary constraints for assigning linear ages, is the one that is evolving most rapidly since the last decade. Historically, time scale building went from an exercise with few and relatively inaccurate radioisotopic dates, as used by Holmes (1947, 1960), to one with many dates with greatly varying analytical precision (like GTS1989), to one with a majority of accurate and often precise dates (like GTS2020). The new philosophy, which was started with GTS2004 and GTS2012, is to select analytical precise radioisotopic dates with high stratigraphic resolution. More than 330 radioisotopic dates were thus selected for their reliability and stratigraphic importance to calibrate the geologic record in linear time.

The uncertainty on older stage boundaries systematically increases owing to potential systematic errors in the different radiogenic isotope methods, rather than to the analytical precision of the laboratory measurements. In this connection, it is good to remember that biostratigraphic error is fossil event and fossil zone dependent, rather than age dependent.

Ages and durations of Cenozoic stages derived from orbital tuning are considered to be accurate to within a precession cycle ($\sim$20 kyr) assuming that all cycles are correctly identified, and that the theoretical astronomical tuning for progressively older deposits is precise.

Table 1.2 lists the age of stage boundaries in this book relative to the GTS2012, published 8 years ago. Comments are provided why these ages changed by 0.5 million years or more. There are minor age changes in Cenozoic and Late Cretaceous and substantial changes of 1 Myr or more in the age of stage boundaries for the Early Cretaceous, Jurassic, late Triassic, lower half of Permian, part of Devonian, part of Silurian and part of Ordovician. Base Phanerozoic is estimated to be about 3-Myr younger than in GTS2012. The large change in age for base Aptian from 126.3 to 121.4 Ma has an effect on stage boundary ages down into Jurassic, all becoming slightly younger. Uncertainties in age for several Early Cretaceous, Jurassic, and Devonian through Ordovician stages changed by more than 0.5 Myr. Details are in the relevant chapters on the geologic periods and in Chapter 14, Geomathematics.

1.3 How this book is arranged?

The foundation of the GTS is the standardized system of international stratigraphic units. In Chapter 2, The Chronostratigraphic Scale, the construction of this international standard, the definition of stage boundaries, and the origin of the main divisions of eons and eras are outlined.

Part I of the book contains chapters detailing astrochronology, magnetostratigraphy with the M and C marine magnetic sequences; radiogenic isotope geochronology; strontium-, osmium-, sulfur-, oxygen-, and carbon isotope stratigraphy; Phanerozoic sea-level changes; and geomathematical and statistical procedures. The evolution and biostratigraphy in Chapter 3 contains (mostly short) chapters on micro– and macro–fossil groups of importance for biostratigraphy and paleoecology and another important mini chapter on major mass extinction events and subsequent evolutionary radiations. The erudite chapter on larger benthic foraminifera is a bit larger for reason that this stratigraphically important group of Late Paleozoic, Mesozoic, and Cenozoic microfossils is not easy to "grasp" from the literature. Another important mini chapter (in Chapter 12: Influence of Large Igneous Provinces) deals with the influence of large igneous provinces. None of the contents in these short chapters received attention in GTS2004 or in GTS2012 and may be welcomed by teachers and students.

Part II of the book deals with the detailed stratigraphy and the new time scale for the Precambrian, Tonian–Cryogenian, Ediacaran, and all Phanerozoic periods plus the Anthropocene. Part II starts with a fascinating overview of the Planetary Time Scale and its stratigraphic underpinning.

Appendix 1 summarizes recommended color coding of stages and in Appendix 2 is the listing of radioisotopic dates, of which the majority were employed for GTS2020.

1.3.1 Conventions and standards

Ages are given in years before "Present" (BP). To avoid a constantly changing datum, "Present" was fixed as CE 1950 (as in ^{14}C determinations), the date of the beginning of modern isotope dating research in laboratories around the world. For most geologists, this offset of official "Present" from "today" is not important. However, for archeologists and researchers into events during the Holocene (the past 11,500 years), the offset between the "BP" convention from radiogenic isotope laboratories and actual total elapsed calendar years becomes significant. The offset between the current year and "Present" has led many Holocene specialists to use a "BP2000," which is relative to the year CE 2000. This practice is used in GTS2020 also.

For clarity, the linear age in years is abbreviated as "*a*" (for annum), and ages are measured in *ka*, *Ma*, or *Ga* for thousands, millions, or billions of years before present.

Elapsed time or duration is abbreviated as "*yr.*" (for year), and longer durations in *kyr* or *Myr*. Therefore the Cenozoic began at 66 Ma and spans 66 Myr (to the present day, defined as the year CE 2000).

The *Ma and Myr* practice is confusing and inconsistent both internally and with respect to SI (Le Système international d'unités). As Holden et al. (2011) elegantly clarify (on behalf of IUPAC and IUGS), the same unit is used for absolute and relative measurements. This is in compliance with quantity calculus, and its unit assignment for continuous and interval scales. Hence, elapsed time or duration would also be abbreviated as in *ka* or *Ma*. Therefore the Cenozoic began at 66 Ma and spans or lasted 66 Ma. This is similar to the use of m (meter) for both absolute depth/distance and a depth/distance difference, and the use of °C for both temperature and temperature difference. For example, we say that interval between two logmarkers in a borehole is 450 m thick and starts 900 m below ground level. Despite this solution to an often fuzzy and confusing debate with respect to the notation of age and duration units in Earth science, we (for now) stick to the same format as used in GTS2004 and in GTS2012, with both Ma and ka, and Myr and kyr units.

The uncertainties in computed ages or durations are expressed as standard deviation (1-sigma or 68% confidence) or 2-sigma (95% confidence). The uncertainty is indicated by "±" and will have implied units of thousands or millions of years as appropriate to the magnitude of the age. Therefore an age cited as "124.6 ± 0.3 Ma" implies a 0.3 Myr uncertainty (2-sigma, unless specified as 1-sigma) on the 124.6 Ma date. We present the uncertainties (±) on summary graphics of the GTS as 2-sigma (95% confidence) values.

Geologic time is measured in years, but the standard unit for time is the second *s*. Because the Earth's rotation is not uniform, this "second" is not defined as a fraction (1/86,400) of a solar day, but as the *atomic second*. The basic principle of the atomic clock is that electromagnetic waves of a particular frequency are emitted when an atomic transition occurs. In 1967 the 13th General Conference on Weights and Measures defined the *atomic second* as the duration of 9,192,631,770 periods of the radiation corresponding to the transition between two hyperfine levels of the ground state of cesium-133. This value was established to agree as closely as possible with the solar-day second. The frequency of 9,192,631,770 Hz, which the definition assigns to cesium radiation was carefully chosen to make it impossible, by any existing experimental evidence, to distinguish the atomic second from the ephemeris second based on the Earth's motion. The advantage of having the atomic second as the unit of time in the International System of Units is the relative ease, in theory, for anyone to build and calibrate an atomic clock with a precision of 1 part per 10^{11} (or better). In practice, clocks are calibrated against broadcast time signals, with the frequency oscillations in hertz being the "pendulum" of the atomic time-keeping device.

1 year is approximately 31.56 mega seconds (1 a = ~31.56 Ms).

The Système International d'Unités (SI) conventions at 10^3 intervals that are relevant for spans of geologic time through sizes of microfossils are:

10^9	giga	G
10^6	mega	M
10^3	kilo	k
10^0	unity	1
10^{-3}	milli	m
10^{-6}	micro	µ
10^{-9}	nano	n

Although dates assigned in the GTS are measured in multiples of the atomic second as unit of time (year), there are two other types of seconds: *mean solar* second and *ephemeris* second.

Universal time is utilized in the application of astronomy to navigation. Measurement of universal time is made directly from observing the times of transits of stars; since the Earth's rotation is not uniform, corrections are applied to obtain a more uniform time system. In essence, universal time is the mean solar time on the Greenwich meridian, reckoned in days of 24 mean solar hours beginning with zero hour at midnight, and derives from the average rate of the daily motion of the Sun relative to the Greenwich meridian. The *mean solar second* is 1/86,400 of the mean solar day, but because of nonuniformity this unit is no longer the standard of international time.

Ephemeris time (ET) is uniform and obtained from observation by directly comparing positions of the Sun, Moon, and the planets with calculated ephemerides of their coordinates. Webster's dictionary defines ephemeris as any tabular statement of the assigned places of a celestial body for regular intervals. ET is based on the *ephemeris second* defined as 1/31,556,925.9447 of the tropical year for 1900 January 0 day 12-hour ET. The ephemeris day is 86400 ephemeris seconds, which unit in 1957 was adopted by the International Astronomical Union as the fundamental invariable unit of time.

1.4 Historical overview of geologic time scales

1.4.1 Paleozoic scales

The Paleozoic spans 286.9 Myr between 538.8 and 251.9 Ma. Its estimated duration has decreased about 60 Myr since the scales of Holmes (1960) and Kulp (1961). Selected key Paleozoic time scales are compared to GTS2020 in Fig. 1.4. Differences in relative estimated

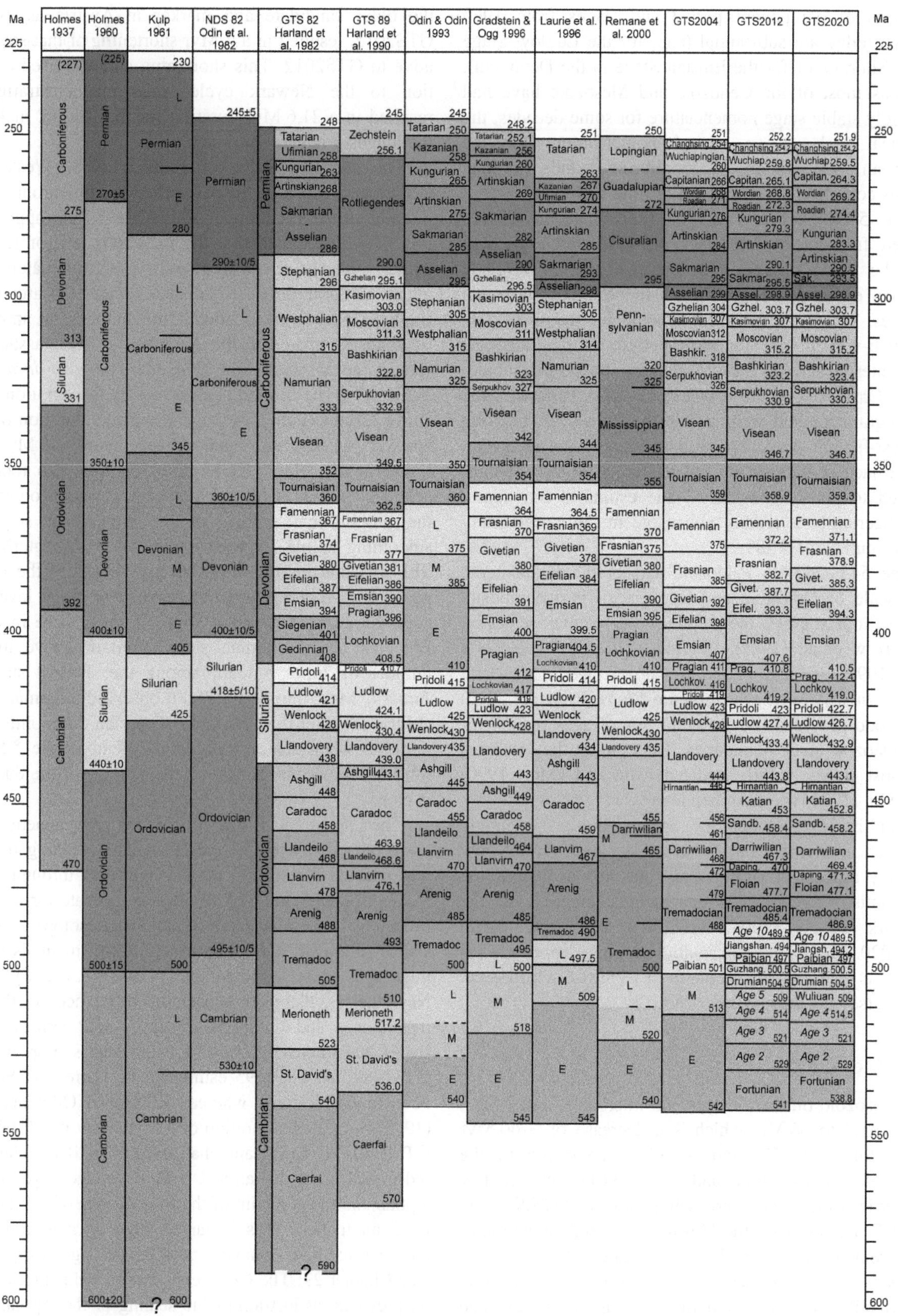

FIGURE 1.4 Comparison of selected Paleozoic time scales with GTS2020. In some columns epochs and stages are stacked together; scales of Holmes (1937, 1960) and Kulp (1961) are more detailed than shown.

durations of component period and stages from 1960 through today are substantial (e.g., for the Ludlow Stage in the Silurian, or for the Emsian Stage in the Devonian). Whereas most of the Cenozoic and Mesozoic have had relatively stable stage nomenclature for some decades, the historical lack of an agreed nomenclature for the Cambrian, Ordovician, Carboniferous, and Permian Periods complicates comparison of time scales.

The 570–245 Ma Paleozoic time scale in GTS89 derived from the marriage of the chronogram method with the chron concept. The chron concept in GTS89 assumed equal duration of zones in prominent biozonal schemes, such as a conodont scheme for the Devonian. The two-way graphs for each period in the Paleozoic were interpolated by hand, weighting tie points subjectively. Error bars on stage boundaries calculated with the chronogram method were lost in the process of drawing the best-fit line. The fact that the Paleozoic suffered both from a lack of data points and relatively large uncertainties led to poorly constrained age estimates for stages; this uncertainty is readily noticeable in the chronogram/chron figures of GTS89.

The 545–248 Ma Paleozoic part of the Phanerozoic time scale of Gradstein and Ogg (1996) is a composite from various sources, including the well-known scales by McKerrow et al. (1985), Harland et al. (1990), Roberts et al. (1995), and Tucker and McKerrow (1995).

The *International Stratigraphic Chart* (Remane, 2000) rather odd provided two different sets of ages for part of the Paleozoic stage boundaries. The column that has ages for most stages slightly updated Odin and Odin (1990) and Odin (1994) and is shown here.

Stability in methodology and a highly systematic approach involving a large slate of key experts, not only in many aspects of stratigraphy, but also in astronomy, geochemistry, geophysics and geomathematics, is the hallmark of GTS2004, GTS2012 and now again GTS2020. This broad and multidisciplinary approach has created a relatively stable platform to utilize and present the diverse data underlying each GTS.

1.4.2 Mesozoic scales

The Mesozoic time scale spans an interval of 185.9 Myr, from 251.9 to 66 Ma, which is a decrease of ~60 Myr since Holmes (1937) and ~35 Myr compared to the scales of Holmes (1960) and Kulp (1961). Selected key Mesozoic time scales are compared to GTS2020 in Fig. 1.5. The GTS for the Mesozoic has undergone major improvements during the last two decades, although weak "spots" remain, for example, the Norian and Rhaetian Stages still lack ratified definitions and have few age dates. For the base of the Rhaetian Stage, the use of its promoted candidate GSSP and marker in Italy, rather than the older candidate and marker in Austria as used in GTS2012, resulted in a 4-Myr shortening of that stage relative to GTS2012. This shortening and a revised correlation to the Newark cycle scale magnetostratigraphy resulted in a 21.6 Myr duration for the Norian, making it the longest Phanerozoic stage.

The Jurassic scales of KG85, EX88, Westermann (1988) and SEPM95 in part relied on biochronology to interpolate the duration of stages. As a first approximation, it was assumed that the numerous ammonite zones and/or subzones of the Jurassic have approximately equal mean duration between adjacent stages. Toarcian and Bajocian Stages have double the number of ammonite subzones compared to the Aalenian, so were assumed to span twice as much time (*but now compare duration in* Table 1.2). The limited age control on the duration of the entire Jurassic indicates that the average duration of each zone is ~1 Myr and each subzone is ~0.45 Myr (e.g., Westermann, 1988). KG85 and SEPM95 also took into account some intra-Jurassic age control points to constrain the proportional scaling of the component stages. A smoothing spline fit was applied by F.P. Agterberg in SEPM95 that incorporates the error limits of the isotope age dates. At the individual subzone or zonal level, this equal-duration assumption is now known to be incorrect. Bajocian and Bathonian stages contain above average number of zones but are among the shortest stages in Jurassic. McArthur et al. (2000) observed a dramatic variability in Pliensbachian and Toarcian ammonite zone duration when scaled to a linear trend in the $^{87}Sr/^{86}Sr$ ratio of the oceans. However, the average of the durations is close.

The Larson and Hilde's (1975) marine magnetic anomaly profile displayed by the Hawaiian spreading lineation was adapted for scaling of the Oxfordian through Aptian Stages in KG85 and SEPM95 to compensate for a paucity of isotope dates. Databases of radiogenic isotope ages were statistically analyzed with various best-fit methods to estimate ages of stage boundaries (GTS1989 and SEPM95). Nevertheless, there are substantial differences in the estimated ages and durations of stages and periods among scales constructed in the last two decades. For example, GTS1989 and SEPM95 estimated the Barremian Stage to be over 6 Myr long, whereas EX88 and Odin and Odin (1990) suggested a duration of 2 Myr. Now it is 5.1 Myr in GTS2020. A significant change in GTS2020, relative to older scales, is the almost 5-Myr younger age of base Aptian and the endpoint of the M-sequence of marine magnetic anomalies. This is largely due to new Barremian radiometric and magnetostratigraphic age assignments (see Chapter 27: The Cretaceous Period) which casts doubt on previous cyclostratigraphic scaling of the Aptian stage. Although a shorter Aptian stage also results in a younger set of stage boundary ages from Oxfordian through

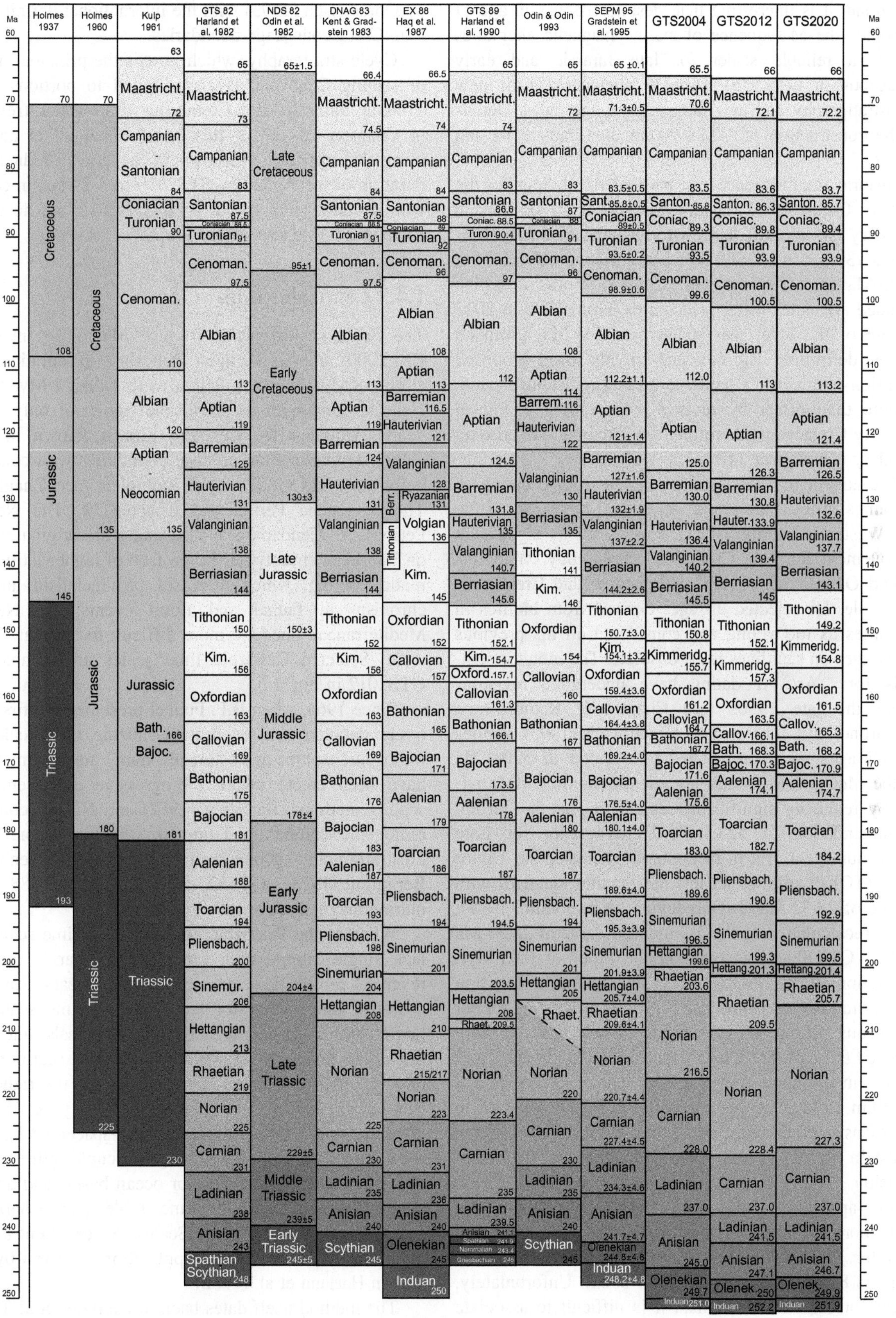

FIGURE 1.5 Comparison of selected Mesozoic time scales with GTS2020.

Barremian, it is interesting that, despite changes in age of tie points, the M-sequence of marine magnetic anomalies is still a reliable scaler for late Jurassic and early Cretaceous in GTS2020, strongly augmented with new cyclostratigraphy and new radioisotopic age dates. Details on the construction of GTS2020 are in Chapters 14 and 25–27.

Historic age differences are particularly obvious for the Jurassic–Cretaceous Transition: the Tithonian–Berriasian Boundary (which still lacks a formal and ratified definition) is 130 Ma in NDS82, 135 Ma in Remane (2000), but ~145 Ma in GTS1989 and SEPM95, both of which excluded age dates using glauconites. From 1995 to 2012 the age of the level was stable near 145 Ma, using an adopted definition. The new and slightly lower proposed definition outlined in Chapter 27, The Cretaceous Period, is more than offset by revised radioisotopic dating of the Early Cretaceous; therefore, the Tithonian–Berriasian boundary is now near 143 Ma.

The advent of $^{40}Ar/^{39}Ar$ radiogenic isotope dating of bentonites in local ammonite zones in a large part of the US Western Interior Cretaceous was a significant improvement for Late Cretaceous chronology. With this method Obradovich (1993) calibrated a Late Cretaceous time scale. He rejected all ages derived from biotites in bentonites as too young and considered all his previous K–Ar ages on sanidines to be obsolete. The monitor standards for $^{40}Ar/^{39}Ar$ dating have undergone revisions during the late 1990s (see Chapter 6: Radioisotope Geochronology). The text of Obradovich (1993) implies that all ages were normalized to a value of 520.4 Ma for the McClure Mountain hornblende monitor MMhb-1, thereby requiring significant recalculation to the current recommendation of 523.1 (~0.5 Myr older for Late Cretaceous ages). But in fact, Obradovich used the Taylor Creek (TC) rhyolite as an internal monitor standard with a value of 28.32 Ma (J. Obradovich, pers. comm., 1999); hence, recalculation to the TC monitor value of 28.34 Ma used in GTS2004 was only on the order of 0.05 Myr. Correlation of the North American ammonite zonation and Obradovich's associated linear scale to Upper Cretaceous European stages and zones was partially achieved through rare interchanges of ammonite and other marine macrofauna (reviewed in Cobban, 1993) and strontium isotope curves for portions of the Campanian and Maastrichtian (e.g., McArthur et al., 1993, 1994). Gradstein et al. (1994, 1995) incorporated the high-precision $^{40}Ar/^{39}Ar$ data of Obradovich (1993); the authors applied a cubic-spline fit to the data set. An even more refined version of this analysis was the basis for the GTS2004 scale for Late Cretaceous (see Chapters 8 and 19 in the GTS2004 book). Unfortunately, except for the basal Turonian, it is difficult to associate the endemic Western Interior ammonite zones calibrated by Obradovich (1993) with the international definitions of Late Cretaceous stage boundaries.

Cycle stratigraphy, which now is the principal method of scaling Cenozoic, is also applied to portions of the Triassic, Jurassic, and Cretaceous time scales (reviewed in Chapters 25–27 of this book). That all is not well using this approach is shown in the drastic reduction in duration of the Aptian in GTS2020 to 8.2 Myr, in conflict with its duration of 13.3 Myr in GTS2012. For details see Chapter 27, The Cretaceous Period.

1.4.3 Cenozoic scales

The Cenozoic time scale from 66 Ma to Recent (set at CE 2000) contains stages that vary in duration from almost 8 Myr for the Lutetian to less than 1 Myr for the Gelasian, and with the Holocene Epoch of only 11,800 years. Although the Cenozoic Era is known in much detail, standardization of stage boundaries with consensus definitions and GSSPs is not complete (see Chapter 28: The Paleogene Period and Chapter 29: The Neogene Period). All Cenozoic standard stages are originally based on European stratotypes. In the face of higher latitude climatic cooling, which increases provincialism and diachronism in faunal and floral events, the Neogene Mediterranean ones are more difficult to correlate worldwide. Selected Cenozoic time scales are compared to GTS2012 in Fig. 1.6.

Since 1964, when B.F. Funnel presented the first, relatively detailed, and accurate Cenozoic time scale with radiogenic isotope age estimates, many marine time scales have been erected with a progressive enhancement of scaling methods. Berggren (1972) and NDS82 combined radiogenic isotope age dating stratigraphic reasoning, and biostratigraphic–geomagnetic calibrations. Hardenbol and Berggren (1978), GTS82, DNAG83 and EX88 added marine magnetic reversal calibrations.

Whereas the Paleozoic and Mesozoic time scales still lack single interpolation methods, the marine magnetic reversals profile (C-sequence) for many years provided a powerful interpolator for the Cenozoic time scale. The large number of geomagnetic field reversals since Late Santonian time, coupled with a wealth of seafloor magnetic profiles and detailed knowledge of the radiogenic isotope age of selected magnetic polarity reversals in lavas and sediments, provide a finely spaced scale. These are combined with orbital tuning and cubic splines to produce spreading-rate models for ocean basins and an associated magnetic polarity time scale (see Chapter 5: Geomagnetic Polarity Time Scale). An excellent account of the method and its early applications is given by A.V. Cox in Harland et al. (1982).

The method itself dates back to Heirtzler et al. (1968), who selected a detailed profile in the South Atlantic from

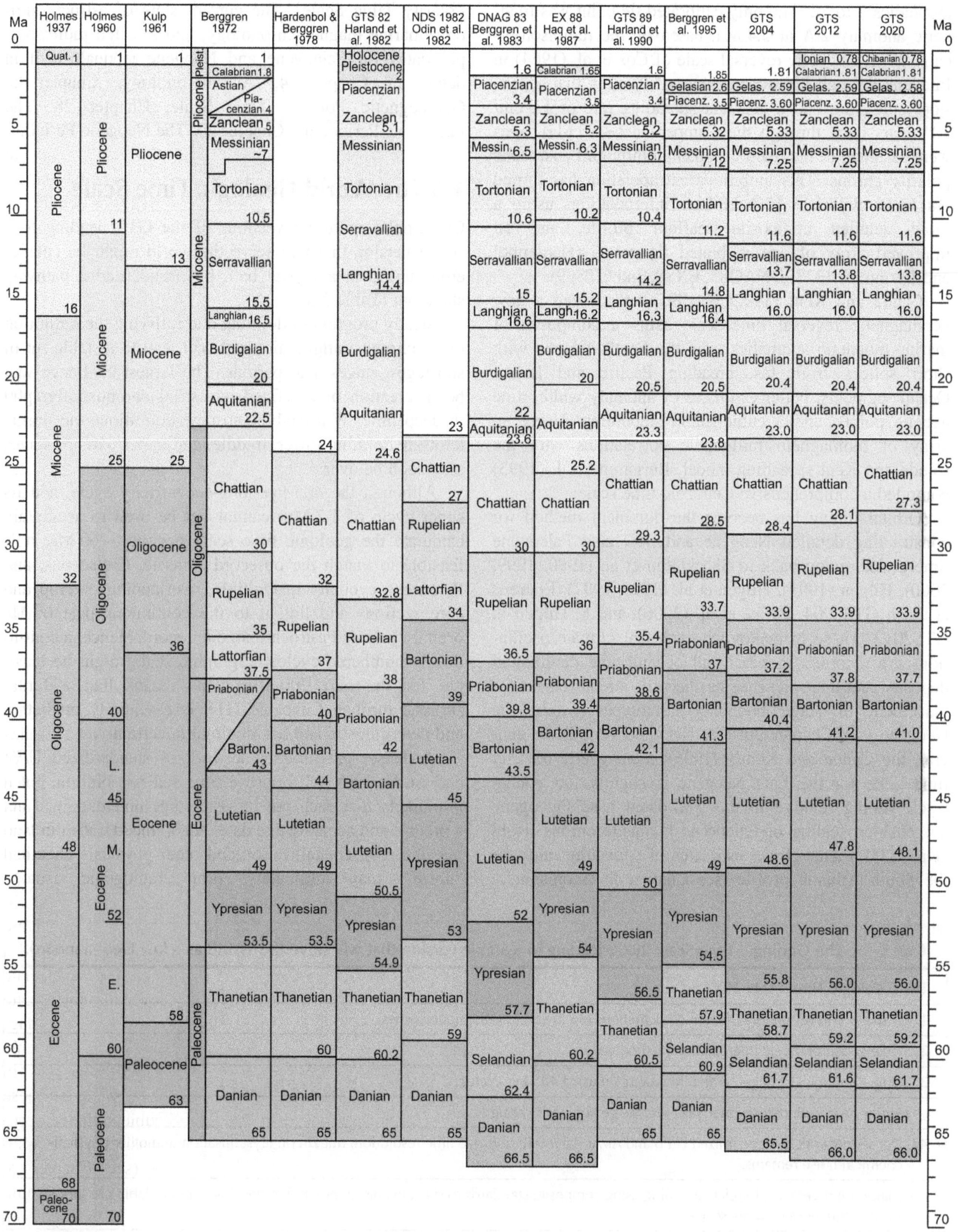

FIGURE 1.6 Comparison of selected Cenozoic time scales with GTS2020.

anomalies 2 to 32. The only calibrated tie point was magnetic anomaly 2 A at 3.4 Ma, based on the radioisotopically dated magnetic reversal scale of Cox et al. (1964) in Pliocene through Pleistocene lavas. Assuming that ocean-floor spreading had a constant spreading rate of 1.9 cm/10^3 years back through the Campanian ($\sim$80 Ma), ages were assigned to the main Campanian through Pleistocene polarity chrons. This ambitious extrapolation has turned out to be within $\sim$10% of later interpolations using a more detailed composite seafloor profile, and an improved array of age-calibrated tie points (Hardenbol and Berggren, 1978, DNAG83, EX88, and GTS89).

Cande and Kent (1992a,b, 1995) constructed a new geomagnetic reversal time scale using a composite of marine magnetic anomalies from the South Atlantic with short splices from fast-spreading Pacific and Indian Ocean segments, better estimates of anomaly width, nine age tie points, and a cubic-spline smoothing. Using an array of biomagnetostratigraphic correlations with the Cande and Kent spreading model, Berggren et al. (1995) compiled a comprehensive Cenozoic time scale.

Orbital tuning has become the dominant method for constructing detailed Neogene and now also Paleogene time scales, going back to Shackleton et al. (1990, 1999, 2000), Hilgen (1991), Hilgen et al. (1995, 1997), Lourens et al. in GTS2004, Pälike et al. (2006), and F. Hilgen in GTS2012. These Milankovitch cycles of climate oscillations are recorded in nearly all oceanic and continental deposits, and their presence has become a requirement for placement of stage boundary stratotypes within the Neogene (see Chapter 29; The Neogene Period). In general, the Cande and Kent's (1995) geomagnetic polarity time scale for the Late Neogene is slightly too young. Cycle tuning relative to the well-dated base Paleogene has enabled scaling of Paleocene magnetic chrons (Röhl et al., 2001) and refined estimates of spreading rates for the South Atlantic profile (see Chapter 5: Geomagnetic Polarity Time Scale). The current state of astrochronology, marine magnetochronology, and selected radioisotopic dates for Paleogene and Neogene is dealt with in detail in Chapter 4, Astrochronology, Chapter 5, Geomagnetic Polarity Time Scale, Chapter 28, The Paleogene Period, and Chapter 29, The Neogene Period.

1.5 The World Geologic Time Scale

Contemplating future versions of the GTS, leading to a stable version that will serve the world might be considered staring in a crystal ball, but trends and a pathway stand out (Table 1.3).

Steady progress in defining and ratifying the definition of all chronostratigraphic units will lead to a stable set of substages, stages, and periods. The largest challenge will be in creation of a refined terrestrial chronostratigraphy in deep time. With stable substage definitions the uncertainty in defining lower, middle, and upper parts of stages may soon be over.

Although the 405-kyr long-eccentricity cycle, and its super cycle of 1.2 Myr cannot yet be used to accurately calculate the geologic time scale beyond $\sim$60 Ma, it is feasible to match the observed Jurassic, Cretaceous, and Paleocene cyclicity in multiple, overlapping outcrop and core sections and link it to the continuous post 60 Ma orbital cycle and astrochronozone record. Hence, a continuously numbered cyclostratigraphic scale might be feasible for the past 200 Myr. This means that a future Jurassic through Cenozoic GTS is essentially predictive and deterministic and has minimal uncertainty.

A denser pre-Jurassic network of standardized U/Pb and Ar/Ar dates will improve time scale resolution, but it is unlikely that each pre-Jurassic stage boundary will get a precise and accurate age date. Also, uncertainties in timing of zircon crystallization and other physical–chemical "noise" may ultimately limit radiogenic isotope

TABLE 1.3 The Geologic Time Scale 20XX, leading to a stable version that will serve the World as a key Geo-standard.

The Geologic Time Scale 20XX
1. All stages and substages with ratified definitions (no lower, middle, upper issues).
2. Stable geochronologic interpolation methodology.
3. Stable Cenozoic, Cretaceous and Jurassic scale using 405 kyr cycles.
Hence, near truth deterministic post Triassic geologic time scale !
4a. Denser network of standardized U/Pb and Ar/Ar dates will improve time resolution, but zircon crystallisation and other physical-chemical noise remains.
4b. Major improvements in relative scaling using composite standards to stack events, zones and stages. Long and reliable pre-Jurassic cyclic sequences (floating scales).
Hence, detailed and probabilistic Cambrian through Triassic time scale.
5. World Geologic Time Scale for Deep-Time Earth Science !

chronology. More promising is the creation of long sequences of orbital cycles in the Mesozoic and Paleozoic, anchored on precise and accurate radioisotopic dating of key stratigraphic events. This, together with the construction of stable composite standard stacks of bio-magneto and geochemical events throughout the Paleozoic and older Mesozoic will create a superior deep-time scale. Proper documentation and geomathematical–statistical treatment of such a massive set of data is a critical issue.

The input for the calculation of a numerical time scale is a set of radioisotopic dates with variable uncertainty in both time (in Myr) and in biochronostratigraphic position. These selected input dates are irregularly distributed with respect to a biostratigraphic scale derived from graphical correlation, constrained optimization, or a stack of successive biozonal units. For selected intervals such scaling may also be adjusted for cyclostratigraphic and magnetochronologic durations. Spline fitting of such a complete dataset with two ways error estimation produces a linear time scale with error bars on the geologic stage boundary ages. The current methodology has served well since 1989 (see Chapter 14: Geomathematics).

Ultimately, the Paleozoic-early Mesozoic deep-time scale will still be probabilistic, but finely resolved, with effective applications for both terrestrial and marine strata. I refrain from speculating on the deep-time scale for Precambrian. It will get a stable set of Earth science, rather than abstract definitions, for its units; but scattering and erosion of all the broken Precambrian earth record pieces is so severe, that global resolution is wanting.

The message of GTS2020 is that the World GTS for regional and global Deep-Time Earth Science is well underway, leading to its stability as a key scientific, cultural, and educational standard.

A practical issue is that the World GTS since 2012 is fostered and has been published through the efforts of the Geologic Time Scale Foundation. Major updates have come every 8 years and a concise version, meant as a handy summary booklet of the standard Geologic Time Scale book was provided every 4 years. One should bear in mind that the summary booklet does not replace the main book with the standard international GTS. Publishing stability with the standard Geologic Time Scale book is important, bearing in mind that the standard time scale is the result of close and loyal *long-term* academic cooperation of stable isotope geochemists, geophysicists and radiogenic isotope experts, an astronomer, a geomathematics specialist, many "different discipline" biostratigraphers, chronostratigraphers, and geomagnetic specialists. To maintain this large specialist geo-network for the future Geologic Time Scale is vital. What is currently needed is the creation of a bureaucratic body in Earth Sciences that controls and communicates standards and conventions. Such a "Bureau of Geostandards" ultimately will be able to maintain a master and more final version of the World GTS, under advise and service of a group of impartial, non-nationalistic scientific specialists. Hence, numeric time scale stability will be taken care of to the benefit of science, economy and culture on Earth.

Bibliography

Berggren, W.A., 1972, A Cenozoic time-scale—some implications for regional geology and paleobiogeography. *Lethaia*, **5**: 195–215.

Berggren, W.A., Kent, D.V., Swisher III, C.C., and Aubry, M.-P., 1995, A revised Cenozoic geochronology and chronostratigraphy. *In* Berggren, W.A., Kent, D.V., Aubry, M.-P., and Hardenbol, J. (eds), *Geochronology, Time Scales, and Global Stratigraphic Correlation.* SEPM Special Publications, **54**: 129–212.

Cande, S.C., and Kent, D.V., 1992a, A new geomagnetic polarity time scale for the Late Cretaceous and Cenozoic. *Journal of Geophysical Research*, **97**: 13917–13951.

Cande, S.C., and Kent, D.V., 1992b, Ultrahigh resolution of marine magnetic anomaly profiles: a record of continuous paleointensity variations? *Journal of Geophysical Research*, **97**: 15075–15083.

Cande, S.C., and Kent, D.V., 1995, Revised calibration of the geomagnetic polarity timescale for the Late Cretaceous and Cenozoic. *Journal of Geophysical Research*, **100**: 6093–6095.

Cobban, W.A., 1993, Diversity and distribution of Late Cretaceous ammonites, Western Interior, United States. *In* Caldwell, W.G.E., and Kauffman, E.G. (eds), *Evolution of the Western Interior Basin.* Geological Association of Canada Special Paper, **Vol. 39**: 435–451.

Cox, A., Doell, R.R., and Dalrymple, G.B., 1964, Reversals of Earth's magnetic fields. *Science*, **144**: 1537–1543.

Gradstein, F.M., and Ogg, J.G., 1996, A Phanerozoic time scale. *Episodes*, **19**: 3–5.

Gradstein, F.M., Agterberg, F.P., Ogg, J.G., Hardenbol, J., van Veen, P., Thierry, T., et al., 1994, A Mesozoic time scale. *Journal of Geophysical Research*, **99** (B12), 24051–24074.

Gradstein, F.M., Agterberg, F.P., Ogg, J.G., Hardenbol, J., Van Veen, P., Thierry, J., et al., 1995, A Triassic, Jurassic and Cretaceous time scale. *In* Berggren, W.A., Kent, D.V., Aubry, M.-P., and Hardenbol, J. (eds), *Geochronology, Time Scales, and Global Stratigraphic Correlation.* SEPM Special Publications, **Vol. 54**: 95–126.

Gradstein, F.M., Ogg, J.G., and Smith, A.G. (eds), 2004. *A Geologic Time Scale 2004.* Cambridge University Press, Cambridge, 589 pp.

Gradstein, F.M., Ogg, J.G., Schmitz, M.D. and Ogg, G.M. (eds.), 2012. *The Geologic Time Scale 2012.* Elsevier Publ. Co., 1144 pp.

Hardenbol, J., and Berggren, W.A., 1978, A new Paleogene numerical time scale. *In* Cohee, G.V., Glaessner, M., and Hedberg, H. (eds), *Contributions to the Geologic Time Scale*. American Association of Petroleum Geologists Studies in Geology, **Vol. 6**: 213–234.

Hardenbol, J., Thierry, J., Farley, M.B., Jacquin, T., de Graciansky, P.-C., and Vail, P.R., 1998, Mesozoic and Cenozoic sequence chronostratigraphic framework of European basins. *In* de Graciansky, P.-C., Hardenbol, J., Jacquin, T., and Vail, P.R. (eds), *Mesozoic and Cenozoic Sequence Stratigraphy of European Basins.* SEPM Special Publication, **60**: 3–13.

Harland, W.B., 1978, Geochronologic scales, 1978. *In* Cohee, G.V., Glaessner, M., and Hedberg, H. (eds), *Contributions to the Geologic Time Scale*. American Association of Petroleum Geologists Studies in Geology, **Vol. 6**: 9–32.

Harland, W.B., Cox, A.V., Llewellyn, P.G., Pickton, C.A.G., Smith, A.G., and Walters, R., 1982, *A Geologic Time Scale*. Cambridge University Press, Cambridge, 131 pp.

Harland, W.B., Armstrong, R.L., Cox, A.V., Craig, L.A., Smith, A.G., and Smith, D.G., 1990, *A Geologic Time Scale 1989*. Cambridge University Press, Cambridge, 263 pp.

Heirtzler, J.R., Dickson, G.O., Herron, E.M., Pitman, W.C., and Le Pichon, X., 1968, Marine magnetic anomalies, geomagnetic field reversals, and motions of the ocean floor and continents. *Journal of Geophysical Research*, **73**: 2119–2139.

Hilgen, F.J., 1991, Extension of the astronomically calibrated (polarity) time scale to the Miocene-Pliocene boundary. *Earth and Planetary Science Letters*, **107**: 349–368.

Hilgen, F.J., Krijgsman, W., Langereis, C.G., Lourens, L.J., Santarelli, A., and Zachariasse, W.J., 1995, Extending the astronomical (polarity) time scale into the Miocene. *Earth and Planetary Science Letters*, **136**: 495–510.

Hilgen, F.J., Krijgsman, W., and Wijbrans, J.R., 1997, Direct comparison of astronomical and $^{40}Ar/^{39}Ar$ ages of ash beds: potential implications for the ages of mineral dating standards. *Geophysical Research Letters*, **24**: 2043–2046.

Hilgen, F.J., Lourens, L.J., Pälike, H., and research support team, 2020, Should unit-stratotypes and astrochronozones be formally defined? A dual proposal (including postscriptum). *Newsletters on Stratigraphy*, 32: 19–39, doi: 10.1127/nos/2019/0514.

Holden, N.E., Bonardi, M.L., De Bièvre, P., Renne, P.R., and Villa, I. M., 2011, IUPAC-IUGS common definition and convention on the use of the year as a derived unit of time (IUPAC Recommendations 2011). *Pure and Applied Chemistry*, **93**: 1159–1162.

Holmes, A., 1937, *The Age of the Earth*, second ed. Thomas Nelson, London.

Holmes, A., 1947, The construction of a geological time-scale. *Transactions of the Geological Society of Glasgow*, **21**: 117–152.

Holmes, A., 1960, A revised geological time-scale. *Transactions of the Edinburgh Geological Society*, **17**: 183–216.

Holmes, A., 1965, *Principles of Physical Geology*. Nelson Printers, London.

Kulp, J.L., 1961, Geologic time-scale. *Science*, **133**: 1105–1114.

Larson, R.L., and Hilde, T.W.C., 1975, A revised time scale of magnetic reversals for the Early Cretaceous and Late Jurassic. *Journal of Geophysical Research*, **80**: 2586–2594.

Lourens, L.J., Hilgen, F.J., Laskar, J., Shackleton, N.J., and Wilson, D., 2004. The Neogene Period. *In* Gradstein, F.M., Ogg, J.G., and Smith, A.G. (eds), *A Geological Time Scale 2004*. Cambridge University Press, Cambridge, 409–440.

McArthur, J.M., Thirlwall, M.F., Gale, A.S., Chen, M., and Kennedy, W.J., 1993, Strontium isotope stratigraphy in the Late Cretaceous: numerical calibration of the Sr isotope curve and intercontinental correlation for the Campanian. *Paleoceanography*, **8**: 859–873.

McArthur, J.M., Kennedy, W.J., Chen, M., Thirlwall, M.F., and Gale, A. S., 1994, Strontium isotope stratigraphy for the Late Cretaceous: direct numerical age calibration of the Sr-isotope curve for the US. Western Interior Seaway. *Palaeogeography, Palaeoclimatology, Palaeoecology*, **108**: 95–119.

McArthur, J.M., Donovan, D.T., Thirlwall, M.F., Fouke, B.W., and Mattey, D., 2000, Strontium isotope profile of the early Toarcian (Jurassic) Oceanic Anoxic Event, the duration of ammonite biozones, and belemnite paleotemperatures. *Earth and Planetary Science Letters*, **179**: 269–285.

McKerrow, W.S., Lambert, R.S.J., and Cocks, L.R.M., 1985, The Ordovician, Silurian and Devonian Periods. *In* Snelling, N.J. (ed), *The Chronology of the Geological Record*. Geological Society of London Memoir, **10**: 73–80.

Obradovich, J.D., 1993, A Cretaceous time scale, Special Paper. *In* Caldwell, W.G.E., and Kauffman, E.G. (eds), *Evolution of the Western Interior Basin*. Geological Association of Canada, **39**: 379–396.

Odin, G.S., 1994, Geologic Time Scale (1994). *Comptes rendus de l'Académie des Sciences de Paris*, **318**: 59–71.

Odin, G.S., and Odin, C., 1990, Échelle numérique des temps géologiques. *Géochronologie*, **35**: 12–20.

Ogg, J.G., Ogg, G., and Gradstein, F.M., 2008, *The Concise Geologic Time Scale*. Cambridge University Press, Cambridge.

Ogg, J.G., Ogg, G.M., and Gradstein, F.M., 2016, *A Concise Geologic Time Scale 2016*. Elsevier, Cambridge, 234 pp.

Pälike, H., Norris, R.D., Herrie, J.O., Wilson, P.A., Coxall, H.K., Lear, C.H., et al., 2006, The heartbeat of the Oligocene climate system. *Science*, **414**: 1894–1898.

Remane, J., 2000, International Stratigraphic Chart, with Explanatory Note. Sponsored by ICS, IUGS and UNESCO. *31st International Geological Congress, Rio de Janeiro* (p. 16).

Roberts, J., Claoué-Long, J.C., and Jones, P.J., 1995, Australian Early Carboniferous time. *In* Berggren, W.A., Kent, D.V., Aubry, M.-P., and Hardenbol, J. (eds), *Geochronology, Time Scales and Global Stratigraphic Correlations: A Unified Temporal Framework for a Historical Geology*. SEPM Special Publication, **54**: 23–40.

Röhl, U., Ogg, J.G., Geib, T., and Weber, G., 2001, Astronomical calibration of the Danian time scale. *In* Kroon, D., Norris, R.D., and Klaus, A. (eds), *Western North Atlantic Paleogene and Cretaceous Palaeoceanography*. Geological Society of London Special Publication, **Vol. 183**: 163–183.

Shackleton, N.J., Berger, A., and Peltier, W.A., 1990, An alternative astronomical calibration of the lower Pleistocene time scale based on ODP Site 677. *Transactions of the Royal Society of Edinburgh Earth Sciences*, **81**: 251–261.

Shackleton, N., Crowhurst, S., Weedon, G., and Laskar, J., 1999, Astronomical calibration of Oligocene-Miocene time. *Philosophical Transactions: Mathematical, Physical and Engineering Sciences*, **357**: 1907–1929.

Shackleton, N.J., Hall, M.A., Raffi, I., Tauxe, L., and Zachos, J., 2000, Astronomical calibration age for the Oligocene-Miocene boundary. *Geology*, **28**: 447–450.

Tucker, R.D., and McKerrow, W.S., 1995, Early Paleozoic chronology: a review in light of new U-Pb zircon ages from Newfoundland and Britain. *Canadian Journal of Earth Sciences*, **32**: 368–379.

Weedon, G.P., Jenkyns, H.C., Coe, A.L., and Hesselbo, S.P., 1999, Astronomical calibration of the Jurassic time-scale from cyclostratigraphy in British mudrock formations. *Philosophical Transactions of the Royal Society of London, Series A*, **357**: 1787–1813.

Westermann, G.E.G., 1988. Duration of Jurassic stages based on average and scaled subzones. *In* Agterberg, F.P., and Rao, C.N. (eds), *Recent Advances in Quantitative Stratigraphic Correlation*. Hindustan Publishing, Delhi, 90–100.

Young, G.C., and Laurie, J.R., 1996, *An Australian Phanerozoic Timescale*. Oxford University Press, Oxford.

Chapter 2

F.M. Gradstein and J.G. Ogg

The Chronostratigraphic Scale

Chapter outline

Abstract

Geologic stages and other international subdivisions of the Phanerozoic portion of the geologic scale are defined by their lower boundaries at Global Boundary Stratotype Sections and Points (GSSPs). The main criteria for a GSSP are that primary and secondary markers provide the means for global correlation. GSSP theory and criteria are outlined, and the status of ratified GSSPs provided. Global Standard Stratigraphic Age (GSSA) levels provide the abstract Precambrian scale. Subdivisions of the *Standard Stratigraphic Chart* are summarized and illustrated.

2.1 History of geologic stratigraphic standardization

The stratigraphic schemes erected by the pioneering stratigraphers of the 19th century challenged the first International Geological Congress (IGC) in Paris in 1878 to undertake the creation of a standard stratigraphic scale. Suggestions were made for standard colors (Anonymous, 1882), uniformity of geologic nomenclature, and the adoption of uniform subdivisions. There was also a review of regional stratigraphic problems.

In the succeeding congress in Bologna in 1881, many of the above suggestions were taken substantially further, that is, the international geologic maps were planned with standard colors for stratigraphic periods and rock types (e.g., Anonymous, 1882) and annexes contained national contributions toward standardization of stratigraphic classification.

In spite of this promising start, the IGCs did not have the continuing organization to carry these proposals through, except for the commissions established to produce international geologic maps. The latter is now the invaluable Commission for the Geologic Map of the World (CGMW; see https://cgmw.org). Guides setting out the stratigraphic principles, terminology, and classificatory procedures were prepared by the International Commission on Stratigraphic Terminology created in 1952 by the 19th IGC in Algiers, and now the International Subcommission on Stratigraphic Classification under the International Commission of Stratigraphy (ICS). The *International Stratigraphic Guide* was published in 1976 (Hedberg, 1976) and is now in its second edition (Salvador, 1994; Murphy and Salvador, 1999). A digital version of this rather boring, but critical bible, may be consulted at http://timescalefoundation.org/strat_guide/abguid.html.

It was not until the establishment of the International Union of Geological Sciences (IUGS) around 1960 that the goal of establishing an international chronostratigraphic scale had a means of fulfillment, through the IUGS's ICS and its many subcommissions. The International Commission on Stratigraphy (www.stratigraphy.org) is the largest and oldest constituent scientific body in IUGS. Guidelines for defining global chronostratigraphic units were established (e.g., Cowie et al., 1986 and enhanced by Remane et al., 1996). At the occasion of the 28th IGC the ICS published the first *Global Stratigraphic Chart* that reflects much current stratigraphic use. At the 31st IGC in Rio de Janeiro, the 32nd in Florence, and the 33rd in Oslo, new editions of that chart indicated the current international standardization and included abbreviations and colors of the stratigraphic units as adopted by the CGMW (Remane, 2000; Gradstein et al., 2004, 2012; Ogg et al., 2008, 2016; see also Appendix 1 in this book). The 2020 version of the Standard Stratigraphic Chart is reproduced in Fig. 2.1, with stratigraphic updates provided by ICS at its website, listed above and also at https://timescalefoundation.org. Between 2012 and 2020, 10 new GSSPs have

Geologic Time Scale 2020. DOI: https://doi.org/10.1016/B978-0-12-824360-2.00002-4

PHANEROZOIC and PRECAMBRIAN CHRONOSTRATIGRAPHY

Eonothem Eon	Erathem Era	System Period	Series/ Epoch	Stage/Age	Age Ma	GSSP
Phanerozoic	Cenozoic	Quaternary	Anthropocene *			
			Holocene U	Meghalayan	4.3 ka	
			Holocene M	Northgrippian	8.2 ka	
			Holocene L	Greenlandian	11.7 ka	
			Pleistocene	Upper	126 ka	
				Chibanian	773 ka	
				Calabrian	1.81	
				Gelasian	2.58	
		Neogene	Pliocene	Piacenzian	3.60	
				Zanclean	5.33	
			Miocene	Messinian	7.25	
				Tortonian	11.63	
				Serravallian	13.82	
				Langhian	15.99	
				Burdigalian	20.45	
				Aquitanian	23.04	
		Paleogene	Oligocene	Chattian	27.3	
				Rupelian	33.9	
			Eocene	Priabonian	37.7	
				Bartonian	41.0	
				Lutetian	48.1	
				Ypresian	56.0	
			Paleocene	Thanetian	59.2	
				Selandian	61.7	
				Danian	66.0	
	Mesozoic	Cretaceous	Upper	Maastrichtian	72.2	
				Campanian	83.7	
				Santonian	85.7	
				Coniacian	89.4	
				Turonian	93.9	
				Cenomanian	100.5	
			Lower	Albian	113.2	
				Aptian	121.4	
				Barremian	126.5	
				Hauterivian	132.6	
				Valanginian	137.7	
				Berriasian	143.1	
		Jurassic	Upper	Tithonian	149.2	
				Kimmeridgian	154.8	
				Oxfordian	161.5	
			Middle	Callovian	165.3	
				Bathonian	168.2	
				Bajocian	170.9	
				Aalenian	174.7	
			Lower	Toarcian	184.2	
				Pliensbachian	192.9	
				Sinemurian	199.5	
				Hettangian	201.4	
		Triassic	Upper	Rhaetian	205.7	
				Norian	226.8	
				Carnian	237.0	

* Anthropocene under discussion

Eonothem Eon	Erathem Era	System Period	Series/ Epoch	Stage/Age	Age Ma	GSSP
					237.0	
Phanerozoic	Mesozoic	Triassic	Middle	Ladinian	241.5	
				Anisian	246.7	
			Lower	Olenekian	249.9	
				Induan	251.9	
	Paleozoic	Permian	Lopingian	Changhsingian	254.2	
				Wuchiapingian	259.5	
			Guadalupian	Capitanian	264.3	
				Wordian	269.2	
				Roadian	274.4	
			Cisuralian	Kungurian	283.3	
				Artinskian	290.5	
				Sakmarian	293.5	
				Asselian	298.9	
		Carboniferous – Pennsylvanian	Upper	Gzhelian	303.7	
				Kasimovian	307.0	
			Middle	Moscovian	315.2	
			Lower	Bashkirian	323.4	
		Carboniferous – Mississippian	Upper	Serpukhovian	330.3	
			Middle	Visean	346.7	
			Lower	Tournaisian	359.3	
		Devonian	Upper	Famennian	371.1	
				Frasnian	378.9	
			Middle	Givetian	385.3	
				Eifelian	394.3	
			Lower	Emsian	410.5	
				Pragian	412.4	
				Lochkovian	419.0	
		Silurian	Pridoli		422.7	
			Ludlow	Ludfordian	425.0	
				Gorstian	426.7	
			Wenlock	Homerian	430.6	
				Sheinwoodian	432.9	
			Llandovery	Telychian	438.6	
				Aeronian	440.5	
				Rhuddanian	443.1	
		Ordovician	Upper	Hirnantian	445.2	
				Katian	452.8	
				Sandbian	458.2	
			Middle	Darriwilian	469.4	
				Dapingian	471.3	
			Lower	Floian	477.1	
				Tremadocian	486.9	
		Cambrian	Furongian	Stage 10	491.0	
				Jiangshanian	494.2	
				Paibian	497.0	
			Miaolingian	Guzhangian	500.5	
				Drumian	504.5	
				Wuliuan	509.0	
			Series 2	Stage 4	514.5	
				Stage 3	521.0	
			Terreneuvian	Stage 2	529.0	
				Fortunian	538.8	

Eonothem Eon	Erathem/ Era	System/ Period	Age Ma	GSSP/ GSSA
			541	
Precambrian – Proterozoic	Neoproterozoic	Ediacaran	635	
		Cryogenian	720	
		Tonian	1000	
	Mesoproterozoic	Stenian	1200	
		Ectasian	1400	
		Calymmian	1600	
	Paleoproterozoic	Statherian	1800	
		Orosirian	2050	
		Rhyacian	2300	
		Siderian	2500	
Precambrian – Archean	Neoarchean		2800	
	Mesoarchean		3200	
	Paleoarchean		3600	
	Eoarchean		4000	
Hadean (informal)			~4560	

Units of the international chronostratigraphic scale with estimated numerical ages.

Colors are according to the Commission for the Geological Map of the World.

Subdivisions of the Phanerozoic (~538.8 Ma to Present) and the base of the Ediacaran are defined by a basal Global Boundary Stratotype Section and Point (GSSP), whereas the Precambrian units are formally subdivided by absolute age (Global Standard Stratigraphic Age, GSSA).

Stratigraphic information and details on international and regional geologic units can be found on the websites of the **Geologic TimeScale Foundation** *https://timescalefoundation.org/* and the **ICS** *www.stratigraphy.org*.

FIGURE 2.1 The 2020 version of the Standard Stratigraphic Chart, showing with a "golden spike," which Phanerozoic and Ediacaran stages, series, and period units have formally defined boundary definitions. As of early 2020, 75 out of 102 units are defined by such Global Boundary Stratotype Section and Point (GSSP). Precambrian units are formally defined by absolute age (Global Standard Stratigraphic Age, GSSA). The chart is kept updated on the website https://timescalefoundation.org.

been formalized, for a current total of 75. More than 25 GSSPs remain to be formally defined. The main intervals currently (early 2020) having few ratified GSSPs are the Serpukhovian through Kungurian and the Callovian through Aptian, with shorter intervals without formalized stages in parts of Cambrian, Triassic, Upper Eocene, and Lower Miocene.

2.2 Stage unit stratotypes

It is not too long ago that stratigraphers were spending time in dealing with type sections of stages and correlation of stage units in terms of zones, and not in terms of fossil or other geo-events. The "New Paleogene Numerical Scale" published in 1978 by Hardenbol and Berggren was a classical study that took its chronostratigraphic starting point from the definition and duration of stages, in this case the classical Paleocene, Eocene and Oligocene stage unit stratotypes. The concept of boundary stratotypes at that time was still in its infancy, and boundaries between Paleogene stages were arbitrarily interpolated using carefully selected biostratigraphic criteria. The stratotypes span less than half of Paleogene time; some are simply facies equivalents rather than chronostratigraphically distinct units. Only a few of these competing stage concepts are preserved in the nomenclature of the present Paleogene geologic time scale. As may be readily observed in Fig. 2.2, none of the modern Paleogene stages have their boundaries defined in these unit stratotypes. International stages for the Paleogene are defined at boundary stratotypes in which the basal boundary of the stage is positioned relative to primary and secondary biostratigraphic, geochemical, or magnetic polarity events for global correlation, and as it turned out, none of the sections now selected as boundary stratotypes (Chapter 28: The Paleogene Period) also serve as potential unit stratotypes.

It is readily understood that the absence of stage boundary definitions may lead to uncertainty in stage correlation. This is particularly so if a regional or ad hoc definition of a stage boundary provides no basis for "global correlation." A classic example is the existing regional suite of stages or series in the Ordovician that was found unsatisfactory in its entirety for global application. Reasons are the marked faunal provincialism and facies differentiation throughout most of the Ordovician. The Ordovician subcommission of ICS, therefore, undertook to identify the best fossil-based datums, wherever they are found, for global correlation and to use these for the definition of global chronostratigraphic (and chronologic) units (Chapter 20: The Ordovician Period). In this respect, it deviated from the course followed by the Silurian and Devonian subcommissions of ICS, both of which recommended the adoption of preexisting (regional) stage or

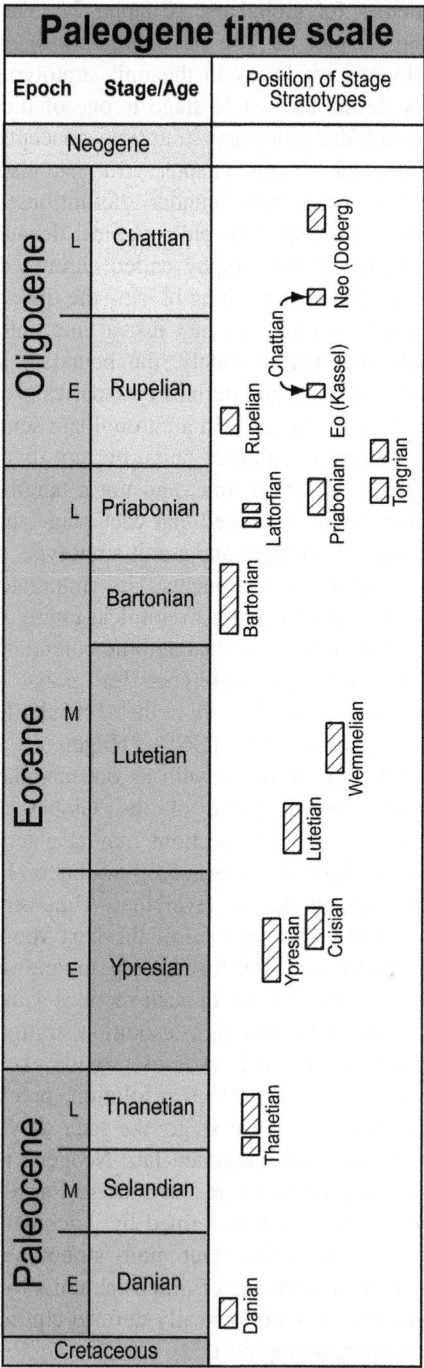

FIGURE 2.2 Stratigraphic range of 14 historical stratotypes of Paleogene stages. The stratotypes span less than half of Paleogene time; some are simply facies equivalents rather than chronostratigraphic distinct units. Only eight of these competing stage concepts are preserved in the nomenclature of the present Paleogene geologic time scale. International stages for the Paleogene are now defined through boundary stratotypes in which the basal boundary of the stage is positioned relative to primary and secondary biostratigraphic, geochemical, or magnetic polarity events for global correlation. *Modified from Hardenbol and Berggren (1978).*

series schemes for global use (Chapter 21: The Silurian Period, and Chapter 22: The Devonian Period).

The obvious weakness in the unit stratotype concept to actually define the whole stage is one of the defining arguments for the boundary stratotype concepts, as outlined further on in this chapter. But, as also can be argued, a stage with only boundary definitions (base and top) opens up an important philosophical debate, namely that the branch of stratigraphy called chronostratigraphy has as its fundamental building block—the time-rock unit. A stage is a time-rock unit, not just a time unit, and not just a rock unit. Unfortunately, the boundary stratotype concept only outlines and defines boundaries of units, and not the content of the unit. In a chronologic sense, it provides the abstract duration of units, but not its content. It defines an abstraction in time, and not a tangible unit in rock. Hence, it can be argued that each stage should both have boundary stratotypes and a unit stratotype.

Now, recent developments in integrated high-resolution stratigraphy and astronomical tuning of continuous deep marine successions combine potential unit stratotypes and boundary stratotypes for global stages as basic building blocks of the standard Global Chronostratigraphic Scale (GCS) (Hilgen et al., 2006, 2020). For the late Neogene with its outstanding orbitally tuned stratal record, some of the Global Stratotype Section and Point (GSSP) sections may also serve as unit stratotypes, defined as coverage of the interval from the base of a stage up to the level that—time stratigraphically—correlates with the base of the next younger stage in a continuous and well-tuned deep marine succession (Fig. 2.3). The added value of such sections as unit stratotype lies in the integrated high-resolution stratigraphy and astronomical tuning. Such sections provide excellent age control with an unprecedented resolution, precision, and accuracy within the entire stage. As such they form the backbone of the new integrated late Neogene time scale and provide the basis for reconstructing Earth's history. In this way a stage is also defined by its content and not only by its boundaries. Our unit stratotype concept strengthens the importance of time-rock units by allowing the introduction of astronomically defined chronozones as formal chronostratigraphic units, thereby arguing against the elimination of the dual classification of chronostratigraphy and geochronology. Extending this concept to older time intervals requires that well-tuned, continuous deep marine sections are employed, thus necessitating the employment of multiple deep-sea drilling sites for defining (remaining) stages and stage boundaries in at least the Cenozoic and Cretaceous, and possibly the entire Mesozoic. Evidently, the construction of the geologic time scale should be based on the most appropriate sections available while, where possible, taking the historical concept of global stages into account.

A major outcome of this progressive stratigraphic philosophy is the formal definition of unit stratotypes and [astro]chronozones (Hilgen et al., 2020). The [astro]chronozones imply that cycles used for the orbital tuning of strata can be formally defined as chronostratigraphic units, independent of the standard hierarchy in global chronostratigraphy. More information is in Chapter 29, The Neogene Period, of this GTS volume where the astronomically age calibrated chronozones (Milankovitch chronozones) are presented for the Neogene System/Period, although they are not formally defined yet and incorporated in the standard chronostratigraphic scale. Thus in the Neogene 405-kyr cycles are identified (Fig. 29.1) which correspond to Neogene astrochronozones 7 through 57.

2.3 Global Boundary Stratotype Section and Point (GSSP)

How can one standardize such fragmentary and disparate material as the stratigraphic record?

Even by the first IGC in 1878, the belief that the stratigraphic systems and other divisions being described in any one place were natural chapters of Earth history was fading, and the need to adopt some conventions was widely recognized. Even so, the practice continued treating stratal divisions largely as biostratigraphic units, and even today it is an article of faith for many Earth scientists that divisions of the developing international stratigraphic scale are defined by the fossil content of the rocks. To follow this through, however, leads to difficulties: boundaries may change with new fossil discoveries, boundaries defined by particular fossils will tend to be diachronous, and there will be disagreement as to which taxa shall be definitive.

As elaborated by Hedberg (1976), one of the major champions of practical and rational thinking in stratigraphic standardization:

> *In my opinion, the first and most urgent task in connection with our present international geochronology scale is to achieve a better definition of its units and horizons so that each will have standard fixed-time significance and the same time significance for all geologists everywhere. Most of the named international chronostratigraphic (geochronology) units still lack precise globally accepted definitions and consequently their limits are controversial and variably interpreted by different workers. This is a serious and wholly unnecessary impediment to progress in global stratigraphy. What we need is simply a single permanently fixed and globally accepted standard definition for each named unit or horizon, and this is where the concept of stratotype standards (particularly boundary stratotypes and other horizon stratotypes) provides a satisfactory answer.*

The standardization advocated by Hedberg and other stratigraphers has been the major task of ICS through the

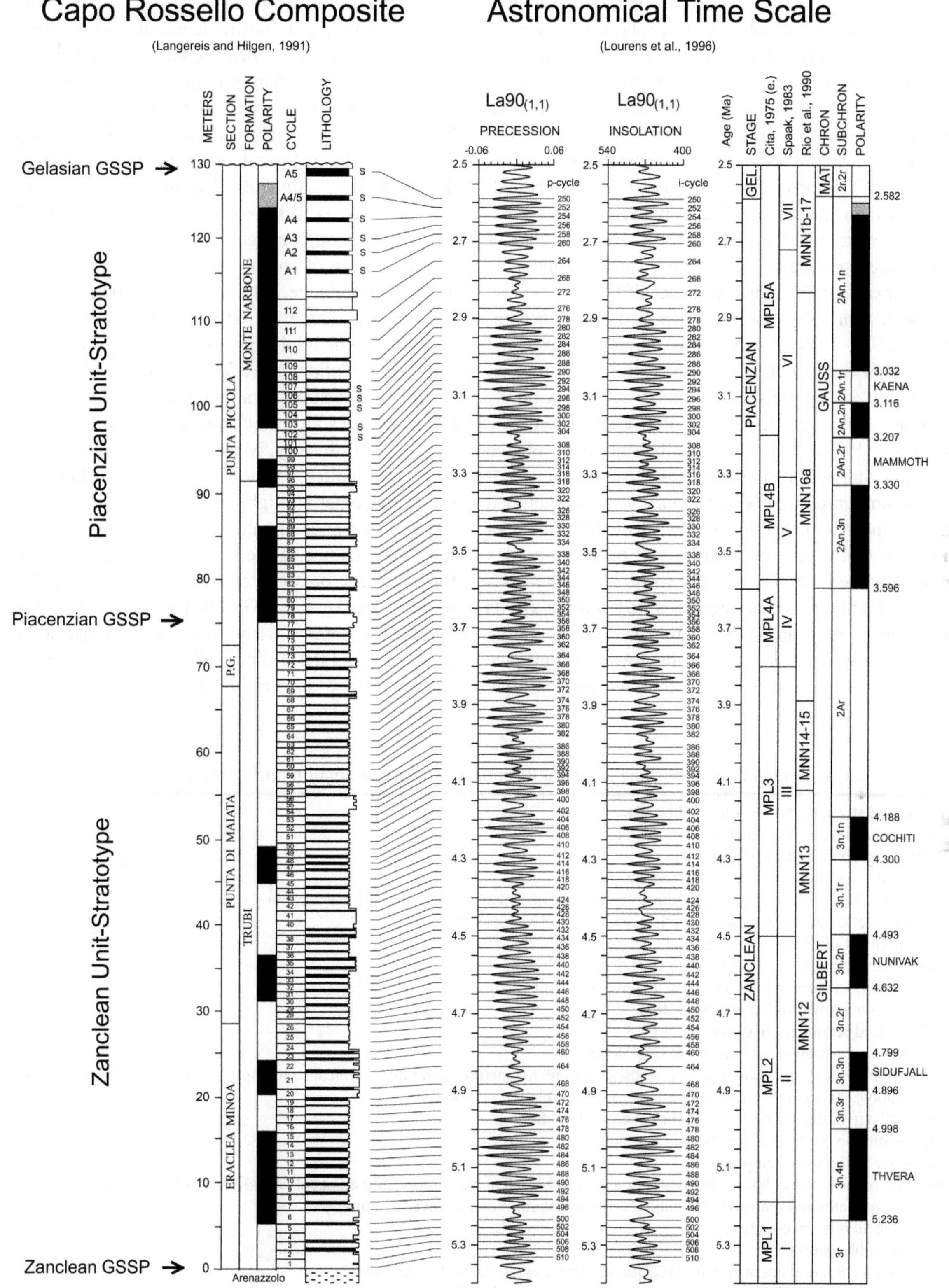

FIGURE 2.3 The RCS (Sicily, Italy) is a prime example of the modified unit stratotype approach showing the orbital tuning of the basic precession-controlled sedimentary cycles and the resulting astronomical time scale with accurate and precise astronomical ages for sedimentary cycles, calcareous plankton events, and magnetic reversal boundaries. The Zanclean and Piacenzian GSSPs are formally defined in the RCS while the level that time stratigraphically correlates with the Gelasian GSSP is found in the topmost part of the section. The well-tuned RCS lies at the base of the Early–Middle Pliocene part of the Neogene Time Scale and the Global Standard Chronostratigraphic Scale and as such could serve as unit stratotype for both the Zanclean and Piacenzian Stages. *RCS*, Rossello Composite Section.

application of the principle of boundary stratotypes; as mentioned above, the current status of this application is actively maintained in the official website of ICS. The traditional stratigraphic scale using stage stratotypes has evolved into a standard chronostratigraphic scale in which the basal boundary of each stage is standardized at a point in a single reference section within an interval exhibiting continuous sedimentation. This precise reference point for each boundary is known as the Global Stratotype Section and Point (GSSP) and represents the point in time when that part of the rock succession began. The global chronostratigraphic scale is ultimately defined by a sequence of GSSPs.

It is now nearly 45 years since the first boundary stratotype or GSSP "golden spike" was defined. It fixed the lower limit of the Lochkovian Stage, the oldest stage of the Devonian, at a precise level in an outcrop with the appropriate name of Klonk in the Czech Republic (Martinsson, 1977). Paleontologically, the base of the Lochkovian Stage coincides with the first occurrence of the Devonian graptolite *Monograptus uniformis* in bed No. 20 of the Klonk Section northeast of the village of Suchomasty (Chlupáč, 1993). However, once the golden spike has been agreed, the discovery, say, of *M. uniformis* below the GSSP does not require a redefinition of its position, but simply an acknowledgment that the initial level chosen was not in fact at the lowest occurrence of the particular graptolite. For this reason, multiple secondary correlation markers, including nonbiostratigraphic methods, are desirable within each GSSP section.

Each GSSP must meet certain requirements and secondary desirable characteristics (Remane et al., 1996; Table 2.1). The main considerations are as follows: (1) the boundary is recognizable outside the GSSP locality; therefore it must be tied to other events in Earth history that are documented in sediments elsewhere and (2) the reference GSSP section is well exposed with the GSSP level within an interval of apparent continuous sedimentation.

The choice of an appropriate boundary level is of paramount importance. "Before formally defining a geochronologic boundary by a GSSP, its practical value—*i.e.* its correlation potential—has to be thoroughly tested. In this sense, *correlation precedes definition*" (Remane, 2003). Without correlation, stratigraphic units and their constituent boundaries are of not much use, and devoid of meaning for Earth history. Most GSSPs coincide with a single "primary marker," which is generally a biostratigraphic event, but other stratigraphic events with widespread correlation potential should coincide or bracket the GSSP level. The choice of the criteria for an international stage boundary can be a contentious issue (e.g., Fig. 2.4). Most primary markers for GSSPs have been biostratigraphic events, but some have utilized other global stratigraphic episodes (e.g., the iridium spike at the base-Cenozoic, the carbon isotope anomaly at the base-Eocene, the base of

TABLE 2.1 Requirements for establishing a Global Boundary Stratotype Section and Point (GSSP).

1. Name and stratigraphic rank of the boundary
Including a concise statement of GSSP definition
2. GSSP geographic and physical geology
Geographic location, including map coordinates
Geologic setting (lithostratigraphy, sedimentology, paleobathymetry, postdepositional tectonics, etc.)
Precise location and stratigraphic position of GSSP level and specific point
Stratigraphic completeness across the GSSP level
Adequate thickness and stratigraphic extent of the section above and below
Accessibility, including logistics, national politics, and property rights
Provisions for conservation and protection
3. Primary and secondary markers
Principal correlation event (marker) at GSSP level
Other primary and secondary markers—biostratigraphy, magnetostratigraphy, chemical stratigraphy, sequence stratigraphy, cycle stratigraphy, other event stratigraphy, marine-land correlation potential
Potential age dating from volcanic ashes and/or orbital tuning
Demonstration of regional and global correlation
4. Summary of the selection process
Relation of the GSSP to historical usage; references to historical background and adjacent (stage) units; selected publications
Other candidates and reasons for rejection; summary of votes and received comments
Other useful reference sections
5. Official publication
Summary for full documentation in IUGS journal *Episodes* or *Newsletter on Stratigraphy*
Digital stratigraphy (lith, paleo, mag, chem.), images and graphic files submitted to ICS for public archive
Full publication in an appropriate journal

Revised from Remane et al. (1996) according to current procedures and recommendations of the IUGS International Commission on Stratigraphy (ICS). *IUGS*, International Union of Geological Science.

Different Concepts of Stage Boundaries
modified from cartoon in Birkelund et al., 1983

FIGURE 2.4 One reason that decisions on international boundaries of stages are difficult. Two experts with different paleontological specialties arguing over the suitable primary marker based on different biostratigraphic criteria. *Modified from Birkelund et al. (1983).*

magnetic polarity Chron C6Cn.2n at the base-Neogene, and a specific Milankovitch cycle for base-Pleistocene).

The requirement for continuous sedimentation across the GSSP level and the bracketing correlation markers is to avoid assigning a boundary to a known "gap" in the geologic record. This requirement has generally eliminated most historical stratotypes for stages (see Fig. 2.2), which were commonly delimited by flooding or exposure surfaces and, formally, represent synthems. As a result, the scope of classical stages is modified, and either the traditional nomenclature is abandoned (e.g., the revised stage nomenclature for the Ordovician and Cambrian periods) or a historical name is given a slightly new meaning to update its practical usage.

Era	Period	Series/ Epoch	Stage	GSSPs
Cenozoic	Quaternary	Holocene	Meghalayan	Mawmluh Cave, Meghalaya, India
			Northgrippian	North GRIP ice core, Greenland
			Greenlandian	North GRIP ice core, Greenland
		Pleistocene	Upper	
			Chibanian	Chiba, Japan
			Calabrian	Vrica, Calabria, Italy
			Gelasian	Monte San Nicola, Sicily, Italy
	Neogene	Pliocene	Piacenzian	Punta Picola, Sicily, Italy
			Zanclean	Eraclea Minoa, Sicily, Italy
		Miocene	Messinian	Oued Akrech, Rabbat, Morocco
			Tortonian	Monte dei Corvi Beach, Ancona, Italy
			Serravallian	Ras il Pellegrin, Fomm Ir-Rih Bay, Malta
			Langhian	
			Burdigalian	
			Aquitanian	Lemme-Carrosio, N. Italy
	Paleogene	Oligocene	Chattian	Monte Cagnero, Umbria-Marche region, Italy
			Rupelian	Massignano, Ancona, Italy
		Eocene	Priabonian	Alano, Italy
			Bartonian	
			Lutetian	Gorrondatxe, N. Spain
			Ypresian	Dababiya, Luxor, Egypt
		Paleocene	Thanetian	Zumaia, Spain
			Selandian	Zumaia, Spain
			Danian	El Kef, Tunisia
Mesozoic	Cretaceous	Upper	Maastrichtian	Tercis-les-Bains, Landes, SW. France
			Campanian	
			Santonian	Olazagutia, Northern Spain
			Coniacian	
			Turonian	Rock Canyon, Pueblo, Colorado, USA
			Cenomanian	Mont Risou, Rosans, Haute-Alpes, France
		Lower	Albian	Col de Pré- Guittard, Drôme, France
			Aptian	
			Barremian	
			Hauterivian	La Charce, Drôme, France
			Valanginian	
			Berriasian	
	Jurassic	Upper	Tithonian	
			Kimmeridgian	
			Oxfordian	
		Middle	Callovian	
			Bathonian	Ravin du Bès, Provence, France
			Bajocian	Cabo Mondego, W. Portugal
			Aalenian	Fuentelsaz, Spain
		Lower	Toarcian	Ponta do Trovao, Peniche, Portugal
			Pliensbachian	Robin Hood's Bay, Yorkshire, UK
			Sinemurian	East Quantox Head, West Somerset, UK
			Hettangian	Kuhjoch, Tyrol, Austria
	Triassic	Upper	Rhaetian	
			Norian	
			Carnian	Prati di Stuores, Italy
		Middle	Ladinian	Bagolino, Italy
			Anisian	
		Lower	Olenekian	
			Induan	Meishan, Zhejiang, China

FIGURE 2.5 Distribution of ratified GSSPs in the Mesozoic and Cenozoic Eras (status of early 2020).

Era	Period	Series/ Epoch	Stage	GSSPs
Paleozoic	Permian	Lopingian	Changhsingian	Meishan, Zhejiang, China
			Wuchiapingian	Penglaitan, Guangxi, China
		Guadalupian	Capitanian	Guadalupe Mountains, TX, USA
			Wordian	Guadalupe Mountains, TX, USA
			Roadian	Stratotype Canyon, TX, USA
		Cisuralian	Kungurian	
			Artinskian	
			Sakmarian	Usolka, Russia
			Asselian	Aidaralash, Ural Mountains, Kazakhstan
	Carboniferous	Penn-sylvanian Upper	Gzhelian	
			Kasimovian	
		Penn-sylvanian Middle	Moscovian	
		Penn-sylvanian Lower	Bashkirian	Arrow Canyon, Nevada, USA
		Missis-sippian Upper	Serpukhovian	
		Missis-sippian Middle	Visean	Pengchong, South China
		Missis-sippian Lower	Tournaisian	La Serre, Montagne Noir, France
	Devonian	Upper	Famennian	Coumiac, Cessenon, Montagne Noir, France
			Frasnian	Col du Puech, Montagne Noir, France
		Middle	Givetian	Jebel Mech Irdane, Tafilalt, Morocco
			Eifelian	Wetteldorf Richtschnitt, Eifel Hills, Germany
		Lower	Emsian	Zinzil'ban Gorge, Uzbekistan
			Pragian	Velka Chuchle, SW Prague, Czech Rep.
			Lochkovian	Klonk, SW of Prague, Czech Republic
	Silurian	Pridoli		Pozary, Prague, Czech Republic
		Ludlow	Ludfordian	Sunnyhill, Ludlow, UK
			Gorstian	Pitch Coppice, Ludlow, UK
		Wenlock	Homerian	Whitwell Coppice, Homer, UK
			Sheinwoodian	Hughley Brook, Apedale, UK
		Llandovery	Telychian	Cefn Cerig, Llandovery, UK
			Aeronian	Trefawr, Llandovery, UK
			Rhuddanian	Dob's Linn, Moffat, UK
	Ordovician	Upper	Hirnantian	Wangjiawan, Yichang, Hubei, China
			Katian	Black Knob, Oklahoma, USA
			Sandbian	Fågelsång, Scania, Sweden
		Middle	Darriwilian	Huangnitang, Zhejiang, China
			Dapingian	Huanghuachang, Yichang, Hubei, China
		Lower	Floian	Diabasbrottet, Hunneberg, Sweden
			Tremadocian	Green Point Newfoundland, Canada
	Cambrian	Furongian	*Stage 10*	
			Jiangshanian	Duibian, Zhejiang, China
			Paibian	Paibi, Hunan, China
		Miaolingian	Guzhangian	Louyixi, Guzhang, Hunan, China
			Drumian	Drum Mountains, Utah, USA
			Wuliuan	Wuliu-Zengjiayan, Guizhou, China
		Series 2	*Stage 4*	
			Stage 3	
		Terreneuvian	*Stage 2*	
			Fortunian	Fortune Head, Newfoundland, Canada

FIGURE 2.6 Distribution of ratified GSSPs in the Paleozoic Era (status of early 2020).

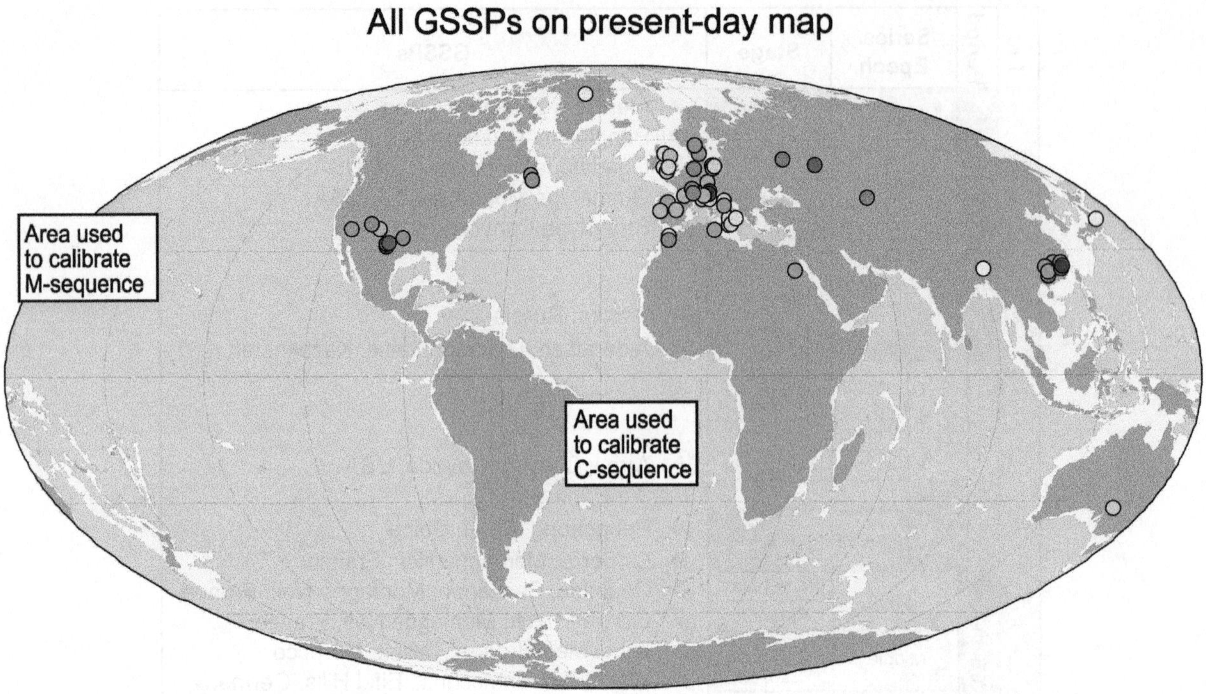

FIGURE 2.7 Geographic distribution of ratified GSSPs on a present-day (0 Ma) map (*status of early 2020*). Most of the GSSPs are located in western Europe, where the clustering has overlapped many GSSPs on this diagram. The approximate oceanic areas used to calibrate the C- and M-sequences of the magnetic polarity time scale are indicated by large rectangles (for details see Chapter 5: Geomagnetic Polarity Time Scale). Small circles are color coded according to their stage colors.

Difficulties in identifying global correlation criteria, problems introduced by biogeographic provincialism, and the occasional need to abandon stage concepts based on historical regional usage have slowed the assignment of GSSPs in some periods, as will be elaborated in the period chapters of this volume. Suitable GSSPs with full documentation are proposed by stratigraphic subcommissions or working groups under ICS, undergo approval voting through ICS and ratification by IUGS, and then are published.

At the time of this writing (early 2020), 75 of the 102 Phanerozoic stage units have been defined by boundary stratotypes, and the criteria for most primary markers to be associated with GSSPs for other stages have been decided. The base of the Cretaceous, the only Phanerozoic period without a formal definition, is still an issue; although an elegant solution now exists with geomagnetics and planktonic biota in deep-water Tethyan sections, rather than with traditional but unpractical ammonites (see Chapter 27: The Cretaceous Period, for details). The great majority of defined and probable GSSPs are in Western Europe (Figs. 2.5–2.7). This distribution mostly reflects the historical accident that stratigraphic studies first developed in Western Europe, but is also due to tectonic processes that kept Western Europe in low-latitude shallow-sea environments for much of the Phanerozoic Eon and have subsequently exposed the richly fossiliferous sections that were the basis of the historical compilations of the chronostratigraphic scale.

GSSP information is kept up to date on the websites http://stratigraphy.org and https://timescalefoundation.org/ with the latest stage names (e.g., within the Cambrian and the Quaternary) and which stages have received formal and ratified boundary definitions.

2.4 Global Standard Stratigraphic Age (GSSA)

Due to the fact that most Proterozoic and Archean rocks lack adequate fossils for correlation, a different type of boundary definition was applied for subdividing these eons into eras and periods [see Chapter 16: Precambrian (4.56 Ga to 1 Ga)]. For these two eons the assigned boundary, called a Global Standard Stratigraphic Age (GSSA), is a chronometric boundary and is not represented by a GSSP in rocks, nor can it ever be. However, although there appears to be consensus that the division into eras is possible, the assignment of strata into these types of finer period subdivisions can be very challenging. An alternative Precambrian classification based on stages in planetary evolution with, in most cases, possible associated GSSPs has been suggested by Van Kranendonk et al. (2012).

2.5 Other considerations for choosing a GSSP

The basic requirements for a GSSP are that it is located in a stratigraphically continuous section, should be readily accessible and well exposed, and should ideally contain multiple markers suitable for global correlation. A GSSP is the precise definition of the base of a stratigraphic boundary in a rock sequence, but that boundary is defined only at one point on Earth. The assignment of the chronostratigraphic boundary within other stratigraphic sections requires correlation to the GSSP.

The ideal GSSP would be in a low-latitude highly fossiliferous marine section (for global biostratigraphic correlation) that contains cyclic sediments or interbedded volcanic ash or lava beds (for isotopic dating or measurement of durations), unambiguous magnetic polarity changes (for high-precision global correlation), and one or more geochemical signatures (to provide additional high-precision global correlation markers).

Surprisingly perhaps, GSSPs located in sections that have an abundant fauna may also introduce unknown correlation errors, particularly if they are in shallow-water shelf environments likely contain hiatuses (Sadler, 1981; Sadler and Strauss, 1990). It is unclear what contribution such a hiatus makes to the overall global correlation uncertainties, as opposed to GSSP events of purely evolutionary origin, such as the presence or absence of a given fossil or fossils.

GSSPs are necessarily part of an outcrop exposed by uplift and erosion, and most are in relatively undistorted strata. However, some GSSPs, such as the Late Devonian GSSP at the Montagne Noire of southeastern France and base-Maastrichtian GSSP, are in tightly folded strata and may no longer retain magnetostratigraphic, geochemical or other secondary markers for global correlation.

The absence of precise global markers for high-precision time scale work is a key problem that was glossed over in some GSSP decisions. If the GSSP is defined in purely biostratigraphic or lithostratigraphic terms and there are no accompanying high-precision secondary markers, such as is the case for some of the Silurian GSSPs, then the likely correlation errors are at least 0.5 Myr and in some cases perhaps as high as 5 Myr. Such GSSPs are unsatisfactory and will eventually need reconsideration (e.g., by working groups of the Silurian Subcommission of ICS established in 2002).

The ideal GSSP is at a horizon amenable to radiogenic isotope and/or astronomical cycle calibration or is bracketed by dateable horizons. This coincidence has been achieved for only a few GSSP placements (e.g., bases of all Pliocene and Upper Miocene stages, the base of the Turonian Stage of the Cretaceous, the base of the Triassic, and some Carboniferous stage levels). If such a horizon is absent, it is essential to be able to correlate to dateable horizons elsewhere using precise global correlation markers.

The stratigraphic advances made by ocean drilling (e.g., the Deep Sea Drilling Project and the Ocean Drilling Program) were from multidisciplinary teams utilizing a wide array of shipboard and down-hole investigations. By contrast, GSSP golden spikes are most commonly placed in well-exposed continental sections where the excellence of the outcrop seems to preclude the need for more expensive methods of sampling such as coring. Coring and multimethod analysis of GSSP sections could provide a wealth of data for high-precision time scale work as well as providing secondary correlation markers. Previously unsuspected events, such as a hiatus or subtle rhythmic sedimentary patterns that cannot easily be detected by outcrop sampling, might also be revealed. For example, magnetic susceptibility has been fundamental for correlating Late Pleistocene sediments over a wide area of the northeast Atlantic (Robinson et al., 1995) and for correlating and identifying the orbital components in latest Triassic–Jurassic successions in England (Weedon et al., 1999). The GSSP for the base of the Holocene Series (Quaternary System) is in an archived Greenland ice core; with the Holocene itself now formally subdivided into the Greenlandian, Northgrippian and Meghalayan stages.

References

Anonymous, 1882, Congrès International de Géologie, Comptes Rendus de la 2ème Session, Bologna 1881. Bologna: Fava and Garagni, 661 pp.

Birkelund, T., Callomon, J.H., Clausen, C.K., Nøhr Hansen, H., and Salinas, I., 1983, The Lower Kimmeridge Clay at Westbury, Wiltshire, England. *Proceedings of the Geologists' Association*, **94**: 289–309.

Chlupáč, I., 1993, *Geology of the Barrandian: A Field Trip Guide*. Senckenberg Bücher, p. 163.

Cowie, J.W., Ziegler, W., Boucot, A.J., Bassett, M.G., and Remane, J., 1986, Guidelines and statutes of the International Commission of Stratigraphy (ICS). *Courier Forschungsinstitut Senckenberg*, **83**: 1–14.

Gradstein, F.M., Ogg, J.G., and Smith, A.G. (eds), 2004. *A Geologic Time Scale 2004*. Cambridge University Press, Cambridge, pp. 589.

Gradstein, F.M., Ogg, J.G., Schmitz, M.D., and Ogg (coordinators), G.M., 2012, *The Geologic Time Scale 2012*. Elsevier Publ., p. 1176.

Hardenbol, J., and Berggren, W.A., 1978, A new Paleogene numerical time scale, 1978, Contributions to the geologic time scale. *In* Cohee, G.V., Glaessner, M., and Hedberg, H. (eds), *American Association of Petroleum Geologists Studies in Geology*. 6. 213–234.

Hedberg, H. (ed), 1976. *International Stratigraphic Guide: A Guide to Stratigraphic Classification, Terminology and Procedure*. Wiley, New York.

Hilgen, F., Brinkhuis, H., and Zachariasse, J.W., 2006, Unit stratotypes for global stages: the Neogene perspective. *Earth-Science Reviews*, **74**: 113–125.

Hilgen, F.J., Lourens, L.J., Pälike, H., and research support team, 2020, Should Unit-Stratotypes and Astrochronozones be formally defined? A dual proposal (including postscriptum). *Newsletters on Stratigraphy*, **53**: 19–39, https://doi.org/10.1127/nos/2019/0514.

Martinsson, A. (ed), 1977. *The Silurian-Devonian Boundary: final report of the Committee of the Siluro-Devonian Boundary within IUGS Commission on Stratigraphy and a state of the art report for Project Ecostratigraphy. International Union of Geological Sciences, Series A.*

Murphy, M.A., and Salvador, A., 1999, International Stratigraphic Guide – an abridged version. *Episodes*, **22**: 255–271.

Ogg, J.G., Ogg, G., and Gradstein, F.M., 2008, *The Concise Geologic Time Scale*. Cambridge University Press, p. 177.

Ogg, J.G., Ogg, G., and Gradstein, F.M., 2016, *A Concise Geologic Time Scale 2016*. Elsevier Publ., p. 234.

Remane, J., 2000, International Stratigraphic Chart, with Explanatory Note. Sponsored by ICS, IUGS and UNESCO. In: 31st International Geological Congress, Rio de Janeiro, p. 16.

Remane, J., 2003, Chronostratigraphic correlations: their importance for the definition of geochronologic units. *Palaeogeography, Palaeoclimatology, Palaeoecology*, **196**: 7–18.

Remane, J., Bassett, M.G., Cowie, J.W., Gohrbandt, K.H., Lane, H.R., Michelsen, O., et al., 1996, Revised guidelines for the establishment of global chronostratigraphic standards by the International Commission on Stratigraphy (ICS). *Episodes*, **19** (3), 77–81.

Robinson, S.G., Maslin, M.A., and McCave, I.N., 1995, Magnetic susceptibility variations in Upper Pleistocene deep-sea sediments of the NE Atlantic: implications for ice rafting and paleocirculation at the last glacial maximum. *Paleoceanography*, **10**: 221–250.

Sadler, P.M., 1981, Sediment accumulation rates and the completeness of stratigraphic sections. *The Journal of Geology*, **89**: 569–584.

Sadler, P.M., and Strauss, D.J., 1990, Estimation of completeness of stratigraphical sections using empirical data and theoretical models. *Journal of the Geological Society*, **147**: 471–485.

Salvador, A. (ed), 1994. *International Stratigraphic Guide: A Guide to Stratigraphic Classification, Terminology, and Procedure*. second ed. *International Subcommission on Stratigraphic Classification of IUGS International Commission on Stratigraphy*, Trondheim.

Van Kranendonk, M.J., Altermann, W., Beard, B.L., Hoffman, P.F., Johnson, C.J., and Kasting, J.F., 2012, A chronostratigraphic division of the Precambrian: possibilities and challenges. *In* Gradstein, F.M., Ogg, J.G., Schmitz, M., and Ogg, G. (eds), *The Geologic Time Scale*. Elsevier Publ., **357**: 299–392, https://doi:10.1016/B978-0-444-59425-9.00023-8.

Weedon, G.P., Jenkyns, H.C., Coe, A.L., and Hesselbo, S.P., 1999, Astronomical calibration of the Jurassic time-scale from cyclostratigraphy in British mudrock formations. *Philosophical Transactions of the Royal Society of London. Series A*, **357**: 1787–1813.

Part II

Concepts and Methods

Coordinated by F.M. Gradstein

Chapter 3

Evolution and Biostratigraphy

Chapter outline

Abstract

Twelve mini chapters in *Geologic Time Scale 2020* address Evolution and Biostratigraphy in key micro- and macrofossil groups. The chapters assist readers of the Geologic Period chapters to better understand and appreciate the role played by paleontology in describing and understanding Life on Earth in Deep Time.

The last decades have witnessed tremendous progress in understanding the evolution, catastrophies, paleoecology, and biostratigraphy of macro- and microfossils. The standard Geologic Time Scales in 2004, in 2012 and now in 2020 (GTS2004, GTS2012, and GTS2020) have benefitted enormously from these quantum leaps in our knowledge of biota in Deep Time. At the same time the relevant literature is massive and not portrayed in handy manuals side by side with the current time scale volumes. Both GTS2004 and GTS2012 have special chapters on physical and chemical applications in geology (e.g., on carbon and oxygen isotopes) and outline many such applications critical to our understanding of Deep Time and its event dynamics. But no such critical chapters were provided for the biota in Deep Time.

This we wanted to rectify, but without publishing a complete textbook in the GTS2020 volumes. The result is 12 mini chapters on 11 key fossil groups, briefly presenting evolution, biostratigraphy and paleoecology with attractive illustrations. The final section 3L, Three Major Mass Extinctions and Evolutionary Radiations in Their Aftermath, summarizes some (but not all!) major mass extinctions. The authors of these 12 chapters have taken pains to keep the content short and avoid too much Latin. The choice of chapters is ours, and it is not complete with respect to all fossil groups utilized in the time scale book. Also, the chapters are not rigidly edited for conformity in outline and style, and we kindly request the reader to accept this. We trust readers will appreciate that this is an attempt to address an imbalance in chapters contributing to a better understanding and use of the standard Geologic Time Scale. Digest and Enjoy!

Geologic Time Scale 2020. DOI: https://doi.org/10.1016/B978-0-12-824360-2.00003-6

Subchapter 3A

Trilobites

S. Peng, L.E. Babcock and P. Ahlberg

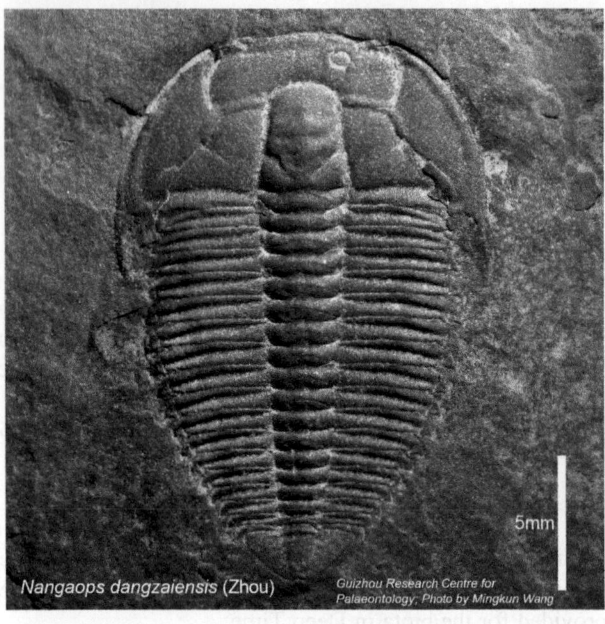

Abstract

Trilobites are marine arthropods that appeared in Cambrian Epoch 2 and became extinct at the end of the Permian. In some Paleozoic deposits, they number among the most abundant macrofossils. Trilobites are important for early Paleozoic biostratigraphy, especially Cambrian.

Trilobites comprise a group of marine arthropods—the class Trilobita, which appeared in the earliest part of Cambrian Epoch 2 (provisional name), lived through nearly the entire Paleozoic Era, and became extinct at the end of the Permian Period. Their remains thus span a time interval of approximately 270 million years. Trilobites have an excellent fossil record, in large part because the animals added calcite to their chitinous protective layer (integument), primarily on the dorsal side, and because they molted as they grew. In some Paleozoic deposits, they number among the most abundant macrofossils. Trilobites are one of the principal biostratigraphic tools used in the lower Paleozoic, and especially in the Cambrian System.

The word "trilobite" was coined about 250 years ago by Walch (1771). The name alludes to the distinctive appearance of the dorsal exoskeleton, which is divided lengthwise into three ("tri") lobes or regions: a central axial lobe and two laterally disposed pleural lobes. The dorsal exoskeleton of an adult trilobite is also divided transversely into three parts: the cephalon (head shield), thorax, and pygidium (tail shield). The axial region, or axis, consists of a glabella on the cephalon, and a series of rings in the thorax and pygidium. The hypostome is a rather broad plate, or sclerite, located beneath the anterior region of the glabella. Its manner of attachment to the rostral plate or doublure is considered to be of significance for understanding the evolution and higher level classification of trilobites (Fortey and Chatterton, 1988; Fortey, 1990; Fortey and Owens, 1997).

The evolutionary record shows that trilobites underwent considerable changes in morphology and position within marine ecosystems during the 270 million years that they existed on Earth. They experienced a number of episodes of phylogenetic diversification, extinction, recovery, and replacement. Rapid evolutionary changes of trilobites, including some distinct faunal turnovers, have led to the recognition of distinct assemblages of taxa and have provided the basis for identifying short biostratigraphic and chronostratigraphic intervals. The combination of evolution and extinction has led to the recognition of assemblages that not only characterize each period of the Paleozoic but also allow us to finely subdivide some periods, especially the Cambrian and Ordovician (see Chapter 19: The Cambrian Period and Chapter 20: The Ordovician Period). The Cambrian Period is colloquially known as the "Age of Trilobites" because of the extraordinary abundance and number of species in strata of that time interval. This information has been used to great effect especially for the Cambrian System. All internal subdivisions of the

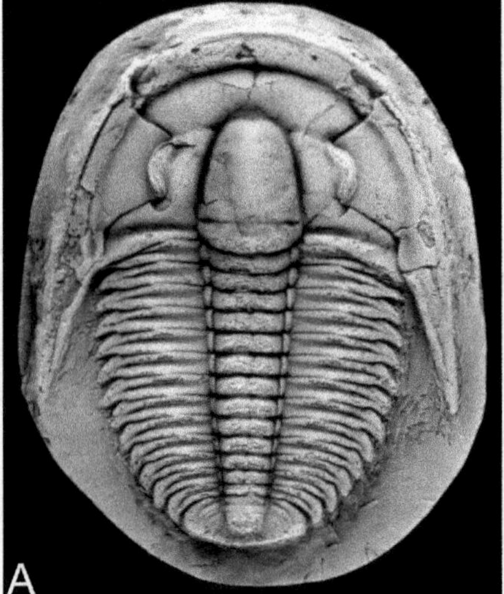

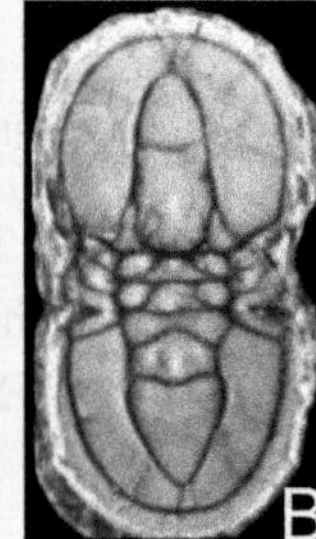

FIGURE 3A.1 Comparison of the calcified dorsal exoskeletons of a typical polymerid trilobite, *Modocia kohli* (Robison and Babcock, 2011), length 25 mm (A), and an agnostoid, *Ptychagnostus atavus* (Tullberg, 1880), length 8 mm (B), both from the Wheeler Formation (Cambrian: Drumian Stage), House Range, Utah, United States. Conventionally, both agnostoids and polymerids have been classified as "trilobites," but morphological differences, especially in the ventral appendages, and ecological differences, have led to suggestions that the two groups may not share close phylogenetic affinities. Photographs by R.A. Robison.

Cambrian recognized so far are defined by Global Boundary Stratotype Section and Points that coincide with the first appearances of a cosmopolitan agnostoid or an intercontinentally distributed polymerid trilobite species (Peng et al., 2004, 2009, 2012b; Babcock et al., 2007; Peng and Zhao, 2018) and are discussed in Chapter 19, The Cambrian Period. More than half of all described trilobite species are from rocks of Cambrian Series 2 through the Lower Ordovician. After the mid-Ordovician, trilobites declined progressively in diversity, although their remains are quite abundant in some strata.

More than 5100 trilobite genera have been proposed, of which about 4100 are regarded as valid (Jell and Adrain, 2003). These genera embrace at least 15,000 valid species (Hughes, 2007). Currently they are classified into eight orders and 13 suborders, plus numerous family-level taxa. For simplicity the "trilobites" (sensu lato) can be classified into two informal morphological forms, polymerids and agnostoids (Fig. 3A.1). These two groups of arthropods show great differences in morphology, especially in the morphology of ventral appendages and in ecology (Fig. 3A.1; see Babcock et al., 2017 for detailed review). Even though agnostoids are commonly included within the class Trilobita, it is debated whether agnostoids are trilobites or comprise a sister group to trilobites.

Important evolutionary changes in trilobite morphologies were discussed or summarized by, among others, Robison (1972a,b), Bergström (1973), Clarkson (1975), McNamara (1986), Fortey and Chatterton (1988), Fortey and Owens (1990, 1997), Babcock (1994a, 2003), Sundberg (2000), and Hughes (2007). Notable evolutionary innovations include changes in the shape, proportion, and segmentation of the exoskeleton; the size of the pygidium; the position and size of the eyes; the size and shape of the glabella, the type of eye construction; segmental articulation related to enrollment, specialization of the hypostome, and spinosity of the dorsal surface and margins. Other changes include secondary loss of eyes, loss of facial sutures, and effacement of the dorsal surface. Multiple biological factors played a role in the spectacular morphological diversification of trilobites, including position in the water column, feeding behavior, or other aspects of ecology. Babcock (2003) drew attention to morphological changes coinciding with changing predator–prey interactions; and McNamara (1986) emphasized the role of heterochrony (i.e., morphological changes through timing and rate in the development of characters) in propelling rapid morphological changes.

Orders, suborders, and superfamilies follow Fortey (1997), and families follow Fortey (1997) and Jell and Adrain (2003) although not all families are shown in the illustration (Fig. 3A.2). Trilobite orders are indicated by bars of varied colors, and within each colored bar, suborders or superfamilies are indicated by infills.

3A.1 Earliest trilobites

Trilobites are considered to have affinities with either chelicerates or mandibulates (e.g., Wills et al., 1994; Budd, 2002; Cotton and Braddy, 2004; see Babcock et al., 2017 for review). Polymerids, the first group to appear in the fossil record, are commonly regarded as having closest affinities with arachnomorph arthropods (chelicerates). Agnostoids have been treated alternately as a highly derived group having an ancestry with polymerids such as the ptychopariids, or as a group having closest affinities with crustaceanomorph arthropods (mandibulates).

The earliest known trilobite taxa are fallotaspidoids (Fig. 3A.3A–E) and bigotinids. The ancestor of the fallotaspidoids is unknown, but it is often assumed to have been an uncalcified and segmented creature within the Arthropoda (sensu lato), perhaps having a wormlike, or lobopodian, form. Fallotaspidoids first appear in Cambrian strata belonging to Cambrian Stage 3 of Series 2 (provisional names), and they appear within a rather narrow stratigraphic window on three paleocontinents in what is now Siberia, Morocco (Gondwana) and western North America (Laurentia) (see review in Zhang et al., 2017). Among the earliest taxa, *Profallotaspis* is probably the oldest known and is the common ancestor of the Olenellina and all other trilobites.

3A.2 Trilobite phylogeny

Cambrian Period. Trilobites first appear in the fossil record at the horizon where, provisionally, the base of Cambrian Stage 3 (Series 2) is marked (e.g., Zhang et al., 2017). Shortly after their first appearance, trilobites became highly diversified and widely dispersed. At least three major evolutionary stages occurred during the Cambrian. The first, extending through Epoch 2, was the rise and flourishing of olenellinid (including fallotaspidoids and their descendants, the olenelloids) and redlichiid trilobites (Jell, 2003) as two broad trilobite provinces that continued through Epoch 2 (Zhang, 1989). Olenellid trilobites, including fallotaspidoids (Fig. 3A.3A–E), were distributed in the Olenellid Faunal Province (mainly Laurasia and Siberia). Redlichiid trilobites (Fig. 3A.3F) characterized the Redlichiid Faunal Province (mainly Gondwana and the present-day Mediterranean region). One striking difference between trilobites of the Olenellina and the Redlichiina is the absence of dorsal facial sutures in Olenellina. Jell (2003) viewed the Redlichiina as a polyphyletic group, having at least five lineages that evolved separately from early fallotaspidoid ancestors, and this scheme is followed in Fig. 3A.2.

The fallotaspidoids also gave rise to the ellipsocephaloids and corynexochinids (Jell, 2003), both of which

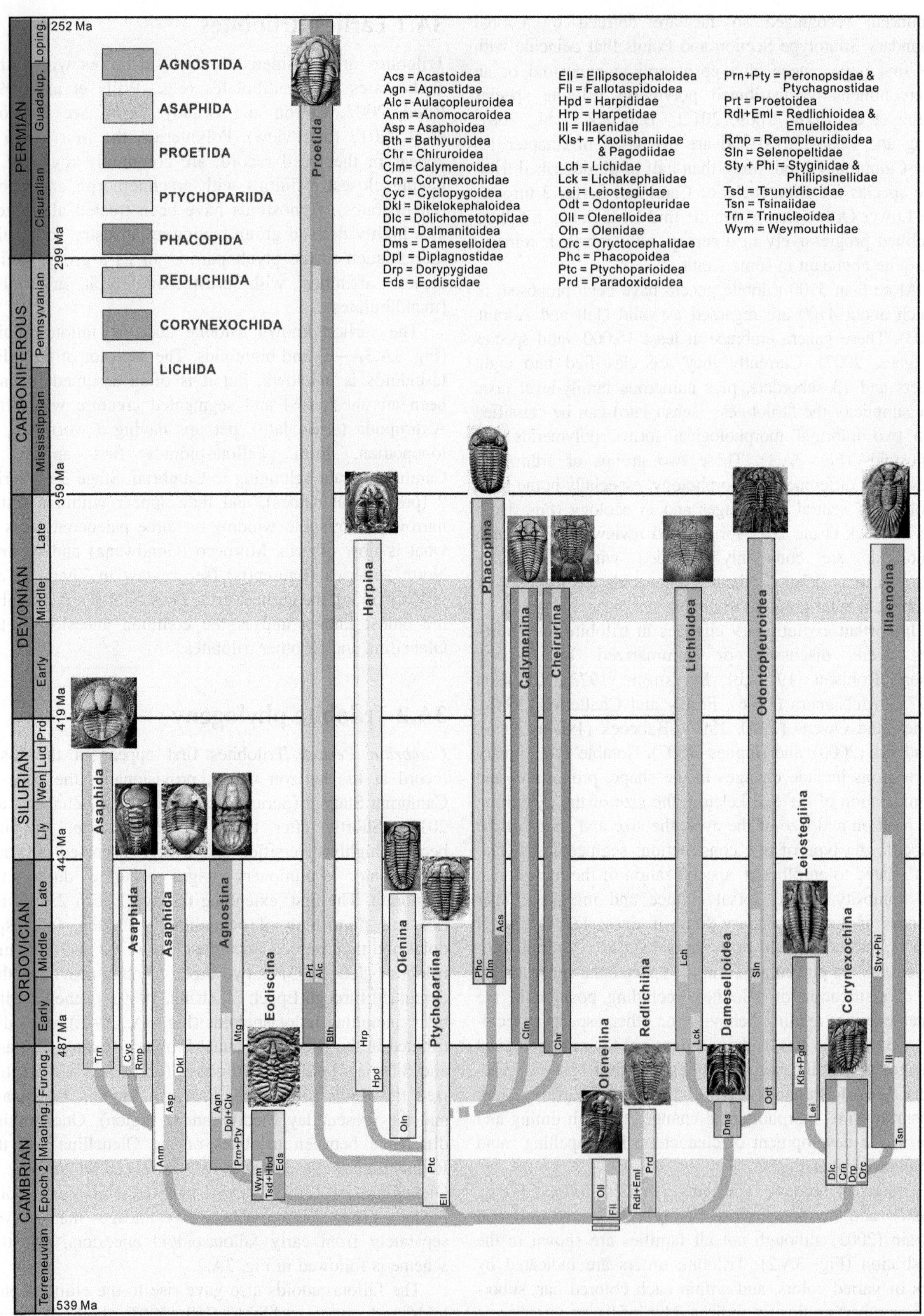

FIGURE 3A.2 Inferred phylogenetic history of trilobites following Fortey (1997), and Jell and Adrain (2003). Trilobite orders are indicated by bars of varied colors, and within each colored bar, suborders or superfamilies are indicated by infills. Miaoling. = Miaolingian; Furong. = Furongian; Lly = Llandovery; Wen = Wenlock; Lud = Ludlow; Prd = Pridoli; Guadalup. = Guadalupian; Loping. = Lopingian.

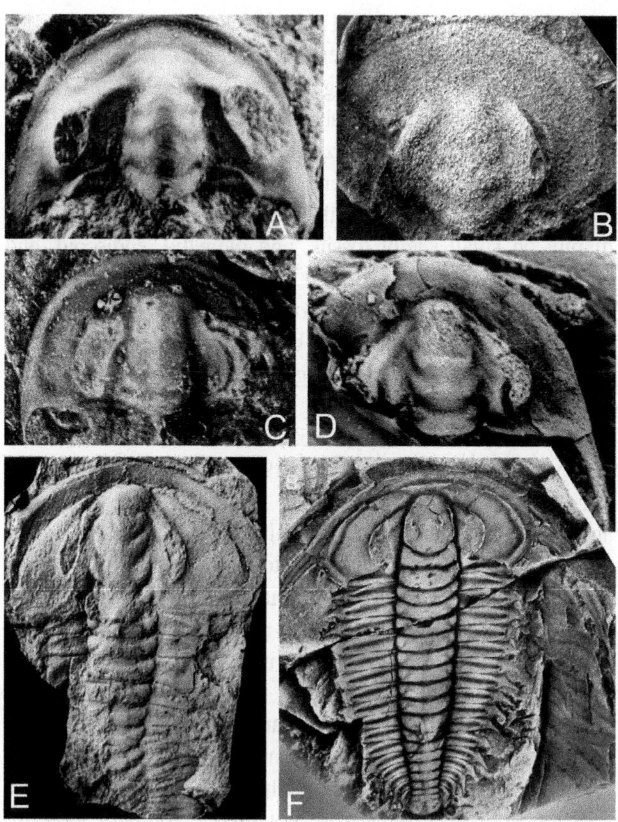

FIGURE 3A.3 Early trilobites, fallotaspidoids (A–E) and a redlichiid (F). A, *Profallotaspis jakutensis* (Repina in Khomentovskii and Repina, 1965), holotype, southeastern Siberia, Russia; B, *Fritzaspis generalis* Hollingsworth, 2007, holotype, Slate Ridge, Nevada, USA; C, *Repinaella sibirica* (Repina in Khomentovskii and Repina, 1965), holotype, southeastern Siberia, Russia; D, *Eofallotaspis tioutensis* Sdzuy, 1978, holotype, Anti-Atlas Mountains, Morocco; E, *Fallotaspis typica* Hupé, 1953, holotype, Anti-Atlas Mountains, Morocco; F, *Eoredlichia intermedia* (Lu, 1940), Kunming, Yunnan, China. Photos from Palmer and Repina, 1997 (A, D, E); Hollingsworth, 2007 (B); Geyer, 1996 (C); Zhang et al., 1980 (F).

became diverse during Age 4 (Epoch 2) through the end of the Miaolingian Epoch. Ellipsocephaloids gave rise to eodiscoids in Age 3, and to ptychoparioids near the end of Age 4 (Jell, 2003; Cotton and Fortey, 2005). Close to the end of Epoch 2, redlichiids and olenellids became extinct.

The second evolutionary stage, lasting through the Miaolingian Epoch, is marked by the diversification of ptychoparioids in two provinces. Paradoxidoids are characteristic of the Atlantic (or Acado-Baltic) faunal province (Baltica through present-day Mediterranean area, including the Middle East). Corynexochinids and dameselloids are characteristic of the Pacific (or North American) faunal province (mainly present-day China, Australia, Antarctica, North America, and Greenland) (Poulsen, 1969; Cowie, 1971; Zhang, 1989). Some of the biogeographic differentiation of trilobites may have been a function of a thermally stratified marine water column, leading to endemic faunas on the shelves of paleocontinents in low latitudes, and more widespread taxa present on the shelves of paleocontinents in higher latitudes and in deeper, cooler waters (Taylor and Cook, 1976; Theokritoff, 1979; Babcock, 1994b). An extinction event near the end of the Miaolingian Epoch eliminated dameselloids and paradoxidoids.

Near the beginning of the Wuliuan Age, agnostoids, which are characterized by the absence of eyes and dorsal facial sutures, made their first appearance. They may have evolved from a group of eodiscoids, the Weymouthiidae, which secondarily lost their facial sutures (Jell, 2003; Naimark, 2008). During the latter half of the Cambrian, agnostoids evolved rapidly and became highly diverse. Many species were cosmopolitan, and the presence of their remains in rock successions over most of the world provides a means of precisely subdividing and correlating these rocks.

The third evolutionary stage, lasting through the Furongian Epoch, involved the diversification of some new groups of Ptychopariida. The Olenina flourished in the Atlantic faunal province. In the Pacific faunal province, some Asaphida and Corynexochiina families became prominent. These and other groups disappeared in an extinction event near the end of the Furongian Epoch and were replaced by other taxa in the Ordovician.

Ordovician Period. The Early Ordovician age was the time of the last great diversification of trilobites, and the members of most trilobite clades that became dominant in the Middle Ordovician through the Devonian are present in rocks of Early Ordovician age. Most of these trilobites probably descended from Cambrian redlichiids or olenellids, but the ancestors of some of other clades, such as the ancestors of the Phacopida, are uncertain (Fig. 3A.2). Except for phillipsiids (Proetida; not shown in Fig. 3A.2), no new family or higher taxon appeared after the Early Ordovician Epoch. After the Early Ordovician, trilobite diversity declined, and by the Middle Ordovician, they were no longer the major elements of marine shelly faunas. Trilobites were much affected by the end-Ordovician (Hirnantian) mass extinction event, which wiped out many trilobite families, including all agnostoid, olenid, and asaphid families (with the exception of one raphiophoridean genus, *Raphiophorus*).

Silurian–Devonian periods. The diversity of the surviving trilobite families remained low. Trilobites sometimes make up a large fraction of shelly fossils in Silurian or Devonian deposits, but typically the assemblages have few species. Dominant groups include the Proetida, Cheirurina, lichids, odontopleurids, styginids, and Phacopida. By the Middle Devonian, trilobite assemblages were characterized mostly by phacopids and proetids. Except for a few Proetida (Fortey and Owens, 1997; Clarkson, 1998), trilobites were eliminated in pulses of extinction during the Late Devonian, beginning near the end of the Frasnian Age.

Carboniferous–Permian periods. The only trilobites to survive into the Early Carboniferous were the members of the order Proetida (aulacopleurids, brachymetopids, and proetids). Their diversity in the late Paleozoic was moderate. Seventeen phillipsiid genera, one proetid genus, and one brachymetopid genus survived into the Guadalupian Epoch of the Permian Period, and only two genera, *Pseudophillipsia* and *Acropyge*, survived to the latest Permian (Fortey and Owens, 1997). Trilobites were completely exterminated in the end-Permian mass extinction event.

3A.3 Trilobite biostratigraphy

Cambrian trilobite biostratigraphy. Macroscopic fossils, primarily trilobites, were used to identify the base of the Cambrian at the time the system was initially proposed (Sedgwick in Sedgwick and Murchison, 1835). Formal biostratigraphic zonation of the system dates to the work of Brøgger (1886) and Walcott (1889, 1890a,b) who established the *Olenellus* Zone in North America as the lowermost Cambrian biozone. Walcott (1889, 1890a,b) also coined the term "pre-cambrian" for all strata underlying the first appearance of *Olenellus*.

Until the 1970s, Cambrian biostratigraphic schemes in most regions of the world were primarily based on the stratigraphic arrangement of trilobite assemblages, and most emphasized polymerids. The concept of extinction-bounded evolutionary units, or biomeres, based on trilobite biostratigraphy (Palmer, 1965) has a close relationship to the development of modern biostratigraphic schemes. Babcock et al. (2015, 2017) showed a relationship between biomere boundaries and eustatic sea level changes and suggested a link with global climatic cycles.

More refined zonal schemes, including range zones and interval zones (Murphy, 1977), provided increased resolution, but the most important breakthrough in our understanding of the utility of trilobites in Cambrian biostratigraphy came from recognition of separate zonal schemes for agnostoid and polymerid trilobites (Robison, 1976; see also Peng and Robison, 2000; Robison and Babcock, 2011; Peng et al., 2012a) and of differing assemblages in open-shelf regions and restricted-shelf regions, particularly for continents in low paleolatitudes. Agnostoids make their evolutionary first appearance in the lower part of the Wuliuan Stage. Upward from that position, agnostoids are among the principal intercontinental biostratigraphic guides for the Cambrian. Many agnostoid genera and species have been shown to have intercontinental to cosmopolitan distributions, making them especially useful for correlation in open-shelf and slope lithofacies around all continents. Polymerid trilobites, in contrast, have varying levels of biostratigraphic utility. Many polymerids were endemic to individual paleocontinents and thus have utility regionally in shelf lithofacies. Some polymerids, primarily pelagic forms from open-shelf, slope, or basinal lithofacies, also have utility for correlating strata intercontinentally (Robison, 1976; Sundberg and McCollum, 1997; Peng and Robison, 2000; Babcock et al., 2011; Robison and Babcock, 2011; Peng et al., 2012a). Updated biostratigraphic zonations for the main paleocontinents are in Chapter 19, The Cambrian Period. Biostratigraphic zonation of the pre-agnostoid Cambrian relies mainly on small shelly fossils, and olenellid, eodiscoid, and oryctocephalid (corynexochoid) trilobites as guides.

Post-Cambrian trilobite biostratigraphy. Trilobites have been used mostly as secondary biostratigraphic guides in post-Cambrian strata. The biostratigraphic utility of trilobites in Ordovician rocks has been long recognized (e.g., Stubblefield and Bulman, 1927; Sdzuy, 1955, 1958; Jell and Stait, 1985; Fortey and Owens, 1987; Peng, 1990a,b; Zhou et al., 2014). For the most part, zonal schemes were based on polymerids and have had mostly regional value. Some polymerids, and especially some widespread agnostoids, played important roles in reorganization of the Tremadocian and Floian stages of the Lower Ordovician. Reliance on trilobites, both polymerids and agnostoids, as guide fossils diminishes in stepwise fashion near the Cambrian–Ordovician boundary, in the Ashgill regional stage of the Ordovician, and in the Middle Devonian (Eifelian–Givetian) (e.g., Fortey and Owens, 1997; Zhen and Zhou, 2008; Peng et al., 2012a; Choi et al., 2016). In contrast to the Cambrian, trilobites are not used as primary tools for the recognition of formal chronostratigraphic units.

In the Silurian through Permian, members of various clades of polymerid trilobites serve as secondary biostratigraphic tools that for the most part are applicable only regionally (e.g., Zhen and Zhou, 2008).

Bibliography

Babcock, L.E., 1994a, Systematics and phylogenetics of polymeroid trilobites from the Henson Gletscher and Kap Stanton formations (Middle Cambrian), North Greenland. *Grønlands Geologiske Undersøgelse Bulletin*, **169**: 79-12.

Babcock, L.E., 1994b, Biogeography and biofacies patterns of Middle Cambrian polymeroid trilobites from North Greenland: palaeogeographic and palaeo-oceanographic implications. *Grønlands Geologiske Undersøgelse Bulletin*, **169**: 129–147.

Babcock, L.E., 2003, Trilobites in Paleozoic predator-prey systems, and their role in reorganization of early Paleozoic ecosystems. *In* Kelley, P.A., Kowalewski, M., and Hansen, T.A. (eds), *Predator-Prey Interactions in the Fossil Record*. New York: Kluwer Academic/Plenum Publishers, 55–92.

Babcock, L.E., Robison, R.A., Rees, M.N., Peng, S.C., and Saltzman, M. R., 2007, The Global boundary Stratotype Section and Point (GSSP) of the Drumian Stage (Cambrian) in the Drum Mountains, Utah, USA. *Episodes*, **30**: 85–95.

Babcock, L.E., Robison, R.A., and Peng, S.C., 2011, Cambrian stage and series nomenclature of Laurentia and the developing chronostratigraphic scale. *Museum of Northern Arizona Bulletin*, **67**: 12–26.

Babcock, L.E., Peng, S.C., Brett, C.E., Zhu, M.Y., Ahlberg, P., Bevis, M., et al., 2015, Global climate, sea level cycles, and biotic events in the Cambrian Period. *Palaeoworld*, **24**: 5–15.

Babcock, L.E., Peng, S., and Ahlberg, P., 2017, Cambrian trilobite biostratigraphy and its role in developing an integrated history of the Earth system. *Lethaia*, **50**: 381–399.

Bergström, J., 1973, Organization, life and systematics of trilobites. *Fossils and Strata*, **2**: 1–69.

Brøgger, W.C., 1886, Om alderen af Olenelluszonen i Nordamerika. *Geologiska Föreningens i Stockholm Förhandlingar*, **8**: 182–213.

Budd, G.E., 2002, A palaeontological solution to the arthropod head problem. *Nature*, **417**: 271–275.

Choi, D.K., Lee, J.G., Lee, S.B., Park, T.Y.S., and Hong, P.S., 2016, Trilobite biostratigraphy of the lower Paleozoic (Cambrian–Ordovician) Joseon Supergroup, Taebaeksan Basin, Korea. *Acta Geologica Sinica (English Edition)*, **90**: 1976–1999.

Clarkson, E.N.K., 1975, The evolution of the eye in trilobites. *Fossils and Strata*, **4**: 7–31.

Clarkson, E.N.K., 1998, *Invertebrate Palaeontology and Evolution*, 4th ed. Oxford: Wiley/Blackwell Science, 452 p.

Cotton, T.J., and Braddy, S.J., 2004, The phylogeny of arachnomorph arthropods and the origin of the Chelicerata. *Transactions of the Royal Society of Edinburgh: Earth Sciences*, **94**: 169–193.

Cotton, T.J., and Fortey, R.A., 2005, Comparative morphology and relationships of the Agnostida. *In* Koenmann, S., and Jenner, R.A. (eds), *Crustacea and Arthropod Relationships. Crustacean Issues 16*. Boca Raton: CRC Press, pp. 95–136.

Cowie, J.W., 1971, Lower Cambrian faunal provinces. *In* Middlemiss, F.A., Rawson, P.F., and Newall, G. (eds), Faunal Provinces in Space and Time. *Geological Society of London Special Publication*, **4**: 31–46.

Fortey, R.A., 1990, Ontogeny, hypostome attachment and trilobite classification. *Palaeontology*, **33**: 529–576.

Fortey, R.A., 1997, Classification. *In* Kaesler, R.L. (ed), Treatise on Invertebrate Paleontology, Part O, Arthropoda 1, Trilobita, Revised. *Lawrence, KS: Geological Society of America and University of Kansas Press*, **Vol. 1**: 289–302.

Fortey, R.A., and Chatterton, B.D.E., 1988, Classification of the trilobite suborder Asaphina. *Palaeontology*, **31**: 165–222.

Fortey, R.A., and Owens, R.M., 1987, The Arenig Series in South Wales. *Bulletin of the British Museum (Natural History). Geology*, **41**: 69–307.

Fortey, R.A., and Owens, R.M., 1990, Trilobites. *In* McNamara, K.J. (ed), *Evolutionary Trends*. London: Belhaven Press, pp. 121–142.

Fortey, R.A., and Owens, R.M., 1997, Evolutionary history. *In* Kaesler, R.L. (ed), Treatise on Invertebrate Paleontology, Part O, Arthropoda 1, Trilobita, Revised. *Lawrence, KS: Geological Society of America and University of Kansas Press*, **Volume 1**: 249–287.

Geyer, G., 1996, The Moroccan fallotaspidid trilobites revisited. *Beringeria*, **18**: 89–199.

Hollingsworth, J.S., 2007, Fallotaspidoid trilobite assemblage (Lower Cambrian) from the Esmeralda Basin (western Nevada, U.S.A): the oldest trilobites from Laurentia. *Memoirs of the Association of Australasian Palaeontologists*, **32**: 123–140.

Hughes, N.C., 2007, The evolution of trilobite body patterning. *Annual Review of Earth and Planetary Sciences*, **35**: 401–434.

Hupé, P., 1953, Contribution a l'étude du Cambrien Inférieur et du Précambrien III de l'Anti-Atlas Marocain. *Division des Mines et de la Géologie, Service Géologique, Notes et Memoires*, **103**: 1–402.

Jell, P.A., 2003, Phylogeny of Early Cambrian trilobites. In: Lane, P.D., Siveter, D.J., Fortey, R.A. (Eds.), Trilobites and their relatives. *Special Papers in Palaeontology*, **70**: 45–57.

Jell, P.A., and Adrain, J.M., 2003, Available generic names for trilobites. *Memoirs of the Queensland Museum*, **48**: 331–551.

Jell, P.A., and Stait, B., 1985, Tremadoc trilobites from the Florentine Valley Formation, Tim Shea area, Tasmania. *Memoirs of the Museum of Victoria*, **46**: 1–34.

Khomentovskii, V.V., Repina, L.N., 1965, *Nizhnii kembrii stratotipicheskogo razreza Sibiri* [The Lower Cambrian stratotype section of Siberia]. Moscow: Sibirskoe Otdelenie, Institute Geologii i Geofiziki, Akademiia Nauk SSSR, p. 196.

Lu, Y.H., 1940, On the ontogeny and phylogeny of *Redlichia intermedia* Lu (sp. nov.). *Bulletin of the Geological Society of China*, **20**: 333–342.

McNamara, K.J., 1986, The role of heterochrony in the evolution of Cambrian trilobites. *Biological Reviews*, **61**: 121–156.

Murphy, M.A., 1977, On time-stratigraphic units. *Journal of Paleontology*, **51**: 213–219.

Naimark, E.B., 2008, Morphogenesis in the genus *Peronopsis* Hawle et Corda, 1847 (Agnostina). *Palaeontological Journal*, **42**: 389–400.

Palmer, A.R., 1965, Biomere – a new kind of biostratigraphic unit. *Journal of Paleontology*, **39**: 149–153.

Palmer, A.R., and Repina, I.N., 1997. Introduction to Suborder Olenellina. *In* Kaesler, R.L. (ed). *Treatise on Invertebrate Paleontology*, Part O, Arthropoda 1, Trilobita, Revised. The Palaeontological Society, The University of Kansas Press, 405–428.

Peng, S.C., 1990a, Trilobites from the Nantsinkwan Formation of the Yangtze Platform. *Beringeria*, **2**: 3–53.

Peng, S.C., 1990b, Trilobites from the Panjiazui Formation and the Madaoyu Formation in the Jiangnan Slope Belt. *Beringeria*, **2**: 54–171.

Peng, S.C., and Robison, R.A., 2000, *Agnostoid biostratigraphy across the Middle-Upper Cambrian Boundary in Hunan, China*. Memoir (The Paleontological Society), Vol, 53 (Suppl. to Vol. 74 of the *Journal of Paleontology)*, 1–104.

Peng, S.C., and Zhao, Y.L., 2018, The proposed Global Standard Stratotype-Section and Point (GSSP) for the conterminous base of Miaolingian Series and Wuliuan Stage at Balang, Jianhe, Guizhou, China was ratified by IUGS. *Journal of Stratigraphy*, **42**: 325–327.

Peng, S.C., Babcock, L.E., Robison, R.A., Lin, H.L., Rees, M.N., and Saltzman, M.R., 2004, Global Standard Stratotype-Section and Point (GSSP) of the Furongian Series and Paibian Stage (Cambrian). *Lethaia*, **37**: 365–379.

Peng, S.C., Babcock, L.E., Zuo, J.X., Lin, H.L., Zhu, X.J., Yang, X.F., et al., 2009, The Global boundary Stratotype Section and Point (GSSP) of the Guzhangian Stage (Cambrian) in the Wuling Mountains, northwestern Hunan, China. *Episodes*, **32**: 41–55.

Peng, S.C., Babcock, L.E., and Cooper, R.A., 2012a, The Cambrian Period. *In* Gradstein, F.M., Ogg, J.G., Schmitz, M.D., and Ogg, G.M. (eds), *The Geologic Time Scale 2012*. Amsterdam: Elsevier BV, **Vol. 2**: 437–488.

Peng, S.C., Babcock, L.E., Zuo, J.X., Lin, H.L., Zhu, X.J., Yang, X.F., et al., 2012b, Global Standard Stratotype-Section and Point (GSSP) for the base of the Jiangshanian Stage (Cambrian: Furongian) at Duibian, Jiangshan, Zhejiang, Southeast China. *Episodes*, **35**: 1–16.

Poulsen, V., 1969, An Atlantic Middle Cambrian fauna from North Greenland. *Lethaia*, **2**: 1–14.

Robison, R.A., 1972a, Hypostoma of agnostid trilobites. *Lethaia*, **5**: 239–248.

Robison, R.A., 1972b, Mode of life of agnostid trilobites. *24th International Geological Congress, Montreal, Canada, Section 7 (Paleontology)*, pp. 33–40.

Robison, R.A., 1976, Middle Cambrian trilobite biostratigraphy of the Great Basin. *Brigham Young University Geology Studies*, **23**: 93–109.

Robison, R.A., and Babcock, L.E., 2011, Systematics, paleobiology, and taphonomy of some exceptionally preserved trilobites from Cambrian Lagerstätten of Utah. *Paleontological Contributions*, **5**: 1–47.

Sdzuy, K., 1955, Die Fauna der Leimitz-Schiefer (Tremadoc). *Abhandlungen der Senckenbergischen Naturforschenden Gesellschaft*, **492**: 1–74.

Sdzuy, K., 1958, Fossilien aus Tremadoc der Montagne Noire. *Senckenbergiana Lethaea*, **39** (3–4), 255–286.

Sdzuy, K., 1978, The Precambrian-Cambrian boundary beds in Morocco (Preliminary Report). *Geological Magazine*, **115**: 83–94.

Sedgwick, A., and Murchison, R.I., 1835, On the Silurian and Cambrian Systems, exhibiting the order in which the older sedimentary strata succeed each other in England and Wales. *The London and Edinburgh Philosophical Magazine and Journal of Science*, **7**: 483–535.

Stubblefield, C.J., and Bulman, O.M.B., 1927, The Shineton Shales of the Wrekin district: with notes on their development in other parts of Shropshire and Herefordshire. *Quarterly Journal of the Geological Society*, **83**: 96–146.

Sundberg, F.A., 2000, Homeotic evolution in Cambrian trilobites. *Paleobiology*, **26**: 258–270.

Sundberg, F.A., and McCollum, L.B., 1997, Oryctocephalids (Corynexochida: Trilobita) of the Lower-Middle Cambrian boundary interval from California and Nevada. *Journal of Paleontology*, **71**: 1065–1090.

Taylor, M.E., and Cook, H.E., 1976, Continental shelf and slope facies in the Upper Cambrian and lowest Ordovician of Nevada. *Brigham Young University Geology Studies*, **23** (2), 181–214.

Theokritoff, G., 1979, Early Cambrian provincialism and biogeographic boundaries in the North Atlantic region. *Lethaia*, **12**: 281–295.

Tullberg, S.A., 1880, Om *Agnostus*-arterna i de kambriska aflagringarne vid Andrarum. *Sveriges Geologiska Undersökning, Series C*, **42**: 1–37.

Walch, J.E., 1771, *Die Naturgeschichte der Versteinerungen, Dritter Theil*. Nuremberg: Paul Jonathan Felstecker, 235 p.

Walcott, C.D., 1889, Stratigraphic position of the *Olenellus* fauna in North America and Europe. *American Journal of Science*, **37**: 374–392, **38**: 29–42.

Walcott, C.D., 1890a, The fauna of the Lower Cambrian or *Olenellus* Zone. *Tenth Annual Report of the Director, 1888–1889, Part 1*. United States Geological Survey, Washington, DC, p. 509–774.

Walcott, C.D., 1890b, Descriptive notes on new genera and species from the Lower Cambrian or *Olenellus* Zone of North America. *Proceedings of the United States National Museum*, **12**: 33–46.

Wills, M.A., Briggs, D.E.G., and Fortey, R.A., 1994, Disparity as an evolutionary index: a comparison of Cambrian and Recent arthropods. *Paleobiology*, **20**: 93–130.

Zhang, W.T., 1989, World Cambrian biogeography. *In* Chinese Academy of Sciences (ed), *Developments in Geosciences, Contribution to 28th International Geological Congress, 1989*. Washington, DC, Beijing: Science Press, pp. 209–220.

Zhang, W.T., Lu, Y.H., Zhu, Z.L., Qian, Y.Y., Lin, H.L., Zhou, Z.Y., et al., 1980, *Cambrian Trilobite Faunas of Southwestern China. Palaeontologia Sinica (New Series B) 16 (159)*. Beijing: Science Press, 497 p.

Zhang, X.L., Ahlberg, P., Babcock, L.E., Choi, D.K., Geyer, G., Gozalo, R., et al., 2017, Challenges in defining the base of Cambrian Series 2 and Stage 3. *Earth-Science Reviews*, **172**: 124–139.

Zhen, Y.Y., and Zhou, Z.Y., 2008, History of trilobite biodiversity: a Chinese perspective. *In* Zhou, Z.Y., and Zhen, Y.Y. (eds), *Trilobite Record of China*. Beijing: Science Press, pp. 301–330.

Zhou, Z.Y., Yin, G.Z., and Zhou, Z.Q., 2014, Ordovician (Darriwilian–early Katian) trilobite faunas of northwestern Tarim, Xinjiang, China. *Memoirs of the Association of Australasian Palaeontologists*, **46**: 1–142.

Subchapter 3B

Graptolites

J. Zalasiewicz, M. Williams and A. Rushton

Graptolites as commonly understood are extinct colonial zooplankton, the fossilized remains of which are common in, and are central to, the dating and correlation of lower Paleozoic strata. They often resemble scratch-like markings on bedding surfaces—and hence, their name, which can be loosely translated as "writing in the rocks." They are indeed hugely important for biostratigraphy and possess some distinctive and unique attributes both biologically and geologically, which lie behind this utility, while recent advances in understanding (reviewed in Maletz, 2017) have considerably modified our understanding of what these fossils fundamentally are.

Looked at closely, the "scratches" are slender tubular structures of one or more branches (termed stipes), typically millimeter scale in width and centimeter scale in length, from which grew a succession of short open-ended tubes (thecae), each of which in life housed one (or perhaps more?) of the colony animals, termed zooids. The soft-bodied zooids themselves are almost never fossilized, so it is just the tubes, made of a tough organic substance perhaps related to collagen, which make up the fossil material that paleontologists work on (Fig. 3B.1). Each preserved colony is commonly now referred to as a tubarium, though older literature uses the term "rhabdosome."

3B.1 Graptolite construction and relationships

When graptolites are well preserved—for instance within carbonate or chert nodules, from which they can be freed by acid—then the tubular construction can be seen to be made of a succession of rings (fusellar) above which is an outer layer termed the cortex, rather like a layer of plaster coating a brick wall. The analogy is a functional one, too, for the fusellar and cortical structure is very similar to that of, and

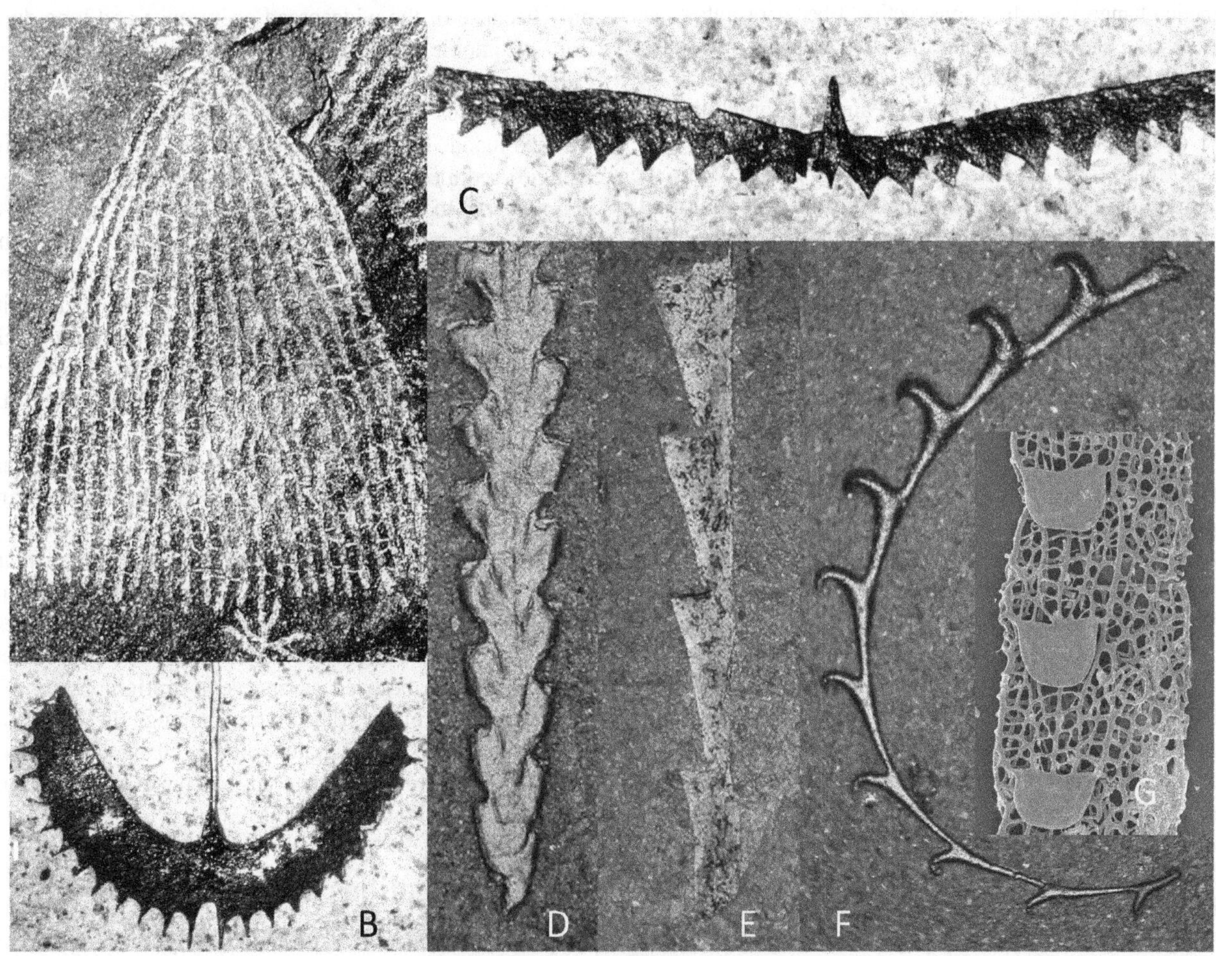

FIGURE 3B.1 Photographs of a few typical graptolite genera: (A) *Rhabdinopora*; (B) *Isograptus*; (C) *Expansograptus*; (D) *Glyptograptus*; (E) *Pristiograptus*; (F) *Torquigraptus*; (G) *Gothograptus*, showing range of form and preservation.

indicates close evolutionary relationship with, the modern pterobranch hemichordates, somewhat obscure tube-dwelling colonial marine benthic organisms—a link shown by Kozłowski (1949).

The pterobranchs do not secrete their tubes passively, as molluscs secrete their shells or we grow our bones. Rather, pterobranchs actively build their tubes, ring by ring, by means of a specialized secretory lobe, rather as spiders build their webs or termites construct their nests.

There is good evidence that the graptolites did the same, as their layer of cortical tissue is made of irregularly criss-crossing "bandages" (Crowther and Rickards, 1977), which can only plausibly have been "plastered" on to the tube wall by the zooids, actively and indeed cooperatively (as the individual thecae needed to be integrated to produce the specific, and often elaborate, construction of the whole colony). In so far as the tubaria of the graptolites represents the active work of animals, they might be thought akin to trace fossils, albeit extraordinarily sophisticated ones. This does not diminish their biostratigraphical usefulness, and may even enhance it, as one might speculate that the extraordinarily rapid rates of morphological evolution may be related to the expression of genetic change via active constructional behavior rather than via passive skeletal secretion, and this in some way might have added an "extra gear" to their evolution.

The similarity of the fossil Paleozoic graptolites to one of the two living genera of pterobranchs indeed suggests that this extant genus, *Rhabdopleura*, can be regarded as a graptolite, in something like the way modern birds are now classified within the dinosaurs. Thus the graptolites (like the dinosaurs) are not extinct, though their remnants today possess little of the ecological importance and biological sophistication their extinct relatives possessed.

The graptolites arose in the mid-Cambrian as conical many-branched benthic colonies, attached to the sea floor by a root-like structure, as filter feeders, perhaps with a similar ecological position to sponges; they possessed two kinds of thecae, paired large autothecae and small bithecae, which may represent different sexes. These were the dendroid graptolites, and they persisted until the Carboniferous. The dendroids are mostly of little practical use for biostratigraphy.

Very early in the Ordovician, one lineage of dendroids left the benthos to join the plankton. The root-like structure was lost and replaced by a tiny initial elongated cone, the sicula (which originated by sexual reproduction), from which the thecae of the stipe(s) successively budded by asexual reproduction. A little later, the bithecae were lost (perhaps as the zooids became hermaphrodite) to yield the major clade of the graptoloid graptolites. These, wholly planktonic and wholly marine, are what most people think of as "the graptolites" and what biostratigraphers use (Fig. 3B.2). The graptoloids (we will only discuss these thereafter, and so simply speak of "graptolites") flourished—albeit with episodes of drastic diversity loss—throughout the Ordovician, Silurian, and Early Devonian periods. The last of the diversity crashes, in the Mid-Devonian, was total and terminal.

3B.2 Paleogeography, paleoecology, and sedimentology

The practical use of the graptolites depends strongly on their geological setting. Wholly marine, the graptolites showed maximum abundance and diversity in open ocean settings, and so are of most use for basinal successions. Shallow water/shelf strata may include graptolites, and sometimes commonly so, but these tend to be low-diversity assemblages that may be strongly provincial. Provinces may be recognized among the ocean-going graptolites too (Cooper et al., 2012), but overall these were more cosmopolitan, sufficiently so to widely afford high-resolution correlation, particularly in low- and mid-latitude settings.

Their distribution, though, strongly depends on paleoceanographic conditions. Graptolites are now common only because of the widespread occurrence and long duration of anoxic deep-sea floor conditions in the early Paleozoic, so that after death the graptolite tubaria could sink on to sea floors from which a scavenging benthos was excluded. Once buried within the (commonly hemipelagic) sediment, some became infilled with early diagenetic pyrite to yield three-dimensional preservation, or without such infill they were simply flattened upon compaction. The organic material of the tubaria became progressively darker (becoming more carbonized) with increasing depth of burial (the white-graptolite-on-black-shale silhouettes so commonly seen reflect a growth of pale phyllosilicate minerals on the graptolites in late diagenetic/early metamorphic conditions).

In "oxic" bioturbated facies, though, graptolites are typically rare or absent, presumably through scavenging by benthic organisms. Many basinal successions show an alternation between dark graptolitic shales, where primary lamination is preserved, and pale "barren beds" reflecting alternations between anoxic and oxic conditions. These alternations (biostratigraphically dated by the graptolites) may themselves be used as an event stratigraphy, and at least in part reflect (and were among the feedback mechanisms of) global paleoclimate change, with oxic episodes being linked with cold, and anoxic with warm, climate phases (Page et al., 2007).

3B.3 Practicalities and history of study

Graptolites are macrofossils, but mostly *small* macrofossils, and moreover ones that can resemble fractures, scratches, or patches of chemical alteration on rock surfaces. Hence, part of the skill involved in graptolite biostratigraphy is simply in finding them, particularly once one is away from graptolite-rich black shale facies, to be in, say, expanded turbidite facies in which graptolites are scarce through dilution (e.g., Cooper et al., 2004), or shelf successions where graptolites may be both rare and damaged by bioturbation. Honed observation skills allied to patience can give rich rewards, as in the graptolite biostratigraphy applied to the "shelly" Ashgill succession of the English Lake District by Rickards (2002), or in terrain where pervasive slaty cleavage means that the rock does not often split along the bedding (Davies et al., 1997). Graptolites may be located in both natural exposures and in borehole material, although, in the latter, cores are necessary, as little identifiable material is preserved in borehole cuttings.

Graptolites are mostly identified from rock fragments using a binocular microscope with a good light source, a process that may be time-consuming when graptolites need to be freed from matrix with a mounted needle. In some circumstances, it is effective to use a scanning electron microscope, especially on graptolites dissolved out of limestone or chert (Bates et al., 2015). There is now a very considerable literature to aid identification (see Zalasiewicz et al., 2009 and references therein).

The current biostratigraphic literature still owes much to some of the classic early studies, with key works by Barrande (1850) in Bohemia, Hall (1865) in Canada, Linnarsson (1871) in Scandinavia, and Charles Lapworth (1878) in southern Scotland. A key question was debated between Barrande and Lapworth: they each saw repetition of recognizable graptolite assemblages, whether this was due to recurring paleoenvironmental control (as Barrande argued for), or whether such repetition was structural, by folding or faulting (as Lapworth inferred in his studies of the tectonically complex Southern Uplands of Scotland). The argument was firmly resolved in Lapworth's favor, effectively setting the scene for the detailed biostratigraphic frameworks that followed, set out in such publications as Elles and Wood's (1901) influential monograph

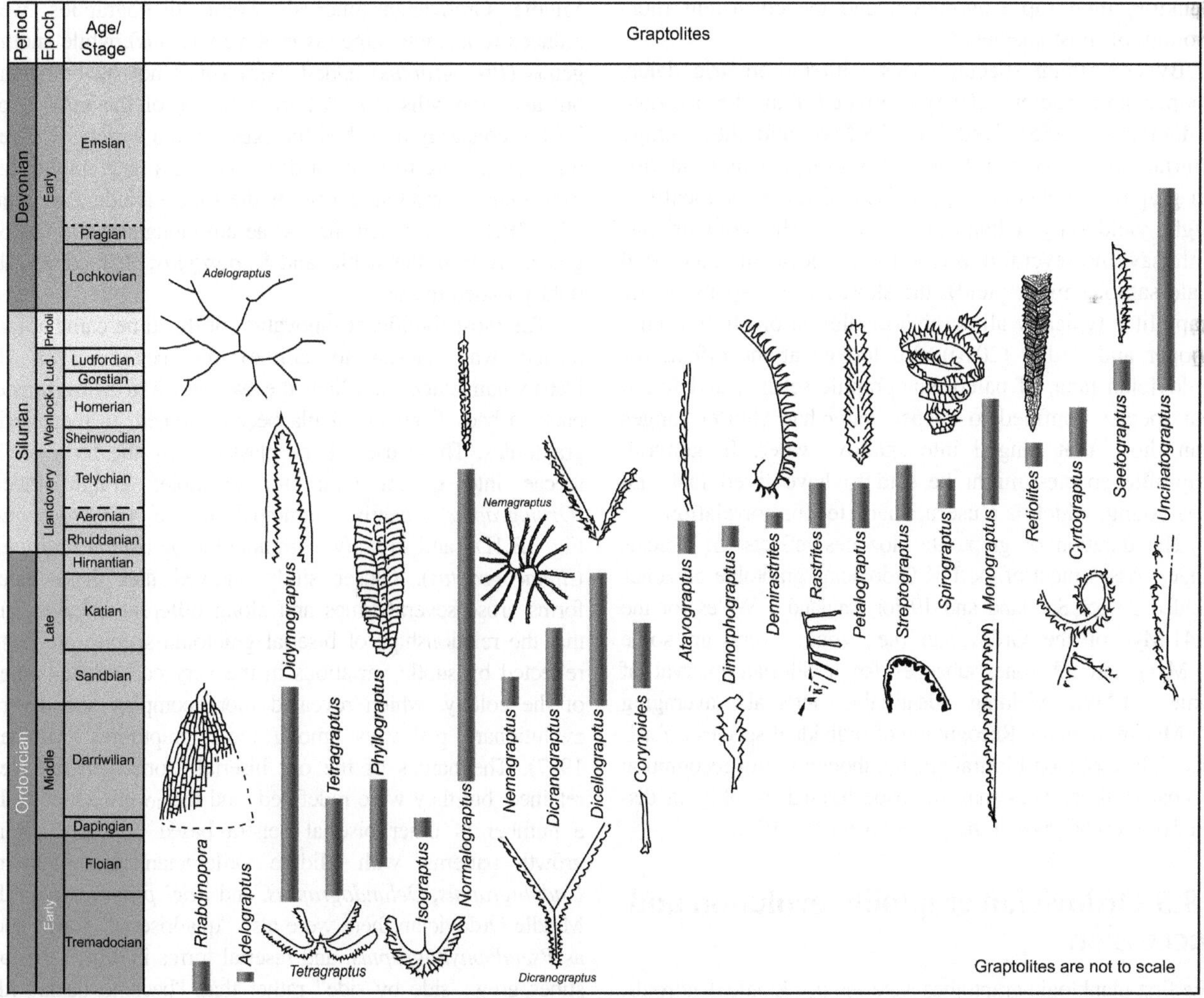

FIGURE 3B.2 Ranges of key genera through the Ordovician, Silurian, and Early Devonian.

and elaborated subsequently in many publications (e.g., Hutt, 1974; Bjerreskov, 1975; Loydell, 1992; Štorch, 1998; Chen et al., 2005; VandenBerg and Cooper, 1992). Much of the early (pre-WWII) work was done when the biological affinities of graptolites were still mysterious, a reminder that paleobiological understanding and biostratigraphic utility are independent of each other.

3B.4 Biostratigraphy

The total number of graptolite species continues to be refined as new species are discovered (and some older species are lost through synonymy). Cooper and Sadler's (2010) CONOP database listed 1446 species through the Ordovician, Silurian, and Early Devonian, while the most recent compilation just for Britain (Zalasiewicz et al., 2009) yielded 697 taxa for the Ordovician and Silurian (minus the Pridoli, which is in nongraptolitic facies in the United Kingdom). These are modest numbers by comparison with, say, trilobites, but the effectiveness of graptolite biostratigraphy reflects the wide dispersal of these plankton, their rapid evolution, and the consistent morphology of most species.

By combining species spans with radiometric dates, Cooper and Sadler (2010) estimated that the average Ordovician species lived for 2.78 Myr, and the average Silurian species only 1.47 Myr. So, though many individual graptolite collections at individual levels or localities might yield only a handful of species (by comparisons with, say, the several dozen acritarch species that a coeval shale sample might yield), the short species spans of the graptolites typically allow high-resolution biostratigraphy. Cooper and Sadler (2010) also looked at the effect, for Ordovician taxa, of paleoceanographic setting, and found that species confined to deeper water had shorter ranges than those that ranged into shallow water. In general, graptolite species might be said to have lived fast and died young, which is a useful character for correlation.

The duration of graptolite biozones reflects the species ranges. Assessment of the UK Ordovician graptolite biozones yielded 23 for Scotland and 19 for England + Wales for the ~41 Myr of the Ordovician (i.e., zones averaging some 2 Myr) and 39 zones/subzones for a Silurian interval of some 23 Myr, yielding identifiable intervals averaging 0.5 Myr in duration. Recognition of individual species affords this high-resolution biostratigraphy, though useful recognition of coarser time slices may be made through identifying distinctive morphotypes at the genus level (Fig. 3B.2).

3B.5 Ordovician graptolite evolution and succession

The first planktonic graptolites were the planktonic dendroids, including those such as *Rhabdinopora* (Fig. 3B.1A), which morphologically closely resembled their benthic ancestors, except for having a sicula rather than holdfast. Albeit not yet finely tuned to the planktonic environment, these taxa were nevertheless successful enough to become abundant worldwide, and the first graptolite biozone, based on forms of *Rhabdinopora flabelliformis*, provides effective correlation at a level just above the basal Ordovician boundary.

From that beginning, graptolites quickly evolved into shapes more suited to life in the plankton, notably by a great reduction in the number of stipes (branches), so that by the Floian Stage of the Ordovician four- and two stiped forms of the dichograptid graptolites dominated the assemblages, and these continued to be common through the Dapingian and much of the Darriwilian. In the dichograptids such as *Expansograptus* (Fig. 3B.1C), the thecae were mostly simple tubes, and a good deal of the morphological variation was expressed by different growing directions of the stipes: either growing more or less upward and outward from the sicula, horizontally away from it, or downward to form the "tuning fork"—shaped graptolites that were especially common in the Darriwilian. Other forms arose in this Early to Middle Ordovician interval. Some dichograptids were reduced to a single stipe (as in *Azygograptus*), while another genus (*Pterograptus*) added extra stipes not by branching, but as outgrowths (*Cladia*) from thecae of the main stipe. Such secondarily branched lineages, from a variety of ancestral forms, were to recur at different times in graptolite history. Other important forms of the time include *Isograptus* (Fig. 3B.1B), in which the thecae are elongated and fan out gracefully from the sicula, and *Sinograptus*, characterized by tightly folded thecae.

The most significant innovation of this time came at (and indeed was chosen to define) the beginning of the Darriwilian Stage, in which the two stipes growing upward back to back from the sicula became joined, in the biserial graptolites. These used to be classified by the form of the thecae into genera with, for example, straight thecae (*Orthograptus*), gently sigmoidal thecae (*Glyptograptus*: Fig. 3B.1D), and strongly sigmoidal thecae (*Amplexograptus, Climacograptus*). Closer study showed that these thecal forms arose several times and along different lineages, and that the relationships of biserial graptolite species are better reflected by subtle variations in the very early development of the colony, which revealed more complex and diverse evolutionary pathways among these graptolites (Mitchell, 1987). The names of the old biserial "form genera" were retained, but they were redefined, and they were added to by a number of other biserial genera based on early colony growth patterns, with Middle Ordovician taxa including *Undulograptus*, *Oelandograptus*, and *Eoglyptograptus*. In the Middle Ordovician there were also "quadriserial" forms such as *Pseudophyllograptus*, and biserial forms in which the two stipes grew "side by side" rather than "back to back," like *Glossograptus* and *Cryptograptus*. The biserial graptolites overall dominated many assemblages in the Middle and Late Ordovician and continued to be important in the early Silurian. In many of these, spines (perhaps used as "feeding platforms" by the zooids, and/or of hydrodynamic significance) grew out from the thecal apertures, either in just the first few thecae, or throughout the colony.

The Late Ordovician saw the evolution of distinctive new genera of graptolites, including the Y-shaped *Dicranograptus*, which started off as a biserial graptolite before separation and divergence of the stipes took place, and the V-shaped *Dicellograptus*. In addition to their distinctive overall shapes, their thecae now were also elaborated into more complex shapes, with the apertures commonly being "introverted" into a concavity developed in the succeeding theca. Other typical Late Ordovician forms are *Nemagraptus* and *Pleurograptus* in which new stipes (as *Cladia*) were added to create multiple-branched forms. These graptolites often developed graceful helically spiraling morphologies, likely a hydrodynamic adaptation. Another useful and distinctive form is *Corynoides*, reduced only to an elongated sicula and 2–3 thecae.

The end of the Ordovician showed a dramatic decline in graptolite diversity, likely precipitated by environmental changes associated with the Hirnantian glaciation. Most groups became extinct, and only a handful of biserial species survived into the Silurian.

3B.6 Silurian graptolite evolution and succession

From the few survivors of the Late Ordovician crisis, there radiated new and highly successful graptolite lineages. The most important innovation was the appearance, very early in the Silurian, of the monograptid graptolites. These were not the first uniserial graptolites—they were preceded by the azygograptids in the Early Ordovician. But, while the azygograptids arose by "amputation" of one of the horizontal stipes of a dichograptid ancestor, the monograptids arose via suppression of one of the vertical thecal rows of a biserial ancestor (not an easy step, as it also included the simplification of that ancestor's complex early colony development).

Once that step was made, a whole new range of morphologies became possible. This included a wide variety of geometries of the single monograptid stipe (including curves of various kinds, plane spirals and helical spirals) while a wide range of thecal types also emerged, which included morphologies that were hooked, lobed, coiled symmetrically or asymmetrically, and also developed a range of spine- or flange-like projections.

The striking new morphologies that appeared help characterize subdivisions of the Silurian. For instance, Aeronian graptolite assemblages include *Pristiograptus*, with simple thecae (Fig. 3B.1D) are typified by the triangulate monograptids, that quickly (the rate of morphological change was notably rapid) gave rise, by pronounced elongation of the triangulate thecae, to the rastritid monograptids (Sudbury, 1958) (Fig. 3B.3, left-hand side); the Aeronian also saw the beginning of *Torquigraptus* (Fig. 3B.1F) with thecae that are triangulate in outline but twisted to one side rather than symmetrically hooked. The succeeding Telychian includes a succession of streptograptid monograptids, with distinctively coiled thecae and *Monograptus* sensu stricto, with hooked thecae; Wenlock assemblages are characterized by the cyrtograptid monograptids, which, like *Nemagraptus* and *Pleurograptus* in the Late Ordovician, grew secondary branches (*Cladia*); and Ludlow assemblages (following another near-extinction crisis et the end of the Wenlock, again associated with oceanographic change) showed a radiation of the spinose saetograptid monograptids.

Biserial graptolites remained important in the early part of the Silurian but most did not survive beyond the end of the Llandovery. Nevertheless, even in this short span they showed some striking developments, among which is the evolutionary trend from the petalolithid graptolites to the enormously elongated thecae of species of *Cephalograptus* in the mid-Llandovery (Snelling and Zalasiewicz, 2011) (Fig. 3B.3, right-hand side).

An extraordinary development among the biserial graptolites (again, with its roots among the petalolithids, in the mid-Llandovery) is the emergence and radiation of the retiolitid graptolites (Kozłowska-Dawidziuk, 2004). These superficially resemble some biserial graptolites of the Ordovician such as *Orthoretiolites* in having a meshwork rather than solid-walled tubaria. However, their construction is quite different. Instead of simply reducing the thecal walls to their frameworks, as was the case with the Ordovician examples, the Silurian retiolitids built their meshwork constructions by enormous elongation and branching of a spine (the virgella) that extended from the base of the sicula. As this new sicula-derived structure (called the ancora sleeve) built upward, the thecal walls inside became reduced to sets of rods that combine with the ancora sleeve. Despite their considerable geometrical complexity (e.g., *Gothograptus*: Fig. 3B.1G, there is good evidence that the retiolitids, like the other graptolites, were actively and cooperatively constructed by the zooids, for much of the construction is made of successively applied bandages. The retiolitids outlived other biserial graptolites, ranging through into the Ludlow.

The last planktonic graptolites, those of the Early Devonian, are mostly relatively straight and simple monograptids, of low diversity. The graptolites—in their prime a key fossil group, which provide the primary guide for 12 out of 15 current GSSPs in the Ordovician–Silurian interval—simply faded away,

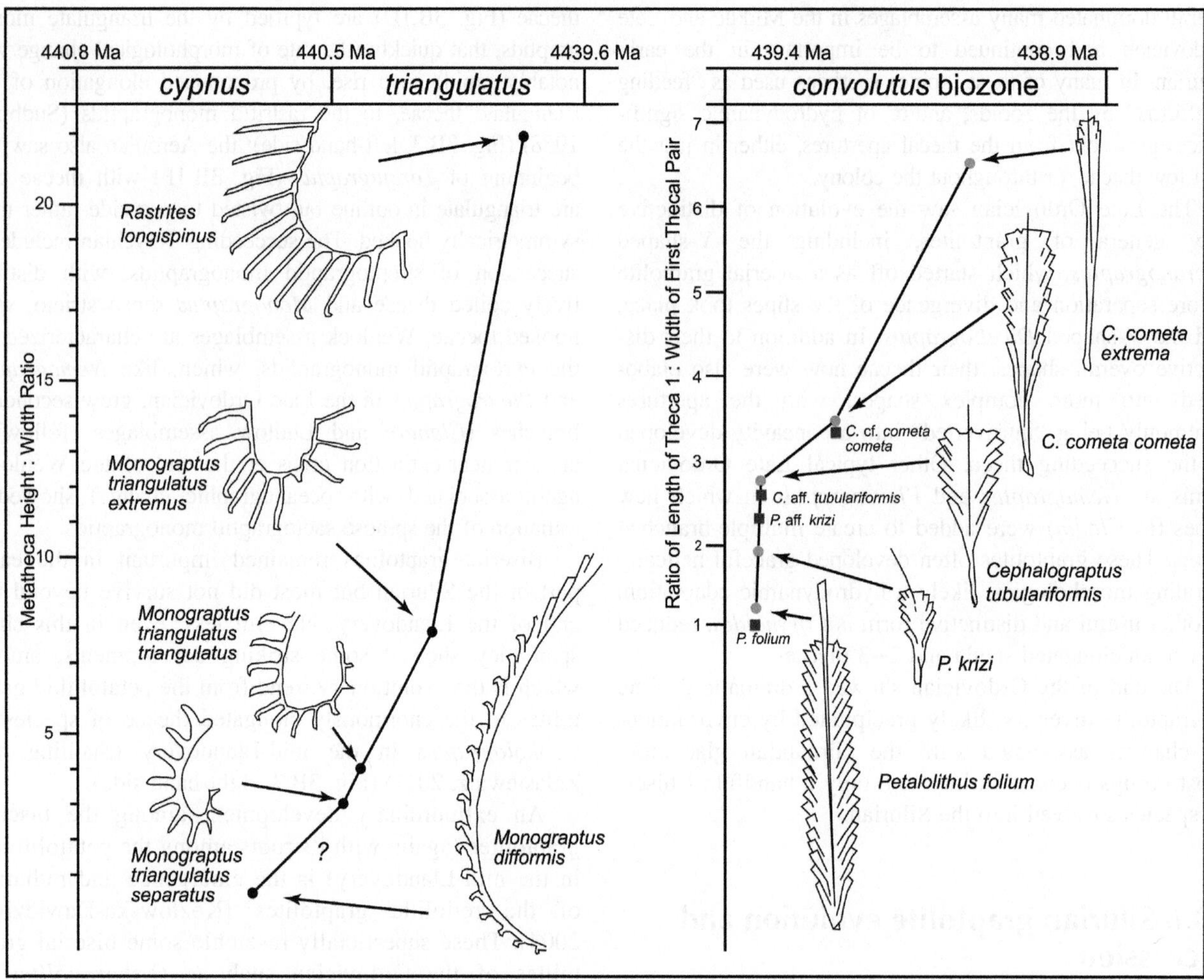

FIGURE 3B.3 Two examples of biostratigraphically useful microevolution, in the early Silurian triangulate monograptid–rastritid and *Petalolithus–Cephalograptus* lineages, modified after Sudbury (1958) and Snelling and Zalasiewicz (2011), respectively.

leaving only the obscure benthic pterobranchs to represent them today. They have no analog in the modern plankton, and thus many aspects of their biology and ecology remain mysterious. Their value for biostratigraphy, though, has proved durable.

Bibliography

Barrande, J., 1850, *Graptolites de Bohême*. Prague: Published by the Author.

Bates, D.E., Maletz, J., and Zalasiewicz, J., 2015, Graptolite preparation and illustration techniques. Part V, Revised Chapter 11 *Treatise Online*, **65**: 1–20 17 fig.

Bjerreskov, M., 1975, Llandoverian and Wenlockian graptolites from Bornholm. *Fossils & Strata*, **8**: 94.

Chen, Xu, Fan, J.X., Melchin, M.J., and Mitchell, C.E., 2005, Hirnantian (Latest Ordovician) graptolities from the Upper Yangtze region, China. *Palaeontology*, **48**: 235–280.

Cooper, R.A., and Sadler, P.M., 2010, Facies preference predicts extinction risk in Ordovician graptolites. *Paleobiology*, **36**: 167–187.

Cooper, A.H., Fortey, N.J., Hughes, R.A., Molyneux, S.G., Moore, R.M., Rushton, A.W.A., et al., 2004, *Skiddaw Group of the English Lake District. Memoir of the British Geological Survey*. London: The Stationary Office.

Cooper, R.A., Rigby, S., Loydell, D.K., and Bates, D.E.B., 2012, Palaeoecology of the Graptoloidea. *Earth Science Reviews*, **112**: 23–41.

Crowther, P., and Rickards, B., 1977, Cortical bandages and the graptolite zooid. *Geologica et Palaeontologica*, **11**: 9–46.

Davies, J.R., Fletcher, C.J.N., Waters, R.A., Wilson, D., Woodhall, D.G., and Zalasiewicz, J.A., 1997, *Geology of the country around Llanilar and Rhayader. Memoir of the British Geological Survey*. Sheets 178 and 179 (England and Wales).

Elles, G.L., and Wood, E.M.R., 1901, *A Monograph of British Graptolites*. London: The Palaeontographical Society.

Hall, J., 1865, *Graptolites of the Quebec Group. Figures and Descriptions of Canadian Organic Remains*. Geological Survey of Canada Dec. 2, 1-151, pls 1-21.

Hutt, J.E., 1974, *The Llandovery Graptolites of the English Lake District*. London: The Palaeontographical Society Publ. 540 part of vol. 128 (1974), 1-56; publ. 542 part of vol. 129 (1975), 57-137.

Kozłowska-Dawidziuk, A., 2004, Evolution of retiolitid graptolites – a synopsis. *Acta Palaeontologica Polonica*, **49**: 505–518.

Kozłowski, R., 1949, Les graptolithes et quelques noveax groupes d'animaux du Tremadoc de la Pologne. *Palaeontologia Polonica*, **3**: 1–235.

Lapworth, C., 1878, The Moffat series. *Quarterly Journal of the Geological Society, London*, **34**: 240–346.

Linnarsson, J.G.O., 1871, Om några försteningar från Sveriges och Norges Primordialzon. *Öfversikt af Kongliga Vetenskaps-Akademiens Förhandlingar*, **6**: 789–797.

Loydell, D.K., 1992, *Upper Aeronian and Lower Telychian (Llandovery) Graptolites From Western Mid-Wales*. London: The Palaeontographical Society Publ. 589 for vol. 146 (1992), 1-55; publ. 592 for vol. 147 (1993), 56-180.

Kozłowska-Dawidziuk, A., Bates, D., Zalasiewicz, J., and Radzevičius, S., 2019, Evolutionary significance of the retiolitine *Gothograptus* (Graptolithina) with four new species from the Silurian of the East European Platform (Baltica), Poland and Lithuania. *Zootaxa*, **4568** (3), 435–469.

Maletz, J. (ed), 2017. Graptolite Palaeobiology. Wiley-Blackwell.

Mitchell, C.E., 1987, The evolution and classification of the Diplograptacea. *Palaeontology*, **30**: 353–405.

Page, A., Zalasiewicz, J.A., Williams, M., and Popov, L.E., 2007, Were transgressive black shales a negative feedback modulating glacioeustasy in the Early Palaeozoic Icehouse? *In* Williams, M., Haywood, A.M., Gregory, F.J., and Schmidt, D.N. (eds), *Deep-Time Perspectives on Climate Change: Marrying the Signal from Computer Models and Biological Proxies*. London: The Micropalaeontological Society, Special Publications. The Geological Society, 123–156.

Rickards, R.B., 2002, The graptolitic age of the type Ashgill Series (Ordovician), Cumbria, UK. *Proceedings of the Yorkshire Geological Society*, **54**: 1–16.

Snelling, A.M., and Zalasiewicz, J.A., 2011, The evolutionary lineage of *Petalolithus* to *Cephalograptus*: evidence from Coalpit Bay, northern Ireland. *Proceedings of the Yorkshire Geological Society*, **58**: 345–350.

Štorch, P., 1998, Graptolites of the *Pribylograptus leptotheca* and *Lituigraptus convolutus* biozones of Tmaň (Silurian, Czech Republic). *Journal of the Czech Geological Society*, **43**: 209–272.

Sudbury, M., 1958, Triangulate monograptids from the *Monograptus gregarius* Zone (lower Llandovery) of the Rheidol Gorge (Cardiganshire). *Philosophical Transactions of the Royal Society of London*, **B241**: 485–555.

VandenBerg, A.H.M., and Cooper, R.A., 1992, The Ordovician graptolite sequence of Australasia. *Alcheringa*, **16**: 33–85.

Zalasiewicz, J.A., Taylor, L., Rushton, A.W.A., Loydell, D.K., Rickards, R.B., and Williams, M., 2009, Graptolites in British stratigraphy. *Geological Magazine*, **146**: 785–850.

Subchapter 3C

Chitinozoans

A. Butcher

Abstract

Chitinozoans are Paleozoic marine organic-walled microfossils of unknown animals thought to be egg cases. The bottle-, flask-, or urn-shaped vesicles are important for Ordovician through Devonian biostratigraphy.

3C.1 Introduction

Chitinozoans are a group of extinct Paleozoic marine organic-walled microfossils of unknown biological affinity, which have proven to be extremely valuable biostratigraphic tools in Ordovician to Devonian studies worldwide. Comprising bottle-, flask-, or urn-shaped vesicles with a sealing plug, they are thought to be the egg cases of pelagic soft-bodied animals (not yet identified in the fossil record), termed "chitinozoophorans" by Grahn (1981).

The name "chitinozoa" was introduced by Alfred Eisenack (1931) to describe unknown microfossils with an apparently chitinous wall, which were extracted from erratic boulders of Ordovician–Silurian age on the Baltic coastline of the former East Prussia. Eisenack (1930) continued to study this enigmatic group throughout the 1930s, though there were very few other investigations worldwide until an acceleration in their study during the 1960s, in relation largely to hydrocarbon exploration. An excellent summary of the history of the study of chitinozoans was provided by Servais et al. (2013).

Despite their name, chitinozoan vesicles in fact contain no true chitin—the vesicles comprise a chitin-like organic compound, termed "pseudochitin," and it is uncertain whether the vesicles did contain chitin originally (which did not survive taphonomic processes), or whether it was never present (Voss-Foucart and Jeuniaux, 1972; Dutta et al., 2007; Jacob et al., 2007).

3C.2 Phylogeny and taxonomy

That chitinozoans may be egg cases was first proposed by Kozłowski (1963), due to their occurrence in coiled chain-like structures considered to have been surrounded by an organic-walled cocoon, similar to those produced by some polychaetes today (Grahn and Paris, 2011). Such structures have been recorded and described subsequently by several authors (e.g., Paris and Nõlvak, 1999; see discussions in Grahn and Paris, 2011, and Servais et al., 2013). Paris and Verniers (2005) suggested that all chitinozoans were probably linked at some point during their development, but that the less resistant linkages were destroyed by either taphonomic processes and/or palynological processing.

Chitinozoan workers generally agree that, unlike the acritarchs, the chitinozoans are most likely a monophyletic group, but due to the uncertainty of their biological affinities their classification is based purely upon morphology (see Fig. 3C.1). While the relatively small number of chitinozoan workers over the decades has limited the research and outputs on this group (as compared with some other Paleozoic fossil groups), it has had the positive effects of creating close collaboration between the different workers at any one time, and also a more general acceptance of taxonomic and biostratigraphic concepts (Servais et al., 2013).

Paris (1981) proposed a robust and comprehensive suprageneric classification scheme for the chitinozoans, based upon distinct morphological features. Chitinozoan workers worldwide adopted this scheme, ensuring an increased level of ease and consistency of identifications. The scheme was revised by Paris et al. (1999) and remains in use today. The emended classification scheme encompasses taxonomic ranks from order to genus, and a definition of each of the 56 valid genera was provided (with 83 genera being rejected on the basis of synonymy). Only a very few new genera have been described since, meaning that this classification scheme can be used by anyone working upon chitinozoans today. Several chitinozoan databases have been developed over the years, in order to collate taxa and occurrences, and provide a platform through which data can be retrieved for both geographical and temporal distribution/diversity studies (see discussion in Hints et al., 2018). The "CHITINOVOSP" database is perhaps the most comprehensive, and, as of 2017, listed 1282 chitinozoan species (Hints et al., 2018). Other databases, such as the Canadian "CHITINOS" (Achab et al., 2000), are no longer active, while the newly created "CHITDB" database for the Baltic is open access (Hints et al., 2018). With any database, however, there are biases inherent from the data entered—inaccuracies/uncertainty in taxonomic identifications, stratigraphic ranges, calculation of time slices, and the number of samples studied per time slice can all introduce bias—as such, resulting models, diversity curves, etc. should take account of the data utilized and its limitations.

Naturally, taxonomic problems do arise, particularly among taxa that possess few morphological features (e.g., processes or other ornamentation)—many species of *Conochitina*, for example, are characterized purely by vesicle dimensions in the absence of other diagnostic features, which can prove problematic in terms of species

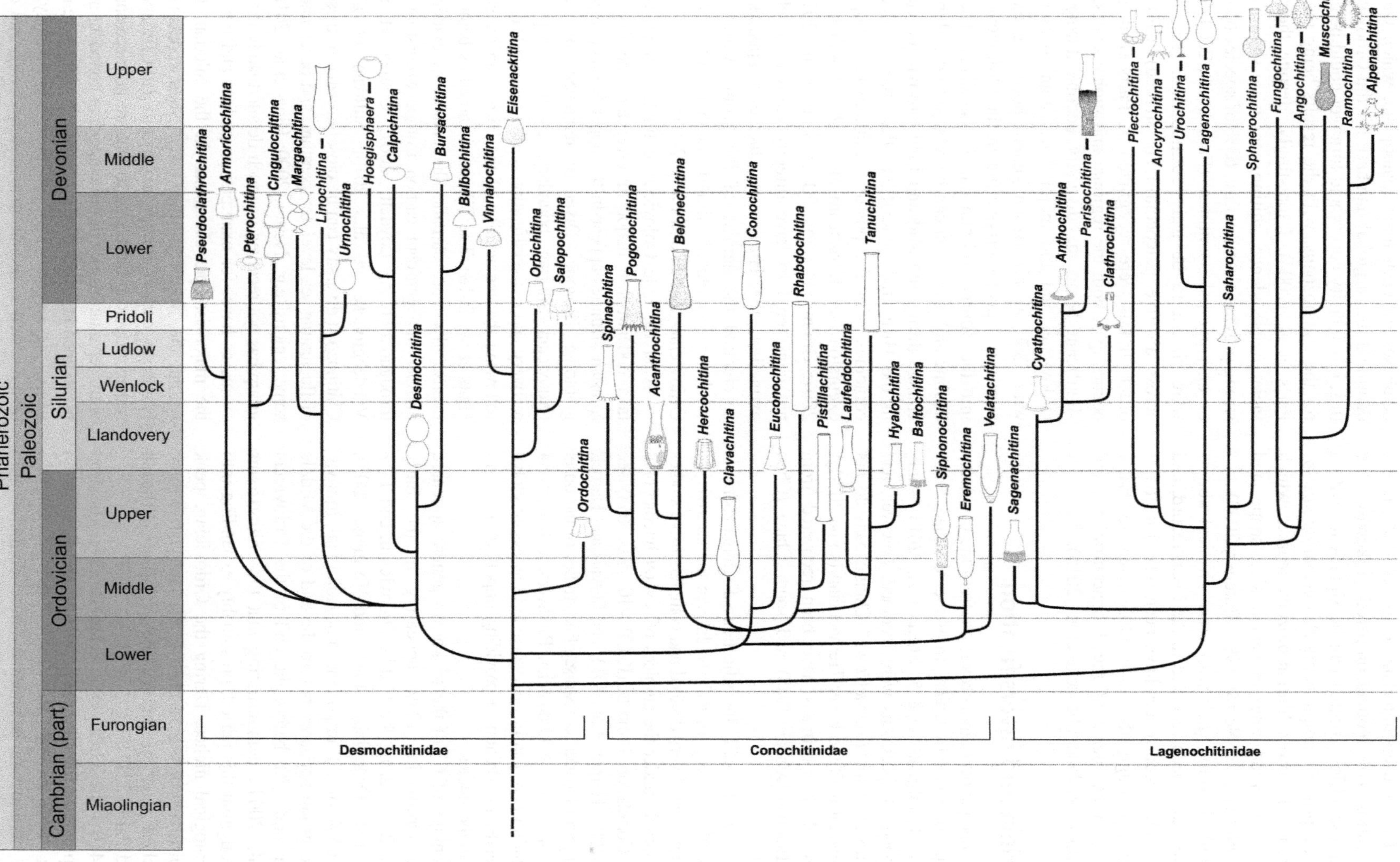

FIGURE 3C.1 Approximate ranges of selected chitinozoan genera. Note that the relationships shown are not necessarily phylogenetic, but based purely upon morphological characteristics (see Paris and Verniers, 2005). Ranges and chitinozoan drawings modified after Paris and Verniers (2005, Figs. 3 and 4).

definitions if a large enough data set is not studied, and dimension ratios not plotted/compared. Likewise, the range of intraspecific variation can be significant within certain taxa, a prime example being *Belonechitina postrobusta*, an important lower Silurian biozonal marker, which possesses a very broad range of vesicle size, shape, and ornamentation (e.g., see Nestor, 1994; Butcher, 2009).

Teratological forms (i.e., with clear physical abnormalities) have also been recorded in the fossil record, and their stratigraphic occurrences have been linked to major ocean events through the Late Ordovician to Early Devonian, such as increased metal concentrations and anoxic events (see Vandenbroucke et al., 2015).

3C.3 Origin and diversification

The earliest unequivocal chitinozoans are from the Cambrian Duyun fauna of southern China, from the Wuliuan Stage (=previously Cambrian Stage 5; Shen et al., 2013)—only three phosphatised specimens were recorded, however, and tentatively assigned to "*Eisenackitina*." Chitinozoans do not become abundant until the lower Tremadocian (some 20 Myr later), from which specimens have been recovered from Morocco (Elaouad-Debbaj, 1988) and south China (Chen et al., 2008).

The subsequent rapid diversification of chitinozoans is extremely well recorded, particularly through the Ordovician, thanks to a number of very detailed and comprehensive studies undertaken largely under the auspices of several International Geological Correlation Projects (IGCP 410, 503, 653; see Paris et al., 2004, Harper et al., 2011, and Servais and Harper, 2018). As a part of wider, cross-discipline studies of the onset and effects of the Great Ordovician Biodiversification Event (GOBE), chitinozoan data proved valuable in assessing global diversity trends, in addition to providing important age constraint data to the studies.

A percentage of 63 of the 56 known genera appeared during the Ordovician (28% appearing in the Early Ordovician, 24% during the Middle Ordovician, and 11% during the Late Ordovician; Paris and Verniers, 2005). Likewise, 65% of all important morphological innovations in the group appeared before the end of the Middle Ordovician, and 77% before the end of the Ordovician (Paris et al., 2004), demonstrating that the chitinozoans thrived throughout this period, presumably expanding into various ecological niches. During the Ordovician, peak chitinozoan diversity was reached in the late Darriwilian, only matched later in the Middle and Late Silurian (Grahn and Paris, 2011).

IGCP 410 (The Great Ordovician Biodiversification Event: Implication for Global Correlation and Resources) included a "Chitinozoan Clade Team," led by Florentin Paris, and chitinozoan occurrences were compiled into databases for each major paleoplate, which were in turn compiled into a global database for the Ordovician. From this, biodiversity curves and turnover could be established for the chitinozoans, with the results being presented by Paris et al. (2004). Interestingly, despite their apparent facies independence, chitinozoans were shown to display strong provincialism, with c. 63% of species being present on only one paleocontinent (Paris et al., 2004)—only 2% were shown to be truly cosmopolitan (i.e., distributed across all five paleocontinents studied). Certain "first-order" trends were recognized by Paris et al. (2004), as occurring at both the regional and global scales, the most significant being the diversity decline during the Late Ordovician and the major Hirnantian extinction event with 33% of chitinozoan genera becoming extinct, and almost no species originating in the Ordovician survived into the Silurian (Grahn and Paris, 2011). The diversity decline and extinction can be related to the global climate change during the Mid and Late Ordovician, culminating in the Hirnantian glaciation—the onset of decline also coincides with the positive Guttenberg isotopic carbon excursion (see Bergström et al., 2009; Achab and Paris, 2007; Grahn and Paris, 2011; Hints et al., 2018). While not considered to have directly caused the chitinozoan extinction, the Hirnantian glaciation appears to have accelerated the demise of the group, which had been weakened by global climatic change earlier in the Late Ordovician (Achab and Paris, 2007).

After the Late Ordovician extinction event, chitinozoan taxa underwent a major turnover and the first taxa with Silurian affinities appear in the upper Hirnantian *persculptus* graptolite Biozone. Diversity remained low across the Ordovician–Silurian boundary, as the group underwent recovery and rediversification during the rapid sea-level rises following the deglaciation of the Hirnantian ice sheets (e.g., Hints et al., 2018). The Silurian is noted as being a time of intense, dynamic, climatic fluctuation, as evidenced by a number of significant carbon isotope excursions occurring throughout (e.g., Loydell, 2007; Cramer et al., 2011; Vandenbroucke et al., 2013; Sullivan et al., 2018). Chitinozoan diversity can be closely related to these episodes of fluctuating sea level, temperature, and ocean chemistry, in some regions (e.g., Nestor, 2009; Hints et al., 2018), but the group has not received as much detailed study through these events as have, for example, graptolites and conodonts. Of the major isotopic excursions in the Silurian, two occur within the Wenlock—the early Sheinwoodian and late Homerian carbon isotope excursions (ESCIE and LHCIE, respectively) can be related to, but are not necessarily coeval with, separate major but not coincident conodont and graptolite extinction events (the Ireviken and Mulde events, respectively; see Loydell, 2007). Chitinozoan diversity has been demonstrated to decline dramatically during, and commonly just following, these isotopic excursions, and high-resolution studies in the Baltic in particular have linked these events, along with the period immediately following the mid-Ludfordian carbon isotope excursion, to decreases in chitinozoan diversity (e.g., Nestor, 2009; Hints et al., 2018)—the general trends are reflected also on a global scale (although not with such high precision; see Grahn and Paris, 2011).

Through the Early Devonian, global regression during the Pragian once again caused chitinozoan diversity to decrease dramatically (see Grahn and Paris, 2011, Fig. 1), and while the abundance of chitinozoans increased once again during a transgressive phase during the Emsian, diversity did not recover and remained low (see Grahn and Paris, 2011). The trend of high absolute abundance but low diversity continued through the remainder of the Devonian, although with a significant peak in the Givetian (see Grahn and Paris, 2011, Fig. 1). The Kellwasser events in the latest Frasnian are associated with ocean anoxia (and a mass extinction, one of the "Big 5"; see Percival et al., 2018, and references therein), and these events can be linked to a decrease in diversity of the group. A final "surprising" increase in chitinozoan diversity, immediately prior to the extinction of the group in the late Famennian, was noted in Brazilian strata by Grahn and De Melo (2002).

The youngest occurrences of chitinozoans are from the upper Famennian of Brazil and Algeria (see Grahn and Paris, 2011, and references therein), immediately prior to the latest Famennian glaciation. Grahn and Paris (2011) provided several explanations for the demise and extinction of the chitinozoans, and the reader is directed to their paper (and references therein) for a comprehensive summary of these hypotheses.

3C.4 Applications

The main application of chitinozoans has been in biostratigraphical studies—being widespread, generally abundant, rapidly evolving, and chemically resistant, the group has proved to be a valuable tool providing age constraints in Ordovician, Silurian, and Devonian strata worldwide. As mentioned previously, much of the early biostratigraphical work in the 1960s–80s was driven by hydrocarbon exploration, where chitinozoans, often occurring in very high abundances, could be readily obtained from cores, cuttings, and outcrop samples. The group has now become one of the three major groups of fossils used for biostratigraphy in the Ordovician and Silurian (alongside graptolites and conodonts) and has been applied not only to hydrocarbon exploration, but also to the definition of stage boundaries and time slices (e.g., Webby et al., 2004; see Servais et al., 2013). Due to their general facies independence, chitinozoans also enable correlation between deeper water (graptolitic) facies and shallower water (conodont) facies, thus being important contributors to the increasing trend for high-resolution integrated biostratigraphical studies (e.g., Albani et al., 2001; Loydell et al., 2003, 2010; Männik et al., 2015; Vandenbroucke et al., 2008).

In addition to regional biozonations, global biozonation schemes have been developed for the Ordovician, Silurian, and Devonian, see, for example, Paris and Verniers (2005) and Gradstein et al. (2012). While still useful, chitinozoan workers generally agree that these global biozonations are overdue a review, due to the numerous local and regional schemes being further developed and refined (e.g., the global biozonation for the Silurian was developed by Verniers et al. (1995)—much has been published since then). Precision for the Ordovician and parts of the Silurian approaches 0.5 Myr for the shortest duration zones. For the Ordovician, three distinct paleocontinental/paleolatitudinal biozonations have been recognized, for the low-latitude Laurentian, the mid-latitude Baltican, and the high-latitude Northern Gondwanan realms (Paris and Verniers, 2005). Paris (in Gradstein et al., 2012) presented a biozonal scheme for the Ordovician of Northern Gondwana comprising 28 biozones/subbiozones, showing a refinement from Paris and Verniers (2005) (=25 biozones). For the Silurian a single biozonation was presented by Paris and Verniers (2005), which remained unchanged in Gradstein et al. (2012), consisting of 17 biozones, while the biozonal scheme for the Devonian has received some revision (e.g., by Grahn et al., 2010) between the two publications, although the overall number of biozones (19) has remained consistent.

In addition to their application in biostratigraphical studies, chitinozoan data have more recently also been applied to global paleoclimatology studies. Vandenbroucke et al. (2010a) utilized chitinozoan biotopes to recognize subtropical, subpolar, and polar climate belts during the Late Ordovician, in relation to cooling trends preceding the Hirnantian glaciation, while Vandenbroucke et al. (2010b) were able to show that the polar front shift during the Hirnantian glaciation was similar to that seen between Pleistocene glacial–interglacial periods. Indeed, Servais et al. (2013) stated that chitinozoans "may be able to play a more important role than previously thought in lower Paleozoic climate studies."

In summary, while they have received relatively little study by comparison with other major Paleozoic fossil groups, chitinozoans have proven to be invaluable tools for lower Paleozoic high-resolution biostratigraphic studies in a range of different fields. Continued study, and expansion and refinement of chitinozoan data by the next generation of Paleozoic palynologists, will only strengthen further their place as an important tool in Ordovician to Devonian studies.

Bibliography

Achab, A., and Paris, F., 2007, The Ordovician chitinozoan biodiversification and its leading factors. *Palaeogeography, Palaeoclimatology, Palaeoecology*, **245**: 5–19.

Achab, A., Asselin, E., and Liang, B., 2000, A structured database and image acquisition system in support of palynological studies: CHITINOS. *Review of Palaeobotany and Palynology*, **113**: 12–26.

Albani, R., Bagnoli, G., Maletz, J., and Stouge, S., 2001, Integrated chitinozoan, conodont, and graptolite biostratigraphy from the upper part of the Cape Cormorant Formation (Middle Ordovician), western Newfoundland. *Canadian Journal of Earth Sciences*, **38**: 387–409.

Bergström, S., Chen, X., Guitiérrez-Marco, J.C., and Dronov, A., 2009, The new chronostratigraphic classification of the Ordovician System and its relations to major regional series and stages and to δ^{13}C chemostratigraphy. *Lethaia*, **42**: 97–107.

Butcher, A., 2009, Early Llandovery chitinozoans from Jordan. *Palaeontology*, **52**: 593–629.

Chen, X.H., Paris, F., and Zhang, M., 2008, Chitinozoans from the Fenxiang Formation (Early Ordovician) of Yichang, Hubei Province, China. *Acta Geologica Sinica*, **82**: 287–294.

Cramer, B.D., Brett, C.E., Melchin, M.J., Männik, P., Kleffner, M.A., McLaughlin, P.I., et al., 2011, Revised correlation of Silurian Provincial Series of North America with global and regional chronostratigraphic units and $\delta^{13}C_{carb}$ chemostratigraphy. *Lethaia*, **44**: 185–202.

Dutta, S., Brocke, R., Hartkopf-Froder, C., Littke, R., Wilkes, H., and Mann, U., 2007, Highly aromatic character of biogeomacromolecules in Chitinozoa: a spectroscopic and pyrolytic study. *Organic Geochemistry*, **38**: 1625–1642.

Eisenack, A., 1930, Neue Mikrofossilien des baltischens Silurs (Vorläufige Mitteilung). *Der Naturwissenschaften*, **18**: 180–181.

Eisenack, A., 1931, Neue Mikrofossilien des baltischens Silurs, I. *Paläontologische Zeitschrift*, **13**: 74–118.

Elaouad-Debbaj, Z., 1988, Acritarches et Chitinozoaires du Tremadoc de l'Anti-Atlas central (Maroc). *Revue de Micropaleontologie*, **31**: 85–128.

Gradstein, F.M., Ogg, J.G., Schmitz, M., and Ogg, G., 2012, *The Geologic Timescale 2012*. Elsevier Publisher, 1144 p.

Grahn, Y., 1981, Ordovician Chitinozoa from the Stora Åsbotorp boring in Västergötland, south-central Sweden. *Sveriges Geologiska Undersökning Serie C*, **787**: 1–40.

Grahn, Y., and De Melo, J.H.G., 2002, Chitinozoan biostratigraphy of the Late Devonian formations in well Caima PH-2, Tapajós River area, Amazonas Basin, northern Brazil. *Review of Palaeobotany and Palynology*, **118**: 115–139.

Grahn, Y., and Paris, F., 2011, Emergence, biodiversification and extinction of the chitinozoan group. *Geological Magazine*, **148**: 226–236.

Grahn, Y., Mauller, P.M., Pereira, E., and Loboziak, S., 2010, Palynostratigraphy of the Chapada Group and its significance in the stratigraphy of the Paraná Basin, south Brazil. *Journal of South American Earth Sciences*, **29**: 354–370.

Harper, D.A.T., Li, J., Munnecke, A., Owen, A.W., Servais, T., and Sheehan, P., 2011, Concluding IGCP 503: towards a holistic view of Ordovician and Silurian Earth systems. *Episodes*, **34**: 32–38.

Hints, O., Antonovitš, L., Bauert, G., Nestor, V., Nõlvak, J., and Tammekänd, M., 2018, CHITDB: a database for documenting and analysing diversification of Ordovician–Silurian chitinozoans in the Baltic region. *Lethaia*, **51**: 218–227.

Jacob, J., Paris, F., Monod, O., Miller, M.A., Tang, P., George, S.C., et al., 2007, New insights into the chemical composition of the chitinozoans. *Organic Geochemistry*, **38**: 1782–1788.

Kozłowski, R., 1963, Sur la nature des Chitinozoaires. *Acta Palaeontologia Polonica*, **8**: 425–455.

Loydell, D.K., 2007, Early Silurian positive δ^{13}C excursions and their relationship to glaciations, sea-level changes and extinction events. *Geological Journal*, **42**: 531–546.

Loydell, D.K., Männik, P., and Nestor, V., 2003, Integrated biostratigraphy of the lower Silurian of the Aizpute-41 core, Latvia. *Geological Magazine*, **140**: 205–229.

Loydell, D.K., Nestor, V., and Männik, P., 2010, Integrated biostratigraphy of the lower Silurian of the Kolka-54 core, Latvia. *Geological Magazine*, **147**: 253–280.

Männik, P., Loydell, D.K., Nestor, V., and Nõlvak, J., 2015, Integrated Upper Ordovician–lower Silurian biostratigraphy of the Grötlingbo-1 core section, Sweden. *Geologiska Föreningens Förhandlingar*, **137**: 226–244.

Nestor, V., 1994, Early Silurian chitinozoans of Estonia and North Latvia. *Academia*, **4**: 1–163.

Nestor, V., 2009, Chitinozoan diversity in the East Baltic Silurian. *Estonian Journal of Earth Sciences*, **58**: 311–316.

Paris, F., 1981, Les Chitinozoaires dans la Paleózoïque du sud-ouest de l'Europe. *Mémoire de la Société géologique et minéralogique de Bretagne*, **26**: 1–492.

Paris, F., and Nõlvak, J., 1999, Biological interpretation and palaeodiversity of a cryptic fossil group: the 'chitinozoan animal'. *Geobios*, **32**: 315–324.

Paris, F., and Verniers, J., 2005, Chitinozoa. *In* Selley, R.C., Cocks, L.R. M., and Plimer, I.R. (eds), *Encyclopaedia of Geology*. Elsevier Publisher, **Vol. 3**: 428–440.

Paris, F., Grahn, Y., Nestor, V., and Lakova, I., 1999, A revised chitinozoan classification. *Journal of Paleontology*, **73**: 547–568.

Paris, F., Achab, A., Asselin, E., Chen, X.H., Grahn, Y., Nõlvak, J., et al., 2004, Chitinozoans. *In* Webby, B.D., Paris, F., Droser, M.L., and Percival, I.G. (eds), *The Great Ordovician Biodiversification Event*. Columbia University Press, pp. 294–311.

Percival, L.M.E., Davies, J.H.F.L., Schaltegger, U., De Vleeschouwer, D., Da Silva, A.C., and Follmi, K.B., 2018, Precisely dating the Frasnian–Famennian boundary: implications for the cause of the Late Devonian mass extinction. *Scientific Reports*, **8** (9578), 10.

Servais, T., and Harper, D.A.T., 2018, The Great Ordovician Biodiversification Event (GOBE): definition, concept and duration. *Lethaia*, **51**: 151–164.

Servais, T., Achab, A., and Asselin, E., 2013, Eighty years of chitinozoan research: from Alfred Eisenack to Florentin Paris. *Review of Palaeobotany and Palynology*, **197**: 143–151.

Shen, C., Aldridge, R.J., Williams, M., Vandenbroucke, T.R.A., and Zhang, X.G., 2013, Earliest chitinozoans discovered in the Cambrian Duyun fauna of China. *Geology*, **41**: 191–194.

Sullivan, N.B., Loydell, D.K., Montgomery, P., Molyneux, S.G., Zalasiewicz, J., Ratcliffe, K.T., et al., 2018, A record of Late Ordovician to Silurian oceanographic events on the margin of Baltica based on new carbon isotope data, elemental geochemistry, and biostratigraphy from two boreholes in central Poland. *Palaeogeography, Palaeoclimatology, Palaeoecology*, **490**: 95–106.

Vandenbroucke, T.R.A., Williams, M., Zalasiewicz, J.A., Davies, J.R., and Waters, R.A., 2008, Integrated Upper Ordovician graptolite-chitinozoan biostratigraphy of the Cardigan and Whitland areas, southwest Wales. *Geological Magazine*, **145**: 199–214.

Vandenbroucke, T.R.A., Armstrong, H.A., Williams, M., Paris, F., Sabbe, K., Zalasiewicz, J.A., et al., 2010a, Epipelagic chitinozoan biotopes map a steep latitudinal temperature gradient for earliest Late Ordovician seas: implications for a cooling Late Ordovician. *Palaeogeography, Palaeoclimatology, Palaeoecology*, **294**: 202–219.

Vandenbroucke, T.R.A., Armstrong, H.A., Williams, M., Paris, F., Zalasiewicz, J.A., Sabbe, K., et al., 2010b, Polar front shift and atmospheric CO_2 during the glacial maximum of the Early Paleozoic Icehouse. *Proceedings of the National Academy of Science, United States of America*, **107**: 14983–14986.

Vandenbroucke, T.R.A., Munnecke, A., Leng, M.J., Bickert, T., Hints, O., Gelsthorpe, D., et al., 2013, Reconstructing the environmental conditions around the Silurian Ireviken Event using the carbon isotope composition of bulk and palynomorph organic matter. *Geochemistry, Geophysics, Geosystems*, **14**: 86–101.

Vandenbroucke, T.R.A., Emsbo, P., Munnecke, A., Nuns, N., Duponchel, L., Lepot, K., et al., 2015, Metal-induced malformations in early Palaeozoic plankton are harbingers of mass extinction. *Nature Communications*, **6** (7966), 1–7.

Verniers, J., Nestor, V., Paris, F., Dufka, P., Sutherland, S., and Van Grootel, G., 1995, A global Chitinozoa biozonation for the Silurian. *Geological Magazine*, **132**: 651–666.

Voss-Foucart, M.F., and Jeuniaux, C., 1972, Lack of chitin in a sample of Ordovician Chitinozoa. *Journal of Paleontology*, **46**: 769–770.

Webby, B.D., Cooper, R.A., Bergström, S.M., and Paris, F., 2004, Stratigraphic framework and time slices. *In* Webby, B.D., Paris, F., Droser, M.L., and Percival, I.G. (eds), *The Great Ordovician Biodiversification Event*. Columbia University Press, pp. 41–47.

Subchapter 3D

Conodonts

C.M. Henderson

Abstract

Conodonts are small (1 mm average size) bioapatitic teeth elements of a rarely preserved eel-like animal; the fossil elements are recovered mostly from dissolving carbonate rocks and are important for biostratigraphy from late Cambrian through Triassic.

3D.1 Introduction

Conodonts were discovered by Pander (1856) and are among the best biostratigraphic index fossils over their 300 million year evolutionary history. The distribution of conodonts in space and time has proven that they are important biostratigraphic tools for correlation of marine rocks from the Upper Cambrian until the end of the Triassic. The first appearance datum (FAD) of conodont species has been used to define Global Boundary Stratotype Sections and Points (GSSP) for many Phanerozoic stages in the Geologic Time Scale (see details at http://stratigraphy.org). The fossil record of conodonts is almost completely composed of small (typically averaging 1 mm in length) bioapatitic elements that resemble teeth; the soft body of the eel-like animal has rarely been preserved.

The small size of conodont elements makes them ideal index fossils to study in outcrop, in subsurface core and even in cuttings. Sedimentary reworking is always possible, but because of their size, they behave hydrodynamically as medium to coarse grained sand particles. One significant biostratigraphic advantage is that many samples collected from marine successions will yield at least some specimens. In the case of GSSP studies, continuous sampling around the boundary interval may precisely reveal the speciation level. A disadvantage is that recovery is usually unknown, until substantial processing of the rock has been completed. Conodonts are sometimes seen on bedding planes, but in most cases they are recovered by the dissolution of carbonate rock in 10% solution of acetic (Jeppsson et al., 1999) or formic acid, or disaggregation of shale by boiling in Quaternary-O detergent, or combinations of the two methods. This is followed by sieving to retain at least all sand-size particles greater than 75 μm, which are subsequently dried and density separated at specific gravity of 2.85 in heavy liquids, including tetrabromoethane or sodium polytungstate; elements have a specific gravity of 2.9–3.0. The conodont elements are hand-picked from the heavy fraction under a binocular microscope, using a fine brush with wet bristles or a single bristle with a static charge. Specimens are then selected and photographed with a Scanning Electron Microscope, although other techniques using synchrotron (Goudemand et al., 2011) and microtomographic imaging (Murdock et al., 2013) have been used more recently. Ideally, a paleontologic plate or figure will depict numerous specimens showing specific variability and ontogenetic or growth series.

Conodonts are also used in thermal maturity studies since their color changes from nearly clear amber to brown, to black, to gray and finally crystal clear as a result of heat associated with burial or contact metamorphism (Epstein et al., 1977; Rejebian et al., 1987). The same carbonization process that alters trace amounts of organic matter within conodont elements also alters organic matter into hydrocarbons. Therefore conodonts can be used to predict the types of hydrocarbons, which is particularly valuable in frontier regions (Utting et al., 1989).

Conodonts originally comprised protoconodonts, paraconodonts, and euconodonts. Protoconodonts are now known to be the grasping spines of arrow worms or chaetognaths and unrelated. True conodonts or euconodonts developed from middle Cambrian paraconodonts by developing a mineralized crown tissue.

3D.2 Biologic affinity

The euconodont animal body was not known until a small eel-like animal was revealed from the Granton Shrimp Beds near Edinburgh, complete with an apparatus comprising numerous phosphatic conodont elements (Briggs et al., 1983). The biological affinity of conodonts continues to be debated. Conodont elements compositionally resemble vertebrate enamel, while histological studies show evidence of occlusion and wear (Donoghue and Purnell, 1999; Purnell and Jones, 2012), leading some to conclude that conodont elements were homologous with vertebrate teeth (Purnell, 1995). Recent work has concluded that conodont elements are the result of convergent evolution and not homologous with other vertebrate teeth (Murdock et al., 2013), but the elements and soft body still provide considerable evidence for vertebrate affinity. As conodonts first appear during the Cambrian Period (Bengston, 1976), they potentially represent a significant step in the evolution of vertebrates. The soft-body discovery (Briggs et al., 1983) provides some of the strongest evidence of chordate and vertebrate affinity, including the interpreted presence of a notochord, chevron-shaped myomeres or muscles bundles, ray-supported caudal fins, and paired eye structures (Aldridge et al., 1993; Purnell, 1995). Some studies have concluded that conodonts are stem gnathostomes (jawed fishes) (Donoghue et al., 2000) and others have rejected this hypothesis (Turner et al., 2010). Other studies point to a stem-cyclostome origin (Dzik, 2000, 2008; Krejsa et al., 1990; Goudemand et al., 2011; Sansom et al., 1992; Terrill et al., 2018). Classification at the superfamily and order level is still being resolved (Donoghue et al., 2008) and phylogenetic analyses provide inconsistent taxonomic clusters. This does not restrict their use as the "most useful fossils in the world" for biostratigraphy, paleoecology, paleobiogeography (Mei and Henderson, 2001), thermal maturity, and geochemical characterization using trace elements and oxygen isotopes (Joachimski et al., 2012).

3D.3 Paleoecology and biofacies

The conodont animal had musculature that pointed to a free swimming or nektic life mode, but it is likely that some forms were nekto-benthic. The apparatus of numerous elements within an individual (usually 15–19 elements) were used to either filter plankton or for grasping and crushing its prey. It is known that the teeth or elements show wear patterns. As such the conodont animal lived within the water column, possibly at different depths according to temperature. Many forms are regarded as shallow-water and even living in restricted conditions of higher than normal salinity. Many of these forms have characteristic morphologies that reoccur (e.g., *Mestognathus*, *Cavusgnathus*, *Clydagnathus*, *Adetognathus* in the Carboniferous and Permian; or Prioniodinids like *Ellisonia* in the Pennsylvanian to Early Triassic). These taxa were probably specialized for these environments and usually have long ranges. Other forms would be considered shelfal [e.g., *Icriodus* and *Polygnathus* in the Devonian; *Sweetognathus* and *Hindeodus* in the Permian and Permian–Triassic Boundary (PTB)], or offshore (e.g., *Palmatolepis*, *Ancyrodella*, and *Siphonodella* in Late Devonian to Early Carboniferous; *Jinogondolella* and *Clarkina* in the Permian and PTB), but may actually be depth stratified according to a thermocline. These taxa tend to have much shorter ranges and are normally utilized for biostratigraphy. This depth-related pelagic model can be well demonstrated in association with cyclothems of the Pennsylvanian and Early Permian. Biofacies therefore play a key role in the development of conodont biozones. Conodonts have never been recovered from fresh water.

3D.4 Biostratigraphy and evolution

Conodonts exhibit cyclic patterns of evolutionary development throughout their history from Late Cambrian to Late Triassic (Sweet, 1988). Most studies describe interval biozones based on the distribution of species from closely spaced samples and are too numerous to summarize in a single figure. Fig. 3D.1 highlights the ranges of key genera. Classifications at familial to order level are still evolving. Conodonts have been utilized in many GSSP definitions where many other correlation tools are available. This concentrated effort on boundary intervals means that sometimes the details between GSSP levels are poorly known. Arguably conodonts represent the best index fossil for biostratigraphy, when considering their entire 300 million year history is subdivided into at least 240 interregional biozones (1.25 Myr/zone on average) and many additional regional zones and subzones. This will be evident by looking at all of the "system" chapters in this volume.

3D.5 Cambrian

Biostratigraphic zonation of the Cambrian is still in early stages of development. Paraconodonts and euconodonts appear during the Miaolingian Series (middle Cambrian) and species define about 10 zones over the last 16 million years of the Cambrian. The near-base of the Drumian Stage is marked by the *Gapparodus bisulcatus–Westergaardodina brevidens* assemblage zone in south China; there is a zonal scheme for the Furongian Series (upper Cambrian) in North America. Cambrian Stage 10 (uppermost Cambrian) includes *Cordylodus* and the first appearance of *Eoconodontus notchpeakensis*. The Cambrian–Ordovician boundary coincides with the extinction of many conodont species.

3D.6 Ordovician

The base of the Ordovician (Tremadocian Stage) is defined as the FAD of *Iapetognathus fluctivagus* at a GSSP section in Newfoundland, Canada (Cooper et al., 2001). The Dapingian Stage is defined by the FAD of *Baltoniodus triangularis*, but all other Ordovician stages are defined by graptolite species. The Ordovician marked the highest diversity of conodonts over their history and distinct faunal provinces are developed among conodonts between North America and Europe. The 42 Myr of the Ordovician is subdivided into at least 27 zones.

3D.7 Silurian

All Silurian stages are defined by graptolite species. The Llandovery Series includes a zonation of several species of *Pterospathodus*, including *Pterospathodus amorphognathoides*; the last occurrence of the latter species approximates the base of the Wenlock Series. Conodonts with multimembrate apparatuses of coniform elements (*Panderodus* and *Walliserodus*) are common in Silurian strata. The most useful taxa however are those that have apparatuses comprising ramiform and pectiniform elements (e.g., *Distomodus*, *Icriodella*, *Pelekysgnathus*, *Pterospathodus*, *Ozarkodina*, and *Kockelella*). The 25 Myr of the Silurian is subdivided into at least 23 zones.

3D.8 Devonian

All stages, but the base of the Devonian are defined by the FAD of conodont species, including Pragian (*Eognathodus sulcatus sulcatus* and *Latericriodus steinachensis*), Emsian

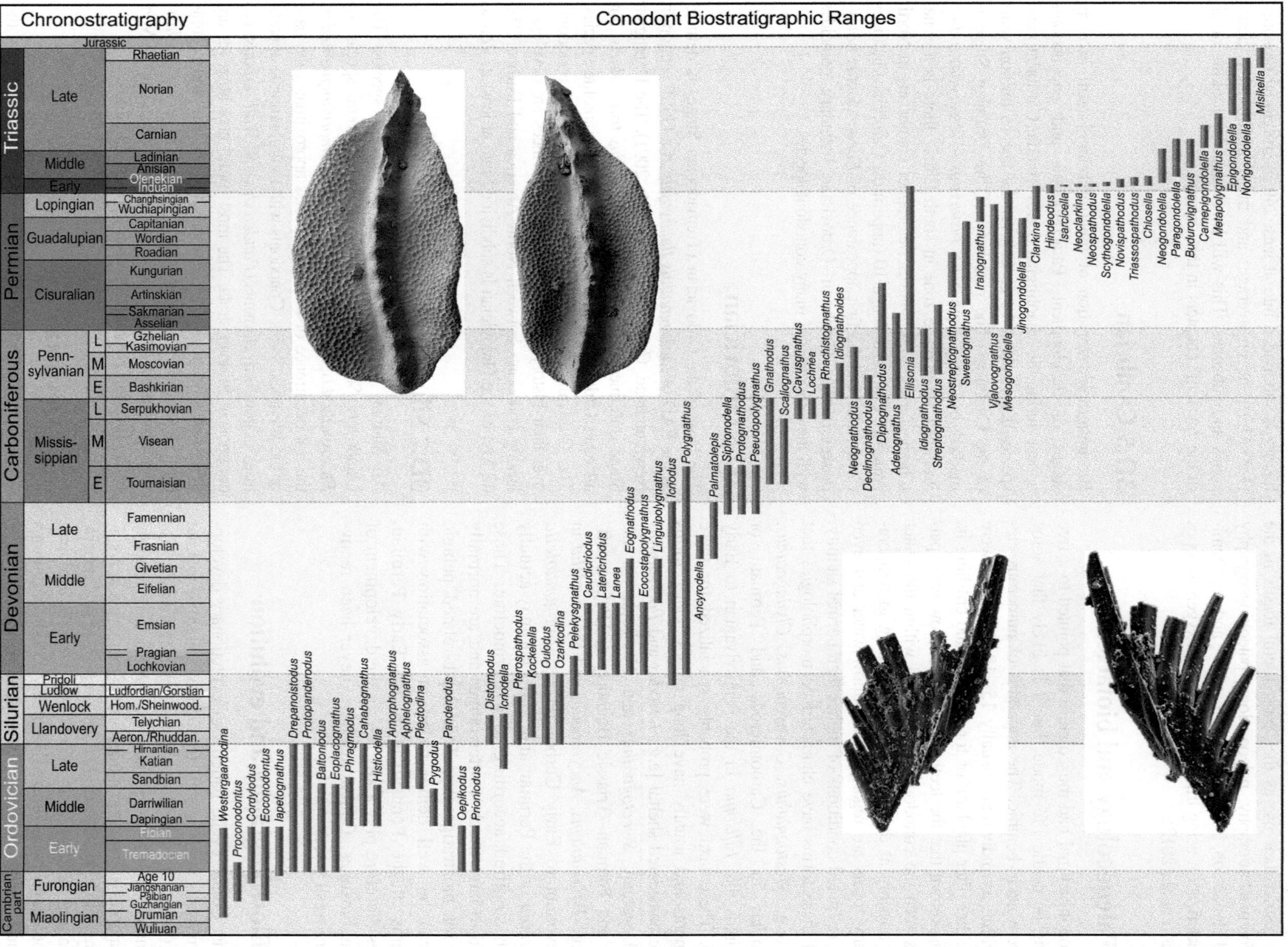

FIGURE 3D.1 Ranges of 75 conodont genera in the interval in which species identifications are most commonly used for biostratigraphy. Some taxa have longer ranges (e.g., *Hindeodus* ranges to Lower Mississippian and *Pelekysgnathus* into Famennian) in which they are rarely used as biostratigraphic indices. Some taxa are more useful for biofacies (e.g., *Ellisonia*, *Cavusgnathus*, and *Adetognathus* are often euryhaline and found in shallow-water environments). Biostratigraphy is normally related to specific level morphologic variation of ornament on pectiniform platform or P1 elements (upper left; *Clarkina wangi* from Lopingian in China), whereas familial identifications are often recognized by ramiform elements [lower right; these S2 (were S1) elements of *Clarkina* from Lopingian of China unite the family Gondolellidae ranging from Pennsylvanian to Triassic]. Each figured element is about 1 mm long and shows a bilaterally symmetrical pair. All taxa are euconodonts except for the paraconodontid *Westergaardodina*.

(*Polygnathus kitabicus*), Eifelian (*Polygnathus costatus partitus*), Givetian (*Polygnathus hemiansatus*), Frasnian (*Ancyrodella rotundiloba*), and Famennian (*Palmatolepis triangularis*). The latter stage is defined just above the Kellwasser Event, which included the extinction of *Ancyrodella* and *Ozarkodina* and many *Polygnathus* and *Ancyrognathus*. The diversity of Late Devonian conodonts is very high but drops dramatically into the Carboniferous. Conodonts are essentially in crises mode from this point. The 60 Myr of the Devonian is subdivided into at least 60 zones.

3D.9 Carboniferous

The bases of the Mississippian and Pennsylvanian subsystems are, respectively, defined by the FAD of *Siphonodella sulcata* and *Declinognathodus noduliferus* and four additional stages may be defined by conodont species. Mississippian zones are defined by the evolution within *Siphonodella*, *Gnathodus*, *Polygnathus*, *Pseudopolygnathus*, and *Lochriea* lineages. Other important taxa include *Scaliognathus*, *Dollymae*, *Patrognathus*, *Mestognathus*, and *Cavusgnathus*. Pennsylvanian zones are defined by the evolution within *Declinognathodus*, *Idiognathoides*, *Neognathodus*, *Diplognathodus*, *Streptognathodus*, and *Idiognathodus* lineages. Shallow-water taxa include *Adetognathus* and *Ellisonia*. The 60 Myr of the Carboniferous is subdivided into at least 38 zones (17 Mississippian and 21 Pennsylvanian).

3D.10 Permian

All nine stages of the Permian are defined by the FAD of conodont species, but two are not yet ratified. Henderson (2018) described 40 global biozones and 35 additional regional zones for the entire Permian. The Cisuralian (Lower Permian) is zoned on the basis of partial range lineage zones of *Streptognathodus*, *Sweetognathus*, *Neostreptognathodus*, and *Mesogondolella*. Carboniferous holdover taxa such as *Streptognathodus* and *Adetognathus* disappear during the latest Asselian or earliest Sakmarian, which basically coincides with the end of the Late Paleozoic Ice Age P1 phase. The Guadalupian (Middle Permian) and Lopingian (Upper Permian) are, respectively, zoned by lineages of *Jinogondolella* and *Clarkina*, but shallow-water taxa such as *Sweetognathus* species are locally useful up to the early Changhsingian Stage. The 47 Myr of the Permian is subdivided into at least 40 zones (Henderson, 2018; Yuan et al., 2019).

3D.11 Triassic

The base of the Triassic (Induan Stage) is defined by the FAD of *Hindeodus parvus*, which nearly coincides with the first occurrence of *Clarkina taylorae*. These two taxa represent "first" evolutionary events above the end-Permian extinction event (EPME), but the respective genera become extinct before the end of the Induan Stage. The EPME is the largest Phanerozoic extinction and yet no conodont genera and only a few conodont species became extinct at this level. The end of the Triassic is also marked by a major extinction event, and in contrast, this extinction resulted in the complete extinction of the conodont clade. Four additional stages in the Triassic may be defined within conodont lineages. Important Early Triassic taxa include species of *Neoclarkina*, *Neospathodus*, *Novispathodus*, and *Triassospathodus*. Locally, shallow-water taxa such as *Ellisonia*, *Hadrodontina*, and *Eurygnathodus* are useful. Important Middle Triassic taxa include species of *Chiosella*, *Neogondolella*, and *Budurovignathus*. Important Late Triassic taxa include species of *Metapolygnathus*, *Epigondolella*, *Paragondolella*, *Parvigondolella*, *Norigondolella*, and *Misikella*. New taxa are being described regularly (see Orchard, 2014, 2018); this does not mean that biostratigraphic studies are in their infancy, but rather they are constantly being refined given their considerable abundance and variability. The topmost Triassic conodont zone is *Misikella ultima* and also includes *Misikella posthernsteini*, *Zieglericonus rhaeticus*, and *Neohindeodella detrei*. The 50 Myr of the Triassic is subdivided into at least 42 zones (Henderson et al., 2018; Orchard, 2010).

Bibliography

Aldridge, R.J., Briggs, D.E.G., Smith, M.P., Clarkson, E.N.K., and Clark, D.L., 1993, The anatomy of Conodonts. *Philosophical Transactions of the Royal Society of London B*, **340**: 405–421.

Bengston, S., 1976, Structure of some Middle Cambrian conodonts, and early evolution of conodont structure and function. *Lethaia*, **9**: 185–206.

Briggs, D.E.G., Clarkson, E.N.K., and Aldridge, R.J., 1983, The conodont animal. *Lethaia*, **16**: 1–14.

Conway-Morris, S., and Caron, J.B., 2014, A primitive fish from the Cambrian of North America. *Nature*, **512**: 419–422.

Conway-Morris, S., and Caron, J.B., 2012, *Pikaia gracilens* Walcott, a stem-group chordate from the Middle Cambrian of British Columbia. *Biological Reviews*, **87**: 480–512.

Cooper, R.A., Nowlan, G.S., and Williams, S.H., 2001, Global Stratotype Section and Point for base of the Ordovician System. *Episodes*, **24** (1), 19–28.

Donoghue, P.C.J., and Purnell, M.A., 1999, Growth, function and the conodont fossil record. *Geology*, **27**: 251–254.

Donoghue, P.C.J., Forey, P.L., and Aldridge, R.J., 2000, Conodont affinity and chordate phylogeny. *Biological Reviews*, **75**: 191–251.

Donoghue, P.C.J., Purnell, M.A., Aldridge, R.J., and Zhang, S., 2008, The interrelationships of complex conodonts (Vertebrata). *Journal of Systematic Palaeontology*, **6** (2), 119–153.

Dzik, J., 2000, The origin of the mineralized skeleton. *Evolutionary Biology*, **31**: 105–154.

Dzik, J., 2008, Evolution of morphogenesis in 360 million year old conodont chordates calibrated in days. *Evolution and Development*, **10**: 769–777.

Epstein, A.G., Epstein, J.B., Harris, L.D., 1977, *Conodont Color Alteration – an Index of Organic Metamorphism*. U.S. Geological Survey, Professional Paper, **995**: 27 pp.

Goudemand, N., Orchard, M.J., Urdy, S., Bucher, H., and Tafforeau, P., 2011, Synchrotron-aided reconstruction of the conodont feeding apparatus and implications for the mouth of the first vertebrates. *Proceedings of the National Academy of Sciences of the United States of America*, **108**: 8720–8724.

Henderson, C.M., 2018, Permian conodont biostratigraphy, Special Publications. *In* Lucas, S.G., and Shen, S.Z. (eds), The Permian Timescale. *London: Geological Society,* **450**: pp. 119–142.

Henderson, C.M., Golding, M.L., and Orchard, M.J., 2018, Conodont sequence biostratigraphy of the Lower Triassic Montney Formation. *Bulletin of Canadian Petroleum Geology*, **66** (1), 1–16.

Janvier, P., 2008, Early jawless vertebrates and cyclostomes origins. *Zoological Science*, **25**: 1045–1056.

Jeppsson, L., Anehus, R., and Fredholm, D., 1999, The optimal acetate buffered acetic acid technique for extracting phosphatic fossils. *Journal of Paleontology*, **73** (5), 964–972.

Joachimski, M.M., Lai, X.L., Shen, S.Z., Jiang, H.S., Luo, G.M., Chen, B., et al., 2012, Climate warming in the latest Permian and the Permian-Triassic mass extinction. *Geology*, **40**: 195–198.

Krejsa, R.J., Bringas Jr., P., and Slavkin, H.C., 1990, A neontological interpretation of conodont elements based on agnathan cyclostome tooth structure, function, and development. *Lethaia*, **23**: 359–378.

Mei, S.L., and Henderson, C.M., 2001, Evolution of Permian conodonts provincialism and its significance in global correlation and paleoclimate implication. *Palaeogeography, Palaeoclimatology, Palaeoecology*, **170**: 237–260.

Murdock, D.J.E., Dong, X.P., Repetski, J.E., Marone, F., Stamponi, M., and Donoghue, P.C.J., 2013, The origin of conodonts and of vertebrate mineralized skeletons. *Nature*, **502**: 546–549.

Orchard, M.J., 2010. Triassic conodonts and their role in stage boundary definition. *In* Lucas, S.G. (ed), *The Triassic Timescale*. Geological Society London, Special Publication, **334**: 139–161. https://doi.org/10.1144/SP334.7.

Orchard, M.J., 2014, Conodonts from the Carnian-Norian boundary (Upper Triassic) of Black Bear Ridge, northeastern British Columbia. *New Mexico Museum of Natural History and Science Bulletin*, **64**: 139.

Orchard, M.J., 2018, The Lower-Middle Norian (Upper Triassic) Boundary: new conodonts taxa and a refined biozonation. *In* D. Jeffrey Over and C.M. Henderson (eds), *Conodont Studies Dedicated to the Careers and Contributions of Anita Harris, Glen Merrill, Carl Rexroad, Walter Sweet and Bruce Wardlaw*, Bulletins of American Paleontology, **395–396**: 165–193.

Pander, C.H., 1856, Monographie der fossilen Fische der silurischen Systems der Russisch-Baltischen Gouvernements. Obersilurische Fische. *Kaiserlichen Akademie des Wissenschaften*, pp. 37–91.

Purnell, M.A., 1995, Microwear on conodont elements and macrophagy in the first vertebrates. *Nature*, **374**: 798–800.

Purnell, M.A., and Jones, D., 2012, Quantitative analysis of conodont tooth wear and damage as a test of ecological and functional hypotheses. *Paleobiology*, **38**: 605–626.

Purnell, M.A., Aldridge, R.J., Donoghue, P.C.J., and Gabbott, S.E., 1995, Conodonts and the first vertebrates. *Endeavor*, **19**: 20–27.

Rejebian, V.A., Harris, A.G., and Huebner, J.S., 1987, Conodont color and textural alteration: an index to regional metamorphism, contact metamorphism, and hydrothermal alteration. *Geological Society of America Bulletin*, **99**: 471–479.

Sansom, I.J., Smith, M.P., Armstrong, H.A., and Smith, M.M., 1992, Presence of the earliest vertebrate hard tissues in conodonts. *Science*, **256**: 1308–1311.

Sansom, R.S., Freedman, K., Gabbott, S.E., Aldridge, R.J., and Purnell, M.A., 2010, Taphonomy and affinity of an enigmatic Silurian vertebrate, *Jamoytius kerwoodi* White. *Palaeontology*, **53**: 1393–1409.

Sweet, W.C., 1988, *The Conodonta: Morphology, Taxonomy, Paleoecology, and Evolutionary History of a Long-Extinct Phylum*, 10. New York: Clarendon Press, 212 p. Oxford Monographs on Geology and Geophysics.

Terrill, D.F., Henderson, C.M., and Anderson, J.S., 2018, New applications of spectroscopy techniques reveal phylogenetically significant soft tissue residue in Paleozoic conodonts. *Journal of Analytical Atomic Spectrometry*, **33**: 992–1002, https://doi.org/10.1039/c&ja00386b.

Turner, S., Burrow, C.J., Schultze, H., Blieck, A., Reif, W., Rexroad, C.B., et al., 2010, False teeth: conodont-vertebrate phylogenetic relationships revisited. *Geodiversitas*, **32**: 545–594.

Utting, J., Goodarzi, F., Dougherty, J., and Henderson, C.M., 1989, *Thermal maturity of Carboniferous and Permian sediments of the Sverdrup Basin. Canadian Arctic Archipelago*. Geological Survey of Canada, 20 p. Paper 89-19.

Yuan, D.X., Shen, S.Z., Henderson, C.M., Chen, J., Zhang, H., Zheng, Q.F., et al., 2019, Integrative timescale for the Lopingian (Late Permian): a review and update from Shangsi, South China. *Earth-Science Reviews*, **188**: 190–209.

Subchapter 3E

Ammonoidea

A.S. Gale, D. Korn, A.J. McGowan, J. Cope and C. Ifrim

Abstract

Ammonoidea are cephalopods that provide an exceptionally high-resolution marine biostratigraphic scale from Devonian through Cretaceous. In some stratigraphic intervals, such as across the Jurassic–Cretaceous boundary, they displayed considerable endemism that is a challenge for interregional correlation.

The cephalopod class Ammonoidea (Devonian to Cretaceous) provides an exceptionally high-resolution marine biostratigraphic scale, because many lineages evolved rapidly and successive species dispersed widely, both in life and as postmortem-drifted shells (Klug et al., 2015). They thus provide a key means of correlation for Late Paleozoic and Mesozoic marine sediments and have underpinned the development of many marine stages for over 150 years. However, their shells are constructed of the metastable carbonate phase aragonite, which is susceptible to dissolution both within the water column and in the sediment, and they are virtually absent in some marine facies, including the deep ocean basins. In addition, in some intervals they displayed considerable endemism, which has provided a significant challenge to correlation.

Next, the expert contributors briefly outline salient morphologic–stratigraphic features of key taxa, organized in Paleozoic, Triassic, Jurassic, and Cretaceous. Figs. 3E.1–3E.4 show shell morphology for key taxa in these time intervals.

3E.1 Paleozoic Ammonoidea

Dieter Korn

The ammonoids are for long regarded as important index fossils for the Paleozoic sedimentary rocks and played a key role for the biostratigraphy before conodonts and other microfossils occupied the leading role. Their value

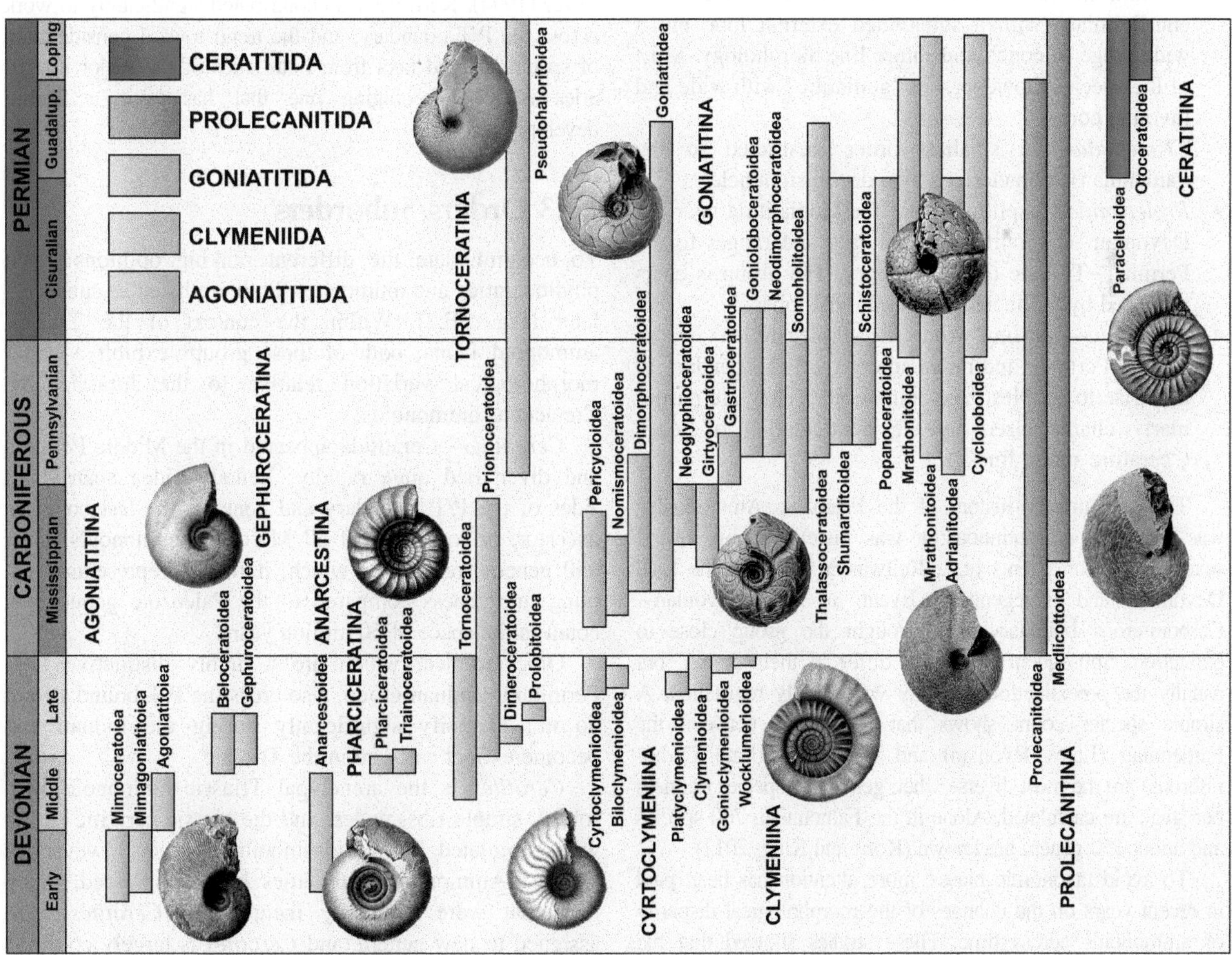

FIGURE 3E.1 Paleozoic ammonoidea stratigraphy.

had two reasons: (1) the ammonoids were rapidly evolving and particularly in the Devonian and Early to early Late Carboniferous, very high evolutionary rates allow for the separation of numerous biozones with durations of 200–500 kyr. However, a problem for global correlation purposes using ammonoids is their well-developed provincialism. In the Late Viséan and Serpukhovian, for instance, clearly separated ammonoid provinces (American Midcontinent and West, Northern Gondwana, Subvariscan Region, and South Urals–Central Asian) were separated (Korn and Klug, 2012); only few ammonoids occurred as index species and genera in several of these provinces.

Currently, there are about 3300 species of Paleozoic ammonoids known, 950 from the Devonian, 1450 from the Carboniferous, and 900 from the Permian are listed in the AMMON database (Korn and Ilg, 2007) and recent publications. It is widely accepted that the Paleozoic Ammonoidea is composed of the following five orders (Fig. 3E.1):

- *Agoniatitida*—the most ancient ammonoids (occurring from the Emsian to Frasnian) with very simple suture line morphology at the beginning but with repeated multilobate forms in various lineages.
- *Goniatitida*—the species-richest order (Eifelian to end-Permian) with a subdivided external lobe but a wide range of conch and suture line morphology. Most of the species, however, are "goniatitic" with wide and involute conch.
- *Clymeniida*—the smallest order (restricted to the Famennian) characterized by a dorsal siphuncle.
- *Prolecanitida*—splitting from the Goniatitida near the Devonian–Carboniferous boundary and ranges to the Permian–Triassic (P/T) boundary. The group is characterized by the increase of umbilical lobes.
- *Ceratitida*—splitting from the Prolecanitida in the Middle Permian and range across the P/T boundary to give rise to all Mesozoic ammonoids. They are particularly characterized by the denticulation of lobes ("ceratitic suture lines").

The evolutionary history of the Paleozoic Ammonoidea was strikingly discontinuous; it was punctuated by several severe extinction events (e.g., Kellwasser Event in the Late Devonian and Hangenberg Event at the Devonian–Carboniferous boundary) that brought the group close to extinction. Subsequent recoveries differ in their timing, but usually the preextinction diversity was rapidly reinstalled. A simple species count shows that the stages between the Famennian (Late Devonian) and Bashkirian (Late Carboniferous) are the most diverse when genus and species richness per stage are calculated. Alone in the Famennian, 700 species and about 150 genera are known (Korn and Klug, 2012).

To avoid taxonomic biases, more attention has been paid in recent years on the changes of the morphological disparity of ammonoids across time. These studies showed that the morphological richness of the group had drastic reductions at the main crises in Earth History; the ammonoids can thus serve as key study objects for the analysis of biotic crises in deep time.

3E.2 Triassic Ammonoidea

Alistair J. McGowan

Triassic ammonid history is bracketed by two major marine extinctions: the P/T and the Triassic/Jurassic (T/J) boundaries. Currently, most Triassic ammonoid systematic schemes propose three orders. However, most Jurassic–Cretaceous classifications rank phylloceratids as a suborder (Phylloceratina rather than Phylloceratida). Evidence has mounted that Ammonitina is represented in the latest Triassic (Rhaetian) by members of the Psiloceratoidea (Guex, 1982; Yin et al., 2007). Debate continues about the hierarchical rank of various groups, and Page (1996) proposed an alternative high-level classification that made greater use of subordinal ranks. The classification schemes of Tozer (1981, 1994) remain the most widely accepted basis for classification and, at the superfamily level, there is close agreement between Page (1996) and Tozer (1994). Korn has also contributed significantly to work across the P/T boundary, and the trend toward consideration of specimens and taxa from both sides of the major boundaries is an encouraging one that has been a fruitful development.

3E.3 Orders/Suborders

To accommodate the different ranking opinions about phylloceratids and ammonites, both are listed as suborders later (Fig. 3E.2). Within the context of the Triassic ammonoid fauna, both of these groups exhibit a wider morphological variation relative to the Jurassic and Cretaceous ammonoids.

Ceratitida—Ceratitida appeared in the Middle Permian and diversified quite rapidly. Xenodiscoidea spans both sides of the P/T Boundary and contains the last common ancestor, or rootstock, of all Mesozoic ammonoids. Over 450 genera are known, which, if robust, represents a tripling in richness compared to the Paleozoic genus-level count in the space of 50 million years.

Otoceratoidea, which are a highly distinctive Late Permian to Induan group, also cross the P/T boundary but do not diversify significantly during the Induan and become extinct early on in the Triassic.

Ceratites is the archetypal Triassic ammonoid with robust, simple ribs, nodes, and the classic ceratitic suture with crenulated lobes and smooth saddles. However, as Triassic Ammonoid systematics have progressed, many taxa that were originally included in *Ceratites* were assigned to new genera, and *Ceratites* is largely confined

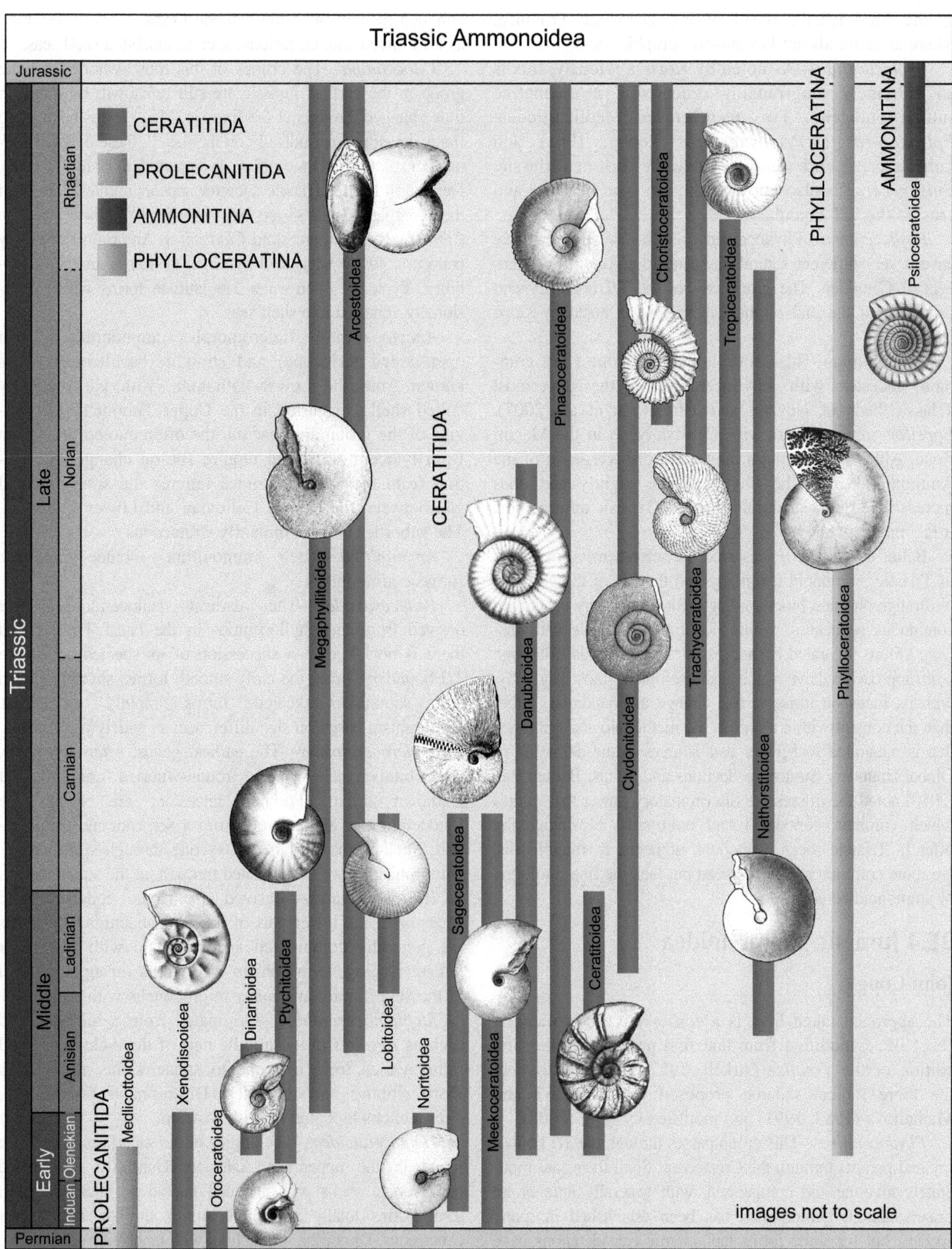

FIGURE 3E.2 Triassic ammonoidea stratigraphy.

to the Muschelkalk Basin of the Germanic Province, where ammonoids are key biostratigraphic tools.

Prolecanitida—As noted by Korn previously, this is an extremely long-ranging order with a distinctive sutural ontogeny. Two members of Medlicottiodea, *Episageceras* (=*Protosageceras* Popov, 1961) and *Latisageceras*, are known from the Lower Triassic. *Episageceras* is also known from the Late Permian and crosses the P/T boundary.

Phylloceratina—Phylloceratida, such as Prolecanitida, have a very different sutural ontogeny to co-occurring members of Ceratitida. The group crosses the T/J boundary and persists until the end of the Cretaceous, as noted by Cope later.

Ammonitina—This group is derived from a last common ancestor with Phylloceratina in the uppermost Triassic beds of Nevada and Tibet (Yin et al., 2007). *Eopsiloceras* co-occurs with *Choristoceras* in the Marshi Zone. Although this alters the timing of divergence of the Ammonitina from the Phylloceratina slightly and does increase the richness and disparity of Triassic ammonoids, it is a modest change.

Balini et al. (2010) presented a comprehensive overview of Triassic ammonoid taxonomy and the use of the group in biostratigraphy and biochronology. Biostratigraphy deals with continuous sequences, while biochronology deals with discrete groups separated by nonfossiliferous intervals. Although both approaches have value and usefulness, biostratigraphy, with its focus on turnover and change at boundaries, rather than the content within a unit, is the methodological approach that is integrated with other data sources in the definition of Global Boundary Stratotype Sections and Points. Balini et al. (2010) noted the impressive discriminatory power that studies which combine conodonts and ammonoid biostratigraphy offer in Triassic rocks. Conodont elements, as microfossils, are more common and widespread but lack the fine resolution of ammonoid zonation.

3E.4 Jurassic Ammonoidea

John Cope

The approach taken here is a conservative classification (Fig. 3E.3), modified from that first proposed in the first edition of the *Treatise* (Arkell, 1957, 1970) rather than the more radical scheme proposed by Bessenova and Michailova (1983, 1991) and modified by Page (2008).

Phylloceratina—This group passes through the T/J boundary and persists through the Cretaceous. Shell forms are moderately involute and compressed, with generally little or no ornamentation. Dimorphism has been established in many species, but for some forms taphonomic considerations have resulted in the nonpreservation of body-chambers, so rendering recognition of maturity (and hence dimorphism) is difficult. They are characteristics of open-water environments and although thought of as low latitude forms, occur as far north as East Greenland. Occasional species inhabited shelf seas.

Lytoceratina—The origins of this round-whorled evolute group in the earliest Jurassic are still unknown; they remain little changed throughout the Jurassic. Many forms have sharp flares developed periodically on their shell; these overlie internal constrictions. Dimorphism is apparent in a few species. Derivation from a Triassic ancestor appears unlikely, although the complex sutures are remarkably like those of the Carnian–Rhaetian arcestoid *Cladiscites*. An origin from early psiloceratoids as suggested by Guex (1982) is another possibility. Typically open-water low-latitude forms which occasionally ventured into shelf seas.

Ancyloceratina—Heteromorph ammonoids, with open-coiled (criocone) and straight (baculicone) forms known from the Lower Tithonian, with part helically coiled shells appearing in the Upper Tithonian. The origins of the group are obscure: the often quoted derivation from lytoceratids would require sutural changes; derivation from the Spiroceratoidea ignores the stratigraphical gap between the Middle Callovian and Lower Tithonian. The suborder is predominantly Cretaceous.

Ammonitina—The Ammonitina include all the Jurassic ammonites.

Psiloceratoidea—The earliest psiloceratoids were derived from the phylloceratids in the latest Triassic and there is now known a succession of its species across the T/J boundary. From the early smooth forms, strongly ribbed and sometimes keeled forms rapidly developed. Dimorphism based on size differences is widely recognized.

Eoderoceratoidea—The earliest genus, *Microderoceras*, is a bituberculate evolute round-whorled ammonite of unknown origin. Possible ancestors are within the Lytoceratina or alternatively from a serpenticone psiloceratoid. Shell forms vary from oxycone through sphaerocone. Dimorphism is well established throughout the superfamily.

Hildoceratoidea—Derived from an eoderoceratoid ancestor in the lower part of the Pliensbachian, the shells are generally compressed and planulate with falcoid or falcate ribbing. Dimorphism is obvious throughout most of the superfamily and many microconchs with lappets.

Stephanoceratoidea—Originated from a hildoceratoid such as *Erycites* in the middle part of the Aalenian. Shell shape varies from oxycone to sphaerocone; many with sharp ribbing and tubercles. Dimorphism pronounced; microconchs lappeted or with rostrum.

Haploceratoidea—The origins of the superfamily are to be found in the uppermost Aalenian. Generally compressed or oxyconic shells with subdued falcoid or falcate ribbing; some forms totally smooth. Continue through into Lower Cretaceous. Dimorphic throughout with lappeted microconchs.

Perisphinctoidea—Derived from stephanoceratoids in the uppermost part of the Lower Bajocian. Most forms are evolute planulates but varying from platycones to

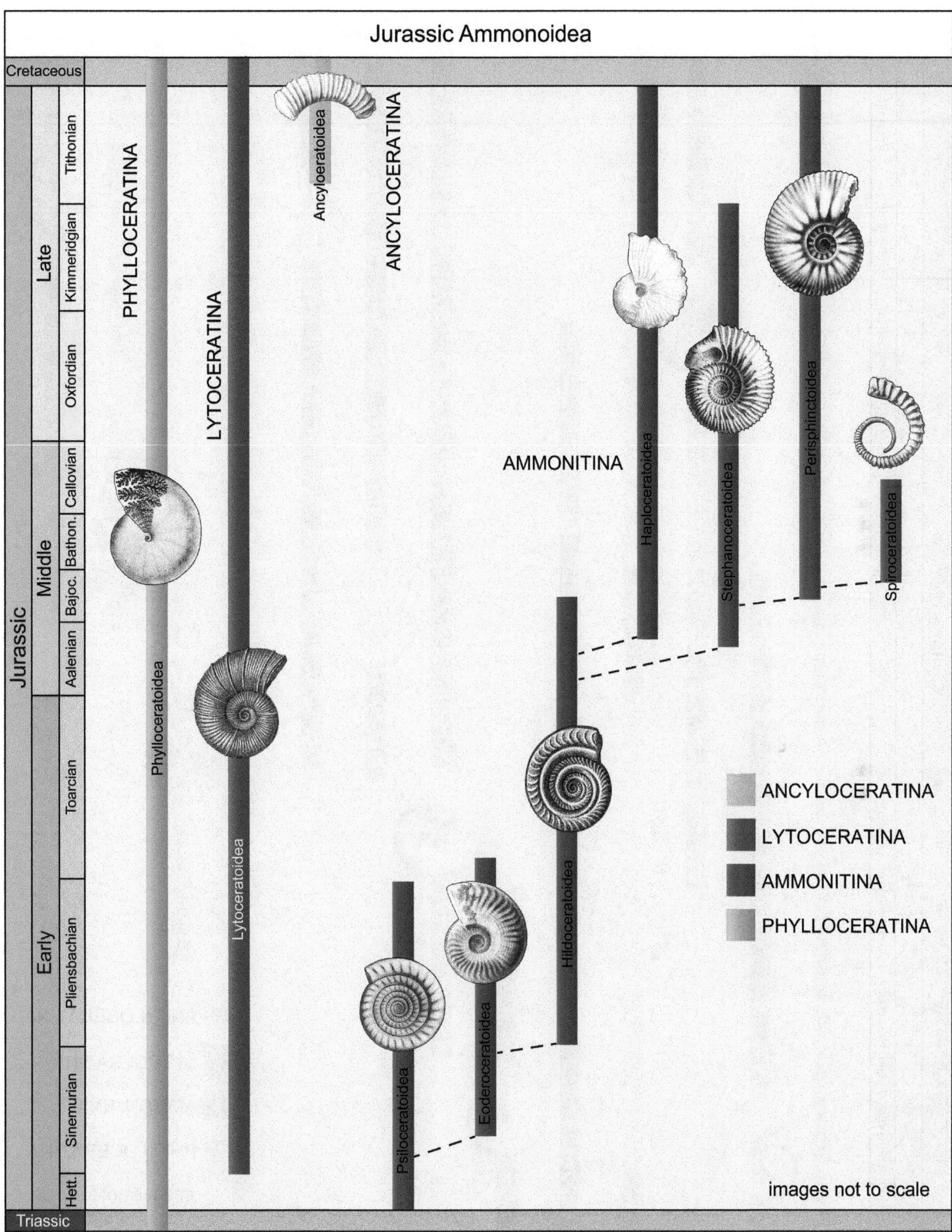

FIGURE 3E.3 Jurassic ammonoidea stratigraphy.

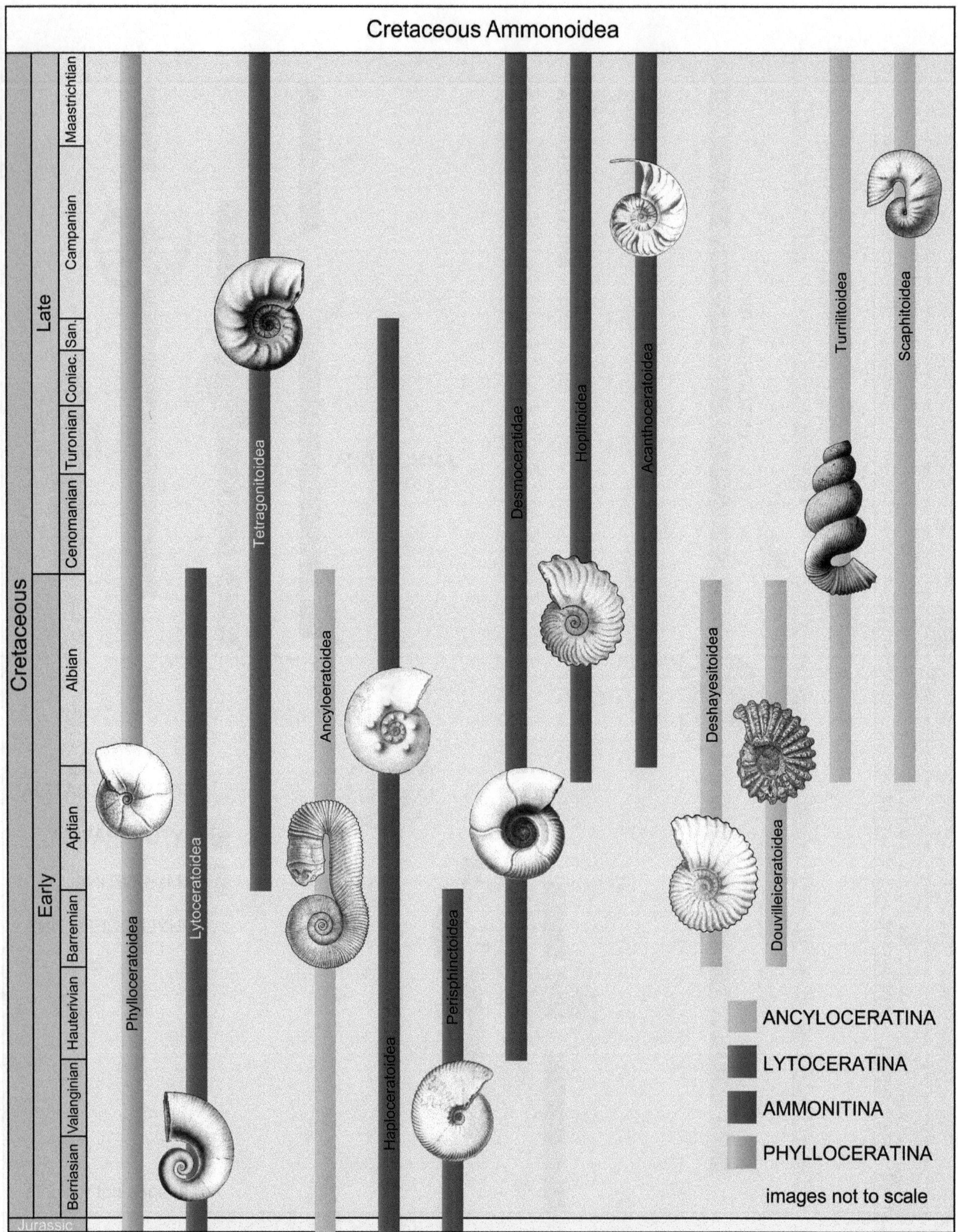

FIGURE 3E.4 Cretaceous ammonoidea stratigraphy.

cadicones. All typically have ribbing which is bifurcate at least on the inner whorls; and outer whorls with a variety of rib styles, often with multiple-branched ribs. Smooth and tuberculate forms are rare. Continue through Cretaceous.

Spiroceratoidea—These uncoiled forms are often claimed to have arisen from *Tmetoceras* in the early Aalenian. A more convincing origin may be from an early parkinsoniid such as *Strenoceras* in the lower part of the Upper Bajocian. An origin from within the lytoceratids (Arkell, 1957) can no longer be countenanced.

3E.5 Cretaceous Ammonoidea

Christina Ifrim

Cretaceous ammonoids (Fig. 3E.4) are traditionally subdivided into Phylloceratina, Lytoceratina, Ammonitina, and heteromorph Ancyloceratina (Wright et al., 1996), although this is in flux (Guex, 1987, 1995; Hoffmann, 2015).

Phylloceratina—a surviving Triassic group (Guex, 2006) with low evolutionary rates, comprise of only one superfamily. They were rare in most ammonoid assemblages (e.g., Ifrim et al., 2004) but range up to the Cretaceous–Paleogene (K/Pg) boundary (Ward and Kennedy, 1993; Salazar et al., 2010).

Lytoceratina—similarly conservative and rare, and both groups do not provide biostratigraphic index species. The Lytoceratoidea are Lower Cretaceous representatives but became extinct in the early Cenomanian, whereas the Tetragonitoidea, which evolved in the Barremian, are typical Upper Cretaceous lytoceratoids. They also range up to the K/Pg boundary and are among the last species (Ward and Kennedy, 1993).

Ancyloceratina— the heteromorph ammonites are considered to have a polyphyletic origin (Wiedmann, 1966; Wiedmann and Kakabadze, 1993). Ancyloceratoidea become increasingly important in the Hauterivian (Lehmann et al., 2015). From then on, they have a fast evolution and provide useful index species for correlation in the Barremian. From the Cenomanian on Turrilitoidea and Scaphitoidea provide excellent index species up to the K/Pg boundary. Some Turrilitoidea are suitable for long-distance correlation, for example, *Nostoceras hyatti*, whereas both superfamilies provide fast successions of biozone indicators, for example, in the Western Interior Seaway (e.g., Cobban et al., 2006), although in the Cenomanian and Coniacian–Santonian pronounced endemism restricts correlation to regional scale (Ifrim et al., 2015). Heteromorphs dominate the last ammonoid assemblages in North America before extinction (Ifrim et al., 2015; Witts et al., 2018) and are among the last taxa anywhere else (Machalski et al., 2012; Stinnesbeck et al., 2012; Ifrim et al., 2015; Witts et al., 2015), providing biozonation up to the K/Pg boundary.

Ammonitina—also have a fast evolution. Perisphinctes dominate the ammonoid assemblages in the Berriasian and Valanginian, but marked provincialism and strong endemism prevent long-distance correlation. In the Hauterivian, long-distance correlation is enhanced by widespread taxa (Lehmann et al., 2015). Haploceratoidea are present throughout their occurrence but provide index species at maximum regional scale. In the Barremian Perisphinctoidea decline and are stepwise replaced by Desmoceratoidea and Pulchellioidea. Whereas the latter provide index species at regional scale, the former dominate the assemblages and allow for repeated long-distance correlation from the Aptian up to the K/Pg boundary, including the primary boundary marker for the base of the Maastrichtian (Odin and Lamaurelle, 2001). In the Albian, Hoplitoidea, and Acanthoceratoidea emerge and add to the index species in the Upper Cretaceous up to longer distance correlation and the primary boundary marker for the base of the Turonian (Kennedy et al., 2005). All three superfamilies are among the last species at the end of the Cretaceous (Stinnesbeck et al., 2012).

Bibliography

Arkell, W.J., 1957, Introduction to Mesozoic Ammonoidea. *In* Moore, R.C. (ed), *Treatise on Invertebrate Paleontology, part L, Mollusca 4, Cephalopoda, Ammonoidea.* University of Kansas Press.

Arkell, W.J., 1970, *The Jurassic System in Great Britain.* University Press, Oxford, UK: pp. 1–681.

Balini, M., Lucas, S.G., Jenks, J.F., and Spielmann, J.A., 2010. *Triassic Ammonoid Biostratigraphy: An Overview.* Geological Society, London, Special Publications, **334**: 221–262. https://doi.org/10.1144/SP334.10

Bessenova, N.V., and Mikhailova, I.A., 1983, The evolution of the Jurassic-Cretaceous ammonoids. *Doklady Akademii nauk SSSR*, **269**: 733–797 [in Russian].

Bessenova, N.V., and Mikhailova, I.A., 1991, Higher taxa of Jurassic and Cretaceous Ammonitida. *Journal of Paleontology*, **25**: 1–19.

Cobban, W.A., Walaszczyk, I., Obradovich, J.D., McKinney, K.C., 2006, A USGS zonal table for the Upper Cretaceous middle Cenomanian—Maastrichtian of the Western Interior of the United States based on ammonites, inoceramids and radiometric ages. *United States Geological Survey Open File Report*, 2006-1250, 1–47.

Guex, J., 1982, Relations entre le genre Psiloceras et les Phylloceratida au voisinage de la limite Trias-Jurassique. *Bulletin de la Société Vaudoise des Sciences Naturelles*, **76**: 47–51, https://doi.org/10.5169/seals-278144.

Guex, J., 1987, Sur la phylogenèse des ammonites du Lias inférieur. *Bulletin de la Société Vaudoise des Sciences Naturelles*, **78**: 455–469.

Guex, J., 1995, Ammonites hettangiennes de la Gabbs Valley Range (Nevada, USA). *Mémoires de Géologie, Lausanne*, **27**: 1–130.

Guex, J., 2006, Reinitialization of evolutionary clocks during sublethal environmental stress in some invertebrates. *Earth and Planetary Science Letters*, **242**: 240–253.

Hoffmann, R., 2015. Part L, Revised, Volume 3B, Chapter 3: Lytoceratoidea. *Treatise Online*, **70**: 34.

Ifrim, C., Stinnesbeck, W., and Lopez-Oliva, J.G., 2004, Maastrichtian Cephalopods from the Méndez Formation at Cerralvo, Northeastern Mexico. *Palaeontology*, **47**: 1575–1627.

Ifrim, C., Lehmann, J., and Ward, P.D., 2015, Paleobiogeography of the Late Cretaceous Ammonoidea. *In* Klug, C., Korn, D., De Baets, K., Kruta, I., and Mapes, R.H. (eds), *Ammonoid Paleobiology – From Macroevolution to Paleogeography*. Topics in Geobiology. Heidelberg: Springer, **44**: pp. 259–274.

Kennedy, W.J., Walaszczyk, I., and Cobban, W.A., 2005, The global boundary stratotype section and point for the base of the Turonian stage of the Cretaceous: Pueblo, Colorado, U.S.A. *Episodes*, **28**: 93–104.

Klug, C., Korn, D., De Baets, K., Kruta, I., Mapes, R.H., (eds), 2015. *Ammonoid Paleobiology: From Macroevolution to Paleogeography.* Topics in Geobiology, Springer, Dordrecht, **44**: 615 pp.

Korn, D., and Ilg, A. 2007. *AMMON.* (Database of Palaeozoic Ammonoidea), http://www.wahre-staerke.com/ammon/.

Korn, D., and Klug, C., 2012. Palaeozoic ammonoids- diversity and development of conch morphology. *In* Talent, J. (ed.). *Earth and Life*. Springer, Dordrecht. 491–534. https://doi.org/10.1007/978-90-481-3428-1_15.

Lehmann, J., Ifrim, C., Bulot, L., and Frau, C., 2015, Paleobiogeography of Early Cretaceous Ammonoids. *In* Klug, C., Korn, D., De Baets, K., Kruta, I., and Mapes, R.H. (eds), *Ammonoid Paleobiology: From Macroevolution to Paleogeography.* Topics in Geobiology. Dordrecht: Springer, **44**: 229–257.

Machalski, M., Jagt, J.M.W., Alekseev, A.S., and Jagt-Yazykova, E., 2012, Terminal Maastrichtian ammonites from Turkmenistan, Central Asia. *Acta Palaeontologica Polonica*, **57**: pp. 729–735.

Odin, G.S., and Lamaurelle, M.A., 2001, The global Campanian-Maastrichtian stage boundary. *Episodes*, **24**: 229–238.

Page, K.N., 1996, Mesozoic Ammonoids in Space and Time. *In* Landman, N.H., Tanabe, K., and Davis, R.A. (eds), *Ammonoid Paleobiology,* Boston, MA: Springer US, 755–794, https://doi.org/10.1007/978-1-4757-9153-2_18.

Page, K.N., 2008, The evolution and geography of Jurassic ammonoids. *Proceedings of the Geological Association*, **119**: 35–57.

Popov, Y.N., 1961, Some Early Triassic ammonoids from the northern Caucasus. *International Geological Review*, **6**: 700–705.

Quinzio-Sinn, L.A., 2010, Ammonites from the Maastrichtian (Upper Cretaceous) Quiriquina Formation in central Chile. *Neues Jahrbuch für Geologie und Paläontologie, Abhandlungen*, **257**: 181–236.

Salazar, C., Stinnesbeck, W., and Quinzio-Sinn, L.A., 2010, Ammonites from the Maastrichtian (Upper Cretaceous) Quiriquina Formation in central Chile. *Neues Jahrbuch für Geologie und Paläontologie*, **257**: 181–236.

Stinnesbeck, W., Ifrim, C., and Salazar, C., 2012, The last Cretaceous ammonites in Latin America. *Acta Geologica Polonica*, **57**: 717–728, https://doi.org/10.4202/app.2011.0042.

Tozer, E.T., 1981, Triassic Ammonoidea: classification, evolution and relationship with Permian and Jurassic forms. *In* House, M.R., and Senior, J.R. (eds), *The Ammonoidea*, Systematics Association Special. London; New York: Academic Press, **Vol. 18**: 66–100.

Tozer, E.T., 1994, Canadian Triassic ammonoid faunas. *Bulletin Geological Survey of Canada*, **467**: 663 pp.

Yin, J., Smith, P.L., Pálfy, J., and Enay, R., 2007, Ammonoids and the Triassic/Jurassic boundary in the Himalayas of southern Tibet. *Palaeontology*, **50**: 711–737, https://doi.org/10.1111/j.1475-4983.2007.00648.x.

Ward, P.D., and Kennedy, W.J., 1993, Maastrichtian ammonites from the Biscay Region. *Journal of Paleontology*, **67** (Suppl. 5), 1–58 II.

Wiedmann, J., 1966, Stammesgeschichte und System der posttriadischen Ammonoideen: ein Überblick. *Neues Jahrbuch für Geologie und Paläontologie, Abhandlungen*, **125**, **127**: 49–78, 13–81.

Wiedmann, J., and Kakabadze, M.V., 1993, Suture investigations and the classification of Cretaceous heteromorph ammonites. *Geobios*, **26**: 393–399.

Witts, J.D., Bowman, V.C., Wignall, P.B., Crame, J.A., Francis, J.E., and Newton, R.J., 2015, Evolution and extinction of Maastrichtian (Late Cretaceous) cephalopods from the López de Bertodano Formation, Seymour Island, Antarctica. *Palaeogeography, Palaeoclimatology, Palaeoecology*, **418**: 193–212.

Witts, J.D., Landman, N.H., Garb, M.P., Boas, C., Larina, E., Rovelli, R., et al., 2018, A fossiliferous spherule-rich bed at the Cretaceous–Paleogene (K–Pg) boundary in Mississippi, USA: Implications for the K–Pg mass extinction event in the Mississippi Embayment and Eastern Gulf Coastal Plain. *Cretaceous Research*, **91**: 147–167.

Wright, C.W., Calloman [sic], J.H., Howarth, M.K., 1996, Cretaceous Ammonoidea. *In* Kaesler, R.L. (ed), *Treatise on Invertebrate Paleontology Part L, Mollusca 4*, revised. Boulder, CO, Lawrence, KS: University of Kansas & Geological Society of America, p. xx + 362.

Subchapter 3F

Calcareous nannofossils

D.K. Watkins and I. Raffi

Abstract

Most calcareous nannofossils belong to the coccolithophores, a group of haptophyte protists that produce calcareous skeletal elements through the biomineralization of external organic scales. Size range is 1–40 μm. The first coccolithophores are documented near the Norian–Rhaetian boundary. These pioneer taxa would radiate and evolve into thousands of species in more than 35 families in 10 major orders. Since the Tithonian, the group has been a major component of oceanic oozes, and the phylogeny of the group often is closely linked to paleoceanographic turnover events; biostratigraphy is detailed and contributes significantly to Earth geologic history.

3F.1 Introduction

The term "calcareous nannofossils" is used to denote a diverse group of minute calcareous fossils that are united by their small size (1–40 μm), calcareous (low-Mg calcite, dominantly) skeletal elements, and marine distribution. The vast majority of calcareous nannofossils can be attributed directly to the coccolithophores, a group of haptophyte protists that produce calcareous skeletal elements (coccoliths) through the biomineralization of external organic scales. The "calcareous nannofossils" also include a collection of minute, calcareous microfossils, biological affinities of which are either uncertain or are clearly aligned with some other (noncoccolithophore) protist groups. In some cases the uncertainty of their biological affinities is related to the highly derived nature of the skeletal material so that they no longer have clear indications (e.g., proximal/distal shields) of their coccolithophore ancestry.

Calcareous nannofossils are assumed to have been exclusively marine phytoplankton, based on the distribution of modern coccolithophores and the facies relationships evident in ancient, nannofossil-bearing sedimentary deposits. Diversity tends to be the highest in depositional settings located in subtropical to subtemperate regions with stable surface water stratification. Calcareous nannofossils are often rare in marginal marine settings (i.e., coastal areas), with oligotaxic assemblages of generalist species often evident. Recent discovery of taxa believed to have suffered extinction in the Paleogene have been made by examining coastal environments (e.g., Hagino et al., 2015) and suggest that coastal environments may have served as refugia for coccolithophores during parts of their history.

Calcareous nannoplankton is responsible for about one-half of all precipitation of calcium carbonate in the modern oceanic system (Milliman, 1993) and is a major driver of the pelagic biological pump. For the most part, nannofossil skeletal elements are transferred from their site of production in oceanic surface waters to the sediment–water interface by the action of grazing zooplankton that packages the coccoliths in sand-sized fecal pellets, which rapidly descend through the water column (Honjo, 1976). This carbonate accumulates in thick deposits of nannofossil ooze everywhere in the ocean where the sediment–water interface lies above the carbonate compensation depth. This encompasses about one-third of the modern ocean system. Rates of coccolith ooze accumulation vary from about 1 to 10 m/Myr in the oligotrophic open ocean; however, accumulation rates in the marginal "chalk" seas of the Late Cretaceous, during the height of chalk deposition, were as high as 100 m/Myr.

3F.2 Evolution

Although calcareous nannoliths of uncertain biological affinities are known from older parts of the Triassic, it is only near the Norian–Rhaetian boundary that the first true coccolithophore fossils are documented in the fossil record (Bown, 1998; Gardin et al., 2012). These pioneer taxa would radiate and evolve into thousands of species in more than 35 geologically important families in 10 major orders (Figs. 3F.1 and 3F.2).

Widespread adaptive radiation and species turnover characterized the Early Jurassic, with steady increase of species richness continuing through the Jurassic (Bown et al., 2004). The Hettangian and Sinemurian were an important time for the adaptive radiation of the two existing murolith coccolithophore families with the evolution of the biostratigraphically important genera *Parhabdolithus* in the Stephanolithiales and the *Crepidolithus* in the Eiffellithales. These forms were joined by the enigmatic nannolith *Schizosphaerella* that quantitatively dominates the nannofossil assemblages of the Early Jurassic. The invention of the interlocking, placolith coccolith occurred with the evolution of the Podorhabdales during the late Sinemurian, with both two-shield placoliths (*Similiscutum*) and three-shield forms (*Triscutum*, *Mazaganella*). The Pliensbachian and early Toarcian were a time of major adaptive radiation within the placolith coccolithophores, including the evolution of the biostratigraphically important genera *Axopodorhabdus* and *Biscutum*. In addition, the order Watznaueriales arose during this interval, with the important genera *Lotharingius* and *Watznaueria* arising during the Pliensbachian and Toarcian, respectively (de Kaenel, et al., 1996). The Toarcian Oceanic Anoxic Event (OAE)

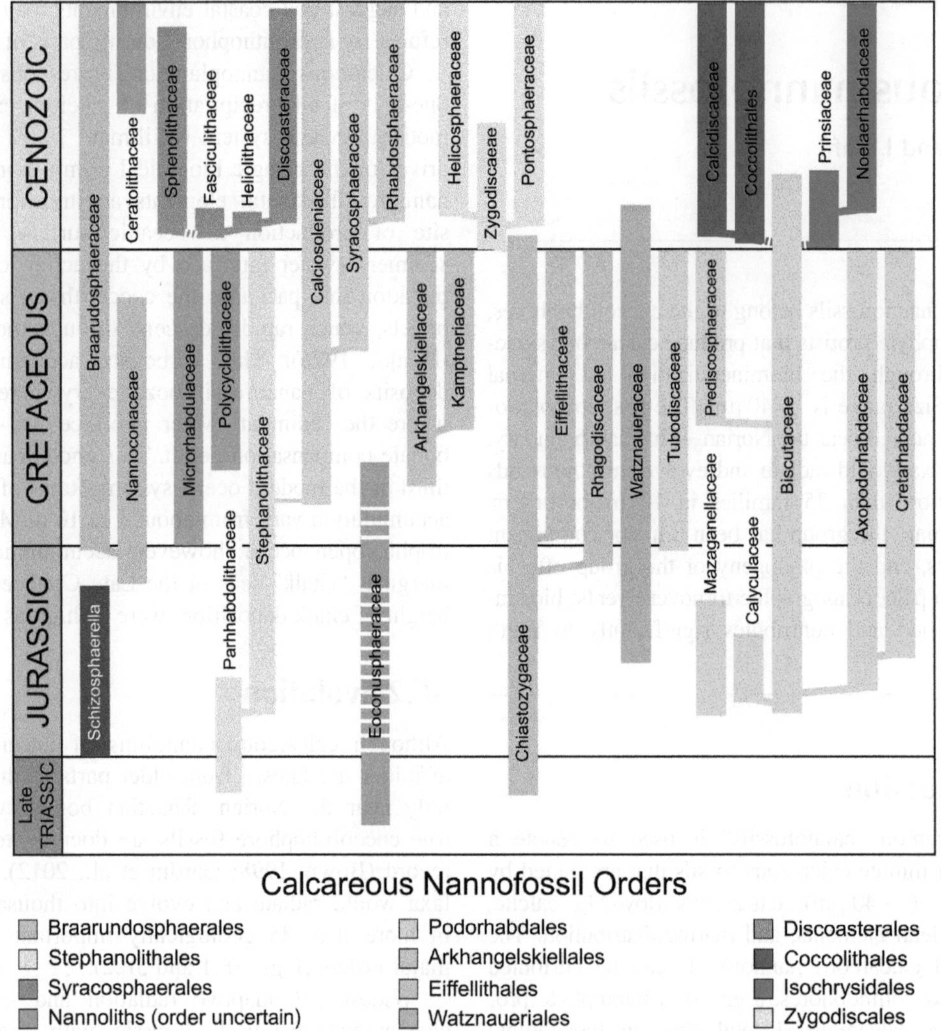

FIGURE 3F.1 Distribution in time of the major orders and families of nannofossils as well as important nannolith "families" and the genus *Schizosphaerella*.

apparently disrupted the pelagic environment enough to cause a substantial species turnover, leading to the rise of a distinctive Middle Jurassic nannofossil assemblage.

The Middle Jurassic was characterized by substantial adaptive radiation in the Watznaueriales, with evolution of the genus *Watznaueria*, which would be the numerically dominant genus in most nannofossil assemblages for the rest of the Mesozoic. This adaptive radiation is evident in the higher biostratigraphic resolution (= more closely spaced zonal units) in the Middle Jurassic. The opening of the Atlantic and other continental plate rearrangements during the Middle Jurassic led to a rise in nannofossil provincialism, as is evidenced by the divergence of tethyan and boreal zonations.

The Late Jurassic was characterized initially by low rates of evolution of nannofossils, as reflected by the low biostratigraphic resolution in the Oxfordian and Kimmeridgian. Rates of evolution substantially accelerated in the Tithonian, and particularly in the late Tithonian, with the origin of the Braarudosphaerales and its two important groups the pentaliths (Braarudosphaeraceae) and the nannoconids (Nannoconaceae). Continued provincialism is evident by the divergent zonations, with the boreal biostratigraphy based on evolution of the *Stephanolithion bigotii* lineage while the Tethyan sequences include the first appearances of a diverse group of nannoliths and coccolithophores (e.g., de Kaenel et al, 1996).

The Early Cretaceous nannofossil record featured the continued dominance of the Watznaueriaceae (especially *Watznaueria barnesiae*) and the diversification and rise of the nannoconids as a significant rock-forming component of Lower Cretaceous pelagic and hemipelagic sediments, leading to the deposition of "nannoconid limestones" in many low-latitude sites. Nannoconid diversity and abundance were reduced by a series of mid-Cretaceous OAEs such as the "nannoconid crises" associated with OAE1 (Erba, 2004). The addition of the Microrhabdulaceae, Rhagodiscaceae, and Tubodiscaceae

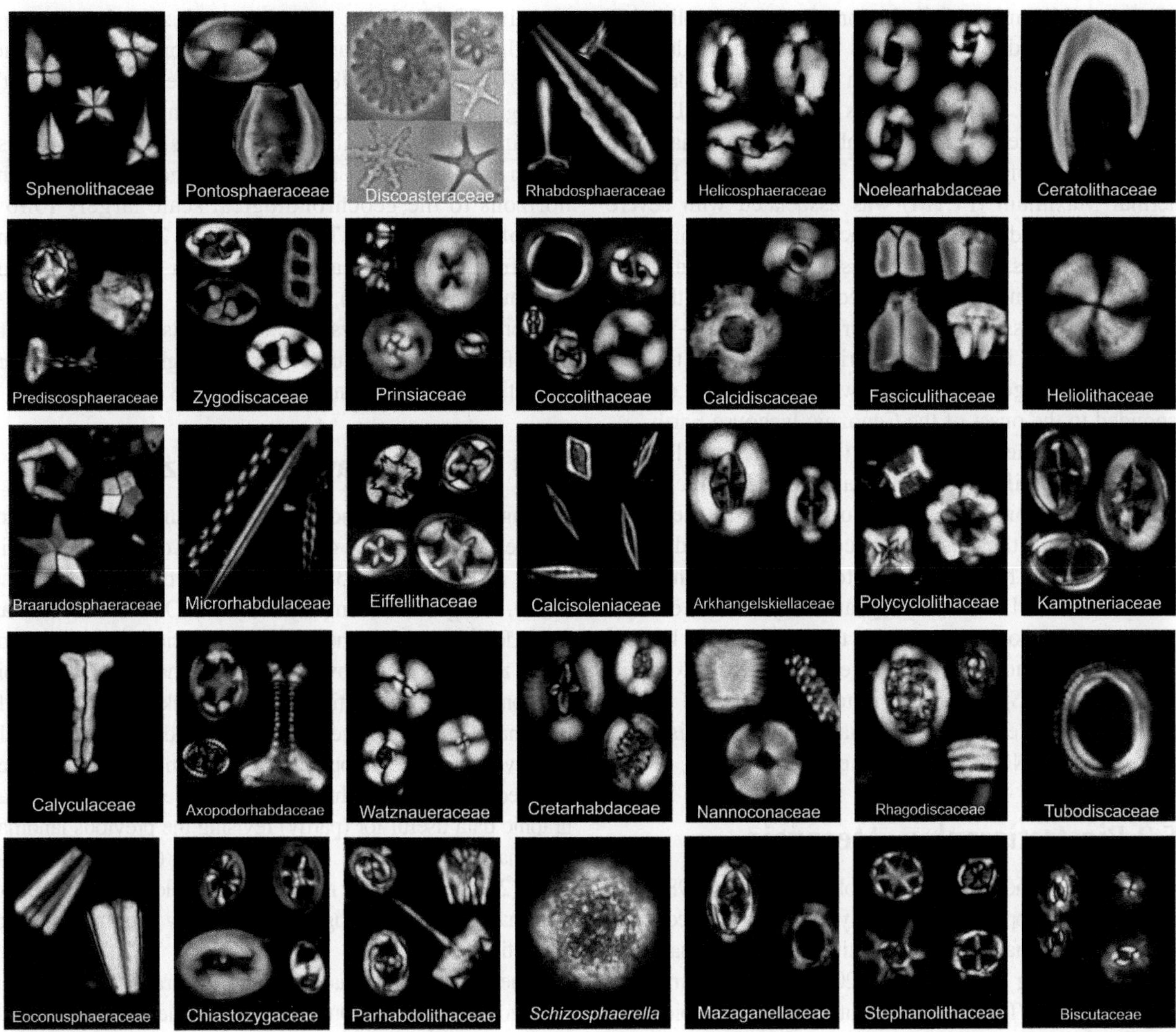

FIGURE 3F.2 Illustrations of representative taxa of the major families of nannofossils as well as important nannolith "families" and the genus *Schizosphaerella*, placed approximately in stratigraphic order of first appearance, from the bottom left to the top right of the illustrations. The scale bar at the base of the figure represents 10 μm.

near the Jurassic–Cretaceous boundary, as well as continued diversification of the Eiffellithales, resulted in a gradual increase in nannofossil species richness through much of the Early Cretaceous.

The Late Cretaceous was characterized by an acceleration in evolutionary activity in the calcareous nannofossils. Widespread and voluminous chalk deposition was evident throughout the global pelagic and hemipelagic environments, with coccolithophores and nannoliths comprising the majority of the sediments. The Polycyclolithaceae and the Arkhangelskiellaceae, minor components in the Early Cretaceous, became an important component quantitatively of the nannofossil assemblages, especially from the Coniacian through the Maastrichtian. Marked provinciality reestablished in the Santonian to Maastrichtian, with supplementary high-latitude zonations needed (Watkins et al., 1996; Burnett, 1998).

The Mesozoic ended with a catastrophic extinction among the calcareous nannofossils. It effectively ended widespread chalk deposition—now relegated largely to the deep ocean. Estimates vary but there is universal agreement that more than 90% of species extant just before the boundary event suffered extinction, with only about 10 species surviving the event (e.g., Bown et al. (2004)). These severely depleted assemblages comprised generalist taxa served as the base for the subsequent explosive adaptive radiation of the nannofossils during the early part of the Paleogene.

The Early Cenozoic (Paleogene) was characterized by the rapid adaptive radiation of the calcareous nannofossils, with the establishment of the Isochrysidales, Coccolithales, Zygodiscales, and Discoasterales during the Paleocene (Figs. 3F.1 and 3F.2). From an initial assemblage of approximately 10 survivor species in the earliest Danian, nannofossil species richness climbed to more than 100 taxa by the end of the Paleocene. The Paleocene–Eocene Thermal Maximum (PETM) was associated with severe stress in the world's oceanic surface waters, resulting in a substantial species turnover and assemblage reorganization in the early Eocene. Cenozoic species richness in the calcareous nannofossils peaked during the early–middle Eocene, followed by a decline in richness through the late Eocene and Oligocene as the world's oceanic system responded to the onset of the Cenozoic Icehouse Earth.

Climatic amelioration in the Miocene led to renewed diversification of nannofossils, including adaptive radiation in the Sphenolithaceae in the early Miocene and in the Discoasteraceae in the middle and late Miocene. The climatic deterioration of the late Cenozoic (late Pliocene and Quaternary) led to extinctions in the Discoasterales, with the progressive loss of two of the most diverse generic complexes in the Cenozoic (*Sphenolithus* and *Discoaster*). These assemblages instead were dominated by generalist taxa evolving in the Noelaerhabdaceae line.

3F.3 Biostratigraphy—Mesozoic

The zonation of the Late Triassic follows Bown (1998) who documented the appearance and early stratigraphic succession of the calcareous nannofossils. The timing of events has been adjusted following Gardin et al. (2012) where appropriate. The three Upper Triassic zonal units yield a low biostratigraphic resolution that is probably a function of both the paucity of well-preserved Triassic sections as well as low initial rates of evolution for these assemblages. The Jurassic biostratigraphic zonation for the Boreal areas follows that of Bown et al. (1998) as modified by Bown and Cooper (1998). Nannofossil provincialism rendered some of the Bown and Cooper (1998) zones difficult to resolve in more tropical areas; however, so Mattioli and Erba (1999) proposed an alternative set of zones based on Tethyan sections. This Tethyan scheme was refined and expanded in the Upper Jurassic by Casselato (2010) and partially recalibrated by Bergen et al. (2014).

There was a major species turnover associated with the Jurassic–Cretaceous boundary interval (Bown et al., 2004), with renewed increase in species richness characterizing the Cretaceous record. Two zonation schemes spanning the entire Cretaceous have had widespread use: the CC zonation of Perch-Nielsen (1985) (herein PN1985), and the NC scheme, originally proposed by Roth (1978) and subsequently modified for wider application by Bralower et al. (1995) (herein BLST1995). An additional zonation for only the Upper Cretaceous has been proposed by Burnett (1998) (herein B1998), which addresses some of the ambiguities of the CC and NC schemes, as well as offering a large number of subzones that may be useful in some areas. Calibration of the biostratigraphic horizons to the geochronological scale largely follows that of the Geologic Time Scale 2012, with additional data from Corbett et al. (2014), Erba et al. (1995), and Thibault et al. (2012).

For a listing of zones and taxon events, please refer to the nannofossil columns in the Jurassic through Neogene biochronostratigraphic figures in Chapters 25–28 of this book.

3F.4 Biostratigraphy—Cenozoic

Among the several Cenozoic calcareous nannofossil biozonations established about 45 years ago, two of them (Martini, 1971; and Bukry, 1973, 1975, 1978 refined in Okada and Bukry, 1980) are still employed by the IODP community and individual biostratigraphers and are considered as the "standard" zonations. The obvious reason is that many of the biohorizons used in Martini's and in Bukry's zonations for biozonal definitions have proven to provide consistent results. However, the huge amount of new information that has accumulated over the past three decades made available biostratigraphic data useful for (partly) revising the previous landmark biozonations. Therefore Backman et al. (2012) and Agnini et al. (2014) proposed a revision of the calcareous nannofossil biozonations for the Neogene–Quaternary and the Paleogene, respectively.

The calcareous nannofossil biostratigraphy of the Cenozoic (Neogene–Quaternary and Paleogene) is reported in Martini (1971) (M1971) and Okada and Bukry (1980) (OM1980) with the revision by Backman et al. (2012) (BRRFP2012) and Agnini et al. (2014) (AFRCPBR2014). Biochronologic information for the marker biohorizons is from Backman et al. (2012) and Agnini et al. (2014), in which details and discussion on the proposed biostratigraphy can be found.

Bibliography

Agnini, C., Fornaciari, E., Raffi, I., Catanzariti, R., Pälike, H., Backman, J., et al., 2014, Biozonation and biochronology of Paleogene calcareous nannofossils from low and middle latitudes. *Newsletters on Stratigraphy*, **47/2**: 131–181, https://doi.org/10.1127/0078-0421/2014/0042.

Backman, J., Raffi, I., Rio, D., Fornaciari, E., and Pälike, H., 2012, Biozonation and biochronology of Miocene through Pleistocene calcareous nannofossils from low and middle latitudes. *Newsletters on Stratigraphy*, **45**: 221–244, https://doi.org/10.1127/0078-0421/2012/0022.

Bergen, J.A., Boesiger, T.M., and Pospichal, J.J., 2014, Low-latitude Oxfordian to Early Berriasian nannofossil biostratigraphy and its application to the subsurface of Eastern Texas. *In* Hammes, U., and

Gale, J. (eds), Geology of the Haynesville Gas Shale in East Texas and West Louisiana. *AAPG Memoir,* **105**: 69–102.

Bown, P.R., 1998, Triassic. *In* Bown, P.R. (ed), *Calcareous Nannofossil Biostratigraphy*. British Micropalaeontological Society Publication Series. London: Chapman & Hall, pp. 29–33.

Bown, P.R., and Cooper, M.K.E., 1998, Jurassic. *In* Bown, P.R. (ed), *Calcareous Nannofossil Biostratigraphy*. British Micropalaeontological Society Publication Series. London: Chapman & Hall, pp. 34–85.

Bown, P.R., Cooper, M.K.E., and Lord, A.R., 1998, A calcareous nannofossil zonation scheme for the early to mid Mesozoic. *Newsletters on Stratigraphy*, **20**: 91–114.

Bown, P.R., Lees, J.A., and Young, J.R., 2004, Calcareous nannoplankton evolution and diversity. *In* Thierstein, H., and Young, J.R. (eds), *Coccolithophores – From Molecular Processes to Global Impact*. Springer-Verlag, pp. 481–508.

Bralower, T.J., Leckie, R.M., Sliter, W.V., and Thierstein, H.R., 1995, An integrated Cretaceous microfossil biostratigraphy. *SEPM Special Publication*, **54**: 65–79.

Bukry, D., 1971, Cenozoic calcareous nannofossils from the Pacific Ocean. *Transactions of the San Diego Society of Natural History*, **16**: 303–327.

Bukry, D., 1973, Low-latitude coccolith biostratigraphic zonation. *In* Edgar, N.T., Saunders, J.B., et al., (eds), *Initial Reports DSDP*. Washington, DC: U.S. Govt. Printing Office, Vol. 15, p. 685–703. https://doi.org/10.2973/dsdp.proc.15.116.1973.

Bukry, D., 1975, Coccolith and silicoflagellate stratigraphy, northwestern Pacific Ocean, Deep Sea Drilling Project Leg 32. *In* Larson, R.L., Moberly, R., et al., (eds), *Initial Reports DSDP*. Washington, DC: U.S. Govt. Printing Office, Vol. 32, p. 677–701. https://doi.org/10.2973/dsdp.proc.32.124.1975.

Bukry, D., 1978, Biostratigraphy of Cenozoic marine sediments by calcareous nannofossils. *Micropaleontology*, **24**: 44–60.

Burnett, J.A., 1998, Upper Cretaceous. *In* Bown, P.R. (ed), *Calcareous Nannofossil Biostratigraphy*. Kluwer Academic Publishers, pp. 132–199.

Casselato, C.E., 2010, Calcareous nannofossil biostratigraphy of Upper Callovian-Lower Berriasian successions from the Southern Alps, North Italy. *Rivista Italiana di Paleontologia e Stratigrafia*, **116**: 357–404.

Corbett, M., Watkins, D., and Pospichal, J., 2014, A quantitative analysis of calcareous nannofossil bioevents of the Late Cretaceous (Late Cenomanian–Coniacian) Western Interior Seaway and their reliability in established zonation schemes. *Marine Micropaleontology*, **109**: 30–45.

de Kaenel, E., Bergen, J.A., and von Salis Perch-Nielsen, K., 1996, Jurassic calcareous nannofossil biostratigraphy of western Europe. Compilation of recent studies and calibration of bioevents. *Bulletin de la Société géologique de France*, **67**: 15–28.

Erba, E., 2004, Calcareous nannofossils and Mesozoic oceanic anoxic events. *Marine Micropaleontology*, **52**: 85–106.

Erba, E., Premoli Silva, I., and Watkins, D.K., 1995, Cretaceous calcareous plankton biostratigraphy of Sites 872 to 879. *In* Haggerty, J.A., Premoli Silva, I., and Rack, F.R., (eds), *Proceedings, Ocean Drilling Program, Scientific Results*, College Station, TX, USA, **144**: 157–169.

Gardin, S., Krystyn, L., Richoz, S., Bartolini, A., and Galbrun, B., 2012, Where and when the earliest coccolithophores? *Lethaia*, **45**: 507–523.

Hagino, K., Young, J.R., Bown, P.R., Godrijan, J., Kulhanek, D.K., Kogane, K., and Horiguchi, T., 2015, Re-discovery of a "living fossil" coccolithophore from the coastal waters of Japan and Croatia. *Marine Micropaleontology*, **116**: 28–37.

Honjo, S., 1976, Coccoliths: production, transportation and sedimentation. *Marine Micropaleontology*, **1**: 65–79.

Martini, E., 1971, Standard Tertiary and Quaternary calcareous nannoplankton zonation. *In* Farinacci, A. (ed), *Proceedings 2nd International Conference Planktonic Microfossils Roma: Rome* (ed. Tecnosci.) Vol. 2, p. 739–785.

Mattioli, E., and Erba, E., 1999, Synthesis of calcareous nannofossil events in Tethyan lower and middle Jurassic successions. *Rivista Italiana di Paleontologia e Stratigrafia*, **105** (3): 343–376.

Milliman, J.D., 1993, Production and accumulation of calcium carbonate in the ocean – budget of a non-steady state. *Global Biogeochemical Cycles*, **7**: 927–957.

Okada, H., and Bukry, D., 1980, Supplementary modification and introduction of code numbers to the low-latitude coccolith biostratigraphic zonation (Bukry, 1973; 1975). *Marine Micropaleontology*, **5**: 321–325.

Perch-Nielsen, K., 1985, Mesozoic calcareous nannofossils. *In* Bolli, H.M., Saunders, J.B., and Perch-Nielsen, K. (eds), *Plankton Stratigraphy*. Cambridge University Press, pp. 329–437.

Roth, P.H., 1978, Cretaceous nannoplankton biostratigraphy and oceanography of the northwestern Atlantic Ocean. *Initial Reports DSDP*. Washington, DC: U.S. Govt. Printing Office, Vol. **44**, p. 731–760.

Thibault, N., Husson, D., Harlou, R., Gardin, S., Galbrun, B., Huret, E., et al., 2012, Astronomical calibration of upper Campanian–Maastrichtian carbon isotope events and calcareous plankton biostratigraphy in the Indian Ocean (ODP Hole 762C): Implication for the age of the Campanian–Maastrichtian boundary. *Palaeogeography, Palaeoclimatology, Palaeoecology*, **337–338**: 52–71.

Watkins, D.K., Wise Jr., S.W., Pospichal, J.J., and Crux, J., 1996, *Upper Cretaceous Calcareous Nannofossil Biostratigraphy and Paleoceanography of the Southern Ocean. Microfossils and Oceanic Environments*. British Micropalaeontological Society, University of Wales, Aberystwyth Press, pp. 355–381.

Subchapter 3G

Planktonic foraminifera

M.R. Petrizzo, B.S. Wade and F.M. Gradstein

Abstract

Planktonic foraminifera are marine protozoa with a calcareous and chambered test. The group evolved since late Early Jurassic, and from mid-Cretaceous onward, it has significantly proliferated and is a major component of oceanic oozes. Planktonic foraminifera phylogeny often is closely linked to paleoceanographic turn-over events, and its detailed biostratigraphy contributes significantly to Earth's geologic history.

3G.1 Introduction

Planktonic foraminifera are marine protozoa, single-celled eukaryotes with calcareous shells and chambered tests that show high diversity and adaptability and have undergone significant evolution since their first development in the Jurassic. Molecular phylogeny indicates that they are polyphyletic, derived multiple times from different benthic ancestors (Darling et al., 1997). Because of their relatively rapid evolutionary changes, abundance and taxonomic diversity in marine sediments, planktonic foraminifera have been used extensively in biostratigraphic studies and are considered one of the most important microfossil groups for understanding Mesozoic and Cenozoic paleoceanography (e.g., Premoli Silva and Sliter, 1999; Kucera, 2007).

The application of a hierarchic system of diagnostic morphological features and the identification and/or construction of lineages translated in generic names (so that natural groups coincide with genera) is currently the approach used by the planktonic foraminiferal workers. In this paper we present the stratigraphic distribution of the most common genera to highlight important evolutionary steps in terms of modification of the wall microstructure and shell morphology from which biozonal schemes and phylogenetic relationships can be established. Genera and species concepts used in this work can be found on the taxonomic database for planktonic foraminifera (pforams@mikrotax) available online at http://www.mikrotax.org (see Huber et al., 2016 for further details).

3G.2 Jurassic

Planktonic foraminifera originated in late Early Jurassic (e.g., Gradstein, 1976; Hart, 1980; Caron, 1983; Wernli, 1988; BouDagher-Fadel et al., 1997; Wernli and Görög, 2007) and, for reasons poorly understood, only underwent proliferation of species and geographic spreading from mid-Cretaceous onward (Fig. 3G.1). Early planktonic foraminifera from the Jurassic are known to be usually of low frequency and only seldom reach sporadic mass occurrences. One issue is that the aragonitic tests of these Jurassic microfossils hampered fossilization. Indeed, a majority of samples in wells or outcrop sections may lack specimens of these taxa. In this context it is not so much surprising that Jurassic foraminifera were only rarely encountered in samples and are limited to low- and mid-latitude marine basins of Pangaea, adjacent to the true oceans (e.g., Görög and Wernli, 2003; Hudson et al., 2009; Gradstein et al., 2018). The Jurassic oceans themselves were empty of planktonic foraminifera.

The early planktonic foraminiferal record from Toarcian through Tithonian is represented by only two trochospiral genera possessing a microperforate wall texture and a cancellate (*Conoglobigerina*) or smooth/pustulose (*Globuligerina*) surface pattern and fewer than 10 species have been identified so far (see review by Gradstein et al., 2017a,b and references herein). Therefore the evolution of planktonic foraminifera does not follow the evolutionary diversity pattern of nannofossils and dinoflagellates, and the Tithonian appears to be a bottleneck for planktonic foraminifera, with a sparse record and virtual extinction of taxa. Jurassic *Globuligerina oxfordiana* likely evolved into the Cretaceous *Favusella hoterivica*.

3G.3 Cretaceous

Planktonic foraminifera from the Berriasian to Barremian still have a scattered geographic and stratigraphic record that makes biostratigraphy and interpretation of their evolutionary trends quite difficult (Fig. 3G.2). The few species observed with rare specimens in Berriasian sediments possess both microperforate and finely perforate wall textures, show a very variable trochospiral morphology and wall ornamentation that has been described as smooth (*Gorbachikella*) and cancellate (*Favusella* and *Conoglobigerina*). To date these taxa have been reported only in hemipelagic, continental margin basins of the Tethys (Crimea, Azerbaijan, Eastern Canada, Mexico: Gorbachik and Poroshina, 1979; Gorbachik and Kuznetsova, 1983; Omana et al., 2017; Wernli et al., 1995). The trochospiral and finely perforate *Hedbergella* (with/without perforation cones) first occurs in the middle Berriasian (Gradstein et al., 2018) or early Valanginian (Boudagher-Fadel et al., 1997; Coccioni and Premoli Silva, 1994; Robaszynski and Caron, 1995; Premoli Silva and Sliter, 1999).

The appearance of the first planispiral, and finely perforate *Globigerinelloides*, is reported from the late Valanginian (Coccioni and Premoli Silva, 1994; Premoli Silva and Sliter, 1999; Coccioni et al., 2007) in a

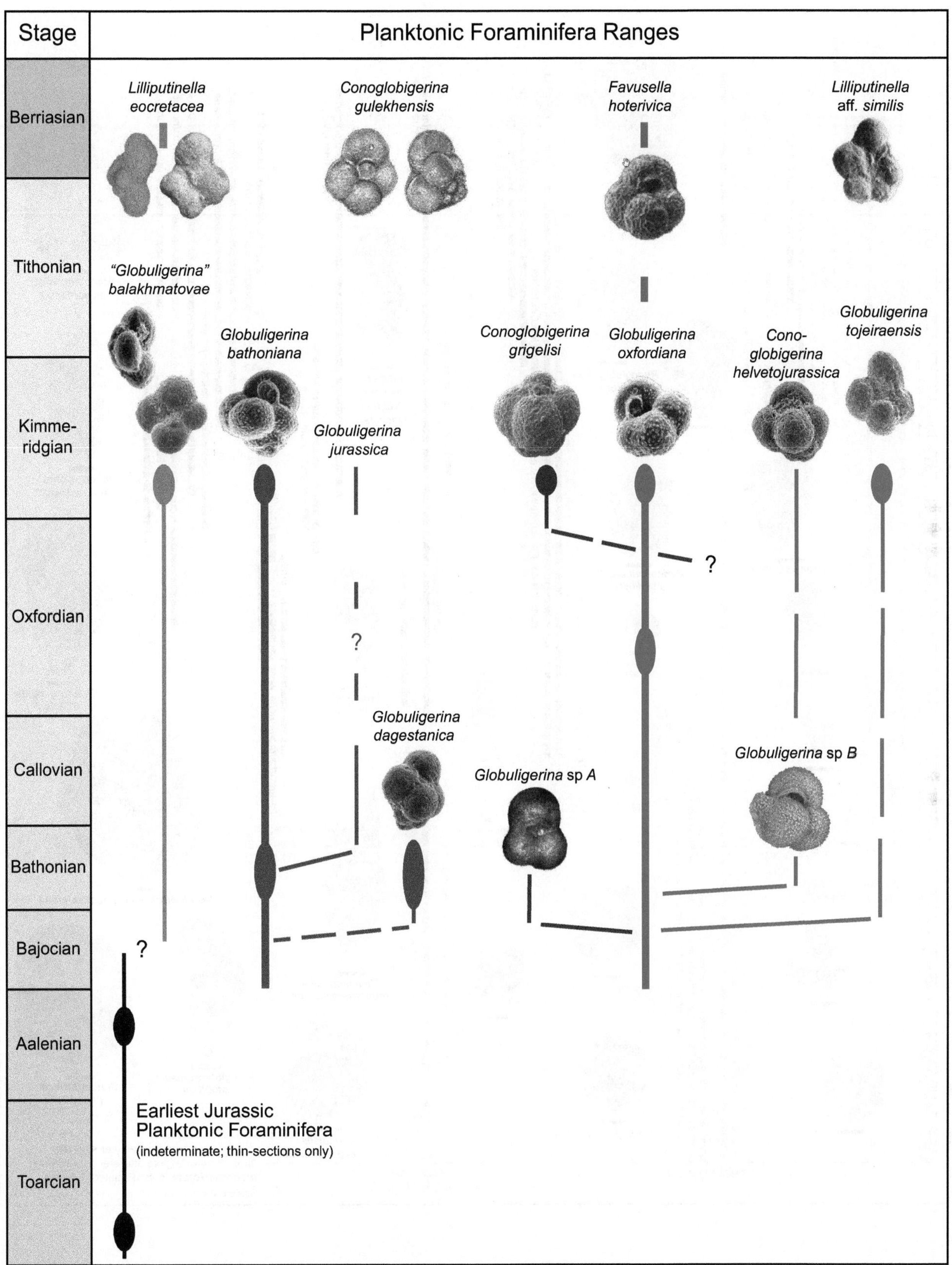

FIGURE 3G.1 Stratigraphic ranges of Jurassic planktonic foraminiferal species according to Gradstein et al. (2017a,b, 2018) and references herein.

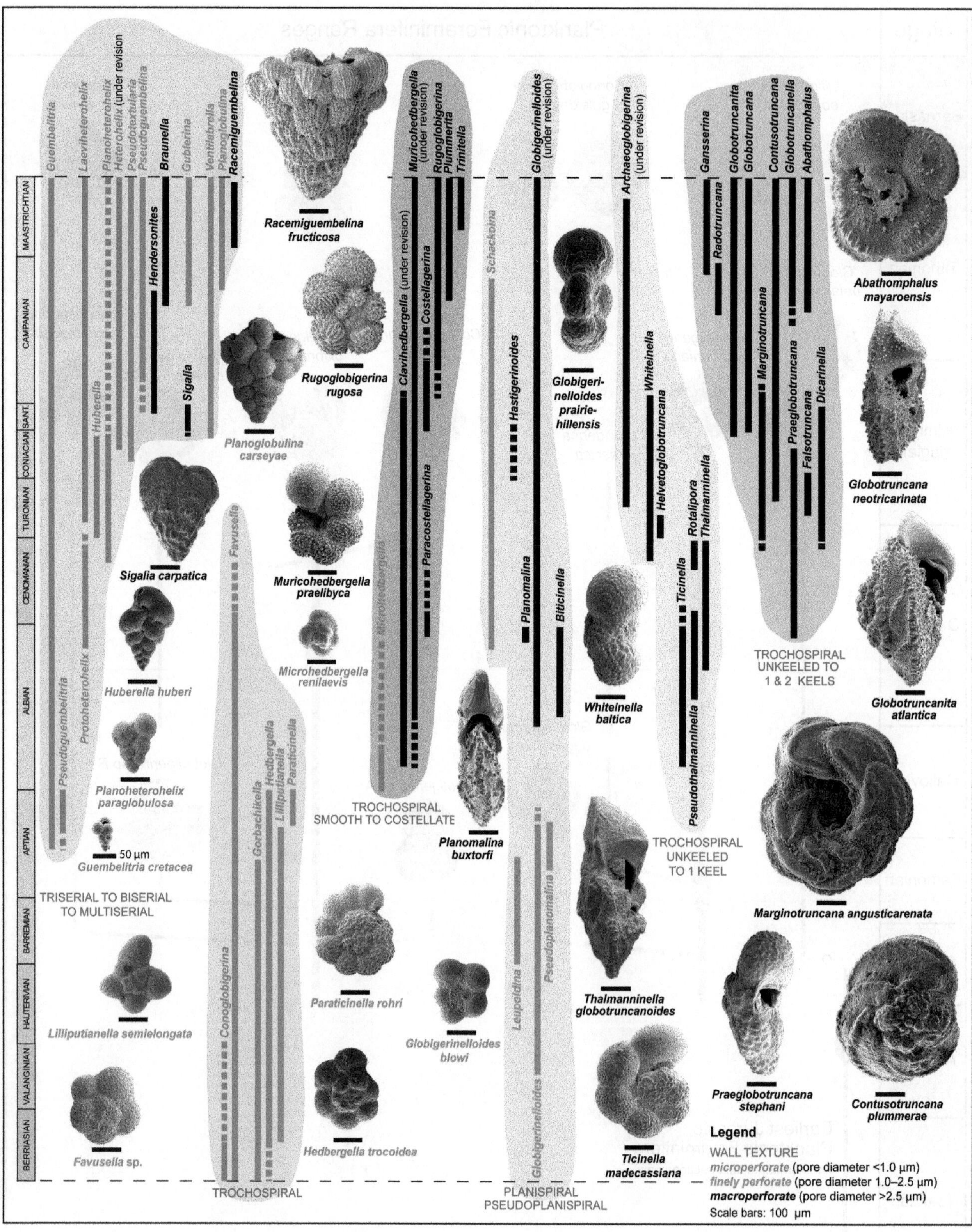

MAASTRICHTIAN
CAMPANIAN
SANT.
CONIACIAN
TURONIAN
CENOMANIAN
ALBIAN
APTIAN
BARREMIAN
HAUTERIVIAN
VALANGINIAN
BERRIASIAN
Guembelitria
Laeviheterohelix
Planoheterohelix
Heterohelix (under revision
Pseudotextularia
Pseudoguembelina
Braunella
Gublerina
Ventilabrella
Planoglobulina
Racemiguembelina
Hendersonites
Sigalia
Huberella
Protoheterohelix
Pseudoguembelitria
Racemiguembelina fructicosa
Rugoglobigerina rugosa
Planoglobulina carseyae
Sigalia carpatica
Muricohedbergella praelibyca
Microhedbergella renilaevis
Huberella huberi
Planoheterohelix paraglobulosa
50 μm
Guembelitria cretacea
TRISERIAL TO BISERIAL TO MULTISERIAL
Lilliputianella semielongata
Favusella sp.
Favusella
Conoglobigerina
Gorbachikella
Hedbergella
Lilliputianella
Paraticinella
Microhedbergella
Muricohedbergella (under revision)
Clavihedbergella (under revision)
Costellagerina
Paracostellagerina
Rugoglobigerina
Plummerita
Trinitella
TROCHOSPIRAL SMOOTH TO COSTELLATE
Paraticinella rohri
Hedbergella trocoidea
Globigerinelloides blowi
TROCHOSPIRAL
Schackoina
Hastigerinoides
Globigerinelloides (under revision)
Planomalina
Biticinella
Planomalina buxtorfi
Leupoldina
Pseudoplanomalina
Globigerinelloides
PLANISPIRAL PSEUDOPLANISPIRAL
Globigeri-nelloides prairie-hillensis
Whiteinella baltica
Thalmanninella globotruncanoides
Ticinella madecassiana
Archaeoglobigerina (under revision)
Whiteinella
Helvetoglobotruncana
Ticinella
Rotalipora
Thalmanninella
Pseudothalmanninella
TROCHOSPIRAL UNKEELED TO 1 KEEL
Gansserina
Radotruncana
Globotruncanita
Globotruncana
Marginotruncana
Contusotruncana
Praeglobotruncana
Globotruncanella
Falsotruncana
Abathomphalus
Dicarinella
TROCHOSPIRAL UNKEELED TO 1 & 2 KEELS
Abathomphalus mayaroensis
Globotruncana neotricarinata
Globotruncanita atlantica
Marginotruncana angusticarenata
Praeglobotruncana stephani
Contusotruncana plummerae
Legend
WALL TEXTURE
microperforate (pore diameter <1.0 μm)
finely perforate (pore diameter 1.0–2.5 μm)
macroperforate (pore diameter >2.5 μm)
Scale bars: 100 μm

stratigraphic interval correlated with the OAE Weissert Event (e.g., Erba et al., 2004). The radiation of finely perforate hedbergellids with radially elongated chambers (*Lilliputianella*) occurs in middle Berriasian (Gradstein et al., 2018), and rare planispirals with bulb-shaped chambers (*Leopoldina*) are recorded in the late Hauterivian (e.g., BouDagher-Fadel et al., 1997; Premoli Silva et al., 2018), the latter genus close to the Faraoni Level (Cecca et al., 1994; Coccioni et al., 1998, 2006).

A progressive increase in abundance and number of species is observed from the mid-Barremian (Aguado et al., 2014) to the lower Aptian where the diversification of the leupoldinids correlates with the Selli Level (OAE1a, e.g., Erba et al., 1999; Premoli Silva et al., 1999; Coccioni et al., 2006, 2007). The middle to late Aptian record is characterized by the appearances of a planispiral species possessing a peripheral pseudo-keel formed by the concentration of perforation cones (*Pseudoplanomalina chenouriensis*) and of the trochospiral finely perforate and with perforation cones that coalesce to form irregular imperforate ridges (*Paraticinella*).

Planktonic foraminiferal turnover across the Aptian–Albian boundary interval is the most dramatic event in the Cretaceous evolutionary history of planktonic foraminifera after the mass extinction at the Cretaceous/Paleogene (K/Pg) Boundary (e.g., Brèhèret et al., 1986; Leckie, 1989; Tornaghi et al., 1989; Premoli Silva and Sliter, 1999; Kennedy et al., 2000; Leckie et al., 2002). It coincides with the extinction of most of the Aptian lineages (*Hedbergella*, *Paraticinella*, *Pseudoguembelitria*) and with the appearance of microperforate small-sized, globigeriniform specimens (*Microhedbergella*) in the earliest Albian (Huber and Leckie, 2011; Petrizzo et al., 2012, 2013; Kennedy et al., 2014). The change in assemblage composition occurs within a protracted interval of organic carbon burial from the latest Aptian to the early Albian (OAE1b, e.g., Erbacher et al., 1996; Larson and Erba, 1999), a long-term sea level fall (Haq et al., 1988; Haq, 2014) and is associated with the latest Aptian prolonged cooling phase, and possibly acidification, following the Kerguelen submarine volcanism (Zeebe, 2001; Leckie et al., 2002; Erba et al., 2015).

The subsequent pattern of evolutionary changes in the planktonic foraminifera during the Albian–Turonian time interval mirrors the overall trend of rising sea level and global warming and increase of the density gradient within the surface water. During the early to middle Albian planktonic foraminifera diversified rapidly with the continuous increase in morphological complexity and species diversity. The newly evolving lineages are all characterized by a macroperforate wall texture. Novel morphological features are the development of (1) a thick-encrusted wall in trochospiral (*Ticinella*) and planispiral (*Biticinella*) taxa, (2) muricae (*Muricohedbergella*), (3) peripheral keel and raised sutures in trochospiral taxa (*Pseudothalmanninella* and *Thalmanninella*), and (4) the appearance of a true keel in the planispiral (*Planomalina*) taxa. The biserials taxa (*Protoheterohelix*) first occur in the geological record along productive continental margins and in the expanding shallow waters of epicontinental seas, and thus interpreted as evolving from a benthic ancestor (Leckie, 2009).

The progressive diversification trend is marked by a turnover phase in the late Albian with the appearances of taxa with muricae peripherally aligned (*Praeglobotruncana*) and partially fused to form costellae (*Paracostellagerina*), and the disappearance of *Ticinella*, *Biticinella*, and *Planomalina* in the latest Albian around the OAE1d (e.g., Caron, 1985; Lipson-Benitah and Almogi-Labin, 2001; Petrizzo et al., 2008).

The Cenomanian Stage corresponds to the appearance and diversification of trochospiral taxa with coarse pustules (*Whiteinella*) and with a single-keel (*Rotalipora*). A significant change occurs across the Cenomanian–Turonian boundary interval as the last representative of the *Rotalipora* lineage (*Rotalipora cushmani*) disappears shortly after the onset of OAE 2 (e.g., Premoli Silva and Sliter, 1999; Leckie et al., 2002; see review in Falzoni et al., 2018), and the two double-keeled *Dicarinella* and *Marginotruncana* first appear in the record and diversify and dominated the assemblages until the latest Santonian (e.g., Caron, 1985; Hart, 1999; Premoli Silva and Sliter, 1999; Petrizzo et al., 2017).

FIGURE 3G.2 Cretaceous genera plotted according to wall texture (microperforate, finely perforate, macroperforate) and coiling mode. Lower Cretaceous: the stratigraphic distribution of genera is based on the work by Moullade (1966), implemented and/or modified according to subsequent taxonomic and biostratigraphic studies or syntheses by Kuhry (1971, 1972), Longoria (1974, 1977), Moullade (1974), Neagu (1975), Sigal (1977, 1979), Salaj (1980, 1984), Pflaumann and Cepek (1982), Caron (1985), Gorbatchik (1986), Weidich (1990), Aguado et al. (1992), Banner et al. (1993), Coccioni and Premoli Silva (1994), Robaszynski and Caron (1995), BouDagher-Fadel et al. (1997), Moullade et al. (2002, 2005), Verga and Premoli Silva (2002, 2003a,b, 2005), Coccioni et al. (2007, 2006), Lipson-Benitah and Almogi-Labin (2004), Premoli Silva et al. (2018).
Upper Cretaceous: the stratigraphic distribution of genera is based on Caron (1966), Pessagno (1967), Douglas (1969), Robaszynski and Caron (1979), Robaszynski et al. (1984, 1990, 2000), Masters (1977, 1980), Peryt (1980), Lipson-Benitah (1980), Caron (1985), Robaszynski and Caron (1995), Premoli Silva and Sliter (1995) and implemented and/or modified according to studies by Tur et al. (2001), Abramovich et al. (2003), Petrizzo (2000, 2001, 2002, 2003), Bellier and Moullade (2002), Lamolda et al. (2007), Georgescu and Huber (2006, 2007, 2009), Ando and Huber (2007), Petrizzo and Huber (2006a, 2006b), González-Donoso et al. (2007), Huber et al. (2008), Desmares et al. (2008), Georgescu and Abramovich (2008), Lipson-Benitah (2008), Georgescu et al. (2009), Premoli Silva et al. (2009), Walaszczyk et al. (2010), Falzoni and Petrizzo (2011), Gale et al. (2011), Huber and Leckie (2011), Petrizzo et al. (2011, 2015, 2017), Pérez-Rodríguez et al. (2012), Ando et al. (2013), Huber and Petrizzo (2014), Elamri and Zaghbib-Turki (2014), Falzoni et al. (2013, 2014, 2016a,b, 2018), Coccioni and Premoli Silva (2015), Haynes et al. (2015), Sari et al. (2016), Huber et al. (2017), Petrizzo (2019).

After the maximum global warmth of the Late Cretaceous registered in the early Turonian, a time of prolonged global warmth characterized the Turonian and Coniacian time (e.g., Forster et al., 2007; Friedrich et al., 2012; Linnert et al., 2014; O'Brien et al., 2017; Huber et al., 2018), and planktonic foraminifera progressively increased in species richness and abundances. The evolution of planktonic foraminifera through the early middle Turonian is marked by increased speciation and enlargement in test size among the double-keeled taxa *Marginotruncana* and *Dicarinella*, by the origination of the single-keeled *Helvetoglobotruncana* and of the double-keeled *Falsotruncana*, *Contusotruncana*, and by the diversification of existing trochospirals (*Muricohedbergella*, *Praeglobotruncana*), planispirals (genus *Globigerinelloides* under revision) and biserial (*Huberella*, *Laeviheterohelix*, genus *Heterohelix* under revision) taxa. After a relatively stasis from the late Turonian to the early middle Coniacian, planktonic foraminiferal assemblages underwent a major compositional changes in the late Coniacian–Santonian (e.g., Hart and Bailey, 1979; Wonders, 1980; Caron and Homewood, 1983; Hart, 1999; Premoli Silva and Sliter, 1999) marked by high rates of species diversification among the double keeled taxa and by the appearance of newly evolved keeled (*Globotruncanita* and *Globotruncana*), biserial, and multiserial (*Pseudotextularia*, *Ventilabrella*, and *Sigalia*) genera. This radiation phase is followed by the extinction of *Marginotruncana* and *Dicarinella* in the latest Santonian–earliest Campanian. The two steps are regarded as due to a broader, turnover (the so-called Santonian turnover) that especially affected the more oligotrophic, keeled taxa (Wonders, 1980; Hart, 1999; Premoli Silva and Sliter, 1999). Overall, the Coniacian–Santonian interval represents the transition from the mid-Cretaceous extreme greenhouse characterized by elevated temperatures, increased volcanic activity, high sea-level and regional-to-global ocean anoxic events, to more temperate climatic conditions in the Late Cretaceous. Specifically, the Campanian–Maastrichtian long-term climate cooling, combined with significant plate rearrangements and opening and closing of seaways, influenced the paleobiogeographic distribution of marine species and determined the onset of climatic bioprovinces (e.g., Huber et al., 1995, 2002; Clarke and Jenkyns, 1999; Wilson et al., 2002; Hay, 2011; Bornemann et al., 2008; Robinson et al., 2010; MacLeod et al., 2011; Linnert et al., 2014, 2018). Superimposed on the long-term cooling trend are short-term cooling and warming pulses characterized by changes in stable oxygen and carbon isotope record. The most pronounced are the Campanian–Maastrichtian Boundary Event (CMBE) that corresponds to a deep-water cooling (e.g., Frank and Arthur, 1999; Barrera and Savin, 1999; Li and Keller, 1999; Voigt et al., 2012; Thibault et al., 2012), and the Mid-Maastrichtian Event (MME) that marks a time of deep-sea warming (Voigt et al., 2012; Jung et al., 2013) and an inoceramid extinction event in numerous open-ocean sites (MacLeod et al., 1996). Such climatic perturbations may have surely influenced the short and long-term evolution of planktonic foraminifera (e.g., photosymbiosis, dwarfism; Houston and Huber, 1998; Houston et al., 1999; Abramovich et al., 2003, 2010) and their vertical and geographic distribution at local and global scale, but understanding the cause–effect relationships between environmental perturbations and evolution needs further investigations.

In general, planktonic foraminifera increase in species richness during the Campanian and Maastrichtian when the rate of origination exceeds extinction resulting in a change in composition that reflects a progressive increase in bioprovinciality. Distinct biostratigraphic zonation schemes for the Tethyan, Boreal, Austral, and Transitional Provinces have been developed because of discrepancies and diachronism in the stratigraphic range of planktonic foraminiferal species among different paleolatitudes (e.g., Caron, 1985; Nederbragt, 1990; Huber, 1992; Premoli Silva and Sliter, 1999; Robaszynski and Caron, 1995; Li et al., 1999; Petrizzo, 2003; Campbell et al., 2004).

Diversification mainly involved heterohelicids that exhibit biserial (*Pseudotextularia*, *Pseudoguembelina*, *Braunella*, *Hendersonites*), biserial-to-multiserial (*Sigalia*, *Gublerina*), and multiserial (*Ventilabrella*, *Planoglobulina*, and *Racemiguembelina*) chambers growth. Globotruncanids diversify with the appearance of the single keeled *Radotruncana* and *Gansserina*. Test wall ornamentation became extremely complex and also variable among species assigned to the same lineage (i.e., fine-to-thick costellae and costae, ribs on the sutures, cameral flanges, and raised sutures on multiserial and trochospiral unkeeled taxa). For example, the meridionally arranged ornamentation (i.e., aligned pustules or costellae that converge toward the external pole of each chamber) in *Rugoglobigerina* is a primary shell feature that shows a high degree of variability throughout the geographic and stratigraphic distribution of the genus as specimens at high latitude show reduced meridional ornamentation (Blow, 1979; Huber, 1992). This observation confirms the increased provincialism at the end of the Cretaceous Period and points to changing environmental conditions that may have played a key role in triggering the external expression of genetically controlled wall ornamentation in the planktonic foraminifera (Falzoni et al., 2014).

The mass extinction event of the K/Pg Boundary eliminated almost all species of planktonic foraminifera (e.g., Luterbacher and Premoli Silva, 1964; Smit 1982; Arenillas et al., 2002, 2018; Molina et al., 2009) except for few survivors (*Guembelitria cretacea*, *Muricohedbergella holmdelensis*, and *Muricohedbergella monmouthensis*). Remarkably, the meridionally arranged ornamentation and the peripheral margin with double keels are morphological features that have never been observed again in the evolutionary history of planktonic foraminifera and are absent in extant species.

3G.4 Cenozoic

Planktonic foraminifera provide an excellent means to study macroevolution through the Cenozoic (Fig. 3G.3). Whilst generic names have changed over the last 60 years, the tropical/subtropical biostratigraphic zonations have remained largely robust, with many of the marker species from the earlier works of Bolli (1957), Jenkins (1965), and Blow (1969) still used in zonations today (Wade et al., 2011). Though zonal schemes have been erected for all latitudes, the discussion here focuses on low latitude planktonic foraminifera, their evolution, and biostratigraphic application.

The lineage phylogeny and paleoecology of macroperforate Cenozoic planktonic foraminifer morphospecies was compiled by Aze et al. (2011) and recently updated on Time Scale Creator to allow easy transfer between different time scales (Fordham et al., 2018). New insights into planktonic foraminiferal evolution and wall texture have been gained through sites with exceptional preservation (Pearson and Wade, 2009, 2015). The main families that dominate the Cenozoic planktonic foraminifera are the Globigerinidae, with the Truncorotaloididae and Globanomalidae being important components of the Paleogene, and the Globorotalidae becoming a key constituent from the early Miocene to the Recent. Microperforate planktonic foraminifera may have great potential to refine the biochronology, but few species are currently utilized, the exception being species of *Globigerinatella* and *Cassigerinella* in the Miocene and *Chiloguembelina* at the Rupelian–Chattian boundary (King and Wade, 2017; Coccioni et al., 2018).

Cenozoic planktonic foraminifera evolved from three survivors of the K/Pg extinction (Olsson et al., 1999) and then diversified and proliferated rapidly. The evolution and extinction of *Parvularugoglobigerina* provides the earliest markers of the basal Danian. The spinose *Subbotina* and *Parasubbotina* originated and the muricate Truncorotaloididae evolved and diversified (Quillévéré and Norris, 2003). The genus *Praemurica* gave rise to the muricate genera *Igorina* and *Morozovella*, from which *Acarinina*, *Planorotalites*, and ultimately *Morozovelloides* evolved (Berggren et al., 2006). These genera provide a series of zonal markers from the Danian through to the base Priabonian.

The Ypresian and Lutetian was a time of diversification in planktonic foraminifera with the appearance of ornate and distinctive forms (Norris, 1991). Within the tropical/subtropical assemblages, marked and rapid abundance shifts occur in key genera at the start of the Early Eocene Climatic Optimum (Luciani et al., 2017). *Globoturborotalita* evolves at the basal Eocene (Ypresian) from *Subbotina* and is one of the few Paleogene genera that are extant. From *Parasubbotina* many important Paleogene genera evolved including *Paragloborotalia* and *Globorotaloides*, with *Catapsydrax* subsequently originating from the latter. *Guembelitrioides* gave rise to the spinose and spherical genus *Globigerinatheka* and then to the short ranging monospecific genus *Orbulinoides* (Premoli Silva et al., 2006). The Hantkeninidae evolved in the Lutetian and their extinction marks the end of the Priabonian. *Pseudohastigerina* and *Turborotalia* originated from *Globanomalina* in the Ypresian and both went extinct in the Rupelian. *Ciperoella*, *Turborotalita*, *Dentoglobigerina*, and *Globigerina* evolved in the Eocene, though these genera do not provide any biostratigraphic control during the Epoch. A major turnover in planktonic foraminifera occurs near the base of the Priabonian with the extinction of all large muricate forms (*Acarinina* and *Morozovelloides*) which dominated the tropical/subtropical surface oceans since the Paleocene (Quillévéré and Norris, 2003; Wade et al., 2012). The mechanism for the turnover is still unknown, as no major shift in sea surface or deep water temperature is associated with the extinction (Wade, 2004; Okafor et al., 2009).

The Eocene–Oligocene Transition was an interval of cooling, ice-sheet growth, and sea level fall (Zachos et al., 1996; Coxall et al., 2005; Houben et al., 2019). Through the end of the Eocene and at the Eocene–Oligocene boundary transpired a major diversity loss in planktonic foraminifera, with the extinction of many distinctive groups such as *Globigerinatheka* and the Hantkeninidae (Wade and Pearson, 2008).

Morphologically Oligocene planktonic foraminifera are generally devoid of distinguishing characteristics, with many low trochospiral forms, with 3–5 globular chambers in the final whorl (Wade et al., 2018). More distinctive genera possessing supplementary apertures evolve in the Chattian (*Trilobatus*), with *Globigerinoides* evolving and diversifying in the Aquitanian (Spezzaferri et al., 2015). These two genera become the principal mixed-layer dwellers of the Neogene. Paragloborotaliids diversify and provide important biostratigraphic markers in the late Oligocene through late Miocene.

Several genera diversified in the early Miocene, particularly *Globigerinoides*, *Globigerinella*, and *Globorotalia* sensu lato (without a keel) (Cifelli, 1969). The *Praeorbulina* lineage originated from *Trilobatus* with early forms possessing a final chamber that partly encases the preceding coil, evolving into *Orbulina*, distinguished by its entirely spherical test (Olsson, 1964). This evolution of increasingly spherical forms provides a series of markers in the Burdigalian and Langhian. The monospecific genus *Clavatorella* evolves and goes extinct in the Langhian. The evolution and extinction of species within the *Globorotalia fohsi* lineage (*peripheroacuta, "praefohsi," robusta*, and *fohsi*) provide zonal and subzonal markers in the Langhian and Serravallian (Zones M7–M9), an interval of climatic cooling termed the Miocene Climate Transition. *Sphaeroidinellopsis* and *Sphaeroidinella* with their distinctive cortex evolved. Endemism was heightened between the

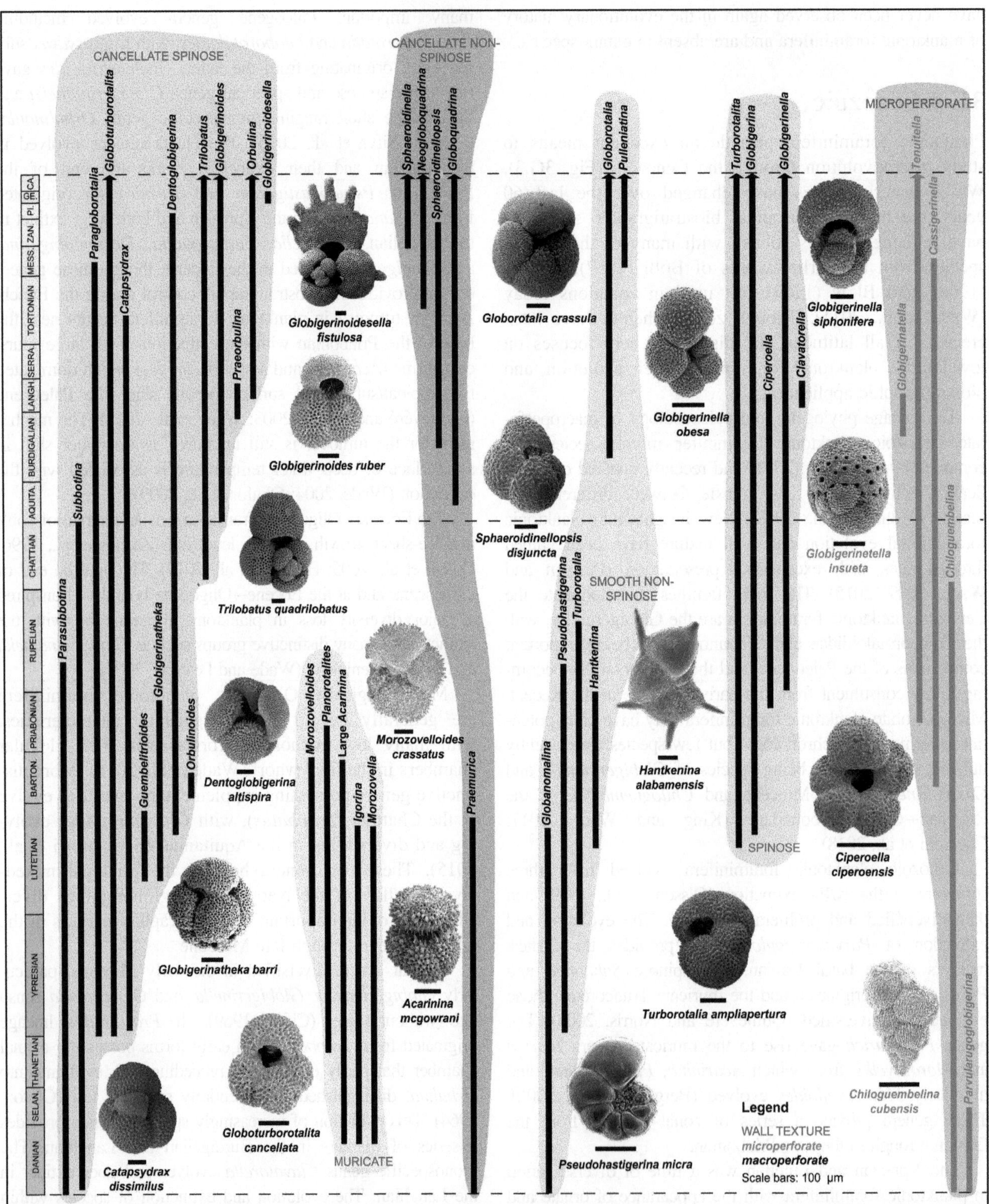

FIGURE 3G.3 Key Cenozoic genera plotted according to wall texture. Stratigraphic distribution of genera is based on stratigraphic ranges as recorded in Aze et al. (2011), Wade et al. (2011), and Mikrotax (Huber et al., 2016). Arrows indicate extant genera.

Pacific and Atlantic Oceans from the middle Miocene due to progressive closure of the Central American Seaway (Haug and Tiedemann, 1998; Spezzaferri and Spiegler, 2005). The smooth-walled, low-trochospiral species of *Globorotalia* processing nonperforate keels are key zonal markers for the middle Miocene and younger (Sierro et al., 1993). Several significant changes occur in the Tortonian and Messinian, with the extinction of the long-ranging genus *Paragloborotalia. Neogloboquadrina* and *Pulleniatina* evolved in the late Miocene and quickly diversified (Bolli and Saunders, 1985).

Following the Miocene/Pliocene boundary, all the modern genera can be recognized in planktonic foraminiferal assemblages, dominated by diverse species of the genus *Globorotalia.* During the Pliocene the short-lived, monospecific genus *Globigerinoidesella* becomes a distinctive component of tropical assemblages (Poole and Wade, 2019).

Bibliography

Abramovich, S., Keller, G., Stüben, D., and Berner, Z., 2003, Characterization of late Campanian and maastrichtian planktonic foraminiferal depth habitats and vital activities based on stable isotopes. *Palaeogeography, Palaeoclimatology, Palaeoecology*, **202** (1), 1–29.

Abramovich, S., Yovel-Corem, S., Almogi-Labin, A., and Benjamini, C., 2010, Global climate change and planktic foraminiferal response in the Maastrichtian. *Paleoceanography*, **25**: PA2201, https://doi.org/10.1029/2009PA001843.

Aguado, R., Company, M., O'Dogherty, L., Sandoval, J., and Tavera, J. M., 1992, Biostratigraphic analysis of the pelagic Barremian/Aptian in the Betic Cordillera (southern Spain): preliminary data. *Cretaceous Research*, **13**: 445–452.

Aguado, R., de Gea, G.A., and O'Dogherty, L., 2014, Integrated biostratigraphy (calcareous nannofossils, planktonic foraminifera, and radiolarians) of an uppermost Barremian–lower Aptian pelagic succession in the Subbetic Basin southern Spain. *Cretaceous Research*, **51**: 153–173.

Ando, A., and Huber, B.T., 2007, Taxonomic revision of the late Cenomanian planktonic foraminifera *Rotalipora greenhornensis*. *Journal of Foraminiferal Research*, **37** (2), 160–174.

Ando, A., Huber, B.T., and Premoli Silva, I., 2013, *Paraticinella rohri* (Bolli 1959) as the valid name for the latest Aptian zonal marker species of planktonic foraminifera traditionally called *bejaouaensis* or *eubejaouaensis*. *Cretaceous Research*, **45**: 275–287.

Arenillas, I., Arz, J.A., and Molina, E., 2002, Quantifying the evolutionary turnover across the K/T boundary catastrophic planktic foraminiferal extinction event at El Kef, Tunisia. *Geologiska Föreningens Förhandlingen*, **124**: 121–126.

Arenillas, I., Arz, J.A., and Gilabert, V., 2018, Blooms of aberrant planktic foraminifera across the K/Pg boundary in the Western Tethys: causes and evolutionary implications. *Paleobiology*, **44** (3), 1–30.

Aze, T., Ezard, T.H.G., Purvis, A., Coxall, H.K., Stewart, D.R.M., Wade, B.S., et al., 2011, A phylogeny of Cenozoic macroperforate planktonic foraminifera from fossil data. *Biological Reviews*, **86**: 900–927.

Banner, F.T., Copestake, P., and White, M.R., 1993, Barremian-Aptian Praehedbergellidae of the North Sea area: a reconnaissance. *Bulletin of the Natural History Museum, Geology, Series*, **49**: 1–30.

Barrera, E., and Savin, S.M., 1999, Evolution of late Campanian-Maastrichtian marine climates and oceans. *Special Papers-Geological Society of America*, **332**: 245–282.

Bellier, J.P., and Moullade, M., 2002, Lower Cretaceous planktonic foraminiferal biostratigraphy of the western North Atlantic (ODP Leg 171B), and taxonomic clarification of key index species. *Revue de Micropaléontologie*, **45** (1), 9–26.

Berggren, W.A., Pearson, P.N., Huber, B.T., and Wade, B.S., 2006, Taxonomy, Biostratigraphy and Phylogeny of Eocene *Acarinina*. *In* Pearson, P.N., Olsson, R.K., Huber, B.T., Hemleben, C., and Berggren, W.A. (eds), Atlas of Eocene Planktonic Foraminifera. *Cushman Foundation Special Publication,* **41**: 257–326.

Blow, W.H., 1969, Late Middle Eocene to Recent planktonic foraminiferal biostratigraphy. *In* Brönnimann, P., and Renz, H.H. (eds), *Proceedings of the First International Conference on Planktonic Microfossils*. Leiden: E.J. Brill, 199–422.

Blow, W.H., 1979, The Cainozoic Globigerinida. Atlas. Volume 2 of *The Cainozoic Globigerinida: A Study of the Morphology, Taxonomy, Evolutionary Relationships and the Stratigraphical Distribution of Some Globigerinida*. Brill Archive.

Bolli, H.M., 1957, Planktonic foraminifera from the Oligocene-Miocene Cipero and Lengua formations of Trinidad, B.W.I. *Bulletin U.S. National Museum*, **215**: 97–123.

Bolli, H.M., and Saunders, J.B., 1985, Oligocene to Holocene low latitude planktic foraminifera. *In* Bolli, H.M., Saunders, J.B., and Perch-Nielsen, K. (eds), *Plankton Stratigraphy*. Cambridge: Cambridge University Press, 155–262.

Bornemann, A., Norris, R.D., Friedrich, O., Beckmann, B., Schouten, S., Damsté, J.S.S., et al., 2008, Isotopic evidence for glaciation during the Cretaceous supergreenhouse. *Science*, **319** (5860), 189–192.

BouDagher-Fadel, M.K., Banner, F.T., and Whittaker, J.E., 1997, *Early evolutionary history of planktonic foraminifera*. Chapman & Hall, pp. 1–269.

Brèhèret, J.-G., Caron, M., and Delamette, M., 1986, Niveaux riches en mati.re organique dans l'Albien vocontien: quelques caractéres du paléoenvironment; essai d'interprétation génétique. *Documents du Bureau des Recherches Géologiques et Miniéres*, **110**: 141–191.

Campbell, R.J., Howe, R.W., and Rexilius, J.P., 2004, Middle Campanian–lowermost Maastrichtian nannofossil and foraminiferal biostratigraphy of the northwestern Australian margin. *Cretaceous Research*, **25** (6), 827–864.

Caron, M., 1966, Globotruncanidae du Crétacé supérieur du synclinal de la Gruyére Préalpes medians, Suisse. *Revue de Micropaléontologie*, **9**: 68–93.

Caron, M., 1983, La spéciation chez les Foraminiféres planctiques: une réponse adaptée aux contraints de l'environnement. *Zitteliana*, **10**: 671–676.

Caron, M., 1985, Cretaceous planktonic foraminifera. *In* Bolli, H.M., Saunders, J.B., and Perch-Nielsen, K. (eds), *Plankton Stratigraphy*. Cambridge: Cambridge University Press, 17–86.

Caron, M., and Homewood, P., 1983, Evolution of early planktic foraminifers. *Marine Micropaleontology*, **7** (6), 453–462.

Cecca, F., Pallini, G., Erba, E., Premoli Silva, I., and Coccioni, R., 1994, Hauterivian-Barremian chronostratigraphy based on ammonites, nannofossils, planktonic foraminifera and magnetic chrons from the Mediterranean domain. *Cretaceous Research*, **15** (4), 457–467.

Cifelli, R., 1969, Radiation of Cenozoic planktonic Foraminifera. *Systemic Zoology*, **18**: 154–168.

Clarke, L.J., and Jenkyns, H.C., 1999, New oxygen isotope evidence for long-term Cretaceous climatic change in the Southern Hemisphere. *Geology*, **27** (8), 699–702.

Coccioni, R., and Premoli Silva, I., 1994, Planktonic foraminifera from the Lower Cretaceous of Rio Argos sections (southern Spain) and biostratigraphic implications. *Cretaceous Research*, **15** (6), 645–687.

Coccioni, R., and Premoli Silva, I., 2015, Revised Upper Albian–Maastrichtian planktonic foraminiferal biostratigraphy and magneto-stratigraphy of the classical Tethyan Gubbio section Italy. *Newsletters on Stratigraphy*, **48** (1), 47–90.

Coccioni, R., Baudin, F., Cecca, F., Chiari, M., Galeotti, S., Gardin, S., et al., 1998, Integrated stratigraphic, palaeontological, and geochemical analysis of the uppermost Hauterivian Faraoni Level in the Fiume Bosso section, Umbria-Marche Apennines, Italy. *Cretaceous Research*, **19** (1), 1–23.

Coccioni, R., Luciani, V., and Marsili, A., 2006, Cretaceous oceanic anoxic events and radially elongated chambered planktonic foraminifera: paleoecological and paleoceanographic implications. *Palaeogeography, Palaeoclimatology, Palaeoecology*, **235** (1-3), 66–92.

Coccioni, R., Premoli Silva, I., Marsili, A., and Verga, D., 2007, First radiation of Cretaceous planktonic foraminifera with radially elongate chambers at Angles (Southeastern France) and biostratigraphic implications. *Revue de Micropaléontologie*, **50** (3), 215–224.

Coccioni, R., Montanari, A., Bice, D.M., Brinkhuis, H., Deino, A., Frontalini, F., et al., 2018, The Global Stratotype Section and Point (GSSP) for the base of the Chattian Stage (Paleogene System, Oligocene Series) at Monte Cagnero, Italy. *Episodes*, **41**: 17–32.

Coxall, H.K., Wilson, P.A., Pälike, H., Lear, C.H., and Backman, J., 2005, Rapid stepwise onset of Antarctic glaciation and deeper calcite compensation in the Pacific Ocean. *Nature*, **433** (7021), 53–57.

Darling, K.F., Wade, C.M., Kroon, D., and Brown, A.J.L., 1997, Planktic foraminiferal molecular evolution and their polyphyletic origins from benthic taxa. *Marine Micropaleontology*, **30** (4), 251–266.

Desmares, D., Grosheny, D., and Beaudoin, B., 2008, Ontogeny and phylogeny of Upper Cenomanian rotaliporids Foraminifera. *Marine Micropaleontology*, **69** (2), 91–105.

Douglas, R.G., 1969, Upper Cretaceous planktonic foraminifera in Northern California. Part 1: Systematics. *Micropaleontology*, **15**: 151–209.

Elamri, Z., and Zaghbib-Turki, D., 2014, Santonian-Campanian biostratigraphy of the Kalaat Senan area west-central Tunisia. *Turkish Journal of Earth Sciences*, **23** (2), 184–203.

Erba, E., Channell, J.E., Claps, M., Jones, C., Larson, R., Opdyke, B., et al., 1999, Integrated stratigraphy of the Cismon Apticore (southern Alps, Italy); a "reference section" for the Barremian-Aptian interval at low latitudes. *Journal of Foraminiferal Research*, **29** (4), 371–391.

Erba, E., Bartolini, A., and Larson, R.L., 2004, Valanginian Weissert oceanic anoxic event. *Geology*, **32** (2), 149–152.

Erba, E., Duncan, R.A., Bottini, C., Tiraboschi, D., Weissert, H., Jenkyns, H.C., et al., 2015. Environmental consequences of Ontong Java Plateau and Kerguelen Plateau volcanism. In: Neal, C.R., Sager, W.W., Sano, T., and Erba, E. (Eds.), *The Origin, Evolution, and Environmental Impact of Oceanic Large Igneous Provinces*, Geological Society of America Special Paper, 511, 271–303.

Erbacher, J., Thurow, J., and Littke, R., 1996, Evolution patterns of radiolaria and organic matter variations: a new approach to identify sea-level changes in mid-Cretaceous pelagic environments. *Geology*, **24** (6), 499–502.

Falzoni, F., and Petrizzo, M.R., 2011, Taxonomic overview and evolutionary history of *Globotruncanita insignis*. *Journal of Foraminiferal Research*, **41** (4), 371–383.

Falzoni, F., Petrizzo, M.R., MacLeod, K.G., and Huber, B.T., 2013, Santonian–Campanian planktonic foraminifera from Tanzania, Shatsky Rise and Exmouth Plateau: species depth ecology and paleoceanographic inferences. *Marine Micropaleontology*, **103**: 15–29.

Falzoni, F., Petrizzo, M.R., Huber, B.T., and MacLeod, K.G., 2014, Insights into the meridional ornamentation of the planktonic foraminiferal genus *Rugoglobigerina* (Late Cretaceous) and implications for taxonomy. *Cretaceous Research*, **47**: 87–104.

Falzoni, F., Petrizzo, M.R., Clarke, L.J., MacLeod, K.G., and Jenkyns, H.C., 2016a, Long-term Late Cretaceous oxygen-and carbon-isotope trends and planktonic foraminiferal turnover: A new record from the southern midlatitudes. *Geological Society of America Bulletin*, **128** (11-12), 1725–1735.

Falzoni, F., Petrizzo, M.R., Jenkyns, H.C., Gale, A.S., and Tsikos, H., 2016b, Planktonic foraminiferal biostratigraphy and assemblage composition across the Cenomanian–Turonian boundary interval at Clot Chevalier Vocontian Basin, SE France. *Cretaceous Research*, **59**: 69–97.

Falzoni, F., Petrizzo, M.R., Caron, M., Leckie, R.M., and Elderbak, K., 2018, Age and synchronicity of planktonic foraminiferal bioevents across the Cenomanian-Turonian boundary interval Late Cretaceous. *Newsletters on Stratigraphy*, **51** (3), 343–380.

Fordham, B.G., Aze, T., Haller, C., Zehady, A.K., Pearson, P.N., Ogg, J.G., et al., 2018, Future-proofing the Cenozoic macroperforate planktonic foraminifera phylogeny of Aze & others 2011. *PLoS One*, **13** (10), e0204625, https://doi.org/10.1371/journal.pone.0204625.

Forster, A., Schouten, S., Baas, M., and Sinninghe Damsté, J.S., 2007, Mid-Cretaceous (Albian–Santonian) sea surface temperature record of the tropical Atlantic Ocean. *Geology*, **35** (10), 919–922.

Frank, T.D., and Arthur, M.A., 1999, Tectonic forcings of Maastrichtian ocean-climate evolution. *Paleoceanography*, **14** (2), 103–117.

Friedrich, O., Norris, R.D., and Erbacher, J., 2012, Evolution of middle to Late Cretaceous oceans—a 55 my record of Earth's temperature and carbon cycle. *Geology*, **40** (2), 107–110.

Gale, A.S., Bown, P., Caron, M., Crampton, J., Crowhurst, S.J., Kennedy, W.J., et al., 2011, The uppermost Middle and Upper Albian succession at the Col de Palluel, Haute-Alpes, France: An integrated study ammonites, inoceramid bivalves, planktonic foraminifera, nannofossils, geochemistry, stable oxygen and carbon isotopes, cyclostratigraphy. *Cretaceous Research*, **32**: 59–130.

Georgescu, M.D., and Abramovich, S., 2008, Taxonomic revision and phylogenetic classification of the Late Cretaceous (upper Santonian-Maastrichtian) serial planktonic foraminifera (Familiy Heterohelicidae Cushman, 1927) with peripheral test wall flexure. *Revista Española de Micropaleontología*, **40** (1), 97–114.

Georgescu, M.D., and Huber, B.T., 2006, *Paracostellagerina* nov. gen., a meridionally costellate planktonic foraminiferal genus of the middle Cretaceous late Albian-earliest Cenomanian. *Journal of Foraminiferal Research*, **36**: 368–373.

Georgescu, M.D., and Huber, B.T., 2007, Taxonomic revision of the late Campanian-Maastrichtian (Late Cretaceous) planktonic foraminiferal genus *Rugotruncana* Brönnimann and Brown, 1956, and A new paleontological species concept for planktonic foraminifera. *Journal of Foraminiferal Research*, **37**: 150–159.

Georgescu, M.D., and Huber, B.T., 2009, Early evolution of the Cretaceous serial planktic foraminifera late Albian–Cenomanian. *Journal of Foraminiferal Research*, **39** (4), 335–360.

Georgescu, M.D., Saupe, E., and Huber, B.T., 2009, Morphometric and stratophenetic basis for phylogeny and taxonomy in Late Cretaceous gublerinid planktonic foraminifera. *Micropaleontology*, **54**: 397–424.

González-Donoso, J.M., Linares, D., and Robaszynski, F., 2007, The rotaliporids, a polyphyletic group of Albian-Cenomanian planktonic foraminifera: emendation of genera. *Journal of Foraminiferal Research*, **37** (2), 175–186.

Gorbatchik, T.N., 1986, Jurassic and Early Cretaceous planktonic foraminifera of the south of the USSR (in Russian. *AN SSSR, Nauka*, 1-239, Jurskie i Rammelovye planktonye foraminifery Juga SSSR. Akademia NAUK SSSR. Moskovskoi Oschestvo Prirody).

Gorbachik, T.N., and Kuznetsova, K.I., 1983, Jurassic and Early Cretaceous planktonic Foraminifera Favusellidea. Stratigraphy and palaeobiogeography. *Zitteliana*, **10**: 459–466.

Gorbachik, T.N., and Poroshina, L.A., 1979, New Berriasian planktonic foraminifers from Azerbaydzhan. *Palaeontology Journal*, **3**: 283–289 (translated from Russian).

Görög, A., and Wernli, R., 2003, Palaeobiogeography of the Middle Jurassic protoglobigerinids Foraminifera. *Eclogae Geologicae Helvetiae*, **96**: 237–248.

Gradstein, F.M., 1976, Biostratigraphy and biogeography of Jurassic Grand Banks Foraminifera. In: *Ist International Symposium on Benthic Foraminifera*, Pt. B. Maritime Sediments Special Publication, **1**: p. 557–583.

Gradstein, F.M., Gale, A., Kopaevich, L., Waskowska, A., Grigelis, A., and Glinskikh, L., 2017a, The Planktonic foraminifera of the Jurassic. Part 1: Material and taxonomy. *Swiss Journal of Paleontology*, **136**: 187–257.

Gradstein, F.M., Gale, A., Kopaevich, L., Waskowska, A., Grigelis, A., Glinskikh, L., et al., 2017b, The planktonic foraminifera of the Jurassic. Part II: Stratigraphy, palaeoecology and palaeobiogeography. *Swiss Journal of Paleontology*, **136**: 259–271.

Gradstein, F.M., Waskowska, A., Kopaevich, L., Watkins, D.K., Friis, H., and Perez Panera, J.P., 2018, Berriasian planktonic foraminifera and calcareous nannofossils from Crimea Mountains, with reference to microfossil evolution. *Swiss Journal of Paleontology*, **138**: 213–236.

Hart, M.B., 1980, A water depth model for the evolution of the planktonic Foraminiferida. *Nature*, **286**: 252–254.

Hart, M.B., 1999, The evolution and biodiversity of Cretaceous planktonic Foraminiferida. *Geobios*, **32** (2), 247–255.

Hart, M.B., and Bailey, H.W., 1979, The distribution of planktonic Foraminiferida in the mid-Cretaceous of NW Europe. *Aspekte der Kreide Europas*, **6**: 527–542.

Hart, M.B., Hylton, M.D., Oxford, M.J., Price, G.D., Hudson, W., and Smart, C.W., 2003, The search for the origin of the planktic Foraminifera. *Journal of the Geological Society*, **160** (3), 341–343.

Hart, M.B., Hudson, W., Smart, C.W., and Tyszka, J., 2012, A reassessment of *Globigerina bathoniana* Pazdrowa, 1969 and the palaeoceanographic significance of Jurassic planktic foraminifera from southern Poland. *Journal of Micropalaeontology*, **31**: 97–109.

Haq, B.U., 2014, Cretaceous eustasy revisited. *Global and Planetary Change*, **113**: 44–58.

Haq, B.U., Hardenbol, J., Vail, P.R., Stover, L.E., Colin, J.P., Ioannides, N.S., et al., 1988, Mesozoic and Cenozoic chronostratigraphy and cycles of sea-level change. *In* Wilgus, C.K., Hastings, B.S., Posimentier, H., Van Wagoner, J., Ross, C.A., and Kendall, C.G.St.C. (eds), *Sea-Level Changes: An Integrated Approach.* SEPM Special Publication, **42**: 71–108.

Haug, G.H., and Tiedemann, R., 1998, Effect of the formation of the Isthmus of Panama on Atlantic Ocean thermohaline circulation. *Nature*, **393**: 673–676.

Hay, W.W., 2011, Can humans force a return to a 'Cretaceous' climate? *Sedimentary Geology*, **235** (1-2), 5–26.

Haynes, S.J., Huber, B.T., and Macleod, K.G., 2015, Evolution and phylogeny of mid-Cretaceous (Albian–Coniacian) biserial planktic foraminifera. *Journal of Foraminiferal Research*, **45** (1), 42–81.

Houben, A.J.P., Quaijtaal, W., Wade, B.S., Schouten, S., and Brinkhuis, H., 2019, Organic-walled dinoflagellate cysts from the Eocene-Oligocene Transition in the Gulf of Mexico: indicators of climate- and sea-level change during the onset of Antarctic glaciation. *Newsletters on Stratigraphy*, **52** (2), 131–154.

Houston, R.M., and Huber, B.T., 1998, Evidence of photosymbiosis in fossil taxa? Ontogenetic stable isotope trends in some Late Cretaceous planktonic foraminifera. *Marine Micropaleontology*, **34** (1), 29–46.

Houston, R.M., Huber, B.T., and Spero, H.J., 1999, Size-related isotopic trends in some Maastrichtian planktic foraminifera: methodological comparisons, intraspecific variability, and evidence for photosymbiosis. *Marine Micropaleontology*, **36** (4), 169–188.

Huber, B.T., 1992, Paleobiogeography of Campanian-Maastrichtian foraminifera in the southern high latitudes. *Palaeogeography, Palaeoclimatology, Palaeoecology*, **92** (3–4), 325–360.

Huber, B.T., and Leckie, R.M., 2011, Planktic foraminiferal species turnover across deep-sea Aptian/Albian boundary sections. *Journal of Foraminiferal Research*, **41** (1), 53–95.

Huber, B.T., and Petrizzo, M.R., 2014, Evolution and taxonomic study of the Cretaceous planktic foraminiferal genus *Helvetoglobotruncana* Reiss, 1957. *Journal of Foraminiferal Research*, **44** (1), 40–57.

Huber, B.T., Hodell, D.A., and Hamilton, C.P., 1995, Middle–Late Cretaceous climate of the southern high latitudes: stable isotopic evidence for minimal equator-to-pole thermal gradients. *Geological Society of America Bulletin*, **107** (10), 1164–1191.

Huber, B.T., Norris, R.D., and MacLeod, K.G., 2002, Deep-sea paleotemperature record of extreme warmth during the Cretaceous. *Geology*, **30** (2), 123–126.

Huber, B.T., MacLeod, K.G., and Tur, N.A., 2008, Chronostratigraphic framework for upper Campanian-Maastrichtian sediments on the Blake Nose subtropical North Atlantic. *Journal of Foraminiferal Research*, **38** (2), 162–182.

Huber, B.T., Petrizzo, M.R., Young, J.R., Falzoni, F., Gilardoni, S.E., Bown, P.R., et al., 2016, Pforams@ mikrotax: A new online taxonomic database for planktonic foraminifera. *Micropaleontology*, **62** (6), 429–438.

Huber, B.T., Petrizzo, M.R., Watkins, D.K., Haynes, S.J., and MacLeod, K.G., 2017, Correlation of Turonian continental margin and deep-sea sequences in the subtropical Indian Ocean sediments by integrated planktonic foraminiferal and calcareous nannofossil biostratigraphy. *Newsletters in Stratigraphy*, **50**: 141–185.

Huber, B.T., MacLeod, K.G., Watkins, D.K., and Coffin, M.F., 2018, The rise and fall of the Cretaceous Hot Greenhouse climate. *Global and Planetary Change*, **167**: 1–23.

Hudson, W., Hart, M.B., and Smart, C.W., 2009, Palaeobiogeography of early planktonic foraminifera. *Bulletin de la Societé géologique de France*, **180** (1), 27–38.

Jenkins, D.G., 1965, Planktonic foraminiferal zones and new taxa from the Danian to Lower Miocene of New Zealand. *New Zealand Journal of Geology and Geophysics*, **8**: 1088–1126.

Jung, C., Voigt, S., Friedrich, O., Koch, M.C., and Frank, M., 2013, Campanian-Maastrichtian ocean circulation in the tropical Pacific. *Paleoceanography*, **28**: 562–573.

Kennedy, W.J., Gale, A.S., Bown, P.R., Caron, M., Davey, R.J., Gröcke, D., et al., 2000, Integrated stratigraphy across the Aptian-Albian boundary in the Marnes Bleues, at the Col de Pre-Guittard, Arnayon (Drome), and at Tartonne (Alpes-de-Haute-Provence), France: A candidate global boundary stratotype section and boundary point for the base of the Albian stage. *Cretaceous Research*, **21** (5), 591–720.

Kennedy, W.J., Gale, A.S., Huber, B.T., Petrizzo, M.R., Bown, P., Barchetta, A., et al., 2014, Integrated stratigraphy across the Aptian/Albian boundary at Col de Pré-Guittard (southeast France): A candidate global boundary stratotype section. *Cretaceous Research*, **51**: 248–259.

King, D.J., and Wade, B.S., 2017, The extinction of *Chiloguembelina cubensis* in the Pacific Ocean: implications for defining the base of the Chattian upper Oligocene. *Newsletters on Stratigraphy*, **50**: 311–339.

Kucera, M., 2007, Chapter six planktonic foraminifera as tracers of past oceanic environments. *Developments in Marine Geology*, **1**: 213–262.

Kuhry, B., 1971, Lower Cretaceous planktonic Foraminifera from the Miravetes, Argos, and Represa formations Southeastern Spain. *Revista Espanola de Micropaleontologıa*, **3** (3), 219–237.

Kuhry, B., 1972, Stratigraphy and micropaleontology of the Lower Cretaceous in the Subbetic south of Caravaca Province of Murcia, SE Spain. I and II. *Koninklijk Nederlands Akademie van Wetenschappen Proceedings, Series B*, **75**: 193–222.

Lamolda, M.A., Peryt, D., and Ion, J., 2007, Planktonic foraminiferal bioevents in the Coniacian/Santonian boundary interval at Olazagutia, Navarra province, Spain. *Cretaceous Research*, **28** (1), 18–29.

Larson, R.L., and Erba, E., 1999, Onset of the Mid-Cretaceous greenhouse in the Barremian-Aptian: Igneous events and the biological, sedimentary, and geochemical responses. *Paleoceanography*, **14** (6), 663–678.

Leckie, R.M., 1989, A paleoceanographic model for the early evolutionary history of planktonic foraminifera. *Palaeogeography, Palaeoclimatology, Palaeoecology*, **73** (1-2), 107–138.

Leckie, R.M., 2009, Seeking a better life in the plankton. *Proceedings of the National Academy of Sciences United States of America*, **106** (34), 14183–14184.

Leckie, R.M., Bralower, T.J., and Cashman, R., 2002, Oceanic anoxic events and plankton evolution: Biotic response to tectonic forcing during the mid-Cretaceous. *Paleoceanography*, **17** (3), 13-1.

Li, L., and Keller, G., 1999, Variability in Late Cretaceous climate and deep waters: evidence from stable isotopes. *Marine Geology*, **161** (2–4), 171–190.

Li, L., Keller, G., and Stinnesbeck, W., 1999, The Late Campanian and Maastrichtian in northwestern Tunisia: palaeoenvironmental inferences from lithology, macrofauna and benthic foraminifera. *Cretaceous Research*, **20** (2), 231–252.

Linnert, C., Robinson, S., Lees, J., Bown, P., Pérez-Rodríguez, I., Petrizzo, M.R., et al., 2014, Evidence for global cooling in the Late Cretaceous. *Nature Communications*, **5**: 4194.

Linnert, C., Robinson, S.A., Lees, J.A., Pérez-Rodríguez, I., Jenkyns, H. C., Petrizzo, M.R., et al., 2018, Did Late Cretaceous cooling trigger the Campanian–Maastrichtian Boundary Event? *Newsletters on Stratigraphy*, **51** (2), 145–166.

Lipson-Benitah, S., 1980, Albian to Coniacian zonation of the western coastal plain of Israel. *Cretaceous Research*, **1** (1), 3–12.

Lipson-Benitah, S., 2008, Phylogeny of the Middle Cretaceous (late Albian-late Cenomanian) planktonic foraminiferal genera *Parathalmanninella* nov. gen. and *Thalmanninella*. *Journal of Foraminiferal Research*, **38** (2), 183–189.

Lipson-Benitah, S., and Almogi-Labin, A., 2001, A revision of the Albian planktonic foraminifera *Biticinella breggiensis* (Gandolfi, 1942) with emphasis on its apertural system. *Revue de Paléobiologie*, **20** (1), 235–243.

Lipson-Benitah, S., and Almogi-Labin, A., 2004, Aptian planktonic foraminifera from Israel. *Israel Journal of Earth Sciences*, **53** (1), 27–46.

Longoria, J.F., 1974, Stratigraphic, morphologic and taxonomic studies of Aptian planktonic foraminifera. *Revista Espanola de Micropaleontologìa. Numero Extraordinario*, 1–150.

Longoria, J.F., 1977, Bioestratigrafıa del Cretàcico Inferior basada en microfòsiles planctònicos. *Boletìn de la Sociedad Geològica Mexicana*, **38** (1), 2–17.

Luciani, V., D'Onofrio, R., Dickens, G.R., and Wade, B.S., 2017, Planktic foraminiferal response to early Eocene carbon cycle perturbations in the southeast Atlantic Ocean (ODP Site 1263). *Global and Planetary Change*, **158**: 119–133.

Luterbacher, H.P., and Premoli Silva, L., 1964, Biostratigrafia del limite Cretaceo–Terziario nel'Appennino centrale. *Rivista Italiana di Paleontologia e Stratigrafia*, **70**: 631–730.

MacLeod, K.G., Huber, B.T., Ward, P.D., 1996, The biostratigraphy and paleobiogeography of Maastrichtian inoceramids. In The Cretaceous-Tertiary event and other catastrophes in Earth history. In: Ryder, G., Fastovsky D.E., and Gartner, S., (Eds.), *The Cretaceous-Tertiary Event and Other Catastrophes n Earth History*, Geological Society of America Special Paper, 307: 361–373.

MacLeod, K.G., Londoño, C.I., Martin, E.E., Berrocoso, Á.J., and Basak, C., 2011, Changes in North Atlantic circulation at the end of the Cretaceous greenhouse interval. *Nature Geoscience*, **4** (11), 779.

Masters, B.A., 1977, Mesozoic planktonic foraminifera. A world-wide review and analysis. *Oceanic Micropaleontology*, **1**: 301–731.

Masters, B.A., 1980, Reevaluation of selected types of Ehrenberg's Cretaceous planktic foraminifera. *Eclogae Geologicae Helvetiae*, **73**: 95–107.

Molina, E., Alegret, L., Arenillas, I., Arz, J.A., Gallala, N., Grajales-Nishimura, J.M., et al., 2009, The Global Boundary Stratotype Section and Point for the base of the Danian Stage (Paleocene, Paleogene, "Tertiary", Cenozoic): auxiliary sections and correlation. *Episodes*, **32** (2), 84.

Moullade, M., 1966, Etude stratigraphique et micropaléontologique du Crétacé inférieur de la « Fosse Vocontienne ». *Documents des Laboratoires de Géologie de Lyon*, **15**: 1–369.

Moullade, M., 1974, Zones de Foraminiféres du Crétacé inférieur éogeen. *Comptes rendus de l'Académie des Sciences de Paris (D)*, **278**: 1813–1816.

Moullade, M., Bellier, J.P., and Tronchetti, G., 2002, Hierarchy of criteria, evolutionary processes and taxonomic simplification in the classification of Lower Cretaceous planktonic foraminifera. *Cretaceous Research*, **23** (1), 111–148.

Moullade, M., Tronchetti, G., and Bellier, J.P., 2005, The Gargasian (Middle Aptian) strata from Cassis-La Bédoule (Lower Aptian historical stratotype, SE France): planktonic and benthic foraminiferal assemblages and biostratigraphy. *Carnets de Geologie*, Article 2005/2 (CG2005 A02): 1–20.

Neagu, T., 1975, Monographie de la faune des Foraminiféres éo crétacés du couloir de la Dimbovicioara, de Codlea et des Monts Persani Couches de Carhaga. *Memorii Institutul de Geologie si Geofizica. Bucaresti*, **25**: 1–141.

Nederbragt, A.J., 1990, *Biostratigraphy and paleoceanographic potential of the Cretaceous planktic foraminifera Heterohelicidae* (Doctoral dissertation, Centrale Huisdrukkerij Vrije Universiteit).

Norris, R.D., 1991, Parallel evolution in the keel structure of planktonic foraminifera. *Journal of Foraminiferal Research*, **21**: 319–331.

O'Brien, C.L., Robinson, S.A., Pancost, R.D., Sinninghe Damsté, J.S., Schouten, S., Lunt, D.J., et al., 2017, Cretaceous sea-surface temperature evolution: Constraints from TEX86 and planktonic foraminiferal oxygen isotopes. *Earth-Science Reviews*, **172**: 224–247.

Okafor, C.U., Thomas, D.J., Wade, B.S., and Firth, J., 2009, Environmental change in the subtropics during the late middle Eocene greenhouse and global implications. *Geochemistry, Geophysics, Geosystems*, **10**: Q07003, https://doi.org/10.1029/2009GC002450.

Olsson, R.K., 1964, *Praeorbulina* Olsson, a new foraminiferal genus. *Journal of Paleontology*, **4**: 770–771.

Olsson, R.K., Hemleben, C.H., Berggren, W.A., and Huber, B.T., 1999, Atlas of Paleocene planktonic foraminifera. *Smithsonian Contributions to Paleobiology*, **(n. 85)**, 252.

Omana, L., Gonzales-Arreola, C., and Nunez-Useche, F., 2017, The Berriasian-Valanginian boundary interval based in calpionellids from the Taraises Formation, Cuencame de Ceniceros, Durango, NW Mexico: biostratigraphic, paleoecologic and paleobiogeographic significance. *Journal of South America Earth Sciences*, **80**: 589–600.

Pearson, P.N., and Wade, B.S., 2009, Taxonomy and stable isotope paleoecology of well-preserved planktonic foraminifera from the uppermost Oligocene of Trinidad. *Journal of Foraminiferal Research*, **39** (3), 191–217.

Pearson, P.N., and Wade, B.S., 2015, *Systematic taxonomy of exceptionally well-preserved planktonic foraminifera from the Eocene/ Oligocene boundary of Tanzania*. Cushman Foundation for Foraminiferal Research Special Publication, No. **45**: 1–85.

Pérez-Rodríguez, I., Lees, J.A., Larrasoaña, J.C., Arz, J.A., and Arenillas, I., 2012, Planktonic foraminiferal and calcareous nannofossil biostratigraphy and magnetostratigraphy of the uppermost Campanian and Maastrichtian at Zumaia, northern Spain. *Cretaceous Research*, **37**: 100–126.

Peryt, D., 1980, Planktic foraminifera zonation of the Upper Cretaceous in the Middle Vistula river Valley, Poland. *Palaeontologia Polonica*, **41**: 3–101.

Pessagno, E.A., 1967, Upper Cretaceous planktonic foraminifera from the western Gulf Coastal Plain. *Palaeontographica Americana*, **5**: 245–445.

Petrizzo, M.R., 2000, Upper Turonian–lower Campanian planktonic foraminifera from southern mid–high latitudes (Exmouth Plateau, NW Australia): biostratigraphy and taxonomic notes. *Cretaceous Research*, **21** (4), 479–505.

Petrizzo, M.R., 2001, Late Cretaceous planktonic foraminifera from Kerguelen Plateau (ODP Leg 183): new data to improve the Southern Ocean biozonation. *Cretaceous Research*, **22** (6), 829–855.

Petrizzo, M.R., 2002, Palaeoceanographic and palaeoclimatic inferences from Late Cretaceous planktonic foraminiferal assemblages from the Exmouth Plateau ODP Sites 762 and 763, eastern Indian Ocean. *Marine Micropaleontology*, **45** (2), 117–150.

Petrizzo, M.R., 2003, Late Cretaceous planktonic foraminiferal bioevents in the Tethys and in the Southern Ocean record: an overview. *Journal of Foraminiferal Research*, **33** (4), 330–337.

Petrizzo, M.R., 2019, A critical evaluation of planktonic foraminiferal biostratigraphy across the Coniacian-Santonian boundary interval in Spain, Texas, and Tanzania. *In* Denne, R.A., and Kahn, A. (eds), *Geologic Problem Solving with Microfossils* IV. *SEPM Special Publication,* **111**: 186–198, http://doi.org/10.2110/sepmsp.111.04.

Petrizzo, M.R., and Huber, B.T., 2006a, Biostratigraphy and taxonomy of late Albian planktonic foraminifera from ODP Leg 171B western North Atlantic Ocean. *Journal of Foraminiferal Research*, **36** (2), 166–190.

Petrizzo, M.R., and Huber, B.T., 2006b, On the phylogeny of the late Albian genus Planomalina. *The Journal of Foraminiferal Research*, **36** (3), 233–240.

Petrizzo, M.R., Huber, B.T., Wilson, P.A., and MacLeod, K.G., 2008, Late Albian paleoceanography of the western subtropical North Atlantic. *Paleoceanography*, **23**, article #PA1213, 17 pp. https://doi.org/10.1029/ 2007PA001517.

Petrizzo, M.R., Falzoni, F., and Premoli Silva, I., 2011, Identification of the base of the lower-to-middle Campanian *Globotruncana ventricosa* Zone: comments on reliability and global correlations. *Cretaceous Research*, **32** (3), 387–405.

Petrizzo, M.R., Huber, B.T., Gale, A.S., Barchetta, A., and Jenkyns, H. C., 2012, Abrupt planktic foraminiferal turnover across the Niveau Kilian at Col de Pré-Guittard (Vocontian Basin, southeast France): new criteria for defining the Aptian/Albian boundary. *Newsletters on Stratigraphy*, **45** (1), 55–74.

Petrizzo, M.R., Huber, B.T., Gale, A.S., Barchetta, A., and Jenkyns, H. C., 2013, Erratum. Abrupt planktic foraminiferal turnover across the Niveau Kilian at Col de Pré-Guittard (Vocontian Basin, southeast France): new criteria for defining the Aptian/Albian boundary. *Newsletters on Stratigraphy*, **46** (1), 93.

Petrizzo, M.R., Caron, M., and Premoli Silva, I., 2015, Remarks on the identification of the Albian/Cenomanian boundary and taxonomic clarification of the planktonic foraminifera index species *globotruncanoides, brotzeni* and *tehamaensis*. *Geological Magazine*, **152** (3), 521–536.

Petrizzo, M.R., Jiménez Berrocoso, Á., Falzoni, F., Huber, B.T., and Macleod, K.G., 2017, The Coniacian–Santonian sedimentary record in southern Tanzania (Ruvuma Basin, East Africa): Planktonic foraminiferal evolutionary, geochemical and palaeoceanographic patterns. *Sedimentology*, **64** (1), 252–285.

Pflaumann, U., and Cepek, P., 1982, Cretaceous foraminiferal and nannoplankton biostratigraphy and paleoecology along the West African continental margin. *In* Rad, Uv, Hinz, K., Sarnthein, M., and Seibold, E. (eds), *Geology of Northwestern African Continental Margin*. Springer Publ, 309–353.

Poole, C.R., and Wade, B.S., 2019, Systematic taxonomy of the *Trilobatus sacculifer* plexus and descendant *Globigerinoidesella fistulosa* (planktonic foraminifera). *Journal of Systematic Palaeontology*, 17 (23): 1989–2030. https://doi.org/10.1080/14772019.2019.1578831.

Premoli Silva, I., and Sliter, W.V., 1995, Cretaceous planktonic foraminiferal biostratigraphy and evolutionary trends from the Bottaccione section, Gubbio, Italy. *Palaeontographia Italica*, **82**: 1–89.

Premoli Silva, I., Sliter, W.V., 1999. Cretaceous paleoceanography: evidence from planktonic foraminiferal evolution. *In* Barrera, E., and Johnson, C.C., (eds), *Evolution of the Cretaceous Ocean-Climate System*, Special Papers-Geological Society of America, **332**: 301–328.

Premoli Silva, I., Erba, E., Salvini, G., Locatelli, C., and Verga, D., 1999, Biotic changes in Cretaceous oceanic anoxic events of the Tethys. *Journal of Foraminiferal Research*, **29** (4), 352–370.

Premoli Silva, I., Wade, B.S., and Pearson, P.N., 2006, Taxonomy of *Globigerinatheka* and *Orbulinoides*. *In* Pearson, P.N., Olsson, R.K., Huber, B.T., Hemleben, C., and Berggren, W.A. (eds), Atlas of Eocene Planktonic Foraminifera. *Cushman Foundation Special Publication*, **41**: 169–212.

Premoli Silva, I., Caron, M., Leckie, R.M., Petrizzo, M.R., Soldan, D., and Verga, D., 2009, *Paraticinella* n. gen. and taxonomic revision of *Ticinella bejaouaensis* Sigal, 1966. *Journal of Foraminiferal Research*, **39** (2), 126–137.

Premoli Silva, I., Soldan, D.M., and Petrizzo, M.R., 2018, Upper Hauterivian-upper Barremian planktonic foraminiferal assemblages from the Arroyo Gilico section (Southern Spain). *Journal of Foraminiferal Research*, **48** (4), 314–355.

Quillévéré, F., Norris, R.D., 2003. Ecological development of acarininids (planktonic foraminifera) and hydrographic evolution of Paleocene surface waters. In: Wing, S.L., Gingerich, P.D., Schmitz, B., and Thomas, E. (Eds.), *Causes and Consequences of Globally Warm Climates in the Early Paleogene*, Special Papers-Geological Society of America, **369**: 223–238.

Robaszynski, F., and Caron, M.C., 1979, Atlas of mid-Cretaceous planktonic foraminifera (Boreal Sea and Tethys). *Cahiers de Micropaléontologie*, **1**: 1–185.

Robaszynski, F., and Caron, M., 1995, Foraminiferes planctoniques du Cretace; commentaire de la zonation Europe-Mediterranee. *Bulletin de la Société géologique de France*, **166** (6), 681–692.

Robaszynski, F., Caron, M., Gonzalez Donoso, J.M., Wonders, A.H., and The European working group on Planktonic Foraminifera, 1984, Atlas of Late Cretaceous globotruncanids. *Revue de Micropaléontologie*, **26**: 145–305.

Robaszynski, F., Caron, M., Dupuis, C., Amédro, F., Gonzalez-Donoso, J.M., Linares, D., et al., 1990, A tentative integrated stratigraphy in the Turonian of Central Tunisia: formations, zones and sequential stratigraphy in the Kalaat Senan area. *Bulletin des Centres de Recherches Exploration-Production Elf Aquitaine*, **14**: 213–384.

Robaszynski, F., Gonzalez Donoso, J.M., Linares, D., Amédro, F., Caron, M., Dupuis, C., et al., 2000, Le Crétacé supérieur de la région de Kalaat Senan, Tunisie Centrale. Litho-biostratigraphie intégrée: zones d'ammonites, de foraminifères planctoniques et de nannofossiles du Turonien supérieur au Maastrichtien. *Bulletin des Centres de Recherche et d'Exploration-Production d'Elf-Aquitaine*, **22**: 359–490.

Robinson, S.A., Murphy, D.P., Vance, D., and Thomas, D.J., 2010, Formation of "southern component water" in the Late Cretaceous: evidence from Nd-isotopes. *Geology*, **38** (10), 871–874.

Salaj, J., 1980. Microbiostratigraphie du Crétacé et du Paléogéne de la Tunisie septentrionale et orientale (Hypostratotypes tunisiens). *Geologicky Ustav Dionyza Stura*, 1-238. Slovenskej Akadémie vied v Bratislave.

Salaj, J., 1984, Foraminifers and detailed microbiostratigraphy of the boundary beds of the Lower Cretaceous stages in the Tunisian Atlas. *Geologicky Zbornik*, **35**: 583–599.

Sari, B., Yildiz, A., Korkmaz, T., and Petrizzo, M.R., 2016, Planktonic foraminifera and calcareous nannofossils record in the upper Campanian-Maastrichtian pelagic deposits of the Malatya Basin in the Hekimhan area (NW Malatya, eastern Anatolia). *Cretaceous Research*, **61**: 91–107.

Sierro, F.J., Flores, J.A., Civis, J., Gonzalez Delgado, J.A., and Frances, G., 1993, Late Miocene globorotaliid event-stratigraphy and biogeography in the NE-Atlantic and Mediterranean. *Marine Micropaleontology*, **21**: 143–168.

Sigal, J., 1977, Essai de zonation du Crétacé méditerranéen à l'aide des foraminiféres planctoniques. *Géologie Méditerranéenne*, **4** (2), 99–108.

Sigal, J., 1979, Chronostratigraphy and ecostratigraphy of Cretaceous formations recovered on DSDP Leg 47B, Site 398, (2). *In* Sibuet, J.-C., Ryan, W.B.F., et al., (eds), Initial Reports of Deep Sea Drilling Project. *Washington: U.S. Government Printing Office*, **47**: pp. 287–326.

Smit, J., 1982. Extinction and evolution of planktonic foraminifera at the Cretaceous/Tertiary boundary after a major impact. In: *Geological Implications of Impacts of Large Asteroids and Comets on the Earth: Geological Society of America Special Paper*, **190**: 329–352.

Spezzaferri, S., and Spiegler, D., 2005, Fossil planktic foraminifera (an overview). *Palaeontogische Zeitschrift*, **79**: 149–166.

Spezzaferri, S., Kucera, M., Pearson, P.N., Wade, B.S., Rappo, S., Poole, C.R., et al., 2015, Fossil and genetic evidence for the polyphyletic nature of the planktonic foraminifera "*Globigerinoides*", and description of the new genus *Trilobatus*. *PLoS One*, **10** (5), e0128108, https://doi.org/10.1371/journal.pone.0128108.

Thibault, N., Harlou, R., Schovsbo, N., Schiøler, P., Minoletti, F., Galbrun, B., et al., 2012, Upper Campanian–Maastrichtian nannofossil biostratigraphy and high-resolution carbon-isotope stratigraphy of the Danish Basin: towards a standard $\delta^{13}C$ curve for the Boreal Realm. *Cretaceous Research*, **33** (1), 72–90.

Tornaghi, M.E., Premoli Silva, I., and Ripepe, M., 1989, Lithostratigraphy and planktonic foraminiferal biostratigraphy of the Aptian–Albian "Scisti a Fucoidi" in the Piobbico core, Marche, Italy: background for cyclostratigraphy. *Rivista Italiana di Paleontologia e Stratigrafia*, **95**: 223–264.

Tur, N.A., Smirnov, J.P., and Huber, B.T., 2001, Late Albian–Coniacian planktic foraminifera and biostratigraphy of the northeastern Caucasus. *Cretaceous Research*, **22**: 719–734.

Verga, D., and Premoli Silva, I., 2002, Early Cretaceous planktonic foraminifera from the Tethys: the genus *Leupoldina*. *Cretaceous Research*, **23**: 189–212.

Verga, D., and Premoli Silva, I., 2003a, Early Cretaceous planktonic foraminifera from the Tethys. The small-sized representatives of the genus *Globigerinelloides*. *Cretaceous Research*, **24**: 305–334.

Verga, D., and Premoli Silva, I., 2003b, Early Cretaceous planktonic foraminifera from the Tethys. The large, many-chambered representatives of the genus *Globigerinelloides*. *Cretaceous Research*, **24**: 661–690.

Verga, D., and Premoli Silva, I., 2005, Early Cretaceous planktonic foraminifera from the Tethys: the Upper Aptian, planispiral morphotypes with elongate chambers. *Cretaceous Research*, **26**: 239–259.

Voigt, S., Gale, A.S., Jung, C., and Jenkyns, H.C., 2012, Global correlation of Upper Campanian–Maastrichtian successions using carbon-isotope strati-graphy: development of a new Maastrichtian timescale. *Newsletters on Stratigraphy*, **45** (1), 25–53.

Wade, B.S., 2004, Planktonic foraminiferal biostratigraphy and mechanisms in the extinction of *Morozovella* in the late Middle Eocene. *Marine Micropaleontology*, **51**: 23–38.

Wade, B.S., and Pearson, P.N., 2008, Planktonic foraminiferal turnover, diversity fluctuations and geochemical signals across the Eocene/Oligocene boundary in Tanzania. *Marine Micropaleontology*, **68**: 244–255.

Wade, B.S., Pearson, P.N., Berggren, W.A., and Pälike, H., 2011, Review and revision of Cenozoic tropical planktonic foraminiferal biostratigraphy and calibration to the geomagnetic polarity and astronomical time scale. *Earth Science Reviews*, **104**: 111–142.

Wade, B.S., Premec-Fucek, V., Kamikuri, S., Bartol, M., Luciani, V., and Pearson, P.N., 2012, Successive extinctions of muricate planktonic foraminifera (*Morozovelloides* and *Acarinina*) mark the base Priabonian. *Newsletters on Stratigraphy*, **45**: 245–262.

Wade, B.S., Pearson, P.N., Olsson, R.K., Premoli Silva, I., Berggren, W.A., Spezzaferri, S., et al., 2018, Taxonomy, biostratigraphy, phylogeny, and diversity of Oligocene and early Miocene planktonic foraminifera. *In* Wade, B.S., Olsson, R.K., Pearson, P.N., Huber, B.T., and Berggren, W.A. (eds), Atlas of Oligocene Planktonic Foraminifera. *Cushman Foundation of Foraminiferal Research, Special Publication,* **No. 46**: 11–28.

Walaszczyk, I., Wood, C.J., Lees, J.A., Peryt, D., Voigt, S., and Wiese, F., 2010, The Salzgitter-Salder quarry (Lower Saxony, Germany) and Słupia Nadbrzeżna river cliff section (Central Poland): a proposed candidate composite global boundary stratotype section and point for the Coniacian stage (upper Cretaceous). *Acta Geologica Polonica*, **60** (4), 445–477.

Weidich, K.F., 1990, Die kalkalpine Unterkreide und ihre Foraminiferen fauna. *Zitteliana*, **17**: 1–312.

Wernli, R., 1988, Les protoglobigerines (foraminifers) du Toarcien et de L'Aalenien du Domuz Dag (Taurus Occidental, Turquie). *Eclogae Geologicae Helvetiae*, **81** (3), 661–668.

Wernli, R., 1995, Les foraminiféres globigériniformes (Oberhauserellidae) du Toarcien inférieur de Teysachaux (Préalpes médianes), Fribourg, Suisse. *Revue de Paléobiologie*, **14**: 257–269.

Wernli, R., and Görög, Á., 2007, Protoglobigérines et Oberhauserellidae (Foraminifères) du Bajocien-Bathonien du Jura méridional, France. *Revue de Micropaléontologie*, **50** (2), 185–205.

Wernli, R., Ascoli, P., and Williams, G.L., 1995, *Favusella hoterivica* (Subbotina) from the Berriasian and Valanginian of offshore Eastern Canada. *Revue de Paléobiologie*, **14** (2), 379–398.

Wilson, P.A., Norris, R.D., and Cooper, M.J., 2002, Testing the Cretaceous greenhouse hypothesis using glassy foraminiferal calcite from the core of the Turonian tropics on Demerara Rise. *Geology*, **30** (7), 607–610.

Wonders, A.A.H., 1980. *Middle and Late Cretaceous planktonic foraminifera of the western Mediterranean area* (Doctoral dissertation, Utrecht University).

Zachos, J.C., Quinn, T.M., and Salamy, K.A., 1996, High-resolution (10^4 years) deep-sea foraminiferal stable isotope records of the Eocene-Oligocene climate transition. *Paleoceanography*, **11**: 251–266.

Zeebe, R.E., 2001, Seawater pH and isotopic paleotemperatures of Cretaceous oceans. *Palaeogeography, Palaeoclimatology, Palaeoecology*, **170** (1-2), 49–57.

Subchapter 3H

Larger benthic foraminifera

M.D. Simmons with a contribution by M. Aretz

Abstract

Larger benthic foraminifera are an informal group of protists, grouped together because of their relatively large size and complex internal structure, requiring study using thin-sections. They have a rich geologic history that extends from the Carboniferous to the recent. The group has long-proven biostratigraphic value for local and regional correlation, despite uncertainties in their taxonomy, stratigraphic ranges of species, calibration of these ranges against chronostratigraphic standards, and provincialism and endemism. During the Carboniferous and Permian, large fusulinid foraminifera are dominant but disappeared with the end-Permian extinction event. The Triassic is relatively impoverished in larger benthic foraminifera, although the involutinids, which first appear during this period, represent a distinctive and biostratigraphically useful group. Jurassic assemblages are dominated by large and complex textulariids that show repeated trends toward increasing morphological complexity and larger size with time. These textulariids diversified in the Early Cretaceous, with, for example, the appearance of the biostratigraphically important orbitolinids. Alveolinids, a group of globular to fusiform larger miliolids, are common and diverse in mid-Cretaceous shallow marine carbonates. Other large miliolids such as the rhapydioninids appeared in the Late Cretaceous alongside the first large rotaliid orbitoid foraminifera. Recovery from the end-Cretaceous extinction event was slow, but by the Late Paleocene, large rotaliids, such as nummulitids and discocyclinids, were abundant in tropical seas along with a resurgence of the alveolinids. In Tethys the larger benthic foraminifera reached an acme of abundance and diversity during the Middle Eocene, including some of the largest known forms. Large textulariids, such as the dictyoconids, are also present in the Paleogene but, along with the nummulitids, are of reduced importance after the end of the Eocene. Neogene assemblages are dominated by a variety of large miliolids such as the soritids and by rotaliids (including the stratigraphically useful miogypsinids and lepidocyclinids during the Miocene).

3H.1 Introduction

Larger benthic foraminifera (LBF) are an informal taxonomic group of protists. They are characterized by their comparatively large size (often fusiform, planispiral or discoidal in shape), complex internal structures, and high internal-surface-area-to-volume ratios (Fig. 3H.1). These structures represent functional morphological adaptations to the culture of algal and diatom photosymbionts (e.g., Hohenegger, 2011). This presence of photosymbionts restricts LBF to photic zone depths (Fig. 3H.2). They are useful paleoenvironmental indicators, especially within warm water, shallow marine, oligotrophic, carbonate shelves (Langer and Hottinger, 2000), where they can occur in rock-forming quantities (Fig. 3H.1).

The LBF are an extremely morphologically diverse group (Fig. 3H.1). The composition of the test wall and its structure can vary, along with which there can be many variations in coiling mode and subdivision of the chambers into chamberlets by a variety of architectural elements. Of particular taxonomic importance are the size and shape of the first chamber (proloculus) and the growth pattern of the second chamber (deuteroloculus) and subsequent chambers. Hottinger (2006) and BouDagher-Fadel (2018) describe the great variety of morphological elements of the LBF and their likely function.

During the 350-million-year evolutionary history of the LBF, many morphological features have shown convergent evolutionary trends. Identical gross morphologies and structures have appeared repeatedly within the same lineage or in parallel lineages from different stocks, for example, the fusiform test morphology in the fusulines and alveolinids. LBF thrive on tropical carbonate shelves in the Cenozoic (Beavington-Penney and Racey, 2004) and Mesozoic but are known from cool-water tropical settings in the Late Paleozoic (Davydov, 2014). Provincialism and endemism are typical of most LBF taxonomic groups.

Many LBF taxonomic groups are useful for biostratigraphic studies in late Paleozoic, Mesozoic, and Cenozoic sedimentary basins (Fig. 3H.3). However, their accurate identification requires study in thin-section (ideally multiple sections through different orientations), with many species defined by morphometrics. Furthermore, because they rarely occur in association with planktonic fossils, the calibration of the stratigraphic ranges of LBF species to standard biozonation schemes and subsequent chronostratigraphic calibration can be challenging (Adams, 1984). Possible techniques to resolve this are calibration via strontium isotope stratigraphy in suitable sediments (e.g., Frijia et al., 2015), or studies targeting fore-reef facies where LBF and planktonic microfossils may cooccur (e.g., van Gorsel et al., 2014).

3H.2 Key groups of larger benthic foraminifera

The suprageneric classification of foraminiferids remains in a state of flux (see, e.g., Vachard, 2016 and references therein for discussion). Therefore herein we simply highlight the main

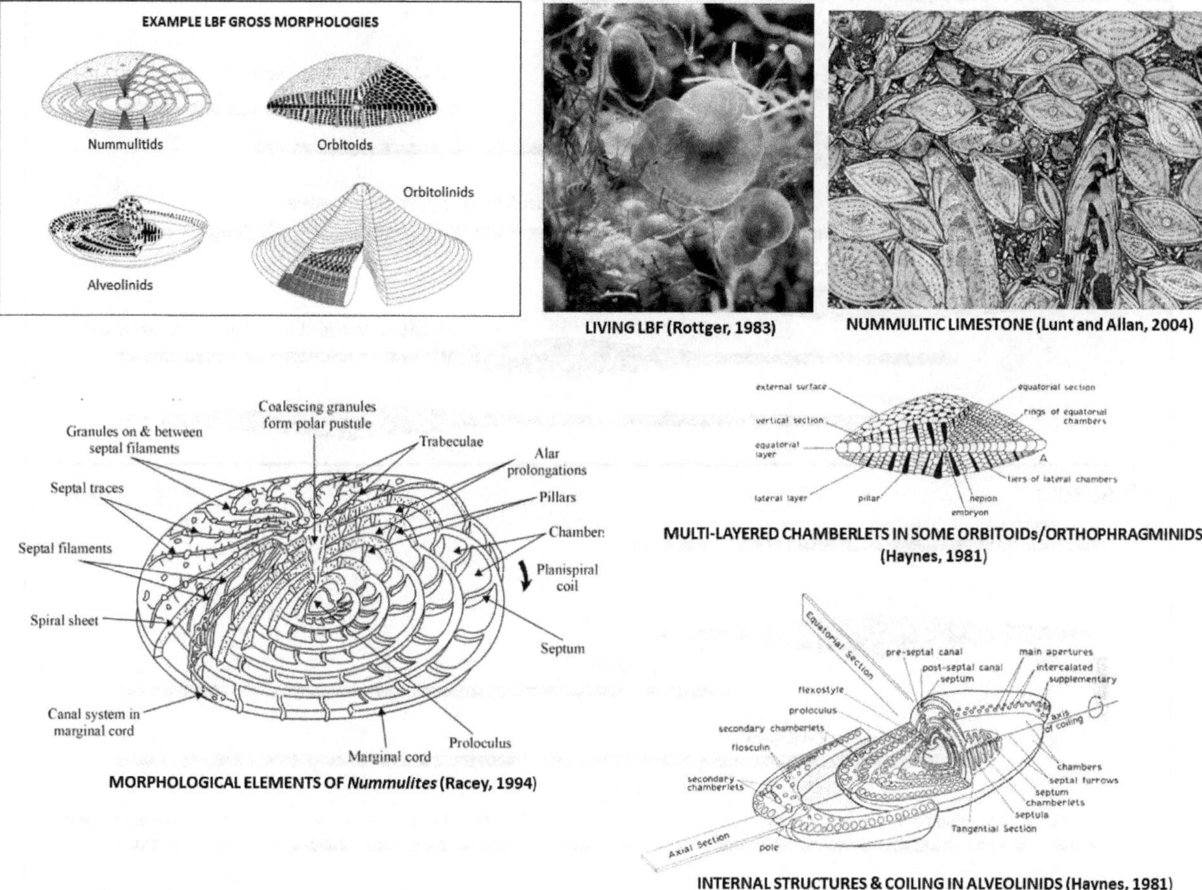

FIGURE 3H.1 Examples of typical external morphologies of Larger Benthic Foraminifers (LBF) and the complexity of their internal morphology. Figures are reproduced courtesy of Wyn Hughes, Peter Lunt, Andy Racey, and Rudolf Röttger.

broad higher groups of foraminifera, based on wall structure, that include LBF.

3H.2.1 Textulariids

The textulariids include LBF with a test wall composed of detrital particles held together by a calcareous cement, although the test wall often appears to be microgranular as opposed to displaying clear agglutinated grains (Banner et al., 1991). A number of those are large enough and complex enough internally to qualify as LBF. Typical features can include an alveolar wall and chamber partitions. Examples of the morphological complexity achieved by textulariid LBF are those with a conical, orbitoliniform shape, mostly occurring within the Cretaceous–Oligocene (e.g., *Orbitolina*, *Dictyoconus*), although Middle Jurassic isomorphs also exist. These typically have a wide conical shape, with an apical proloculus, followed by a series of trochospiral chambers, subdivided by radial septulae into chamberlets, which can host further morphological elements. Other textulariid LBF include lituolids, which include those with planispiral or streptospiral tests (e.g., *Alveosepta* or *Spirocyclina*). Trochospiral forms (e.g., *Kurnubia*) and multiserial forms (e.g., *Chrysalidina*) of textulariid LBF are common.

3H.2.2 Fusulinids

The fusulinids include LBF with a calcareous microgranular perforate test wall. Typical LBF within this order comprise the larger fusulinids of the Carboniferous–Permian (e.g., *Fusulina, Schwagerina*, and *Neoschwagerina*), extensively referred to in Chapter 23, The Carboniferous Period, and Chapter 24, The Permian Period (this book). A typical fusulinid test has planispiral chambers, which are strongly elongated along the coiling axis (the name of the group is derived from the Latin *fusus*, meaning spindle). They display a progressively more complex internal structure with time, with folded septa and secretion of chomata connecting the mid-floor of each chamber. Early forms have a simple wall structure but from the

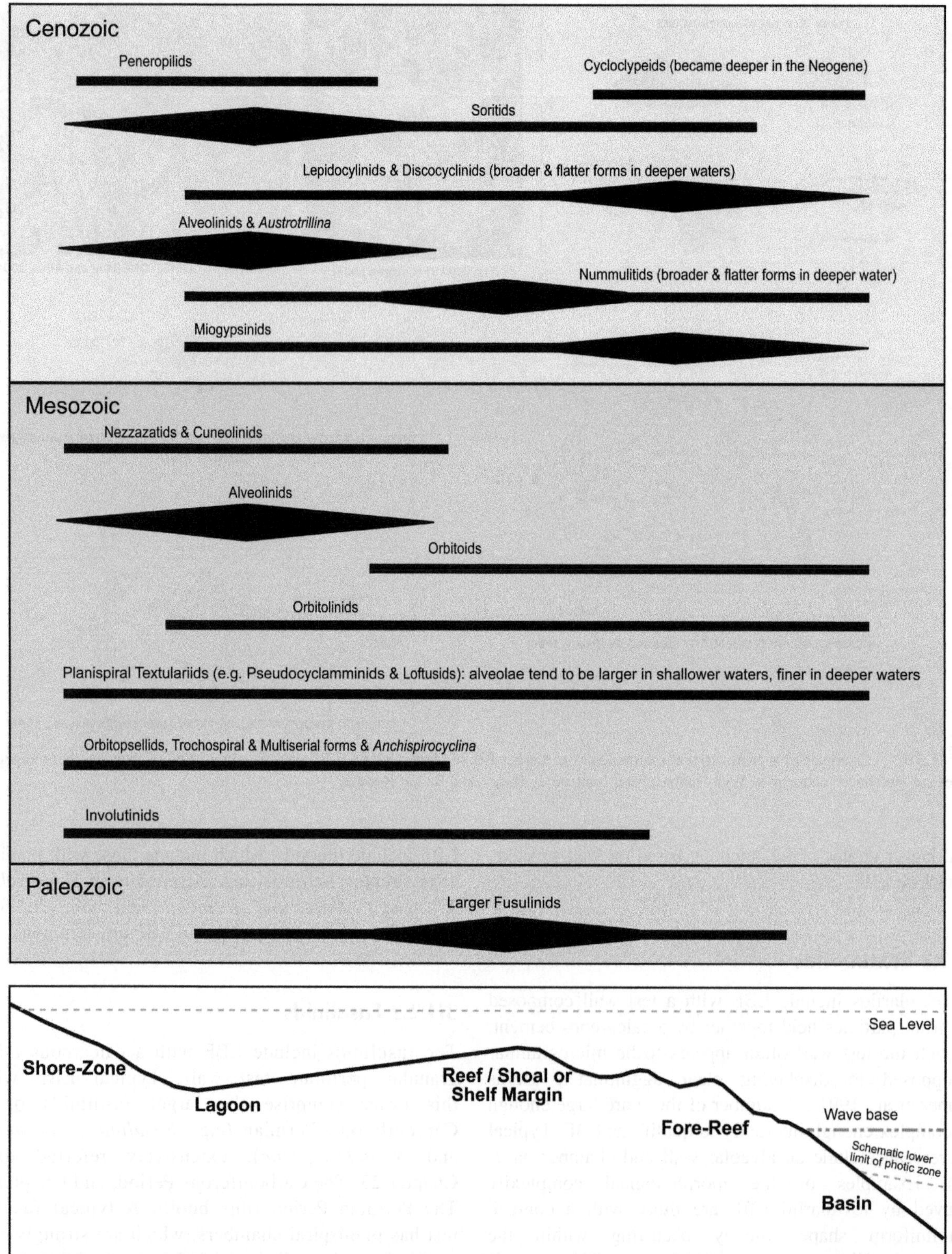

FIGURE 3H.2 Highly generalized lateral distribution of major informal Larger Benthic Foraminifers (LBF) groups across a schematic back-reef/lagoon–reef/shoal–fore-reef transect. The detailed distribution of individual genera and species is difficult to visualize in this format due to the strong influences of other environmental factors that affect distribution such as hydrodynamic energy, water clarity/turbidity, light penetration/intensity, symbiont-type, temperature, and nutrient and oxygen levels.

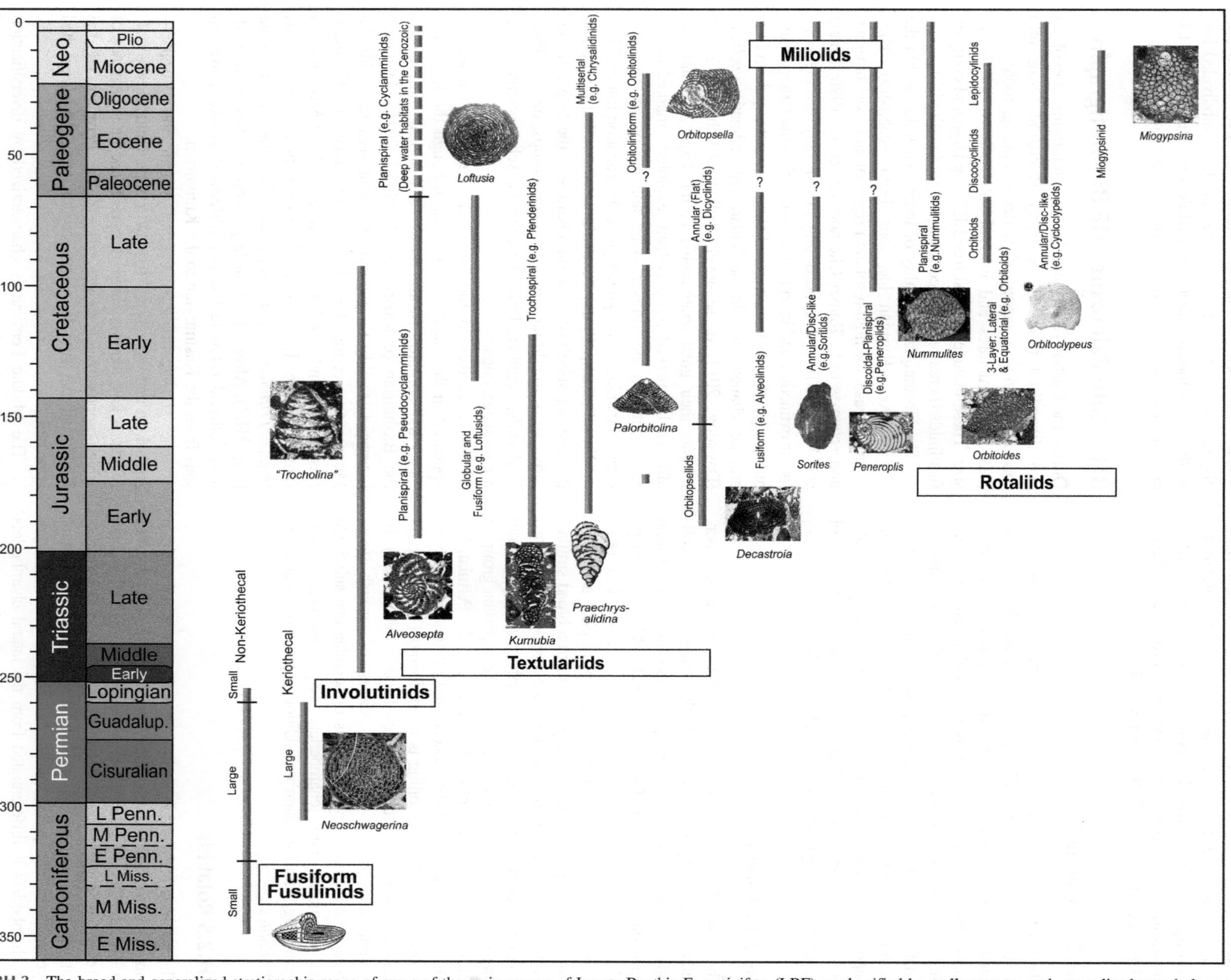

FIGURE 3H.3 The broad and generalized stratigraphic range of some of the main groups of Larger Benthic Foraminifers (LBF) as classified by wall structure and generalized morphology. Genera shown are examples and do not range throughout the time-intervals of the relevant group. Examples of typical external morphologies of LBF and the complexity of their internal morphology. Some images of LBF are reproduced courtesy of Wyn Hughes, Peter Lunt, and The Natural History Museum, London.

Kasimovian to the Middle Permian forms with a keriothecal (alveolar) wall are common. The larger fusulinds became extinct at the end of the Permian, although some relatively small related forms with a fusulinid wall structure survived into the Triassic (Groves and Altiner, 2005) and possibly later.

3H.2.3 Involutinids

The involutinids consist of a group of calcareous foraminifera with perforate, radiate walls that were originally aragonite, usually recrystallized to a microgranular calcite structure. A proloculus is usually followed by an enrolled tubular second chamber (e.g., *Trocholina*, *Involutina*). Although many are small and simple, they typically require identification in thin-section and consequently are often treated as LBF. They are important biostratigraphically in Cenomanian and older strata, especially in the Triassic. Important taxonomic revisions of this group are ongoing (e.g., Rigaud et al., 2013).

3H.2.4 Miliolids

The miliolids include LBF with imperforate calcareous porcellanous tests. Typical LBF within this order are the alveolinids that evolved in the Early Cretaceous and became common in the mid-Cretaceous and Paleogene (e.g., *Alveolina* and *Praealveolina*). Some taxa are extant (e.g., *Borelis*). Coiling is fusiform to ovate planispiral and often elongated along the coiling axis, giving them a broad similarity to the large fusulinds. Perforate septa subdivide the test interior into chambers, which are further subdivided into chamberlets in one or more rows. Another important group of miliolid LBF are the soritids that evolved in the Permian but are not abundant until the Eocene and occur abundantly in modern tropical seas. Coiling is often discoidal or planispiral further modified to cyclical, fan-shaped (flabelliform) or straight uniserial in the later stages of growth (e.g., *Peneropolis*). Interseptal buttresses or septulae can subdivide the chambers into chamberlets (e.g., *Archaias*). All-embracing, annular chamber additions can also occur (e.g., *Orbitolites*).

3H.2.5 Rotaliids

The rotaliids include LBF with test walls formed of multilaminar, perforate, hyaline calcite. They evolved several times in the history of the LBF, most notably in the Late Cretaceous and Cenozoic. A typical morphology is a discoidal mode of growth, with chambers arranged in annular cycles rather than plane spirals. A median (equatorial) layer of chamberlets is differentiated from the lateral chamberlets as seen in axial thin-sections (e.g., *Orbitoides, Discocyclina*, and *Lepidocyclina*). Radiating calcite pillars give rise to granules on the outer test surface. The nummulitids are perhaps the most well-known group of rotaliid LBF (e.g., *Nummulites*, *Assilina*, and *Operculina*) and have convex planispiral coiling. Chambers may be simple or subdivided into median (equatorial) chamberlets, while some genera have lateral chamberlets (e.g., *Spiroclypeus*) seen in axial sections.

3H.3 Late Paleozoic LBF Biostratigraphy

During the Carboniferous and Permian, foraminifera evolved and diversified from simple Early Paleozoic forms into forms displaying a variety of modes of coiling, more complex wall structures and internal subdivisions, and larger size. These include the first true LBF, the large and complex fusulinids (hereafter referred to as "larger fusulinids").

The biostratigraphic utility of larger fusulinids within the Carboniferous–Permian has long been established. They form the basis for high-resolution regional and local biozonation schemes (e.g., Rauser-Chernousova et al., 1996; Zhang and Wang, 2018). It is becoming increasingly accepted that major extinction and inception events within the larger fusulinids might be related to geodynamic events, paleoceanographic change and, in particular, paleoclimatic cyclicity (Davydov, 2014) or sea-level cyclicity (Wahlman, 2013). Despite their great stratigraphic utility, larger fusulinds are affected by marked provincialism, exhibiting marked differences between the Tethyan–Ural and the North American regions, making an integrated global biozonation impossible.

Based principally on the evolution of wall structure and the internal subdivision of the chambers, the larger fusulinids can be subdivided into six main groups: ozwainellids, staffellids, schubertellids, fusulinoids, schwagerinids, and neoschwagerinids.

The ancestors to the larger fusulinids (ozwainellids) appeared in the latest Tournaisian, although the first truly large and complex fusulinids did not appear until within the Bashkirian or Moscovian (Vachard, 2016). Diversity increased steadily throughout the Pennsylvanian, with the Moscovian seeing the global appearance of *Fusulina*, *Fusulinella*, and *Beedeina*. At the end of the Moscovian a faunal turnover leads to the rise of the first schwagerinids (e.g., *Triticites*) that appeared in the Kasimovian (Fig. 3H.3). After this event large, complex fusulinids with a keriothecal (alveolar) wall proliferated in warm tropical seas from the Kasimovian to the Kungurian.

The schwagerinids diversified within the Asselian–Artinskian and were joined by new groups, including the staffellids. A key genus is *Pseudoschwagerina*, the appearance of which approximates to the base of the Permian. By the Kungurian the first neoschwagerinids (e.g., *Misellina*) had appeared.

The Middle Permian is characterized by diversification within the neoschwagerinids (e.g., the appearance of *Neoschwagerina* near the base Roadian). By the Capitanian, gigantism was typical of many schwagerinid and neoschwagerinid fusulinids. The larger fusulinids suffered a major extinction at the end of the Middle Permian (Fig. 3H.3). Globally, all the large and morphologically complex forms of the schwagerinids and neoschwagerinids were eliminated by an end-Guadalupian event.

A reduced larger fusulinid assemblage is present within the Late Permian of Tethys (e.g., schubertellids such as *Codonofusiella*). Following a brief diversification of the schubertellids in the Changhsingian (e.g., *Paleofusulina*), larger fusulinids were eliminated by the major global end-Permian extinction event (Fig. 3H.3).

3H.4 Triassic LBF Biostratigraphy

The end-Permian extinction event was catastrophic for the foraminifera with over 90% of calcareous foraminiferal genera becoming extinct at this time (Groves and Altiner, 2005). True LBF disappeared completely with the extinction of the larger fusulinids, although a few smaller simple fusulinids survived before becoming extinct in the Late Triassic.

It was not until the Anisian that any significant recovery in foraminiferal diversity and complexity took place in Tethyan shallow marine carbonates (Payne et al., 2011) with the rise of the miliolids, lageninids, ammodiscids, and involutinids. During the Middle and Late Triassic, some small foraminifera with complex internal structures, placing them into LBF, reappeared.

Despite taxonomic uncertainties, and that many taxa are apparently relatively long-ranging, foraminifera are important for biostratigraphic correlation in Triassic Tethyan shallow marine carbonates, notwithstanding ongoing uncertainties in calibration to ammonoid or conodont-based biochronostratigraphy. In addition to the biozonation and bioevents compilation by Peybernes in Hardenbol et al. (1998), there are a number of regional biozonation schemes (e.g., Salaj et al., 1983; Davies and Simmons, 2018).

Miliolids first appeared within the Late Carboniferous and almost became extinct at the end of the Permian. However, despite an apparent gap in the Induan, *Hoyenella* and *Meandrospira* appear in the Olenekian, although it is not until the middle Anisian that more complex forms such as *Meandropspiranella* and *Turriglomina* evolve. Textulariids are important in the Early and Middle Triassic, especially the ammodiscids.

The involutinids are an important group for Triassic biostratigraphy. The oldest representatives of this group are *Praetriadodiscus* and *Triadodiscus*, which appear abruptly in the Olenekian and have uncertain ancestry (Altiner and Payne, 2017) (Fig. 3H.3). In the Anisian the planispirally coiled *Triadodiscus* evolved into the streptospirally coiled *Aulotortus*. The Middle Triassic also saw the appearance of the distinctive trochospiral involutinids such as *Lamelliconus* and *Trocholina*. During the Norian significant diversification occurred, with changes in the shape of the coiled tests and the appearance of pillars (e.g., *Triasina*, an important genus for Late Triassic biostratigraphy).

3H.5 Jurassic LBF Biostratigraphy

Following the end Triassic extinction, Hettangian LBF are rare and are dominated by small involutinids and textulariids. However, from the Sinemurian, and especially the Pliensbachian onward, the textulariids developed larger, morphologically more complex forms (Septfontaine, 1988; Kaminski et al., 2010) that provide good biostratigraphic utility in Tethyan shallow marine carbonate facies. These include planispiral forms (e.g., *Everticyclammina* and *Paleomayncina* appearing in the Early Jurassic, and *Alveosepta* appearing in the Late Jurassic), a variety of trochospiral forms (e.g., *Pfenderina, Kurnubia*), and broadly annular/discoidal forms (e.g., *Orbitopsella*).

A number of studies have proposed LBF-based biozonation schemes for Jurassic Tethyan sediments (e.g., Septfontaine, 1984; Septfontaine et al., 1991; Bassoullet, 1997; Velić, 2007; Hughes, 2018; BouDagher-Fadel, 2018). Although these schemes have great utility for correlation, their calibration to chronostratigraphic standards remains a topic for ongoing research.

Septfontaine (1988) has demonstrated that Jurassic textulariid LBF underwent similar and sometimes repeated (recapitulated) morphological evolution in several lineages. For example, simple mesoendothyrids present from the Hettangian onward developed into forms that are more complex during the Late Sinemurian and Pliensbachian (e.g., *Lituosepta*). Eventually these forms became discoidal with annular chambers as in *Orbitopsella. Labyrinthina* may represent a Late Jurassic recapitulation of this evolutionary trend.

Jurassic planispiral textulariids, similar to *Lituola*, but with an alveolar wall, first appeared in the Sinemurian (*Everticyclammina praevirguliana, Paleomayncina*). The more complex *Pseudocyclammina* appeared in the Pliensbachian. This genus and its descendants form a stratigraphically important group throughout the remainder of the Jurassic and the Cretaceous. In the Oxfordian and Kimmeridgian, *Alveosepta*, with fine and complex alveoles and septa with many apertures is a key zonal genus (e.g., Gradstein, 1976).

In the Hettangian, small simple textulariids developed a twisted siphonal canal connecting successive apertures (*Siphovalvulina*). These forms evolved gradually within the Sinemurian to the Bathonian into *Pseudopfenderina*. In the Middle Jurassic, more evolved forms such as *Pfenderella* appeared, which are probably the ancestors of *Pfenderina*. *Pfenderina* persists into the Early Cretaceous. The pfenderinoids underwent a spectacular diversification in the Middle Jurassic. Particularly notable among this diversification is the development of *Kurnubia* in the Callovian, which has a peripheral zone divided by radial partitions. Related forms include *Praekurnubia* and *Conicokurnubia*.

3H.6 Cretaceous LBF Biostratigraphy

During the Early Cretaceous the relatively large, complex textulariids continued to dominate the biota of the inner carbonate platform environments, which were widespread along the margins of the Tethys Ocean. Many species have limited stratigraphic ranges and are useful for biostratigraphic correlation. During the late Early Cretaceous, another group, the alveolinids, joined them (Fig. 3H.3). These large miliolids proliferated in the mid-Cretaceous. In the Late Cretaceous, rotaliids evolved into forms with complex three-layered structures, the orbitoids (Fig. 3H.3). Involutinids are present in the Early Cretaceous and the Cenomanian and have some biostratigraphic value pending ongoing taxonomic revisions (Arnaud-Vanneau et al., 1988; Schlagintweit et al., 2015).

Cretaceous LBF have been intensively studied for many decades. In addition to the compilation of biozones and bioevents by Arnaud-Vanneau in Hardenbol et al. (1998), there are also many local Cretaceous biozonation schemes based on LBF. However, few biozonations can be applied to large regions of Tethys. Taxonomic uncertainties and lack of calibration to ammonite or planktonic foraminifera standards means that the full biostratigraphic value of some groups is still to be fully realized (Frijia et al., 2015). Examples of LBF biozonation and bioevents schemes applied to Cretaceous sediments include Schroeder and Neumann (1985) and Velić (2007).

Within the textulariids a number of groups are important for biostratigraphy. These include the orbitolinids, chrysalidinids, complex planispiral or fusiform lituolids, cuneolinids, and nezzazatinids. A faunal turnover occurred during the Cenomanian, with the appearance of many new genera, but the extinction of some others (Kaminski et al., 2010).

The orbitolinids are a conical group of textulariids that can be rock forming during the mid-Cretaceous, although range younger with an apparent gap in the late Cenomanian and Turonian (Schlagintweit et al., 2016). The earliest formed chambers of the megalospheric generation can form a complex embryonic apparatus, the size, shape, and subdivision of which can be the most important feature for taxonomic subdivision (e.g., Simmons et al., 2000; Schroeder et al., 2010). There are many genera (e.g., *Palorbitolina*, *Orbitolina*, *Montseciella*) and species, some of which provide very precise biostratigraphy.

Stratigraphically important chrysalidinids have trochospiral tests and triserial or quadriserial, coiling modes. Important genera include *Praechrysalidina, Dukhania, Chrysalidina*, and *Accordiella* (Banner et al., 1991).

Complex lituolids are typically initially planispiral (e.g., *Choffatella*) and can become flabelliform (e.g., *Pseudochoffatella*), spherical (e.g., *Barkerina*, *Reticulinella*), or fusiform (e.g., *Loftusia*). The chamber walls are typically alveolar. Genera such as *Everticyclammina*, *Hemicyclammina*, and *Pseudocyclammina* can have biostratigraphic value in the Early and mid-Cretaceous (e.g., Banner and Whittaker, 1991).

The earliest alveolinid, *Archaealveolina*, appears in the Aptian, with subsequent mid-Cretaceous assemblages dominated by forms commonly referred to *Praealveolina*, *Ovalveolina*, or *Cisalveolina* (e.g., Calonge et al., 2002). However, Vicedo and Puiz (2017) have shown that with careful study there is much more subtle morphological variation than has commonly been recognized, leading to the recognition of a number of new, biostratigraphically useful, genera and species. Maximum alveolinid taxonomic diversity occurred in the Cenomanian, with relatively few new genera appearing in the remaining Late Cretaceous. A closely related group, the rhapydioninids (e.g., *Pseudedomia*, *Chubbina*, and *Rhapydionina*), were relatively abundant and diverse and, thus, useful in Late Cretaceous biostratigraphy (e.g., Vicedo et al., 2009).

Large rotaliid foraminifera with orbitoidal growth first appeared in the Late Cretaceous (van Gorsel, 1978). A typical orbitoid test varies from lenticular to subglobular and is composed of a median layer, consisting of concentrically arranged equatorial chamberlets, flanked on either side by layers of lateral chamberlets. The arrangement of the embryonic chambers is one of the most important characters needed for species identification. Genera include *Orbitoides* and *Lepidorbitoides* and these are particularly useful for biostratigraphy in the Campanian and Maastrichtian (e.g., Caus et al., 1996, Albrich et al., 2014), although they do display provincialism with the Caribbean Province being particularly taxonomically diverse.

3H.7 Cenozoic LBF Biostratigraphy

After the end-Cretaceous extinction the Early Paleocene was a period of recovery for LBF. Large miliolids (e.g., alveolinids) and rotaliids [especially nummulitids and orthophragminids (orbitoidal larger foraminifera, e.g., *Discocyclina*)] did not appear before the Selandian. Upon their return the LBF were often abundant, taxonomically diverse, and often mimicked some of the successful morphologies that had been present in the Cretaceous. In the Paleocene some large and complex forms such as *Ranikothalia* and *Miscellanea* occurred (Hottinger, 2014), but it was during the warm Early to Middle Eocene that the LBF reached an acme of diversity as well as size of individuals. Within the later Bartonian, *Alveolina*, *Assilina*, and large, strongly dimorphic nummulitids become extinct. Consequently, the Late Eocene is mainly characterized by relatively small *Nummulites* that persist into the Oligocene.

In the American province the recovery period for LBF was later than in Tethys, and it was not until the Middle

Eocene that rotaliids developed a new evolutionary lineage in the form of the three-layered lepidocyclinids *Lepidocyclina* and *Eulepidina*. These American forms migrated eastward into Tethys in the Oligocene (Adams, 1983).

LBF have long played an important role in the subdivision and correlation of Cenozoic strata. Differing zonations are required for back-reef and fore-reef paleoenvironments, which mainly use alveolinids and nummulitids/orthophragminids, respectively (Fig. 3H.2). Furthermore, provincialism and endemism mean that separate zonation schemes are required for the American, Tethyan, and Southeast Asian provinces (e.g., Adams, 1967; Butterlin, 1981).

The value of LBF in Cenozoic biostratigraphy is exemplified by the "East Indies Letter classification" or "Letter Stages" that use successive assemblages of LBF to subdivide the Cenozoic stratigraphy of Indonesia and subsequently more widely in Southeast Asia (see Lunt, 2013 for a history). It began with six divisions, based on different combinations of nummulitid, orthophragminid, and alveolinid genera, named Ta ... upwards to Tf, with the uppermost stages Tg and Th being mollusc assemblage defined. Subdivisions (zones) were added to the divisions Ta, Te, and Tf. Calibration to classical European chronostratigraphy was initially fraught with problems, but nonetheless, the scheme proved valuable for local correlation, not least within the oil industry, and was ultimately proven as a valuable biostratigraphic tool by Adams (1970, 1984). In fact, as pointed out by Lunt (2013), the "Letter Stages" were intended to be more than simple biozones; they were the basic units of Tertiary stratigraphy in Southeast Asia, used for mapping, given that the classical European stages initially had little meaning in this region. Issues in calibration to global standards are being progressively resolved, alongside further refinements to the subdivision of the letter stages (Adams, 1984; Lunt and Allan, 2004; van Gorsel et al., 2014).

Serra-Kiel et al. (1998) and Cahuzac and Poignant (1997) developed a well-established LBF biozonation for the Paleogene–Miocene of the Mediterranean Tethyan province by defining a series of shallow benthic zones (SBZ) mainly using the ranges of orthophragminid, alveolinid and nummulitid taxa (see Chapter 28: The Paleogene Period, in this book for zonal succession). This zonation has been broadly correlated to the classic "Letter Stage" biozonation of the Indo-Pacific by Lunt and Allan (2004), van Gorsel et al. (2014), BouDagher-Fadel (2018), and others, although further ties to plankton-based chronostratigraphic proxies are required (Papazzoni et al., 2017). These zonations were subsequently correlated (Less, 1998; Less et al., 2007) with the evolutionary pattern of orthophragminids for the Paleocene–Eocene of the Mediterranean to create a series of "OZ" zones (OZ1a–16).

Although secondary to the large rotaliids and miliolids for biostratigraphic purposes, Paleogene textulariid LBF contain a number of stratigraphically useful genera and species (Hottinger and Drobne, 1980). These occur in two main morphological groups: first, multiserial forms that are homeomorphs or isomorphs of Mesozoic chrysalidinids (e.g., *Pseudochrysalidina*) and second, conical orbitolinids, similar to many Cretaceous taxa, including coskinolinids (e.g., *Coskinolina*) and dictyoconids (e.g., *Dictyoconus*), which are common and diverse in the Early and Middle Eocene, with most lineages ending at the Middle–Late Eocene boundary. Only *Dictyoconus* ranges up into the Oligocene.

The most important groups of miliolid LBF for biostratigraphy in the Paleogene are the alveolinids (e.g., Hottinger, 1960) and soritids. Among the alveolinids, *Glomalveolina* is the ancestral form, appearing in the Selandian. Its descendent, *Alveolina*, evolved into larger forms through the Eocene and reached gigantic sizes before the end of the Middle Eocene. *Alveolina* species then became smaller, before disappearing at the end of the Middle Eocene. The various species of *Alveolina* are extremely useful biostratigraphic indices. Only the cosmopolitan form, *Borelis*, survived from the Paleogene into the Neogene (and still thrives today). Within the Neogene of the Indo-Pacific province, alveolinids underwent a slow, yet stratigraphically useful evolution.

Oligocene and younger shallow-water foraminiferal communities are often dominated by soritids (e.g., Sirel et al., 2013), which are miliolids with peneropliform–planispiral, flabelliform, and annular tests. This group developed a great variety of external and internal morphologies, leading to a number of stratigraphically useful genera and species, including *Peneroplis*, *Praerhapydionina*, *Neotaberina*, *Rhipidionina*, *Archiaias*, *Orbitolites*, and *Sorites*. In the Caribbean the ecological equivalents of the Tethyan soritids include discoidal *Yaberinella*, and *Cyclorbiculinoides*. The soritids are very common in Miocene and younger tropical carbonates and form a major constituent of many modern LBF assemblages. In the Cenozoic the rotaliids thrived in the warm shallow waters of Tethys and they became very large, reaching up to ca. 15-cm diameter in nummulitid forms such as *Cycloclypeus*. Three groups are particularly important for biostratigraphy—the nummulitids, the orbitoidal rotaliids (e.g., orthophragminids and lepidocyclinids) and the miogypsinids.

Members of the planispirally coiled nummulitids became very abundant in the Paleogene. They evolved rapidly and developed complex, large tests, making them very valuable for biostratigraphy (e.g., Schaub, 1981; Racey, 1995). Large *Nummulites* become extinct at the end of the Middle Eocene and only a few, small species of *Nummulites* and none of *Assilina*, survive into the Late Eocene, with *Nummulites* becoming extinct near the end of the Early Oligocene, although the closely allied form *Palaeonummulites* continues to the present day.

The orthophragminids are orbitoidal larger foraminifera, characterized by a discoidal, lenticular test with a fine equatorial layer of rectangular chamberlets and small lateral chamberlets who exhibit both cyclical and involute growth. The best known and most stratigraphically useful orthophragminids in the Paleogene are the discocyclinids (e.g., *Discocyclina*) with species often defined by biometrics (e.g., Özcan et al., 2006).

In the Americas the unrelated lepidocyclinids evolved in the Middle Eocene (Adams, 1967) and have gross morphological similarities to the discocyclinids. The lepidocyclinids did not appear in Tethys until the Early Oligocene and the latest Early Oligocene in the Indo-Pacific region. They are valuable for biostratigraphic dating and correlation (Adams, 1967, 1970; Butterlin, 1981; BouDagher-Fadel and Price, 2010). There is distinct provincialism between the American, Mediterranean, and Indo-Pacific LBF faunal provinces. The lepidocyclinids become extinct in the Americans toward the end of Early Miocene but range into the Middle Miocene in the Mediterranean and Indo-Pacific, with the youngest occurring in the Late Miocene of Southeast Asia.

The miogypsinids have a flattened to biconvex test with the megalospheric form having a bilocular embryonic stage followed by a fan of median chamberlets. They are a particularly well known group of LBF having great stratigraphic utility in Oligocene to Middle Miocene sediments, although they do show distinct provincialism. Many independent lineages of *Miogypsina* and related forms have been recognized in the Mediterranean, Indo-Pacific, and Central American bioprovinces (e.g., Drooger, 1993; BouDagher-Fadel and Price, 2013). The extinction of the Mediterranean miogypsinids occurred in the Langhian, but miogypsinids survived in the Indo-Pacific province into the Serravallian.

As in the Mesozoic and late Paleozoic, the Paleogene saw a turnover in LBF taxa due to paleoceanographic and climatic changes. For example, a large number of taxa disappeared at the Paleocene–Eocene boundary in response to the sudden, short, thermal maximum event (PETM) (Scheibner et al., 2005). The subsequent Early Eocene saw the appearance of many new LBF genera with provincialism becoming pronounced in the Lutetian. Major extinctions of LBF occur at the Middle/Late Eocene boundary (extinction of large *Nummulites*, *Assilina*, and *Alveolina*) and Eocene/Oligocene boundary (Cotton and Pearson, 2011) (extinction of *Discocyclina*).

In comparison to other periods, episodes of turnover of LBF in the Neogene are less clear and their relationship to global events is less obvious. This is partly because of the marked provincialism in Neogene LBF, and the likelihood that local tectonic controls on paleoenvironments played an important role. For example, increasing isolation of the proto-Mediterranean led to extinctions of taxonomic groups that persisted longer in the Indo-Pacific region (e.g., lepidocyclinids), culminating in major extinction in the Mediterranean synchronous with the Messinian salinity crisis. From the Pliocene to the present day the Indo-Pacific has been the center for LBF abundance and diversification, although there is also good species diversity and richness in the Caribbean.

Acknowledgments

Peter Lunt, Mike Bidgood, Andy Racey, Wyn Hughes, Michel Septfontaine and Vicent Vicedo kindly provided unpublished data and/or commented on early drafts of the text. However, responsibility for errors of fact or interpretation is mine alone.

Bibliography

Adams, C.G., 1967, Tertiary Foraminifera in the Tethyan, American and Indo-Pacific provinces. *In* Adams, C.G., and Ager, D.V. (eds), *Aspects of Tethyan Biogeography*. Systematics Association, 195–217 Special Volume, 7.

Adams, C.G., 1970, A reconsideration of the East Indian letter classification of the Tertiary. *Bulletin of the British Museum (Natural History). Geology*, **19**: 87–137.

Adams, C.G., 1983, Speciation, phylogenesis, tectonism, climate and eustasy: factors in the evolution of Cenozoic larger Foraminifera. *In* Sims, R.W., Price, J.H., and Whalley, P.E.S. (eds), *Evolution, Time and Space: The Emergence of the Biosphere*. Academic Press, 255–289.

Adams, C.G., 1984, Neogene larger Foraminifera, evolutionary and geological events in the context of datum planes. *In* Ikebe, N., and Tsuchi, R. (eds), *Pacific Neogene Datum Planes*. University of Tokyo Press, 47–67.

Albrich, S., Frijia, G., Parente, M., and Caus, E., 2014, The evolution of the earliest representatives of the genus *Orbitoides*: Implications for Upper Cretaceous biostratigraphy. *Cretaceous Research*, **51**: 22–34.

Altiner, D., and Payne, J.L., 2017, Origination and early evolution of Involutinida in the aftermath of the end-Permian mass extinction: *Praetriadodiscus* n. gen., and two new species. *Revue de Micropaléontologie*, **60**: 573–584.

Arnaud-Vanneau, A., Boisseau, T., and Darsac, C., 1988, Le genre *Trocholina* Paalzow 1922 et ses principals especès au Crétacé. *Revue de Paléobiologie Volume Spéciale*, **2**: 353–377.

Banner, F.T., and Whittaker, J.E., 1991, Redmond's "new lituolid Foraminifera" from the Mesozoic of Saudi Arabia. *Micropaleontology*, **37**: 41–59.

Banner, F.T., Simmons, M.D., and Whittaker, J.E., 1991, The Mesozoic Chrysalinidae (Foraminifera, Textulariacea) of the Middle East: the Redmond (Aramco) taxa and their relatives. *Bulletin of the British Museum (Natural History)*, **47**: 101–152.

Bassoullet, J.P., 1997. Foraminifères – Les Grands Foraminifères. In: Cariou, E., Hantzpergue, P. (Coord.) Groupe Francais d'Etude du Jurassique. Biostratigraphie du Jurassique ouest-européen et méditerranéen: zonations parallels et distribution des invertébrés et microfossiles. *Bulletin du Centre Recherche Elf Exploration et Production*, **17**, 293-304.

Beavington-Penney, S.J., and Racey, A., 2004, Ecology of extant nummulitids and other larger benthic foraminifera: applications in Paleoenvironmental analysis. *Earth-Science Reviews*, **67**: 219–265.

BouDagher-Fadel, M.K., 2018, *Evolution and Geological Significance of Larger Benthic Foraminifera*, second ed. London: UCL Press 693 pp.

BouDagher-Fadel, M.K., and Price, G.D., 2010, Evolution and paleogeographic distribution of the lepidocyclinids. *The Journal of Foraminiferal Research*, **40**: 79–108.

Boudagher-Fadel, M.K., and Price, G.D., 2013, The phylogenetic and paleogeographic evolution of the miogypsinid larger benthic foraminifera. *Journal of the Geological Society*, **170**: 185–208.

Butterlin J., 1981. *Claves para la determinación de macroforaminíferos de México y del Caribe, del Cretácico Superior al Mioceno Medio*. Instituto Mexicano del Petróleo, Subdirección de Tecnología de Exploración, México, 219 pp.

Cahuzac, B., and Poignant, A., 1997, Essai de biozonation de l'Oligo-Miocène dans les bassins européens à l'aide des grands foraminifères néritiques. *Bulletin de la Société géologique de* ***France***, **168**: 155–169.

Calonge, A., Caus, E., Bernaus, J.M., and Aguilar, M., 2002, *Praealveolina* (Foraminifera) species; a tool to date Cenomanian platform sediments. *Micropaleontology*, **48**: 53–66.

Caus, E., Bernaus, J.M., and Gomez Garrido, A.N., 1996, Biostratigraphic utility of species of the genus *Orbitoides*. *Journal of Foraminiferal Research*, **26**: 24–36.

Cotton, L.J., and Pearson, P.N., 2011, Extinction of larger benthic foraminifera at the Eocene/Oligocene boundary. *Palaeogeography, Palaeoclimatology, Palaeoecology*, **311**: 281–296.

Davies, R.D., and Simmons, M.D., 2018, Triassic sequence stratigraphy of the Arabian Plate. *In* Pöppelreiter, M.C. (ed), *Lower Triassic to Middle Jurassic Sequence of the Arabian Plate*. The Netherlands: EAGE Publications bv, 101–162.

Davydov, V.I., 2014, Warm water benthic foraminifera document the Pennsylvanian – Permian warming and cooling events – The record from the Western Pangea tropical shelves. *Paleogeography, Paleoclimatology, Paleoecology*, **414**: 284–295.

Drooger, C.W., 1993, Radial Foraminifera, morophometrics and evolution. *Verhandelingen der Koninklijke Nederlandse Akademie Wetenschappen*, **41**: 1–241.

Frijia, G., Parente, M., Di Lucia, M., and Mutti, M., 2015, Carbon and strontium isotope stratigraphy of the Upper Cretaceous (Cenomanian-Campanian) shallow-water carbonates of southern Italy: Chronostratigraphic calibration of larger Foraminifera biostratigraphy. *Cretaceous Research*, **53**: 110–139.

Gradstein, F.M., 1976. Biostratigraphy and biogeography of Jurassic Grand Banks Foraminifera. In: *Proceedings of the First International Conf. Benthonic Foraminifera*, Halifax, N.S., 1975; Maritime Sediments, Special Publication, **2**, 557-583, 8 figs., 8 pl.

Groves, J.R., and Altiner, D., 2005, Survival and recovery of calcareous Foraminifera pursuant to the end-Permian mass extinction. *Comptes Rendus Palevol*, **4**: 487–500.

Hardenbol, J., Thierry, J., Farley, M.B., Jacquin, T., de Graciansky, P.C., and Vail, P.R., 1998, Mesozoic and Cenozoic sequence chronostratigraphic framework of European basins. *In* de Graciansky, Hardenbol, J., Jacquin, T., and Vail, P.R. (eds), Mesozoic and Cenozoic Sequence Stratigraphy of European Basins. *SEPM Special Publication,* **60**: 3–13.

Haynes, J.R., 1981, *Foraminifera*. Macmillian Publishers Ltd 433 pp.

Hohenegger, J., 2011, Large Foraminifera: greenhouse constructions and gardeners in the oceanic microcosm. *The Kagoshima University Museum Bulletin*, **5**: 81 pp.

Hottinger, L., 1960, Recherches sur les Alvéolines du Paléocène et de l'Eocène. *Memoire Suisses Paleontologie*, **75/76**: 1–243.

Hottinger, L., 2006, *Illustrated glossary of terms used in foraminiferal research*. Carnets de Geologie, Memoir 2006/02. <http://paleopolis.rediris.es/cg/CG2006_M02/>.

Hottinger, L., 2014, *Paleogene Larger Rotaliid Foraminifera from the Western and Central Neotethys*. Springer 196 pp.

Hottinger, L., and Drobne, K., 1980, Early Tertiary conical imperforate Foraminifera. *Slovenska Akademija Znanosti in Umetnosti*, **22**: 188–276.

Hughes, G.W., 2018, A new thin-section based micropaleontological biozonation for the Saudi Arabian Jurassic carbonates. *Micropaleontology*, **64**: 331–364.

Kaminski, M.A., Setoyama, E., and Cetean, C.G., 2010, The Phanerozoic diversity of agglutinated Foraminifera: origination and extinction rates. Acta Paleontologica Polonica 55, 529-539. Langer, M.R., Hottinger, L., 2000. Biogeography of selected "larger" Foraminifera. *Micropaleontology*, **46**: 105–126.

Langer, M.R., and Hottinger, L., 2000, Biogeography of selected "larger" foraminifera. *Micropaleontology*, **46** (Suppl. 1): 105–126.

Less, G., 1998, Zonation of the Mediterranean Upper Paleocene and Eocene by Orthophragminae. *Opera Dela Slovenska Akademija Znanosti in Umetnosti*, **34**: 21–43.

Less, G., Özcan, E., Baldi-Beke, M., and Kollanyi, K., 2007, Thanetian and early Ypresian orthophragmines (Foraminifera: Discocyclinidae and Orbitoclypeidae) from the central Western Tethys (Turkey, Italy and Bulgaria) and their revised taxonomy and biostratigraphy. *Rivista Italiana di Paleontologia e Stratigrafia*, **113**: 415–448.

Lunt, P., 2013, Foraminiferal micropalaeontology in SE Asia. *In* Bowden, A.J., Gregory, F.J., and Henderson, A.S. (eds), Landmarks in Foraminiferal Micropalaeontology: History and Development. *The Micropalaeontological Society Special Publication,* **6**: 193–206.

Lunt, P., and Allan, T., 2004, Larger Foraminifera in Indonesian biostratigraphy, calibrated to isotopic dating. *GRDC Museum Workshop on Micropalaeontology, Bandung*, 1–109.

Özcan, E., Less, G., Báldi-Beke, M., Kollányi, K., and Kertész, B., 2006, Biometric analysis of middle and upper Eocene Discocyclinidae and Orbitoclypeidae (Foraminifera) from Turkey and updated orthophragmine zonation in the Western Tethys. *Micropaleontology*, **52**: 485–520.

Papazzoni, C.A., Ćosović, V., Briguglio, A., and Drobne, K., 2017, Towards a calibrated larger Foraminifera biostratigraphic zonation: Celebrating 18 years of the application of shallow benthic zones. *Palaios*, **32**: 1–4.

Payne, J.L., Summers, M., Rego, B.L., Altiner, D., Wei, J., Yu, M., et al., 2011, Early and Middle Triassic trends in diversity, evenness, and size of foraminifers on a carbonate platform in south China: implications for tempo and mode of biotic recovery from the end-Permian mass extinction. *Paleobiology*, **37**: 5409–5425.

Racey, A., 1995, Lithostratigraphy and larger foraminiferal (nummulitid) biostratigraphy of the Tertiary of northern Oman. *Micropaleontology*, **41** (Suppl.), 123.

Rauser-Chernousova, D.M., Bensh, F.R., Vdovenko, M.V., Gibshman, N.B., Leven, E.J., Lipina, O.A., et al., 1996, *Guidebook on the Systematics of Foraminifers of the Paleozoic*. Moscow: Nauka Publishing House (in Russian).

Rigaud, S., Blau, J., Martini, R., and Rettori, R., 2013, Taxonomy and phylogeny of the Trocholinidae (Involutinina). *Journal of Foraminiferal Research*, **43**: 317–339.

Röttger, R., 1983, A complicated protozoon, *Heterostegina depressa*: test structures and their function. *German Research Reports of the DFG*, **2** (83), 11–13.

Salaj, J., Borza, K., and Samuel, O., 1983, Triassic Foraminifera of the West Carpathians. *Geologicky ustav Dionyza Stura*, 213 pp.

Schaub, H., 1981, Nummulites et Assilines de la Tethys Paleogene. Taxinomie, phylogenese et biostratigraphie. *Schweizerische Paläontologisches Abhandlungen*, **104-106**: 236.

Scheibner, C., Speijer, R.P., and Marzouk, A.M., 2005, Turnover of larger Foraminifera during the Paleocene-Eocene Thermal Maximum and paleoclimatic control on the evolution of platform ecosystems. *Geology*, **33**: 493–496.

Schlagintweit, F., Rigaud, S., and Wilmsen, M., 2015, Insights from exceptionally preserved Cenomanian trocholinids (benthic foraminifera) of northern Cantabria, Spain. *Facies*, **61**: 416.

Schlagintweit, F., Rashidi, K., and Babapidour, M., 2016, Orbitolinid Foraminifera from the late Maastrichtian of the Tarbur formation (Zagros zone, SW Iran). *Acta Paleontologica Romaniae*, **12**: 29–46.

Schroeder, R., Neumann, M. (Coords.) 1985. *Les grands Foraminifères du Crétacé moyen de la région méditerranéenne*. Geobios Mémoire Special, **7**, 160 pp.

Schroeder, R., van Buchem, F.S., Cherchi, A., Baghbani, D., Vincent, B., Immenhauser, A., et al., 2010, Revised orbitolinid biostratigraphic zonation for the Barremian–Aptian of the eastern Arabian Plate and implications for regional stratigraphic correlations. *GeoArabia Special Publication*, **4**: 49–96.

Septfontaine, M., 1984, Biozonation (a l'aide des foraminiferes imperforés) de la plate-forme interne carbonatee Liasique du Haut Atlas (Maroc). *Revue de Micropaléontologie*, **27**: 209–229.

Septfontaine, M., 1988, Vers une classification évolutive des Lituolidés (Foraminifères) jurassiques en milieu de plate-forme carbonatée. *Revue de Paléobiologie, Volume Spécial*, **2**: 229–256.

Septfontaine, M., Arnaud-Vanneau, A., Bassoullet, J.P., Gusic, Y., Ramalho, M., and Velic, I., 1991, Les foraminifères imperforés des plates-formes carbonatées jurassiques: état des connaissances et perspectives d'avenir. *Bulletin de la Societé Vaudoise des Sciences naturelles*, **80**: 255–277.

Serra-Kiel, J., Hottinger, L., Caus, E., Drobne, K., Ferrandez, C., Jauhri, A.K., et al., 1998, Larger foraminiferal biostratigraphy of the Tethyan Paleocene and Eocene. *Bulletin de la Société géologique de France*, **169**: 281–299.

Simmons, M.D., Whittaker, J.E., and Jones, R.W., 2000, Orbitolinids from Cretaceous sediments of the Middle East –a revision of the F. R.S. Henson and Associates Collection. *In* Hart, M.B., Kaminski, M. A., and Smart, C.W. (eds), Proceedings of the Fifth International Workshop on Agglutinated Foraminifera. *Gryzbowski Foundation Special Publication*, **7**: 411–437.

Sirel, E., Ozgen Erdem, N., and Kangal, O., 2013, Systematics and biostratigraphy of Oligocene (Rupelian-Early Chattian) Foraminifera from lagoonal-very shallow water limestone in the eastern Sivas Basin (central Turkey). *Geologia Croatica*, **66**: 83–110.

Vachard, D., 2016, Macroevolution and biostratigraphy of Paleozoic foraminifers. *In* Montenari, M. (ed), Stratigraphy & Timescales. *Elsevier*, **1**: 257–323.

van Gorsel, J., 1978, Late Cretaceous orbitoidal Foraminifera. In: Hedley, R.H., Adams, C,G. (Eds.), *Foraminifera*, vol. 3, 1–120.

van Gorsel, J.T., Lunt, P., and Morley, R., 2014, Introduction to Cenozoic biostratigraphy of Indonesia-SE Asia. *Berita Sedimentologi*, **29**: 6–40.

Velić, I., 2007, Stratigraphy and paleobiogeography of Mesozoic benthic foraminifera of the Karst Dinarides (SE Europe). *Geologia Croatica*, **60**: 1–113.

Vicedo, V., and Puiz, A., 2017, Evolutionary trends and biostratigraphic application of new Cenomanian alveolinids (Foraminifera) from the Natih Formation of Oman. *Journal of Systematic Palaeontology*, **15**: 9–12.

Vicedo, V., Aguilar, M., Caus, E., and Hottinger, L., 2009, Fusiform and laterally compressed alveolinaceans (Foraminiferida) from both sides of the Late Cretaceous Atlantic. *Neues Jahrbuch für Geologie und Paläontologie Abhandlungen*, **253**: 229–247.

Wahlman, G.P., 2013, Pennsylvanian to Lower Permian (Desmoinesian – Wolfcampian) fusulinid biostratigraphy of Midcontinent North America. *Stratigraphy*, **10**: 73–104.

Zhang, Y.-C., and Wang, Y., 2018, Permian fusuline biostratigraphy, Special Publications. *In* Lucas, S.G., and Shen, S.Z. (eds), The Permian Timescale. *London: Geological Society*, **450**: pp. 253–288.

Subchapter 3I

Dinoflagellates

R.A. Fensome and D.K. Munsterman

Abstract

Most dinoflagellates are free-living single-celled organisms that inhabit aquatic environments with a mostly organic-walled cyst stage in their life cycle. The evolution of dinoflagellates through their cyst fossils goes back to Middle Triassic. The intricate Jurassic through Cenozoic organic walled cyst taxonomy allows a refined marine biostratigraphy.

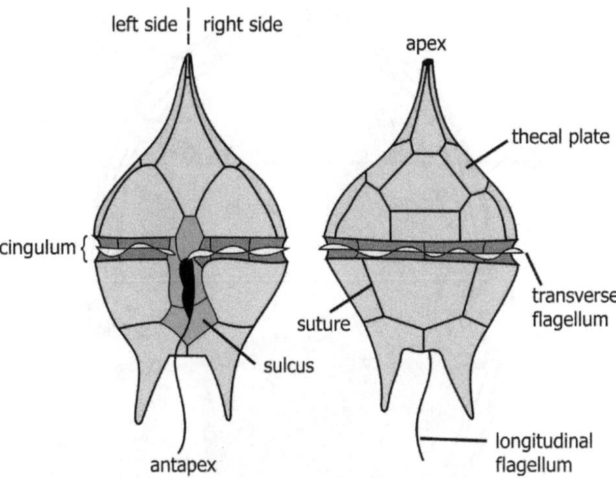

FIGURE 3I.1 General morphology of a motile dinoflagellate cell showing the position of the two flagella. This cell is an "armored" form with cellulosic thecal plates, which together constitute a cell wall known as a theca. The arrangement of plates is known as tabulation and may be reflected (but not separable into constituent plates) in fossils as a paratabulation.

3I.1 Dinoflagellates as organisms

Most dinoflagellates are free-living single-celled organisms that inhabit aquatic environments; some forms live in wet sand or snow, and a few have multicellular life-cycle stages. They may be autotrophic, heterotrophic, or both, and the group also includes endosymbionts and parasites. Dinoflagellates are particularly common in marine nearshore and neritic settings, being most diverse in the latter. Under the right conditions, some marine dinoflagellate species "bloom," becoming so abundant that their cell pigments color the water with a red, brown or even greenish hue. Such "red tides" may be associated with shellfish poisoning due to the toxins secreted by some dinoflagellate species; the poisoning may cause serious or fatal illness in people who consume shellfish that have accumulated the toxin from large numbers of ingested dinoflagellates. Other marine dinoflagellates are responsible for luminescence, sometimes seen at night in breaking surf or a ship's wake.

Historically dinoflagellates have been classified as both animals (protozoans) and plants (algae) and so have been treated nomenclaturally under both the International Code of Zoological Nomenclature (ICZN) and International Code of Botanical Nomenclature (ICBN). Nowadays, most researchers consider the group as algae for nomenclatural purposes, and thus under the successor to the ICBN, the International Code for Algae, Fungi, and Plants (Turland et al., 2018). As organisms, dinoflagellates are considered to be protists rather than protozoa or algae, which are informal vernacular terms. They are part of the supergroup Chromalveolata within the domain Eukaryota.

Dinoflagellates have one or, usually, both of two defining criteria. The first criterion is the presence during the life cycle of a swimming (motile) cell with two flagella: a transverse flagellum that encircles the cell and is ribbon-like, and a longitudinal flagellum that is cylindrical and trails the cell posteriorly (Fig. 3I.1). The combined actions of the flagella propel motile cells through water in a corkscrew manner, inspiring the name "dinoflagellate" from the Greek *dinos* (rotation) and the Latin *flagellum*, "small whip." The second defining criterion is the possession of a special type of nucleus, called a dinokaryon, that lacks histones (proteins generally found in eukaryotic cell nuclei that help organize DNA) and in which the chromosomes remain condensed during interphase (i.e., between episodes of cell division) (Fig. 3I.2). Beyond the two defining criteria, living dinoflagellates show an amazing array of morphologies (Fig. 3I.3), including ameboid, multinucleate, tentacle-bearing (Fig. 3I.3I), ribbon-like (Fig. 3I.3M), filamentous multicellular, and tripod-like (Fig. 3I.3F) forms. Individual taxa can have a very complicated life cycle (Fig. 3I.4), with several morphologically different stages, although generally including the typical biflagellated motile stage. Among the variety of living dinoflagellate cells are types that have a continuous wall, lacking flagella; most such cells are considered to be cysts, discussed later.

In size, living dinoflagellate cells range mostly from 5 to 100 μm in diameter, although some may be up to 2 mm across. The outer part of dinoflagellate cells (known as the amphiesma) comprises a series of membranes and a layer of enclosed vesicles (amphiesmal vesicles, homologous with the alveolae of related protists such as ciliates) that may be empty or contain cellulosic plates, known as thecal plates. The ensemble of thecal plates on a single cell constitutes a cell wall and is known as a theca. The arrangement of amphiesmal vesicles with or without thecal plates is termed tabulation.

Tabulation on dinoflagellate motile cells (and represented, or "reflected," on fossils, as we discuss later) is fundamental in classifying the group and understanding

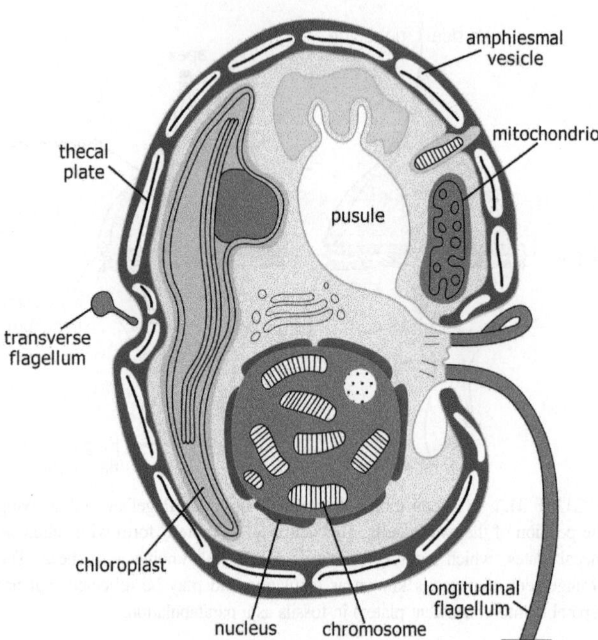

FIGURE 3I.2 Cross-section of a motile dinoflagellate cell. Note that the chromosomes remain condensed (and thus visible) between episodes of cell division (i.e., during interphase). The series of membranes, vacuoles, and thecal plates around the periphery of the cell is called the Amphiesma. Adapted from Taylor (1980).

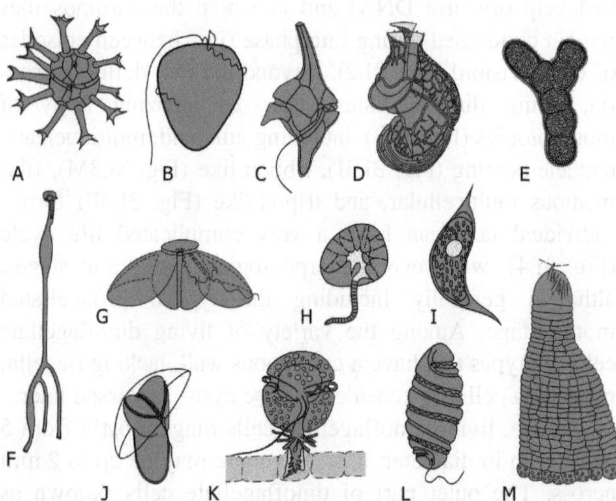

FIGURE 3I.3 A diversity of modern dinoflagellate cells. (A) *Cladopyxis*—generally considered a motile cell, despite processes; flagella not shown. (B) *Prorocentrum* motile cell, which has two very large thecal plate, one on each side. (C) *Ceratium* motile cell. (D) *Histioneis*, motile cell. (E) *Dinothrix*, a filamentous multicellular form. (F) *Amphisolenia*, motile cell. (G) *Cymbodinium*, motile cell. (H) *Noctuluca* cell with tentacle. (I) *Cystodinium*, living vegetative cell. (J) *Kofoidinium*, miotile cell with umbrella-like structure probably used to concentrate the flow of potential food particles. (K) *Protoodinium*, motile cell simultaneously feeding and bearing chloroplasts (in *green*). (L) *Cochlodinium*, a pseudocolonial motile cell. (M) *Haplozoon*, a ribbon-like multicellular form. Adapted from Fensome et al. (1993).

its evolution. The system of plate nomenclature generally adopted for many dinoflagellates, including most fossils, is based on that proposed by Kofoid (1907a,b, 1909). He related latitudinal series of plates to "landmarks" such as the apex (at the cell's leading, or anterior, end), the antapex (opposite the apex), and cingulum (the generally equatorially positioned furrow containing the transverse flagellum; Fig. 3I.1). Peridinioid tabulation (Fig. 3I.5) is one of the two principal types of tabulation found in the fossil record, the other main type being gonyaulacoid (Fig. 3I.6). The differences between the two may seem subtle, and variations on these two themes occur, but essentially peridinioid and gonyaulacoid lineages of dinoflagellates dominate much of the fossil record and have been separate since the Early Jurassic.

3I.2 Dinoflagellates as fossils

As noted, the life cycle of many dinoflagellates includes a cyst stage, in which the cell lacks flagella and is enclosed in a continuous wall (Fig. 3I.4C). In vegetative cysts, life processes continue, whereas in resting cysts life processes are suspended. Some species (about 13% among modern motile forms) produce long-term resting cysts (hypnozygotes) in which the wall is composed of a fossilizable organic material (dinosporin), calcium carbonate or, very rarely, silica. Fossil dinoflagellate cysts (dinocysts) are common in many Mesozoic and Cenozoic fine-grained marine sediments and sedimentary rocks. Extraction techniques similar to those developed for foraminifers and other hard-shelled microfossils are used to concentrate calcareous and siliceous dinoflagellate cysts. Organic-walled cysts are recovered through a processing technique (e.g., Wood et al., 1996) that usually involves hydrochloric and hydrofluoric acids to dissolve carbonates and silicates, respectively, and, if needed, careful oxidation to refine the organic residue and remove superfluous kerogen. The resulting residue potentially contains palynomorphs (organic-walled microfossils) such as pollen and spores, as well as dinocysts.

Most geological applications using dinocysts are based on organic-walled forms, extracted through palynological processing. However, the earliest observations of fossil organic-walled dinocysts were made from thin sections of flint flakes. In 1838 Christian Ehrenberg published his observations from Cretaceous flints of two types of microfossils, identifying one as fossil dinoflagellates because of their resemblance to the modern dinoflagellate *Peridinium*. The other was a small spiny sphere that he attributed to the extant green alga *Xanthidium*. From the 1930s to early 1960s the spiny forms became known as "ova hispida" (spiny eggs) or "hystrichospheres" (spiny spheres). Palynological processing was increasingly used by the 1950s, leading to the seminal discoveries of Evitt (1961, 1963a,b). He recognized that regular openings in fossils classified as dinoflagellates were excystment openings

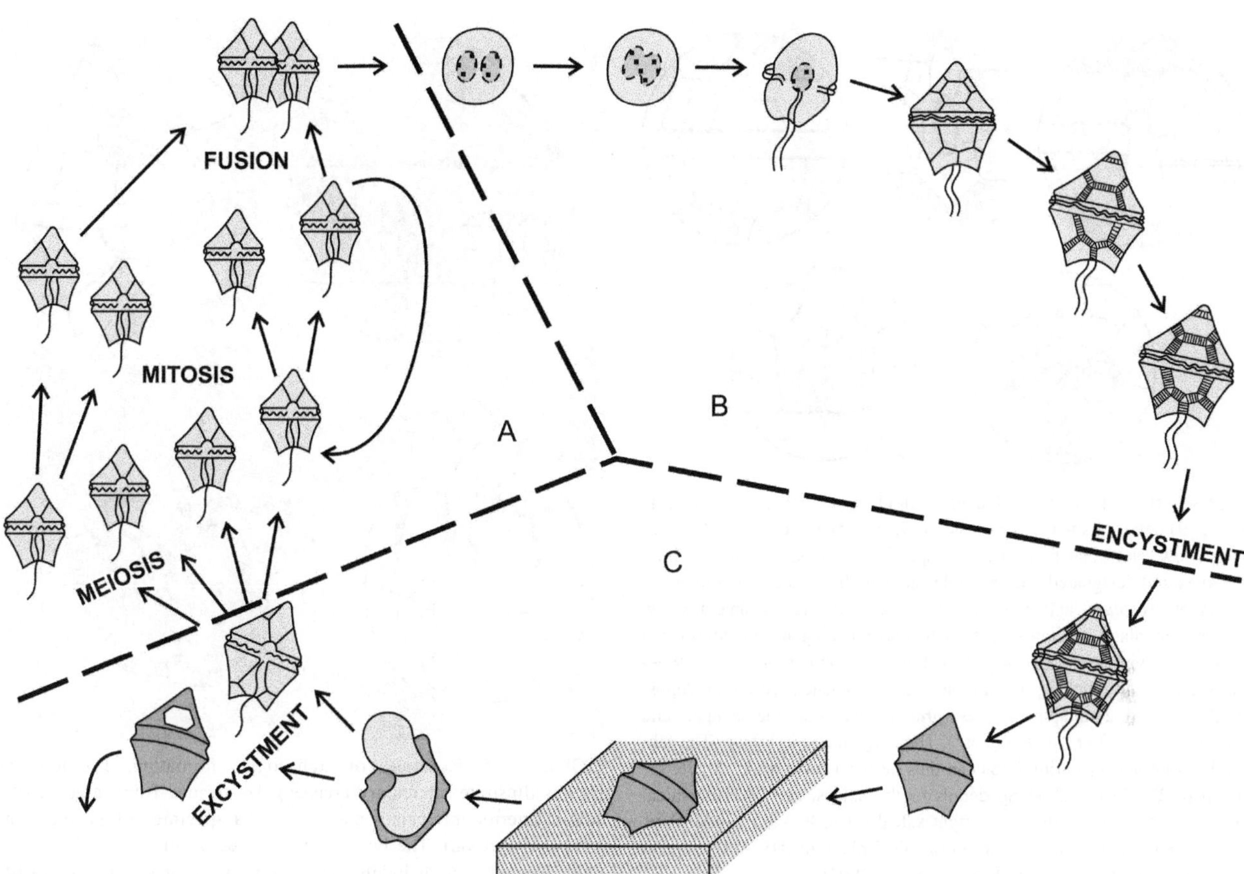

FIGURE 3I.4 A simplified dinoflagellate life cycle involving sexual reproduction and cyst formation. The cells in sector A are haploid (i.e., with half the usual number of chromosomes). Fusion (top of sector A) produces diploid cells (with the full complement of chromosomes), as shown in sector B, which may undergo fusion. Encystment leads to the formation of resting cysts (brown in sector C), which may be preservable in the fossil record. Excystment usually leads to the development of haploid cells. Adapted from Evitt (1985).

that, in living cells, facilitate the escape of the incipient motile stage: the fossils themselves were, therefore, preserved cysts (Fig. 3I.7). Moreover, he identified similar openings in many Mesozoic–Cenozoic hystrichospheres and realized that in many such microfossils the arrangement of the spines, or processes, could be related to the tabulation on a motile dinoflagellate cell (Fig. 3I.8). Outlines of excystment openings, or archaeopyles, in both spiny and nonspiny forms tended to reflect the outlines of one or more thecal plates of the motile cells. For hystrichospheres that remained of unknown affinity (predominantly pre-Mesozoic forms), Evitt established a group that he called the acritarchs.

Armed with this new understanding, it was recognized that fossil dinoflagellate cysts come in a variety of shapes, including "chorate" forms with processes, and "proximate" forms that generally lacked processes and showed a variety of surface ornament, some of which reflected aspects of the motile parent cell, such as thecal plates (Fig. 3I.9). On the cyst, however, such reflected thecal features are nonfunctional, and hence are described using the prefix "para" (e.g., paraplates and paracingulum).

Some calcareous forms in inorganic-walled microfossil assemblages (alongside fossils such as foraminifera and ostracods) have been recognized as calcareous dinocysts because they exhibit paratabulation and have archaeopyles (Elbrächter et al., 2008). They are not preserved in palynological assemblages, however, and have not been used extensively for biostratigraphy.

3I.3 Evolution of dinoflagellates

Despite its incompleteness, the dinoflagellate fossil record shows some clear evolutionary patterns and trends (Fensome et al., 1996; MacRae et al., 1996). Common to the evolution of many groups of organisms is an early radiation of diverse morphotypes and "experimentation"; for dinoflagellates, this phase took place during the Middle Triassic to Middle Jurassic. It was followed by a long period of greater stability with the success of a relatively few fundamental types but with diversification within those groups. Thus since the Middle Jurassic, peridinioids and gonyaulacoids became stabilized as the predominant types among dinoflagellates preserved as fossils.

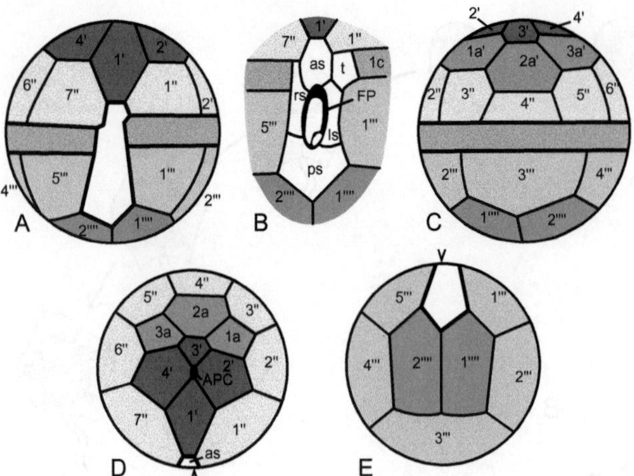

FIGURE 3I.5 Tabulation of a peridinioid dinoflagellate. (A) Ventral view, (B) detail of sulcus, (C) dorsal view, (D) apical view, and (E) antapical view. Note that there are four apical plates (*red*—plates touching the apex and designated with a single "apostrophe"), three anterior intercalary plates (*blue*—between apical plates and precingular plates), seven precingular plates (*yellow*—anterior to and touching the cingulum and designated with two "apostrophes"), five postcingular plates (*green*—posterior to and touching the cingulum and designated with three "apostrophes"), and 2 antapical plates (*orange*—plates at the antapex and designated with four "apostrophes"). The cingulum is in brown. The tabulation formula for peridinioids can thus be formulated as 4′, 3a, 7″, xc, 5‴, 0 p, 2⁗. In (B) showing details of the sulcus, as = anterior sulcal plate, t = transitional plate, rs = right sulcal plate, ls = left sulcal plate, FP = flagellar pore, and ps = posterior sulcal plate. In (D), APC = apical pore complex. Adapted from Fensome et al. (1993).

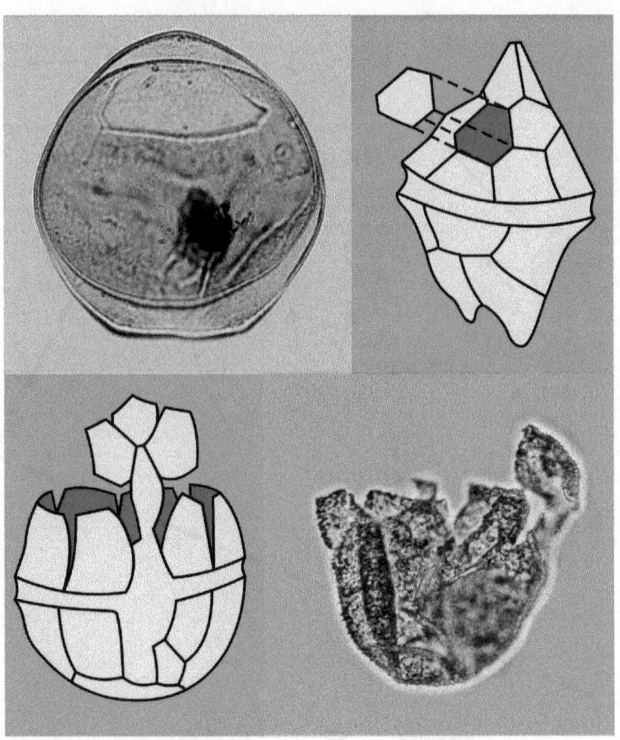

FIGURE 3I.7 Examples of archaeopyle formation. The top two figures illustrate intercalary archaeopyles formed from removal of a single anterior intercalary plate (left is a specimen of *Lentinia* and right is a cartoon). The bottom two figures illustrate apical archaeopyles formed from dislodging of all four apical plates and "accessory sutures" between precingular plates (left is a cartoon and right is a specimen of *Sentusidinium*).

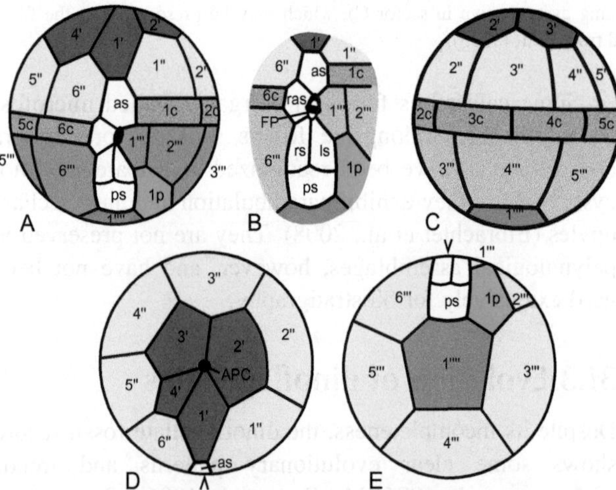

FIGURE 3I.6 Tabulation of a gonyaulacioid dinoflagellate. (A) Ventral view, (B) detail of sulcus, (C) dorsal view, (D) apical view, and (E) antapical view. Note that there are 4 apical plates (*red*), 6 precingular plates (*yellow*), 6 cingular plates (*brown*), 6 postcingular plates (*green*), 1 posterior intercalary plate (*light blue*—between postcingular and antapical plates) and 1 antapical plate (*orange*—plates at the antapex). The basic tabulation formula for gonyaulacoids is thus 4′, 0a, 6″, 6c, 6‴, 1p, 1⁗. In (B), showing details of the sulcus, as = anterior sulcal plate, ras = right anterior sulcal plate, FP = Flagellar Pore, rs = right sulcal plate, ls = left sulcal plate, and ps = posterior sulcal plate. In (D), APC = apical pore complex. Adapted from Fensome et al. (1993).

FIGURE 3I.8 Interpretation of a chorate (spiny) dinoflagellate cyst. From a cartoon based on an actual fossil species (left) the processes can be related to plates in a dinoflagellate tabulation (center), and hence some idea of the original motile dinoflagellate cell can be postulated (right).

In order to fully explain dinoflagellate evolution, we need to introduce additional tabulation types beyond the gonyaulacoid–peridinioid pattern, with its tabulation arranged essentially into five or six latitudinal plate series (Fig. 3I.10). Subdivision of the gonyaulacoids (or gonyaulacaleans), shown in Fig. 3I.11, is also important.

The earliest record of a fossil confidently assigned to the dinoflagellates is a single dinocyst species, *Sahulidinium ottii*, from the Middle Triassic (Stover and Helby, 1987). The tabulation is unclear, but probably of gonyaulacoid–peridinioid type (although not closely similar to later gonyaulacaleans or

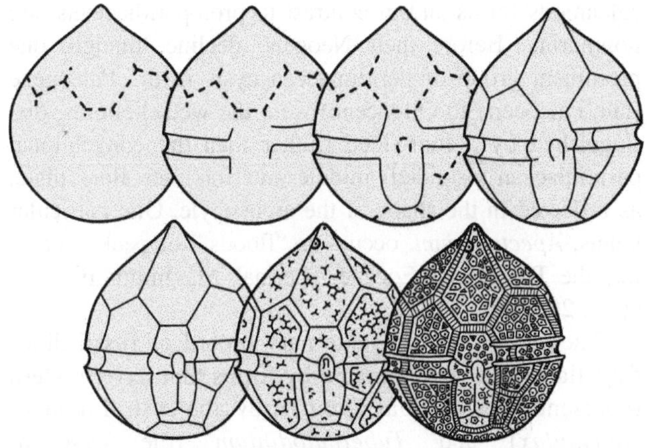

FIGURE 31.9 Variation in the degree of reflection of motile cell features on dinoflagellate cysts found in the fossil record. It is important to note that the reflected plates and suture ("paraplates" and "parasutures") are nonfunctional on cysts except insofar as they may be involved in archaeopyle formation. Adapted from Gocht (1983).

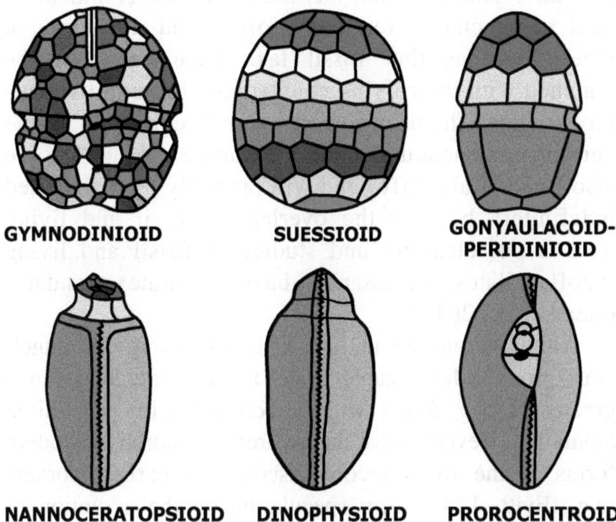

FIGURE 31.10 Tabulation types among living and fossil dinoflagellates. In the gymnodinioid type, amphiesmal vesicles are numerous, and usually lack thecal plates, the cells being thus "unarmored." In all the other types the vesicles contain thecal plates, the cells thus being "armored." In the suessioid type, amphiesmal vesicles are arranged in seven to ten latitudinal series. In the gonyaulacoid–peridinioid type, well-developed thecal plates are arranged in five or six latitudinal series and a longitudinal sulcal seres. Dinophysioid tabulation involves four latitudinal series of relatively few plates and a sagittal suture, which separates the dinoflagellate into two lateral halves; usually the cingulum is located toward the anterior end of the cell, in contrast to the usually more or less mid-length cingular position in the gonyaulacoid–peridinioid type. The nannoceratopsioid tabulation type involves shows an episome (that part of the cell anterior to the cingulum) similar to that of gonyaulacoid–peridinioid type and a hyposome (that part of the cell posterior to the cingulum) practically identical to the dinophysioid type. Unlike all other types, the prorocentroid type lacks a cingulum or (obvious) sulcus and the flagella are located anteriorly rather than ventrally. The theca consists of large plates, separated by a sagittal suture resembling that of dinophysioids, and a series of small plates anteriorly. Adapted from Fensome et al. (1993).

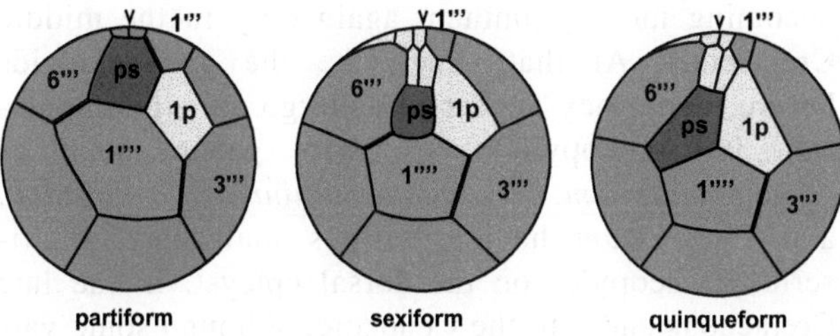

FIGURE 31.11 Variations on the tabulation of the gonyaulacalean hyposome. In the quinqueform pattern the single antapical plate is five-sided; in the sexiform pattern the antapical plate is six-sided and the anterior boundary of the ps plate abuts against the first posterior intercalary (1p) plate; in the partiform pattern the antapical plate is also six-sided, but the anterior boundary of the ps plate abuts against the first postcingular (1''') plate. *ps*, Posterior sulcal. Based on Evitt (1985).

peridinialeans). During the Late Triassic a variety of dinocysts appeared, including forms with a suessioid tabulation and forms with a diversity of gonyaulacoid–peridinioid patterns, although again not closely related to later classic gonyaulacaleans or peridinialeans. Many of these taxa became extinct at the end of the Triassic.

The record of dinocysts in the Early Jurassic is sporadic both in time and space. The isolated occurrence of *Liasidium variabile* in the Sinemurian (Riding and Thomas, 1992) is significant in which the paratabulation appears in part to be peridinioid, although critical features that would confirm its affinity are not apparent. Although geographically restricted, assemblages in the Pliensbachian were the most diverse since the Triassic; they include partiform gonyaulacoids, the earliest true gonyaulacaleans (Fig. 31.11) and *Nannoceratopsis*, with its unique nannoceratopsioid paratabulation (see Fig. 31.10). The later Toarcian saw the radiation of the *Parvocysta* group of peridinioids, the first fully confirmed peridinialean tabulation, which differs from most later members of the order only in having five rather than four apical plates.

The Middle Jurassic witnessed the burgeoning of sexiform gonyaulacoids, Bajocian taxa being characterized by an "experimentation" of archeopyle types — notably the multiplated precingular archeopyles of *Dissiliodinium* (Wiggan et al., 2018). By the Callovian and Oxfordian the archeopyle had stabilized to single plate precingular or epicystal (in which all plates anterior to the cingulum are removed), with genera such as *Gonyaulacysta* and *Dichadogonyaulax*, respectively. The first areoligeraceans (sexiform gonyaulacoids with a tendency to be asymmetrical, with the sulcus offset to the left) appear in the early Kimmeridgian, with *Senoniasphaera jurassica*. The similarly asymmetrical, horn-bearing ceratioids appear during the Tithonian, with species of *Muderongia*. Partiform gonyaulacoids such as *Pareodinia* and *Batioladinium* are also notable in the Late Jurassic and Early Cretaceous.

After the Toarcian peak of the *Parvocysta* group, peridinioids occur only sporadically in the Jurassic, becoming more prominent again only in the middle Cretaceous. At that time, like the gonyaulacoids before them, they appear to undergo an experimentation in archeopyle types, with genera such as *Chichaouadinium*, *Palaeoperidinium*, *Ovoidinium*, and *Luxadinium* having various multiplate, multiseries archeopyles on the dorsal epicyst. In the late Cretaceous and into the Cenozoic, although some variation persists, most peridinioids settled on a single-plate intercalary archaeopyle.

Among gonyaulacoids, areoligeraceans with subdued ornamentation, such as *Cyclonephelium* and *Aptea*, are important through much of the Cretaceous, as are ceratioids such as *Odontochitina*. But the most common Cretaceous gonyaulacoids are the sexiforms: they show a range of morphologies, from proximate (e.g., *Cribroperidinium* and *Apteodinium*) to chorate (*Oligosphaeridium* and *Kleithriasphaeridium*). Most Cretaceous gonyaulacoids have a single-plate precingular or an apical archeopyle. In the latest Cretaceous and Paleogene, areoligeraceans with high ornamentation become common, with specimens of *Glaphyrocysta* and *Areoligera* complex "flooding" many marine Paleocene assemblages. Surprisingly, given their abundance in present waters, ceratioids had largely disappeared from the fossil record by the end of the Cretaceous and are almost absent from the Cenozoic record. In the Paleogene, chorate gonyaulacoids with a precingular archeopyle, notably *Cordosphaeridium* and its allies, are important, as are quinqueform chorate gonyaulacoids such as *Hystrichosphaeridium* and *Homotryblium*.

Peridinioids continue to be important components in the Cenozoic record, although two groups need to be recognized, the peridiniaceans and the protoperidiniaceans. The difference recognized among modern forms is that peridiniaceans have four to six cingular plates, whereas protoperidiniaceans have three cingular plates. Such detail is rarely seen among fossils, but from observations on modern forms, protoperidiniacean cysts tend to have a single wall layer (in contrast to the usual two in peridiniaceans), and are often pigmented brown (in contrast to the transparent walls of peridiniacean cysts). Protoperidiniacean cysts also sometimes have an archeopyle (reflecting the middle anterior intercalary plate) that is asymmetrical and offset from the midline of the dorsal surface. Based on such features, it appears that protoperidiniacean cysts first appear in the latest Cretaceous or earliest Paleogene with *Phelodinium* and *Lejeunecysta* and become increasing prominent through the Cenozoic. Today, protoperidiniaceans are important, exclusively marine dinoflagellates. Intriguingly, peridiniacean cysts in the earlier Cenozoic as exclusively marine fossils, flourishing in the Paleogene, but wane in the Neogene, disappearing as organic-walled cysts from the marine fossil record in the Tortonian with the last *Palaeocystodinium*. Modern peridiniaceans, except for calcareous forms and in contrast to protoperidiniaceans, are nonmarine. Before their Neogene decline, though, one prominent group of peridiniacean cysts in the Paleogene (late Paleocene to Oligocene) were the wetzelielloids, distinguished by a four-sided (rather than the conventional peridiniacean six-sided) middle anterior intercalary plate, as reflected in the shape of the archeopyle. One particular genus, *Apectodinium*, occurs as "floods," or peaks, marking the Paleocene–Eocene Thermal Maximum (Crouch et al., 2001).

The Neogene and Quaternary record of fossil dinoflagellate cysts is dominated by forms that have modern representatives, such as *Spiniferites* (the cyst of modern *Gonyaulax*) and *Tuberculodinium* (the cyst of *Pyrophacus*). This leads us to the observation that fossil dinoflagellates have been described almost exclusively on the basis of the cyst stage, whereas living dinoflagellates have been described mainly on the basis of the motile stage, with separate sets of experts and histories of study. This situation has led to the development of dual nomenclature for many forms, and it is only in recent decades that fossil taxa have begun to be matched with their living counterparts through live culture studies. The dual nomenclature is condoned by the current nomenclatural code (Turland et al., 2018; see also Head et al., 2016) and will probably be maintained indefinitely because the overlap of fossil and living taxa is not clear-cut and studies of fossil and living dinoflagellates necessarily have separate mandates (Head et al., 2017).

Although only about 13% of motile living dinoflagellates produce fossilizable cysts, the percentage is much greater among forms with a gonyaulacoid–peridinioid tabulation. Nevertheless, the low representation of modern forms in the fossil record discouraged earlier workers (e.g., Evitt, 1981) from speculating on the evolution of dinoflagellates. However, the fact that we do have a significant fossil record of dinoflagellates, in contrast to that of other groups such as ciliates, is to be celebrated. Indeed, in combination with other evidence such as molecular, the fossil record can contribute significantly to a meaningful phylogenetic scenario for the group (Fensome et al., 1993; Janouškovec et al., 2017). A possible evolutionary scenario based on all lines of evidence is shown in Fig. 3I.12.

One aspect that was predicted by the fossil record (Fensome et al., 1996) and is now supported by molecular data is that the dinoflagellates underwent an early Mesozoic radiation that produced the dinoflagellate morphology as we recognize it today. Dinoflagellates must of course have had pre-Mesozoic ancestors, but exactly what they were is unknown. Suggestions have been made on morphological grounds that the ancestors of dinoflagellates might be found among the

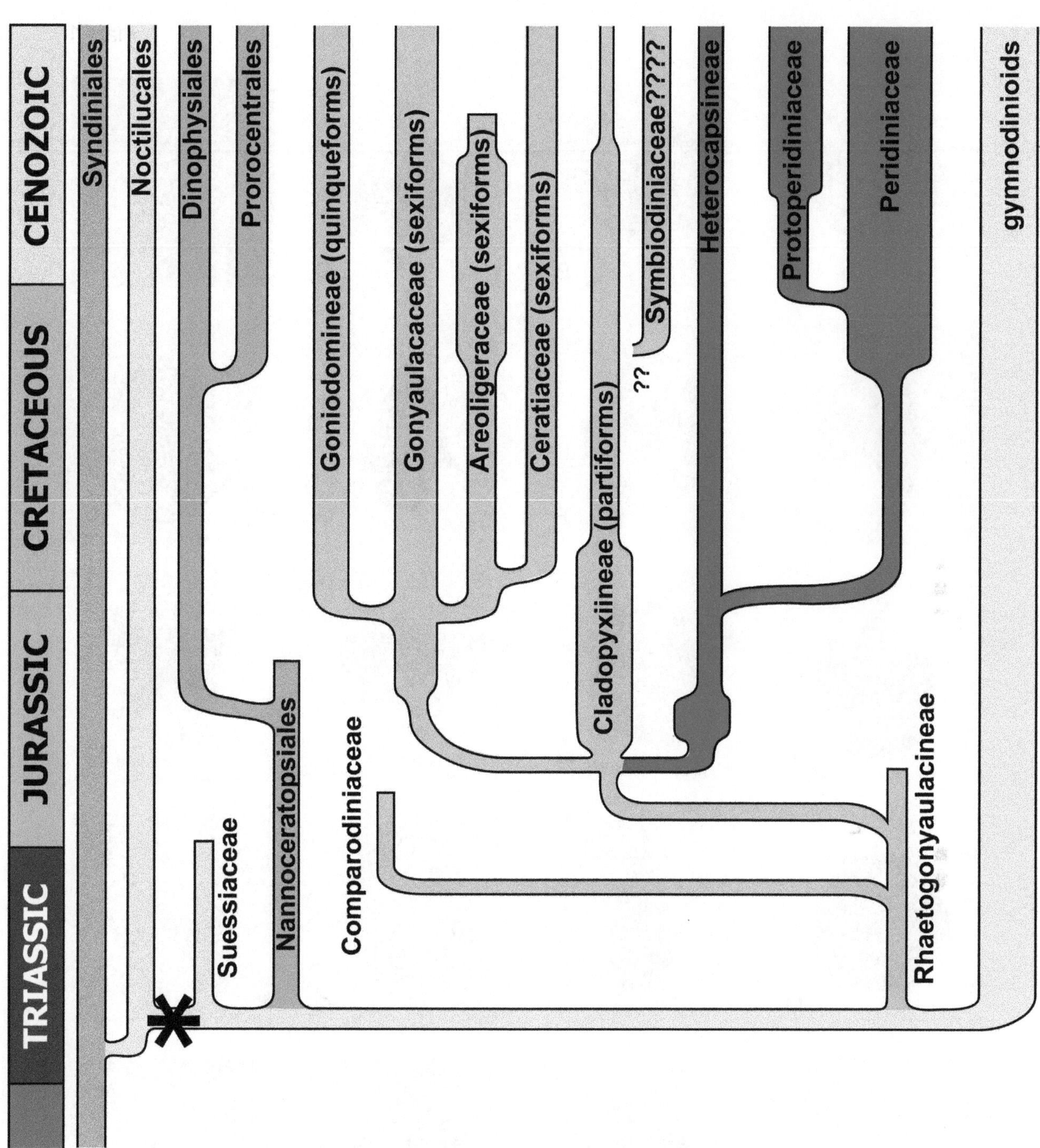

FIGURE 3I.12 Phylogenetic scheme for dinoflagellates based on fossil, biological and molecular evidence. The asterisk indicates the possible stage at which dinosterols began to be present in dinoflagellates. Adapted and updated from Fensome et al. (1993).

acritarchs (Downie, 1973), but regularly arranged processes and polygonal openings are characteristic of other organisms, not just dinoflagellates (Fensome et al., 2000). The presence of dinoflagellates as far back as the Proterozoic has been postulated based on the detection of dinosteranes in sedimentary rocks (Moldowan and Talyzina, 1998). However, other groups of organisms are known to produce dinosterols (from which dinosteranes are derived) (Janouškovec et al., 2017). Janouškovec et al. also noted that based on the latest molecular evidence, early derived dinoflagellates did not have dinosterols (Fig. 3I.12). So the pre-Mesozoic history of the dinoflagellate lineage remains open to speculation (Plates 3I.1 and 3I.2).

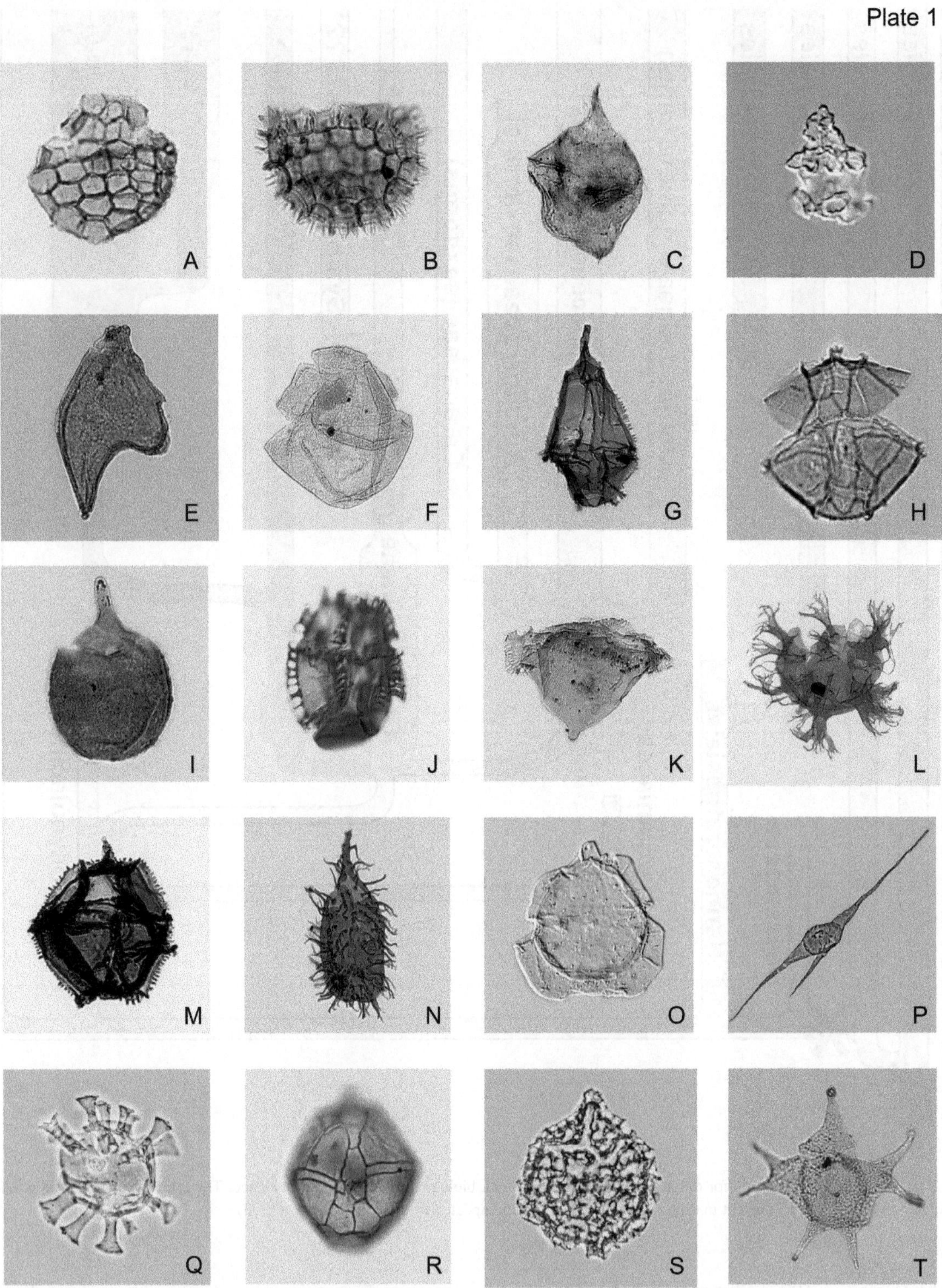

PLATE 3I.1 A variety of Late Triassic to Early Cretaceous dinoflagellate cysts. Specific sizes are not available due to the archival sources of most of the images, but most specimens range 20–100 μm in maximum dimension; exceptions include the specimen shown on Plate 3I.1, Fig. P, which is about 400 μm long, and that shown in this figure, Fig. D, which is less than 20 μm long. (A) *Suessia swabiana*, (B) *Wanneria listeri*, (C) *Liasidium variabile*, (D) *Susadinium scrofoides*, (E) *Nannoceratopsis pellucida*, (F) *Dissiliodinium caddaense*, (G) *Gonyaulacysta jurassica*; (H) *Korystocysta gochtii*, (I) *Pareodinia* sp., (J) *Stephanelytron redcliffense*, (K) *Wanaea fimbriata*, (L) *Perisseiasphaeridium pannosum*, (M) *Rhynchodiniopsis serrata*, (N) *Gochteodinia villosa*, (O) *Sirmiodinium grossii*, (P) *Odontochitina costata*, (Q) *Oligosphaeridium totum*, (R) *Leptodinium mirabile*, (S) *Aptea cassis*, (T) *Nyktericysta davisii*.

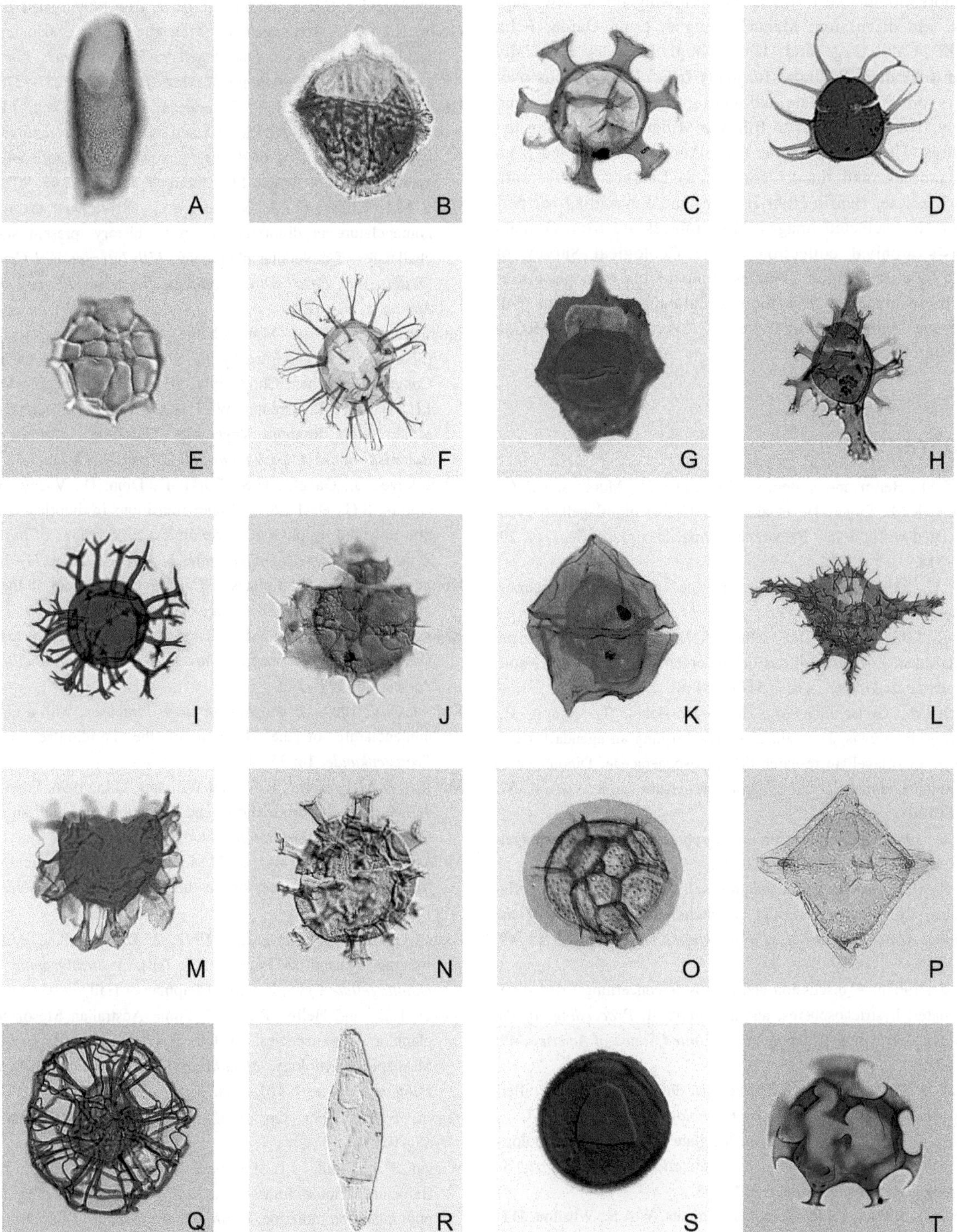

PLATE 3I.2 A variety of Cretaceous and Cenozoic dinoflagellate cysts. Specific sizes are not available due to the archival sources of the images, but most specimens range 20–100 μm in maximum dimension. (A) *Batioladinium micropodum*, (B) *Cribroperidinium orthoceras*, (C) *Callaiosphaeridium asymmetricum*, (D) *Cauca parva*, (E) *Cladopyxidium saeptum*, (F) *Surculosphaeridium longispinatum*; (G) *Chatangiella coronata*, (H) *Xenascus ceratioides*, (I) *Achomosphaera* sp., (J) *Palynodinium grallator*, (K) *Palaeoperidinium pyrophorum*, (L) *Apectodinium augustum*, (M) *Glaphyrocysta extensa*, (N) *Homotryblium tenuispinosum*, (O) *Heteraulacacysta fehmarnense*, (P) *Rhombodinium porosum*, (Q) *Nematosphaeropsis reticulensis*, (R) *Svalbardella cooksoniae*, (S) *Tectatodinium pellitum*, and (T) *Selenopemphix armageddonensis*.

Acknowledgments

The authors would like to thank the following for review, suggestions, and discussion: Manuel Bringué, Lynn Dafoe, Felix Gradstein, Gabi Ogg, and James Ogg. RAF is especially indebted to Graham Williams for many fruitful discussions over the years on dinoflagellate morphology, biostratigraphy, and taxonomy. We are grateful to Bill MacMillan for preparing the text-figures. The images for the two plates were compiled from various sources, and thanks are due to Laurent de Verteuil, Andrew MacRae, Henrik Nøhr-Hansen, and Jim Riding for permission to use selected images. Most images are from Graham Williams's archival collection at the Geological Survey of Canada (Atlantic), which contains some of his own photos as well as those inherited from the late colleagues Dan Beju, Bill Evitt, Dave McIntyre, and Lew Stover. This is NRCan Contribution no. 20180332.

Bibliography

Crouch, E.M., Heilmann-Clausen, C., Brinkhuis, H., Morgans, H.E.G., Rogers, K.M., Egger, H., et al., 2001, Global dinoflagellate event associated with the late Paleocene thermal maximum. *Geology*, **29**: 315–318.

Downie, C., 1973, Observations on the nature of acritarchs. *Palaeontology*, **16**: 239–259.

Ehrenberg, C.G., 1838, Die Infusionsthierchen als volkommene Organismen. Ein Blick in das tiefere organische Leben der Natur. *Leipzig, Leopold Voss*, xvii + 547 p., 64 pl.

Elbrächter, M., Gottschling, M., Hildebrand-Habel, T., Keupp, H., Kohring, R., Lewis, J., et al., 2008, Establishing an agenda for calcareous dinoflagellate research (Thoracosphaeraceae, Dinophyceae) including a nomenclatural synopsis of generic names. *Taxon*, **57**: 1289–1303.

Evitt, W.R., 1961, Observations on the morphology of fossil dinoflagellates. *Micropaleontology*, **7**: 385–420.

Evitt, W.R., 1963a, A discussion and proposals concerning fossil dinoflagellates, hystrichospheres, and acritarchs, I. *Proceedings of the National Academy of Sciences of the United States of America*, **49**: 158–164.

Evitt, W.R., 1963b, A discussion and proposals concerning fossil dinoflagellates, hystrichospheres, and acritarchs, II. *Proceedings of the National Academy of Sciences of the United States of America*, **49**: 298–302.

Evitt, W.R., 1981, The difference it makes that dinoflagellates did it differently. *International Commission for Palynology Newsletter*, **4**: 6–7.

Evitt, W.R., 1985, Sporopollenin dinoflagellate cysts: their morphology and interpretation. *American Association of Stratigraphic Palynologists, Monograph Series*, **1**: 333.

Fensome, R.A., Taylor, F.J.R., Norris, G., Sarjeant, W.A.S., Wharton, D.I., and Williams, G.L., 1993, A classification of fossil and living dinoflagellates. *Micropaleontology Press Special Paper*, **7**: 351.

Fensome, R.A., MacRae, R.A., Moldowan, J.M., Taylor, F.J.R., and Williams, G.L., 1996, The early Mesozoic radiation of dinoflagellates. *Paleobiology*, **22**: 329–338.

Fensome, R.A., Saldarriaga, J., and Taylor, F.J.R., 2000, Dinoflagellate phylogeny revisited: reconciling morphological and molecular based phylogenies. *Grana*, **38**: 66–80 (Cover date 1999, issued 2000).

Gocht, H., 1983, Morphogenetische Deutung und Bezeichnung ausgewählter Merkmale bei Dinoflagellaten-Zysten. *Neues Jahrbuch für Geologie und Paläontologie, Monatshefte*, **1983-5**: 257–276.

Head, M.J., Fensome, R.A., Herendeen, P.S., and Skog, J.E., 2016, Proposals to amend Article 11.8 and its examples to remove ambiguity in the sanctioning of dual nomenclature for dinoflagellates, and an amendation of Article 11.7, Example 29. *Taxon*, **65**: 902–903.

Head, M.J., Ellegaard, M., Versteegh, G., 2017. Dual taxonomy and nomenclature in dinoflagellate cysts: history, present status, and challenges of molecular phylogeny. *11th International Congress on Modern and Fossil Dinoflagellates, Bordeaux 17 to 21-07-2017, Abstracts*, 60–61.

International Code of Nomenclature for algae, fungi, and plants (Shenzhen Code) adopted by the Nineteenth International Botanical Congress Shenzhen, China, July 2017. *In* Turland, N.J., Wiersema, J.H., Barrie, F.R., Greuter, W., Hawksworth, D.L., Herendeen, P.S., et al., (eds), Regnum Vegetabile. *Glashütten, Germany: Koeltz Botanical Books, https://doi.org/10.12705/Code.2018.*

Janouškovec, J., Gavelis, G.S., Burki, F., Dinh, D., Vachvaroff, T.R., Gornik, S.G., et al., 2017, Major transitions in dinoflagellate evolution unveiled by phylotranscriptomics. *Proceedings of the National Academy of Sciences United States of America*, **114**: 171–180.

Kofoid, C.A., 1907a, The plates of *Ceratium* with a note on the unity of the genus. *Zoologischer Anzeiger*, **32**: 177–183.

Kofoid, C.A., 1907b, Dinoflagellata of the San Diego region. III. Descriptions of new species. *University of California Publications in Zoology*, **3**: 299–340.

Kofoid, C.A., 1909, On *Peridinium steini* Jörgensen, with a note on the nomenclature of the skeleton of the Peridinidae. *Archiv für Protistenkunde*, **16**: 25–47.

MacRae, R.A., Fensome, R.A., and Williams, G.L., 1996, Fossil dinoflagellate diversity, originations, and extinctions and their significance. *Canadian Journal of Botany*, **74**: 1687–1694.

Moldowan, J.M., and Talyzina, N.M., 1998, Biogeochemical evidence for dinoflagellate ancestors in the Early Cambrian. *Science*, **281**: 1168–1170.

Riding, J.B., and Thomas, J.E., 1992, 2. Dinoflagellate cysts of the Jurassic System. *In* Powell, A.J. (ed), *A Stratigraphic Index of Dinoflagellate Cysts*. London: Chapman & Hall, 7–98.

Stover, L.E., and Helby, R., 1987, Some Australian Mesozoic microplankton index species. *In* Jell, P.A. (ed), Studies in Australian Mesozoic Palynology. *Memoir of the Association of Australasian Palaeontologists*, **4**: 101–134.

Taylor, F.J.R., 1980, On dinoflagellate evolution. *BioSystems*, **13**: 65–108.

Wiggan, N.J., Riding, J.B., Fensome, R.A., and Mattioli, E., 2018, The Bajocian (Middle Jurassic): a key interval in the early Mesozoic phytoplankton radiation. *Earth-Science Reviews*, **180**: 126–146.

Wood, G.D., Gabriel, A.M., and Lawson, J.C., 1996, Chapter 3. Palynological techniques—processing and microscopy. *In* Jansonius, J., and McGregor, D.C. (eds), Palynology: Principles and Applications. *Dallas: American Association of Stratigraphic Palynologists Foundation,* **Volume 2**: 29–50.

Subchapter 3J

Plants, spores, and pollen

H. Kerp, G. Mangerud and S.R. Gradstein

Abstract

The greening of our planet is a fascinating story. The vast majority of the Earth's biomass is produced by plants, ranging from microscopically small phytoplankton to complex rainforest ecosystems. The evolution of plants can be traced back to the Archean and is intrinsically connected with the evolution of the Earth's geosphere and atmosphere.

Paleobotany, the study of fossil plants, and palynology, the study of organic-walled, acid-resistant microfossils (palynomorphs), is widely used in biostratigraphy and enables reconstructions of ancient ecosystems.

Anatomically preserved plant remains contribute to a better understanding of the histology and physiology of these fossil organisms. The more common impression and compression fossils provide useful information on the paleoecology and paleoclimate. Cuticles show a variety of features, including the distribution and density of the stomata, that are widely used as proxies for reconstructing ancient CO_2 levels. Palynomorphs have very resistant organic walls and an excellent preservation potential. They comprise not only reproductive parts of plants, such as pollen and spores, but also whole organisms such as unicellular algae. Most palynomorphs belong to the plant kingdom sensu lato except for a few groups, for example, chitinozoans (an extinct group of marine microfossils) and scolecodonts (jaw elements of polychaete annelid worms). Palynomorphs are classified and named based on their morphology. Pollen and spores are usually between 10 and 100 μm in diameter. Most plant species produce their own typical pollen or spore type. However, some types can only be related to the genus or family level. Moreover, the natural affinity of dispersed fossil pollen and spores is often unclear. However, this does not limit their use in biostratigraphy. Palynology has the clear advantage that only a few grams of sediment are needed for an analysis. Pollen and spores are produced in large quantities and disperse easily over wide distances. They are the only fossils that enable direct correlations of terrestrial and marine sequences. Although pollen and spore assemblages not necessarily reflect the compositional abundance of the macroflora, they are excellent proxies for reconstructing past vegetation types and provide valuable information on paleoenvironments and paleoclimate.

3J.1 The Precambrian

The earliest putative life forms may be as old as 3.77 Ga and possibly 4.28 Ga (Dodd et al., 2017). Prior to the Proterozoic, cyanobacteria and microbial mats probably represented the only forms of life on the Earth. They are known from Greenland (Nutman et al., 2016) and Australia (Van Kranendonk et al., 2008). The early atmosphere contained only minor quantities of oxygen. Anoxygenic photosynthesis does not use water as an electron donor but rather can use a variety of substrates, including sulfide, iron, and hydrogen (Shih, 2015). Around 2.45 Ga a major oxygenation event took place, when a new type of photosynthesis evolved. This was a major first step toward the future life on land. The origin of eukaryotes probably dates back to the early Mesoproterozoic (1.4–1.5 Ga); the earliest eukaryotes are described from basinal and lagoonal sediments of the Roper Group in Northern Australia (Javaux and Knoll, 2016).

Acritarchs, originally defined as unicellular marine palynomorphs of unknown origin (Evitt, 1963), are among the oldest fossils from the Proterozoic (Traverse, 2007), maybe even dating back to the Archean (Javaux et al., 2010). Early forms seem to be linked to the appearance of eukaryotic organisms. The robust-walled, mostly planktonic acritarchs range up until the present (Fig. 3J.1). However, they show the greatest diversity and fastest evolution from the latest Proterozoic to the end of the Silurian. They are excellent biostratigraphic markers for this time interval and also are applied as markers in younger successions. More complex life forms developed during the Neoproterozoic, and this appears to coincide with the increasing oxygenation of the ocean (Lenton et al., 2014).

Eukaryotes adapted to freshwater environments appeared much earlier than previously thought. Lake deposits from the Nonesuch Formation (Michigan; c. 1 Ga) and fluviolacustrine sediments of the Torridon Group (NW Scotland; 1.2–1.0 Ga) have yielded a fairly wide variety of organic microfossils, including microbial mats in ephemeral pools (Prave, 2002), multicellular organisms, complex-walled cysts, and dorsiventral compressed thalli up to 1 mm in diameter (Strother et al., 2011; Strother and Wellman, 2016; Wellman and Strother, 2015). Other forms include *Vaucheria*-like multicellular algae from the Neoproterozoic (800–700 Ma) of Spitsbergen (Knoll et al., 1984). Vascular

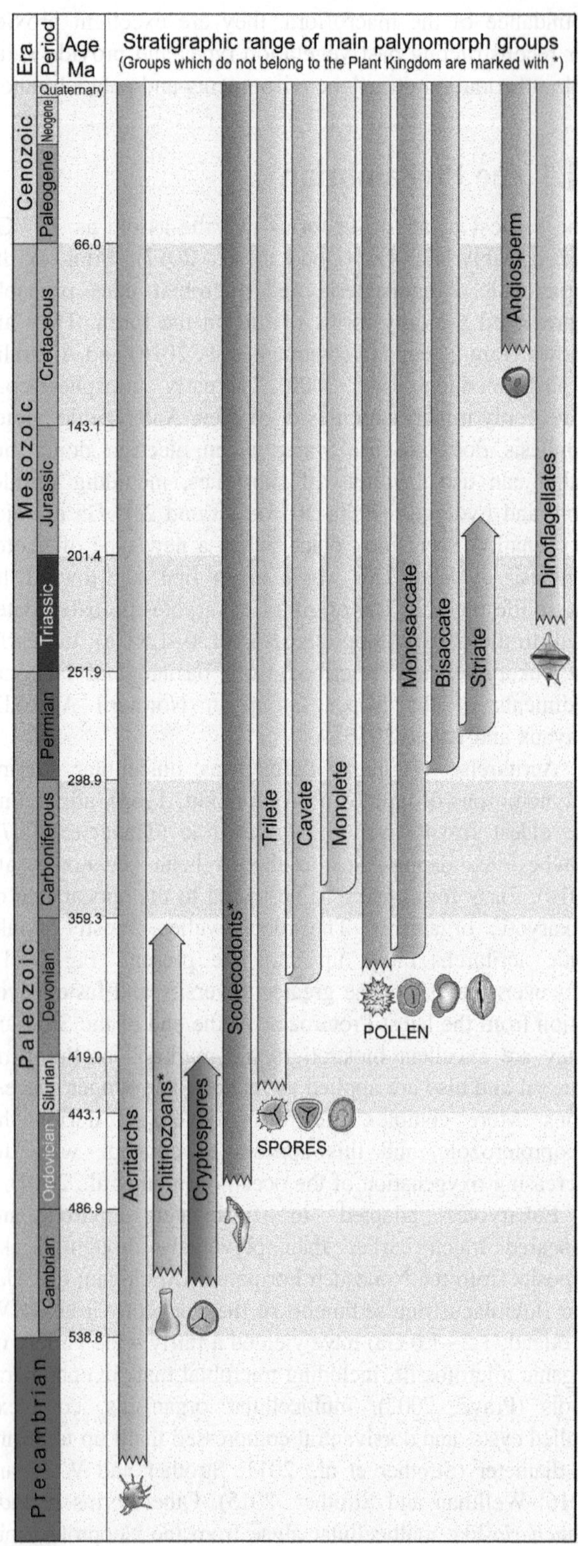

FIGURE 3J.1 Stratigraphic ranges of main palynomorph groups.

land plants are assumed to have evolved from green freshwater algae; the most closely related living ones are coleochaetes and charophytes.

3J.2 Paleozoic

The dramatic change in the fossil record, known as the Cambrian explosion, is also reflected in the diversification of acritarchs that show a great structural and sculptural complexity. Together with chitinozoans, acritarchs are widely used for biostratigraphic studies of Ordovician–Silurian successions (e.g., Al-Shawareb et al., 2017; Servais et al., 2018).

The evolution of early Paleozoic marine phytoplankton is well documented, but the record of the earliest terrestrial plant life is much scantier. The land surface was likely inhabited as early as the mid-Cambrian by cyanobacteria, fungi, lichens, algae, and presumably liverworts. However, definite proof is difficult because terrestrial successions are rare, not easily recognizable, and the organisms had very little preservation potential. The systematic position of cryptospores, organic-walled spore-like microfossils that often form permanent dyads or tetrads but lack a trilete mark, is problematic. Cryptospores first appeared in the middle Cambrian (Taylor and Strother, 2009; Strother, 2015), diversified in the Late Ordovician and Silurian, and disappeared when vascular land plants started to rise in the Early Devonian. The oldest cryptospore monads that are probably of liverwort affinity are from the Dapingian of Argentina (Rubinstein et al., 2010).

The colonization of the land surface is one of the most significant steps in the Earth and life history. Life on land, a basically hostile environment, required, apart from major physiological changes, a number of major adaptations: (1) a cuticle protecting the plant against desiccation and UV-B radiation, (2) a vascular system to provide sufficient support for upright growth and for the transport of water, nutrients, and photosynthesis products, and last but not least (3) sporangia and spores for sexual reproduction, providing optimal protection and assuring a wide dispersal of the precious genetic material. Early vascular land plants are defined by the combination these three features. Cuticles and spores are composed of very resistant material. The vascular strand consists of two tissues of which the xylem with its dead, thick-walled tracheids serving for the transport of water and nutrients is very resistant. Land plants having sporangia and spores but lacking a vascular system and/or a cuticle are classified as bryophytes, a group that includes liverworts, hornworts, and mosses. Bryophytes are relatively rare in the fossil record as they have limited preservation potential. The oldest macroscopic bryophyte is *Metzgeriothallus*, a liverwort from the Givetian of New York State (VanAller Hernick et al., 2008). In addition, several enigmatic forms, some with well-developed cuticle-like sheets and spores, such as the Late Devonian *Protosalvinia*, have been described. The palynological record of the Upper Ordovician and Silurian includes various types of organic debris superficially resembling remains of vascular land plants, such as tracheid-like banded tubes, cuticle-like sheets and cryptospores, but these cannot be directly related to vascular land plants. Nevertheless, they indicate that moist terrestrial habitats were already inhabited long before the advent of vascular land plants.

The earliest bona fide vascular land plants (Fig. 3J.2), belonging to the group of the rhyniophytes, are known from the Wenlock, that is, *Cooksonia barrandei* from the Sheinwoodian of the Czech Republic (Libertín et al., 2018) and *Cooksonia* cf. *pertonii* from the Homerian of Ireland (Edwards and Feehan, 1980). They were tiny, just a few centimeters high or even less, with naked bifurcating axes, a simple vascular strand, a cuticle with stomata, and terminal sporangia. More complex, but poorly preserved is *Baragwanathia*, a putative early lycophyte with remarkably robust axes covered with leafy structures from the Ludlow of southern Australia. Although these are the earliest records of vascular land plants, it can be assumed that they were already around in the Late Ordovician, as is evidenced by the dispersed spore record (Edwards et al., 2014). A recently published account on a flora from the Pridoli (latest Silurian) of the Prague Basin (Czech Republic) comprising six species nicely illustrates the initial land plant diversification and dispersal (Kraft et al., 2019). Nevertheless, it is astonishing, how long the land surface remained uninhabited, whereas life in the marine realm had quickly diversified since the development of calcareous and chitinous inner and exoskeletons. Desiccation may have been a limiting factor for colonizing the land, but probably not the only or even not the most important one, as all known early land plants grew in temperate regions in moist habitats such as floodplains. A decrease of UV-B radiation may well have been the trigger enabling plants to settle on land; all early land plants had robust cuticles——even coeval nonvascular plants had well-developed protective, cuticle-like layers, for example, *Nematothallus*, *Protosalvinia*, and *Bitelaria* (Taylor et al., 2009).

Four groups of vascular land plants are known from the late Silurian and early Devonian (Taylor et al., 2009). Rhyniophytes show the same basic organization as *Cooksonia* but Devonian representatives could reach a height of up to 25 cm. Zosterophyllophytes had repeatedly bifurcating axes with laterally attached sporangia consisting of two valves; they could be arranged in a strobilus. Trimerophytes often had a more complex vascular strand and the most advanced forms possessed an upright main stem with lateral, repeatedly bifurcating axes. The spindle-shaped sporangia were standing in dense clusters at the ends of ultimate branchlets. Axes of the zosterphyllophytes and trimerophytes were naked or covered with small spine-like enations. Early lycophytes looked remarkably similar to modern lycopsids, but the leafy appendages lacked a mid-vein. One of the most famous Lower Devonian (Pragian) plant occurrences is the Rhynie Chert from Scotland. Hot-spring deposits conserved a complete early terrestrial ecosystem, including vascular plants and a wide variety of micro-organisms (for an overview see: Trewin and Kerp, 2017). Plants are preserved in situ, often still in upright position, showing an amazing amount of detail down to the subcellular level. Apart from complete life cycles with germinating spores and male reproductive organs releasing sperm cells (Kerp, 2017), interactions of plants with other organisms like fungi have been demonstrated (Krings et al., 2007), including the oldest known mycorrhizae (Remy et al., 1994). Plants diversified rapidly during the Devonian and Emsian trimerophytes already attained a height of 1.5–2 m.

The first fern-like plants appeared in the Middle Devonian. The most remarkable example is *Eospermatopteris* from the Givetian of Gilboa, New York State, where a fossil forest with upright standing tree stumps associated with slightly smaller lycophyte trees has been uncovered (Stein et al., 2007, 2012). The leafless *Eospermatopteris* trees were up to 8 m tall and had a crown of branches with lateral branches bearing several orders of repeatedly bifurcating, three-dimensionally arranged branchlets. Scars on the main stem indicate that complete branching systems were abscised. A slightly younger in situ preserved fossil forest consisting of lycophytes has been found in Spitsbergen (Berry and Marshall, 2015). Smaller but still a few meters tall was *Rhacophyton*, a leafless, early fern-like plant. In *Rhacophyton*, two orders of branches were arranged in the same plane; only the ultimate branchlets that bifurcated only a few times were three-dimensionally arranged.

All early spore-producing land plants were bound to at least periodically humid environments like floodplains, because water was required for conveying the free-swimming sperm to the egg cells. Heterospory and ultimately the development of the seed habit were crucial evolutionary innovations, enabling plants to colonize drier habitats further away from the humid floodplains and water bodies. The heterosporous life history is characterized by haploid plant life stages (=gametophytes) that are strictly unisexual, and thus incapable of self-fertilization. Heterospory has developed a number of times, independently in different groups of plants and at different times. It co-occurs with the maturation of the gametophytes while housed within the spore walls, instead of being free-living. Heterosporous plants show a differentiation into large megaspores containing the female gametophyte

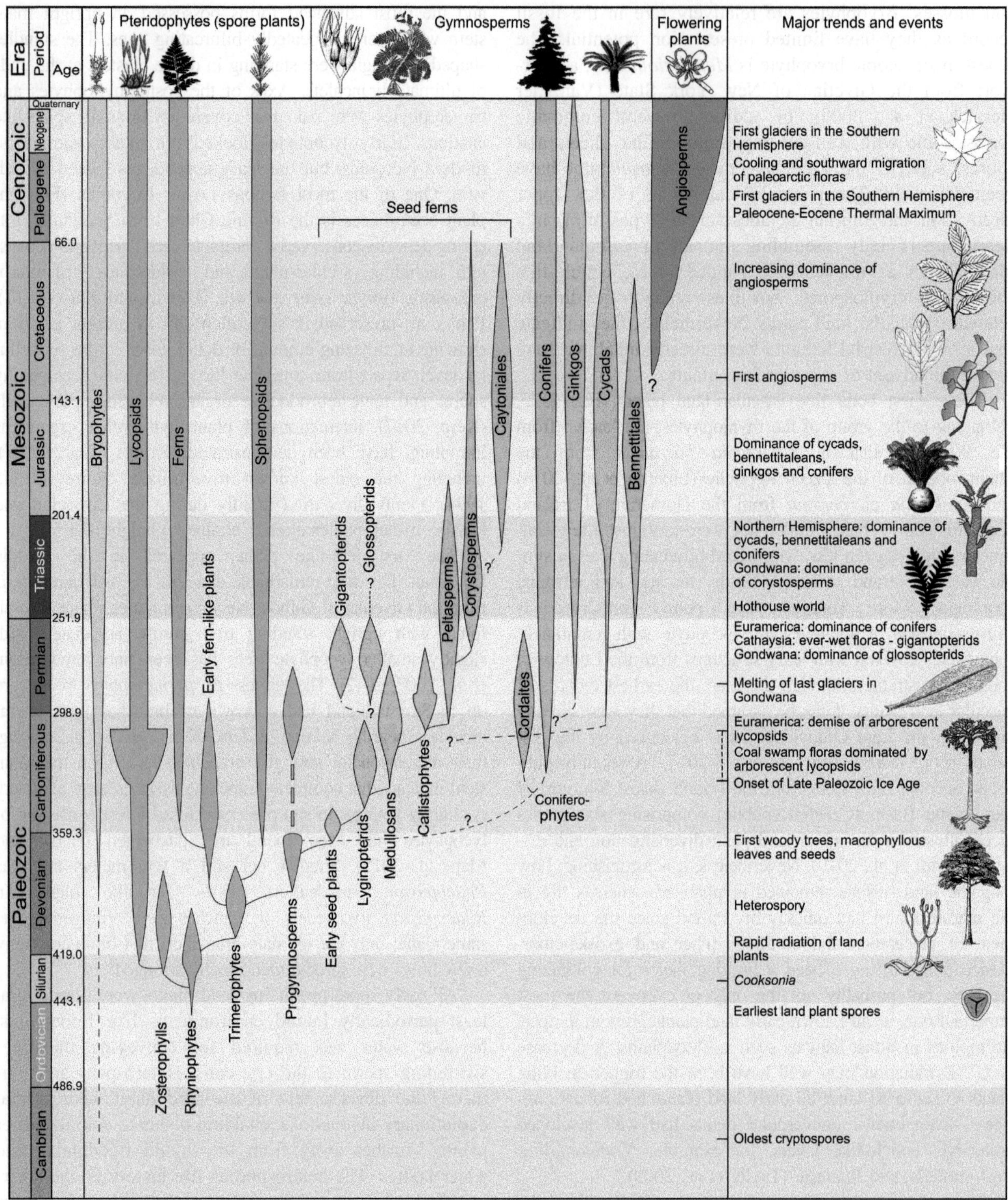

FIGURE 3J.2 Evolution and stratigraphic ranges of major groups of land plants.

and small microspores containing the male gametophyte. The female gametophyte is protected by the thick megaspore wall and the megaspore contains a nutrient supply for the developing embryo. Fertilization takes place via free-swimming, flagellate sperm cells released by the microspores. The oldest dispersed megaspores have been reported from the upper Emsian. The development of the seed in which the female gametophyte is even better protected, and pollination and fertilization are more efficient, is the next logical step. In early seed plants the female gametophyte is enclosed by several protective layers and has a liquid-filled pollen chamber in which free-swimming sperms are released, whereas in more advanced seed plants a pollen tube serves for the passive transport of the male nuclei.

When plants became taller, they needed more robust stems that provided sufficient strength. Some plants, for example, *Eospermatopteris*, achieved this with a stem composed of a large number of individual vascular strands embedded in a groundmass of thin-walled cells. An efficient and most successful alternative is a woody stem with secondary growth as in all modern trees. In arborescent lycophytes, which were dominant during most of the Pennsylvanian, secondary growth primarily took place in the outermost layer of the stem or cortex.

The Late Devonian, particularly the Famennian, which is characterized by a global sea-level drop exposing huge areas of land, witnessed a number of major evolutionary innovations. *Archaeopteris* was a tree with woody stems that could reach a diameter of more than 1 m and a height of several tens of meters. *Archaeopteris* formed extensive woodlands in coastal lowland areas in the middle and late Frasnian. The wood of this heterosporous progymnosperm was remarkably similar to some types of modern conifer wood. Moreover, it was the first plant with true macrophyllous leaves. Pre-Famennian plants were leafless, except for the lycophytes that had narrow, single-veined microphyllous leaves. The development of the macrophyllous leaf can be related to several factors: (1) due to the rise of the terrestrial vegetation during the Devonian, the atmospheric CO_2 concentration gradually dropped from c. 16 to 4 times the current value; as a consequence, plants had to "process" more air to take up sufficient CO_2 for photosynthesis; (2) also the increase in plant size resulted in a rising CO_2 demand; and (3) in woody trees the photosynthetic surface is reduced to the green parts of the plant. In order to compensate these limitations, plants had to increase their photosynthetic surface. The arrangement of axes in a single plane was a first step to the development of a macrophyllous leaf. The earliest seed plants, *Moresnetia* and *Elkinsia*, appeared in the Famennian. They belong to the pteridosperms or seed ferns, a heterogeneous group of Paleozoic and Mesozoic gymnosperms. Archetypical pteridosperms had fern-like foliage and true seeds; the anatomy of the axes was cycad like. The seed habit was an excellent and most efficient adaptation to survive in drier environments. In humid settings the first horsetails evolved.

Although the parent plants of palynomorphs often cannot be identified, it is obvious that there was an explosion of morphotypes during the Devonian, reflecting the rapid evolution and diversification of plants. Many forms were endemic to one of the two Devonian supercontinents, Gondwana and Euramerica, even though these were situated at comparable paleolatitudes; but also mixed and transitional floras are known. Consequently, local as well as regional palynostratigraphic schemes exist, using several different palynomorph groups. A cosmopolitan species, *Retispora lepidophyta*, allows worldwide correlations; its last appearance closely coincides with the Devonian–Carboniferous boundary. Acritarch diversity dropped dramatically at the end of the Devonian, making them less useful for biostratigraphy. However, in younger strata pollen and spores become more important.

By the end of the Devonian, all major lineages of land plants had evolved, except for the angiosperms. The explosive radiation and strong diversification of land plants during the late Silurian and Devonian, from tiny leafless bifurcated axes to tall trees with large leaves, are unique and only comparable to the rapid radiation and expansion within the angiosperms in the Late Cretaceous and Cenozoic. The rise of land plants had major impacts on the composition of the atmosphere, on erosion, on weathering, on sediment fluxes, on sedimentological processes, on soil formation, and on the hydrological cycle. A plant cover reduces erosion rates and the runoff. With the increasing size of plants roots penetrated deeper into the substrate. Plant-derived humic acids are crucial for weathering processes, including the formation of clay minerals. Weathering in pre-Devonian times was primarily physical but became predominantly chemical when the land vegetation developed (Davies and Gibling, 2010; Gibling and Davies, 2012; Gibling et al., 2014).

Little is known about plant life in the Mississippian, because large parts of the land surface were covered by a shallow sea. The few Tournaisian floras show a strong diversification of the ferns. The most diverse floras are from the upper Visean. These consist of horsetails (*Archaeocalamites*), sphenophylls, a few arborescent lycophytes, ferns, and a wide variety of pteridosperms. In the middle Mississippian (345 Ma) a global cooling resulted in the formation of an ice cover in Gondwana, the transition to an icehouse world and the beginning of a distinct floral provincialism.

Two centuries of extensive coal mining and the abundance of plant fossils, including anatomically preserved remains uncovered by these activities, have provided a wealth of information on Pennsylvanian floras. In the paleo-equatorial wetlands of Europe and North America, immense amounts of plant biomass accumulated and were later transformed into coal. The climate was hot and humid and the lush vegetation gave rise to elevated atmospheric oxygen levels with values of up to 28%–30%. As a consequence, wildfires were frequent. The waxing and waning of the Gondwanan ice sheet resulted in periodic sea-level changes. Some of these episodic warming and cooling intervals had relatively little effect on the composition of the flora because plants could retreat in refugia and subsequently recolonize their former habitats. One period of extreme global change, however, had devastating effects and resulted in the demise of the iconic coal swamp forests and marks a floristic turnover.

Arborescent lycophytes provided up to 90% of the biomass of the paleoequatorial lowland coal swamp forests in Europe and North America. Their stems primarily consisted of bark tissue. *Lepidodendron*, the tallest form, could reach a height of 45 m and had a crown of repeatedly bifurcating axes with long narrow leaves. *Sigillaria* was up to 20 m high and the main stem bifurcated terminally up to two times. Many arborescent lycophytes were heterosporous. *Calamites* or giant horsetails were up to 20 m high and grew along rivers and lake sides. In slightly drier places, like sandy levees, pteridosperms flourished. The most common seed ferns, the medullosans, included medium-sized trees with several meter long leaves. Medullosan pollen organs were large and often very complex. Pollen grains could be over 200 μm large and were apparently dispersed by insects. Medullosan pollen grains still have a proximal tetrad mark like spores. Inside the seed's pollen chamber free-swimming sperm cells were released through the tetrad mark to fertilize the egg cells. Medullosan seeds could be up to 10 cm long and many had a fleshy outer layer, which suggests distribution by larger animals. Medullosans were probably the first plants of which the dispersal of reproductive units fully depended on animal activity. Other pteridosperms were smaller and had a thicket- or vine-like growth habit or creeping rhizomes, like several ferns. Cordaitales were gymnosperms with woody stems and strap-shaped leaves. Some cordaites were over 40 m high trees, whereas others were medium sized with a mangrove-like growth or low bushy plants with creeping axes.

The vegetation of these paleoequatorial wetlands flourished for some 15 Myr. By the end of the Westphalian (~Desmoinesian–Missourian boundary), lepidodendrids disappeared suddenly, which is also reflected in the abrupt demise of *Lycospora*. The reasons for this major floristic turnover in Euramerica have long been a matter of debate, but the current opinion is that the coal forest collapse was closely linked to intensification of glacial cycle amplitude involving both extreme episodes of global warming and cooling (Falcon-Lang et al., 2018). Only few arborescent lycophytes persisted as minor constituents of the vegetation until they eventually vanished. However, in Cathaysia arborescent lycophytes survived until the late Permian. The dramatic demise of lepidodendrids in Euramerica was immediately followed by a first, short appearance of walchian conifers in the macrofossil record.

The composition of the coal swamp vegetation is well known, but information on the coeval vegetation of elevated hinterland areas is scarce. However, palynological data suggest that conifers were already present long before, because pollen typical for walchian conifers (*Potonieisporites*) has been recorded from the Lower Pennsylvanian. The swamp vegetation of the latest Pennsylvanian that replaced the lycophyte-dominated coal-forming vegetation was strongly dominated by marattialean tree ferns (e.g., *Psaronius*). During the Late Pennsylvanian, several new groups of seed ferns appeared. The callistophytes were creeping, scrambling, and climbing plants. They were the first plants without free-swimming sperm cells but they had a true pollen tube through which the male gamete cells were passively conveyed to the egg cell; consequently, their pollen lacks a proximal tetrad mark but shows a distal wall thinning where the pollen tube extruded (e.g., *Vesicaspora*).

The Late Pennsylvanian also marks the collision of Gondwana with Laurasia and their amalgamation into the supercontinent Pangaea. The widely extending paleoequatorial wetlands did no longer exist, and deposition was restricted to intramontane basins of variable size. Particularly the smaller basins are of great interest, because rapid facies changes reveal glimpses of the vegetation of ecologically stressed extrabasinal areas where the major evolutionary innovations within the gymnosperms took place. During the latest Pennsylvanian the peltasperms, a group of pteridosperms with small-to-medium-sized leaves and fan- to umbrella-shaped seed-bearing structures arranged in a strobilus, evolved. This group, originally regarded to be typical Mesozoic, is now recognized to have been most diverse and widespread in the Permian.

The need for dating and correlation tools for coal exploration resulted in important pioneer work in the field of palynology (e.g., Ibrahim, 1933; for an overview see Traverse, 2007). An informal classification system was developed (Potonié, 1956, 1958, 1960, 1966, 1970) that is still partly used today. The early evolution of terrestrial plants is clearly reflected in the palynological record, as can be seen, for example, in the development of pseudosaccate spores, superficially resembling bisaccate pollen but with a different saccus structure, followed by mono- and bisaccate and pollen that were optimally adapted to wind dispersal. Also, various types of pollen ornamentation evolved. This diversification is the basis for the successful application of palynology in biostratigraphy (e.g., Clayton et al., 1977).

The Pennsylvanian–Permian boundary in the terrestrial realm remains difficult to assess. Plant macrofossil taxa originally regarded as markers for the Permian, such as walchian conifers and certain pteridosperms now recognized as peltasperms, appeared to have been present in the Late and latest Pennsylvanian, respectively, when they were part of the paleo(sub)equatorial extrabasinal vegetation. Palynologically the boundary has been defined on the basis of changing dominance patterns, particularly the dominance of saccate conifer pollen. However, this is fairly ambiguous as the occurrence of these forms is primarily facies dependent, and short-term dominance shifts are to be interpreted as paleoecological signals rather than as biostratigraphic boundaries. The transition from the latest Pennsylvanian to the Permian is not marked by abrupt changes in the palynological record but is characterized by a gradual increase of pollen of plants adapted to drier conditions, mostly conifers. The most distinct feature of Permian palynofloras is the appearance of striate pollen, in particular the genus *Vittatina*, and taeniate bisaccate pollen.

With the deglaciation of the Southern Hemisphere during the Artinskian, the Permian witnessed the transition from an icehouse to a greenhouse world; this global warming trend would eventually lead to the Early Triassic hothouse world. Floral provincialism culminated in the Permian and four provinces can be distinguished, that is, the cool to temperate Gondwanan Province in the Southern Hemisphere, the temperate Angaran Province covering Siberia and the northernmost parts of Greenland and Canada, paleoequatorial Euramerica, and Cathaysia. The latter province encompasses China, Korea, and parts of directly adjacent regions in SE-Asia. Although occurring at comparable latitudes, Euramerican and Cathaysian Permian floras show marked differences. In Euramerica the flora clearly shows a warming and increasing aridification during the Permian, as indicated by the increasing rareness and eventual disappearance of humid elements such as sphenopsids and tree ferns, the growing dominance of conifers, and the early, but rare, occurrences of cycad- and ginkgophyte-like taxa. In Cathaysia, humid conditions continued to exist until the late Permian and most Chinese coals are of latest Pennsylvanian–Permian age. The Cathaysian flora was initially rather similar to that of Euramerica but during the Permian the number of endemic taxa increased. This diverse flora included arborescent lycophytes, sphenophytes, noeggerathialeans, tree ferns, various seed ferns, including the largely endemic gigantopterids, cordaites, and additional early cycads and putative ginkgophytes. In contrast the vegetation of Gondwana was rather monotonous and dominated by glossopterids, a group of deciduous gymnospermous trees with simple lancet-shaped leaves that was more diverse than the rather uniform foliage suggests; a wide variety of partly very complex fertile organs is correlated glossopterid foliage. Cordaites and peltasperms were important elements of the of Angaran floras, where also the first osmundalean ferns, one of the two groups of Paleozoic ferns still present today, evolved. Several examples of mixed floras containing elements of two or more floral provinces have been reported, for example, from the Arabian Peninsula (Berthelin et al., 2003).

The end of the Permian is marked by the most severe mass extinction in Earth history. This catastrophic extinction is particularly evident in the marine realm, less so in the terrestrial realm as continuous, fossil-bearing terrestrial successions covering the uppermost Permian–Lower Triassic boundary interval are scarce. Although several widespread Paleozoic groups had vanished by the end of the Permian, such as arborescent lycophytes and sphenophytes in Cathaysia and glossopterids in Gondwana, the timing of their disappearance is not always sharp and many species seem to have disappeared earlier. Rather, it seems that a gradual reduction of the number of species took place.

Botanical knowledge of the Permian–Triassic (P–T) transition is primarily based on the marine palynological record. In the Tethyan realm a sudden demise of gymnospermous, primarily conifer pollen, is observed. Moreover, in many successions, just below the P–T boundary, palynological associations contain a remarkable number of unseparated spore tetrads and malformed pollen with distorted sacci. These aberrant forms are interpreted to have been subjected to raised UV stress, caused by severe disruptions of the stratospheric ozone balance during a period of excessive emission of hydrothermal organohalogens related to the Siberian Traps volcanism (Visscher et al., 2004). Recently, these morphological aberrations have been ascribed to atmospheric pollution linked to the Siberian Traps emissions (Hochuli et al., 2017). A spike of *Reduviasporonites* (also known as *Tympanicysta*), a palynomorph that is either interpreted to be of fungal (Eshet et al., 1995; Visscher et al., 1996, 2011) or algal affinity (Afonin et al., 2001; Foster et al., 2002; Spina et al., 2015), is associated with the P–T boundary. The assemblages from the lowermost part of the Triassic are dominated by bryophyte and lycophyte spores.

Mid-latitudinal sequences are less condensed and document the changes at the P–T transition in greater detail, with a time resolution in the order of 10 kyr (Hochuli et al., 2010a,b). They reveal that after gradual changes during the latest Permian, ecosystems suffered from a major environmental perturbation leading to a rapid turnover from gymnosperm-dominated ecosystems to assemblages dominated by lycophytes. At the base of the Triassic, the appearance of spore species led to an increased diversity. This change is also marked by the massive reduction of *Vittatina*, a pollen type associated with peltaspermalean seed ferns. Together with other typical Permian elements (e.g., the conifer pollen *Lueckisporites virkkiae*), this group is rare but consistently present in the lower part of the Griesbachian, and it gradually disappears in its upper part. The distribution of other groups such as taeniate and nontaeniate bisaccate gymnosperm pollen (pteridosperms and conifers) shows no significant change across the boundary, whereas spores and other gymnosperm pollen increase in diversity and abundance (Hochuli et al., 2010a,b).

Although continuous terrestrial, plant macrofossil-bearing boundary sequences are lacking, recent finds from the upper Permian of the Jordan shed new light on extinction and survival patterns at the P–T boundary. The formation palynologically dated as late Permian and immediately underlying the lowermost Triassic has yielded different types of floral associations. These comprise a mixture of elements of different floral provinces, primarily Gondwanan and Cathaysian elements and a minor number of Euramerican and subcosmopolitan taxa. The flora of the humid facies mainly consists of Cathaysian elements, such as gigantopterids and the sphenophyte *Lobatannularia*, whereas drier associations include a number of Gondwanan species. Especially the latter are of great interest because they include several species of *Dicroidium* (Kerp et al., 2006), a seed fern from the group of the corystospermales with distinctive forked leaves. *Dicroidium* is traditionally considered to be typical for the Triassic of Gondwana (Anderson et al., 1999) where it replaced the glossopterids. The Jordan occurrence of *Dicroidium* predates its "traditional" Triassic occurrences in central and southern Gondwana and is located much further to the north. Recently, the first appearances of two other clades of typical Mesozoic gymnosperms were reported from these *Dicroidium*-bearing beds (Blomenkemper et al., 2018). These new findings show that evolutionary innovations took place in stressed extrabasinal, seasonally dry environments. While humid elements became extinct at the P–T boundary, taxa that evolved in and were adapted to drier environments survived the extinction event and spread during the Triassic, eventually becoming major constituents of Mesozoic floras. Similar patterns are seen in the palynological record (Lindström and McLoughlin, 2007). Comparable occurrences of precocious taxa have been found in the Southwestern United States, where typical late P–T elements occur in lower Permian strata (DiMichele et al., 2001; Looy and Stevenson, 2014).

3J.3 Mesozoic

Worldwide, earliest Triassic macrofloras are extremely rare and associations show a very low diversity. It should be noted, however, that the number of plant-bearing localities is limited and nearly all are in the Paleotethyan region. All over Eurasia, the lowermost Triassic is dominated by *Pleuromeia*, an up to 1.2 m high lycophyte that could form dense stands along shores and streams, growing associated with a few horsetails and ferns (Grauvogel-Stamm and Ash, 2005). The dominance of *Pleuromeia* is also apparent from the palynological record, that is, its spore *Densoisporites nejburgii*. Younger, early Anisian floras from France and Germany are more diverse and dominated by herbaceous conifers (*Aethophyllum*) and several genera of voltzialean conifer trees; other common elements are sphenopsids, ferns, and ginkgophytes. Pteridosperms and cycadophytes are present but rather rare. A late Anisian flora from the Alps is similar in composition, but ferns and cycadophytes are far more common. This gradual increase in diversity continued and Ladinian floras from the Alps and the Germanic Basin are characterized by a fairly wide variety of sphenopsids, lycophytes, ferns, cycadophytes, pteridosperms and ginkgophytes, and conifers. The increasing diversity is ascribed to a change of climate that became less arid. During the Middle Triassic, several new groups appeared, including matoniaceous and dipteridaceous ferns and probably caytonialean seed ferns. These groups spread rapidly and soon became typical for Northern Hemisphere Mesozoic floras together with podocarpalean conifers and bennettitales; the latter group was recently traced back to the late Permian (Blomenkemper et al., 2018). The bennettitaleans were a group of plants with cycad-like leaves—in fact bennettitalean and cycadalean leaves are often hardly distinguishable without cuticle; they partly also had a similar growth habit. However, the complex flower-like reproductive organs, which are bisexual in several species, clearly separate them from cycads.

The oldest coal-forming Triassic vegetations are known from the Ladinian but it was not until the Carnian that large amounts of plant biomass were deposited on a wide scale; the Carnian is often associated with a pluvial event. Carnian coal-forming floras are typically dominated by bennettitaleans and cycads, commonly associated with sphenopsids and ferns. Northern Hemisphere Rhaetian floras are the most diverse floras of the Triassic and remarkably similar over large distances; regional differences are mainly of quantitative nature. Prominent constituents were the peltaspermalean seed fern *Lepidopteris* and the Caytoniales, a group of seed ferns with characteristic quadripartite leaves possessing a cuticle with simple stomata, similar to those of angiosperms, and very small seeds deeply hidden in a semienclosed cup-shaped structure, and simple pollen sacs containing small bisaccate pollen. Also common were sphenopsids, various ferns, a wide variety of cycads and bennettitaleans, and various types of conifers, including several new families such as Voltziaceae, Cheirolepidiaceae, Araucariaceae, Podocarpaceae, and Pinaceae; the latter three survive until today. Triassic Gondwana floras also show an increasing diversity throughout the Triassic. They are often strongly dominated by the seed fern *Dicroidium*, a species-rich genus that during the Triassic spread over the entire Southern Hemisphere. Peltasperms did not arrive in the Southern Hemisphere until the Triassic. Other typical elements are conifers, including podocarpaceous conifers and

Heidiphyllum, a conifer that was widespread and common throughout Gondwana. Sphenopsids, ferns, cycads, bennettitaleans, and ginkgophytes were also represented. Within the Southern Hemisphere, different subprovinces related to the paleoclimatic and paleogeographical position can be distinguished, varying from relatively dry and warm to more temperate (Césari and Colombi, 2013). *Dicroidium* species from northern and central Gondwana often had relatively large leaves, whereas trees from the Antarctic were deciduous and had small leaves, being an adaptation to the long period of darkness during the polar winter (Bomfleur and Kerp, 2010).

Like the macroflora, palynological associations show a strong increase in diversity during the Triassic. Earliest Triassic microfloras are dominated by lycophyte and bryophyte spores and two species of acritarchs. Striate pollen is a typical feature of Triassic palynomorph assemblages, disappearing near the end of the Triassic. A characteristic and widespread Triassic genus is *Aratrisporites*, a double-layered, monolete lycophyte spore. In the marine realm, dinoflagellate cysts first appeared in the Upper Triassic (see, e.g., Mangerud et al., 2019). From then on, these organic-walled phytoplankton cysts, now commonly found in marine, brackish and freshwater environments, play a prominent role in biostratigraphy (e.g., Stover et al., 1996).

Although the Triassic–Jurassic boundary marks one of the big mass extinctions, only one plant group, the common and widespread genus *Lepidopteris* (peltasperms) was affected severely and became extinct. In some regions in central Europe, the Triassic–Jurassic boundary is not clearly expressed in the terrestrial macrofossil record, whereas in other regions such as East Greenland highly diverse Triassic communities of *Podozamites*, a broad-leafed conifer, and bennettitaleans were replaced by lower diversity forests, dominated by taxa that had been relatively minor components of Late Triassic forests such as the Czekanowskiales, a group of plants with narrow, strongly dissected leaves and seed-bearing structures consisting of two valves, ginkgophytes (*Sphenobaiera*) and osmundaceous ferns (McElwain et al., 2007).

Cycads and bennettitaleans were important components of vegetation during the Jurassic and Early Cretaceous and ginkgophytes reached their maximum diversity. Pteridosperms were still present (*Pachypteris*, *Caytonia*), but as a whole, the group shows a gradual and steady decline. New groups of modern conifers evolved such as the Cephalotaxaceae, Taxaceae, and Cupressaceae; the latter have small, scale-like leaves. In general, the Triassic and Jurassic were periods of major radiation within the ferns and the conifers.

The Triassic–Jurassic boundary is much clearer expressed in the palynological record than in the macrofossil record. In the Northern Hemisphere, up to 90% of the pollen and spore species became locally or regionally extinct. Highly diverse assemblages of monosulcates and monosaccates were replaced by low diversity assemblages dominated by *Classopollis*, the pollen of cheirolepidiaceous conifers, which first appeared in the Rhaetian and persisted until the earliest Paleogene. Cheirolepidiaceae were conifers with small scale–like leaves and extremely, up to 100 μm, thick cuticles. They were widespread at low latitudes and adapted to arid and (hyper)saline environments. They formed monospecific forest in coastal and lagoonal settings but were also part of mixed forests in fluvial environments.

Until the end of the Early Cretaceous, gymnosperms ruled the world. The first angiosperms flowers, carpels, and stamens appeared in the late Barremian–early Aptian (Friis et al., 2011). Angiosperms differ from gymnosperms in a number of features, for example, in having true flowers, pollen with a much more complex wall structure, and in leaf morphology (leaf shape, venation, and cuticle). Although angiosperms are a highly diverse and extremely successful group, their origin is still enigmatic, even though in recent years many fossils of early flowering plants have been found. Various gymnosperm groups have been discussed as potential ancestors. Pollen showing remarkable similarities to angiosperm pollen have been reported from the Middle and Upper Triassic (Cornet, 1989; Hochuli and Feist-Burkhardt, 2013), but there are no convincing records of coeval angiosperm macrofossils. The earliest pollen grains unequivocally assigned to angiosperms are small (<10 μm); they are very rare in the Hauterivian. Angiosperms originated in paleoequatorial regions being small herbs growing in humid environments, maybe even partly submersed. Initially, they played a minor role, but they diversified and spread rapidly and during the Late Cretaceous they were already dominant, except for the high latitudes where the vegetation was still mainly composed of conifers and ferns. During the Cretaceous, groups that had been most successful in the Jurassic were outcompeted and several became extinct, for example, the bennettitaleans and pteridosperms, but also cycads and ginkgophytes show a drastic decline. A part of the success of angiosperms is probably related to the efficiency of insect pollination; angiosperms and insects show a remarkable coevolution.

The rapid radiation and spreading of angiosperms are well documented by the microfossil record; palynological associations from the successive stages show a fast diversification and increasing abundances. *Aquilapollenites* is a typical Cretaceous pollen type that has been recorded throughout the Northern Hemisphere but is also found in South America (Vajda and Bercovici, 2014); it reached its maximum distribution during the Maastrichtian. In the tropical areas, palm pollen became characteristic elements of the assemblages. By the end of the Cretaceous, provincialism reached its peak and several floral provinces had developed (Herngreen et al., 1996), mostly along latitudinal lines.

3J.4 Cenozoic

The extinction event at the Cretaceous–Paleogene boundary did not result in the extinction of major groups, although several families of angiosperms were diminished severely and a number of genera disappeared. The extinction seems to have been highly selective. Especially insect-pollinated and evergreen taxa were affected, whereas extinction rates among wind-pollinated species and deciduous trees were much lower. Angiosperms still dominated the scene, but many typical Cretaceous pollen taxa disappeared during the Paleogene, including *Classopollis*, *Wodehouseia*, *Aquilapollenites*, and *Normapollis*. Early Paleogene associations are less diverse, but the flora recovered rapidly, much faster than after the P–T extinction (McElwain and Punyasena, 2007; Vajda and Bercovici, 2014). A global warming that culminated in the Paleocene–Eocene (P–E) Thermal Maximum at the P–E boundary resulted in a new phase of angiosperm radiation and an expansion of tropical floras covering large parts of the Northern Hemisphere. These so-called paleotropical evergreen floras comprised palms (up to a latitude of 55°N), Lauraceae (laurel family), Moraceae (mulberry family), and various tropical ferns. The Arcto–Tertiary floras in the far North, for example, Northern Scandinavia and Arctic Canada, consisted of temperate forests with deciduous trees such as oak (*Quercus*), maple (*Acer*), beech (*Betula*), elm (*Ulmus*), and conifers such as pine (*Pinus*) and spruce (*Picea*). *Ginkgo* and the bald cypress (*Taxodium*) were also part of the temperate flora. The early Eocene is characterized by a climate optimum, but the late Eocene is marked by a steady global cooling that led to a first glaciation in Antarctic in the early Oligocene. As a consequence, Arcto–Tertiary elements migrated southward where they replaced the tropical floras, which, in turn, retreated to lower latitudes. Subsequent climate fluctuations resulted in deglaciations and reglaciations in the Antarctic until a permanent ice cover developed in the middle Miocene, and the transition from a greenhouse into an icehouse world was eventually completed. The most dramatic events in the vegetation history are these changes in composition and distribution in response to global climate changes. They led to a strong diversification in plant community composition and distribution that gave rise to the latitudinal belts reflecting the temperature zones that we know today. However, also geotectonics and paleogeography, changing oceanic and atmospheric circulations patterns, and the formation of mountain chains played an important role. Large palm leaves recently collected from Eocene deposits in Tibet at an altitude of c. 6000 m nicely illustrate that this region, where nowadays hardly any plant can survive, once, before the uplift of the Himalayas, supported a lush tropical vegetation.

One of the most successful angiosperm groups today is the wind-pollinated grasses that cover large areas. Little is known about their early history. The oldest unambiguous grass fossils are from the lower Eocene, but phytoliths, typical siliceous secretion bodies, suggest that the earliest grasses appeared in the late Maastrichtian (Friis et al., 2011), when many extant angiosperm families had already evolved. It was not until the early-to-middle Miocene that grass-dominated ecosystems became widespread (Edwards et al., 2010). Crucial was the development of C_4 carbon fixation, a different photosynthesis pathway with the advantages of fast growth, and resistance to drought, high temperatures, and strong solar radiation.

Since the Oligocene the proportion of modern taxa increased and more and more dispersed pollen and spore types can be assigned to living genera, in the Late Pleistocene and Holocene even to living species. Palynological studies of Pliocene and younger successions are solely based on quantitative analyses, and pollen diagrams enable the reconstruction of past vegetation types and successions. Major shifts in composition and abundances indicate climatic and/or environmental changes. Thermophilous taxa-like palms, *Liquidambar* and *Nyssa*, disappeared in Europe at the Pliocene–Pleistocene boundary. They did not become extinct but migrated to and survived in warmer regions. In the course of the Pleistocene, which is characterized by a series of glacials and interglacials, the number of thermophilous taxa diminished steadily. Global cooling forced forest elements to migrate southward to refugia in the Mediterranean and Asia Minor. They were replaced by a scarce tundra vegetation in areas that were not covered by ice. During warmer intervals, thermophilous plants successively reappeared; the timing depended on their temperature constraints. Many but not all forest taxa migrated back northward.

Palynology plays an important role in Quaternary stratigraphy. It serves, for example, in recognizing the Younger Dryas, a widely recognized cold interval in the Northern Hemisphere characterized by a tundra vegetation with *Dryas octopetala*. The Holocene vegetation history is well documented by palynological data, which, all together, form a unique long-term climate archive that shows the effects of climate fluctuations and human activity such as the Little Ice Age in the 16th–17th century and the beginning of agriculture. The latter is reflected by a strong decrease in tree pollen indicating deforestation, in combination with an increase of pollen of cultivated plants (e.g., wheat, barley, rye, and crops) and associated crop weeds (e.g., *Centaurea cyanus*). Events such as the major "Barbarian" migrations and the fall of the Roman Empire in the 4th century, and the widespread 14th-century Black Death pandemics, finally, can be recognized by an increase of pollen of ruderal plants (e.g., *Artemisia*) and even trees.

3J.5 Final remarks

In this chapter, we have tried to give an integrated overview of the geologic history of plant life on the Earth. As it is impossible to provide a comprehensive overview in the limited number of pages, our text mainly focused on selected crucial intervals and events. We realize that some important aspects may be missing. Nevertheless, we hope to have unveiled some glimpses of the fascinating story of the greening of our planet.

Bibliography

Afonin, S.A., Barinova, S.S., and Krassilov, V.A., 2001, A bloom of *Tympanicysta* Balme (green algae of zygnematalean affinities) at the Permian-Triassic boundary. *Geodiversitas*, **23**: 481–487.

Al-Shawareb, A., Miller, M., and Vecoli, M., 2017, Late Ordovician (Katian) chitinozoans from northwest Saudi Arabia: biostratigraphic and paleoenvironmental implications. *Revue de Micropaléontologie*, **60**: 333–369.

Anderson, J.M., Anderson, H.M., Archangelsky, S., Bamford, M., Chandra, S., Dettmann, M., et al., 1999, Patterns of Gondwana plant colonisation and diversification. *Journal of African Earth Sciences*, **28**: 145–157.

Berry, C.M., and Marshall, J.E.A., 2015, Lycopsid forests in the early Late Devonian paleoequatorial zone of Svalbard. *Geology*, **43**: 1043–1046.

Berthelin, M., Broutin, J., Kerp, H., Crasquin-Soleau, S., Platel, J.P., and Roger, J., 2003, The Oman Gharif mixed paleoflora: a key tool for testing Permian Pangea reconstructions. *Palaeogeography, Palaeoclimatology, Palaeoecology*, **196**: 85–98.

Blomenkemper, P., Kerp, H., Abu Hamad, A., DiMichele, W.A., and Bomfleur, B., 2018, A hidden cradle of plant evolution in Permian tropical lowlands. *Science*, **362**: 1414–1416.

Bomfleur, B., and Kerp, H., 2010, *Dicroidium* diversity in the Upper Triassic of north Victoria Land, East Antarctica. *Review of Palaeobotany and Palynology*, **160**: 67–101.

Césari, S.N., and Colombi, C.E., 2013, A new Late Triassic phytogeographical scenario in westernmost Gondwana. *Nature Communications*, **4**: 1889.

Clayton, G., Coquel, R., Doubinger, J., Gueinn, K.J., Loboziak, S., Owens, B., et al., 1977, Carboniferous miospores of western Europe: illustration and zonation. *Mededelingen Rijks Geologische Dienst*, **29**: 1–71.

Cornet, B., 1989, Late Triassic angiosperm-like pollen from the Richmond Rift Basin of Virginia, U.S.A. *Palaeontographica B*, **213**: 37–87.

Davies, N.S., and Gibling, M.R., 2010, Cambrian to Devonian evolution of alluvial systems: the sedimentological impact of the earliest land plants. *Earth-Science Reviews*, **98**: 171–200.

DiMichele, W.A., Mamay, S.H., Chaney, D.H., Hook, R.W., and Nelson, W.J., 2001, An Early Permian flora with Late Permian and Mesozoic affinities from north-central Texas. *Journal of Paleontology*, **75**: 449–460.

Dodd, M.S., Papineau, D., Grenne, T., Slack, J.F., Rittner, M., Pirajno, F., et al., 2017, Evidence for early life in Earth's oldest hydrothermal vent precipitates. *Nature*, **543**: 60–64.

Edwards, D., and Feehan, J., 1980, Records of *Cooksonia*-type sporangia from the late Wenlock strata in Ireland. *Nature*, **287**: 41–42.

Edwards, E.J., Osborne, C.P., Strömberg, C.A.E., and Smith, S.A., 2010, The origins of C_4 grasslands: integrating evolutionary and ecosystem science. *Science*, **328**: 587–591.

Edwards, D., Morris, J.L., Richardson, J.B., and Kenrick, P., 2014, Cryptospores and cryptophytes reveal hidden diversity in early land floras. *New Phytologist*, **202**: 50–78.

Eshet, Y., Rampino, M.R., and Visscher, H., 1995, Fungal event and palynological record of ecological crisis and recovery across the Permian–Triassic boundary. *Geology*, **23**: 967–970.

Evitt, W.R., 1963, A discussion and proposals concerning fossil dinoflagellates, hystrichospheres and acritarchs, I and II. *Proceedings of the National Academy of Sciences of the United States of America*, 49, 158–164 and 49, 298–302.

Falcon-Lang, H.J., Nelson, J.W., Heckel, O.H., DiMichele, W.A., and Elrick, S.D., 2018, Evidence from cyclothems and coniferopsid tree-stumps near the Desmoinesian–Missourian boundary in Peoria County, Illinois, USA. *Palaeogeography, Palaeoclimatology, Palaeoecology*, **490**: 375–392.

Foster, C.B., Stephenson, M.H., Marshall, C., Logan, G.A., and Greenwood, P.F., 2002, A revision of *Reduviasporonites* Wilson 1962: description, illustration, comparison and biological affinities. *Palynology*, **26**: 35–58.

Friis, E.M., Crane, P.R., and Pedersen, R.K., 2011, *Early Flowers and Angiosperm Evolution*. New York: Cambridge University Press.

Gibling, M.R., and Davies, N.S., 2012, Palaeozoic landscapes shaped by plant evolution. *Nature Geoscience*, **5**: 99–105.

Gibling, M.R., Davies, N.S., Falcon-Lang, H.J., Bashforth, A.R., DiMichele, W.A., Rygel, M.C., et al., 2014, Palaeozoic co-evolution of rivers and vegetation: a synthesis of current knowledge. *Proceedings of the Geologists' Association*, **125**: 524–533.

Grauvogel-Stamm, L., and Ash, S.R., 2005, Recovery of the Triassic land flora from the end-Permian life crisis. *Comptes Rendus Palevol*, **4**: 593–608.

Herngreen, G.F.W., Kedves, M., Rovnina, L.V., and Smirnova, S.B., 1996, Cretaceous palynofloral provinces: a review. *In* Jansonius, J., and McGregor, D.C. (eds), Palynology: Principles and Applications. *American Association of Stratigraphic Palynologists Foundation*, **3**: 1157–1188.

Hochuli, P.A., and Feist-Burkhardt, S., 2013, Angiosperm- like pollen and *Afropollis* from the Middle Triassic (Anisian) of the Germanic Basin (Northern Switzerland). *Frontiers in Plant Science*, **4** (344), 1–14.

Hochuli, P.A., Vigran, J.O., Hermann, E., and Bucher, H., 2010a, Multiple climatic changes around the Permian-Triassic boundary event revealed by an expanded palynological record from mid-Norway. *Geological Society of America Bulletin*, **122**: 884–896.

Hochuli, P.A., Hermann, E., Vigran, J.O., Bucher, H., and Weissert, H., 2010b, Rapid demise and recovery of plant ecosystems across the end-Permian extinction event. *Global and Planetary Change*, **74**: 144–155.

Hochuli, P.A., Schneebeli-Hermann, E., Mangerud, G., and Bucher, H., 2017, Evidence for atmospheric pollution across the Permian–Triassic Transition. *Geology*, **45**: 1123–1126.

Ibrahim, A.C., 1933, *Sporenformen des Aegirhorizonts des Ruhr-Reviers*. Würzburg: Konrad Triltsch.

Javaux, E.J., and Knoll, A.H., 2016, Micropaleontology of the lower Mesoproterozoic Roper Group, Australia, and implications for early eukaryotic evolution. *Journal of Paleontology*, **91**: 199–229.

Javaux, E.J., Marshall, C.P., and Bekker, A., 2010, Organic-walled microfossils in 3.2-billion-year-old shallow-marine siliciclastic deposits. *Nature*, **463**: 934–938.

Kerp, H., 2017, Organs and tissues of Rhynie chert plants. *Philosophical Transactions of the Royal Society B*, **373** (20160495), 1–16.

Kerp, H., Abu Hamad, A., Vörding, B., and Bandel, K., 2006, Typical Triassic Gondwanan floral elements in the Upper Permian of the paleotropics. *Geology*, **34**: 265–268.

Knoll, A.H., Niklas, K.J., Gensel, P.G., and Tiffney, B.H., 1984, Character diversification and patterns of evolution in early vascular plants. *Paleobiology*, **10**: 34–47.

Kraft, P., Pšenička, J., Sakala, J., and Frýdac, J., 2019, Initial plant diversification and dispersal event in upper Silurian of the Prague Basin. *Palaeogeography, Palaeoclimatology, Palaeoecology*, **514**: 144–155.

Krings, M., Taylor, T.N., Hass, H., Kerp, H., Dotzler, N., and Hermsen, E.J., 2007, Fungal endophytes in a 400-million-yr-old land plant: infection pathways, spatial distribution, and host responses. *New Phytologist*, **174**: 648–657.

Lenton, T.M., Boyle, R.A., Poulton, S.W., Shields-Zhou, G.A., and Butterfield, N.J., 2014, Co-evolution of eukaryotes and ocean oxygenation in the Neoproterozoic era. *Nature Geoscience*, **7**: 257–265.

Libertín, M., Kvaček, J., Bek, J., Žárský, V., and Štorch, P., 2018, Sporophytes of polysporangiate land plants from the early Silurian period may have been photosynthetically autonomous. *Nature Plants*, **4**: 269–271.

Lindström, S., and McLoughlin, S., 2007, Synchronous palynofloristic extinction and recovery after the end-Permian event in the Prince Charles Mountains, Antarctica: implications for palynofloristic turnover across Gondwana. *Review of Palynology and Palaeobotany*, **145**: 89–122.

Looy, C.V., and Stevenson, R.A., 2014, Earliest occurrence of autorotating seeds in conifers: The Permian (Kungurian-Roadian) *Manifera talaris* gen. et sp. nov. *International Journal of Plant Sciences*, **175**: 841–854.

Looy, C.V., Brugman, W.A., Dilcher, D.L., and Visscher, H., 1999, The delayed resurgence of equatorial forests after the Permian–Triassic ecological crisis. *Proceedings of the National Academy of Sciences of the United States of America*, **96**: 13857–13862.

Looy, C.V., Twitchett, R.J., Dilcher, D.L., Van Konijnenburg-van Cittert, J.H.A., and Visscher, H., 2001, Life in the end-Permian dead zone. *Proceedings of the National Academy of Sciences of the United States of America*, **98**: 7879–7883.

Looy, C.V., Kerp, H., Duijnstee, I., and DiMichele, W.A., 2014, The late Paleozoic ecological-evolutionary laboratory, a land-plant fossil record perspective. *The Sedimentary Record*, **12** (2), 4–10.

Mangerud, G., Paterson, N.W., and Riding, J.B., 2019, The temporal and spatial distribution of Triassic dinoflagellate cysts. *Review of Palynology and Palaeobotany*, **261**: 53–66.

McElwain, J.C., and Punyasena, S.W., 2007, Mass extinction events and the plant fossil record. *Trends in Ecology & Evolution*, **22**: 548–557.

McElwain, J.C., Popa, M.E., Hesselbo, S.P., Haworth, M., and Surlyk, F., 2007, Macroecological responses of terrestrial vegetation to climatic and atmospheric change across Triassic–Jurassic boundary in East Greenland. *Paleobiology*, **33**: 547–573.

Nutman, A.P., Bennett, V.C., Friend, C.R.L., Van Kranendonk, M.J., and Chivas, A.R., 2016, Rapid emergence of life shown by discovery of 3,700-million-year-old microbial structures. *Nature*, **537**: 535–538.

Potonié, R., 1956, Synopsis der Gattungen der Sporae dispersae. I. Teil: Sporites. *Beihefte zum Geologischen Jahrbuch*, **23**: 1–103.

Potonié, R., 1958, Synopsis der Gattungen der Sporae dispersae. II. Teil: Sporites (Nachträge), Saccites, Aletes, Praecolpates, Polyplicates, Monocolpates. *Beihefte zum Geologischen Jahrbuch*, **31**: 1–114.

Potonié, R., 1960, Synopsis der Gattungen der Sporae dispersae. III. Teil: Nachträge Sporites, Fortsetzung Pollenites. Mit Generalregister zu Teil I-III. *Beihefte zum Geologischen Jahrbuch*, **39**: 1–189.

Potonié, R., 1966, Synopsis der Gattungen der Sporae dispersae. IV. Teil: Nachträge zu allen Gruppen (Turmae). *Beihefte zum Geologischen Jahrbuch*, **72**: 1–244.

Potonié, R., 1970, Synopsis der Gattungen der Sporae dispersae. Teil V. Nachträge zu allen Gruppen (Turmae). *Beihefte zum Geologischen Jahrbuch*, **79**: 1–156.

Prave, A.R., 2002, Life on land in the Proterozoic: evidence from the Torridonian rocks of northwest Scotland. *Geology*, **30**: 811–814.

Remy, W., Taylor, T.N., Hass, H., and Kerp, H., 1994, Four hundred-million-year-old vesicular-arbuscular mycorrhizae. *Proceedings of the National Academy of Sciences of the United States of America*, **91**: 11841–11843.

Rubinstein, C.V., Gerrienne, P., De la Puente, G.S., Astini, R.A., and Steemans, P., 2010, Early Middle Ordovician evidence for land plants in Argentina (eastern Gondwana). *New Phytologist*, **188**: 365–369.

Servais, T., Molyneux, S.G., Li, J., Nowak, H., Rubinstein, C.V., Vecoli, M., et al., 2018, First Appearance Datums (FADs) of selected acritarch taxa and correlation between Lower and Middle Ordovician stages. *Lethaia*, **51**: 228–253.

Shih, P.M., 2015, Photosynthesis and early Earth. *Current Biology*, **25**: R845–R875.

Spina, A., Cyrilli, S., Utting, J., and Jansonius, J., 2015, Palynology of the Permian and Triassic of the Tesero and Bulla sections (Western Dolomites, Italy) and consideration about the enigmatic species *Reduviasporonites chalastus*. *Review of Palaeobotany and Palynology*, **218**: 3–14.

Stein, W.E., Mannolini, F., VanAller Hernick, L., Landing, E., and Berry, C.M., 2007, Giant cladoxylopsid trees resolve the enigma of the Earth's earliest forest stumps at Gilboa. *Nature*, **446**: 904–907.

Stein, W.E., Berry, C.M., VanAller Hernick, L., and Mannolini, F., 2012, Surprisingly complex community discovered in the mid-Devonian fossil forest at Gilboa. *Nature*, **483**: 78–81.

Stover, L.E., Brinkhuis, H., Damassa, S.P., de Verteuil, L., Helby, R.J., Monteil, E., et al., 1996, Mesozoic-Tertiary dinoflagellates, acritarchs and prasinophytes. *In* Jansonius, J., and McGregor, D.C. (eds), *Palynology: Principles and Applications*. American Association of Stratigraphic Palynologists Foundation, **2**: 641–750.

Strother, P.K., 2015, Systematics and evolutionary significance of some new cryptospores from the Cambrian of eastern Tennessee, USA. *Review of Palaeobotany and Palynology*, **227**: 28–41.

Strother, P., and Wellman, C.H., 2016, Palaeoecology of a billion-year-old non-marine cyanobacterium from the Torridon Group and Nonesuch Formation. *Palaeontology*, **59**: 89–108.

Strother, P., Battison, L., Brasier, M.D., and Wellman, C.H., 2011, Earth's earliest non-marine eukaryotes. *Nature*, **473**: 505–509.

Taylor, T.N., Taylor, E.L., and Krings, M., 2009, *Paleobotany: The Biology and Evolution of Fossil Plants*, 2nd ed. Amsterdam: Elsevier.

Taylor, W.A., and Strother, P.K., 2009, Ultrastructure, morphology, and topology of Cambrian palynomorphs from the Lone Rock Formation, Wisconsin, USA. *Review of Palaeobotany and Palynology*, **153**: 296–309.

Traverse, A., 2007, *Paleopalynology*, 2nd ed. Dordrecht: Springer.

Trewin, N.H., and Kerp, H., 2017, The Rhynie and Windyfield cherts, Early Devonian, Rhynie, Scotland. *In* Fraser, N.C., and Sues, H.-D. (eds), *Terrestrial Conservation Lagerstätten - Windows into the Evolution of Life on Land*. Edinburgh: Dunedin Academic Press Ltd, 1–38.

Vajda, V., and Bercovici, A., 2014, The global vegetation pattern across the Cretaceous–Paleogene mass extinction interval: a template for other extinction events. *Global and Planetary Change*, **122**: 29–49.

VanAller Hernick, L., Landing, E., and Bartowski, K.E., 2008, Earth's oldest liverworts—*Metzgeriothallus sharonae* sp. nov. from the Middle Devonian (Givetian) of eastern New York, USA. *Review of Palaeobotany and Palynology*, **148**: 154–162.

Van Kranendonk, M.J., Philippot, P., Lepot, K., Bodorkos, S., and Pirajno, F., 2008, Geological setting of Earth's oldest fossils in the ca. 3.5 Ga Dresser Formation, Pilbara craton, Western Australia. *Precambrian Research*, **167**: 93–124.

Visscher, H., Brinkhuis, H., Dilcher, D.L., Elsik, W.C., Eshet, Y., Looy, C.V., et al., 1996, The terminal Paleozoic fungal event: evidence of terrestrial ecosystem destabilization and collapse. *Proceedings of the National Academy of Sciences of the United States of America*, **93**: 2155–2158.

Visscher, H., Looy, C.V., Collinson, M.E., Brinkhuis, H., Cittert, J., Kurschner, W.M., and Sephton, M.A., 2004, Environmental mutagenesis during the end-Permian ecological crisis. *Proceedings of the National Academy of Sciences, U.S.A*, **101**: 12952–12956.

Visscher, H., Sephton, M.A., and Looy, C.V., 2011, Fungal virulence at the time of the end-Permian biosphere crisis? *Geology*, **39**: 883–886.

Wellman, C.H., and Strother, P.K., 2015, The terrestrial biota prior to the origin of land plants (embryophytes): a review of the evidence. *Palaeontology*, **58**: 601–627.

Wellman, C.H., Osterloff, P.L., and Mohiuddin, U., 2003, Fragments of the earliest land plants. *Nature*, **425**: 282–285.

Subchapter 3K

Cretaceous microcrinoids

A.S. Gale

Abstract

The abundance and considerable diversity of microcrinoids in the Albian to Maastrichtian, together with a widespread distribution, makes them attractive fossils for biostratigraphy, although they have largely been overlooked by micropaleontologists. The short stratigraphic ranges and widespread distribution of species have allowed establishment of a refined zonation for the Albian through Campanian interval.

Tiny, pelagic crinoids of the Order Roveacrinida are common in parts of the Triassic, Upper Jurassic, and the mid-to-late Cretaceous, although it is not certainly known whether the Triassic forms are closely related to those from the Jurassic and Cretaceous or represent a parallel evolutionary development. Taxa have cup sizes of one to several millimeters, and the arm ossicles (brachials) are often common constituents of residues taken from Late Cretaceous marine sediments. The abundance and considerable diversity of microcrinoids in the Albian to Maastrichtian, together with a very widespread distribution, makes them attractive fossils for biostratigraphy, although they have largely been overlooked by micropaleontologists in the past. The detailed work of Peck (1943) and Hess (2015) on Albian and Cenomanian microcrinoids from the Gulf states of the United States provided a firm taxonomic basis for future studies, and Bruno Ferré (Ferré and Berthou, 1994; Ferré and Granier, 2000, 2001; Ferré et al., 2005) has pioneered the identification of microcrinoids in this section. Recent systematic sampling and processing of chalks and clays and SEM illustration of material (Gale, 2016, 2017, 2018, 2019a,b,c) have demonstrated an unexpected diversity of taxa, many of which are present in North America, Africa, and Europe. The short stratigraphical ranges and widespread distribution of species (Fig. 3K.1) have allowed establishment of a refined zonation for the Albian to Campanian interval, including 12 Albian zones (AlR1-12), 5 Cenomanian zones (CeR1-5), 13 Turonian zones (TuR1-13), 6 Coniacian zones (CuR1-6), 6 Santonian zones (Sa1-6), and 11 Campanian zones (Ca1-11).

Albian faunas are dominated by the roveacrinid genera *Plotocrinus, Poecilocrinus, Hylocrius, Styracocrinus,* and *Euglyphocrinus*. *Plotocrinus* gave rise to *Poecilocrinus* in the early late Albian, and rapid evolutionary changes in *Poecilocrinus* provide a detailed biostratigraphical framework, originally identified in Texas, but applicable also in North Africa (Gale, 2020a,b). The Cenomanian saw the rise of the genus *Roveacrinus*, which together with successive *Euglyphocrinus* and *Styracocrinus* species (giving rise to *Fenestracrinus* in the late Cenomanian) provide a zonal framework. Albian and Cenomanian taxa are dominantly Tethyan in distribution and only extend into Boreal seas at a few levels.

The Turonian Stage marks the maximum geographical extent of the Roveacrininae, with permanent abundance in both Boreal and Tethyan Realms. Rapid evolution in proximal brachial structure of the genera *Drepanocrinus* and *Roveacrinus*, together with brief abundances of *Caveacrinus* and *Dentatocrinus*, provides a very detailed biostratigraphy, which has been used to test models of eustatic sea-level events (Gale, 2019b). The Turonian also saw the emergence of the delicately constructed Hessicrininae, and the reappearance of Saccocomidae, with the genus *Roveacrinoides* appearing in Boreal Chalks. The Coniacian marks a reduction in overall diversity of microcrinoids, with extinction of both *Roveacrinus* and *Drepanocrinus* in the mid-Coniacian.

In the Santonian the Hessicrininae become abundant, and the genus *Stellacrinus* appears, accompanied by a resurgence of saccocomids, with the genera *Costatocrinus* and *Sagittacrinus* undergoing rapid evolutionary change in the late Santonian (Gale, 2019a). *Stellacrinus* shows rapid morphological diversification in the lower Campanian and, together with *Applinocrinus* and Hessicrininae, provides a high-resolution framework which can be correlated between Texas and Europe (Gale, in prep.). The biostratigraphy of later Campanian and Maastrichtian microcrinoids requires further study to refine a zonation. However, they are abundant and moderately diverse in late Maastrichtian sediments, before extinction at the K–Pg boundary (Gale, 2017).

Future work will focus on refinement and geographical extension of the proposed zonation, refinement of the late Campanian and Maastrichtian zonation, and the possible application to deep sea core material. Hess (1972) has described Jurassic microcrinoids from Jurassic DSDP sites.

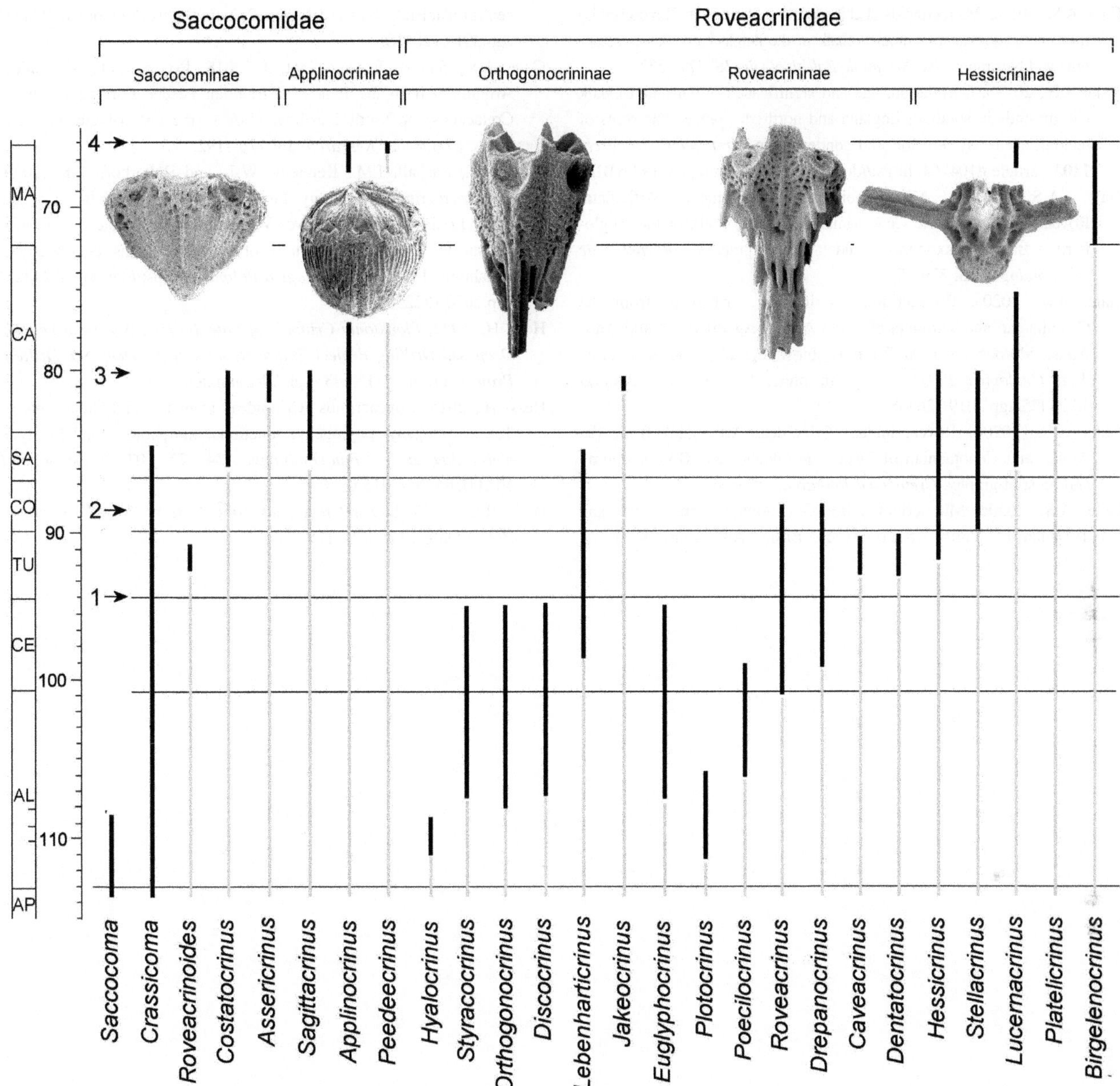

FIGURE 3K.1 Distribution of Cretaceous microcrinoids. The arrowed events represent (1) The extinctions that occurred in the late Cenomanian (five genera). It is not yet known if these are precisely related to the anoxic event OAE2. (2) Coniacian extinction of roveacrinine genera *Roveacrinus* and *Drepanocrinus*. (3) Apparent disappearance of many microcrinoids in the mid-Campanian, possibly an artifact of few study sites in the late Campanian. (4) K—Pg extinction of all microcrinoids.

Bibliography

Ferré, B., and Berthou, P.-Y., 1994, Roveacrinid remains from the Cotinguiba Formation (Cenomanian–Turonian) of the Sergipe Basin (NE-Brazil). *Acta Geologica Leopoldensia*, **17** (39/1), 299–313.

Ferré, B., and Granier, B., 2000, *Roveacrinus berthoui* nov. sp., early Hauterivian representative of Roveacrinidae (Roveacrinida, Crinoidea) of Busot Alicante, Spain. *Geologica Carpathica*, **51**: 101–107.

Ferré, B., and Granier, B., 2001, Albian roveacrinids from the southern Congo Basin, off Angola. *Journal of South American Earth Sciences*, **14**: 219–235.

Ferré, B., Walter, S., and Bengston, P., 2005, Roveacrinids in mid-Cretaceous biostratigraphy of the Sergipe Basin, northeastern Brazil. *Journal of South American Earth Sciences*, **19**: 259–272.

Gale, A.S., 2016, Roveacrinida (Crinoidea, Articulata) from the Santonian-Maastrichtian (Upper Cretaceous) of England, the US Gulf Coast (Texas, Mississippi) and southern Sweden. *Papers in Palaeontology*, **2**: 489–532, https://doi.org/10.1002/spp2.1050.

Gale, A.S., 2017, An integrated microcrinoid zonation for the Lower Campanian chalk of southern England, and its implications for correlation. *Cretaceous Research*, **87**: 312–352, https://doi.org/10.1016/j.cretres.2017.02.002.

Gale, A.S., 2019a, Microcrinoids (Echinodermata: Articulata: Roveacrinida) from the Cenomanian-Santonian chalk of the Anglo-Paris Basin: taxonomy and biostratigraphy. *Revues de Paléobiologie*, **38**: 379–533.

Gale, A.S., 2019b, Correlation, age and significance of Turonian Chalk hardgrounds in southern England and northern France: The roles of tectonics, eustasy, erosion and condensation. *Cretaceous Research*, **1103**: article #104164. https://doi.org/10.1016/j.cretres.2019.06.010.

Gale, A.S., 2019c, Microcrinoids (Echinodermata: Articulata: Roveacrinida) from the Cenomanian-Santonian chalk of the Anglo-Paris Basin: taxonomy and biostratigraphy. *Revues de Paléobiologie*, **38**: 379–533.

Gale, A.S., 2020a, Roveacrinidae (Crinoidea, Articulata) from the Cenomanian and Turonian of North Africa (Agadir Basin and Anti-Atlas, Morocco, central Tunisia): biostratigraphy and taxonomy. *Acta Geologica Polonica*, **70**: in press, 83 pp. https://doi.org/10.24425/agp.2019.126458.

Gale, A.S., 2020b, Roveacrinidae (Crinoidea, Articulata) from the Albian and Cenomanian of Texas and Oklahoma, USA; taxonomy and biostratigraphy. *Cretaceous Research*, in press.

Gale, A.S., 2020c, Microcrinoids from the Albian, Cenomanian and Turonian of North Africa (Agadir Basin, Anti-Atlas, Morocco; central Tunisia). *Acta Geologica Polonica*, https://doi.org/10.24425/agp.2019.126458.

Gale, A.S., Sadorf, E., and Jagt, J., 2018, Roveacrinida (Crinoidea, Articulata) from the Late Maastrichtian Peedee Formation (Upper Cretaceous) of North Carolina, USA – the last pelagic microcrinoids. *Cretaceous Research*, **85**: 176–192.

Gale, A.S., Rashall, J.M., Kennedy, W.J., and Holterhoff, F.K., 2020, The microcrinoid taxonomy, biostratigraphy and correlation of the upper Fredricksburg and lower Washita groups (Cretaceous, middle Albian to lower Cenomanian) of northern Texas and southern Oklahoma, USA. *Acta Geologica Polonica*, https://doi.org/10.24425/agp.2020.132256.

Hess, H., 1972, *Planktonic Crinoids of Late Jurassic Age from Leg 11, Deep Sea Drilling Project, Initial Reports of the Deep Sea Drilling Project*, 11. pp. 631–643 4 pls.;Washington.

Hess, H., 2015, Roveacrinids (Crinoidea) from the mid-Cretaceous of Texas: ontogeny, phylogeny, functional morphology and lifestyle. *Swiss Journal of Palaeontology*, **134**: 77–107, https://doi.org/10.1007/s13358-015-0076-z.

Peck, R.E., 1943, Lower Cretaceous crinoids from Texas. *Journal of Paleontology*, **17**: 451–475.

Subchapter 3L

Three major mass extinctions and evolutionary radiations in their aftermath

S. Esmeray-Senlet

Abstract

Fossil record and geochemical proxies demonstrated that there have been five mass extinctions in the Phanerozoic that are statistically distinct from the background extinction levels and associated with large-scale environmental perturbations in the marine and terrestrial realms. These are Late Ordovician, Late Devonian, end-Permian, end-Triassic, and end-Cretaceous extinctions, each of which killed about 75% of the species globally in a relatively short amount of geologic time. Here we will only focus on the biota events in late Ordovician, latest Permian, and latest Cretaceous. Although there have been major advances in our understanding of mass extinctions, there is still no consensus about the causes and kill mechanisms of these biotic crises. Mass extinctions have vital influence on evolutionary radiation processes. They open up the Earth for new forms of life to emerge. Following extinction events, communities are restructured, surviving groups gain new adaptations, and new species evolve with an increased rate of speciation. Many scientists agree that we are in the middle of the *sixth mass extinction* right now caused by environmentally destructive activities of humans. Studies have shown that the extinction rates today are significantly higher than the background level, underlining the need for effective conservation measures.

3L.1 Introduction

Of the 4 billion species estimated to have evolved on Earth, almost 99% are extinct (Novacek, 2001), illustrating how common extinction and speciation are on our planet. However, at several times in life's history, extinction rates reached a peak intensity above background levels during relatively short interval of geologic time, over geographically widespread areas (Sepkoski, 1986). These events with global ecological and evolutionary effects are called mass extinctions. Although there are several different ecological-severity estimations and rankings (e.g., McGhee et al., 2013), it is clear regardless of the approach that there were five large mass extinctions in the Phanerozoic, referred to as "Big Five" (Table 3L.1). These are Late Ordovician, Late Devonian, end-Permian, end-Triassic, and end-Cretaceous extinctions, each of which killed ~75% of the species globally (Raup and Sepkoski, 1982). In this chapter, we review the key aspects of the Late Ordovician, end-Cretaceous, and end-Permian mass extinctions, and evolutionary radiations in their aftermath.

Several kill mechanisms for Earth's largest biotic crises have been proposed, including global climate change, ocean anoxia, ocean acidification, ocean euxinia, sea-level change, toxic metal poisoning, wildfires, intense continental weathering, and global darkness triggered by major events such as bolide impact, glaciation/deglaciation, and extensive volcanism. Often, a combination of several of these mechanisms is necessary to explain coeval marine and terrestrial extinctions and the teleconnection between the two biospheres via atmospheric drivers.

Advancements in proxies such as sedimentary and geochemical tracers and radiometric dating techniques have refined the link between continental large igneous provinces (LIPs) and mass extinctions. Four of the "Big Five" are associated with LIPs suggesting that large-scale volcanism could be the main driver for the mass extinctions (Wignall, 2001). The most dramatic effects of LIPs are global warming due to greenhouse gas emissions and subsequent cooling caused by CO_2 drawdown due to weathering of LIP-related basalts and/or sulfate aerosols (e.g., Ernst and Youbi, 2017). However, continental configuration must have played a crucial role as well, since some of the most voluminous LIPs during Cretaceous caused minimal species decline, while the major LIP–extinction relationship occurred during the time of Pangea (Bond and Grasby, 2017). The only major extinction since Pangea breakup is the End-Cretaceous extinction that is associated with the bolide impact created the Chicxulub crater, Mexico in addition to Deccan eruptions in India.

Although extinction events are geologically instantaneous, environmental perturbations continue millions of years in their aftermath often tracked by geochemical markers such as carbon isotopes. Carbon isotopes show typically excursions coincident with mass extinctions that do not return back to preextinction values until long after extinction events (e.g., D'Hondt, 2005). That is an example of long-term effects of mass extinctions to biogeochemical cycles and rock record.

Mass extinctions have vital influence on evolutionary radiation processes. Postextinction ecosystems function differently with survivors showing morphological,

TABLE 3L.1 The "Big Five" mass extinction events.

Event	Extinction rates in marine biota	Possible triggers	Associated LIP	Proposed kill mechanisms	Losers	Winners
Late Ordovician (~443 Ma)	~49%–52% of genera ~86% of species	Glaciation and deglaciation	Suordakh event?	Global climate change, change in ocean circulation and chemistry, sea-level change, euxinia	Strophomenid and rhynchonellid brachiopods, nautiloids, trilobites, crinoids, conodonts, graptolites	Siliceous sponges, tabulate corals
Late Devonian (~372 Ma)	~35%–40% of genera ~75% of species	Glaciation and deglaciation	Yakutsk–Vilyui and Kola Dnieper LIPs	Global warming and cooling pulses, ocean anoxia	Stromatoporoids, tabulate corals, trilobites, cricoconarids, eurypterids, brachiopods, ammonoids, agnathans, placoderms	Chondrichthyans, actinopterygians
End-Permian (~252 Ma)	~57% of genera ~80% of species	Volcanism	Siberian Trap LIP	Carbon cycle disruption, ocean anoxia, ocean acidification, global warming, acid rain, ozone destruction, toxic metal poisoning	Brachiopods, crinoids, ammonoids, trilobites, tabulate and rugose corals, fenestrate bryozoans, fusulinoid forams, tetrapods	Bivalves, gastropods, malacostracan, echinoids, scleractinian corals, archosaurs
End-Triassic (~201 Ma)	~33%–40% of genera ~80% of species	Volcanism	CAMP	Global warming, ocean acidification	Calcareous sponges, scleractinian corals, brachiopods, nautiloids, ammonites	Siliceous sponges, dinosaurs
End-Cretaceous (~66 Ma)	~33%–40% of genera ~75% of species	Bolide impact, Volcanism	Deccan Trap LIP	Impact winter, wildfires, soot and sulfur injection, global warming, toxic metal poisoning	Nonavian dinosaurs, ammonites, calcareous plankton, mosasaurs, pterosaurs, rudist bivalves	Birds, mammals, spiny-rayed fishes

CAMP, Central Atlantic Magmatic Province; *LIP*, large igneous province.
Table based on Sepkoski, 1996; Bambach, 2004; Barnosky et al., 2011; McGhee et al., 2013; Hull, 2015; Bond and Grasby, 2017; Ernst and Youbi, 2017.

physiological, and ecological characteristics influenced by the selectivity of the extinction (Hull, 2015 and the references therein). Because of the selective nature of the mass extinctions, they can eliminate the entire branch of the tree of life, cause decline of diverse groups, and lead to the radiation of new species and ecosystems (Raup and Sepkoski, 1982; Bambach, 2006). In fact, the rate of speciation increases after mass extinctions (Sepkoski, 1998). Following extinction events, communities are restructured and surviving groups gain new adaptations that allow them to invade ecological niches that they have not occupied previously. One classical example of this is the evolution of mammals following the End-Cretaceous extinction. Small insectivorous and omnivorous mammals evolved and became herbivores and carnivores replacing dinosaurs in terrestrial ecosystem. Similarly, modern birds and flowering plants present in some diversity before End-Cretaceous mass extinction, exploded to ecological dominance in the aftermath of the extinction (Field et al., 2018). Therefore mass extinctions should not be considered as instantaneous evolutionary point events, but rather a prolonged interval of mass loss and subsequent radiation of taxa (Hull, 2015).

In addition having a vital impact on how life has been evolving on Earth, mass extinctions and extinctions in general also allowed biostratigraphic division of sedimentary rocks, which was proposed by William Smith more than 200 years ago. Still, biotic turnovers recorded in fossil record as a result of dramatic environmental changes are the primary means of relative dating and correlation and therefore used to define many of the boundaries of the Geologic Time Scale.

3L.2 The Late Ordovician mass extinction

3L.2.1 The earliest of the "Big Five"

The Late Ordovician mass extinction is the earliest mass extinction in the Phanerozoic (Sepkoski, 1986; Jablonski, 1991; Bambach et al., 2004) with an elimination of ~86% of species, ~49%–52% of genera, and ~26% of families of marine invertebrates (Jablonski, 1991; Brenchley et al., 2001; Sheehan, 2001). It was ranked as the second largest mass extinction after the end-Permian mass extinction by Sepkoski (1996) and Bambach et al. (2004). However, some recent reevaluations of the severity rankings place the Late Ordovician mass extinction as the third largest mass extinction after the end-Triassic extinction (McGhee et al., 2013). Regardless of its ranking, the Late Ordovician mass extinction caused severe diversity crisis in many marine clades such as conodonts, graptolites, trilobites, brachiopods, nautiloids, and crinoids (Sheehan, 2001 and the references therein). It has been linked to the rapid growth and decay of the large Gondwana ice sheets and related changes in sea level, sea-surface temperatures, and ocean oxygen stratification, all of which resulted in the declining availability of potential niche space in both the pelagic and benthic realms (e.g., Armstrong and Harper, 2014).

Significant changes in the biodiversity and biocomplexity of marine life occurred during Early-to-Mid Ordovician with a profound increase in diversity at the family, genus, and species levels, known as the Great Ordovician Biodiversification Event (e.g., Harper, 2006). Although the cause of the Great Ordovician Biodiversification Event is not fully understood, a cooling climate, increased nutrient availability, increased ecospace after sea-level rise, additional oxygenation of shallow-marine environments, and geochemical fluctuations are among the possible causes suggested (Liu et al., 2019; Edwards, 2019). Late Ordovician mass extinction terminated the Great Ordovician Biodiversification Event by severely disrupting the structure and diversity of benthic and planktonic ecosystems and downgrading the biocomplexity (Brenchley et al., 2001; Harper et al., 2014).

The Ordovician paleogeography and paleoclimate were significantly different from the Recent. Several continental plates were spread along the equator covered by extensive epicontinental seas and the Gondwana supercontinent was close to the South Pole (e.g., Sheehan, 2001). Before a glaciation apparently caused the Late Ordovician mass extinction, the world was in an intense greenhouse interval with atmospheric CO_2 levels about 16 times higher than the pre-industrial Holocene atmospheric levels (Sheehan, 2001). Clumped isotope paleothermometry through the Late Ordovician–Early Silurian showed that the ocean temperatures were 32°C–37°C except for a short-lived cooling by ~5°C during the final Hirnantian stage (Finnegan et al., 2011). Global cooling in Hirnantian was especially devastating because the biota was adapted to greenhouse conditions.

The Late Ordovician mass extinction is considered to consist of two pulses in the Hirnantian Stage (Brenchley et al., 1994). The first pulse is associated with the onset of rapid glaciation on supercontinent Gondwana (Sheehan, 2001; Harper et al., 2014). The growth of the ice sheets drained the large epicontinental seaways eliminating the habitat of many endemic communities (Sheehan, 2001). Cooling-related acceleration in oceanic circulation aerated the deep oceans and brought nutrients and possibly toxic material from deep oceans to the surface waters (Brenchley et al., 1994; Sheehan, 2001). These perturbations impacted planktonic and the deep-sea benthic communities particularly, especially fauna in epicontinental seas and in higher latitudes (Sheehan, 2001; Harper et al., 2014). Some brachiopod, trilobite, and graptolite communities that survived the first pulse of extinction adapted to cool conditions (Wang et al., 2019 and the references therein), and a distinctive benthic fauna called the Hirnantian fauna was introduced and flourished following the glaciation (e.g., Harper et al., 2014).

The second pulse of the extinction is associated with the melting of the Gondwana ice sheet that caused a sea-level rise and slowdown of ocean circulation (Sheehan, 2001). Stagnant ocean circulation caused the development of anoxic ocean conditions documented by widespread black shale deposition close to the Ordovician–Silurian boundary worldwide (e.g., Vecoli et al., 2009). The second pulse of extinction killed many of the survivors from the first extinction phase, including conodonts, cool temperature-adapted Hirnantian fauna, and many other open marine species and left a simple and cosmopolitan ecosystem behind (Brenchley et al., 2001; Sheehan, 2001). Clumped isotope thermometry studies showed that the ice sheets persisted from Late Ordovician to Early Silurian, but tropical cooling was largely limited to the Hirnantian Stage supporting the hypotheses linking the two-pulsed nature of the Late Ordovician mass extinction to rapid climate changes at the beginning and end of this interval (Finnegan et al., 2011).

Geochemical redox indicators suggested that euxinia, generated by the reorganization of nutrient cycling after glaciation and subsequent deglaciation, might be a possible kill mechanism for the Late Ordovician mass extinction.

Zou et al. (2018) suggested that both pulses were coincident with euxinic conditions causing habitat loss for deep-water benthic and nektonic organisms; on the other hand, Hammarlund et al. (2012) proposed that euxinic conditions prevailed and intensified in the early Hirnantian oceans and played only role for the first pulse of the extinction.

It is not common in the Phanerozoic that glaciations are associated with major mass extinctions. One possible reason why the Late Ordovician glaciation was devastating to life might be its short duration. The peak of the glaciation most likely occurred within the course of half a million years, and faunas did not have time to adapt to either the rapid deterioration of climate or, for that matter, the succeeding return to more normal conditions (Brenchley et al., 1994; Sheehan, 2001). Paleogeographic configuration during the Ordovician–Silurian interval may have played a role in the extinction as well. The loss of microcontinents and associated smaller terranes around Laurentia may have restricted shelf and slope habitats during the latest Ordovician (Rasmussen and Harper, 2011). The gradual ventilation of the oceans during the later Paleozoic and Mesozoic helped the biosphere not be subject to glacially induced mass extinction in this intensity again (Armstrong and Harper, 2014).

The Late Ordovician extinction was severe in terms of biodiversity loss but not as severe as the other mass extinctions in terms of ecological consequences (Sheehan, 2001; Harper et al., 2014). There was relatively little innovation in terms of evolution and adaptive strategies during the recovery period, that is, newly evolved fauna from surviving fauna lived in similar ecological settings as the extinct fauna (Brenchley et al., 2001; Sheehan, 2001). For example, reef development was interrupted by the extinction, but the new Silurian reef communities were similar to preextinction communities (Copper, 1994).

Although the resulting fauna had similar ecological patterns to the extinct fauna, the recovery after the Late Ordovician mass extinction took over about 4–5 Myr (Brenchley et al., 2001). Three of the major Paleozoic groups, the brachiopods, graptolites, and trilobites played an important role in the survival period (see the review in Harper et al., 2014). Within the nonarticulate brachiopods, nearly 20 families survived the extinction while nearly 10 families went extinct, with more diverse clades being the survivors. The trilobites lost almost half of the families, with 20 families disappearing at the boundary and 20 surviving. Within the graptolites, ~75% of the dendroid families survived the extinction but less than 15% of the graptolites continued into the Llandovery, where they experienced a great diversification. New, near-cosmopolitan, and low-diversity communities formed the basis for a massive recovery of the shelly fauna during the later Silurian.

Early Silurian ecosystems rapidly reconstructed many of the ecological structures destroyed by the extinction event. Multiple lineages of sponges that survived the Late Ordovician mass extinction played particularly an important role. Diverse sponge communities dominated the postextinction seafloor and aided the ecosystem recovery by stabilizing the sediment surface, allowing sessile suspension feeders such as brachiopods, corals, and bryozoans to recover rapidly (Botting et al., 2017).

3L.3 End-Permian mass extinction

3L.3.1 The greatest of the "Big Five"

Regardless of the approach to assess the severity of the diversity declines in Earth's history, the end-Permian mass extinction is ranked as the largest mass extinction in the Phanerozoic (Sepkoski, 1996; Bambach et al., 2004; McGhee et al., 2013) with an extinction of more than ~80% of marine (e.g., Stanley, 2016) and ~75% of terrestrial genera (Erwin, 2006). The end-Permian mass extinction affected several major marine groups, including brachiopods, crinoids, trilobites, ammonites, rugose and tabulate corals, sponges, fusulinids, and radiolarians (Payne and Clapham, 2012 and the references therein). It also caused widespread devastation on land, including vertebrate species, terrestrial plants, and insects (e.g., Labandeira and Sepkoski, 1993; Retallack, 1995; Smith and Ward, 2001; Ward et al., 2005). The end-Permian mass extinction is not only the cause of the largest global biodiversity decline in the past 538 million years but also largely responsible for much of the biotic structure today by having redirected the evolution of the subsequent marine and terrestrial life.

Before the end-Permian mass extinction, in the Middle Permian, at the end of the Guadalupian (Capitanian), there was another biodiversity crisis that significantly affected Permian diversity trends (Jin et al., 1994). In fact, end-Guadalupian crisis has been traditionally ranked as the third largest mass extinction in the Phanerozoic with ~40% loss in marine genera (Sepkoski, 1996; Bambach et al., 2004). However, biostratigraphic evidence showed that no high-rank phylogenetic clade became extinct at the end-Guadalupian and the turnover of major groups, including rugose corals, brachiopods, conodonts, fusulinids, bivalves, and ammonites occurred at different degrees and temporal levels (Shen and Shi, 2009; Chen and Shen, 2019). In fact, reevaluation of the ecological-severity ranking showed that the end-Guadalupian biotic crisis caused only ~25% marine genera loss and is not as severe as previously thought (Payne and Clapham, 2012; McGhee et al., 2013). Nevertheless, the end-Guadalupian mass extinction is associated with environmental changes such as carbon, strontium, sulfur isotopic changes, and rapid fluctuations in seawater temperatures (Chen and Shen, 2019). Evidence suggests that Emeishan LIP volcanism, southwest China caused or at least largely contributed to the end-Guadalupian mass extinction (Bond et al., 2010; Chen and Xu, 2019). Other suggested trigger is the regression due to the largest Paleozoic sea-level fall (Haq and Schutter, 2008) that eliminated habitats for faunas evolved in the epicontinental seas (Chen and Shen, 2019). After the end-Guadalupian mass extinction, biodiversity gradually increased until it suddenly dropped at the end-Permian.

Unlike the end-Guadalupian mass extinction, the end-Permian mass extinction affected all existent marine invertebrate and protist clades. Trilobites, rugose and tabulate corals, goniatites, brachiopods (Strophomenata, Spiriferida, Orthida), blastoids, rostroconchs, and fenestrate bryozoans suffered complete extinction at the end-Permian mass extinction (Payne and Clapham, 2012 and the references therein). The extinction was devastating for all calcareous foraminifera (Lagenida, Miliolida, and Fusulinida), but especially so for the large and morphologically complex agglutinated superfamily Fusulinoidea, which was entirely eliminated (e.g., Groves et al., 2005). Reef ecosystems changed entirely from Permian to Triassic with complete extinction of rugose and tabulate corals and appearance and diversification of scleractinian corals in Middle-to-Late Triassic (Payne and Clapham, 2012 and the references therein). Although less clearly documented, the end-Permian mass extinction was equally severe for terrestrial vertebrates as demonstrated by the abrupt tetrapod extinction in Karoo Basin, Africa (Ward et al., 2005).

Several kill mechanisms have been proposed for the end-Permian mass extinction, including carbon cycle disruption, ocean anoxia, ocean acidification, global warming, acid rain, ozone destruction, and toxic metal poisoning (Bond and Grasby, 2017 and the references therein). Many of these kill mechanisms were linked to the eruption and emplacement of Siberian Trap LIP, the largest preserved continental basaltic magmatism generated in the Phanerozoic (Wignall, 2001; Courtillot and Renne, 2003; Burgess et al., 2014; Burgess and Bowring, 2015). The U–Pb dates on Siberian Trap LIP rocks demonstrated that the majority of the lava/pyroclastic volume was erupted before and during the end-Permian mass extinction and magmatism continued for at least 500 kyr after the event (Burgess and Bowring, 2015). Rapid injection of massive amounts of greenhouse gases not only from extrusive eruptions but also from intrusive hydrothermal vent complexes drive climate change and subsequent perturbations in the ecosystem (Ernst and Youbi, 2017).

Injection of large amounts of greenhouse gases into the atmosphere possibly induced global warming and ocean anoxia. Paleotemperature proxies showed that sea-surface temperature could have been risen up to 5°C–9°C across the Permian–Triassic transition reaching up to ~30°C with an atmospheric CO_2 of 8000 ppm during the peak extinction event (Cui and Kump, 2015). Such elevated seawater temperatures and atmospheric CO_2 probably were devastating to life both in oceans and on land. Ocean anoxia linked to global warming enhanced the activity of sulfate-reducing bacteria that generated further CO_2 and H_2S, both of which would be delivered to surface ocean and atmosphere by upwelling and causing biota to be exposed to asphyxia (oxygen deprivation), hypercapnia (CO_2 poisoning), H_2S poisoning, and thermal stress (Knoll et al., 2007). Widespread anoxia and euxinia across the Permian–Triassic boundary were further supported by synsedimentary pyrite framboid deposition recorded in many locations worldwide (e.g., Wignall et al., 2005). Knoll et al. (2007) also suggested that release of H_2S from the ocean to the atmosphere possibly increased UV radiation and caused ozone depletion, particularly harmful for terrestrial life. However, a collapse of stratospheric ozone leading to a UV increase is not supported by photochemical model calculations (Kaiho and Koga, 2013).

Ocean acidification is considered as another possible killer for the end-Permian mass extinction (e.g., Payne et al., 2010; Clapham and Payne, 2011; Hinojosa et al., 2012). Ocean acidification occurs when there is rapid (~10^4 years or shorter) CO_2 release, and the rate of CO_2 release is too high to allow sources (weathering) and sinks ($CaCO_3$ burial) to balance, causing a decline in ocean pH and $CaCO_3$ saturation (e.g., Kump et al., 2009). Evidence of Late Permian ocean acidification comes from sedimentological features such as carbonate dissolution surfaces, fossils, and geochemical proxies (e.g., Payne et al., 2007, 2010; Hinojosa et al., 2012; Garbelli et al., 2017). An example of fossil evidence from marine invertebrates is that the loss of Strophomenata brachiopods during the end-Permian mass extinction because of their sensitivity to pH decline, whereas survival of Rhynchonellata brachiopods due to their adaptability to pH changes (Garbelli et al., 2017). Calcium, carbon, and other isotopes used as proxies to quantify the pH changes also showed shifts across the Permian–Triassic boundary (e.g., Payne et al., 2010). However, using some of the isotopic datasets such as calcium isotopes as proxies for paleoenvironmental conditions has been questioned by some studies due to the complexity of primary and secondary processes controlling isotopic composition of ancient oceans (Komar and Zeebe, 2016; Wang et al., 2019).

The end-Permian mass extinction witnessed significant changes in global carbon cycle as recorded by carbon isotopes. A gradual $\delta^{13}C$ excursion across the Permian–Triassic boundary was documented at more than 100 marine and many nonmarine sections (see the review by Korte and Kozur, 2010). The $\delta^{13}C$ excursion has been explained by two hypotheses: (1) collapse of primary productivity as a consequence of the extinction and the resulting isotopic homogenization of the oceans (Strangelove Ocean) and (2) injection of ^{13}C-depleted carbon to the oceans and atmosphere possibly from methane clathrates, methane dissolved in deep-ocean waters, dissolved inorganic carbon in the deep waters of a stratified ocean, a large dissolved marine organic carbon reservoir, or sedimentary organic carbon deposits (see the review by Payne and Clapham, 2012). Most probably both of these mechanisms contributed to the carbon cycle perturbations across the Permian–Triassic boundary.

Although the main pulse of End-Permian mass extinction only lasted shorter than a few hundred thousand years (Payne and Clapham, 2012; Burgess and Bowring, 2015), the highly disturbed ecosystem lasted millions of years and a stable ecosystem did not reestablish until Middle Triassic (Erwin, 2001; Chen and Benton, 2012). Ammonoids, marine tetrapods, conodonts experienced relatively rapid (2–3 Myr) but punctuated diversity rebound during the Early Triassic. Radiolarians that suffered dramatic loss during the End-Permian extinction recovered in the Olenekian (Early Triassic) evolving from the Paleozoic taxa that migrated from tropics to higher paleolatitudes (Feng and Algeo, 2014). For other groups the recovery period was longer. It took until Middle Triassic for brachiopods to reach their preextinction diversity (Chen et al., 2005). Coral and metazoan reef systems were replaced by microbial carbonate mound for up to 6 Myr. Complex burrowing of sediments remained rare for ~4 Myr (Chen and Benton, 2012), and the rediversification of benthic invertebrates took ~5 Myr (Pietsch and Bottjer, 2014). Although some new lineages of predators such as fishes and reptiles appeared soon after the mass extinction (Benton et al., 2004), rediversification was delayed by Anisian (Middle Triassic) (Hu et al., 2011). On land, some ecological strategists revolved immediately, while it took 15 Myr for small fish-eaters, small insect-eaters, large herbivores, and top carnivores to reappear (Benton et al., 2004).

3L.4 End-Cretaceous mass extinction

3L.4.1 The latest of the "Big Five"

The End-Cretaceous extinction is one of the five largest mass extinctions in Earth's history (Raup and Sepkoski, 1982). It was catastrophic both in terrestrial and marine environments. On land, nonavian dinosaurs and pterosaurs disappeared; many bird, lizard, snake, insect, and plant groups underwent drastic changes (D'Hondt, 2005; Schulte et al., 2010). In the oceans, ~75% of species and ~40% of genera extinct (Sepkoski, 1996; McGhee et al., 2013), including ammonites, belemnites, rudist bivalves, and calcareous plankton (Schulte et al., 2010 and the references therein).

Forty years ago, the discovery of anomalously high abundances of iridium (Ir) and other platinum-group elements at several K–Pg boundary sections led to the hypothesis that an asteroid ~10 km in diameter collided with Earth causing environmental perturbations (Alvarez et al., 1980; Smit and Hertogen, 1980). Subsequent recognition of impact-related features such as shocked minerals (Bohor et al., 1987), impact spherules, and Ni-spinels (Smit and Kyte, 1984), the discovery of the Chicxulub crater (165–200 km in diameter) in the Yucatan Peninsula, Mexico (Hildebrand et al., 1991; Morgan et al., 1997), and radiometric dating of the crater (Swisher et al., 1992) substantiated the impact hypothesis. Large earthquakes, massive submarine landslides, and tsunamis from the Caribbean up to North America were caused by the impact (Bralower et al., 1998; Norris et al., 2000), and its hot ejecta caused at least regional if not global wildfires (Melosh et al., 1990; Goldin and Melosh, 2009; Robertson et al., 2013b).

It has been proposed that stratigraphic and micropaleontological data from the Gulf of Mexico show three impacts during the time interval spanning the boundary with the Chicxulub impact predating the K–Pg boundary by ~300 kyr (Keller et al., 2003, 2007). This multiple impact hypothesis (Keller et al., 2003, 2007) is not supported by other K–Pg boundary locations free from stratigraphic complexities of near-impact sites. Moreover, more than 350 K–Pg boundary sites known today show a distinct pattern of decreasing thickness of the ejecta deposits with increasing distance from the Chicxulub crater suggesting a unique source for the ejecta at the K–Pg boundary (Smit, 1999; Claeys et al., 2002; Schulte et al., 2010). Detailed analysis of Ir profiles with a Lagrangian particle-tracking model of sediment mixing across the K–Pg boundary also showed that Ir concentrations are a product of a single global cause (Esmeray-Senlet et al., 2017). However, even closely spaced sites show heterogeneity in preservation of the ejecta layers due to postdepositional modification by bioturbation and geochemical processes (Hull et al., 2011; Esmeray-Senlet et al., 2017).

The impact hypothesis has not been the only explanation for the K–Pg boundary mass extinction. Emplacement of the large Deccan continental flood basalts in India spanning the K–Pg boundary has also been suggested as the cause of the End-Cretaceous mass extinction. The activity of the LIP lasted ~750 kyr causing severe environmental effects due to the eruptive degassing of sulfur and carbon dioxide (Courtillot et al., 1986; Courtillot and Renne, 2003; Self et al., 2006; Chenet et al., 2007, 2009; Schoene et al., 2015). Schoene et al. (2015) used U–Pb dating of zircons interbedded within the Deccan lava flows and showed that the main eruptive phase initiated ~250 kyr before and ended ~500 kyr after the K–Pg boundary contributing to the End-Cretaceous ecosystem crisis. However, this proposal was challenged by Sprain et al. (2019) who suggested that ~75% of the Deccan Traps emplaced after the K–Pg boundary, and Late Cretaceous climate change coincided briefly with the eruption of the smallest Deccan Trap phases. They argued that either the release of climate-modifying gases is not directly related to eruptive volume or Deccan volcanism was not the source of Late Cretaceous climate change (Sprain et al., 2019).

There are multiple hypotheses for the kill mechanism of the K–Pg mass extinction. Alvarez et al. (1980) suggested that injection of impact-related dust and aerosols into the stratosphere might have blocked the solar radiation leading a global decimation of marine and continental photosynthesis and therefore collapse in the food chain both in marine and terrestrial environments (the "impact-winter" hypothesis). Direct evidence for "impact-winter" hypothesis came from TEX_{86} paleothermometry measurements in sediments from the Brazos River section, Texas, and New Jersey paleoshelf, the United States that indicated a decline in sea-surface temperatures during the first months to decades following the impact event. Recent climate simulations suggested that 15,000 Tg of soot, originated from global wildfires ignited after the impact, created a worldwide soot aerosol layer that prevented sunlight penetration for several years (Bardeen et al., 2017). Cessation of photosynthesis even for a short period of time can cause global extinction of phytoplankton taxa with life spans of weeks to months, also causing catastrophic extinction of marine autotrophs that are strongly dependent on daily photosynthetic output (Robertson et al., 2013a).

Another possible kill mechanism proposed is widespread acid rain that resulted from increased atmospheric nitric oxide, carbonic, and sulfuric acid (Toon et al., 1982; Kring, 2007). Models suggest that release of gases from the anhydrite (calcium sulfate) target rocks could have caused injection of sulfur vapor into the stratosphere, producing sulfuric acid rain (e.g., Pierazzo et al., 1998). Recent studies using new constraints on the Chicxulub impact angle and target composition estimated that 325 ± 130 Gt of sulfur were ejected into the atmosphere (Artemieva et al., 2017). Sulfuric acid rain might have had direct deadly biological impacts, as well as negative effects such as extended darkness, global cooling, acidification, and increased weathering (Kring, 2007).

Marine microfossils experienced the End-Cretaceous mass extinction differently showing the selective nature of the extinction. Calcareous plankton suffered catastrophic extinctions, with the disappearance of more than 90% of the Cretaceous species of planktonic foraminifera (e.g., Smit, 1982; Olsson and Liu, 1993; MacLeod et al., 1997; Olsson et al., 1999; Keller et al., 2002) and calcareous nannofossils (e.g., Bernaola and Monechi, 2007). However, organic-walled, opportunistic dinoflagellates experienced minimal turnover (e.g., Brinkhuis et al., 1998), presumably because they employ a resting cyst stage as part of their life cycle. Benthic foraminifera also showed negligible extinctions (Culver, 2003), though the diversity of their assemblages decreased after the End-Cretaceous mass extinction interpreted to be due to high environmental stress (Alegret and Thomas, 2005).

The End-Cretaceous mass extinction is associated with drastic perturbations in the oceanic carbon cycle as shown by a collapse in the carbon isotopic ($\delta^{13}C$) gradient between surface and deep waters recorded by planktonic and benthic foraminifera and a significant drop in bulk carbonate $\delta^{13}C$ values both in open-ocean sites (e.g., Zachos and Arthur, 1986) and shallow-water sites (Esmeray-Senlet et al., 2015). Studies showed that the $\delta^{13}C$ difference between surface-dwelling planktonic and deep-sea benthic foraminiferal tests in the latest Cretaceous was ~2‰ (e.g., D'Hondt, 2005), which is similar to that measured in the modern oceans (Kroopnick, 1985). However, this difference apparently disappeared at the beginning of the Paleocene (Zachos and Arthur, 1986; Stott and Kennett, 1989; Zachos et al., 1989; D'Hondt and Zachos, 1998; D'Hondt, 2005; Coxall et al., 2006; Esmeray-Senlet et al., 2015).

The perturbations in the carbon cycle in the aftermath of the K–Pg event have been explained by several hypotheses: (1) *Strangelove Ocean*: global collapse of primary productivity (Broecker and Peng, 1982; Hsu et al., 1982), (2) *Living Ocean*: greatly reduced export but not primary productivity (D'Hondt and Zachos, 1998; D'Hondt et al., 1998; D'Hondt, 2005; Coxall et al., 2006; Esmeray-Senlet et al., 2015), (3) *Resilient Ocean*: little or no reduction in export productivity (Alegret and Thomas, 2009; Alegret et al., 2012), and (4) *Heterogeneous Ocean*: geographic heterogeneity in the change of export productivity (Hull and Norris, 2011; Sibert et al., 2014). Esmeray-Senlet et al. (2015) tested primary versus export productivity changes in the paleoshelf of New Jersey, United States, where $\delta^{13}C$ values and organic carbon accumulation rates can distinguish among different ocean responses and compared the shelf record with the open ocean sites from Atlantic and Pacific Oceans. They argued that the data support the Living Ocean hypothesis though do not contradict the Heterogeneous Ocean. Uniformity in the change of export productivity in the world shelves and deep-sea oceans cannot be expected; the ocean floor in highly productive regions such as the equatorial Pacific may have continued to receive significant export productivity (Hull and Norris, 2011; Sibert et al., 2014; Esmeray-Senlet et al., 2015; Sepúlveda et al., 2019).

Earlier studies suggested that full recovery to preextinction surface to deep-water $\delta^{13}C$ gradients took

~3 Myr after the K–Pg boundary (D'Hondt et al., 1998; Coxall et al., 2006), though more recent studies suggested that the biological pump was weakened for a shorter duration, less than 2 Myr (Birch et al., 2016). Sepúlvede et al. (2019) suggested that carbon cycling and primary productivity in neritic and upper bathyal regions recovered to preboundary levels faster ($<10^4$ kyr) than in oceanic regions (10^5-10^6 years), likely sustained by resilient noncalcifying phytoplankton with resting stages.

Life did not take too much time to recovery after the End-Cretaceous mass extinction. Lowery et al. (2018) suggested that life reappeared just years after the impact and a high-productivity ecosystem was established within 30 kyr even near the Chicxulub impact crater. However, it took longer time for the marine communities to diversify. Both coccolithophores and planktonic foraminifera were characterized by a succession of short-lived, low-diversity communities in roughly million years after the Chicxulub impact. In each successive community a single species dominated the assemblage, giving rise to the evolution of the successors. For example, the earliest Danian survival interval is dominated by a single planktonic foraminiferal species *Guembelitria cretacea*, and all subsequent planktonic foraminifera are descended from *G. cretacea* and two other species *Hedbergella holmdelensis* and *Hedbergella monmouthensis* (Olsson et al., 1999). These small, opportunistic species rapidly expanded their environmental range in the absence of competitors and quickly diversified as the recovery progressed (Koutsoukos, 1996).

Many of the modern vertebrate groups that exist today appeared in the Cretaceous, yet the End-Cretaceous mass extinction reshaped the evolutionary trends for land vertebrates. Some groups, including ray-finned fishes, multituberculate mammals, eutherian mammals, turtles, lizards, champsosaurs, and crocodiles survived the extinction; however, after the K–Pg boundary the basic organization and dynamics of the larger vertebrate fauna were radically transformed (Novacek, 1999). The loss of nonavian dinosaurs caused larger herbivorous browsers not replenish for some millions of years into the Paleocene (Novacek, 1999). The End-Cretaceous mass extinction also intensely influenced the evolutionary history of modern birds (Field et al., 2018). After the devastation of global forests, no lineages of tree-dwelling birds survived the mass extinction event, therefore; all modern tree-dwelling birds are descended from surviving ground-dwelling lineages (Field et al., 2018).

It is still debated whether the End-Cretaceous mass extinction led directly to the rise of mammals and ultimately to the evolutionary origin of humans. However, evidence suggests that the ancestors of living placentals and marsupials that survived the extinction thrived and radiated extensively during the Cenozoic (Perini, 2016). During the beginning of the Cenozoic, many archaic groups of mammals evolved, as well as the first representatives of modern orders of mammals (Perini, 2016).

3L.5 Concluding remarks

Fossil records and geochemical proxies demonstrated that catastrophic environmental changes created numerous declines in biodiversity in Earth's history impacting ecological structure of both marine and terrestrial biota. The magnitudes of the biodiversity declines have been variable, but at least five times in the last 538 Myr almost 75% of the species extinct globally (Raup and Sepkoski, 1982). Subsequent recoveries of biodiversity in the aftermaths have been slower than the mass extinctions, often taking 5–10 Myr or even more. The patterns of recovery are complex but generally involve outbreaks of disaster species and significant ecological instability over time scales of 10^5-10^6 years (Sepkoski, 2012).

How does the current biodiversity crisis compare with previous mass extinctions? Scientists have been documenting the accelerating rate of modern species extinctions referred to as the *sixth mass extinction* or *Anthropocene mass extinction* caused by environmentally destructive activities of humans (Barnosky et al., 2011; Pievani, 2015; Wagler, 2012, 2018, and the references therein). It is an ongoing event where a large number of living species are threatened with extinction.

Rapid global warming, as a result of input of greenhouse gases due to fossil fuel burning, causes melting of polar glaciers and rapid sea-level rise. Today's CO_2 from the atmosphere is absorbed in the oceans lowering the pH and causing ocean acidification. Ocean acidification will likely affect shelly organisms at the base of the food chain (e.g., pteropods, corals) in the near-future endangering all life up the food chain (Hauri et al., 2015). Payne et al. (2016) stated that activities of humans such as fishing and hunting cause as much threat to modern marine fauna as the ocean chemistry changes if not more.

Modern global biodiversity is estimated to be more than 5 million species (Wagler, 2012, 2018). Among those, 5–150 species become extinct *per day* (Sepkoski, 2012). International Union for Conservation of Nature assessed the current extinction is as 24%–40% of genera overall, with similar loss levels in vertebrates and mollusks. The lower value is twice the background rate, and the higher is comparable to the End-Cretaceous mass extinction (Payne et al., 2016). Barnosky, et al. (2011) estimated similar extinction rates for the past 500 years, namely, 22% in mammals and 47%–56% in gastropods and bivalves. These rates far exceed those recorded in the fossil record for the five major extinctions and are concerning. Since there is still much of the world's biodiversity left to save, the hope is that the humans will work toward reversing the escalating threats.

Bibliography

Alegret, L., and Thomas, E., 2005, Cretaceous/Paleogene boundary bathyal paleo-environments in the central North Pacific (DSDP Site 465), the Northwestern Atlantic (ODP Site 1049), the Gulf of Mexico and the Tethys: the benthic Foraminiferal record. *Palaeogeography, Palaeoclimatology, Palaeoecology*, **224**: 53−82, https://doi.org/10.1016/j.palaeo.2005.03.031.

Alegret, L., and Thomas, E., 2009, Food supply to the seafloor in the Pacific Ocean after the Cretaceous/Paleogene boundary event. *Marine Micropaleontology*, **73**: 105−116, https://doi.org/10.1016/j.marmicro.2009.07.005.

Alegret, L., Thomas, E., and Lohmann, K.C., 2012, End-Cretaceous marine mass extinction not caused by productivity collapse. *Proceedings of the National Academy of Sciences of the United States of America*, **109**: 728−732, https://doi.org/10.1073/pnas.1110601109/-/DCSupplemental/ST01.doc.

Alvarez, L., Alvarez, W., Asaro, F., and Michel, H., 1980, Extraterrestrial cause for the Cretaceous-Tertiary extinction. *Science*, **208**: 1095−1108.

Armstrong, H.A., and Harper, D.A.T., 2014, An earth system approach to understanding the end-Ordovician (Hirnantian) mass extinction. *Geological Society of America Special Papers*, **505**: 287−300, https://doi.org/10.1130/2014.2505(14).

Artemieva, N., Morgan, J., and Expedition 364 Science Party, 2017, Quantifying the release of climate-active gases by large meteorite impacts with a case study of Chicxulub. *Geophysical Research Letters*, **44**: 10,180−10,188, https://doi.org/10.1002/2017GL074879.

Bambach, R.K., 2006, Phanerozoic biodiversity mass extinctions. *Annual Review of Earth and Planetary Sciences*, **34**: 127−155, https://doi.org/10.1146/annurev.earth.33.092203.122654.

Bambach, R.K., Knoll, A., and Wang, S.C., 2004, Origination, extinction, and mass depletions of marine diversity. *Paleobiology*, **30**: 522−542, https://doi.org/10.1666/0094-8373(2004)030 < 0522:OEAMDO > 2.0.CO;2.

Bardeen, C.G., Garcia, R.R., Toon, O.B., and Conley, A.J., 2017, On transient climate change at the Cretaceous − Paleogene boundary due to atmospheric soot injections. *Proceedings of the National Academy of Sciences of the United States of America*, **114**: 1−10, https://doi.org/10.1073/pnas.1708980114.

Barnosky, A.D., et al., 2011, Has the Earth's sixth mass extinction already arrived? *Nature*, **470**: 51−57, https://doi.org/10.1038/nature09678.

Benton, M.J., Tverdokhlebov, V.P., and Surkov, M.V., 2004, Ecosystem remodelling among vertebrates at the Permian-Triassic boundary in Russia. *Nature*, **432**: 97−100, https://doi.org/10.1038/nature02950.

Bernaola, G., and Monechi, S., 2007, Calcareous nannofossil extinction and survivorship across the Cretaceous − Paleogene boundary at Walvis Ridge (ODP Hole 1262C, South Atlantic Ocean). *Palaeogeography, Palaeoclimatology, Palaeoecology*, **255**: 132−156, https://doi.org/10.1016/j.palaeo.2007.02.045.

Birch, H.S., Coxall, H.K., Pearson, P.N., Kroon, D., and Schmidt, D.N., 2016, Partial collapse of the marine carbon pump after the Cretaceous-Paleogene boundary. *Geology*, **44**: 287−290, https://doi.org/10.1130/G37581.1.

Bohor, B., Modreski, P., and Foord, E., 1987, Shocked quartz in the Cretaceous-Tertiary boundary clays: evidence for a global distribution. *Science*, **236**: 705−709.

Bond, D.P.G., and Grasby, S.E., 2017, On the causes of mass extinctions. *Palaeogeography, Palaeoclimatology, Palaeoecology*, **478**: 3−29, https://doi.org/10.1016/j.palaeo.2016.11.005.

Bond, D.P.G., Hilton, J., Wignall, P.B., Ali, J.R., Stevens, L.G., Sun, Y., et al., 2010, The Middle Permian (Capitanian) mass extinction on land and in the oceans. *Earth-Science Reviews*, **102**: 100−116, https://doi.org/10.1016/j.earscirev.2010.07.004.

Botting, J.P., Muir, L.A., Zhang, Y., Ma, X., Ma, J., Wang, L., et al., 2017, Flourishing sponge-based ecosystems after the end-Ordovician mass extinction. *Current Biology*, **27**: 556−562, https://doi.org/10.1016/j.cub.2016.12.061.

Bralower, T.J., Paull, C.K., and Leckie, R.M., 1998, The Cretaceous-Tertiary boundary cocktail: Chicxulub impact triggers margin collapse and extensive sediment gravity flows. *Geology*, **26**: 331−334.

Brenchley, P.J., Marshall, J.D., Carden, G.A.F., Robertson, D.B.R., Long, D.G.F., Meidla, T., et al., 1994, Bathymetric and isotopic evidence for a short-lived Late Ordovician glaciation in a greenhouse period. *Geology*, **22**: 295−298.

Brenchley, P.J., Marshall, J.D., and Underwood, C.J., 2001, Do all mass extinctions represent an ecological crisis? Evidence from the Late Ordovician. *Geological Journal*, **36**: 329−340, https://doi.org/10.1002/gj.880.

Brinkhuis, H., Bujak, J.P., Smit, J., Versteegh, G., and Visscher, H., 1998, Dinoflagellate-based sea surface temperature reconstructions across the Cretaceous−Tertiary boundary. *Palaeogeography, Palaeoclimatology, Palaeoecology*, **141**: 67−83.

Broecker, W.S., and Peng, T.H., 1982, *Tracers in the Sea*. Lamont-Doherty Geological Observatory Palisades. Columbia University Press, p. 620.

Burgess, S.D., and Bowring, S.A., 2015, High-precision geochronology confirms voluminous magmatism before, during, and after Earth's most severe extinction. *Science Advances*, **1**: e1500470, https://doi.org/10.1016/j.epsl.2009.02.012.

Burgess, S.D., Bowring, S.A., and Shen, S.-Z., 2014, High-precision timeline for Earth's most severe extinction. *Proceedings of the National Academy of Sciences of the United States of America*, **111**: 3316−3321, https://doi.org/10.1073/pnas.1403228111.

Chen, Z.-Q., and Benton, M.J., 2012, The timing and pattern of biotic recovery following the end-Permian mass extinction. *Nature Geoscience*, **5**: 375−383, https://doi.org/10.1038/ngeo1475.

Chen, Z.-Q., Kaiho, K., and George, A.D., 2005, Early Triassic recovery of the brachiopod faunas from the end-Permian mass extinction: a global review. *Palaeogeography, Palaeoclimatology, Palaeoecology*, **224**: 270−290, https://doi.org/10.1016/j.palaeo.2005.03.037.

Chen, J., and Shen, S., 2019, *Mid-Permian (End-Guadalupian) extinctions. Reference Module in Earth Systems and Environmental Sciences*Elsevier Inc, http://doi.org/10.1016/B978-0-12-409548-9.11976-1.

Chen, J., and Xu, Y., 2019, Establishing the link between Permian volcanism and biodiversity changes: insights from geochemical proxies. *Gondwana Research*, **75**: 68−96, https://doi.org/10.1016/j.gr.2019.04.008.

Chenet, A., Quidelleur, X., Fluteau, F., Courtillot, V., and Bajpai, S., 2007, ^{40}K-^{40}Ar dating of the Main Deccan large igneous province: further evidence of KTB age and short duration. *Earth and Planetary Science Letters*, **263**: 1−15.

Chenet, A., Courtillot, V., Fluteau, F., Gérard, M., Quidelleur, X., Khadri, S.F.R., et al., 2009, Determination of rapid Deccan eruptions across the Cretaceous-Tertiary boundary using paleomagnetic secular variation: 2. Constraints from analysis of eight new sections and synthesis for a 3500-m-thick composite section. *Journal of Geophysical Research*, **114**: B06103, https://doi.org/10.1029/2008JB005644.

Claeys, P., Kiessling, W., and Alvarez, W., 2002, Distribution of Chicxulub ejecta at the Cretaceous-Tertiary boundary: catastrophic events and mass extinctions: impacts and beyond. *Geological Society of America Special Paper*, **356**: 55–68.

Clapham, M.E., and Payne, J.L., 2011, Acidification, anoxia, and extinction: a multiple logistic regression analysis of extinction selectivity during the Middle and Late Permian. *Geology*, **39**: 1059–1062, https://doi.org/10.1130/G32230.1.

Copper, P., 1994, Ancient reef ecosystem expansion and collapse. *Coral Reefs*, **13**: 3–11, https://doi.org/10.1007/BF00426428.

Courtillot, V., and Renne, P., 2003, On the ages of flood basalt events. *Earth and Planetary Science Letters*, **335**: 113–140.

Courtillot, V., Besse, J., and Vandamme, D., 1986, Deccan flood basalts at the Cretaceous/Tertiary boundary? *Earth and Planetary Science Letters*, **80**: 361–374.

Coxall, H.K., D'Hondt, S., and Zachos, J.C., 2006, Pelagic evolution and environmental recovery after the Cretaceous-Paleogene mass extinction. *Geology*, **34**: 297–300, https://doi.org/10.1130/G21702.1.

Cui, Y., and Kump, L.R., 2015, Global warming and the end-Permian extinction event: proxy and modeling perspectives. *Earth-Science Reviews*, **149**: 5–22, https://doi.org/10.1016/j.earscirev.2014.04.007.

Culver, S., 2003, Benthic foraminifera across the Cretaceous-Tertiary (K-T) boundary: a review. *Marine Micropaleontology*, **47**: 177–226.

D'Hondt, S., 2005, Consequences of the Cretaceous/Paleogene mass extinction for marine ecosystems. *Annual Review of Ecology, Evolution, and Systematics*, **36**: 295–317.

D'Hondt, S., and Zachos, J.C., 1998, Cretaceous foraminifera and the evolutionary history of planktic photosymbiosis. *Paleobiology*, **24**: 512–523.

D'Hondt, S., Donaghay, P., Zachos, J.C., Luttenberg, D., and Lindinger, M., 1998, Organic carbon fluxes and ecological recovery from the Cretaceous-Tertiary mass extinction. *Science*, **282**: 276–279, https://doi.org/10.1126/science.282.5387.276.

Edwards, C.T., 2019, Links between early Paleozoic oxygenation and the Great Ordovician Biodiversification Event (GOBE): a review. *Palaeoworld*, **28**: 37–50, https://doi.org/10.1016/j.palwor.2018.08.006.

Ernst, R.E., and Youbi, N., 2017, How Large Igneous Provinces affect global climate, sometimes cause mass extinctions, and represent natural markers in the geological record. *Palaeogeography, Palaeoclimatology, Palaeoecology*, **478**: 30–52, https://doi.org/10.1016/j.palaeo.2017.03.014.

Erwin, D.H., 2001, Lessons from the past: biotic recoveries from mass extinctions. *Proceedings of the National Academy of Sciences of the United States of America*, **98**: 5399–5403, https://doi.org/10.1073/pnas.091092698.

Erwin, D.H., 2006, *Extinction. How Life on Earth Nearly Ended 250 Million Years Ago*. Princeton, Oxford: Princeton University Press, p. 296.

Esmeray Senlet, S., Wright, J.D., Olsson, R.K., Miller, K.G., Browning, J.V., and Quan, T.M., 2015, Evidence for reduced export productivity following the Cretaceous/Paleogene mass extinction. *Paleoceanography*, **30**: 718–738, https://doi.org/10.1002/2014PA002724.

Esmeray-Senlet, S., Miller, K.G., Sherrell, R.M., Senlet, T., Vellekoop, J., and Brinkhuis, H., 2017, Iridium profiles and delivery across the Cretaceous/Paleogene boundary. *Earth and Planetary Science Letters*, **457**: 117–126, https://doi.org/10.1016/j.epsl.2016.10.010.

Feng, Q., and Algeo, T.J., 2014, Evolution of oceanic redox conditions during the Permo-Triassic transition: evidence from deepwater radiolarian facies. *Earth-Science Reviews*, **137**: 34–51, https://doi.org/10.1016/j.earscirev.2013.12.003.

Field, D.J., Bercovici, A., Berv, J.S., Dunn, R., Fastovsky, D.E., Lyson, T.R., et al., 2018, Early Evolution of modern birds structured by global forest collapse at the end-Cretaceous mass extinction. *Current Biology*, **28**: 1825–1831.e2, https://doi.org/10.1016/j.cub.2018.04.062.

Finnegan, S., Bergmann, K., Eiler, J.M., Jones, D.S., Fike, D.A., Eisenman, I., et al., 2011, The magnitude and duration of Late Ordovician-Early Silurian glaciation. *Science*, **331**: 903–906, https://doi.org/10.1126/science.1200803.

Garbelli, C., Angiolini, L., and Shen, S.-Z., 2017, Biomineralization and global change: a new perspective for understanding the end-Permian extinction. *Geology*, **45**: 19–22, https://doi.org/10.1017/pab.2015.12.

Goldin, T., and Melosh, H., 2009, Self-shielding of thermal radiation by Chicxulub impact ejecta: firestorm or fizzle? *Geology*, **37**: 1135–1138.

Groves, J.R.J., Altiner, D., and Rettori, R., 2005, Extinction, survival, and recovery of Lagenide Foraminifers in the Permian–Triassic Boundary interval, Central Taurides, Turkey. *Journal of Paleontology*, **83**: 718–738, https://doi.org/10.1666/0022-3360(2005)79[1:ESAROL]2.0.CO;2.

Hammarlund, E.U., Dahl, T.W., Harper, D.A.T., Bond, D.P.G., Nielsen, A.T., Bjerrum, C.J., et al., 2012, A sulfidic driver for the end-Ordovician mass extinction. *Earth and Planetary Science Letters*, **331–332**: 128–139, https://doi.org/10.1016/j.epsl.2012.02.024.

Harper, D.A.T., 2006, The Ordovician biodiversification: setting an agenda for marine life. *Palaeogeography, Palaeoclimatology, Palaeoecology*, **232**: 148–166, https://doi.org/10.1016/j.palaeo.2005.07.010.

Harper, D.A.T., Hammarlund, E.U., and Rasmussen, C.M.Ø., 2014, End Ordovician extinctions: a coincidence of causes. *Gondwana Research*, **25**: 1294–1307, https://doi.org/10.1016/j.gr.2012.12.021.

Hauri, C., Friedrich, T., and Timmermann, A., 2015, Abrupt onset and prolongation of aragonite undersaturation events in the Southern Ocean. *Nature Climate Change*, **5**: 1–5, https://doi.org/10.1038/NCLIMATE2844.

Haq, B., and Schutter, S., 2008, A chronology of Paleozoic sea-level changes. *Science*, **322**: 64–68.

Hildebrand, A., Penfield, G., Kring, D., Pilkington, M., and Camargo, Z., 1991, Chicxulub crater: a possible Cretaceous/Tertiary boundary impact crater on the Yucatan Peninsula, Mexico. *Geology*, **19**: 867–871.

Hinojosa, J.L., Brown, S.T., Chen, J., DePaolo, D.J., Paytan, A., Shen, S., et al., 2012, Evidence for end-Permian ocean acidification from calcium isotopes in biogenic apatite. *Geology*, **40**: 743–746, https://doi.org/10.1130/G33048.1.

Hsu, K., He, Q., McKenzie, J., Weissert, H., Perch-Nielsen, K., Oberhansli, H., et al., 1982, Mass mortality and its environmental and evolutionary consequences. *Science*, **216**: 249–256.

Hu, S., Zhang, Q., Chen, Z.-Q., Zhou, C., Lü, T., Xie, T., et al., 2011, The Luoping biota: exceptional preservation, and new evidence on the Triassic recovery from end-Permian mass extinction. *Proceedings of the Royal Society B: Biological Sciences*, **278**: 2274–2282, https://doi.org/10.1098/rspb.2010.2235.

Hull, P., 2015, Life in the aftermath of mass extinctions. *Current Biology*, **25**: R941–R952, https://doi.org/10.1016/j.cub.2015.08.053.

Hull, P.M., and Norris, R.D., 2011, Diverse patterns of ocean export productivity change across the Cretaceous-Paleogene boundary: new insights from biogenic barium. *Paleoceanography*, **26**: PA3205, https://doi.org/10.1029/2010PA002082.

Hull, P.M., Franks, P.J.S., and Norris, R.D., 2011, Mechanisms and models of iridium anomaly shape across the Cretaceous–Paleogene boundary. *Earth and Planetary Science Letters*, **301**: 98–106, https://doi.org/10.1016/j.epsl.2010.10.031.

Jablonski, D., 1991, Extinctions: a paleontological perspective. *Science*, **253**: 754–757.

Jin, Y.G., Zhang, J., and Shang, Q.H., 1994, Two phases of the end-Permian mass extinction. *In* Embry, A.F., Beauchamp, B., and Glass, D.J. (eds), *Pangea: Global Environments and Resources*. Canadian Society of Petroleum Geologists, Memoir, **17**: 813–822.

Kaiho, K., and Koga, S., 2013, Impacts of a massive release of methane and hydrogen sulfide on oxygen and ozone during the late Permian mass extinction. *Global and Planetary Change*, **107**: 91–101, https://doi.org/10.1016/j.gloplacha.2013.04.004.

Keller, G., Adatte, T., Stinnesbeck, W., Luciani, V., Karoui-Yaakoub, N., and Zaghbib-Turki, D., 2002, Paleoecology of the Cretaceous-Tertiary mass extinction in planktonic foraminifera. *Palaeogeography, Palaeoclimatology, Palaeoecology*, **178**: 257–297.

Keller, G., Stinnesbeck, W., Adatte, T., and Stuben, D., 2003, Multiple impacts across the Cretaceous-Tertiary boundary. *Earth-Science Reviews*, **62**: 327–363.

Keller, G., Adatte, T., Berner, Z., Harting, M., Baum, G.R., Prauss, M., et al., 2007, Chicxulub impact predates KT boundary. New evidence from Brazos, Texas. *Earth and Planetary Science Letters*, **255**: 339–356.

Knoll, A.H., Bambach, R.K., Payne, J.L., Pruss, S., and Fischer, W.W., 2007, Paleophysiology and end-Permian mass extinction. *Earth and Planetary Science Letters*, **256**: 295–313, https://doi.org/10.1016/j.epsl.2007.02.018.

Komar, N., and Zeebe, R.E., 2016, Calcium and calcium isotope changes during carbon cycle perturbations at the end-Permian. *Paleoceanography*, **31**: 115–130, https://doi.org/10.1002/2015PA002834.

Korte, C., and Kozur, H.W., 2010, Carbon-isotope stratigraphy across the Permian–Triassic boundary: a review. *Journal of Asian Earth Sciences*, **39**: 215–235, https://doi.org/10.1016/j.jseaes.2010.01.005.

Koutsoukos, E., 1996, Phenotypic experiments into new pelagic niches in early Danian planktonic foraminifera: aftermath of the K/T boundary event. *Geological Society of London, Special Publications*, **102**: 319–335.

Kring, D., 2007, The Chicxulub impact event and its environmental consequences at the Cretaceous-Tertiary boundary. *Palaeogeography, Palaeoclimatology, Palaeoecology*, **255**: 4–21.

Kroopnick, P.M., 1985, The distribution of ^{13}C of ΣCO_2 in the world oceans. *Deep Sea Research*, **32**: 57–84.

Kump, L.R., Bralower, T.J., and Ridgwell, A., 2009, Ocean acidification in deep time. *Oceanologica Acta*, **22**: 94–107.

Labandeira, C.C., and Sepkoski, J.J., 1993, Insect diversity in the fossil record. *Science*, **261**: 310–315, https://doi.org/10.1126/science.11536548.

Liu, M., Chen, D., Zhou, X., Yuan, W., Jiang, M., and Liu, L., 2019, Climatic and oceanic changes during the Middle-Late Ordovician transition in the Tarim Basin, NW China and implications for the Great Ordovician Biodiversification Event. *Palaeogeography, Palaeoclimatology, Palaeoecology*, **514**: 522–535, https://doi.org/10.1016/j.palaeo.2018.10.032.

Lowery, C.M., et al., 2018, Rapid recovery of life at ground zero of the end-Cretaceous mass extinction. *Nature*, **558**: 288–291, https://doi.org/10.1038/s41586-018-0163-6.

MacLeod, N., Rawson, P., Forey, P., Banner, F., Boudagher-Fadel, M., Bown, P., et al., 1997, The Cretaceous-Tertiary biotic transition. *Journal of The Geological Society*, **154**: 265–292.

McGhee Jr, G.R., Clapham, M.E., Sheehan, P.M., Bottjer, D.J., and Droser, M.L., 2013, A new ecological-severity ranking of major Phanerozoic biodiversity crise. *Palaeogeography, Palaeoclimatology, Palaeoecology*, **370**: 260–270, https://doi.org/10.1016/j.palaeo.2012.12.019.

Melosh, H.J., Schneider, N.M., Zahnle, K.J., and Latham, D., 1990, Ignition of global wildfires at the Cretaceous/Tertiary boundary. *Nature*, **343**: 251–254.

Morgan, J., Warner, M., Brittan, J., Buffler, R., Camargo, A., Christeson, G., et al., 1997, Size and morphology of the Chicxulub impact crater. *Nature*, **390**: 472–476.

Norris, R.D., Firth, J., Blusztajn, J., and Ravizza, G., 2000, Mass failure of the North Atlantic margin triggered by the Cretaceous-Paleogene bolide impact. *Geology*, **28**: 1119–1122.

Novacek, M., 1999, 100 million years of land vertebrate evolution: the Cretaceous-Early Tertiary transition. *Annals of The Missouri Botanical Garden*, **86**: 230–258.

Novacek, M.J., 2001, *The Biodiversity Crisis: Losing What Counts*. The New Press.

Olsson, R.K., and Liu, C., 1993, Controversies on the placement of Cretaceous-Paleogene boundary and the K/P mass extinction of planktonic foraminifera. *Palaios*, **8**: 127–139.

Olsson, R.K., Hemleben, C., Berggren, W.A., Huber, B.T., and Editors and Members of the Paleogene Planktonic Foraminifera Working Group, 1999, *Atlas of Paleocene Planktonic Foraminifera: Smithsonian Contributions to Paleobiology*, **85**: 252.

Payne, J.L., and Clapham, M.E., 2012, End-Permian mass extinction in the oceans: an ancient analog for the Twenty-First Century? *Annual Review of Earth and Planetary Sciences*, **40**: 89–111, https://doi.org/10.1146/annurev-earth-042711-105329.

Payne, J.L., Lehrmann, D.J., Follett, D., Seibel, M., Kump, L.R., Riccardi, A., et al., 2007, Erosional truncation of uppermost Permian shallow-marine carbonates and implications for Permian-Triassic boundary events. *Geological Society of America Bulletin*, **119**: 771–784, https://doi.org/10.1130/B26091.1.

Payne, J.L., Turchyn, A.V., Paytan, A., DePaolo, D.J., Lehrmann, D.J., Yu, M., et al., 2010, Calcium isotope constraints on the end-Permian mass extinction. *Proceedings of the National Academy of Sciences of the United States of America*, **107**: 8543–8548, https://doi.org/10.1073/pnas.0914065107.

Payne, J.L., Bush, A.B., Heim, N.A., Knope, M.L., and McCauley, D.J., 2016, Ecological selectivity of the emerging mass extinction in the oceans. *Science*, **353**: 1–4.

Perini, F.A., 2016, Mammals, Origin of. *In* Kliman, R.M. (ed), *Encyclopedia of Evolutionary Biology*. Oxford: Academic Press, 430–439, http://doi.org/10.1016/B978-0-12-800049-6.00282-1.

Pierazzo, E., Kring, D.A., and Melosh, H.J., 1998, Hydrocode simulation of the Chicxulub impact event and the production of climatically active gases. *Journal of Geophysical Research: Planets*, **103**: 28607–28625.

Pietsch, C., and Bottjer, D.J., 2014, The importance of oxygen for the disparate recovery patterns of the benthic macrofauna in the Early Triassic. *Earth-Science Reviews*, **137**: 65–84, https://doi.org/10.1016/j.earscirev.2013.12.002.

Pievani, T., 2015, *Earth's Sixth Mass Extinction Event. Reference Module in Earth Systems and Environmental Sciences,* Elsevier Inc., https://doi.org/10.1016/B978-0-12-409548-9.09216-2.

Rasmussen, C.M.Ø., and Harper, D.A.T., 2011, Did the amalgamation of continents drive the end Ordovician mass extinctions? *Palaeogeography, Palaeoclimatology, Palaeoecology*, **311**: 48–62, https://doi.org/10.1016/j.palaeo.2011.07.029.

Raup, D., and Sepkoski, J.J., 1982, Mass extinctions in the marine fossil record. *Science*, **215**: 1501–1503.

Retallack, G.J., 1995, Permian-Triassic life crisis on land. *Science*, **267**: 77–80, https://doi.org/10.1126/science.267.5194.77.

Robertson, D.S., Lewis, W.M., Sheehan, P.M., and Toon, O.B., 2013a, K-Pg extinction patterns in marine and freshwater environments: the impact winter model. *Journal of Geophysical Research: Biogeosciences*, **118**: 1006–1014, https://doi.org/10.1002/jgrg.20086.

Robertson, D.S., Lewis, W.M., Sheehan, P.M., and Toon, O.B., 2013b, K-Pg extinction: reevaluation of the heat-fire hypothesis. *Journal of Geophysical Research: Biogeosciences*, **118**: 329–336, https://doi.org/10.1002/jgrg.20018.

Schoene, B., Samperton, K.M., Eddy, M.P., Keller, G., Adatte, T., Bowring, S.A., et al., 2015, U-Pb geochronology of the Deccan Traps and relation to the end-Cretaceous mass extinction. *Science*, **347**: 182–184, https://doi.org/10.1126/science.aaa0118.

Schulte, P., Alegret, L., Arenillas, I., Arz, J.A., Barton, P., Bown, P., et al., 2010, The Chicxulub asteroid impact and mass extinction at the Cretaceous-Paleogene boundary. *Science*, **327**: 1214–1218.

Self, S., Widdowson, M., and Thordarson, T., 2006, Volatile fluxes during flood basalt eruptions and potential effects on the global environment: a Deccan perspective. *Earth and Planetary Science Letters*, **248**: 518–532.

Sepkoski, J.J., 1986, Phanerozoic overview of mass extinction. *In* Raup, D.M., and Jablonski, D. (eds), *Patterns and Processes in the History of Life*. Dahlem Workshop Reports, Berlin Heidelberg: Springer, pp. 277–295.

Sepkoski, J.J., 1996, Patterns of Phanerozoic Extinction: a perspective from global data bases. *In* Walliser, O.H. (ed), *Global Events and Event Stratigraphy in the Phanerozoic: Results of the International Interdisciplinary Cooperation in the IGCP-Project 216 Global Biological Events in Earth History,* Berlin, Heidelberg: Springer, 35–51, http://doi.org/10.1007/978-3-642-79634-0_4.

Sepkoski, J.J., 1998, Rates of speciation in the fossil record. *Philosophical Transactions of the Royal Society of London. Series B: Biological Sciences*, **353**: 315–326, https://doi.org/10.1098/rstb.1998.0212.

Sepkoski, J.J., 2012, *Mass Extinctions, Concept of Encyclopedia of Biodiversity (2nd edition),* Elsevier Ltd., http://doi.org/10.1016/B978-0-12-384719-5.00091-5.

Sepúlveda, J., Alegret, L., Thomas, E., Haddad, E., Cao, C., and Summons, R.E., 2019, Stable isotope constraints on marine productivity across the Cretaceous-Paleogene mass extinction. *Paleoceanography and Paleoclimatology*, **34**: 1195–1217, https://doi.org/10.1029/2018PA003442.

Sheehan, P.M., 2001, The Late Ordovician mass extinction. *Annual Review of Earth and Planetary Sciences*, **29**: 331–364.

Shen, S.-Z., and Shi, G.R., 2009, Latest Guadalupian brachiopods from the Guadalupian/Lopingian boundary GSSP section at Penglaitan in Laibin, Guangxi, South China and implications for the timing of the pre-Lopingian crisis. *Palaeoworld*, **18**: 152–161, https://doi.org/10.1016/j.palwor.2009.04.010.

Sibert, E.C., Hull, P.M., and Norris, R.D., 2014, Resilience of Pacific pelagic fish across the Cretaceous/Palaeogene mass extinction. *Nature Geoscience*, **7**: 667–670, https://doi.org/10.1038/ngeo2227.

Smit, J., 1982, Extinction and evolution of planktonic foraminifera after a major impact at the Cretaceous/Tertiary boundary. *Geological Society of London, Special Publications*, **190**: 329–352.

Smit, J., 1999, The global stratigraphy of the Cretaceous-Tertiary boundary impact ejecta. *Annual Review of Earth and Planetary Sciences*, **27**: 75–113.

Smit, J., and Hertogen, J., 1980, An extraterrestrial event at the Cretaceous–Tertiary boundary. *Nature*, **285**: 198–200.

Smit, J., and Kyte, F.T., 1984, Siderophile-rich magnetic spheroids from the Cretaceous–Tertiary boundary in Umbria, Italy. *Nature*, **310**: 403–405.

Smith, R.M.H., and Ward, P.D., 2001, Pattern of vertebrate extinctions across an event bed at the Permian-Triassic boundary in the Karoo Basin of South Africa. *Geology*, **29**: 1147–1150, http://doi.org/10.1130/0091-7613(2001)029 < 1147:POVEAA > 2.0.CO;2.

Sprain, C.J., Renne, P.R., Vanderkluysen, L., Pande, K., Self, S., and Mittal, T., 2019, The eruptive tempo of Deccan volcanism in relation to the Cretaceous-Paleogene boundary. *Science*, **363**: 866–870, https://doi.org/10.1144/jgs2015-133.

Stanley, S.M., 2016, Estimates of the magnitudes of major marine mass extinctions in earth history. *Proceedings of the National Academy of Sciences of the United States of America*, **113**: E6325–E6334, https://doi.org/10.1017/S0094837300013178.

Stott, L.D., and Kennett, J.P., 1989, New constraints on early Tertiary palaeoproductivity from carbon isotopes in foraminifera. *Nature*, **342**: 526–529.

Swisher III, C., et al., 1992, Coeval 40Ar/39Ar ages of 65.0 million years ago from Chicxulub crater melt rock and Cretaceous-Tertiary boundary tektites. *Science*, **257**: 954–958.

Toon, O.B., Pollack, J.B., Ackerman, T.P., Turco, R.P., McKay, C.P., and Liu, M.S., 1982, Evolution of an impact-generated dust cloud and its effects on the atmosphere. *Geological Society of America Special Papers*, **190**: 187–200.

Vecoli, M., Riboulleau, A., and Versteegh, G.J.M., 2009, Palynology, organic geochemistry and carbon isotope analysis of a latest Ordovician through Silurian clastic succession from borehole Tt1, Ghadamis Basin, southern Tunisia, North Africa: palaeoenvironmental interpretation. *Palaeogeography, Palaeoclimatology, Palaeoecology*, **273**: 378–394, https://doi.org/10.1016/j.palaeo.2008.05.015.

Wagler, R., 2012, The sixth great mass extinction. *Science Scope*, **35** (7), 48–55.

Wagler, R., 2018, The sixth great mass extinction. *Encyclopedia of the Anthropocene*, **1**: 9–12, https://doi.org/10.1016/B978-0-12-809665-9.10477-X.

Wang, G., Zhan, R., and Percival, I.G., 2019, The end-Ordovician mass extinction: a single-pulse event? *Earth-Science Reviews*, **192**: 15–33, https://doi.org/10.1016/j.earscirev.2019.01.023.

Ward, P.D., Botha, J., Buick, R., Kock, M.O.D., Erwin, D.H., Garrison, G.H., et al., 2005, Abrupt and gradual extinction among Late Permian land vertebrates in the Karoo Basin, South Africa. *Science*, **307**: 709–714, https://doi.org/10.1126/science.1107068.

Wignall, P.B., 2001, Large igneous provinces and mass extinctions. *Earth-Science Reviews*, **53**: 1–33.

Wignall, P.B., Newton, R., and Brookfield, M.E., 2005, Pyrite framboid evidence for oxygen-poor deposition during the Permian–Triassic crisis in Kashmir. *Palaeogeography, Palaeoclimatology, Palaeoecology*, **216**: 183–188, https://doi.org/10.1016/j.palaeo.2004.10.009.

Zachos, J.C., and Arthur, M., 1986, Paleoceanography of the Cretaceous/Tertiary boundary event: inferences from stable isotopic and other data. *Paleoceanography*, **1**: 5–26.

Zachos, J.C., Arthur, M., and Dean, W., 1989, Geochemical evidence for suppression of pelagic marine productivity at the Cretaceous/Tertiary boundary. *Nature*, **337**: 61–64.

Zou, C., Qiu, Z., Wei, H., Dong, D., and Lu, B., 2018, Euxinia caused the Late Ordovician extinction: evidence from pyrite morphology and pyritic sulfur isotopic composition in the Yangtze area, South China. *Palaeogeography, Palaeoclimatology, Palaeoecology*, **511**: 1–11, https://doi.org/10.1016/j.palaeo.2017.11.033.

J. Laskar

Chapter 4

Astrochronology

Chapter outline

Abstract

The long-term variations of the orbital and rotational parameters of the Earth are the key ingredients for the insolation forcing in the Milankovitch theory. This chapter describes the main aspects of these variations, concentrating on the aspects that are currently recovered in the stratigraphic record. A special emphasis is given to the very long periodic terms (>1 Myr period) that modulate the astronomical solutions and that are essential for understanding the chaotic behavior of the solar system.

4.1 Introduction

According to the Milankovitch theory (Milankovitch, 1941), some of the large climatic changes of the past originate from the variations of the Earth's orbit and of its spin axis resulting from the gravitational pull of the other planets and the Moon. These variations can be traced over many millions of years (Myr) in the geological sedimentary record, although the mechanisms that transfer the forcing insolation to the sedimentary variations are not precisely known.

The recovery of astronomical signal in stratigraphic sequences has allowed local or global calibration of the stratigraphic records, and cyclostratigraphy is now a very active field of research. After the astronomical calibration of the Neogene Period (Lourens et al., 2004; Hilgen et al., 2012), focus turned toward the entire Paleogene Period (e.g., Kuiper et al., 2008; Westerhold et al., 2012, 2014, 2015; Boulila et al., 2018), covering the entire Cenozoic Era.

Extending this procedure through the Mesozoic Era and beyond is difficult, as the solar system motion is chaotic (Laskar, 1989, 1990). It is thus not possible to retrieve the precise orbital motion of the planets beyond 60 Ma from their present state (Laskar et al., 2011b). Nevertheless, the existence of a stable component in the astronomical forcing, the 405-kyr metronome (e.g., Laskar et al., 2004), has allowed the continuation of the astronomical calibration of geologic time deep into the Mesozoic Era and even into the Paleozoic Era and the Precambrian.

Detailed compilations of currently available cyclostratigraphic records have been summarized recently (e.g., Hinnov and Hilgen, 2012; Hinnov, 2018b; Huang, 2018), and we refer to these. In this chapter, we will focus on the astronomical solution and especially on the long cycles of these solutions, with the aim to answer some of the common questions that arise in the analysis of long sequences of stratigraphic records.

4.1.1 Historical introduction

During the 18th century the question of the stability of the solar system was of prime importance, as it was also necessary to decide whether Newton's law properly describes the motion of the celestial bodies (for details, refer to

Geologic Time Scale 2020. DOI: https://doi.org/10.1016/B978-0-12-824360-2.00004-8

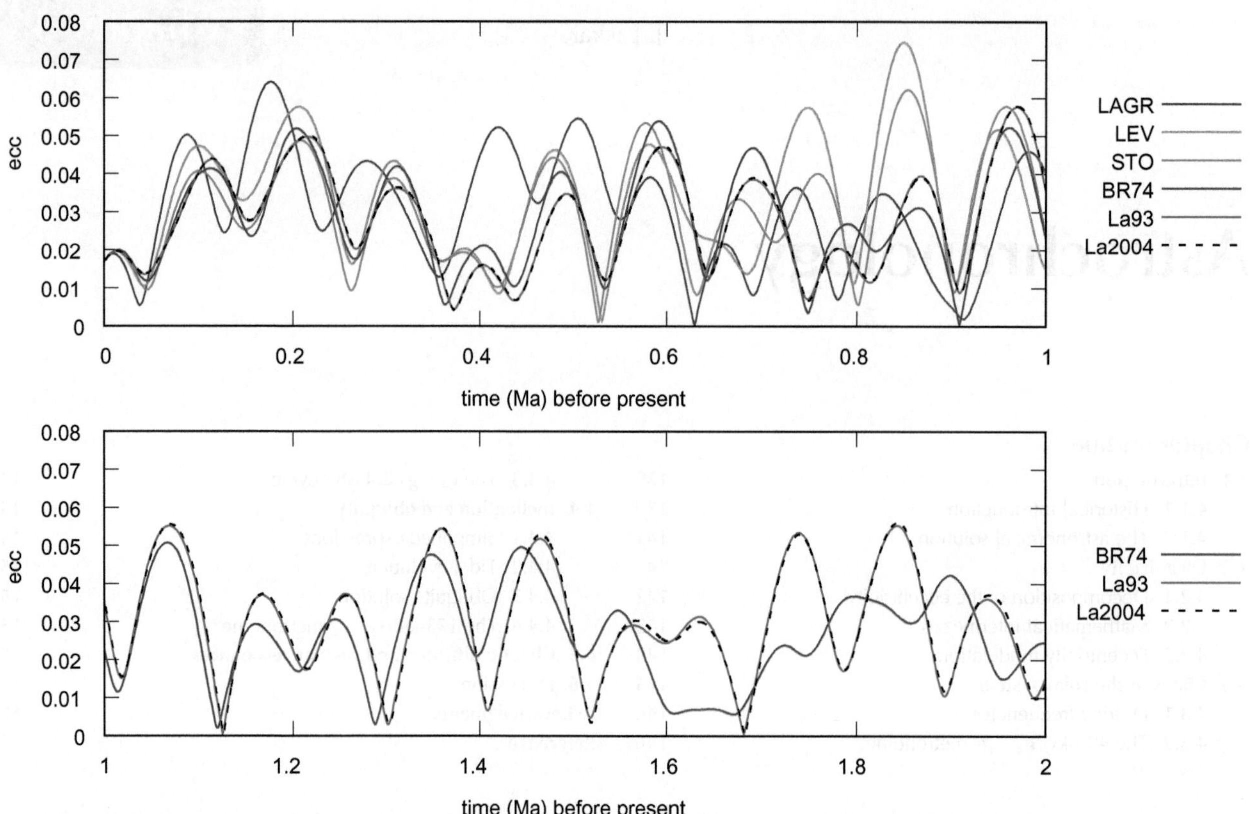

FIGURE 4.1 Improvements in the computation of the past evolution of the Earth's eccentricity. LAGR is the first secular solution for the solar system, with only six planets (Lagrange, 1783,1784); Uranus was added in LEV (Le Verrier, 1840); and Neptune in STO (Stockwell, 1873); BR74 (Bretagnon, 1974) added some terms of order 2 with respect to the masses and degree four in eccentricity and inclination. La93 (Laskar, 1988, 1990; Laskar et al., 1993) is a numerical solution of the averaged equations that contains all terms up to order 2 with respect to the masses and degree six in eccentricity and inclination, the contribution of the Moon and general relativity. La04 (Laskar et al., 2004) is a numerical integration of the full equations of motion.

Laskar, 2013). A very important result of this quest was the derivation of the first long-term models for the solar system orbital evolution. A first result, of fundamental importance for cyclostratigraphy is the demonstration, at first order of the planetary masses, of the invariance of the semimajor axes of the orbits of the planets (Laplace, 1776). This result is also practically verified in the full, nonapproximated system of equations, with the major consequence that the orbital period of the Earth does not change over time. One can thus assume that the length of the year has practically not changed over the past billion years.[1] By contrast, Lagrange and Laplace found that in the linear approximation of the averaged equations of motion, the eccentricity, inclination, and orientation of the orbits change significantly with time, in a quasiperiodic manner with frequencies of several tens of kyr to Myr, but in a way that does not allow for planetary collisions (Lagrange, 1778; Laplace, 1775)[2]; the first full computation of the long-term motion of the Earth's orbit is due to Lagrange at the end of the 18th century (Lagrange, 1783, 1784). Of course, the solution of Lagrange only includes the planets visible to naked eye (Mercury, Venus, Earth, Mars, Jupiter, and Saturn), but it already provides a very accurate representation of the Earth's orbital motion over the past million years. In Lagrange's solution, all the main features of the variation of the Earth's orbital elements are present, but it was only after the work of Agassiz (1840), showing evidence of past Ice Ages, and the new solution of Le Verrier, including Uranus (Le Verrier, 1840, 1841, 1856) that it was advocated that the variations of the Earth's orbit could trigger the large climatic variations of the past (Croll, 1875) (see Hilgen (2010) for more historical details). The orbital solution was upgraded by Stockwell (1873) who added the contribution of Neptune (Fig. 4.1). This latest orbital solution was used by Pilgrim (1904) for the computation of the variation of the Earth spin axis evolution.

1. The relative loss of the mass of the Sun is of about 9×10^{-14}/year. Using the conservation of angular momentum and Kepler's third law, one can deduce that the mass loss of the Sun induces an increase of 9×10^{-5} AU in the Earth semimajor axis and a decrease of only 1.5 hours in the orbital period of the Earth over 1 Ga.

2. Laplace's work was largely inspired by Lagrange's manuscript that was submitted in 1774 (see Laskar, 2013).

Nevertheless, in his theory of the insolation of the Earth, Milankovitch (1941) considered that the solution of Le Verrier (1856) was more reliable and asked his colleague Miškovič to update Le Verrier's solution for the new values of the planetary masses and to use it for the computation of the orientation of the spin axis of the Earth with respect to its orbit. After comparison to the solution of Stockwell (1873) and Pilgrim (1904), Milankovitch decided to limit his insolation computations to the most recent 600,000 years.

With the use of computers, it was possible to extend these analytical computations significantly. The solution of Bretagnon (1974) for the solar system comprises 318 periodic terms, while the secular system of Laskar, 1988 (1990) and Laskar et al. (1993) contains 153,824 terms, including the averaged contribution of the Moon and general relativity. Nevertheless, these analytical perturbative methods always require some truncation in series expansions and thus have some limitations in precision. With the improvement in computer speed and numerical integration algorithms, it is now possible to directly integrate the equations of motion, as in the La2004 solution (Laskar et al., 2004).

When comparing the various solutions that have been used in stratigraphic astrochronology (Fig. 4.1A), it appears that although Lagrange solution is somewhat off in the first 500,000 years, it already provides a good measure of the qualitative behavior of the Earth's orbital solution. The other solutions are in quite good agreement over the first 600,000 years but begin to depart from one another after this date. On the contrary, the semianalytical solution La93 (Laskar, 1988, 1990; Laskar et al., 1993) is a perfect match to the full numerical solution La2004 (Laskar et al., 2004) over the most recent 2 Myr and even over the last 10 Myr (see Laskar et al., 2004). Starting with La93, the orbital solution can thus be considered as perfectly known over the past few Myr. The evolution of the precision of the solutions is particularly striking beyond 1.5 Ma (Fig. 4.1B). The difference is very large with respect to the solution of Bretagnon (1974) and Berger (1978) but insignificant with respect to the more recent La2004.

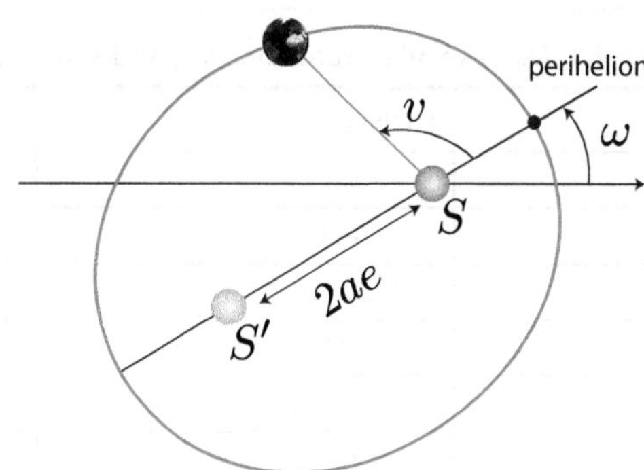

FIGURE 4.2 The eccentricity e is the ratio of the distance between the two foci of the ellipse (SS') and the major axis of the ellipse ($2a$). At perihelion the Earth–Sun distance is $a(1-e)$; at aphelion it becomes $a(1+e)$. The horizontal line is the direction of the ascending node (Fig. 4.3).

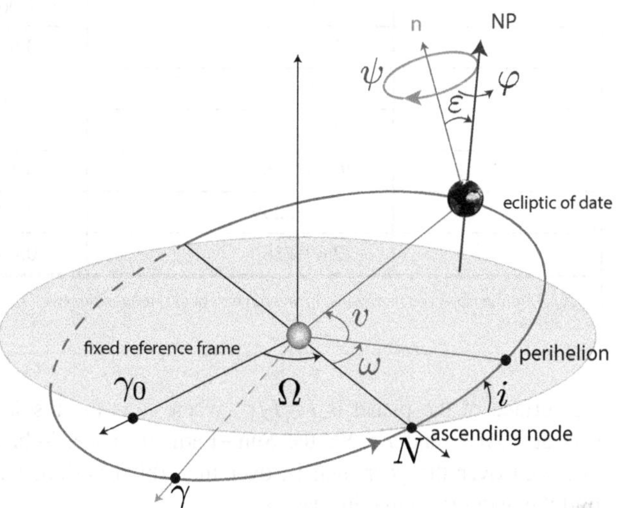

FIGURE 4.3 Earth angular parameters. The instantaneous orbital plane of the Earth, the ecliptic of date, is referred with respect to a fixed reference frame [mean ecliptic J2000 in La2004 (Laskar et al., 2004) and invariant plane in La2010 (Laskar et al., 2011a)], with a fixed origin γ_0 (equinox J2000 in La2004). The ecliptic of date is defined by the longitude of the ascending node Ω and the inclination i. The argument of perihelion ω is the angle from the line of node SN to the perihelion and the true anomaly v the angle from perihelion to the position of the Earth. The equinox of date γ is the intersection of the equator with the ecliptic of date. The spin axis of the Earth is directed toward the North Pole (NP) and φ is the spin angle. The obliquity ε is the angle from the normal to the ecliptic of date (n) to the spin axis (NP). The precession angle ψ describes the motion of the spin axis of the Earth around n. The longitude of perihelion ϖ is the sum of the longitude of the node Ω and the argument of perihelion ω ($\varpi = \Omega + \omega$). It should be noted that the two angles, Ω, ω, are not on the same plane.

4.1.2 The astronomical solution

Due to the gravitational interactions of the planets, the Earth's orbit and spin axis present significant variations in time. The orbit precesses slowly on its plane in space (Fig. 4.2), and the equator precesses around the normal to the orbit (Fig. 4.3). This slow precession motion of the planetary orbits is described by a combination of periodic modes related to the precession of the perihelions with fundamental secular frequencies g_i ($i = 1, 2, \ldots, 8$) and precession of the orbital planes in space with fundamental secular frequencies s_i ($i = 1, 2, \ldots, 8$) (Table 4.1). In addition, the eccentricity of the orbit and the inclination with respect to the fixed reference frame oscillates with the same frequencies. The precessing of the motion of the spin axis enters an additional frequency, the precession frequency p.

4.2 Eccentricity

The eccentricity of the Earth e is a measure of the shape of its orbit (Fig. 4.2). At perihelion the Sun–Earth distance (SE) is $a(1-e)$ and $a(1+e)$ at aphelion. The insolation on

TABLE 4.1 Main secular frequencies g_i and s_i of La2004 and La2010a in arcsec/year.

	La2004	La2010a	Δ_{100}	Period (year)
g_1	5.59	5.59	0.13	231,843
g_2	7.452	7.453	0.019	173,913
g_3	17.368	17.368	0.20	74,620
g_4	17.916	17.916	0.20	72,338
g_5	4.257452	4.257482	0.000030	304,407
g_6	28.2450	28.2449	0.0010	45,884
g_7	3.087951	3.087946	0.000034	419,696
g_8	0.673019	0.673019	0.000015	1,925,646
s_1	− 5.59	− 5.61	0.15	231,843
s_2	− 7.05	− 7.06	0.19	183,830
s_3	− 18.850	− 18.848	0.066	68,753
s_4	− 17.755	− 17.751	0.064	72,994
s_5	0	0		
s_6	− 26.347855	− 26.347841	0.000076	49,188
s_7	− 2.9925259	− 2.9925258	0.000025	433,079
s_8	− 0.691736	− 0.691740	0.000010	1,873,547

Δ_{100} are the observed variations, in arcsec/year, of the frequencies over 100 Myr (Laskar et al., 2011a). The periods of the secular term are given in the last column.

the surface of the planet is $I = I_0/r^2$, where I_0 is the insolation at 1 AU,[3] and $r = SE$ the Sun–Earth distance. When averaged over the year, that is, over the orbital period, we find the average annual insolation

$$I_M = \frac{I_0}{a^2\sqrt{1-e^2}}.$$

As the semimajor axis a is constant, I_M depends only on the eccentricity that varies from 0 to about 0.06 over 10 Ma. The relative variation of I_M is thus 1.8×10^{-5} that is very small. By contrast, the ratio of insolation at perihelion versus aphelion is

$$\rho_I = \left(\frac{1+e}{1-e}\right)^2$$

which amounts to 1.27 at maximum eccentricity $e = 0.06$. Averaging over the Earth surface and using a simple radiative model, this relation translates into a relative variation of temperature of a planet δT, from perihelion to aphelion, considered as a black body, as

$$\frac{\delta T}{T} \approx e$$

where T is the temperature expressed in Kelvin. Considering an average temperature of $T = 285$ K (14.85°C), we obtain $\delta T = 4.8$ K for the present eccentricity ($e = 0.0167$), and $\delta T = 17.1$ K for $e = 0.06$. These simple examples are quoted here to emphasize how the eccentricity can modulate the seasonal insolation. For more complete models, one can refer to Paillard (1998, 2001) and Bosmans et al. (2014).

4.2.1 Decomposition of the eccentricity

The eccentricity signal is one of the major targets for stratigraphic studies, especially for older times, before the Neogene Period. It is thus important to understand the main components of the eccentricity signal. The decomposition of this signal in terms of fundamental frequencies is given in Table 4.2. In this decomposition, all of the terms are recognized as combinations of the fundamental secular frequencies (Table 4.1). More precisely, most terms are differences of two g_i except $\mu_9 = g_2 - g_5 - (g_4 - g_3)$. Indeed, all combinations of frequencies in the periodic decomposition of the eccentricity are of the form $\mu = \sum_i k_i g_i$ with $\mu = \sum_i k_i = 0$. This can be easily understood when one realizes that the

3. Astronomical unit.

TABLE 4.2 First 10 terms (in decreasing amplitude) of the frequency decomposition of the Earth's eccentricity over the time interval [− 15, +5] Ma.

k		μ_k("/year)	P (kyr)	$b_k \times 10^4$
1	$g_2 - g_5$	3.200	405	107
2	$g_4 - g_5$	13.652	95	81
3	$g_4 - g_2$	10.456	124	62
4	$g_3 - g_5$	13.110	99	53
5	$g_3 - g_2$	9.910	131	45
6	$g_4 - g_3$	0.546	2373	30
7	$g_1 - g_5$	1.326	978	28
8	$g_4 - g_1$	12.325	105	21
9	$g_2 - g_5 - (g_4 - g_3)$	2.665	486	20
10	$g_2 - g_1$	1.884	688	18

The eccentricity e can be expressed as $e = e_0 + \sum_{k=1}^{10} b_k \cos(\mu_k t + \eta_k)$ with $e_0 = 0.0275579$. Column two lists the corresponding combination of frequencies where gi are the fundamental frequencies (Table 4.1).
Source: Adapted from Laskar et al. (2004).

TABLE 4.3 The five leading terms in the frequency decomposition of the complex eccentricity variable $z = e \exp i\varpi$ for the Earth over the time interval [− 15, +5] Ma (Laskar et al., 2004) $(z = \sum_k b_k \exp(\mathrm{i} g_k t + \theta_t))$.

n	g_k	k	g_k ("/year)	b_k	θ_k (degree)
1	g_5	5	4.257	0.0189	30.7
2	g_2	2	7.457	0.0163	− 157.8
3	g_4	4	17.910	0.0130	140.6
4	g_3	3	17.367	0.0088	− 55.9
5	g_1	1	5.579	0.0042	77.1

important variable in the dynamical evolution of the solar system is not the eccentricity (e), but the complex variable $z = e \exp(\mathrm{i}\varpi)$, where $\varpi = \Omega + \omega$. As shown in Figs. 4.2 and 4.3, ω is the argument of perihelion and Ω the longitude of the ascending node. This was already known to Lagrange who set up the proper form for the computation of the long-term evolution of the solar system (Lagrange, 1778). This system reduces to a simple linear system of differential equation with constant coefficients, which is now classically studied in the first years of university. In this linear solution, that we will call the Lagrange–Laplace solution, each variable z_i is expressed as a $z_i = \sum_{k=1}^{N} a_{ik} \exp(\mathrm{i}(g_k t + \theta_{ik}))$, where N is the number of planets of the considered system (here $N = 8$) and g_k are the fundamental frequencies. When one considers a more complex model, not limited to the linear secular approximation, the decomposition of z_i is more complex (e.g., Laskar et al., 2004), but the main terms of the solution will still be those corresponding to the Lagrange–Laplace solution, and a large understanding can be gained by considering only these terms.

Let us thus consider the five leading terms of $z = e \exp \mathrm{i}\varpi$ the complex eccentricity of the Earth (Table 4.3 extracted from Table 4 of Laskar et al., 2004). We can construct a solution based only on these five terms, $z^{(5)} = \sum_{k=1}^{5} b_k \exp(\mathrm{i} g_k t + \theta_k)$. As this solution is composed of only five periodic terms, the frequency decomposition of the eccentricity $e^{(5)} = |z^{(5)}|$ is more straightforward and is provided in Table 4.4. In the first column, k is the index of the term in the frequency decomposition (by decreasing amplitude) of $e^{(5)}$, and k' the rank of the same term in the decomposition of the full Earth eccentricity (Tables 2 and 6 from Laskar et al., 2004). It is important to note that all 10 leading terms of the Earth's eccentricity can be explained by only the first 5 terms of z_3. In Section 4.2.3, we will discuss further the outcome of the decomposition of Table 4.4 in the observed aspects of the Earth eccentricity solution and their possible manifestations in the geological data. Before, it is instructive to understand the mathematical origin of the periodic terms involved in Table 4.4.

4.2.2 Mathematical intermezzo

Let consider

$$
\begin{aligned}
z &= \sum_{k=1}^{N} a_k \exp(\mathrm{i}(g_k t + \theta_k)) \\
z &= \sum_{k=1}^{N} a_k \exp(\mathrm{i}\pi_k)
\end{aligned}
\tag{4.1}
$$

the expression of $z = e \exp(\mathrm{i}\varpi)$, where the amplitudes a_k are positive real numbers and $\pi_k = g_k t + \theta_k$. The eccentricity e is then $e = \sqrt{z\bar{z}}$, where $\bar{z}$ is the complex conjugate of z, that is,

$$
\bar{z} = \sum_{k=1}^{N} a_k \exp(-\mathrm{i}\pi_k). \tag{4.2}
$$

We have

$$
\begin{aligned}
z\bar{z} = e^2 &= \textstyle\sum_{k,l} a_k a_l \exp(\mathrm{i}(\pi_k - \pi_l)) \\
&= \textstyle\sum_k a_k^2 + \sum_{k \neq 1} a_k a_l \exp(\mathrm{i}(\pi_k - \pi_l)).
\end{aligned}
\tag{4.3}
$$

We see that the arguments that appear are differences $\pi_k - \pi_l = (g_k - g_l)t + (\theta_k - \theta_l)$ with frequencies $g_k - g_l$,

TABLE 4.4 First 13 periodic terms (in decreasing amplitude) of the frequency decomposition of $e^{(5)} = |z^{(5)}|$, when $z^{(5)}$ is limited to the first five linear terms of z (Table 4.2).

k	k'		μ'_k("/year)	P (kyr)	$b'_k \times 10^4$
1	1	$g_2 - g_5$	3.200	405	109
2	2	$g_4 - g_5$	13.653	95	82
3	3	$g_4 - g_2$	10.453	124	66
4	4	$g_3 - g_5$	13.110	99	53
5	5	$g_3 - g_2$	9.910	131	44
6	6	$g_4 - g_3$	0.543	2387	35
7	7	$g_1 - g_5$	1.322	980	25
8	10	$g_2 - g_1$	1.878	690	21
9	8	$g_4 - g_1$	12.331	105	16
10	12	$g_2 + g_4 - 2g_5$	16.853	77	16
11	18	$g_3 + g_4 - g_2 - g_5$	23.563	55	13
12	9	$g_2 - g_5 - (g_4 - g_3)$	2.657	488	13
13	20	$g_2 - g_5 + (g_4 - g_3)$	3.743	346	13

$e^{(5)} = e_0 \sum_{k=1}^{13} b'_k \cos(\mu'_k t + \theta'_k)$ with $e_0 = 0.0269$. k is the rank of the term by decreasing amplitude in $e^{(5)}$, while k' is the rank of the same term in e (Table 4.2). Column three is the corresponding combination of frequencies. g_i are the fundamental frequencies (Table 4.1).

involving all fundamental frequencies g_i. But this is e^2, and not e. With $e_0^2 = \sum_k a_k^2$, we have

$$e^2 = e_0^2(1 + X) \tag{4.4}$$

with

$$X = \sum_{k \neq l} a_k a_l \exp(i(\pi_k - \pi_l)) \tag{4.5}$$

and thus assuming that X is small with respect to 1, and expanding up to second order in X,

$$e = e_0\sqrt{1+X} = e_0\left(1 + \frac{1}{2}X - \frac{1}{8}X^2 + O(X^3)\right). \tag{4.6}$$

Thus X will involve differences of two frequencies $g_k - g_l$ (Eq. 4.5) as terms 1–9 of Table 4.4, but the terms of the X^2 part will be sums of two differences $\pi_k - \pi_l$. These will be terms of order 4, involving four fundamental frequencies g_i, as terms 10–13 of Table 4.4. It is also interesting to note that the phase of these terms will be opposite to the equivalent combination of arguments because of the minus sign in Eq. (4.6).

Now we can return to the simple example of $e^{(5)} = |z^{(5)}|$. $z^{(5)}$ has only five periodic components. As demonstrated earlier, $e^{(5)}$ will contain only harmonics of even order, sum of terms of the form $g_k - g_l$ (Table 4.4). Indeed, this is well revealed by the spectral analysis of $e^{(5)}$ (Fig. 4.4). For this simple model, all periodic terms are easily identified and can then be related to the corresponding term of the full eccentricity e_3 [Fig. 4.4 (top)]. It is thus remarkable that the most important features of the eccentricity solution of the Earth are provided by the simple model $z^{(5)}$ (Table 4.4).

It should be noted that the largest periodic component of the eccentricity is the 405-kyr term $g_2 - g_5$. This term is fundamental in cyclostratigraphy as its period is very stable and can thus be used as a metronome for the establishment of local and global time scales (Olsen, 1986; Laskar, 1999; Laskar et al., 2004, 2011a; Boulila et al., 2008; Hinnov and Hilgen, 2012; Kent et al., 2018; Hinnov, 2018a; Huang, 2018).

4.2.3 Eccentricity modulations

Due to the importance of the 405-kyr mode ($g_2 - g_5$), it is important to filter the data to retrieve its 405-kyr component. From Fig. 4.4, it is clear that the $g_2 - g_5$ mode does not occur in isolation but is surrounded by two nearby peaks, corresponding to $g_2 - g_5 - (g_4 - g_3)$ and $g_2 - g_5 + (g_4 - g_3)$ (reps. 488 and 346 kyr period). These side terms produce a modulation of the 405-kyr component e_b with frequency $g_4 - g_3$ (Fig. 4.5B). As the $g_4 - g_3$ term also appears in the eccentricity, the $g_4 - g_3$ mode can also be directly retrieved by filtering the eccentricity in the [0:1.1]"/year interval (e_a) (Fig. 4.5A). By superposing e_a with the envelope $\hat{e}_b$ of the 405-kyr component e_b, one can see that e_a is almost identical, although in opposite phase to $\hat{e}_b$ (Fig. 4.5) (see also Laskar et al., 2011a).

The $g_4 - g_3$ modulation appears also in the high frequency ($\sim$100 kyr) eccentricity terms. These main terms appear

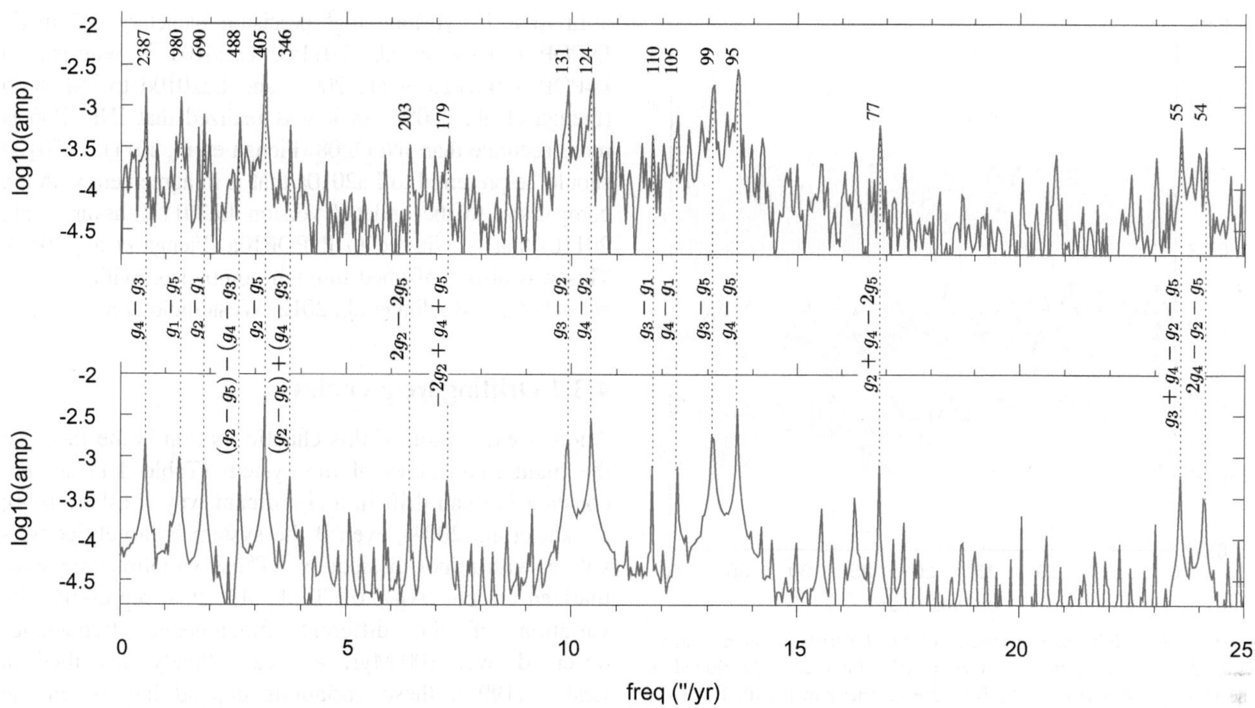

FIGURE 4.4 Fast fourier transform (FFT) of the La2004 eccentricity solution over 33 Myr (top) and Fourier transform of the solution $e^{(5)}$ limited to the five main linear terms of z (Table 4.3). For $e^{(5)}$, all the terms can be easily identified, and a combination of their corresponding frequencies are reported in the figure (see also Table 4.4). The periods of the corresponding terms are displayed (in kyr) in the top figure. Frequencies are expressed in arcsec/year (″/year): 1″/year = 0.7716 cycle/Myr.

(Fig. 4.4) in two sets: $(g_3 - g_2,\ g_4 - g_2)$ and $(g_3 - g_5,\ g_4 - g_5)$. These components will both modulate with a $g_4 - g_3$ frequency (Fig. 4.5C and D). In this case, the modulation envelopes $\hat{e}_c$, $\hat{e}_d$ are similar and in phase with $g_4 - g_3$ (e_a).

We can explain this using our simple 5 term model. Let us consider the filtered eccentricity e_c in the [9.3, 11]″/year band. We will have

$$e_c = a\exp(\mathrm{i}(\pi_3 - \pi_2)) + a'\exp(\mathrm{i}(\pi_4 - \pi_2)), \quad (4.7)$$

where a, a' are both positive (Eq. 4.6). Thus

$$e_c = [a + a'\exp(\mathrm{i}(\pi_4 - \pi_3))]\exp(\mathrm{i}(\pi_3 - \pi_2)), \quad (4.8)$$

and as a' is positive, the slow modulation $a'\exp(\mathrm{i}(\pi_4 - \pi_3))$ appears with the same phase as e_a. This is the same for e_d (Fig. 4.5D) and for all order 2 couples $g_3 - g_j$, $g_4 - g_j$, as for example, $(g_3 - g_1,\ g_4 - g_1$, Fig. 4.4). Now let us consider the modulation of the 405-kyr term, e_b. This term involves three components in its simple approximation (Eq. 4.6)

$$\begin{aligned} e_b &= a\exp(\mathrm{i}(\pi_2 - \pi_5)) - b\exp(\mathrm{i}((\pi_2 - \pi_5) - (\pi_4 - \pi_3))) \\ &\quad - b'\exp(\mathrm{i}((\pi_2 - \pi_5) + (\pi_4 - \pi_3))) \\ &= \exp(\mathrm{i}(\pi_2 - \pi_5)) \\ &\quad \times [a - b\exp(-\mathrm{i}(\pi_4 - \pi_3)) - b'\exp(\mathrm{i}(\pi_4 - \pi_3))], \end{aligned} \quad (4.9)$$

where a, b, and b' are positive. We have now a minus sign before b and b' $(-1/8X^2$ in Eq. 4.6). This induces a modulation of e_b with frequency $g_4 - g_3$, but due to these minus signs, it will be in opposite phase with respect to e_a. Indeed, if instead of the eccentricity, expanded as $1 + 1/2X - 1/8X^2$ (Eq. 4.6), we consider a fictitious eccentricity like expression $1 + 1/2X + 1/8X^2$, with the opposite sign in the terms X^2 of fourth order,[4] then the modulation in the 405-kyr band of this fictitious eccentricity is in phase with $g_4 - g_3$.

4.3 Chaos in the solar system

Since the first semianalytical long-term solutions of Laskar (1988, 1990) and Laskar et al. (1993), it becomes possible to compute reliable orbital solutions starting from the present initial conditions (Section 4.1.1). This was confirmed later on by direct numerical integrations (Quinn et al., 1991; Laskar et al., 1992, 2004). It was previously thought that the progress of computers and of observational techniques would result in an astronomical solution with higher precision, so that time validity could be extended steadily both in the future and in the past as envisioned by Laplace (1812). But the discovery of the chaoticity of the orbital motion of the solar system put an end to this hope (Laskar, 1989, 1990).

4. X is of second order in the g_i (Eq. 4.5).

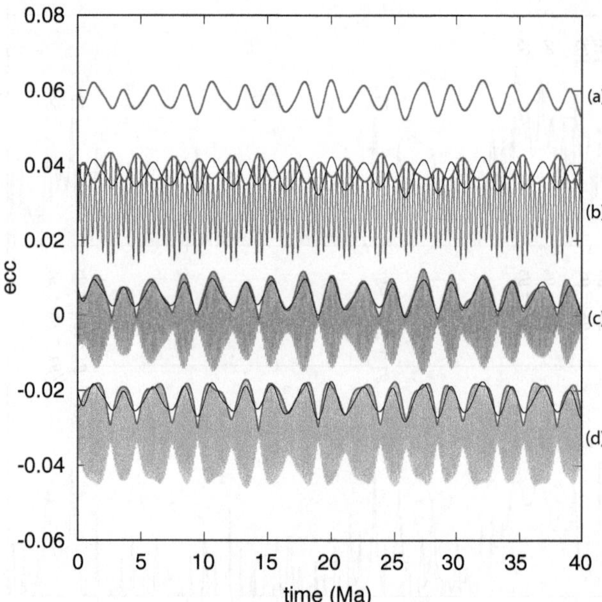

FIGURE 4.5 Filtered eccentricity of the La2010a solution (Laskar et al., 2011a). The filtered solutions are shifted in order to be plotted on the same graph. (A) e_a is the filtered eccentricity in the [0, 1.1]″/year (period > 1.18 Myr) band (+0.03) *(red)*. (B) e_b is filtered in the [2.2, 4.3]″/year ([301, 589] kyr period) band *(purple)*. (C) e_c is filtered in the [9.3, 11]″/year ([139, 118] kyr period) band (−0.03) *(green)*. (D) e_d is filtered in the [12.6, 14.5]″/year ([103, 89] kyr period) band (−0.06) *(blue)*. The upper envelopes of e_b, e_c, e_d, respectively, $\hat{e}_b$, $\hat{e}_c$, $\hat{e}_d$ are plotted in red. The thin black curve is the (e_a) curve, shifted in order to compare to the envelopes $\hat{e}_b$, $\hat{e}_c$, $\hat{e}_d$ of e_b, e_c, e_d. (e_a) nearly coincide with $\hat{e}_c$, $\hat{e}_d$ and is phase opposite to the $\hat{e}_b$. See the text for discussion. *See also Laskar et al., 2011a.*

Indeed, the uncertainty in the solutions grows exponentially, by a factor of 10 every 10 Myr (Laskar, 1989). More recently, it was shown that the motion of the minor planets Ceres and Vesta is itself chaotic, on much shorter time scales than the planets. Due to the perturbation of these celestial bodies on the planets, the possibility for constructing a precise orbital solution for the planets of the solar system from their present state is limited to about 60 Myr (Laskar et al., 2011b). Thus the use of the Earth's eccentricity solution as a template for cyclostratigraphy will suffer the same limitation. In Fig. 4.6, five eccentricity solutions are plotted over 60 Myr into the past (only 2 Myr slices are plotted every 10 Myr). The La2004 model (Laskar et al., 2004) is widely used and has been demonstrated to be precise for the past 40 Myr (Laskar et al., 2011a). The La2010a and La2010d solutions are improved versions, with a model, including the five major asteroids (Ceres, Vesta, Pallas, Iris, and Bamberga). Their initial conditions were obtained using a fit to a 1 Myr long high-precision planetary ephemeris INPOP (Laskar et al., 2011a). La2010a is adjusted to INPOP08 (Fienga et al., 2009) and La2010d to INPOP06 (Fienga et al., 2008). As it was realized that INPOP06 is more accurate than INPOP08 (Fienga et al., 2011), La2010d should be preferred to La2010a that is in agreement with the comparison to the updated version La2011 (Laskar et al., 2011b) that is adjusted to INPOP10a (Fienga et al., 2011). This was also confirmed through comparison with geological data (e.g., Boulila et al., 2012; Westerhold et al., 2012).

4.3.1 Drifting frequencies

Another expression of this chaotic motion is the fact that the main frequencies of the system (Table 4.1) are not constant but can drift in a significant way (Laskar, 1990; Laskar et al., 2004), even if the system is largely conservative, with minor dissipation.[5] These variations are summarized in col Δ_{100} of Table 4.1 that represents the variation of the different fundamental frequencies observed over 100 Myr. As was already described in Laskar (1990), these variations depend largely on the involved planets. Indeed, the chaos is not evenly distributed among the planets. The frequencies related to the outer solar system (g_5, g_6, g_7, g_8, s_6, s_7, s_8) are nearly constant over the age of the solar system and reflect the mostly regular behavior of the outer solar system (Jupiter, Saturn, Uranus, Neptune).[6] By contrast, the frequencies related to the inner planets, (g_1, g_2, g_3, g_4, s_1, s_2, s_3, s_4) undergo significant variations, with some differences in their unstability. They can be put in three classes, depending their Δ_{100} value (Table 4.1):

1. unstable frequencies: g_1, g_3, g_4, s_1, s_2
2. moderately unstable frequencies: s_3, s_4
3. nearly stable frequencies: g_2

This last frequency is of particular interest as it contributes to the $g_2 - g_5$ term with a 405-kyr period that is the largest term of the eccentricity signal (Table 4.2). Despite the chaotic motion of the solar system, this term can thus be used as a metronome for the time calibration of the stratigraphic record in the Mesozoic and beyond.

4.3.2 The 405-kyr $g_2 - g_5$ metronome

The main periodic component of the Earth's eccentricity is the 405-kyr $g_2 - g_5$ term (Table 4.2). The value of g_5 is practically constant, and g_2 presents only small chaotic diffusion (Table 4.1). This component can thus be approximated by a single periodic term that gives an approximate

5. This is not the case for the rotational motion of the Earth which is subject to tidal dissipation in the Earth−Moon system.

6. As a rule of thumb, one can consider that 1″/yr corresponds to a period of 1 Myr (1.296 Myr exactly). A variation of 0.001″/yr will make an offset of 2π after 1 Gyr. More precisely, $1''/\text{yr} = 0.77 \times 10^{-6}$ cycles/year.

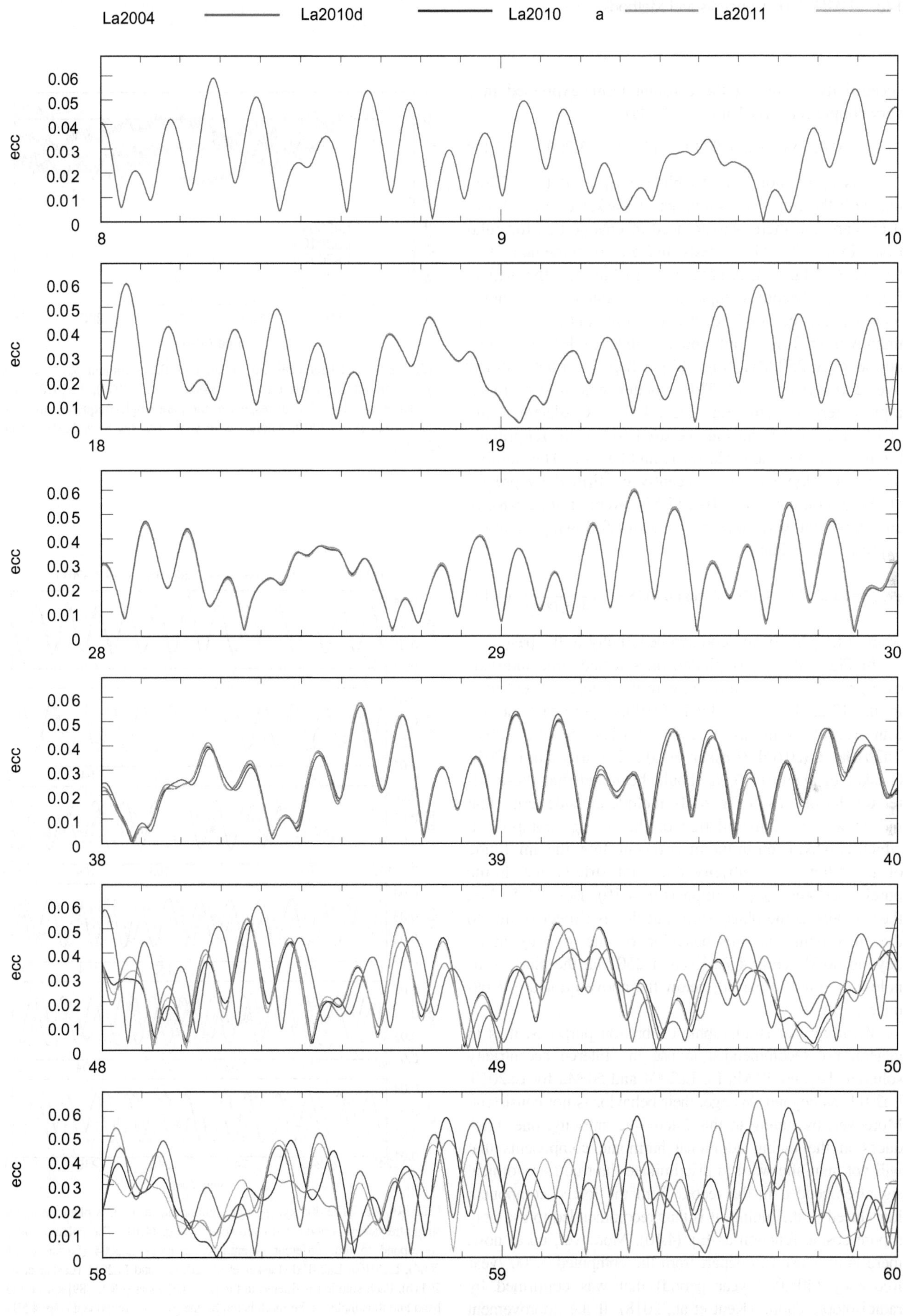

FIGURE 4.6 Evolution of four eccentricity solutions over 60 Myr in the past. For clarity, only 2 Myr slices are plotted, every 10 Myr. La2004 (Laskar et al., 2004), La2010a, La2010d (Laskar et al., 2011a), and La2011 (Laskar et al., 2011b).

eccentricity, including the constant term, expressed in a very simple form Laskar et al. (2004)

$$e_{405} = 0.027558 - 0.010739\cos(2434'' + 3.200''t). \quad (4.10)$$

This expression was established by a fit to La2004, but with the improved solutions of Laskar et al. (2011a), it appears that there was no need to change this formulation (Fig. 4.7). One needs indeed to remember that beyond 60 Ma, as it is obvious from Fig. 4.7, the drift in frequencies becomes apparent and cannot be predicted only by the celestial mechanics computation. But this unknown drift is small and amounts to less than one period over 250 Myr (Fig. 4.7), which is about 405-kyr over 250 Myr ($\sim$1.6‰). This is better than most radioisotopic determinations (e.g., Fig.1.4 from Gradstein et al., 2012). Eq. (4.10) can thus be used for cyclostratigraphic tuning over the whole Mesozoic and beyond. The stability of this 405-kyr term was recently confirmed by precise U–Pb zircon dates at 210–215 Ma (Kent et al., 2018). In an equivalent way, one can use the following formula, expressed in radians

$$e_{405} = 0.027558 - 0.010739\cos\left(0.0118 + 2\pi\frac{t}{405,000}\right) \quad (4.11)$$

where t is in years and counted negatively in the past.

In Fig. 4.8, e_{405} is plotted on selected time intervals over 250 Myr. It is compared with the filtered eccentricity in the [2.2, 4.3]″/year ([301, 589] kyr period) band for four recent solutions La2004 (Laskar et al., 2004), La2010a, La2010d (Laskar et al., 2011a), and La2011 (Laskar et al., 2011b). It should be noted that these filtered solutions, as in Fig. 4.5B, include the side terms that induce a $g_4 - g_3$ modulation of the $g_2 - g_5$ component, which is why, even in the most recent time, the amplitude of the filtered eccentricity does not strictly match the purely periodic e_{405} solution (Eq. 4.10). Beyond 55 Ma, there is also some phase shift, but this is expected, due to the uncertainty of the behavior of the $g_2 - g_5$ mode beyond 60 Ma (Fig. 4.7). Even at 250 Ma, the phase shift is less than half a period, below the above-quoted $\sim$1.6‰ uncertainty.

Warning: For stratigraphic calibration purposes, it is in general not recommended to use the filtered eccentricity solutions beyond 40 Ma for La2004 and 50 Ma for La2010, La2011, as beyond this age, their behavior is not consistent. Moreover, by tuning to this filtered eccentricity, one introduces in the tuning additional harmonic components that will not help afterward to discriminate the true astronomical signal embedded in the record from the forced component introduced in the tuning. It is thus recommended to use only a pure cosine function as Eq. (4.10). Moreover, up to now, there is no reason to depart from the computed 3.200″/year frequency (405,000 year period) that was confirmed by radioisotopic dating (Kent et al., 2018). If the improvement

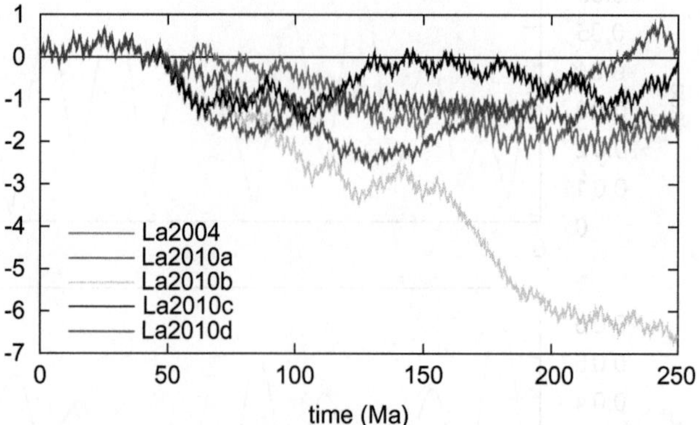

FIGURE 4.7 Differences (in radians) of the argument $\theta_{g2-g5}(t)$ of $g_2 - g_5$ in all solutions La2004 (Laskar et al., 2004), La2010a,b,c,d (Laskar et al., 2011a) with respect to the pure single-frequency approximation $\theta_{405}(t) = 3.200''t$, where t is in year. *Adapted from Laskar et al. (2011a).*

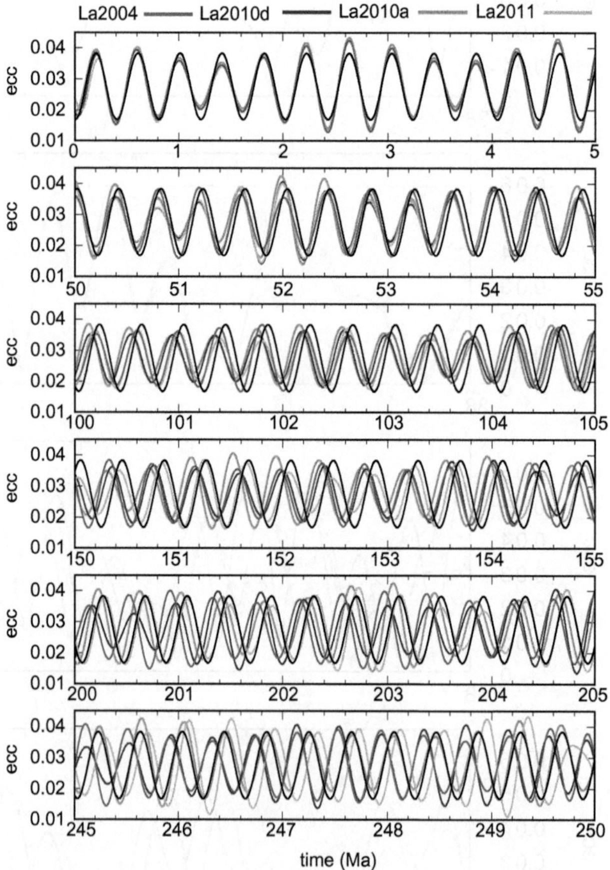

FIGURE 4.8 The 405-kyr $g_2 - g_5$ component. In black is plotted e_{405}, the single-frequency periodic term provided by Eq. (4.10). The colored curves correspond to four different eccentricity solutions La2004 (Laskar et al., 2004), La2010a, La2010d (Laskar et al., 2011a), and La2011 (Laskar et al., 2011b). Each solution is filtered in the [2.2, 4.3]″/year ([301, 589] kyr period) band and thus includes the modulation by the $g_4 - g_3$ component (Fig. 4.5B).

of radioisotopic measures provides more precise time constraints in the future, then it will be possible to improve a tuning target by providing either a slightly different value for the e_{405} frequency or even a varying frequency for this term (Fu and Laskar, 2019). Such improvement is more than welcome, but meanwhile, one should stick to the constant 3.200″/year frequency. By contrast, for ages that are within the validity time of the solution, that is 40 Ma for La2004 and 50 Ma for La2010 and La2011, one can use the full eccentricity solution, as well as the derived filtered eccentricity (Fig. 4.5B).

4.3.3 The $g_4 - g_3$ 2.4 Myr cycle

The g_2 fundamental frequency is the most stable, not considering the outer planet ones. This led to the recognition of the $g_2 - g_5$ metronome. By contrast, g_3 and g_4 are the most unstable frequencies (Table 4.1). Moreover, we have seen the important role of the $g_4 - g_3$ 2.4 Myr term in the eccentricity (Section 4.2.3). $g_4 - g_3$ is the sixth term in amplitude in the eccentricity (Table 4.2) but appears also as the main modulation of the $g_2 - g_5$ 405-kyr term and also as the modulation of the ~100-kyr terms in the eccentricity (Fig. 4.5). However, this term cannot be used for time calibration, as its behavior is not stable, and its frequency, as for $s_4 - s_3$, will evolve because of the chaotic diffusion of the orbits (Fig. 4.9). This modulation has been recognized in sedimentary records of the Cenozoic and Mesozoic eras (Olsen and Kent, 1999; Pälike et al., 2004; Boulila et al., 2014; Fang et al., 2015; Ma et al., 2017; Westerhold et al., 2017), although in Olsen and Kent (1999), the 405-kyr modulation was measured with a period of about 1.7 Myr, instead of the present 2.4 Myr value. The question arises as to whether this difference could be the expression of the chaotic diffusion of the solar system, and this was answered positively in Olsen et al. (2019). Indeed, in Fig. 4.10, extracted from Olsen et al. (2019), the period of the $g_4 - g_3$ argument is plotted versus time for 13 different orbital solutions. For the most recent 40 Myr, they all reveal the same ~2.4 Myr period, but then they depart from each other due to chaotic diffusion (Laskar, 1990; Laskar et al., 2004). The green horizontal line represents the 1.7 Myr value observed in the Newark–Hartford data (Olsen and Kent, 1999; Olsen et al., 2019). This value is attained by many of the solutions and in particular by La2010d (in black) at roughly the same 200 Ma age. It can also be observed that the excursion of the $P_{g_4-g_3}$ period is even larger and can evolve across the [1.4:2.6 Myr] period range during this time interval.

The prediction of the evolution of the actual path of the $P_{g_4-g_3}$ period in the past cannot be retrieved by only considering the present planetary positions and computing their past orbits using the laws of celestial mechanics. As in Olsen et al. (2019), we will have to rely on geological data to retrieve this information. Recovering these long-period cycles in the geological data is in some sense recovering the planetary orbital motions through geological data beyond their horizon of predictability.

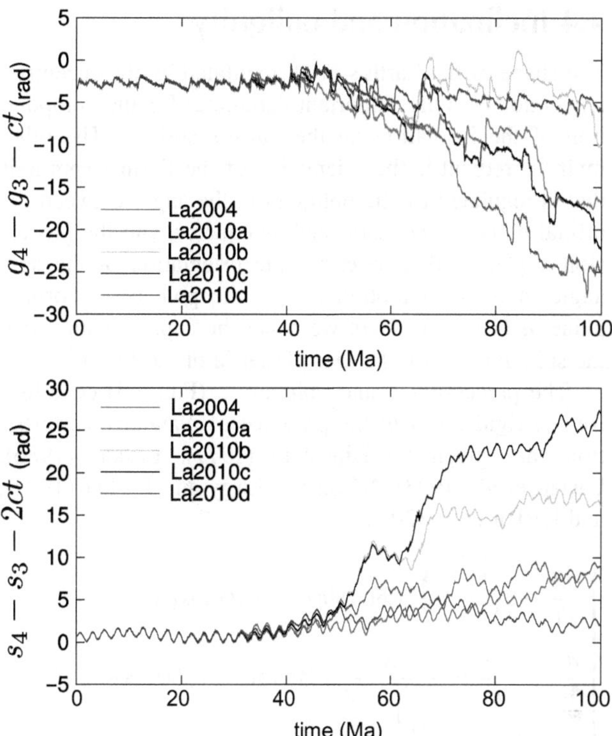

FIGURE 4.9 *Top*: differences (in radians) of the argument of $g_4 - g_3$ in solutions La2004 (Laskar et al., 2004), La2010a,b,c,d (Laskar et al., 2011a) with respect to the linear evolution 2.664*T*, where *T* is in Myr. *Bottom*: differences (in radians) of the $s_4 - s_3 5$ argument in La2004, La2010a,b,c,d with respect to the linear expression 2 × 2.664*T*, where *T* is in Myr. *Adapted from Laskar et al., 2011a.*

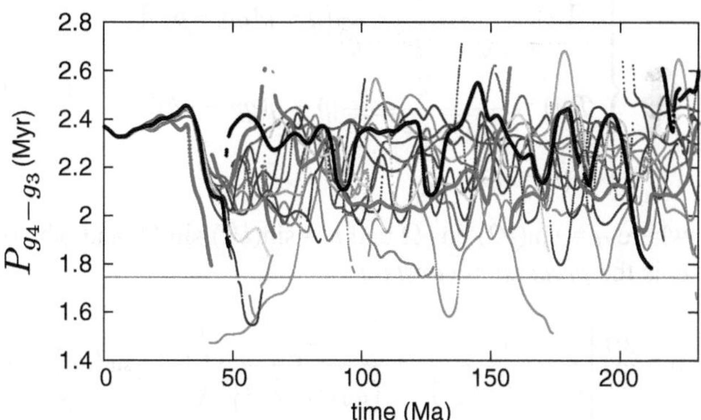

FIGURE 4.10 Evolution of the period of the $g_4 - g_3$ argument for 13 orbital solutions over 250 Myr in the past. The horizontal line is the 1.7 Myr value observed in the Newark–Hartford data. The red curve is La2004, and the black curve La2010d. Over the first 40 Myr, all values are of ~2.4 Myr, but they diverge after 50 Myr due to chaotic diffusion. La2010d (*black*) has nearly the same value as the one found in the Newark–Hartford data around the same age (200–220 Ma) (Olsen et al., 2019).

4.4 Inclination and obliquity

The shape of the Earth's orbit, regulated by the eccentricity, is not the only important parameter for the computation of the insolation on the Earth's surface. The other main ingredient is the orientation of the Earth's spin axis that is regulated by the obliquity ε, the angle between the orbital plane of the Earth and its equator, and the precession angle, ψ, that describes the orientation of the spin angle in its slow motion around the pole of the orbital plane, $\boldsymbol{n}$ (Fig. 4.3). Here we make the approximation that the spin axis is also the axis of inertia of the Earth.[7]

The precession ψ and obliquity ε (Fig. 4.3) equations for the rigid Earth in the presence of planetary perturbations are given by Kinoshita (1977), Laskar (1986), Laskar et al. (1993), Néron De Surgy and Laskar (1997), and Laskar et al. (2004)

$$\begin{cases} \dfrac{dX}{dt} = L\sqrt{1-\dfrac{X^2}{L^2}}(\mathcal{B}(t)\sin\psi - \mathcal{A}(t)\cos\psi) \\ \dfrac{d\psi}{dt} = \dfrac{\alpha X}{L} - \dfrac{X}{L\sqrt{1-\dfrac{X^2}{L^2}}}(\mathcal{A}(t)\sin\psi + \mathcal{B}(t)\cos\psi) - 2C(t) \end{cases} \tag{4.12}$$

with[8] $X = L\cos\varepsilon$, $L = C\gamma$, where γ is the spin rate of the Earth, $A < B < C$ are the principal momentum of inertia of the Earth, and

$$\begin{cases} \mathcal{A}(t) = \dfrac{2}{\sqrt{1-p^2-q^2}}[\dot{q} + p(q\dot{p} - p\dot{q})] \\ \mathcal{B}(t) = \dfrac{2}{\sqrt{1-p^2-q^2}}[\dot{p} - q(q\dot{p} - p\dot{q})] \\ C(t) = q\dot{p} - p\dot{q} \end{cases} \tag{4.13}$$

where $q = \sin(i/2)\cos\Omega$ and $p = \sin(i/2)\sin\Omega$, and where α is the *precession constant*

$$\alpha = \frac{3G}{2\gamma}\left[\frac{m_\odot}{\left(a_\odot\sqrt{1-e_\odot{}^2}\right)^3} + \frac{m_M}{\left(a_M\sqrt{1-e_M{}^2}\right)^3}\left(1-\frac{3}{2}\sin^2 i_M\right)\right]E_d \tag{4.14}$$

where $\odot$ refers to the Sun, and M to the Moon. For a fast rotating planet such as the Earth, the dynamical ellipticity $E_d = (2C - A - B)/C$ can be considered as proportional to γ^2; this corresponds to the hydrostatic equilibrium (e.g., Lambeck, 1980). In this approximation, α is thus proportional to ω. The quantities $\mathcal{A}(t)$, $\mathcal{B}(t)$, and $C(t)$ are related to the secular evolution of the orbital plane of the Earth and are given by the integration of the planetary motions.

TABLE 4.5 First eight terms (in decreasing amplitude) of the frequency decomposition of the Earth's obliquity over the time interval [−20, −10] Ma.

$k1$		ν_k ("/year)	P (kyr)	$b_k \times 10^4$
1	$p+s_3$	32.026	40.5	49
2	$p+s_4$	33.144	39.1	19
3	$p+s_4-(g_4-g_3)$	32.582	39.8	15
4	$p+s_6$	24.527	52.8	14
5	$p+s_3-(g_4-g_3)$	31.475	41.2	9
6	$p+s_2$	43.815	29.6	8
7		32.213	40.2	7
8	$p+s_1$	45.244	28.6	6

$\varepsilon = \varepsilon_0 + \sum_{k=1}^{8} b_k\cos(\nu_k t + \theta_k)$ with $\varepsilon_0 = 0.0275579$. Column two is the corresponding combination of frequencies. s_i are the fundamental frequencies (Table 4.1); p is the precession frequency ($p = 50.87435''$/year in the center of the considered time interval.

4.4.1 Simplified expressions

To understand the main terms that appear in the obliquity and precession, it is useful to look for simplified expressions of Eq. (4.12). Let us consider the case where there is no dissipation in the rotation speed of the Earth (ω is constant) and no planetary perturbations. The elliptical elements are thus constant, and $\mathcal{A} = \mathcal{B} = C = 0$ in Eq. (4.13). Eq. (4.12) reduces then to

$$\begin{cases} \dfrac{d\cos\varepsilon}{dt} = 0 \qquad \text{i.e.}\quad \varepsilon = \varepsilon_0 = Cte. \\ \dfrac{d\psi}{dt} = \alpha\cos\varepsilon_0 \end{cases} \tag{4.15}$$

The obliquity is then constant, and the precession angle ψ evolves linearly with time at a constant angular speed of $\alpha\cos\varepsilon_0$. This is a zero order solution. We can go further by reducing (Eq. 4.12) to the first order terms. We obtain the solution of order one,

$$\frac{d\varepsilon}{dt} = 2(\dot{p}\sin\psi - \dot{q}\cos\psi) = 2\mathcal{Re}(\dot{\zeta}\exp(\mathrm{i}\psi)). \tag{4.16}$$

where $\zeta = \sin(i/2)\exp(\mathrm{i}\Omega)$ and $\mathcal{Re}$ denotes the real part of the complex number. With the quasiperiodic approximation (e.g., Table 4.5 of Laskar et al., 2004),

$$\zeta = \sum_{k=1}^{N} a_k \exp(\mathbf{i}(\nu_k t + \phi_k)), \tag{4.17}$$

7. The angle between the Earth's spin axis and its axis of inertia is less than 1″.

8. There is here a misprint in Laskar et al. (2004). It should be read as here $X = L\cos\varepsilon$, and not $X = \cos\varepsilon$.

The first-order solution of the obliquity will be a similar quasiperiodic function

$$\varepsilon = \varepsilon_0 + 2\sum_{k=1}^{N} \frac{a_k \nu_k}{\nu_k + p} \cos((\nu_k + p)t + \phi_k + \psi_0), \quad (4.18)$$

The terms that appear in the obliquity have thus frequency $\nu_k + p$, where p is the precession frequency, and ν_k are the frequencies of the inclination variables $\zeta_k = \sin(i_k/2) \exp(i\Omega_k)$ (Fig. 4.3). The amplitude of these terms is multiplied by $\nu_k/(\nu_k + p)$. High frequencies are thus favored (factor ν_k). Amplitudes are also divided by $\nu_k + p$, and resonance will occur when $\nu_k + p = 0$. At present, $p = 50.475838''$/year (Laskar et al., 2004), but due to tidal dissipation in the Earth–Moon system, p is not constant but evolves in time, as the spin rate of the Earth and the Earth–Moon distance evolves.

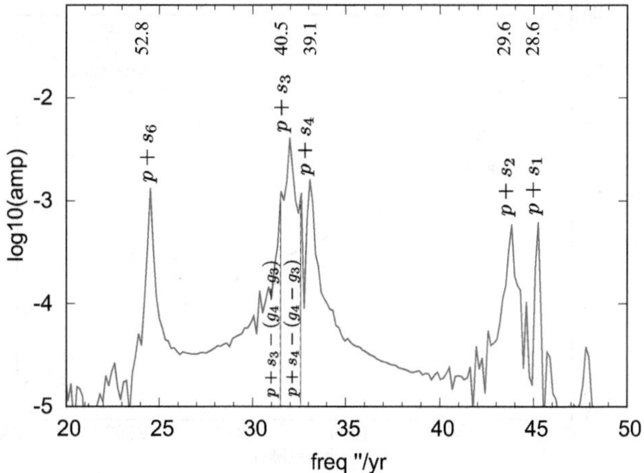

FIGURE 4.11 Spectral analysis of the obliquity ε. The spectral analysis is performed over the interval [10:20] Ma. The main peaks are recognized as $p + s_i$, where s_i is one of the fundamental frequencies of the inclination of the orbital plane (Table 4.1). On top, the periods are given in kyr. Two additional terms of higher order are given: $p + s_3 - (g_4 - g_3)$ and $p + s_4 - (g_4 - g_3)$ (see Table 4.5). Frequencies are expressed in arcsec/yr (''/year): 1''/year = 0.7716 cycle/Myr.

4.4.2 Tidal evolution

The Lunar Laser ranging measurements have taken place since the Apollo and Lunokhod mission installed reflectors on the Moon nearly 50 years ago, with an accuracy that is now less than 2 cm (e.g., Viswanathan et al., 2018). This allows us to monitor the present recession of the Moon, at a rate of ~3.8 cm/year (Dickey et al., 1994; Laskar et al., 2004). Backward integration of the Earth–Moon system provides interpolation formulae for the Earth–Moon distance (a_M, in Earth radius), the length of day (LOD, in hours), and the precession constant (p, in ''/year) as provided in the La2004 solution (Laskar et al., 2004)

$$\begin{aligned} a_M &= 60.142611 + 6.100887T - 2.709407T^2 \\ &\quad + 1.366779T^3 - 1.484062T^4 \\ \text{LOD} &= 23.934468 + 7.432167T - 0.727046T^2 \\ &\quad + 0.409572T^3 - 0.589692T^4 \\ p &= 50.475838 - 26.368583T + 21.890862T^2 \end{aligned} \quad (4.19)$$

where T is the time from the present (J2000), expressed in Gyr and counted negatively in the past (Fig. 4.12). These expressions have been established by a fit over 250 Myr but can be extrapolated over 500 Myr for a first estimate of the past evolution of these quantities. It should nevertheless be reminded that these expressions cannot be extrapolated over the age of the solar system, and the past evolution of the Earth–Moon system is still largely unknown. If one integrates back the evolution of the Earth–Moon system, owing to the present rheology parameters of the Earth, one finds that the Moon hits the Earth at about 1.5 Gyr ago, which is clearly not compatible with our understanding of the origin of the Moon or history of the Earth (Gerstenkorn, 1969; Walker and Zahnle, 1986). In order to reconcile this evolution with

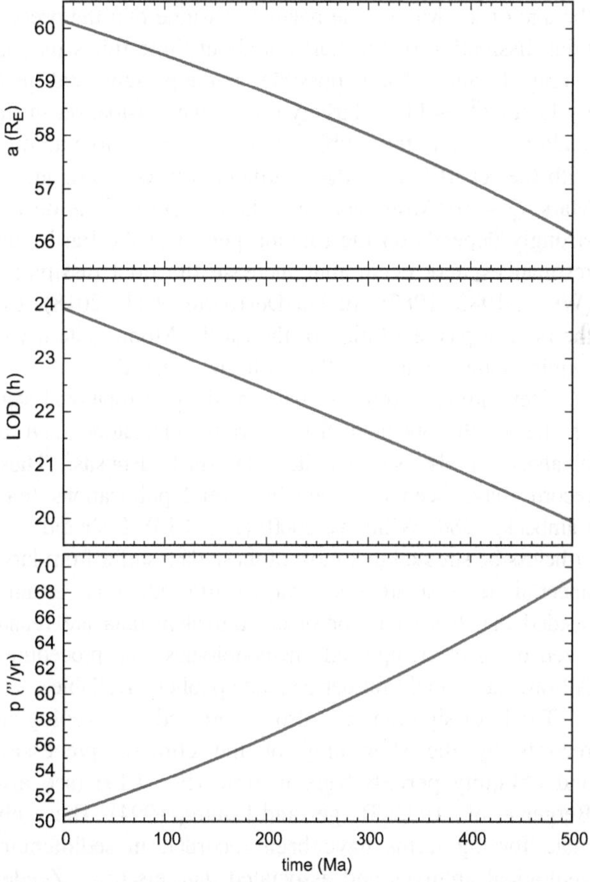

FIGURE 4.12 Past evolution of the Earth–Moon distance a_M (top, in Earth radius R_E), of the LOD (middle, in hours), and precession frequency p (bottom, in arcsec/year). These curves are obtained using Eq. (4.19), which are extrapolated from the La2004 solution over 250 Myr (Laskar et al., 2004). *LOD*, Length of day.

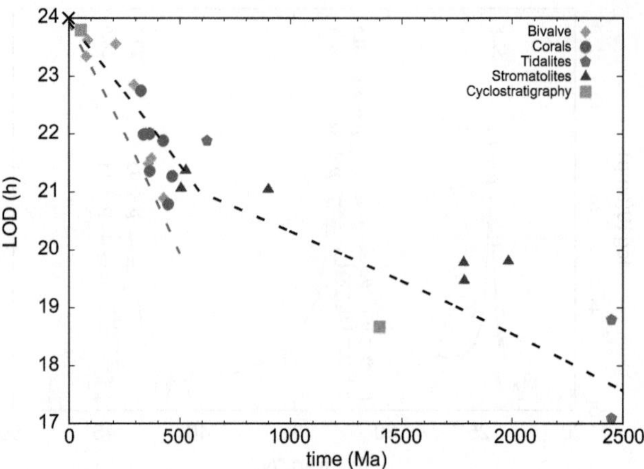

FIGURE 4.13 Length of day (LOD) evolution due to tidal dissipation in the Earth–Moon system. The dotted red line is the LOD provided by Eq. (4.19) (Laskar et al., 2004). The dotted black line is an empirical fit using a simplified tidal model adjusted to the geological data (Walker and Zahnle, 1986; Lambeck, 1980; Berger and Loutre, 1994). *LOD*, Length of day. *Compilation of various data from (Williams, 2000) and references therein. The cyclostratigraphic data are from (Meyers and Malinverno, 2018).*

the age of the Moon, one needs to assume that the present tidal dissipation of the Earth is about three times its past averaged value. This is possible, as the present tidal quality factor Q (~ 11) is largely due to the dissipation in the shallow seas and thus subject to change by a large amount with the repartition of the continents (by comparison, for Mars, $Q \sim 90$). Moreover, the tidal response of the oceans strongly depends on the rotation period of the Earth, and resonances may occur that increase the tidal dissipation (Webb, 1980, 1982; Auclair-Desrotour et al., 2018). But the precise past evolution of the Earth–Moon system will require some input from the geological record.

There are numerous estimates of the past rotational state of the Earth, obtained from various indicators such as bivalves, corals, stromatolites, or tidal deposits. These records have been compiled in several publications (e.g., Lambeck, 1980; Williams, 2000) (Fig. 4.13). It should nevertheless be stressed that most of these data suffer from large uncertainties that are not always estimated. It is certainly needed that these data or other equivalent data are reanalyzed using clear, updated, methodologies, and procedures. All raw data should further be made publicly available.

Tidal dissipation is also expressed in geological records by the shortening of the climatic precession and obliquity periods back in time (Eq. 4.19) (see also Berger et al., 1992; Berger and Loutre, 1994). These climate forcing terms have been recorded in sedimentary geological archives and associated datasets (e.g., Zeeden et al., 2014; Meyers and Malinverno, 2018) (Fig. 4.13). While this tidal dissipation effect can be seen as a phase shift of the precession/obliquity cycle relative to a solution assuming recent tidal dissipation rate in the Neogene (Lourens et al., 2001; Zeeden et al., 2014), a shortening of the precession and obliquity periods relative to the stable eccentricity 405-kyr metronome is observed in Paleozoic and Mesozoic datasets (e.g., Wu et al., 2013a; Boulila et al., 2014, 2019). Such datasets from the Mesozoic and Cenozoic could be used to reconstruct the Earth's precession and obliquity periods in a quantitative manner, and it is desirable that the analysis of such records will be continued in order to improve the knowledge of the past evolution of the Earth–Moon system.

In Fig. 4.13 is also plotted (in *red dashed line*) the computed variation of the LOD as obtained by Eq. (4.19) (Laskar et al., 2004). It should be stressed that this curve has not been fitted to the available geological data (Fig. 4.13) but is obtained through the sole use of the Lunar Laser ranging data over the past few decades.

In addition to the variations expressed in Eq. (4.19), the tidal dissipation induces an average variation in the obliquity itself which can be written as

$$\varepsilon = 23.270773 + 2.011295T \tag{4.20}$$

where T is in billions of years (Laskar et al., 2004), counted negatively in the past. The obliquity was thus smaller going back in time (see Fig. 14 from Laskar et al., 2004). This formula, obtained through a fit over 250 Myr, could also be used over 500 Myr in the past, although as stated earlier, large uncertainties remain, which can only be improved by constraints provided by the geological record.

In addition to the tidal dissipation in the Earth–Moon system, the variations of the Earth's spin rate and orientation can result from changes in the momentum of inertia of the Earth. These can result from change in the ice bold (e.g., Laskar et al., 1993; Levrard and Laskar, 2003) or plate tectonics (e.g., Mitrovica et al., 1997; Morrow et al., 2012). The problem with these effects is that their signature is not easy to disentangle from that of tidal dissipation, as they will also manifest themselves by a change in the precession rate (e.g., Pälike and Shackleton, 2000; Lourens et al., 2001). Over Gyr time scales, it may further be necessary to take into account the mass loss of the sun that will affect also the orbital secular frequencies (e.g., Spalding et al., 2018).

4.4.3 Obliquity solution

Due to the dissipation in the Earth–Moon system described earlier, the analysis of the obliquity solution is complex. It is nevertheless interesting to look to the main features of the solution over a limited time of 20 Myr, where the dissipative aspect is moderate (Fig. 4.14). In Fig. 4.14 the obliquity ε is plotted, as well as various filtered expressions ε_1, ε_2, ε_3, filtered over respectively [28:38], [23:38], [42:47]″/year. These filtering intervals are dictated by the analysis of the Fourier spectrum of the obliquity (Fig. 4.11). The envelopes $\hat{\varepsilon}_1$, $\hat{\varepsilon}_2$,

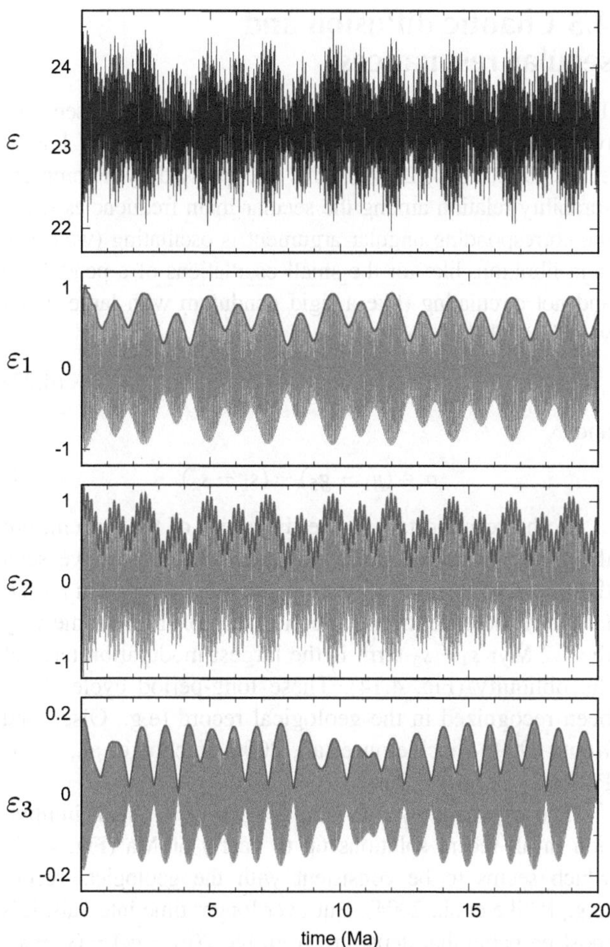

FIGURE 4.14 Obliquity (ε) evolution (in degrees) over 20 Myr from La2004 (Laskar et al., 2004) (top). ε_1 is the filtered obliquity in the window [28:38]″/year ([34.1:46.3] kyr periods) (*green*). In red is plotted the envelope $\hat{\varepsilon}_1$ of ε_1. ε_2 is the filtered obliquity in the wider window [23:38]″/year ([34.1:56.3] kyr periods) (*green*). In red is plotted the envelope $\hat{\varepsilon}_2$ of ε_2. ε_3 is the filtered obliquity in the window [42:47]″/year ([27.6:30.9] kyr periods) (*green*). In red is plotted the envelope $\hat{\varepsilon}_1$ of ε_1. The vertical scale is the same for ε, ε_1, ε_2 and five times larger for ε_3.

and $\hat{\varepsilon}_3$ of these filtered obliquity solutions allow to extract the most important components of the obliquity. In Fig. 4.15 are plotted the Fast Fourier Transform (FFT) analyses of these envelopes $\hat{\varepsilon}_1$, $\hat{\varepsilon}_2$, $\hat{\varepsilon}_3$, of the filtered obliquities ε_1, ε_2, ε_3, with the identification of the main terms.

As expected, the main term in these envelopes is related to the $s_4 - s_3$ term, with a period of $\sim$1.2 Myr. This term results from the beat of the $p + s_4$ and $p + s_3$ obliquity terms (Fig. 4.11 and Table 4.5). However, other terms appear as well. The term $g_4 - g_3$ is also present in the eccentricity solution with a period of $\sim$2.4 Myr. This term results from both the beat of the $p + s_3$ and $p + s_3 - (g_4 - g_3)$ terms and the $p + s_4$ and $p + s_4 - (g_4 - g_3)$ terms (Fig. 4.11 and Table 4.5). Very important, is further the $s_3 - s_6$ term, appearing as the beat of $p + s_6$ with the main obliquity term $p + s_3$. Finally, $s_1 - s_2$ appears as the beat of $p + s_1$ and $p + s_2$.

The important feature of all these spectral terms is that they do not depend on the precession frequency p, but only on the orbital solution with secular main frequencies g_i, s_i. These terms will thus not be affected by the strong variations in p (Eq. 4.19 and Fig. 4.12).

Both $s_4 - s_3$ and $s_3 - s_6$ are of particular importance: the first one because it is at present in resonance with the modulation frequency of the eccentricity $g_4 - g_3$ ($s_4 - s_3 = 2(g_4 - g_3)$), and the second one because s_6 is a stable frequency and s_3 a moderately stable frequency (Section 4.3.1). It is thus possible to use the $s_3 - s_6$ inclination term as an additional chronometer for stratigraphic tuning, with a period of 173 kyr.

4.4.4 The 173-kyr $s_3 - s_6$ metronome

The $g_2 - g_5$ 405-kyr metronome is a fundamental tool for establishing local or global time scales (see Section 4.3.2), but this signal is not always present. Recently, it has been demonstrated that in some cases the $s_3 - s_6$ 173-kyr cycle can also be used as a metronome for the calibration of stratigraphic sequences (Boulila et al., 2018; Charbonnier et al., 2018). This cycle allows to calibrate obliquity dominated stratigraphic sequences.

This $s_3 - s_6$ term, present in the modulation of the obliquity (Figs. 4.14 and 4.15B), does not depend on the precession frequency p and is quite stable in time (Fig. 4.16). Only the variation of the orbital plane of the Earth is involved. We can call this term the 173-kyr *inclination metronome*, analogous to the 405-kyr $g_2 - g_5$ *eccentricity metronome*. The time scale uncertainty associated with the *inclination metronome* is of the order of 400 kyr over 100 Myr that is about 0.4%. But contrary to the eccentricity metronome, the inclination metronome is not the largest term present in the obliquity and not even in the modulation of the obliquity. It is nevertheless quite isolated (Fig. 4.15B) which explains why it can be successfully used for stratigraphic calibration (Boulila et al., 2018; Charbonnier et al., 2018).

A good approximation for this cycle can be given by the following expression

$$\varepsilon_{s3-s6}(t) = 0.144\ \cos(404,444'' + 7.5''t) \qquad (4.21)$$

where t is in years, counted negatively in the past. The angle is in arcseconds and should usually be converted to radians to compute the cosine. The frequency $s_3 - s_6$ has been rounded to 7.5″/year, as it is meaningless to use the exact expression $s_3 - s_6 = 7.497855''$/year obtained from Table 4.1 due to the variability of s_3. Alternatively, one can use the same quantity expressed in radians and years (counted negatively in the past).

$$\varepsilon_{s3-s6}(t) = 0.144\ \cos\left(1.961 + 2\pi\frac{t}{172,800}\right). \qquad (4.22)$$

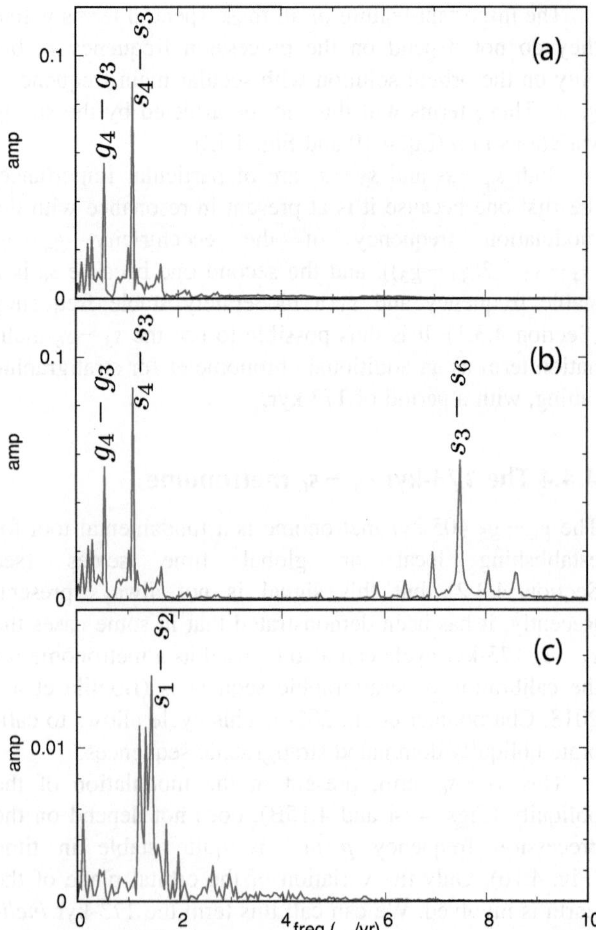

FIGURE 4.15 FFT of the envelopes $\hat{\varepsilon}_1$, $\hat{\varepsilon}_2$, $\hat{\varepsilon}_3$ of the filtered obliquities ε_1, ε_2, ε_3 from Fig. 4.14. Frequencies are expressed in arcsec/yr ("/year): 1"/year = 0.7716 cycle/Myr.

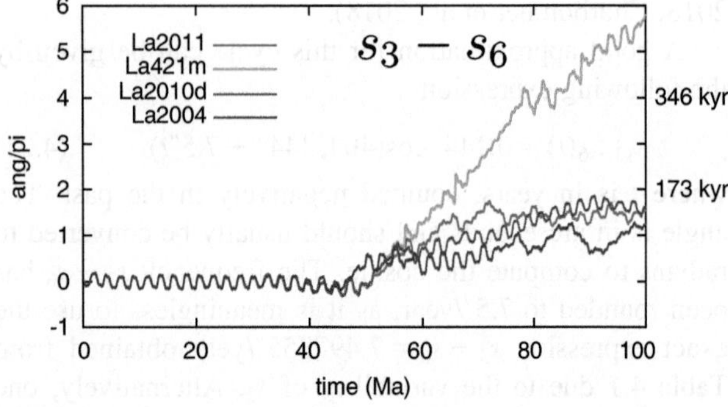

FIGURE 4.16 Stability of the $s_3 - s_6$ argument versus time. The variation of the argument is compared to a pure periodic term for the four solutions La2004 (Laskar et al., 2004) La2010d (Laskar et al., 2011a) La2011 (Laskar et al., 2011b), and the variant La421m that has been made using initial conditions derived from a fit to DE421 (Folkner et al., 2009; Laskar et al., 2004).

4.5 Chaotic diffusion and secular resonances

The present solar system is characterized by the presence of two main secular resonances (Laskar, 1990, 1992; Laskar et al., 1992, 2004, 2011a). This is expressed by a commensurability relation among the secular main frequencies while the corresponding angular argument is oscillating (we say it is in libration, like for the small oscillations of a pendulum) and not circulating (like a rigid pendulum with large initial velocity). These two resonances are

$$\theta = 2(g_4 - g_3) - (s_4 - s_3) \tag{4.23}$$

and

$$\sigma = (g_1 - g_5) - (s_1 - s_2). \tag{4.24}$$

Both are important in the dynamics of the system, but the first one draws particular attention as we have seen that the 2.4 Myr $g_4 - g_3$ term is the main long-term modulation of the eccentricity (Section 4.3.3). In the same way the 1.2 Myr $s_4 - s_3$ term is the largest modulation term of the obliquity (Fig. 4.14). These long-period cycles have been recognized in the geological record (e.g., Olsen and Kent, 1999; Shackleton et al., 2000; Zachos et al., 2001; Pälike et al., 2001, 2004).

The argument φ_θ of $\theta = 2(g_4 - g_3) - (s_4 - s_3)$ is in libration in all recent solutions up to nearly 50 Ma (Fig. 4.17), which seems to be consistent with the geological record (e.g., Pälike et al., 2004). But over longer time intervals, it is most probable that departure from the $2(g_4 - g_3) - (s_4 - s_3)$ occurs, as what is observed in the numerical simulations (Fig. 4.18). It should be noted that observing a change in the $P_{g_4-g_3}$ period only is not sufficient to conclude that the system exit the θ resonance, as the two $P_{g_4-g_3}$ and $P_{s_4-s_3}$ periods can change, but stay in the same 2:1 ratio, corresponding to the black line of Fig. 4.18.

In the recent years, there has been an increasing interest search of chaotic transition in the $\theta = 2(g_4 - g_3) - (s_4 - s_3)$

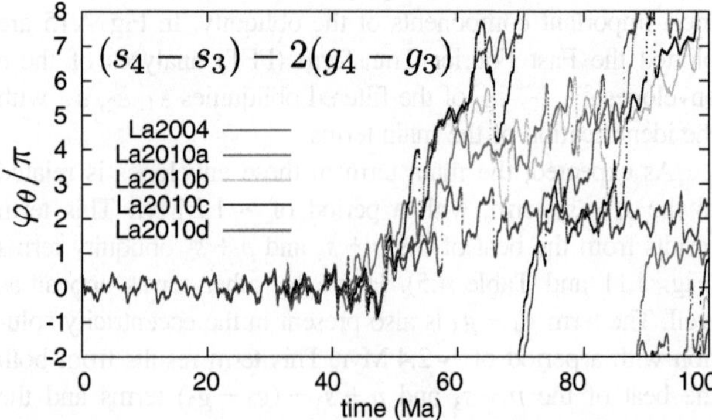

FIGURE 4.17 Evolution (in radians) of the argument φ_θ of the resonant argument $\theta = 2(g_4 - g_3) - (s_4 - s_3)$ in all solutions La2004 (Laskar et al., 2004) and La2010a,b,c,d (Laskar et al., 2011a). *Adapted from Laskar et al. (2011a).*

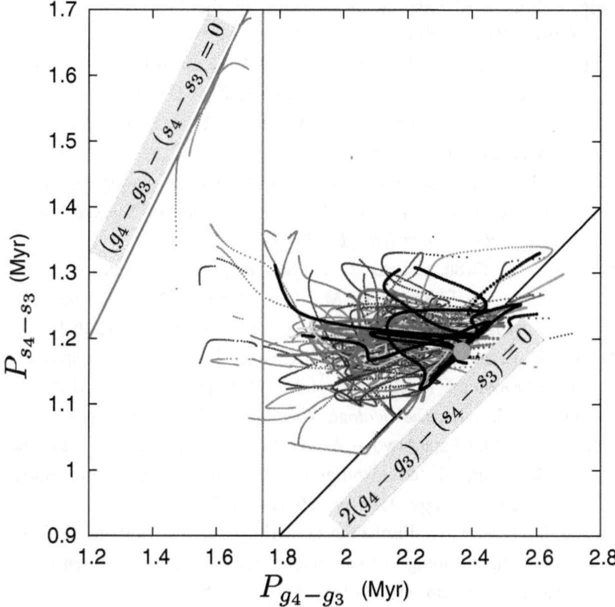

FIGURE 4.18 Evolution of the period $P_{s_4-s_3}$ of the $s_4 - s_3$ argument versus the period $P_{g_4-g_3}$ of $g_4 - g_3$ for 13 orbital solutions over 250 Myr in the past. The vertical line is the 1.7 Myr value observed in the Newark–Hartford data. The red curve is La2004 and the black curve is La2010d. The black line corresponds to the $2(g_4 - g_3) - (s_4 - s_3)$ resonance. The red line corresponds to the $(g_4 - g_3) - (s_4 - s_3)$ resonance. The green dot is the origin of all solutions, corresponding to the present date, where all solutions start in the 2 $(g_4 - g_3) - (s_4 - s_3)$ resonance. *Adapted from Olsen et al. (2019).*

secular resonance (e.g., Grippo et al., 2004; Huang et al., 2010; Wu et al., 2013b; Ikeda and Tada, 2014; Fang et al., 2015; Ma et al., 2017; Gambacorta et al., 2018; Ma et al., 2019). This search is difficult, as it requires very long records of high quality that are not very numerous. Some convincing results are nevertheless obtained (e.g., Ma et al., 2017), and we can expect that more will follow in the near future.

4.6 Discussion

Since GTS2004 (Gradstein et al., 2004) and the astronomical calibration of the Neogene (Lourens et al., 2004), huge progress has been made in the analysis of stratigraphic records, and the astronomical solutions are challenged to follow this evolution. Starting from the present initial conditions, despite a highly accurate fit to the most precise observational data, gathered from spacecraft orbiting around the planets, the astronomical solution is limited to 60 Ma (Laskar et al., 2011b) because of its chaotic behavior. Meanwhile, recent solutions are valid over about 50 Ma (Laskar et al., 2011a). This is not sufficient to address the needs for stratigraphic studies that have covered the Cenozoic and are now being extended to cover the entire Mesozoic. This extension, beyond the 60 Ma limit, is made possible by the use of both the 405-kyr $g_2 - g_5$ eccentricity metronome and the 173-kyr $s_3 - s_6$ inclination metronome (see Sections 4.3.2 and 4.4.4). In order to go beyond the use of these pure periodic terms, it will be necessary to extend the astronomical solutions, and this will only be made possible by using the geological record as an input for constraining the astronomical solution. Encouraging results have been obtained in this direction (Olsen et al., 2019; Zeebe and Lourens, 2019). In the same way the stratigraphic record can be used to constrain the past rotational evolution of the Earth (e.g., Meyers and Malinverno, 2018), and it is most probable that similar studies will help to decipher the past tidal evolution of the Earth–Moon system in the near future. The search for chaotic transitions in the $2(g_4 - g_3) - (s4 - s_3)$ secular resonance is a hunt that is shared by many, as well as analysis of other very long periodic components. But in order to obtain convincing results, the stratigraphic community needs to adopt rigorous methods with open shared data, processing techniques, and protocols. It will be the price to switch from qualitative analysis to quantitative results that can be cross compared and used as input for the next generation of astronomical solutions.

Acknowledgments

The author thanks L. Hinnov and F. Hilgen for helpful discussions and remarks that helped to improve this chapter. The support from ANR-AstroMeso is acknowledged.

References

Agassiz, L., 1840, *Études Sur Les Glaciers*. Neuchatel.

Auclair-Desrotour, P., Mathis, S., Laskar, J., and Leconte, J., 2018, Oceanic tides from Earth-like to ocean planets. *Astronomy & Astrophysics*, **615**: A23.

Berger, A., 1978, Long-term variations of caloric insolation resulting from the Earth's orbital elements. *Quaternary Research*, **9** (2), 139–167.

Berger, A., and Loutre, M., 1994, Astronomical forcing through geological time. *Special Publication of the International Association of Sedimentologists*, **19**: 15–24.

Berger, A., Loutre, M.F., and Laskar, J., 1992, Stability of the astronomical frequencies over the Earth's history for paleoclimate studies. *Science*, **255** (5044), 560–566.

Bosmans, J.H.C., Drijfhout, S.S., Tuenter, E., Hilgen, F.J., and Lourens, L.J., 2014, Response of the North African summer monsoon to precession and obliquity forcings in the EC-Earth GCM. *Climate Dynamics*, **44** (1–2), 279–297.

Boulila, S., Galbrun, B., Hinnov, L.A., and Collin, P.-Y., 2008, Orbital calibration of the Early Kimmeridgian (southeastern France): implications for geochronology and sequence stratigraphy. *Terra Nova*, **20** (6), 455–462.

Boulila, S., Galbrun, B., Laskar, J., and Paelike, H., 2012, A similar to 9 myr cycle in Cenozoic delta C-13 record and long-term orbital eccentricity modulation: is there a link? *Earth and Planetary Science Letters*, **317**: 273–281. WOS:000301616700027.

Boulila, S., Galbrun, B., Huret, E., Hinnov, L.A., Rouget, I., Gardin, S., et al., 2014, Astronomical calibration of the Toarcian

Stage: implications for sequence stratigraphy and duration of the early Toarcian OAE. *Earth and Planetary Science Letters*, **386**: 98–111.

Boulila, S., Vahlenkamp, M., De Vleeschouwer, D., Laskar, J., Yamamoto, Y., Pälike, H., et al., 2018, Towards a robust and consistent middle Eocene astronomical timescale. *Earth and Planetary Science Letters*, **486** (15), 94–107.

Boulila, S., Galbrun, B., Sadki, D., Gardin, S., and Bartolini, A., 2019, Constraints on the duration of the early Toarcian T-OAE and evidence for carbon-reservoir change from the High Atlas (Morocco). *Global and Planetary Change*, **175**: 113–128.

Bretagnon, P., 1974, Termes à longues périodes dans le système solaire. *Astronomy & Astrophysics*, **30**: 141–154. Cited By (since 1996): 42.

Charbonnier, G., Boulila, S., Spangenberg, J.E., Adatte, T., Follmi, K.B., and Laskar, J., 2018, Obliquity pacing of the hydrological cycle during the Oceanic Anoxic Event 2. *Earth and Planetary Science Letters*, **499**: 266–277. WOS:000444359800024.

Croll, J., 1875, *Climate and Time in Their Geological Relations: A Theory of Secular Changes of the Earth's Climate. D. Appleton.* Google-Books-ID: 4j8XAAAAYAAJ.

Dickey, J., Bender, P., Faller, J., Newhall, X., Ricklefs, R., Ries, J., et al., 1994, Lunar laser ranging – a continuing legacy of the Apollo program. *Science*, **265** (5171), 482–490.

Fang, Q., Wu, H., Hinnov, L.A., Jing, X., Wang, X., and Jiang, Q., 2015, Geologic evidence for chaotic behavior of the planets and its constraints on the third-order eustatic sequences at the end of the Late Paleozoic Ice Age. *Palaeogeography, Palaeoclimatology, Palaeoecology*, **440**: 848–859.

Fienga, A., Manche, H., Laskar, J., and Gastineau, M., 2008, INPOP06: a new numerical planetary ephemeris. *Astronomy & Astrophysics*, **477**: 315–327.

Fienga, A., Laskar, J., Morley, T., Manche, H., Kuchynka, P., Le Poncin-Lafitte, C., et al., 2009, INPOP08, a 4-D planetary ephemeris: from asteroid and time-scale computations to ESA Mars Express and Venus Express contributions. *Astronomy & Astrophysics*, **507**: 1675–1686.

Fienga, A., Laskar, J., Kuchynka, P., Manche, H., Desvignes, G., Gastineau, M., et al., 2011, The INPOP10a planetary ephemeris and its applications in fundamental physics. *Celestial Mechanics and Dynamical Astronomy*, **111**: 363–385.

Folkner, W., Williams, J., and Boggs, D., 2009, The planetary and lunar ephemeris de 421. *In IPN Progress Report*, pp. 1–34.

Fu, Y.N., and Laskar, J., 2019, Frequency analysis and representation of slowly diffusing planetary solutions. *Astronomy & Astrophysics*, **628**: A84.

Gambacorta, G., Menichetti, E., Trincianti, E., and Torricelli, S., 2018, Orbital control on cyclical primary productivity and benthic anoxia: astronomical tuning of the Telychian Stage (Early Silurian). *Palaeogeography, Palaeoclimatology, Palaeoecology*, **495**: 152–162.

Gerstenkorn, H., 1969, The earliest past of the earth-moon system. *Icarus*, **11**.

Gradstein, F.M., Ogg, J.G., and Smith, A.G., 2004, *A Geologic Time Scale 2004*. Cambridge University Press.

Gradstein, F., Ogg, J., Schmitz, K., and Ogg, G., 2012, *The Geologic Time Scale 2012*, **Vol. 2**. Elsevier.

Grippo, A., Fischer, A., Hinnov, L., Herbert, T., and Premoli Silva, I., 2004, Cyclostratigraphy and chronology of the Albian stage (Piobbico core, Italy). *Cyclostratigraphy: Approaches and Case Histories*, **81**: 57–81.

Hilgen, F.J., 2010, Astronomical dating in the 19th century. *Earth-Science Review*, **98** (1–2), 65–80.

Hilgen, F.J., Lourens, L.J., Van Dam, J.A., Beu, A.G., Boyes, A.F., Cooper, R.A., et al., 2012, The Neogene Period. *In* Gradstein, F.M., Schmitz, J.G.O.D., and Ogg, G.M. (eds), *The Geologic Time Scale*. Elsevier, Boston, 923–978.

Hinnov, L.A., 2018a, Astronomical metronome of geological consequence. *Proceedings of the National Academy of Sciences of the United States of America*, **115** (24), 6104–6106.

Hinnov, L.A., 2018b, Chapter 3 – Cyclostratigraphy and astrochronology in 2018. *In* Montenari, M. (ed), *Stratigraphy & Timescales*. Cyclostratigraphy and Astrochronology. *Academic Press*, **Vol. 3**: 1–80.

Hinnov, L.A., and Hilgen, F.J., 2012, Chapter 4 – Cyclostratigraphy and astrochronology. *In* Gradstein, F.M., Ogg, J.G., Schmitz, M.D., and Ogg, G.M. (eds), *The Geologic Time Scale*. Elsevier, Boston, 63–83.

Huang, C., 2018, Chapter two – Astronomical time scale for the Mesozoic. *In* Montenari, M. (ed), *Stratigraphy & Timescales*. Cyclostratigraphy and Astrochronology. *Academic Press*, **Vol. 3**: 81–150.

Huang, C., Hinnov, L., Fischer, A.G., Grippo, A., and Herbert, T., 2010, Astronomical tuning of the Aptian Stage from Italian reference sections. *Geology*, **38** (10), 899–902.

Ikeda, M., and Tada, R., 2014, A 70 million year astronomical time scale for the deep-sea bedded chert sequence (Inuyama, Japan): implications for Triassic-Jurassic geochronology. *Earth and Planetary Science Letters*, **399**: 30–43.

Kent, D.V., Olsen, P.E., Rasmussen, C., Lepre, C., Mundil, R., Irmis, R.B., et al., 2018, Empirical evidence for stability of the 405-kiloyear Jupiter-Venus eccentricity cycle over hundreds of millions of years. *Proceedings of the National Academy of Sciences of the United States of America*, **115** (24), 6153–6158.

Kinoshita, H., 1977, Theory of the rotation of the rigid earth. *Celestial Mechanics*, **15** (3), 277–326. Cited By (since 1996): 86.

Kuiper, K.F., Deino, A., Hilgen, F.J., Krijgsman, W., Renne, P.R., and Wijbrans, J.R., 2008, Synchronizing rock clocks of earth history. *Science*, 320.

Lagrange, J.-L., 1778, Recherches sur les équations séculaires des mouvements des nœuds et des inclinaisons des planètes. *In Mémoires de l'Académie des Sciences de Paris, année 1774, Œuvres Complètes*, **Vol. 6**, 635–709 pp.

Lagrange, J.-L., 1783, Théorie des variations séculaires des éléments des planètes, première partie. *In Nouveaux Mémoires de l'Académie des Sciences et Belles-Lettres de Berlin, Année 1781, Œuvres Complètes*, **Vol. 5**, 125–207 pp.

Lagrange, J.-L., 1784, Théorie des variations séculaires des éléments des planètes, seconde partie contenant la détermination de ces variations pour chacune des planètes principales. *In Nouveaux Mémoires de l'Académie des Sciences et Belles-Lettres de Berlin, Année 1782, Œuvres Complètes*, Vol. 5, 211–344 pp.

Lambeck, K., 1980, *The Earth's Variable Rotation: Geophysical Causes and Consequences*. Cambridge University Press.

Laplace, P.-S., 1775, Mémoire sur les solutions particulières des équations différentielles et sur les inégalités séculaires des planètes. *Mémoires de l'Académie royale des sciences de Paris, année 1772. Ie partie; 1775, Œuvres Complètes*, **Vol. 8**, 325–366 pp.

Laplace, P.-S., 1776, Sur le principe de la Gravitation Universelle, et sur les inégalités séculaires des planètes qui en dépendent. *Mémoires de l'Académie des Sciences de Paris, Savants étrangers, année 1773, t. VII, Œuvres Complètes*, **Vol. 8**, 201–275 pp.

Laplace, P.-S., 1812, *Théorie Analytique des Probabilités*. Courcier, Paris.

Laskar, J., 1986, Secular terms of classical planetary theories using the results of general theory. *Astronomy & Astrophysics*, **157**: 59–70.

Laskar, J., 1988, Secular evolution of the solar system over 10 million years. *Astronomy & Astrophysics*, **198**: 341–362.

Laskar, J., 1989, A numerical experiment on the chaotic behaviour of the solar system. *Nature*, **338**: 237.

Laskar, J., 1990, The chaotic motion of the solar system – a numerical estimate of the size of the chaotic zones. *Icarus*, **88**: 266–291.

Laskar, J., 1992, A few points on the stability of the solar system. *In* Ferraz-Mello, S. (ed), *Chaos, Resonance, and Collective Dynamical Phenomena in the Solar System: Proceedings of the 152nd Symposium of the International Astronomical Union held in Angra dos Reis, Brazil.* 15–19 July, 1991. Dordrecht: Kluwer Academic Publishers, p. 1–16.

Laskar, J., 1999, The limits of earth orbital calculations for geological time-scale use. *Philosophical Transactions of the Royal Society of London, Series A*, **357**: 1735.

Laskar, J., 2013, Is the solar system stable? *In* Duplantier, B., Nonnenmacher, S., and Rivasseau, V. (eds), Chaos: Progress in Mathematical Physics. Springer Basel, pp. 239–270.

Laskar, J., Quinn, T., and Tremaine, S., 1992, Confirmation of resonant structure in the solar system. *Icarus*, **95**: 148–152.

Laskar, J., Joutel, F., and Boudin, F., 1993, Orbital, precessional, and insolation quantities for the earth from −20 MYR to +10 MYR. *Astronomy & Astrophysics*, **270**: 522–533.

Laskar, J., Robutel, P., Joutel, F., Gastineau, M., Correia, A.C.M., and Levrard, B., 2004, A long-term numerical solution for the insolation quantities of the earth. *Astronomy & Astrophysics*, **428**: 261–285.

Laskar, J., Fienga, A., Gastineau, M., and Manche, H., 2011a, La2010: a new orbital solution for the long-term motion of the earth. *Astronomy & Astrophysics*, **532**: A89.

Laskar, J., Gastineau, M., Delisle, J., Farrés, A., and Fienga, A., 2011b, Strong chaos induced by close encounters with Ceres and Vesta. *Astronomy & Astrophysics*, **532**: L4.

Le Verrier, U.J.J., 1840, Sur les variations séculaires des éléments elliptiques des sept planètes principales: Mercure, Vénus, la Terre, Mars, Jupiter, Saturne et Uranus. *Journal des Mathématiques Pures et Appliquées, 1ère Série*, **5**: 220–254.

Le Verrier, U.J.J., 1841, Mémoire sur les inégalités séculaires des planètes. *Additions à la Connaissance des Temps Pour l'an 1844*. Paris, Bachelier. pp. 28–110.

Le Verrier, U.J.J., 1856, Recherches astronomiques: (suite). *Annales de L'Observatoire de Paris*, **2**.

Levrard, B., and Laskar, J., 2003, Climate friction and the earth's obliquity. *Geophysical Journal International*, **154**: 970–990.

Lourens, L.J., Wehausen, R., and Brumsack, H.J., 2001, Geological constraints on tidal dissipation and dynamical ellipticity of the Earth over the past three million years. *Nature*, **409** (6823), 1029–1033.

Lourens, L.J., Hilgen, F.J., Shackleton, N.J., Laskar, J., and Wilson, D.S., 2004, The Neogene Period. *In* Gradstein, F.M., Ogg, J.G., and Smith, A. G. (eds), *The Geologic Time Scale.* chapter 21. Cambridge: Cambridge University Press, p. 409–440.

Ma, C., Meyers, S.R., and Sageman, B.B., 2017, Theory of chaotic orbital variations confirmed by Cretaceous geological evidence. *Nature*, **542** (7642), 468–470.

Ma, C., Meyers, S.R., and Sageman, B.B., 2019, Testing Late Cretaceous astronomical solutions in a 15 million year astrochronologic record from North America. *Earth and Planetary Science Letters*, **513**: 1–11.

Meyers, S.R., and Malinverno, A., 2018, Proterozoic Milankovitch cycles and the history of the solar system. *Proceedings of the National Academy of Sciences of the United States of America*, **115** (25), 6363–6368.

Milankovitch, M., 1941, *Kanon der Erdbestrahlung und seine Anwendung auf das Eiszeitenproblem. Spec. Acad. R. Serbe*, Belgrade.

Mitrovica, J.X., Forte, A.M., and Pan, R., 1997, Glaciation-induced variations in the Earth's precession frequency, obliquity and insolation over the last 2.6 Ma. *Geophysical Journal International*, **128** (2), 270–284.

Morrow, E., Mitrovica, J.X., Forte, A.M., Glišović, P., and Huybers, P., 2012, An enigma in estimates of the Earth's dynamic ellipticity. *Geophysical Journal International*, **191**: 1129–1134.

Néron De Surgy, O., and Laskar, J., 1997, On the long term evolution of the spin of the earth. *Astronomy & Astrophysics*, **318** (3), 975–989.

Olsen, P., 1986, A 40-million-year lake record of Early Mesozoic orbital climatic forcing. *Science*, **234** (4778), 842–848.

Olsen, P., Laskar J., Kent D.V., Kinney, S., Reynolds, D., Sha, J., et al., 2019, Mapping solar system chaos with the geological orrery. *Proceedings of the National Academy of Sciences of the United States of America*, **116**.

Olsen, P.E., and Kent, D.V., 1999, Long-period Milankovitch cycles from the Late Triassic and Early Jurassic of eastern North America and their implications for the calibration of the Early Mesozoic time-scale and the long-term behaviour of the planets. *Philosophical Transactions of the Royal Society A*, **357** (1757), 1761–1786.

Paillard, D., 1998, The timing of Pleistocene glaciations from a simple multiple-state climate model. *Nature*, **391** (6665), 378–381.

Paillard, D., 2001, Glacial cycles: toward a new paradigm. *Reviews of Geophysics*, **39** (3), 325–346.

Pälike, H., and Shackleton, N.J., 2000, Constraints on astronomical parameters from the geological record for the last 25 Myr. *Earth and Planetary Science Letters*, **182** (1), 1–14.

Pälike, H., Shackleton, N.J., and Röhl, U., 2001, Astronomical forcing in Late Eocene marine sediments. *Earth and Planetary Science Letters*, **193** (3), 589–602.

Pälike, H., Laskar, J., and Shackleton, N.J., 2004, Geologic constraints on the chaotic diffusion of the solar system. *Geology*, **32** (11), 929–932.

Pilgrim, L., 1904, Versuch einer rechnerischen behandlung des eiszeitenproblems. *Jahreshefte fur Vaterlandische Naturkunde in Wurttemberg*, 60 pp.

Quinn, T.R., Tremaine, S., and Duncan, M., 1991, A three million year integration of the earth's orbit. *The Astronomical Journal*, **101**: 2287–2305.

Shackleton, N.J., Hall, M.A., Raffi, I., Tauxe, L., and Zachos, J., 2000, Astronomical calibration age for the Oligocene-Miocene boundary. *Geology*, **28** (5), 447–450.

Spalding, C., Fischer, W.W., and Laughlin, G., 2018, An orbital window into the ancient sun's mass. *The Astrophysical Journal*, **869** (1), L19.

Stockwell, J.N., 1873, Memoir on the Secular Variations of the Elements of the Eight Principal Planets. *Smithsonian Contributions to Knowledge*, **Vol. 18**.

Viswanathan, V., Fienga, A., Minazzoli, O., Bernus, L., Laskar, J., and Gastineau, M., 2018, The new lunar ephemeris INPOP17a and its application to fundamental physics. *Monthly Notices of the Royal Astronomical Society*, **476**: 1877–1888.

Walker, J.C.G., and Zahnle, K.J., 1986, Lunar nodal tide and distance to the Moon during the Precambrian. *Nature*, **320** (6063), 600–602.

Webb, D.J., 1980, Tides and tidal friction in a hemispherical ocean centred at the equator. *Geophysical Journal International*, **61**: 573–600.

Webb, D.J., 1982, Tides and the evolution of the earth-moon system. *Geophysical Journal International*, **70**: 261–271.

Westerhold, T., Röhl, U., and Laskar, J., 2012, Time scale controversy: accurate orbital calibration of the early Paleogene. *Geochemistry, Geophysics, Geosystems*, **13** (6), Q06015.

Westerhold, T., Röhl, U., Pälike, H., Wilkens, R., Wilson, P.A., and Acton, G., 2014, Orbitally tuned timescale and astronomical forcing in the middle Eocene to early Oligocene. *Climate of the Past*, **10** (3), 955–973.

Westerhold, T., Röhl, U., Frederichs, T., Bohaty, S.M., and Zachos, J.C., 2015, Astronomical calibration of the geological timescale: closing the middle Eocene gap. *Climate of the Past Discussions*, **11** (3), 1665–1699.

Westerhold, T., Röhl, U., Frederichs, T., Agnini, C., Raffi, I., Zachos, J.C., et al., 2017, Astronomical calibration of the Ypresian time scale: implications for seafloor spreading rates and the chaotic behaviour of the solar system? *Climate of the Past Discussions*, **2017**: 1–34.

Williams, G.E., 2000, Geological constraints on the Precambrian history of Earth's rotation and the Moon's orbit. *Reviews of Geophysics*, **38** (1), 37.

Wu, H., Zhang, S., Hinnov, L.A., Jiang, G., Feng, Q., Li, H., et al., 2013a, Time-calibrated Milankovitch cycles for the late Permian. *Nature Communications*, **4**.

Wu, H., Zhang, S., Jiang, G., Hinnov, L., Yang, T., Li, H., et al., 2013b, Astrochronology of the Early Turonian–Early Campanian terrestrial succession in the Songliao Basin, northeastern China and its implication for long-period behavior of the Solar System. *Palaeogeography, Palaeoclimatology, Palaeoecology*, **385**: 55–70.

Zachos, J.C., Shackleton, N.J., Revenaugh, J.S., Pälike, H., and Flower, B.P., 2001, Climate response to orbital forcing across the Oligocene-Miocene boundary. *Science*, **292** (5515), 274–278.

Zeebe, R.E., and Lourens, L.J., 2019, Solar system chaos and the paleocene-eocene boundary age constrained by geology and astronomy. *Science*, **365** (6456), 926–929.

Zeeden, C., Hilgen, F.J., Hüsing, S.K., and Lourens, L.L., 2014, The Miocene astronomical time scale 9–12 Ma: new constraints on tidal dissipation and their implications for paleoclimatic investigations. *Paleoceanography*, **29** (4), 296–307.

J.G. Ogg

Chapter 5

Geomagnetic Polarity Time Scale

Chapter outline

Abstract

The time scale for marine magnetic anomalies for the Late Cretaceous through Neogene (C-sequence) and Middle Jurassic through Early Cretaceous (M-sequence with deep-tow extension) has been calibrated through magnetostratigraphic studies to biostratigraphy, cycle-stratigraphy and selected radioisotope-dated levels. The majority of the geomagnetic polarity time scale for the past 160 Myr is constructed by fitting spreading rate models to these constraints. The status of the geomagnetic polarity time scale for each geologic period is summarized in the appropriate period chapters.

This chapter incorporates some of the discussions from the *Geomagnetic Polarity Time Scale* chapters in GTS2004 and GTS2012 by J.G. Ogg and A.G. Smith. The derivation of age-models for the C-sequence and the M-sequence of polarity chrons are new to GTS2020.

5.1 Principles

5.1.1 Magnetic field reversals and magnetostratigraphy

The principal goals of magnetostratigraphy are to document and calibrate the global geomagnetic polarity sequence in stratified rocks, to apply this geomagnetic polarity time scale for high-resolution correlation of marine magnetic anomalies, and to utilize the calibrated reference pattern of polarity changes to correlate polarity zones among other sections.

Extensive reviews on general paleomagnetism are by Merrill et al. (1996), McElhinny and McFadden (2000), and Tauxe (2010), among others. Magnetostratigraphy concepts, procedures, and selected applications are summarized by Harland et al. (1990), Opdyke and Channell (1996), and by Langereis et al. (2010). The synthesis by Langereis et al. (2010) was intended to become a chapter of the International Stratigraphic Code, which currently consists mainly of definitions for magnetic polarity units (International Subcommission on Stratigraphic Classification, 1979).

Ancient geomagnetic fields can be recorded by preferential orientation of iron-bearing grains when a sedimentary rock was deposited or when such grains in igneous rocks cooled through their Curie points. In practice, secondary magnetizations are acquired by sediments or lavas upon compaction, lithification, diagenesis, long-term exposure to other magnetic field directions, and other processes. Therefore various methods of demagnetization are

Geologic Time Scale 2020. DOI: https://doi.org/10.1016/B978-0-12-824360-2.00005-X

required to separate the later secondary components from the primary magnetization directions. In addition to magnetostratigraphy, the magnetic imprints are useful for determining past paleomagnetic directions for deducing tectonic motions.

The Earth's magnetic field continuously varies in its intensity and direction. Fluid motions of conducting iron-rich molten material in the Earth's outer core generate a magnetic field. About 90% of the observed field at the surface approximates a global dipole field. This dipole component has an irregular drift or secular variation about the Earth's rotational axis; but a time-averaged field spanning about 10,000 years roughly coincides with the Earth's rotational poles.

For reasons that are still not well understood, at irregular times the polarity of the dipole magnetic field can reverse. To a first approximation, geomagnetic reversals reflect a random process with intervals between successive reversals being independent of previous polarity changes. The durations of polarity intervals vary from as little as 30 kyr to several tens of millions of years. The average frequency of geomagnetic reversals during the Cenozoic is about 2 or 3 per million years; and the most recent reversal was about 770,000 years ago. There are intervals, such as the mid-Cretaceous, during which the geomagnetic field did not undergo a reversal for up to 40 Myr.

By convention in paleomagnetism, the present-day polarity is *normal*: lines of magnetic force at the Earth's surface are directed in toward the North magnetic pole and the N-seeking pole of a compass needle points North (its *declination*) (Fig. 5.1). The *inclination* of the magnetic field dips progressively steeper downward with increasing latitude in the northern hemisphere and dips upward in the southern hemisphere. When the polarity is *reversed*, the lines of force are directed in the opposite direction and a compass needle would point to the South. The sign of the inclination is then reversed in both hemispheres.

Reversals of the polarity of the main geomagnetic dipole field are geologically rapid events, typically less than 5000 years in duration, which occur at random intervals. *Polarity chrons* are intervals of geologic time having a predominant (normal or reversed) magnetic field polarity delimited by reversals (International Subcommission on Stratigraphic Classification, 1979). Some publications refer to a "polarity chron" as merely a "chron." Although "chron" in the International Stratigraphic Guide designates a formal subdivision of a geologic stage (e.g., "Mariae Chron" within the Oxfordian stage), it is usually clear from the context whether a chron refers to a magnetic polarity interval. Possible ambiguities can be avoided by retaining the prefix "polarity."

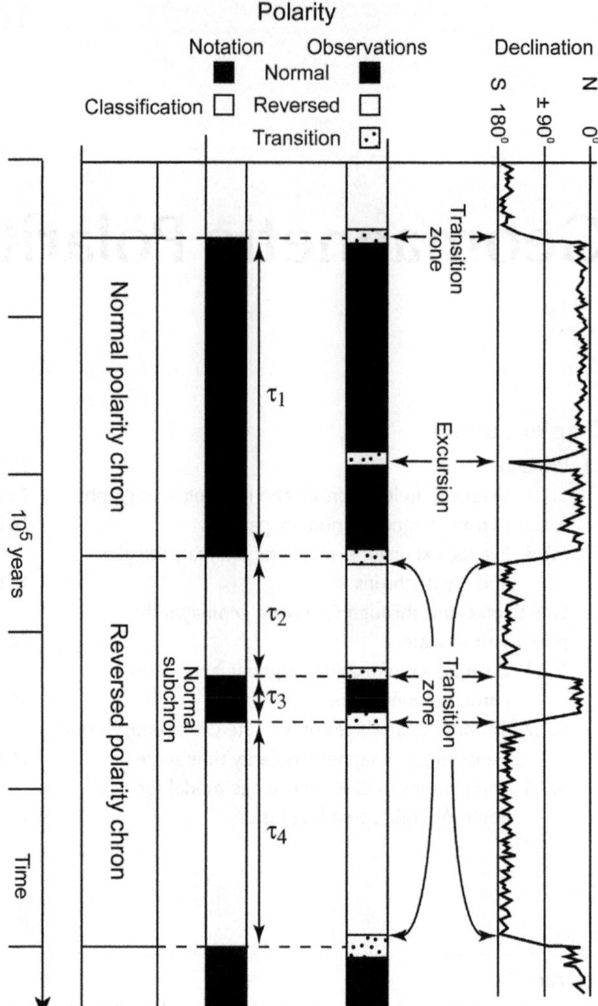

FIGURE 5.1 Polarity chrons, polarity subchrons, transition zones, and excursions. From Harland et al. (1982, their Fig. 4.1).

A *polarity zone* is the corresponding interval in a stratigraphic section deposited during the polarity chron. The zone or chron is called "normal polarity" if the geomagnetic field orientation is similar to the present dipole polarity, and "reversed polarity" if it is opposite in orientation (Fig. 5.1).

Establishing a stable nomenclature for a succession of polarity intervals, especially one that includes events of short durations, is a challenging problem (e.g., Langereis et al., 2010). In the course of paleomagnetic research, each new discovery of a short polarity interval changes the local polarity structure. This situation is schematically shown in Fig. 5.1, where prior to the discovery of the short polarity interval labeled T_3, only one reversed interval would have been recognized spanning the intervals T_2, T_3, and T_4. Therefore in naming or numbering polarity intervals for stratigraphic purposes, a hierarchical set of names is needed that does not change drastically

TABLE 5.1 Suggested hierarchical scheme for magnetostratigraphic (rock) and polarity chron (time) units.

Magnetostratigraphic polarity units (rock record)	Geochronologic unit (time equivalent)	Approximate duration (years)
Polarity megazone	Megachron	10^8-10^9
Polarity superzone	Superchron	10^7-10^8
Polarity zone	Chron	10^6-10^7
Polarity subzone	Subchron	10^5-10^6
Polarity cryptozone	Cryptochron	$<3\times10^4$

Source: Modified from McElhinny and McFadden (2000, their Table 4.3).

with the discovery of additional short polarity intervals. Numbering of polarity intervals in the sequence of their occurrence does not provide such a system, and the current "C-sequence" and "M-sequence of marine magnetic anomalies have several such inconsistencies (e.g., anomaly C14 was removed when it was discovered to be an artifact of miscorrelations).

A hierarchical system for grouping polarity intervals together for successively longer time intervals (International Subcommission on Stratigraphic Classification, 1979) was modified by McElhinny and McFadden (2000) and further modified here in Table 5.1.

The relative timing (position) of an event (level) within a polarity chron (zone) is "defined as the relative position in time or distance between the younger and older chronal boundaries" (system of Hallam et al., 1985, p. 126). In this proportional stratigraphic convention, the placement of the Danian/Selandian boundary occurs at C27n.3, indicating that this level/event is 30% up within of normal-polarity zone/chron C27n. For clarity, the decimal fraction is the best placed after the polarity chron name enclosed in parentheses (Cande and Kent, 1992a); but some chapters in GTS2012 omit these parentheses. [*Note:* Cande and Kent (1992a) *had also recommended an inverted-stratigraphic placement; in which, C27n(0.3) in their notation indicated that 30% of reversed-polarity Chron C27n followed the event. Their suggested system mirrors the convention of measuring geologic time and the numbering magnetic anomalies backwards from the present. GTS2012 uses the stratigraphic-placement system, rather than this inverted-stratigraphic option.*]

Because polarity reversals are potentially recorded simultaneously in rocks all over the world, these magnetostratigraphic divisions, unlike lithostratigraphic and biostratigraphic divisions, are not time transgressive. Thus the pattern of polarity reversals provides a unique global "bar code" for correlating polarity reversals recorded in rock strata, a usage first suggested by Khramov (1958). Therefore magnetostratigraphy enables the correlation of rock strata among diverse depositional and faunal realms and the assignment of geologic ages to anomalies of marine magnetic intensities. Considering that the polarity reversal transition spans only about 5000 years, then paleomagnetic correlation is the most precise method available for global correlation in virtually all stratified rocks of all ages, but only directly at the recorded reversal boundary.

The geomagnetic polarity time scale is a composite reference pattern constructed from paleomagnetic analyses of various sedimentary sections having detailed biostratigraphy and by correlations to marine magnetic anomaly patterns. It is essential to have some biostratigraphic constraints on the polarity zone pattern resolved from any given section in order to propose a nonambiguous correlation to the reference geomagnetic polarity time scale.

5.1.2 Marine magnetic anomaly patterns

When magma cools beneath oceanic spreading ridges, its iron-rich minerals acquire the direction of the ambient field at that time. Marine magnetic anomalies are observed by shipboard magnetometers as an enhanced magnetic field intensity over crust that cooled during normal polarity and as a partially canceled magnetic field intensity over crust formed during reversed polarity. The correlation of the linear patterns of these marine magnetic anomalies was the initial evidence for the theory of seafloor spreading, which was later verified by drilling and dating of the oceanic basalt crust.

For Middle Jurassic to Present, the pattern and nomenclature of preserved ocean-floor magnetic anomalies with their calibrations to biostratigraphy serve as a template against which the polarity reversals in stratigraphic sections, either on land or in deepsea or other cores, can be identified.

5.1.3 Events, excursions, magnetic anomaly wiggles, and cryptochrons

Even when the dipole field has a steady polarity, it undergoes swings in direction with typical amplitudes of 15 degrees and periods of 10^2-10^4 years. This *geomagnetic secular variation* is generally too small to be mistaken for the 180-degree changes in field direction that characterize polarity reversals.

Occasionally, the field appears to undergo an *event* characterized by a change in direction that exceeds 45 degrees in declination or even a brief *excursion* (ca. 2–5 kyr) interval of apparent opposite polarity. Excursions

TABLE 5.2 Named geomagnetic excursions and major polarity chrons of Quaternary.

Geomagnetic Excursions during Quaternary Period

Main Polarity Chrons	Excursions	Base (Ma)		Comments
Matuyama (C1r)		0.000		
	Tianchi	0.010		Tianchi Volcano (NE China) with revised dating as 10.2 ± 1 ka.
	Hilina Pali?	0.017	Dotted	Hilina Pali, Hawaii, has lava flows with low paleointensity (discovery site); but the best dating is Changbaishan Volcano, northeastern China (reviewed in Singer, 2014); but verification is uncertain.
	Rockall	0.026		Excursion at c. 26 ka (MIS3) in Core MD04-2822 from the Rockall Trough (Channell et al., 2016; as reviewed in Channell et al., 2020).
	Mono Lake	0.032		Initially dated by C14 at Mono Lake, eastern California; with improved dating by cosmogenic methods in ice cores, astronomical cycles in ODP cores, and Ar–Ar in Auckland Volcanic Field, New Zealand (reviewed by Laj and Channell, 2007, and Singer, 2014). 32 ± 2 ka.
	Laschamp	0.041		Best documented of the Brunhes Chron excursions. Discovered 1967 in lava flow at Puy de Laschamp, Massif Central, France (reviewed by Laj and Channell, 2007), and dated by Be-10 flux peak in NorthGRIP ice core, Greenland, and at 41.1 ± 0.35 ka by U–Th in Missouri speleothem.
	Skalamaelifell	0.095		First documented in lavas in SW Iceland. Dated as 95 ± 3 ka in stalagmite from southern China.
	Post-Blake	0.104		Documented at several ODP sites, lake sediments, and other places; but an official "discovery site" name has yet to be attached. Near Marine Isotope Stage 5.2/5.3 boundary. Dated as 104 ± 1 ka in stalagmite from southern China.
	Blake	0.114		Discovered 1969 in piston cores from Blake Outer Rise (Central Atlantic, east of Florida) ODP sites near MIS5d/53 boundary, Main excursion lasted 4.5 kyr (116.5–112.0 ka) according to speleothem in northern Spain; but low geomagnetic intensity persisted for more than 20 kyr (summarized in Singer, 2014).
	Iceland Basin	0.188		The most widely recorded excursion in sediments (Channell et al., 2020). Named after documentation in Iceland Basin ODP Sites at Marine Isotope Stage 6/7 boundary.
	Pringle Falls?	0.212	Dotted	Named after discovery in lacustrine deposits at Pringle Falls, Oregon, United States, with dating of 212 ± 13 ka from Albuquerque Volcanoes, New Mexico (Singer, 2014). Exact age remains uncertain, and "the possibility remains that there are two (or more) magnetic excursions in the 240–210 ka interval" (Channell et al., 2020).
	Portuguese Orphan	0.286		Named after discovery in core from Portuguese margin with age during interglacial MIS9a.
	Bermuda	0.412		Named after its discovery in ODP Site 1063 on Bermuda Rise with age during MIS11. Dated as 411.5 ± 3 ka in Saudi Arabia volcanic field and 417 ± 8 ka in northern Italian speleothem
	Orphan Knoll	0.495		Recorded in IODP site 1302 on Orphan Knoll within MIS13a (Channell, 2017).
	Big Lost	0.540		Big Lost names after a reversed magnetized flow in Idaho, United States and also seen in ODP cores within MIS14.
	West Eifel suite	0.560		West Eifel volcanic field in western Germany records five geomagnetic excursions between 0.53 and 0.73 ka (dates from Singer, 2014). "The interpretations of Singer et al. (2008b) and Singer (2014) imply that a significant proportion of the 530–730 ka interval was characterized by anomalous magnetic field behavior during which six excursions occurred" (Channell et al., 2020).
	La Palma	0.580		Discovered in lavas at Los Tilos Barranca (La Palma), and verified in IODP cores within MIS15b/c.
	Osaka Bay	0.680		Excursion in Osaka Bay in Marine Isotope Stage 17.
Brunhes (C1n) base		0.773		Mean age of 773 ± 2 ka from transitional lava flows on Maui (Hawaii) and La Palma (Singer, 2014; Channell et al., 2020). Shortly after peak interglacial of MIS19.
	M-B Precursor	0.794		A drop in geomagnetic intensity close to the MIS19/20 preceded the main polarity reversal of Matuyama–Brunhes boundary.
	Kamikatsura	0.867		Named after excursion in Kamikatsura Tuff (Osaka Group, Japan) excursion with Ar–Ar ages from Tahiti and Hawaii sites (Singer, 2014).
	Santa Rosa	0.932		Santa Rosa I rhyolite dome in New Mexico is the discovery location; with its Ar–Ar age (927 ± 2 ka) agreeing with MIS24/25 boundary (932 ka) in ODP sites (summarized in Singer, 2014).

(Continued)

TABLE 5.2 (Continued)

Geomagnetic Excursions during Quaternary Period				
Main Polarity Chrons	**Excursions**	**Base (Ma)**		**Comments**
Upper Matuyama (C1r.1r) base		0.990		990 ± 4 ka; and base of MIS27.
	Intra-Jaramillo	1.048		A brief excursion during Marine Isotope Stage 30 in Chinese loess and ODP sites in MIS31/30 transition.
Jaramillo (C1r.1n) base		1.070		1070 ± 3 ka (MIS31; and dated lavas in Tahiti; Channell et al., 2020).
	Punaruu	1.115		Lavas in Punaruu valley of Tahiti record this excursion between Cobb Mtn and Jaramillo subchrons. Occurs in MIS34 (1.115 Ma), but Ar–Ar dating is slightly older at 1126 ± 2 ka.
C1r.2r		1.180		End of the Cobb Mountain excursion in ODP/IODP records is approximately 1178 ka (reviewed in Channell et al., 2020).
Cobb Mountain (C1r.2n) base		1.215		Excursion named after Alder Creek rhyolite at Cobb Mountain (California) is near MIS36/37 boundary with onset in ODP/IODP cores at 1215 ka.
	Bjorn	1.255		Bjorn excursion (named after Bjorn Drift ODP Site 984 in North Atlantic) is dated by astronomical cycles.
	Gardar	1.460		Gardar excursion (named after Gardar Drift ODP Site 983) is in MIS49. Age estimates vary from 1455 to 1472–1480 ka.
	Gilsa	1.584		Gilsa excursion (named after river in Iceland) is near MIS54/55 transition.
C1r.3r		1.770		In MIS63. Astrochronology at ODP Site 677 (1.77 Ma) is consistent with that of Italian land sections (1.79Ma).
Olduvai (C2n) base		1.925		Near LAD of *Discoaster brouweri* and MIS71/72 transition. "Site U1308 result implies an age for the base Olduvai, on the LR04 Time Scale, of 1925 ka" (review by Channell et al., 2020, of difficulties dating the onset).
	Huckleberry Ridge	2.078		Huckleberry Ridge Tuff from the Yellowstone Caldera was one of the largest volcanic eruptions during the Cenozoic, and records a transitional geomagnetic direction. It seems to be the last episode of three main excursions (Reunion, Feni, Huckleberry Ridge) during the 150 kyr interval from 2.20 to 2.07 Ma (Singer, 2014).
C2r.1n–C2r.1r	Feni (Réunion)	2.125		C2r.1n was formerly named Reunion; but the type location was discovered to be a brief excursion before the main Normal; therefore Singer (2014) recommended Feni be used after the documented extent and age-control at Feni Drift ODP Site 981 in North Atlantic. Best documented at Feni Drift ODP Site 981 as spanning c. 2.140–2.116 Ma (25 kyr).
	Réunion?	2.200	Dotted	Lower Réunion excursion may be at 2200 ± 10 ka (Singer, 2014).
	Halawa	2.445		Polarity chron "C2r.2n" (anomaly "X" of Heirtzler et al., 1968) was suggested as a "lower Reunion" event, but its reality was questioned by Cande-Kent and omitted from their final scale. Excursion named after Halawa, Oahu, Hawaii by Singer (2014); and his summarized Ar–Ar age is used here.
Lower Matuyama (C2r.2r) base		2.595		MIS104 at 2595 ka; and an Ar/Ar date from Kenya of 2606 ± 6 ka.
	Porcupine?	2.737	Dotted	IODP site near Porcupine Abyssal Plain has an excursion within the MIS G6/G7 transition but has not yet been documented elsewhere.

Source: Modified from syntheses by Singer (2014) and by Channell et al. (2020). These are partially diagrammed in Fig. 30.2 in Gibbard and Head (2020, Ch. 20, The Quaternary Period, this book), although a few names and dates are slightly different in the Channell et al. (2020) compilation.

offer the potential of providing very precise, but rarely observable, stratigraphic markers. Approximately two dozen excursions have been identified and named in the sediment and volcanic records spanning the past 2.5 Myr (e.g., Langereis et al., 1997; Singer, 2014; Channell et al., 2020) (Table 5.2; Fig. 30.2). Therefore similar excursions are probably a common feature of the ancient geomagnetic field through the Phanerozoic.

Detailed studies of magnetic anomalies from fast spreading ridges show several tiny "wiggles" that clearly reflect changes in the paleomagnetic field (Cande and Kent, 1992a, 1992b). Cande and Kent (1992b) suggest that marine anomalies with a time span of <30 kyr should be named *cryptochrons*, whereas anomalies with a time span of >30 kyr are well characterized and are probably true polarity reversals. However, the distinction between "chron," "subchron," or "cryptochron" varies significantly among workers, including the current chron/subchron designations for subdivisions of the Cenozoic C-sequence geomagnetic polarity time scale (e.g., Cande and Kent, 1992a). Some of the larger amplitude marine magnetic anomaly subchrons have been independently demonstrated to be short-lived field reversals from magnetostratigraphic studies. For example, the ~40-kyr subchron C5r.2r-1 has been verified within chron C5r.2r (Abdul Aziz et al., 2003).

5.2 Late Cretaceous through Cenozoic geomagnetic polarity time scale

One of the major achievements of stratigraphy and chronostratigraphy in the past three decades has been the compilation and synthesis of an ultrahigh-resolution cyclo-bio-geomagnetic time scale spanning the entire Cenozoic and latest Cretaceous. This achievement has been a collaboration between geophysicists unraveling the oceanic marine magnetic anomaly record and correlating each of these to polarity zones observed in sediments, geochemists applying improved radioisotopic dating methods and standardization among radioactive decay systems, paleontologists placing their datums relative to those polarity zones, astrophysicists developing progressively more advanced mathematical models of the solar system dynamics, and cyclostratigraphers interpreting and systematically merging these records into an astronomically tuned geomagnetic polarity time scale. Indeed, the assignment of most ages to Cenozoic stages is now based on the relative placement of their GSSPs or the working definitions relative to the astronomically tuned C-sequence.

5.2.1 C-sequence of marine magnetic anomalies and chron nomenclature

The four youngest polarity chrons—Brunhes, Matuyama, Gauss, and Gilbert—that span the past ~6 Myr were named after important scientists in the field of geomagnetism. The existence of these polarity chrons was established largely through dating lava flows on land. Subchrons within these intervals were named after the locality of their discovery—for example, Olduvai normal-polarity subchron after the Olduvai Gorge (eastern Africa).

After the discovery of ocean-floor spreading, the marine magnetic anomaly sequence of a long traverse in the South Atlantic was taken as a marine standard for the polarity pattern spanning the latest Cretaceous through Cenozoic. The anomalies of this Cenozoic or "C-sequence" were numbered from 1 to 34 (oldest). Refinements of this C-sequence led to insertion of many additional anomalies with a complex letter number system, and the deletion of anomaly "14."

The corresponding pair of polarity chrons (time) and polarity zones (stratigraphy) is prefaced by the letter C—for Cenozoic—before the named magnetic anomaly, with a suffix *n* denoting the *younger* normal polarity interval or *r* denoting the *older* reversed polarity interval, for instance Chron C15r (e.g., Tauxe et al., 1984; Cande and Kent, 1992a). When a major numbered polarity chron was further subdivided, the resulting subchrons are denoted by a suffix of a corresponding numbered polarity chron. For example, "C8n.2n" is the second oldest normal-polarity subchron comprising normal-polarity Chron C8n. For the younger part of the time scale (Pliocene–Pleistocene), the traditional names are often used to refer to the chrons and subchrons (e.g., Brunhes = C1n, Matuyama = C1r, and Jaramillo subchron = C1r.1n) sequence of marine magnetic anomalies.

Cryptochrons are designated by appending to a chron or subchron name the designation of "-1" (youngest) and "-2" (next older). For example, one of the younger cryptochron, the Emperor cryptochron, is in Chron C1n and designated "C1n-1."

5.2.2 Calibration and ages of the Late Cretaceous through Cenozoic geomagnetic polarity time scale

A composite C-sequence magnetic anomaly pattern for the latest Cretaceous and Cenozoic was assembled by Cande and Kent (1992a, 1995) from a composite of South Atlantic magnetic survey profiles enhanced by additional high-resolution profiles from selected Pacific surveys. Their numerical age models, "CK92" followed by "CK95," for this synthetic magnetic anomaly pattern were calculated by applying a cubic spline fit to selected radioisotopic age controls (Cande and Kent, 1992a, 1995) (Fig. 5.2). The spline fit method yielded an age model for the scale of "kilometers in the South Atlantic marine magnetic profile," and the numerical ages of the limits of each polarity chron were derived from their assigned placement on this magnetic anomaly distance scale. In a revolutionary compilation, Berggren et al. (1995) calibrated a vast array of biostratigraphic and chronostratigraphic events to magnetostratigraphy and then derived the ages of datums and working versions of Cenozoic stage boundaries from this "CK95" age model for the polarity chrons. Their detailed Cenozoic chronostratigraphic time scale has been progressively enhanced, and the C-sequence is still the main primary scale for assigning numerical ages to the majority of Cenozoic and latest Cretaceous stratigraphic and geochemical data.

Cyclostratigraphy analysis followed by astronomical tuning of biomagnetostratigraphy sections from ocean drilling sites and from exposed pelagic sediments in the Mediterranean and other regions has progressively yielded orbital cycle durations for nearly the entire C-sequence of polarity chrons.

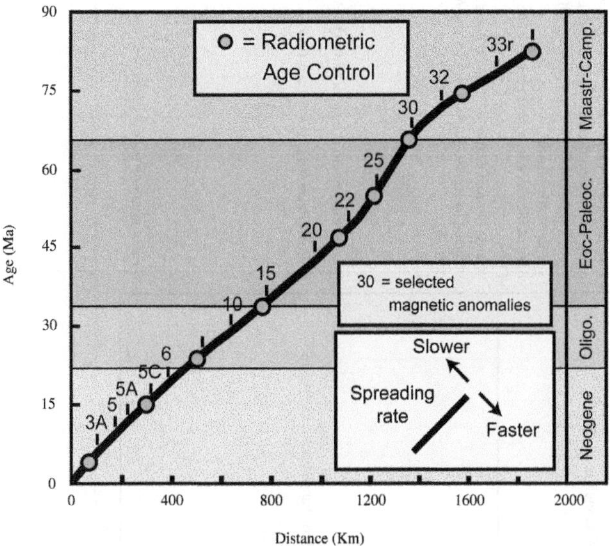

FIGURE 5.2 Age calibration of Cenozoic through Campanian C-sequence of marine magnetic anomalies as compiled by Cande and Kent (1992a). They had applied a spline of the radioisotopic dates on polarity chrons (magnetic anomalies) versus relative distance from the spreading axis of a synthetic flow profile for the South Atlantic.

For the GTS2004 age model for the C-sequence, the late Neogene portion (Chrons C1−C4r at c. 8.3 Ma) had incorporated astronomical tuning tied to the present (Lourens et al., 2004), and the earliest Paleogene portion had used cycle-scaled durations relative to a base-Cenozoic age of 65.5 Ma. Similar to the procedure of Cande and Kent (1992a), these segments had been joined by a spline fit to selected radioisotopic ages.

In GTS2012 the astronomical tuning of the Neogene polarity chrons had now extended through Chron C5Bn (14.9 Ma) in the Langhian Stage. An application of very long period Milankovitch cycles to the sediment record in ocean cores placed the base of the Neogene (base of Chron C6Cn.2n) at 23.03 Ma. The intervening Chrons C5C−C6Cn (16−23 Ma) had the same numerical ages as derived from the spline fit of GTS2004. The age model for the Paleogene polarity chrons (Vandenberghe et al., 2012) was in three segments: (1) astronomical cycle tuning from the base of the Miocene (set as 23.0 Ma) "downward" to the base of the Oligocene (polarity Chron C13r) by Pälike et al. (2006), (2) cycle tuning of durations "upward" from the base Cenozoic (set as 66.0 Ma) through early Eocene to Chron C23n, and (3) a bridge by interpolating a smoothed spreading rate spline applied to the seafloor marine magnetic anomaly record for middle through late Eocene chrons C22n−C13r. In the GTS2016 enhancement (Ogg et al., 2016), that temporary spline bridge for interpolating within the Eocene was replaced by astronomical cycle tuning of the middle and late Eocene from a suite of ocean drilling cores (Westerhold et al., 2014, 2015). In contrast to the GTS2004 spline method the spline fit (and uncertainties on derived ages, including Cenozoic stages) has partially incorporated the statistics on uncertainties for the individual marine magnetic anomalies (Table 4 of Cande and Kent, 1992a); and these values are included in the C-sequence summary compilation of Table 5.3. In the case of short-duration chrons in which direct cycle scaling was inadequate to delimit the boundaries, the combined cycle durations for pairs of chrons, rather than single chrons, were used for the composite scale, and those brief chrons were assigned durations as derived from the GTS2004 spline fit to Cande and Kent's (1992a) marine magnetic anomaly widths. Similar to the Cenozoic portion of the C-sequence, the late Cretaceous portion (Chrons C29r−C32r) in GTS2012/2016 was tuned by cyclostratigraphy studies in ocean drilling cores and outcrops of pelagic sediments relative to the base of the Cenozoic (e.g., Husson et al., 2011; Thibault et al., 2012). The suite of duration-per-chron and numerical age scaling is consistent with the few radioisotopic dates in this interval (Hicks et al., 1995, 1999; Hicks and Obradovich, 1995; *tabulated in Appendix 2 of this volume*).

Finally, in this GTS2020, the entire late Cretaceous through Cenozoic C-sequence has been astronomically tuned. In the synthesis by Heiko Pälicke (Table 5.3), intervals in the late Miocene (Chrons C4−C3A) and the late Oligocene through early Miocene (Chrons C7A−C5B) have been enhanced (Liebrand et al., 2016; Beddow et al, 2018; Kochhann et al., 2016; Drury et al., 2017), with only a c. 2-Myr interval during the late Aquitanian (C6AA−C6A) that still required interpolation. The Paleocene through earliest Eocene portion incorporates revised astronomical tuning (Dinarès-Turell et al., 2014, 2018; Francescone et al., 2019). The base of Chron C33r, which begins the C-sequence, has been radioisotopically dated and astronomically calibrated in cyclic lacustrine sediments in Songliao Basin of north China (Wang et al., 2016; Wu et al., 2020), thereby essentially completing the astronomical tuning of the entire C-sequence.

In general, the relative durations of polarity chrons derived from the composite of South Atlantic magnetic survey profiles (Cande and Kent, 1992a) have been verified by the suites of high-resolution cyclo-magnetostratigraphy, although there are significant differences for some of the shorter chrons. Curiously, in some intervals, the relative proportions of normal and reversed polarity according to the astronomical tuning of durations of polarity chrons in magnetostratigraphy studies are shifted from their proportions in the marine magnetic anomaly model. For example, the early Oligocene interval of Chrons C9n−C11r is projected as 60% reversed polarity according to the marine magnetic anomaly model, but reversed polarity actually comprises 65% of this interval according to the cycle-scaled magnetostratigraphy. The Paleocene interval of Chrons C24r−C29r is projected as 71% reversed polarity in the marine magnetic anomaly model but is observed to

TABLE 5.3 C-sequence marine magnetic anomaly distances and age model.

C-sequence marine magnetic anomaly distances and age calibration

Geologic Age	Age of base (Ma)		Polarity Chron	Distance (km) from South Atlantic spreading center (CK92) Old end	Width (km)	Statistics on uncertainties Table 4 of Cande and Kent (1992a, 1992b) Anomaly	Mean width	95% confidence interval (km)	% error	Orbital tuning Base (Ma)	Duration (Myr)	Source of astronomical tuning	Comments
NEOGENE HOLOCENE	**11.8 ka**			0.00						0.000			
PLEISTOCENE		C1	C1n (Brunhes)	12.14	*12.14*	In	13.43	*0.78*	*6.3*	0.773	*0.773*	No change from GTS2016	Base of Middle Pleistocene (Ionian) = base of Brunhes Chron.
Late (Tarantian)	**0.130**		C1r.1r (Matuyama)	15.37	*3.23*	Ir	15.66	*1.78*	*11.3*	0.990	*0.217*	Channell et al. (2020)	
Middle (Chibanian)	**0.773**		C1r.1n (Jaramillo)	16.39	*1.02*					1.070	*0.080*		
			C1r.2r							1.180	*0.110*		
			C1r.2n (Cobb Mountain)							1.215	*0.035*		Excursion named after Alder Creek rhyolite at Cobb Mountain (California) is near MIS36/37 boundary with onset in ODP/IODP cores at 1215 ka.
			C1r.3r	27.80	*11.41*					1.775	*0.560*	No change from GTS2016	
(Calabrian)	**1.80**	C2	C2n (Olduvai)	31.51	*3.71*	2	13.95	*0.58*	*4.1*	1.934	*0.159*	Channell et al. (2020)	Base of Calabrian is in lower part of Olduvai Chron.
			C2r.1r	35.04	*3.53*					2.116	*0.182*		
			C2r.1n (Feni)	35.57	*0.53*					2.140	*0.024*		Formerly named Reunion; but the type location was discovered to be a brief excursion prior to a more major normal-polarity event with extent and age-control documented at Feni Drift ODP Site 981 in North Atlantic.
Early (Gelasian)	**2.58**		C2r.2r (Matuyama)	41.75	*6.18*					2.595	*0.455*		Base of Pleistocene is near base of Matuyama Chron.
PLIOCENE		C2A	C2An.1n (Gauss)	49.44	*7.69*	2A-3n.1	28.81	*2.12*	*7.3*	3.032	*0.437*	No change from GTS2012/16	"Gauss Normal Chron" (C2An) contains two reversed intervals—Kaena (2An.1r) and Mammoth (2An.2r).
			C2An.1r (Keana)	50.70	*1.26*					3.116	*0.084*		
			C2An.2n	52.31	*1.61*					3.207	*0.091*		
			C2An.2r (Mammoth)	54.10	*1.79*					3.330	*0.123*		
Late (Piacenzian)	**3.60**		C2An.3n (Gauss)	58.03	*3.93*					3.596	*0.266*		Base of Piacenzian is base of Chron C2An.3n.
			C2Ar (Gilbert)	66.44	*8.41*					4.187	*0.591*		"Gilbert Reversed Chron" spans Chrons C2Ar–C3r.
		C3	C3n.1n (Cochiti)	68.23	*1.79*					4.300	*0.113*		
			C3n.1r	70.56	*2.33*					4.493	*0.193*		
			C3n.2n (Nunivak)	73.56	*3.00*	3n.2-3r	26.31	*3.52*	*13.3*	4.631	*0.138*		
			C3n.2r	76.76	*3.20*					4.799	*0.168*		
			C3n.3n (Sidufjall)	78.26	*1.50*					4.896	*0.097*		
			C3n.3r	80.40	*2.14*					4.997	*0.101*		
Early (Zanclean)	**5.34**		C3n.4n (Thvera)	84.68	*4.28*					5.235	*0.238*		Base of Miocene is in uppermost Chron C3r.

MIOCENE			C3r (Gilbert)	96.87	*12.19*					6.023	*0.788*		
		C3A	C3An.1n	101.42	*4.55*	3A-3B	29.61	*1.79*	*6.0*	6.272	*0.249*		
			C3An.1r	103.92	*2.50*					6.386	*0.114*		
			C3An.2n	109.60	*5.68*					6.727	*0.341*		
			C3Ar	116.70	*7.10*					7.104	*0.377*		
		C3B	C3Bn	119.74	*3.04*					7.214	*0.110*		
(Messinian)	**7.246**		C3Br.1r	120.62	*0.88*					7.262	*0.048*		Base of Messinian is in lowermost Chron C3Br.1r.
			C3Br.1n	121.30	*0.68*					7.305	*0.043*	Drury et al. (2017)	
			C3Br.2r	124.68	*3.38*					7.456	*0.151*		
			C3Br.2n	125.35	*0.67*					7.499	*0.043*		
			C3Br.3r	126.48	*1.13*					7.537	*0.038*		
		C4	C4n.1n	129.08	*2.60*	4	25.84	*3.23*	*12.4*	7.65	*0.113*		
			C4n.1r	130.83	*1.75*					7.701	*0.051*		
			C4n.2n	139.37	*8.54*					8.125	*0.424*		
			C4r.1r	142.49	*3.12*					8.257	*0.132*		
			C4r.1n	143.15	*0.66*					8.300	*0.043*		
			C4r.2r	152.32	*9.17*					8.771	*0.471*		*Cryptochron C4r.2r-1 within C4r.2r (c. 8.661–8.699 Ma).*
		C4A	C4An	159.16	*6.84*	4A	20.02	*2.14*	*10.7*	9.105	*0.334*		
			C4Ar.1r	163.49	*4.33*					9.311	*0.206*		
			C4Ar.1n	165.16	*1.67*					9.426	*0.115*		
			C4Ar.2r	171.00	*5.84*					9.647	*0.221*		
			C4Ar.2n	172.34	*1.34*					9.721	*0.074*		
			C4Ar.3r	174.47	*2.13*					9.786	*0.065*		
		C5	C5n.1n	177.49	*3.02*	5	51.19	*2.36*	*4.6*	9.937	*0.151*		
			C5n.1r	178.38	*0.89*					9.984	*0.047*		
			C5n.2n	201.13	*22.75*					11.056	*1.072*		
			C5r.1r	203.44	*2.31*					11.146	*0.090*		
			C5r.1n	204.51	*1.07*					11.188	*0.042*		
			C5r.2r	213.04	*8.53*					11.592	*0.404*	No change from GTS2012/16	*Subchron C5r.2r-1 is within C5r.2r (ca. 11.263–11.308 Ma).*
Late (Tortonian)	**11.63**		C5r.2n	214.28	*1.24*					11.657	*0.065*		Base of Tortonian = near base of Chron C5r.2n.
			C5r.3r	223.52	*9.24*					12.049	*0.392*		
		C5A	C5An.1n	226.81	*3.29*	5A-5AB	41.01	*2.42*	*5.9*	12.174	*0.125*		
			C5An.1r	229.23	*2.42*					12.272	*0.098*		
			C5An.2n	234.25	*5.02*					12.474	*0.202*		
			C5Ar.1r	240.65	*6.40*					12.735	*0.261*		
			C5Ar.1n	241.35	*0.70*					12.770	*0.035*		
			C5Ar.2r	242.90	*1.55*					12.829	*0.059*		
			C5Ar.2n	243.94	*1.04*					12.887	*0.058*		
			C5Ar.3r	247.92	*3.98*					13.032	*0.145*		
		C5AA	C5AAn	251.38	*3.46*					13.183	*0.151*		
			C5AAr	255.19	*3.81*					13.363	*0.180*		
		C5AB	C5ABn	260.03	*4.84*					13.608	*0.245*		
			C5ABr	264.53	*4.50*					13.739	*0.131*		
(Serravalian)	**13.82**	C5AC	C5ACn	273.28	*8.75*	5AC-5AD	25.64	*2.28*	*8.9*	14.070	*0.331*		Base of Serravalian = upper Chron C5ACn.
			C5ACr	275.66	*2.38*					14.163	*0.093*		
		C5AD	C5ADn	285.80	*10.14*					14.609	*0.446*		
			C5ADr	290.17	*4.37*					14.775	*0.166*		
		C5B	C5Bn.1n	292.24	*2.07*	5B	28.22	*1.30*	*4.6*	14.870	*0.095*		
			C5Bn.1r	295.63	*3.39*					15.032	*0.162*	Kochhann et al. (2016)	
			C5Bn.2n	298.45	*2.82*					15.160	*0.128*		

(Continued)

TABLE 5.3 (Continued)

C-sequence marine magnetic anomaly distances and age calibration

Geologic Age	Age of base (Ma)		Polarity Chron	Distance (km) from South Atlantic spreading center (CK92) Old end	Width (km)	Statistics on uncertainties Table 4 of Cande and Kent (1992a, 1992b) Anomaly	Mean width	95% confidence interval (km)	% error	Orbital tuning Base (Ma)	Duration (Myr)	Source of astronomical tuning	Comments
Middle (Langhian)	**15.99**		C5Br	318.39	19.94					15.974	0.814		Base of Langhian = near base of Chron C5Br.
		C5C	C5Cn.1n	324.87	6.48	5C	29.26	4.15	14.2	16.268	0.294		
			C5Cn.1r	325.65	0.78					16.303	0.035		
			C5Cn.2n	329.38	3.73					16.472	0.169		
			C5Cn.2r	330.95	1.57					16.543	0.071	Kochhann et al. (2016)	
			C5Cn.3n	334.88	3.93					16.721	0.178		
			C5Cr	347.64	12.76	5D	23.22	2.39	10.3	17.235	0.514		
		C5D	C5Dn	355.45	7.81					17.533	0.298		
			C5Dr.1r	*360.88*	5.43					17.717	0.184		
			C5Dr.1n	*361.55*	0.68					17.740	0.023		Cryptochron in C5Dr.
			C5Dr.2r	*370.87*	9.32					18.007	0.267	Interpolated by H. Pälicke using relative durations from GTS2012	
		C5E	C5En	382.45	11.58	5E	17.78	1.65	9.3	18.497	0.490		
			C5Er	388.64	6.19					18.636	0.139	Liebrand et al. (2016)	
		C6	C6n	413.88	25.24	6	34.29	3.22	9.4	19.535	0.899		
			C6r	422.93	9.05					19.979	0.444		
		C6A	C6An.1n	427.81	4.88	6A	18.91	1.46	7.7	20.182	0.203	Interpolated by H. Pälicke using relative durations from GTS2012	
(Burdigalian)	**20.45**		C6An.1r	434.18	6.37					20.448	0.266		Base of Burdigalian (working version) = approx. base of Chron C6An.1r (used here) or of Chron C6An.1n.
			C6An.2n	441.85	7.67					20.765	0.317	Liebrand et al. (2016)	
			C6Ar	452.46	10.61					21.130	0.365		
		C6AA	C6AAn	454.63	2.17	6AA	27.13	2.74	10.1	21.204	0.074	Interpolated by H. Pälicke using relative durations from GTS2012	
			C6AAr.1r	461.59	6.96					21.441	0.238		
			C6AAr.1n	463.92	2.33					21.519	0.078		
			C6AAr.2r	468.97	5.05					21.691	0.172	Liebrand et al. (2016)	
			C6AAr.2n	469.79	0.82					21.722	0.031	Interpolated by H. Pälicke using relative durations from GTS2012	
			C6AAr.3r	472.08	2.29					21.806	0.084		
		C6B	C6Bn.1n	475.99	3.91	6B	21.64	2.75	12.7	21.985	0.179		
			C6Bn.1r	477.29	1.30					22.042	0.057		
			C6Bn.2n	483.70	6.41					22.342	0.300	Beddow et al. (2018)	
			C6Br	490.61	6.91					22.621	0.279		
		C6C	C6Cn.1n	495.05	4.44	6Cn	18.79	1.43	7.6	22.792	0.171		
			C6Cn.1r	498.54	3.49					22.973	0.181		

Early (Aquitanian)	**23.04**		C6Cn.2n	501.55	*3.01*					23.040	*0.067*		Base of Miocene = base of Chron C6Cn.2n.
PALEOGENE													
OLIGOCENE			C6Cn.2r	506.47	*4.92*					23.212	*0.172*		
			C6Cn.3n	509.41	*2.94*					23.318	*0.106*	Beddow et al. (2018)	
			C6Cr	524.64	*15.23*	6Cr	17.88	*1.50*	*8.4*	24.025	*0.707*		
		C7	C7n.1n	525.92	*1.28*	7n	8.73	*1.06*	*12.1*	24.061	*0.036*		
			C7n.1r	527.29	*1.37*					24.124	*0.063*		
			C7n.2n	536.04	*8.75*					24.459	*0.335*		
			C7r	543.97	*7.93*					24.654	*0.195*	Liebrand et al. (2016)	
		C7A	C7An	547.82	*3.85*	7r-7A	16.30	*0.65*	*4.0*	24.766	*0.112*		
			C7Ar	552.30	*4.48*					25.099	*0.333*		
		C8	C8n.1n	555.55	*3.25*	8n	18.71	*1.27*	*6.8*	25.264	*0.165*		
			C8n.1r	556.60	*1.05*					25.304	*0.040*		
			C8n.2n	571.04	*14.44*					25.987	*0.683*		
			C8r	583.30	*12.26*	8r	12.19	*0.99*	*8.1*	26.420	*0.433*		
		C9	C9n	607.96	*24.66*	9n	24.74	*3.02*	*12.2*	27.439	*1.019*		Base of Chattian (Early/Late Oligocene Boundary) GSSP is the local highest common occurrence of planktonic foraminifer *Chilogeuembelina cubensis* at Monte Cagnero, Italy with published placement at the GSSP at 15% up in Chron C9n.
Late (Chattian)	**27.29**											No change from GTS2012/16	
			C9r	616.12	*8.16*	9r	8.18	*0.59*	*7.2*	27.859	*0.420*		
		C10	C10n.1n	622.16	*6.04*	10n	12.15	*1.49*	*12.3*	28.087	*0.228*		
			C10n.1r	623.90	*1.74*					28.141	*0.054*		
			C10n.2n	628.29	*4.39*					28.278	*0.137*		
			C10r	645.65	*17.36*	10r	17.27	*2.28*	*13.2*	29.183	*0.905*		
		C11	C11n.1n	652.56	*6.91*	11n	18.59	*1.75*	*9.4*	29.477	*0.294*		
			C11n.1r	655.31	*2.75*					29.527	*0.050*		
			C11n.2n	664.15	*8.84*					29.970	*0.443*		
			C11r	674.26	*10.11*	11r	10.02	*1.38*	*13.8*	30.591	*0.621*		
		C12	C12n	686.50	*12.24*	12n	12.26	*1.24*	*10.1*	30.977	*0.386*		
			C12r	742.63	*56.13*	12r	56.21	*3.09*	*5.5*	33.214	*2.237*	Westerhold et al. (2014) (PEAT)	
		C13	C13n	755.44	*12.81*	13	41.77	*0.46*	*1.1*	33.726	*0.512*		
Early (Rupelian)	**33.90**		C13r	784.40	*28.96*					35.102	*1.376*		Base of Rupellian is at c. Chron C13r.9.
EOCENE		C15	C15n	791.78	*7.38*	15	17.75	*0.73*	*4.1*	35.336	*0.234*		"C14" does not exist.
			C15r	802.15	*10.37*					35.580	*0.244*		
		C16	C16n.1n	806.87	*4.72*	16	32.53	*1.98*	*6.1*	35.718	*0.138*		
			C16n.1r	810.93	*4.06*					35.774	*0.056*		
			C16n.2n	827.67	*16.74*					36.351	*0.577*		
			C16r	834.68	*7.01*					36.573	*0.222*		
		C17	C17n.1n	856.19	*21.51*	17	45.14	*2.75*	*6.1*	37.385	*0.812*		
			C17n.1r	859.46	*3.27*					37.530	*0.145*	Westerhold et al. (2014) PEAT; used in GTS2016	
			C17n.2n	865.54	*6.08*					37.781	*0.251*		Base of Priabonian = submitted GSSP of Tiziano Bed in Italy has astronomical age of 37.71 Ma, or c. C17n.2n.1.
Late (Priabonian)	**37.71**												
			C17n.2r	867.33	*1.79*					37.858	*0.077*		
			C17n.3n	872.10	*4.77*					38.081	*0.223*		
			C17r	879.83	*7.73*					38.398	*0.317*		
		C18	C18n.1n	907.31	*27.48*	18n	41.39	*2.86*	*6.9*	39.582	*1.184*		
			C18n.1r	909.21	*1.90*					39.666	*0.084*		
			C18n.2n	921.21	*12.00*					40.073	*0.407*		
(Bartonian)	**41.03**		C18r	947.96	*26.75*	18r	26.74	*0.75*	*2.8*	41.030	*0.957*		Base of Bartonian (working version; no GSSP yet) assigned as base of Chron C18r.

(*Continued*)

TABLE 5.3 (Continued)

C-sequence marine magnetic anomaly distances and age calibration

Geologic Age	Age of base (Ma)		Polarity Chron	Distance (km) from South Atlantic spreading center (CK92) Old end	Width (km)	Statistics on uncertainties Table 4 of Cande and Kent (1992a, 1992b) Anomaly	Mean width	95% confidence interval (km)	% error	Orbital tuning Base (Ma)	Duration (Myr)	Source of astronomical tuning	Comments
		C19	C19n	954.12	*6.16*	19	29.69	*2.11*	*7.1*	41.180	*0.150*		
			C19r	977.65	*23.53*					42.196	*1.016*	Westerhold et al. (2017) (1258)	
		C20	C20n	1006.06	*28.41*	20n	28.41	*2.05*	*7.2*	43.450	*1.254*	Dinarès-Turell et al. (2018)	
			C20r	1060.24	*54.18*	20r	54.18	*3.58*	*6.6*	46.235	*2.785*	Westerhold et al. (2017) (1258)	
		C21	C21n	1094.71	*34.47*	21n	34.47	*2.90*	*8.4*	47.760	*1.525*	Francescone et al. (2019) = > base of Lutetian shifted older by c. 0.3 Myr (48.2 instead of 47.9 in GTS2016).	
			C21r	1117.55	*22.84*	21r	22.84	*2.92*	*12.8*	48.878	*1.118*		Base of Lutetian at GSSP is 39 precession cycles (0.81 Myr) above base of Chron C21r (therefore near C21r.7).
Middle (Lutetian)	**48.07**												
		C22	C22n	1130.78	*13.23*	22n	13.23	*1.06*	*8.0*	49.666	*0.788*	Francescone et al. (2019)	
			C22r	1150.83	*20.05*	22r	20.05	*2.39*	*11.9*	50.767	*1.101*		
		1C23	C23n.1n	1153.90	*3.07*	23	28.14	*4.87*	*17.3*	50.996	*0.229*		
			C23n.1r	1155.75	*1.85*					51.047	*0.051*		
			C23n.2n	1168.20	*12.45*					51.724	*0.677*		
			C23r	1178.96	*10.76*					52.540	*0.816*		
		C24	C24n.1n	1184.03	*5.07*	24	55.55	*5.22*	*9.4*	52.930	*0.390*		
			C24n.1r	1185.61	*1.58*					53.020	*0.090*	Francescone et al. (2019)	
			C24n.2n	1186.34	*0.73*					53.120	*0.100*		
			C24n.2r	1188.05	*1.71*					53.250	*0.130*		
			C24n.3n	1195.35	*7.30*					53.900	*0.650*		
Early (Ypresian)	***56.00***		C24r	1234.51	*39.16*					57.101	*3.201*		Base of Eocene is c. 1.1 Myr above the base of Chron C24r based on astronomical tuning.
PALEOCENE		C25	C25n	1241.50	*6.99*	25	23.30	*2.26*	*9.7*	57.656	*0.555*	Hilgen et al. (2010); used in GTS2012/2016	
			C25r	1257.81	*16.31*					58.959	*1.303*		
Late (Thanetian)	**59.24**	C26	C26n	1262.74	*4.93*	26	46.00	*2.81*	*6.1*	59.237	*0.278*		Base of Thanetian is base of Chron C26n.
			C26r	1303.81	*41.07*					62.278	*3.041*		Base of Selandian at GSSP is an isotope-shift at 30 precession cycles (0.61 Myr) above base of C26r at GSSP.
Middle (Selandian)	**61.66**												
		C27	C27n	1308.70	*4.89*	27	21.90	*3.02*	*13.8*	62.530	*0.252*	Dinarès-Turell et al. (2014)	
			C27r	1325.71	*17.01*					63.537	*1.007*		
		C28	C28n	1341.99	*16.28*	28	46.14	*4.48*	*9.7*	64.645	*1.108*		
			C28r	1347.03	*5.04*					64.862	*0.217*		
		C29	C29n	1358.66	*11.63*					65.700	*0.838*		
			C29r	1371.84	*13.18*					66.380	*0.680*	Magnetozone duration from Thibault et al. (2012) relative to K/Pg	Base of C29r is 0.406 Myr below K/P (Thibault et al., 2012); or 0.34 Myr (Batenburg et al., 2012; used here and in GTS2020). Mesozoic/Cenozoic boundary event is approx. Chron C29r.4.
Early (Danian)	**66.04**												

CRETACEOUS		C30	C30n	1407.22	*35.38*	30-31n	57.30	*5.73*	*10.0*	68.178	*1.798*	Magnetozone duration from Thibault et al. (2012)	
			C30r	1409.56	*2.34*					68.351	*0.173*		
		C31	C31n	1429.14	*19.58*					69.271	*0.920*	Magnetozone duration from Husson et al. (2011)	
			C31r	1481.12	*51.98*	31r	51.98	*3.43*	*6.6*	71.451	*2.180*	Magnetozone duration from Husson et al. (2011)	Duration of C31r = 2.18 Myr (Husson et al., 2011). Base of C31r is within the lower *Baculites grandis* ammonite zone is constrained by Ar/Ar ages of 70.65 ± 0.65 Ma (2-sigma) within that zone.
		C32	C32n.1n	1487.68	*6.56*	32	68.29	*5.74*	*8.4*	71.691	*0.240*		
			C32n.1r	1493.94	*6.26*					71.851	*0.160*	Magnetozone duration adjusted from Husson et al. (2011)	
MAASTRICHTIAN	***72.17***		C32n.2n	1531.81	*37.87*					73.651	*1.800*		The ratified GSSP boundary is in an abandoned quarry near the village of Tercis les Bains in southwest France, at 90 cm below a coincident lowest occurrence of *Pachydiscus neubergicus* and *Hoploscaphites constrictus* ammonoids. Chron equiv = c. 7/8ths up in C32n.2n.
			C32r.1r	1539.94	*8.13*					73.951	*0.300*	Magnetozone duration from Husson et al. (2011)	
			C32r.1n	1542.32	*2.38*					74.051	*0.100*		
			C32r.2r	1549.41	*7.09*					74.201	*0.150*	Magnetozone duration adjusted from Husson et al. (2011)	
		C33	C33n	1723.76	*174.35*	33n	174.35	*5.75*	*3.3*	79.900	*5.699*	No change from GTS2012	Base of C33n constrained by Ar/Ar dates to be slightly younger than 80.08 ± 0.61 Ma; following Hicks'95, it is extrapolated as 0.2 Myr younger = 79.9 Ma.
			C33r	1862.32	*138.56*	33r	138.56	*5.82*	*4.2*	82.875	*2.975*	Astronomical calibration and ID-TIMS dating (Wu et al., 2020)	Base of C33r in is long-eccentricity cycle 204.6 with astronomical tuned age of 82.875 Ma (Wu et al., 2020); and constrained by ID-TIMS date of 83.27 ± 0.11 Ma on a bentonite below it (Wang et al., 2016).
CAMPANIAN	***83.65***		C33r extension GTS2020							83.650		Assigned basal age (and base of Campanian) in Gale et al. (2020, Ch. 27, The Cretaceous Period, this book)	Base of Campanian is not ratified, but working definition is the base of Chron C33r; which was assigned an age in the GTS2020 Cretaceous chapter of 83.65 Ma with a placement in long-eccentricity cycle 207.
SANTONIAN		C34	C34n										Chron C33r may include uppermost part of the English-Chalk usage of Santonian.

The kilometer placement for the Late Cretaceous through Neogene C-sequence block model of marine magnetic anomalies is from a synthetic flow profile for the South Atlantic using relative distances from the spreading axis (Cande and Kent, 1992a). Distances are tabulated to 2-decimal precision for preserving the relative widths of subchrons and for applying spreading rate models, but the actual accuracy is much less—the relative uncertainties on kilometer widths of each marine magnetic anomaly are tabulated in Cande and Kent (1992a).
The GTS2020 age model for converting the C-sequence of marine magnetic anomalies (km) to numerical ages (Ma) is primarily derived from astronomical orbital tuning of oceanic sediments with constraints from selected radioisotopic ages. The Paleogene and Neogene synthesis was compiled by Heiko Pälicke for Paleogene and Neogene, the Quaternary scale is from Channell et al. (2020; see Table 5.2), and the Campanian and Maastrichtian is modified from Husson et al. (2011), Thibault et al. (2012, and Wu et al. (2020). Details and references for the Neogene and the Paleogene astronomically tuned ages are given in those chapters. The associated time scale framework for geologic stages (ages in bold-font in 2nd column on left) is derived from biostratigraphic correlations to C-sequence polarity chrons or independent ages obtained by astronomical or radioisotopic dating of stage boundaries or zonal datums (see Neogene and Paleogene chapters in this book). Some Paleogene stage boundaries have not yet been defined by a GSSP or an accepted primary marker and therefore are assigned an age according to a possible placement with respect to the C-sequence time scale (see Paleogene chapter). The composite biostratigraphic and geomagnetic polarity time scale are illustrated in the Neogene, Paleogene, and Cretaceous chapters (Raffi et al., 2020, Ch. 29; Speijer et al., 2020, Ch. 28; Gale et al., 2020, Ch. 27; respectively).

have 76% reversed polarity in magnetostratigraphy. One possibility is that the baseline for assigning limits for normal versus reversed polarity blocks for some extended intervals that are dominated by reversed polarity in the marine magnetic anomaly model is shifted and has overemphasized normal polarity. In contrast, within normal polarity–dominated intervals such as the Maastrichtian, the marine magnetic anomaly model may have exaggerated the relative durations of short reversed polarity chrons (e.g., Chron C32n.1r is less than half the marine magnetic anomaly modeled duration according to Husson et al., 2011).

Similar to the procedure used by Berggren et al. (1995), the calibration of biostratigraphic datums and chronostratigraphic boundaries to this geomagnetic polarity time scale yields the main numerical time scale for the latest Cretaceous through Neogene [e.g., Table 5.3 *and Speijer et al. (2020, Ch. 28, The Paleogene Period) and Raffi et al. (2020, Ch. 29, The Neogene Period) in this book].*

5.2.3 Implications of C-sequence age model for South Atlantic spreading history

Applying a smoothed version of these computed chron ages (Table 5.3) to the marine magnetic anomaly profile of Cande and Kent (1992a) yields a schematic representation of South Atlantic spreading rates (Fig. 5.3). The general trends implied by the Cande and Kent (1995) (Fig. 5.2), GTS04, GTS2012, and GTS2020 age models are quite similar—a rapid slowing in spreading rates from Campanian through Paleocene, a progressive increase through the Eocene followed by a moderate Oligocene slowing, a lesser increase during early Miocene, then a rapid slowing from mid-Miocene to the present.

This generalized curve for the spreading rates from the GTS2012 and GTS2020 age models required a multichron averaging within 2- to 5-Myr sliding windows. This was necessary to avoid major distortions when the instantaneous spreading rate derived from the detailed astronomical tuning of the duration of an individual polarity chron and the corresponding anomaly widths of the "standard" marine magnetic pattern as modeled by Cande and Kent (1992a) could produce values that were up to 50% from the smoothed mean. These distortions also imply that some of the uncertainties on magnetic anomaly widths tabulated by Cande and Kent (1992a, their Table 4) are probably underestimates.

Even though there have been shifts in the timing and the relative magnitudes of acceleration and slowing of spreading rates in this South Atlantic reference profile, the detailed curve in GTS2020 from cycle-stratigraphy chron-duration analyses have generally supported the

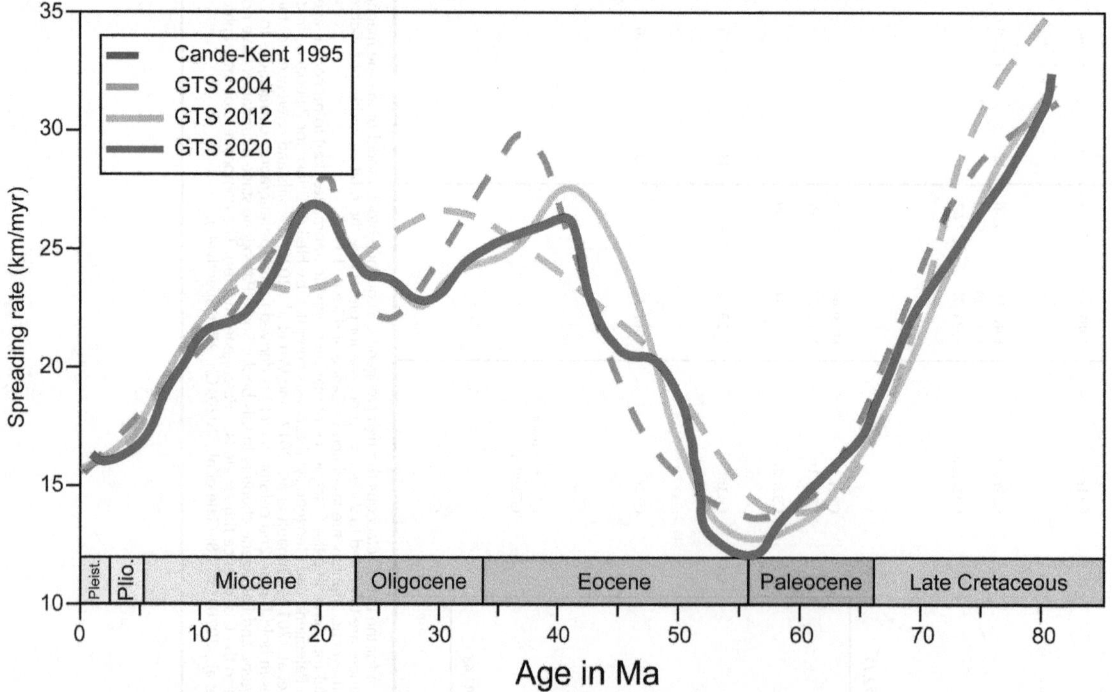

FIGURE 5.3 Spreading history of the South Atlantic. Apparent variation in spreading rates (km/Myr) for marine magnetic anomalies along the synthetic flow profile for the South Atlantic. Dashed lines are the spreading models implied by Cande and Kent (1992a, 1995), by GTS2004 (Gradstein et al., 2004), and by GTS2012 (Gradstein et al., 2012) based on spline fits to calibrate the late Cretaceous through Neogene magnetic polarity time scale. The solid line is the smoothed mean spreading rates from the GTS2020 Campanian through Quaternary astronomical time scale for the magnetic polarity chrons (Table 5.2).

estimates made by Cande and Kent (1995) to a spline fit of a small set of radioisotopic age constraints. Some of these apparent changes in South Atlantic spreading trends might be synchronous with other global plate-motion variations. For example, the early Eocene acceleration at c. 50 Ma coincides with a general change in plate tectonic motions at about Chron C21 (Doug Wilson, written commun., 2011).

5.3 Middle Jurassic through Early Cretaceous geomagnetic polarity time scale

5.3.1 M-sequence of marine magnetic anomalies

An extended ~35-Myr interval of normal polarity, the "Cretaceous Long Normal-Polarity Chron" or polarity Superchron C34n, extends from the early Aptian to approximately the Santonian/Campanian boundary. Oceanic crust of late Middle Jurassic through earliest Aptian age displays a second series of magnetic anomalies that were named the "M"—for Mesozoic—series. The M-sequence for anomalies and corresponding chrons of M0r–M25r was derived from a block model of the Hawaiian lineations by Larson and Hilde (1975) and has undergone relatively minor refinements (e.g., Tamaki and Larson, 1988; Channell et al. 1995). The nomenclature has some anomalies, for example, the M anomalies start at M0 (*not* M1) and the younger set of Chrons M1 and M3 are normal polarity with Chrons M2 and M4 are reversed polarity, whereas all other marine magnetic anomalies/chrons from M5 onward are pairs of normal and reversed polarity (e.g., Chrons M5n and M5r; and M6n and M6r).

After the M-sequence was numbered, three events or clusters of brief reversed polarity excursions or subzones were reported from the Aptian–Albian portion of Chron C34n, especially within drilling cores of deepsea sediments. Ryan et al. (1978) summarized these events and suggested an "upward," hence "negative numbering" continuation to the M-sequence younger than polarity Chron M0r: (1) Chron M"-1r" in late Aptian, with an alternate designation as the "ISEA" event (Tarduno, 1990); (2) Chron M"-2r" set of middle Albian events; and (c) Chron M"-3r" set in late Albian. Further details on these enigmatic brief "negative-numbered" events, which have not been resolved in surveys of coeval marine magnetic anomalies, are in Gale et al. (2020, Ch. 27, The Cretaceous Period) of this book. We did not include a reported Santonian interval of reversed polarity spanning c. 0.4-Myr interval at c. 84.5 Ma from the Songliao Basin scientific drilling (He et al., 2012; Wu et al., 2013; Wang et al., 2016), because this feature has not yet been verified in any other section or in marine magnetic anomaly survey.

5.3.2 Extension to M-sequence from deep-tow magnetometer surveys

Additional marine magnetic surveys in the Pacific had extended the M-sequence to marine magnetic anomaly M29 (e.g., Cande et al., 1978; Handschumacher et al., 1988). Oceanic crust in the Pacific older than M29 was considered to be a "Jurassic Quiet Zone." Magnetic surveys into this region using magnetometers towed at depths near the seafloor ("deep-tow" profiles) revealed that this Quiet Zone contained a complex suite of correlative anomalies (e.g., Sager et al., 1998; Tivey et al., 2006; Tominaga et al., 2008, 2015; Tominaga and Sager, 2010). The apparent "Jurassic Quiet Zone" signature in surface surveys appears to be a consequence of two factors: an apparently weak intensity of the geomagnetic field and a relatively high geomagnetic reversal rates that caused blurring of signals from the narrow bands of normal- and reversed-magnetized oceanic crust at depth when observed at the surface. The deep-tow magnetic features that are correlative among profiles are interpreted as a set of possibly 50 –100 polarity chrons that have been semi-arbitrary grouped into clusters with a nomenclature of "M26"–"M44." Pacific IODP Site 801 is within the marine anomaly cluster "M42," and the interpreted Bajocian–Bathonian age of Site 801 implies that marine magnetic anomalies M26–M44r should span the Oxfordian, Callovian, Bathonian, and Bajocian stages.

The details of the marine anomaly clusters called M25A and M26 are poorly resolved by the magnetic surveys due to very weak amplitude of the magnetic signal recorded in the original Pacific Ocean study (Handschumacher et al., 1988). We used the relative widths of polarity blocks comprising these M25A and M26 anomaly clusters based on survey data from the Eastern Indian Ocean (Sager et al., 1992).

However, unlike the standard polarity pattern model for sea-surface marine magnetic anomalies M0r–M25r, the interpretation of the deep-tow surveys over magnetic anomalies M27r–M44 depends on assumptions of additional factors (Tominaga et al., 2008). A modeling of the direct deep-tow profile overemphasizes the narrow-width paleomagnetic intensity fluctuations just above the oceanic crust relative to the longer distance trends, thereby creating a polarity model of numerous short-duration, low-amplitude polarity intervals. Alternatively, if the deep-tow data are projected to a mid-depth level or to the surface, then the close-spaced fluctuations are tempered, and the longer wavelength features are emphasized. The mid-depth models are potentially a better estimate of the main geomagnetic polarity history (M. Tominaga, pers. commun. to J. Ogg). We include the geophysics models for both the deep-depth and the upward projection interpretations of these pre-M25r deep-tow magnetic anomaly profiles (e.g., Figure 11 in Tominaga et al., 2008). The actual reversal history of the Earth's geomagnetic field is perhaps between these two models.

Outcrop-based magnetostratigraphy for the Oxfordian through Bajocian is generally consistent with an intermediate interpretation between the polarity patterns derived from the direct deep-tow model and the interpreted mid-depth or sea-surface projection for these pre-M25 marine magnetic anomalies (see Hesselbo et al., 2020, Ch. 26, The Jurassic Period, this book). Currently (Aug., 2020), the oldest numbered M-sequence anomaly is M44r with an estimated age of latest Aalenian.

5.3.3 Composite M-sequence

The pre-GTS2020 age models for the C-sequence required a synthetic standardized kilometer scale for the C-sequence marine magnetic anomalies (Cande and Kent, 1992a) followed by a merger of spline fits to select radioisotopic dates and to intervals with cycle-scaled durations to smooth the implied spreading rates and yield an age model for each individual polarity chron. This same procedure is used for the age models for the M-sequence polarity chrons. A synthetic reference M-sequence pattern had been constructed for GTS2012 from reference patterns of magnetic polarity versus ocean-crust kilometers in the Pacific and is used in GTS2020. The concept and philosophy are similar to the construction of a "South Atlantic kilometer scale" for the C-sequence marine magnetic anomalies (Cande and Kent, 1992a, 1995).

The M-sequence pattern is the best documented at the trio of expanding spreading centers that created the current Pacific plate (e.g., Larson and Hilde, 1975). Channell et al. (1995) developed a composite scaling of marine magnetic anomaly block models from approximately M0r–M29r from the individual Pacific spreading centers. This composite "CENT95" scaling is a more robust estimate of the M-sequence pattern than the splicing of selected profiles on the Hawaiian lineations by Larson and Hilde (1975) (Roger Larson, personal communication to J. Ogg, 1997). However, the CENT95 composite did not resolve some of the fine-scale features in individual profiles that are also documented by magnetostratigraphy, and it lacks adequate resolution for anomalies older than approximately M22r. Following the CENT95 procedure, a series of synthetic kilometer distances was added to replicate the fine-scale structure of the Larson–Hilde block model for several intervals and for the revised relative durations of subchrons in M11An observed from magnetostratigraphic studies (Channell et al., 1995, p. 60). Anomalies from M22r to M25n were proportioned according to the Hawaiian lineation of pattern of Larson and Hilde (1975) into the base-M22r to base-M25n distance of the CENT95 composite. The base of Chron M0r is one candidate for the GSSP primary marker of the Aptian stage, and this level was used as the "zero-kilometer" reference for the final scale.

Our synthetic M-sequence polarity kilometer scale is normalized to the kilometer distances from anomaly M0r at a single spreading center (the "Hawaiian" ridge in the Pacific). This normalization is supported by comparison of the three main spreading centers operating in the Pacific during the M-sequence (Tominaga and Sager, 2010). That compilation demonstrated that the relative polarity block widths from the Hawaiian and Japanese, and to some degree from the Phoenix, marine magnetic anomaly lineation sets are similar. Even though the spreading rates may have changed during the M-sequence interval, such changes appear to have occurred nearly synchronously and to the same relative degree in the Hawaiian and Japanese centers.

A synthetic composite M-sequence, normalized to an arbitrary span of 0–100 distance-units for anomalies M0r–M29r, was derived from a statistical fit to multiple magnetic profiles from the three Pacific spreading centers by Tominaga and Sager (2010). They observed that individual polarity blocks seem to have variable widths relative to adjacent blocks among the composite patterns among each spreading center, even though the general characteristics are similar. A comparison of their three spreading center composite to the CENT95 pattern for M25–M0r (which is essentially the GTS2012 hybrid pattern) indicated significant distortions in some polarity block intervals (Figure 13 in Tominaga and Sager, 2010). For example, widths of M16n and M11n are significantly thinner relative to adjacent polarity blocks when compared to the CENT95 model. However, magnetostratigraphy in those intervals generally supports the relative scaling of the CENT95 block model (e.g., Speranza et al., 2005; Channell et al., 2010). Therefore, as in GTS2012, the CENT95 and Hawaiian polarity block models were retained for the GTS2020 synthetic M-sequence.

The continuation of the M-sequence into older oceanic than M25r is the best resolved in the magnetic anomaly lineations created at the "Japanese" spreading center, which were formed at a faster rapid spreading rate than those the Hawaiian set. We proportionally scaled the widths of these oldest Japanese lineations observed by Sager et al. (1998) and their modification/extension by Tominaga et al. (2008) to fit the CENT95 Hawaiian lineation scale by comparing the kilometers between the middle of marine magnetic anomalies M27r and M29r. This comparison implies that the Japanese suite formed at a spreading rate of approximately 2.5 times faster than the Hawaiian suite. Both of the deep-tow models for the pre-M25r marine magnetic anomalies—the direct deep-tow fine-scale features and the computed mid-depth projections

TABLE 5.4 M-sequence marine magnetic anomaly distances and age calibration.

Geologic stage	GTS2020 age of base (Ma)		Polarity chron	Distance (km) from Hawaiian spreading center: Old end	*Width (km)*	Age calibration (spreading rate model): Base Ma	*Duration (Myr)*	Comments
Cenomanian	***100.5***							
Early Cretaceous		within C34n	M″-3r″ ??			~103	*Not known*	Potential "M-1r," "M-2r," and "M-3r) are not fully verified, and ages are projected from reported coincidence with foraminifers.
			M″-2r″ ??			~107.5	*Not known*	
Albian	***113.2***							
			M″-1r″ (or ISEA) ??			~118	0.1?	
		C34n		− 9.808		*120.964*		
		M0	M0r	0.000	9.808	**121.400**	0.436	Duration of Chron M0r is ~0.4 Myr from cycle stratigraphy in Italy.
Aptian	**121.4**							Base of Aptian (working definition for GTS2020) = Base of Chron M0r.
			M1n	53.607	53.607	123.783	2.383	
		M1	M1r (or "M1")	62.439	8.832	124.169	0.386	
		M3	M3n (or "M2")	r74.613	12.174	124.717	0.548	
			M3r (or "M3")	114.185	39.572	126.514	1.797	Base of U. Barrem = upper Chron M3r.
		M5	M5n (or "M4")	136.295	22.110	127.526	1.012	
Barremian	**126.5**							Base of Barremian, if placed at Chron M5n.8 (GTS2012), would be 126.7 Ma.
			M5r (or "M5")	144.678	8.383	127.920	0.393	
		M6	M6n	149.412	4.734	128.145	0.225	
			M6r	152.557	3.145	128.294	0.150	
		M7	M7n	158.782	6.225	128.593	0.299	
			M7r	166.232	7.450	128.951	0.358	
		M8	M8n	173.095	6.863	129.282	0.331	
			M8r	179.674	6.579	129.601	0.319	
		M9	M9n	186.405	6.731	129.926	0.325	
			M9r	194.062	7.657	130.297	0.371	
		M10	M10n	202.040	7.978	130.683	0.386	
			M10r	211.178	9.138	131.125	0.442	
		M10N	M10Nn.1n	218.137	6.959	131.462	0.337	The "N" of M10N was in recognition of Fred Naugle by Larson and Hilde (1975).
			M10Nn.1r	219.117	0.980	131.509	0.047	
Hauterivian	**132.6**							Base of Hauterivian, if assigned as middle of Chron M10Nn (GTS2016), would be 131.6 Ma.
			M10Nn.2n	225.737	6.620	131.829	0.320	
			M10Nn.2r	226.217	0.480	131.852	0.023	
			M10Nn.3n	232.213	5.996	132.139	0.287	
			M10Nr	240.878	8.665	132.552	0.413	
		M11	M11n	257.083	16.205	133.323	0.771	
			M11r.1r	262.217	5.134	133.565	0.242	
			M11r.1n	262.717	0.500	133.588	0.023	

(*Continued*)

TABLE 5.4 (Continued)

Geologic stage	GTS2020 age of base (Ma)		Polarity chron	Distance (km) from Hawaiian spreading center: Old end	Width (km)	Age calibration (spreading rate model): Base Ma	Duration (Myr)	Comments
			M11r.2r	266.946	4.229	133.785	0.197	
		M11A	M11An.1n	277.897	10.951	134.294	0.509	
			M11An.1r	279.117	1.220	134.348	0.054	
			M11An.2n	280.817	1.700	134.426	0.078	
			M11Ar	282.787	1.970	134.515	0.089	
		M12	M12n	287.797	5.010	134.740	0.226	
			M12r.1r	306.148	18.351	135.586	0.846	
			M12r.1n	307.997	1.849	135.668	0.082	
			M12r.2r	311.677	3.680	135.828	0.160	
		M12A	M12An	318.047	6.370	136.104	0.275	
			M12Ar	320.247	2.200	136.198	0.094	
		M13	M13n	324.815	4.568	136.391	0.193	
			M13r	331.276	6.461	136.657	0.266	
		M14	M14n	338.168	6.892	136.936	0.278	
			M14r	356.584	18.416	137.658	0.723	
Valanginian	**137.7**							Base of Valanginian, if assigned as Chron M14r.3 (GTS2012), would be 137.4 Ma.
			M15n	366.264	9.680	138.020	0.362	
		M15	M15r	379.164	12.900	138.482	0.462	
		M16	M16n	412.472	33.308	139.649	1.167	
			M16r	428.465	15.993	140.186	0.537	
		M17	M17n	437.933	9.468	140.492	0.306	
			M17r	477.493	39.560	141.752	1.260	
		M18	M18n	494.915	17.422	142.305	0.553	
			M18r	505.139	10.224	142.626	0.320	
		M19	M19n.1n	508.767	3.628	142.740	0.114	
			M19n.1r	511.217	2.450	142.778	0.038	Shortened M19n.1r duration relative to Hawaiian model (following magnetostratigraphy by Hausa/Pruner, etc.).
Berriasian	**143.1**							Base of Cretaceous (base of Berriasian) if assigned as exact middle of M19n.2n would be 143.3 Ma.
Late Jurassic								
			M19n.2n	540.261	29.044	143.741	0.963	M19n.2n expanded accordingly.
			M19r	547.398	7.137	143.968	0.227	
		M20	M20n.1n	557.487	10.089	144.295	0.327	
			M20n.1r	559.197	1.710	144.351	0.056	
			M20n.2n	580.172	20.975	145.046	0.695	
			M20r	600.286	20.114	145.716	0.671	
		M21	M21n	625.619	25.333	146.580	0.864	
			M21r	638.098	12.479	147.009	0.429	
		M22	M22n.1n	675.017	36.919	148.294	1.285	
			M22n.1r	676.237	1.220	148.337	0.043	

Stage	Base (Ma)	Anomaly	Chron	Distance	Duration	Age (Ma)	Duration (Myr)	Comments
			M22n.2n	677.467	1.230	148.380	0.044	
			M22n.2r	678.677	1.210	148.424	0.043	
			M22n.3n	680.415	1.738	148.486	0.062	
			M22r	697.476	17.061	149.100	0.614	
		M22A	M22An	701.268	3.792	149.237	0.137	
Tithonian	**149.2**							Base of Tithonian (working definition) is base of Chron M22An.
			M22Ar	706.577	5.309	149.431	0.194	
			M23n	717.448	10.871	149.828	0.397	
		M23	M23r.1r	725.791	8.343	150.136	0.308	
			M23r.1n	726.549	0.758	150.164	0.028	
			M23r.2r	745.004	18.455	150.853	0.689	
		M24	M24n	752.069	7.065	151.118	0.265	
			M24r.1r	765.735	13.666	151.632	0.515	
			M24r.1n	766.493	0.758	151.661	0.029	
			M24r.2r	772.561	6.067	151.891	0.230	
		M24A	M24An	776.353	3.792	152.035	0.144	
			M24Ar	784.190	7.837	152.333	0.298	
		M24B	M24Bn	794.808	10.618	152.736	0.404	
			M24Br	799.358	4.551	152.910	0.173	
		M25	M25n	807.954	8.596	153.237	0.328	
			M25r	813.273	5.319	153.442	0.205	Marine magnetic anomaly series from M25r through M27n are rescaled from Handschumacher et al. (1988), Sager et al. (1992).
		M25A	M25An.1n	816.690	3.417	153.574	0.132	
			M25An.1r	818.472	1.783	153.642	0.069	
			M25An.2n	820.552	2.080	153.723	0.080	
			M25An.2r	823.227	2.674	153.826	0.103	
			M25An.3n	824.118	0.891	153.860	0.034	
			M25Ar	828.129	4.011	154.016	0.155	
		M26	M26n.1n	831.850	3.721	154.160	0.144	
			M26n.1r	833.613	1.763	154.228	0.068	
			M26n.2n	834.396	0.783	154.259	0.030	
			M26n.2r	835.963	1.567	154.320	0.061	ODP Site 761 drilled on middle of anomaly M26n yielded Ar/Ar age of 155.3 Ma (± 3.4 Myr; 1-sigma).
			M26n.3n	838.901	2.938	154.434	0.114	
			M26n.3r	841.642	2.742	154.541	0.107	
			M26n.4n	842.230	0.588	154.564	0.023	
			M26r	847.713	5.484	154.778	0.214	
Kimmeridgian	**154.8**							Base of Kimmeridgian (pending GSSP = Sub-boreal/Boreal usage) is base of Chron M26r; which is near a Re–Os dated horizon of 154.1 ± 2.2 Ma.
		M27	M27n	851.934	4.221	154.943	0.165	
		M-sequence extension *(Pacific deep-tow surveys)*						Marine magnetic anomaly series from M27r to M44n are rescaled from deep-tow surveys on Japanese lineations (Sager et al., 1998; Tominaga et al., 2008). These anomalies are also projected upward (bottom table) to sea surface (M27r–M37r) or mid-depth (3 km; M38n–M44n).
			M27r	856.642	4.708	155.128	0.185	
		M28	M28n	865.256	8.614	155.467	0.339	
			M28r	869.563	4.307	155.637	0.170	
			M28An	872.417	2.855	155.750	0.113	
			M28Ar	879.128	6.711	156.016	0.266	
			M28Bn	880.581	1.452	156.074	0.058	

(Continued)

TABLE 5.4 (Continued)

Geologic stage	GTS2020 age of base (Ma)		Polarity chron	Distance (km) from Hawaiian spreading center Old end	*Width (km)*	Age calibration (spreading rate model) Base Ma	*Duration (Myr)*	Comments
			M28Br	883.085	2.504	156.173	0.099	
			M28Cn	886.140	3.055	156.295	0.122	
			M28Cr	888.744	2.604	156.398	0.104	
			M28Dn	891.048	2.304	156.490	0.092	
			M28Dr	894.203	3.155	156.616	0.126	
		M29	M29n.1n	898.660	4.457	156.795	0.178	
			M29n.1r	899.512	0.851	156.829	0.034	
			M29n.2n	901.415	1.903	156.905	0.076	
			M29r	908.176	6.761	157.177	0.272	
			M29An	909.578	1.402	157.233	0.056	
			M29Ar	911.481	1.903	157.310	0.077	
		M30	M30n	915.037	3.556	157.453	0.143	
			M30r	919.645	4.608	157.639	0.186	
			M30An	922.499	2.855	157.755	0.116	
			M30Ar	923.401	0.901	157.791	0.036	
		M31	M31n.1n	927.858	4.457	157.972	0.181	
			M31n.1r	930.212	2.354	158.068	0.096	
			M31n.2n	931.013	0.801	158.100	0.033	
			M31n.2r	932.215	1.202	158.149	0.049	
			M31n.3n	933.467	1.252	158.200	0.051	
			M31r	935.020	1.553	158.263	0.063	
		M32	M32n.1n	935.671	0.651	158.290	0.027	
			M32n.1r	936.522	0.851	158.325	0.035	
			M32n.2n	939.327	2.805	158.439	0.114	
			M32n.2r	940.829	1.502	158.500	0.061	
			M32n.3n	941.681	0.851	158.535	0.035	
			M32r	944.084	2.404	158.633	0.098	
		M33	M33n	952.598	8.514	158.983	0.350	
			M33r	956.405	3.806	159.139	0.157	
			M33An	958.658	2.254	159.232	0.093	
			M33Ar	960.662	2.003	159.315	0.083	
			M33Bn	962.615	1.953	159.395	0.081	
			M33Br	965.870	3.255	159.530	0.135	
			M33Cn.1n	966.972	1.102	159.575	0.046	
			M33Cn.1r	968.474	1.502	159.638	0.062	
			M33Cn.2n	971.980	3.506	159.783	0.145	
			M33Cr	977.840	5.860	160.026	0.243	
		M34	M34n.1n	980.294	2.454	160.121	0.095	
			M34n.1r	982.347	2.053	160.207	0.085	
			M34n.2n	983.699	1.352	160.260	0.053	
			M34n.2r	984.801	1.102	160.295	0.035	

Stage	Age (Ma)	Chron	Subchron	Distance	Duration	Age	Duration	Notes
			M34n.3n	985.702	0.901	160.322	0.027	
			M34n.3r	987.155	1.452	160.389	0.067	
			M34An	987.806	0.651	160.427	0.038	
			M34Ar	991.812	4.007	160.583	0.156	
			M34Bn.1n	994.567	2.754	160.692	0.109	
			M34Bn.1r	995.619	1.052	160.766	0.074	
			M34Bn.2n	996.320	0.701	160.800	0.034	
			M34Br	997.572	1.252	160.838	0.039	
		M35	M35n	1000.076	2.504	160.918	0.079	
			M35r	1005.385	5.309	161.093	0.175	
		M36	M36n.1n	1008.490	3.105	161.220	0.127	
			M36n.1r	1010.543	2.053	161.287	0.068	
			M36An	1011.795	1.252	161.340	0.053	
			M36Ar	1012.396	0.601	161.366	0.025	
			M36Bn	1013.247	0.851	161.401	0.036	
Oxfordian	**161.5**							Base of Oxfordian (working French ammonite version) is assigned as Chron M36Br.25.
Middle Jurassic								
			M36Br	1017.304	4.057	161.573	0.172	
			M36Cn	1019.307	2.003	161.658	0.085	
			M36Cr	1022.863	3.556	161.809	0.151	
		M37	M37n.1n	1029.824	6.961	162.106	0.297	
			M37n.1r	1030.518	3.305	162.247	0.141	
			M37n.2n	1033.711	3.193	162.383	0.136	
			M37r	1036.475	2.765	162.501	0.118	
		M38	M38n.1n	1040.241	3.766	162.663	0.161	
			M38n.1r	1041.644	1.402	162.723	0.060	
			M38n.2n	1045.851	4.207	162.904	0.181	
			M38n.2r	1047.013	1.162	162.954	0.050	
			M38n.3n	1049.256	2.244	163.051	0.097	
			M38n.3r	1052.461	3.205	163.189	0.138	
			M38n.4n	1058.792	6.330	163.463	0.274	
			M38n.4r	1060.755	1.963	163.548	0.085	
			M38n.5n	1065.202	4.447	163.741	0.193	
			M38r	1067.085	1.883	163.823	0.082	
		M39	M39n.1n	1072.053	4.968	164.039	0.217	
			M39n.1r	1075.299	3.245	164.181	0.142	
			M39n.2n	1079.345	4.047	164.358	0.177	
			M39n.2r	1081.228	1.883	164.441	0.082	
			M39n.3n	1084.834	3.606	164.599	0.158	
			M39n.3r	1088.480	3.646	164.759	0.160	
			M39n.4n	1092.647	4.167	164.943	0.184	
			M39n.4r	1097.495	4.848	165.157	0.214	
Callovian	**165.3**		M39n.5n	1100.981	3.486	165.311	0.154	Base of Callovian interpreted as base of Chron M39n.5n (deep tow) = M39n.3n (mid-depth projection).
			M39n.5r	1104.546	3.566	165.469	0.158	
			M39n.6n	1107.271	2.724	165.590	0.121	
			M39n.6r	1110.156	2.885	165.718	0.128	
			M39n.7n	1112.079	1.923	165.804	0.086	
			M39n.7r	1113.361	1.282	165.861	0.057	

(Continued)

TABLE 5.4 (Continued)

Geologic stage	GTS2020 age of base (Ma)		Polarity chron	Distance (km) from Hawaiian spreading center: Old end	*Width (km)*	Age calibration (spreading rate model): Base Ma	*Duration (Myr)*	Comments
			M39n.8n	1116.125	2.765	165.984	0.123	
			M39r	1118.249	2.123	166.079	0.095	
		M40	M40n.1n	1119.371	1.122	166.129	0.050	
			M40n.1r	1124.419	5.048	166.355	0.226	
			M40n.2n	1126.302	1.883	166.439	0.084	
			M40n.2r	1128.826	2.524	166.553	0.113	
			M40n.3n	1130.669	1.843	166.635	0.083	
			M40n.3r	1137.080	6.410	166.924	0.289	
			M40n.4n	1137.961	0.881	166.964	0.040	
			M40r	1139.924	1.963	167.053	0.089	
		M41	M41n.1n	1142.208	2.284	167.156	0.103	
			M41n.1r	1147.457	5.249	167.394	0.238	
			M41n.2n	1149.300	1.843	167.478	0.084	
			M41n.2r	1152.224	2.925	167.611	0.133	
			M41n.3n	1153.907	1.683	167.687	0.077	
			M41n.3r	1156.792	2.885	167.819	0.131	
			M41n.4n	1157.553	0.761	167.853	0.035	
			M41r	1160.638	3.085	167.994	0.141	
		M42	M42n.1n	1163.563	2.925	168.128	0.134	
Bathonian	**168.2**		M42n.1r	1166.528	2.965	168.264	0.136	Base of Bathonian interpreted as base of Chron M42n.1n (mid-depth projection) = mid M42n.1r (deep tow).
			M42n.2n	1167.129	0.601	168.291	0.028	
			M42n.2r	1168.331	1.202	168.346	0.055	
			M42n.3n	1169.733	1.402	168.411	0.064	
			M42n.3r	1170.815	1.082	168.460	0.050	
			M42n.4n	1171.496	0.681	168.492	0.031	
			M42n.4r	1171.977	0.481	168.514	0.022	Site 801C is on anomaly M42n.4r = 168.4 ± 1.7 Ma (Koppers et al., 2003).
			M42n.5n	1173.098	1.122	168.565	0.052	
			M42n.5r	1173.739	0.641	168.595	0.029	
			M42n.6n	1174.421	0.681	168.626	0.031	
			M42n.6r	1174.821	0.401	168.645	0.018	
			M42n.7n	1175.623	0.801	168.682	0.037	
			M42n.7r	1176.304	0.681	168.713	0.031	
			M42n.8n	1176.945	0.641	168.742	0.030	
			M42n.8r	1178.107	1.162	168.796	0.054	
			M42n.9n	1179.990	1.883	168.883	0.087	
			M42n.9r	1183.475	3.486	169.044	0.161	
			M42n.10n	1184.116	0.641	169.074	0.030	
			M42n.10r	1189.245	5.128	169.311	0.238	
			M42n.11n	1189.926	0.681	169.343	0.032	

Stage	Age	Chron	Subchron	Distance	Duration	Age (Ma)	Duration (Myr)	Notes
			M42r	1192.530	2.604	169.464	0.121	
		M43	M43n.1n	1192.971	0.441	169.485	0.020	
			M43n.1r	1196.657	3.686	169.656	0.172	
			M43n.2n	1199.461	2.805	169.787	0.131	
			M43n.2r	1201.745	2.284	169.894	0.107	
			M43n.3n	1203.228	1.482	169.963	0.069	
			M43n.3r	1204.510	1.282	170.023	0.060	
			M43n.4n	1205.431	0.922	170.066	0.043	
			M43n.4r	1207.354	1.923	170.156	0.090	
			M43n.5n	1209.318	1.963	170.248	0.092	
			M43r	1211.561	2.244	170.353	0.105	
		M44	M44n.1n	1212.923	1.362	170.417	0.064	
			M44n.1r	1214.125	1.202	170.474	0.057	
			M44n.2n	1214.806	0.681	170.506	0.032	
			M44n.2r	1216.209	1.402	170.572	0.066	
			M44n.3n	1217.210	1.002	170.619	0.047	
			M44n.3r	1221.057	3.846	170.801	0.182	
			M44n.4n	1221.537	0.481	170.823	0.023	
			M44n.4r	1223.100	1.563	170.897	0.074	
			M44n.5n	1223.581	0.481	170.920	0.023	
Bajocian	**170.9**		M44n.5r	1225.664	2.083	171.019	0.099	Base of Bajocian interpreted as 80% up in Chron M44n.1r (mid-depth projection) = upper Chron M44n.5r (deep tow).
Aalenian			M44n.6n	1225.985	0.321	171.034	0.015	
			M44n.6r	1227.908	1.923	171.125	0.091	
			M44n.7n	1228.188	0.280	171.138	0.013	
			M44n.7r	1229.350	1.162	171.193	0.055	
			M44n.8n	1230.873	1.522	171.265	0.072	
			M44n.8r	1231.594	0.721	171.300	0.034	
			M44n.9n	1232.716	1.122	171.353	0.053	
			M44r	1233.757	1.042	171.402	0.050	
		M45	M45n	1234.398	0.641	171.433	0.030	
			M45r					
		M-sequence extension [*deep-tow upward projection to surface (M27r–M37r or 3 km mid-depth (M38n–M44n)*]						
Kimmeridgian			M27r	856.642	4.708	155.128	0.185	
		M28	M28n.1n	865.256	8.614	155.467	0.339	
			M28n.1r	869.563	4.307	155.637	0.170	
			M28n.2n	872.417	2.855	155.750	0.113	
			M28n.2r	879.128	6.711	156.016	0.266	
			M28n.3n	886.140	7.011	156.295	0.279	
			M28n.3r	888.744	2.604	156.399	0.104	
			M28n.4n	891.048	2.304	156.491	0.092	
			M28r	894.203	3.155	156.617	0.126	
		M29	M29n	901.415	7.212	156.906	0.289	
			M29r	908.176	6.761	157.177	0.272	
		M30	M30n	915.037	6.861	157.454	0.277	
			M30r	919.645	4.608	157.640	0.186	
		M31	M31n	927.858	8.213	157.973	0.333	
			M31r	930.212	2.354	158.069	0.096	
		M32	M32n	939.327	9.115	158.441	0.372	

(Continued)

TABLE 5.4 (Continued)

Geologic stage	GTS2020 age of base (Ma)		Polarity chron	Distance (km) from Hawaiian spreading center		Age calibration (spreading rate model)		Comments
				Old end	*Width (km)*	Base Ma	*Duration (Myr)*	
			M32r	946.939	7.612	158.752	0.311	
		M33	M33n.1n	952.598	5.659	158.984	0.232	
			M33n.1r	956.405	3.806	159.141	0.157	
			M33n.2n	958.658	2.254	159.234	0.093	
			M33n.2r	960.662	2.003	159.316	0.083	
			M33n.3n	962.615	1.953	159.397	0.081	
			M33n.3r	965.870	3.255	159.531	0.135	
			M33n.4n	971.980	6.110	159.785	0.253	
			M33r	977.840	5.860	160.028	0.244	
		M34	M34n.1n	980.123	2.284	160.123	0.095	
			M34n.1r	991.181	11.058	160.586	0.463	
			M34n.2n	993.786	2.604	160.695	0.109	
			M34r	997.271	3.486	160.841	0.146	
		M35	M35n	999.154	1.883	160.920	0.079	
			M35r	1003.321	4.167	161.096	0.175	
		M36	M36n.1n	1010.633	7.312	161.405	0.309	
Oxfordian	**161.5**							Base of Oxfordian (working French ammonite version) is assigned as Chron M36Br.25 (mid-depth) = ca. mid-M36n.1r on upward surface projection.
Middle Jurassic			M36n.1r	1014.692	4.059	161.577	0.172	
			M36n.2n	1016.695	2.003	161.661	0.085	
			M36r	1020.249	3.554	161.812	0.151	
		M37	M37n.1n	1027.212	6.963	162.109	0.297	
			M37n.1r	1030.518	3.305	162.250	0.141	
			M37n.2n	1033.711	3.193	162.386	0.136	
			M37r	1035.754	3.640	162.542	0.156	
		M38	M38n.1n	1038.799	3.045	162.673	0.131	
			M38n.1r	1040.722	1.923	162.755	0.083	
			M38n.2n	1043.567	2.845	162.878	0.122	
			M38n.2r	1045.971	2.404	162.981	0.103	
			M38n.3n	1048.295	2.324	163.081	0.100	
			M38n.3r	1051.500	3.205	163.219	0.138	
			M38n.4n	1057.990	6.491	163.500	0.281	
			M38n.4r	1061.596	3.606	163.657	0.156	
			M38n.5n	1064.080	2.484	163.764	0.108	
			M38r	1069.048	4.968	163.980	0.216	
		M39	M39n.1n	1071.693	2.644	164.096	0.115	
			M39n.1r	1080.107	8.414	164.463	0.367	
			M39n.2n	1092.687	12.581	165.013	0.550	
			M39n.2r	1097.014	4.327	165.203	0.189	
			M39n.3n	1098.977	1.963	165.289	0.086	

Callovian	165.3							Base of Callovian interpreted as base of Chron M39n.3n.
			M39n.3r	1103.505	4.527	165.488	0.199	
			M39n.4n	1105.788	2.284	165.588	0.101	
			M39n.4r	1108.753	2.965	165.719	0.131	
			M39n.5n	1110.516	1.763	165.797	0.078	
			M39n.5r	1113.040	2.524	165.909	0.112	
			M39n.6n	1115.404	2.364	166.014	0.105	
			M39r	1117.768	2.364	166.119	0.105	
		M40	M40n.1n	1119.130	1.362	166.180	0.061	
			M40n.1r	1122.616	3.486	166.336	0.156	
			M40n.2n	1125.821	3.205	166.480	0.144	
			M40n.2r	1128.305	2.484	166.591	0.112	
			M40n.3n	1129.547	1.242	166.647	0.056	
			M40r	1139.684	10.137	167.104	0.457	
		M41	M41n.1n	1141.327	1.643	167.178	0.074	
			M41n.1r	1142.649	1.322	167.238	0.060	
			M41n.2n	1143.650	1.002	167.284	0.045	
			M41n.2r	1144.692	1.042	167.331	0.047	
			M41n.3n	1148.939	4.247	167.524	0.193	
			M41r	1159.356	10.417	167.999	0.475	
		M42	M42n.1n	1163.082	3.726	168.169	0.170	
Bathonian	**168.2**							Base of Bathonian interpreted as base of Chron M42n.1n.
			M42n.1r	1171.376	8.294	168.549	0.380	
			M42n.2n	1173.940	2.564	168.667	0.117	
			M42n.2r	1176.103	2.164	168.766	0.099	
			M42n.3n	1179.629	3.526	168.928	0.162	
			M42n.3r	1180.430	0.801	168.965	0.037	
			M42n.4n	1187.161	6.731	169.274	0.309	
			M42r	1191.128	3.966	169.456	0.182	
		M43	M43n.1n	1192.690	1.563	169.529	0.073	
			M43n.1r	1199.181	6.491	169.831	0.302	
			M43n.2n	1202.426	3.245	169.982	0.151	
			M43n.2r	1205.912	3.486	170.145	0.163	
			M43n.3n	1209.037	3.125	170.291	0.146	
			M43r	1212.883	3.846	170.471	0.180	
		M44	M44n.1n	1219.614	6.731	170.787	0.316	
Bajocian	**170.9**							Base of Bajocian interpreted as 80% up in Chron M44n.1r.
Aalenian			M44n.1r	1231.434	11.819	171.343	0.556	
			M44n.2n	1235.480	4.047	171.533	0.190	
			M44n.2r					

The Middle Jurassic through Early Cretaceous M-sequence of marine magnetic anomalies is a synthetic flow profile for the Hawaiian spreading center of the Pacific. Distances are tabulated to 3-decimal precision for preserving the relative widths of subchrons and for applying spreading rate models, but the actual accuracy is much less. The age model for converting the marine magnetic anomaly pattern to millions of years is from a spline fit of spreading rates as constrained by astronomical orbital tuning of durations of Early Cretaceous stages and selected radioisotopic dates. In turn, the age model for the bases of the Bajocian through Kimmeridgian stages (bold-font ages in 2nd column from left) is derived from the Jurassic portion of that spline fit of smoothed spreading rates. The composite biostratigraphic and geomagnetic polarity time scale are illustrated in the Cretaceous and Jurassic chapters (Gale et al., Ch. 27; and Hesselbo et al., Ch. 26; respectively) of this book.

(Sager et al., 1998; Tominaga et al., 2008)—were transformed to "Hawaiian-distances." This method of projecting pre-M29r marine magnetic anomalies of the Japanese-kilometer block model onto the synthetic Hawaiian-kilometer pattern implicitly assumes that there were no relative changes in spreading rates between these two ridges during the formation of this pre-M29r crust.

The synthetic profile of the full suite of M-sequence marine magnetic anomalies scaled to the relative distances in the Hawaiian lineation composite is in Table 5.4.

5.3.4 Constraints on age models and spreading rates for the composite M-sequence model

5.3.4.1 Spline fit procedure for Early Cretaceous M-sequence age model

Magnetostratigraphic studies in combination with constraints from drilling of oceanic crust have calibrated many Jurassic ammonite zones and the latest Jurassic through early Cretaceous microfossil datums to the M-sequence of marine magnetic anomalies [see Hesselbo et al. (2020, Ch. 26, The Jurassic Period) and Gale et al. (2020, Ch. 27, The Cretaceous Period) of this book]. The interpreted or estimated placement of the Middle Jurassic through Early Cretaceous stage boundaries relative to the M-sequence polarity chrons is summarized in Table 5.4.

However, in contrast to the C-sequence, which has a detailed calibration to the astronomical time scale relative to the present, the M-sequence pattern has only a few intervals of polarity chrons with "floating" cyclostratigraphic interpretation of durations, and only rare radioisotopic ages that are directly on its polarity chrons. Two ODP Sites (765 and 801) have been drilled into oceanic crust on M-sequence magnetic anomalies), but their radioisotopic datings have relatively large uncertainties.

Unfortunately, there are few radioisotopic dating of basement basalts from ocean drilling sites on M-sequence magnetic anomalies or on volcanic ash beds in outcrop sections with magnetostratigraphy; and only about three of these direct dates are considered to meet the level of quality controls used in the GTS2020 radioisotopic database. Therefore the age model for the M-sequence requires a spline fit of a few other radioisotopic dates that can be projected via biostratigraphic constraints to a polarity chron and with the additional constraints from cyclostratigraphic studies of Lower Cretaceous sections that are considered to span multiple polarity chrons.

The age model for the M-sequence polarity time scale in GTS2020 is derived from a smoothed spline fit of the spreading rates (distance versus age) for the relative widths of the composite M-sequence pattern of composite-normalized kilometer scale for the Pacific marine magnetic anomalies. This spline fit of the spreading rates was constrained by the few radioisotopic dates that have been directly correlated to polarity chrons (with uncertainties) and astronomical tuning of time spans of polarity zone intervals (with uncertainties). The "tightness" of the spline fit was adjusted to minimize rapid changes in the computed spreading rates between control points.

In GTS2012/2016 the M-sequence age model had incorporated an Aptian duration of c. 13 Myr from cyclostratigraphy (Huang et al., 2010b) that gave a base-Aptian age estimate of c. 126 Ma relative to radioisotopic dates on the Aptian–Albian boundary interval. That estimated age for the base of the Aptian was also the age for the beginning of Chron M0r, which was a candidate horizon to place the Aptian GSSP. That base-Aptian age was also consistent with radioisotopic dates of c. 124 Ma from the Ontong Java Plateau large igneous province in the Pacific that has been considered to be the cause of the Oceanic Anoxic Event OAE1a of early Aptian. The M-sequence age model used in GTS2012 was also supported by a recalibrated $^{40}Ar/^{39}Ar$ date of 145.5 ± 0.8 Ma on reversed polarity magnetized sills (interpreted as cooled during magnetozone M18r) that intruded earliest Berriasian pelagic sediments drilled at ODP Site 1213B on Shatsky Rise (Mahoney et al., 2005).

However, after the publication of GTS2012, ID-TIMS U–Pb dates from zircon assemblages from bentonites in Early Cretaceous sediments in Svalbard and Argentina have questioned the reliability of the $^{40}Ar/^{39}Ar$ dating of these basalts from ODP sites and implied that those basalt ages were systematically too old by nearly 4 Myr. In addition, ID-TIMS U–Pb dates from a bentonite horizon in Hauterivian-age sediments in Argentina yielded a date that was also nearly 3 Myr younger than the previous SHRIMP-derived U–Pb date of that same horizon (Aguirre-Urreta et al., 2008, 2015, 2019).

5.3.4.2 Spline fit version 1 to only selected radioisotopic dates would imply a near constant spreading rate during the Tithonian through Barremian stages

Therefore, for the Tithonian through early Aptian scaling in GTS2020, we focused mainly on U–Pb radioisotopic dates derived by ID-TIMS methods, of which most were published after 2012. Biostratigraphy of the dated volcanic horizons was used to estimate the placement relative to a polarity chron and equivalent kilometer interval (with uncertainty) based on the previous GTS2012/2016 syntheses of ammonite, calpionellid, and microfossil calibrations from arrays of magnetostratigraphy studies (Table 27.2 in Gale et al., Ch. 27, The Cretaceous Period, and Appendix 2 of this book).

The important suite of ID-TIMS radioisotopic dates from the Tithonian–Berriasian interval in Argentina (Aguirre-Urreta et al., 2015, 2019) are constrained by a regional ammonite zonation, but its correlation to the European standard zonation is debated. These dated horizons in Argentina have an interpreted assignment to M-sequence chrons from cyclo-magnetostratigraphy studies of nearby sections (Kietzmann et al., 2018). We modified those magnetostratigraphic calibrations by incorporating the reported condensations at major regional sequence boundaries, by considering the relative duration of polarity intervals from the succession of M-sequence widths of marine magnetic anomalies and by giving less weight to intervals that had uncertain polarity interpretations. Therefore we merged the interpreted "M19n-M18n" interval of Kietzmann et al. (2018) as only Chron M19n, thereby shifting the overlying calibrations downward by one polarity zone. These adjustments are briefly itemized in Appendix 2.

An initial spline fit to these selected radioisotopic dates as projected onto the M-sequence kilometer scale yielded an apparent linear fit for the Tithonian through basal Aptian (c. chrons M22–M0r), which would imply a nearly constant rate of spreading of the M-sequence of marine magnetic anomalies produced at the Hawaiian spreading center (its main reference location) during this interval. This initial spline fit to only the radioisotope date array is shown by the red-colored line in Fig. 5.4 (see also Section 14A.5.7 in Agterberg et al., Ch. 14A, Geomathemical and statistical procedures, this volume).

This spline-derived relationship would imply ages for the bases and durations of Early Cretaceous stages of:

1. base Barremian (estimated placement is at Chron M5n.8 at 119 km in M-sequence magnetic anomaly model) = 127.2 Ma (with a Barremian duration of 4.4 Myr);
2. base Valanginian (M14r.3; 351 km) = 135.8 Ma (combined Val + Haut stage duration of 8.6 Myr);

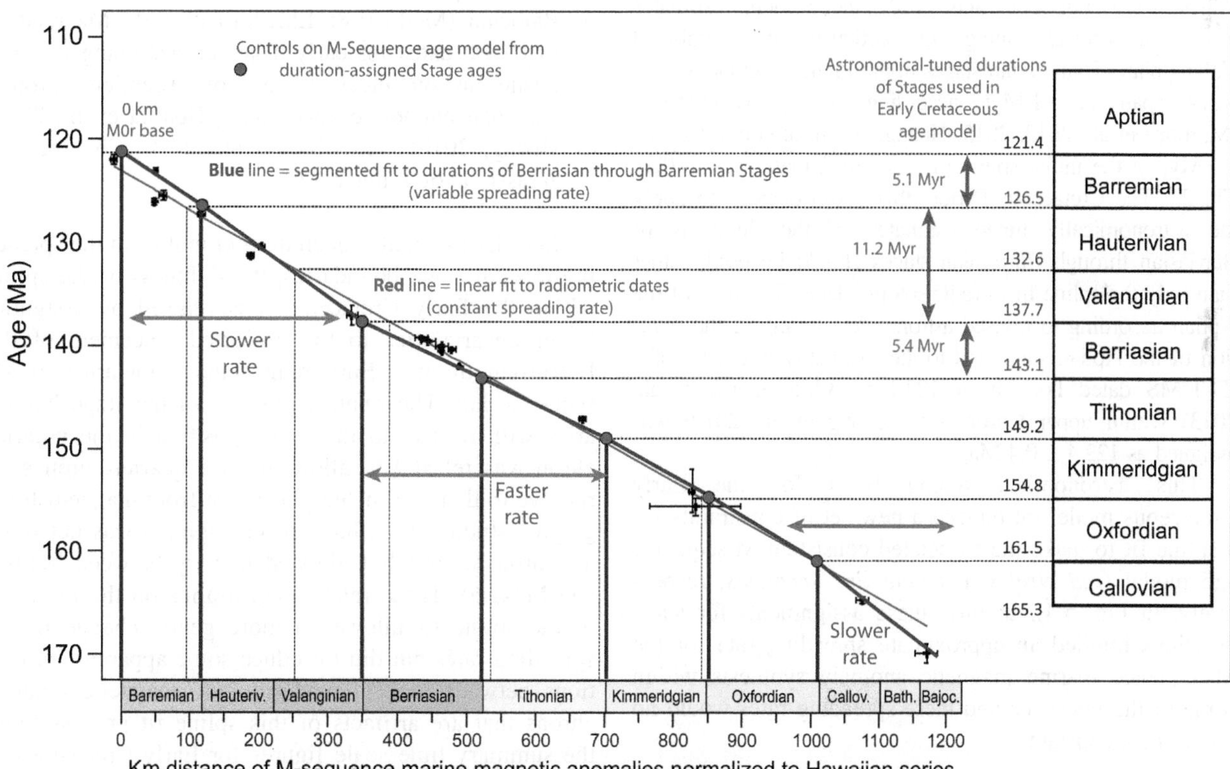

FIGURE 5.4 Late Jurassic–Early Cretaceous spline fit and time scale. A cubic spline was fit (red line) to an array of radioisotopic dates (*black dots* with uncertainties) according to their interpreted calibration to M-sequence polarity zones and the corresponding kilometer distance on the synthetic M-sequence marine magnetic profile normalized for the Hawaiian spreading center of the Pacific. The radioisotopic dates with stratigraphic discussions are given in Appendix 2 of this book. The near-linear cubic spline fit would have implied a nearly constant spreading rate for Kimmeridgian through Barremian. However, the astronomical-tuned durations of Early Cretaceous stages were used for the GTS2020, and therefore the magnetochron placement of the stage boundaries (*red dots*) implied variable spreading rates (*blue line*), which were smoothed with a cubic spline (Fig. 5.5) to interpolate the ages for M-sequence chrons (Table 5.4).

3. base Berriasian = Jurassic–Cretaceous boundary (M19n.2n.5; 526 km) = 142.3 Ma (duration of 6.5 Myr); and
4. base Tithonian (base M22An; 701 km) = 148.9 Ma (duration of 6.5 Myr).

While this set seems to be consistent with the array of radioisotopic dates, it is inconsistent with the astronomical tuning of some of the Early Cretaceous stages. Therefore this spline fit to only radioisotopic dates was not used for either the Early Cretaceous time scale nor for the associated M-sequence of polarity chrons.

5.3.4.3 Spline fit version 2 incorporating astronomically tuned duration of Berriasian through Barremian stage (the GTS2020 Early Cretaceous age model) imply major changes in rates of Pacific Hawaiian spreading center

These "constant-spreading rate" durations for the geologic stages were not consistent with independent estimates from astronomical tuning. In particular, the combined Valanginian–Hauterivian stages in the French regional stratotypes span c. 11 Myr according to cyclostratigraphy (Martinez et al., 2013, 2015; Huang, 2018), in contrast to the 8.6 Myr of the initial spline fit. Therefore, Gale et al. (2020, Ch. 27, The Cretaceous Period, this book) decided to apply the astronomically tuned estimates of the durations of Berriasian through Barremian stages should be used, rather than only the spline fit to radioisotopic dates. The base of the Aptian according to revised astronomical tuning of the duration of the Aptian stage and to the magnetostratigraphy of a ID-TIMS dated horizon of 123.1 ± 0.3 Ma (Corfu et al., 2013) within upper Chron M1r (Zhang et al., 2019) was assigned as 122.4 ± 0.4 Ma.

This astronomical tuning basis for the Early Cretaceous model introduced a new set of constraints for a spline fit to make the associated consistent M-sequence age model (*red circles* and *blue line segments*, respectively, in Fig. 5.4). In turn, these assignments for stage durations implied an approximate spreading rate for the M-sequence marine magnetic anomaly synthesis within some of the intervals; and these spreading rates would no longer be a constant.

1. Aptian (base M0r; 0 km on M-sequence magnetic anomalies) = 121.4 Ma = fixed chron-age assignment
2. Barremian (M5n.8; 119 km) = 126.5 Ma (stage duration of 5.1 Myr, as assigned by Gale et al., Ch. 27, The Cretaceous Period, this book)
3. Valanginian (M14r.3; 351 km) = 137.7 Ma (combined Val + Haut duration of 11.2 Myr according to Martinez et al., 2015; Martinez, 2018)
4. Berriasian (M19n.2n.5; 526 km) = 143.1 Ma (duration of 5.4 Myr, as assigned by Gale et al., Ch. 27, The Cretaceous Period, this book)
5. Tithonian (base M22An) = age depended on the resulting spline fit; but duration of Tithonian is c. 6 Myr (Ogg et al., 1984; Huang et al., 2010a; and C.J. Huang in the Jurassic chapter of GTS2012)

The Jurassic portion of the M-sequence spline has four additional main control points for the spline fit, of which the younger two have relatively large uncertainties

6. Kimmeridgian (base M26r, 848 km) at 154.1 ± 2.2 Ma (Selby, 2007; Przybylski et al., 2010a, 2010b; Ogg et al., 2010a, 2010b) and a cycle-derived duration of c. 5.5 Myr (Huang et al., 2010a; Huang, 2018)
7. Near the base of Callovian (base M39.3n, 1099 km) is a U–Pb radioisotopic date of 164.64 ± 0.27 Ma (Kamo and Riccardi, 2009) but uncertain placement relative to European magnetostratigraphy across boundary interval, and therefore effectively has a c. 20-km uncertainty
8. Pacific magnetic anomaly M42n.4r (1272 km) with radioisotopic date of 168.7 ± 1.7 Ma at DSDP Site 801 (Koppers et al., 2003)
9. Bajocian (M44n.1r.8; 1222 km) at 170.9 Ma relative to U–Pb dates for early Toarcian according to composite astronomical tuning of Toarcian through Aalenian ammonite zones (e.g., Boulila et al., 2014; Huang, 2018) (Hesselbo et al., 2020, Ch. 26, The Jurassic Period, this book)

In order to avoid sudden discontinuities in the spreading rates at stage boundaries, the tightness of the spline within the Early Cretaceous was relaxed by assigning larger uncertainties to the projected placement of the Berriasian through Barremian stage boundaries to M-sequence km. The relative position of the stage boundaries with respect to the target position in the polarity chron was relaxed to allow up to a quarter-chron shift relative to their estimated placement from magnetostratigraphic studies (e.g., base of Valanginian was not fixed as Chron M14r.3 but allowed to vary between M14r.0 and M14r.6). These relaxed constraints on the tightness of the spline fit allowed a more gentle change in the spreading rates but did introduce some apparent correlations between stage boundaries and magnetic polarity chrons that are artifacts of this spline fit process (e.g., the summary time scale figures for Early Cretaceous in Gale et al., Ch. 27, this book) and should not be considered as new calibrations.

5.3.5 GTS2020 age model for the composite M-sequence and implied spreading rates

The spline fit to Early Cretaceous stage durations and selected Middle and Late Jurassic constraints was run with different weighting parameters. The selected solution was the spline fit of spreading rates that was mainly within the uncertainties of the majority of the constraints but did not have artifacts of sudden changes in rates at the Early Cretaceous stage boundaries. The age model for the M-sequence chrons through M44, plus the upward projection of the pre-M26 deep-tow anomalies, is summarized in Table 5.4.

Similar to the chronostratigraphy of the Cenozoic, the age model for the stage boundaries and many of the biostratigraphic zones of the Bajocian through Tithonian of the Jurassic is based upon their calibrations to the M-sequence polarity chrons. The ages implied by the M-sequence spline fit for these Jurassic stage boundaries are included in Table 5.4, and this chronostratigraphic scaling was used for the Jurassic time scale in GTS2020.

The distance scale for the M-sequence of marine magnetic anomalies had been normalized to the Hawaiian spreading center, which had been the original reference region for M25–M0r (Larson and Hilde, 1975). In the previous GTS2012 scale the spreading rate model and implied ages for the M-sequence chrons had been a simple linear line fit to a small set of apparent spreading rates derived from estimates of astronomically tuned durations for relatively small clusters of polarity chrons that had high uncertainties (Fig. 5.5). In the GTS2020 spline fit the total age span of the Bajocian through Barremian is c. 5 Myr longer because the beginning of the Aptian (beginning of Chron M0r) had been shifted from c. 126 to c. 121 Ma. Therefore the implied average spreading rate for the M-sequence interval in the ocean spreading rates is slower.

The spline fit to the Early Cretaceous stage ages requires a significantly slower spreading rate for the Valanginian through Hauterivian (Fig. 5.5), because the duration of this pair of stages from astronomical tuning estimates of French reference sections (Martinez et al., 2013, 2015; Huang, 2018) is much longer than in GTS2012. In contrast, the estimated duration of the Berriasian stage is shorter than in GTS2012; therefore the smoothed spline fit implies an apparent faster spreading rate during Berriasian that then rapidly slows by nearly 25% to the Valanginian–Hauterivian spreading rate.

The spline fit to the selected radioisotopic dates with their relatively large uncertainties in the Jurassic would imply a smooth trend of a slowly increasing rate from Bajocian until the implied rapid spreading rate during the Berriasian. The apparent slower spreading rate of the Bajocian through Callovian interval relative to GTS2012 implies that the duration of these Middle Jurassic stages spans a longer interval in the GTS2020 age model.

Important caveats are that (1) this GTS2020 spline fit and resulting oscillating spreading rate model for the Hawaiian synthetic profile of marine magnetic anomalies was largely a result of the given constraints on the durations of the Berriasian through Barremian stages as assigned from the cyclostratigraphy of single reference sections and (2) similar to the use of the South Atlantic profiles for the initial scaling of the C-sequence (Fig. 5.3), the apparent spreading

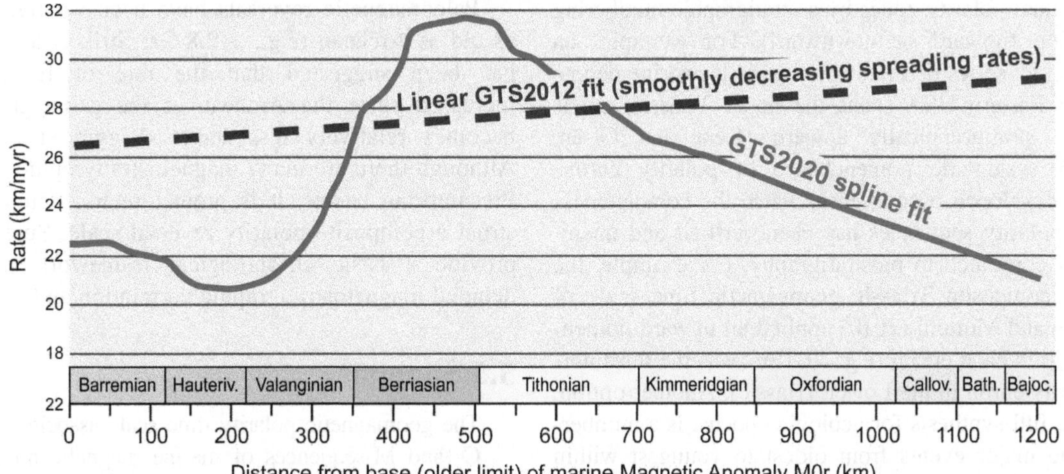

FIGURE 5.5 Spreading rates for the synthetic M-sequence marine magnetic profile normalized for the Hawaiian spreading center of the Pacific. The dashed blue line was the model used in GTS2012 of a simple linear fit to selected estimates of astronomically tuned durations for clusters of polarity chrons within the Oxfordian through Barremian. The red line is the GTS2020 age model according to a spline fit to ages of Early Cretaceous stages (Fig. 5.4) and selected radioisotopic dates in the Jurassic. The apparent slower spreading rates for the Middle Jurassic and for the Valanginian through Barremian reflect the significantly longer durations of those stages relative to the GTS2012 age model. In contrast, the duration of the Berriasian in GTS2020 is shorter than in GTS2012, thereby implying an apparent faster spreading rate.

rate changes for the Hawaiian profile do not indicate global rates of seafloor spreading. Improving the age model for the M-sequence and for the associated Middle Jurassic through Early Cretaceous interval required a combination of verified astronomical tuning of biomagnetostratigraphic reference sections, including oceanic boreholes, additional radioisotopic dating that meets modern EarthTime standards to be accomplished on unambiguous magnetic polarity chrons and European ammonite biozones, and reevaluating previous cyclostratigraphy and magnetostratigraphy studies. This process should eventually enable the M-sequence age model to achieve the same level of precision and high-resolution calibration usage as the C-sequence.

5.4 Geomagnetic polarity time scale for Early Jurassic and older rocks

The oldest M-sequence polarity chron from Pacific marine magnetic anomalies is of Middle Jurassic age. Therefore the geomagnetic polarity time scale for earlier geologic time has to be derived entirely by the progressive assembly and verification of magnetostratigraphic studies from overlapping and coeval stratigraphic reference sections. A schematic pattern of geomagnetic polarity for each individual period is summarized in that corresponding chapter within this book. However, not all of these pre-Triassic polarity patterns have been revised to incorporate an extensive Paleozoic synthesis by Hounslow et al. (2018; see also Hounslow, 2016; Hounslow and Balabanov, 2016).

Polarity chrons older than the numbered system for the corresponding marine magnetic anomaly sequences do not yet have a systematic nomenclature system. Some published magnetostratigraphic sections have designated the individual polarity zones by a stratigraphic numbering or lettering (upward or downward). For example, an extensive "E" series derived from cyclic lacustrine deposits in the Eastern USA spans the upper Triassic and is numbered stratigraphically upward (Kent and Olsen, 1999). A systematic nomenclature of polarity chrons could be developed by consensus when the completeness of these polarity sequences has been verified and unambiguously correlated to biostratigraphy. For example, the proposed composite Triassic geomagnetic time scale of Hounslow and Muttoni (2010) applied an upward nomenclature within each epoch (e.g., "LT3n" was the third normal polarity chron in the Lower Triassic). Another option, pending a full synthesis for geologic epochs, is a numbering of the major events from oldest to youngest within each individual stage—for example, polarity chron "Toarcian-3n" (or "Toar.3n") to indicate the third major normal polarity chron upward from the base of the Toarcian stage. A version of this type of stage-level nomenclature was for a preliminary (and now largely superseded) compilation of polarity patterns by Ogg (1995). However, as with the complexities in terminology within the C-sequence and M-sequence, there is a subjective choice of designating and delimiting chrons versus subchrons within an essentially random pattern.

At a larger scale, some paleomagnetists, especially Soviet workers, have proposed a series of Paleozoic "superzones" or "hyperzones" characterized by a dominant magnetic polarity or frequency of reversals (Irving and Pullaiah, 1976; Khramov and Rodionov, 1981; Algeo, 1996). In particular, the late Carboniferous to late Permian has a reversed polarity Kiaman superzone is followed by the mixed polarity Illawarra superzone. Other suggested first-order polarity features include a "Burskan" reversed polarity bias superzone spanning middle Cambrian to middle Ordovician and a "Nepan" normal polarity bias superzone spanning late Ordovician to late Silurian (Algeo, 1996). The superchrons of semistable geomagnetic polarity seem to have a long-term periodicity, and presumably the long-term changes in the average frequency of geomagnetic reversals are caused by variations in core–mantle boundary heat flow or other deep interior processes (reviewed in Hounslow, 2016). Hounslow et al. (2018) propose a fascinating theory that the long-term variation in core–mantle boundary heat flow, hence the occurrence of superchrons of semistable geomagnetic polarity, is partly caused by changes in the rates of global subduction and sinking of cold lithospheric slabs into the lower mantle. Their statistical analysis of estimated subduction area fluxes and geomagnetic reversal rates through the Phanerozoic suggests a correlation with a c. 120 Myr lag between the subduction flux and the reversal frequency.

Paleomagnetic reversals have been verified in rocks as old as Archean (e.g., ~2.8 Ga; Strik et al., 2003). It has been suggested that the rate of reversals has increased since the Archean as the geomagnetic field becomes relatively less stable (Biggin et al., 2008). Although there are many magnetostratigraphic studies of Precambrian basins, it is premature to attempt to construct a composite polarity reversal scale. Such projects provide a basic chronological framework for future detailed magnetostratigraphic correlation and dating.

5.5 Summary

- The geomagnetic polarity time scale associated with the C- and M-sequences of marine magnetic anomalies of Middle Jurassic through Neogene age is known in detail and calibrated to an array of biostratigraphic datums.
- Astronomical dating by means of Milankovitch cycles provides high-precision ages or chron durations for the majority of the C-sequence polarity time scale of the Cenozoic and for portions of the Mesozoic. The age

model for most of the M-sequence is derived from a spline fit to a synthetic marine magnetic anomaly composite ("Hawaiian" spreading ridge in Pacific for M-sequence) as constrained by astronomical tuning of durations of Tithonian through Barremian stages and the few radioisotopic dates that meet GTS2020 standards.
- Many Phanerozoic polarity patterns from pre–late Jurassic strata are calibrated to biostratigraphic scales, but most of these sequences require additional verification and complete coverage of geologic stages before a systematic nomenclature can be proposed.

Bibliography

Abdul Aziz, H., Hilgen, F.J., Krijgsman, W., and Calvo, J.P., 2003, An astronomical polarity time scale for the late middle Miocene based on cyclic continental sequences. *Journal of Geophysical Research*, **108**: 2159, https://doi.org/10.1029/2002JB001818.

Agterberg, F.M., da Silva, A.C., and Gradstein, F.M., 2020, Geomathematical and statistical procedures. *In* Gradstein, F.M., Ogg, J.G., Schmitz, M.D., and Ogg, G.M. (eds), *The Geologic Time Scale 2020*. Elsevier Publ., **Vol. 1** (this book).

Aguirre-Urreta, B., Pazos, P.J., Lazo, D.G., Fanning, C.M., and Litvak, V.D., 2008, First U/Pb SHRIMP age of the Hauterivian stage, Neuquen Basin, Argentina. *Journal of South American Earth Sciences*, **26**: 91–99.

Aguirre-Urreta, B., Lescano, M., Schmitz, M.D., Tunik, M., Concheyro, A., Rawson, P.F., et al., 2015, Filling the gap: new precise Early Cretaceous radioisotopic ages from the Andes. *Geological Magazine*, **152** (3), 557–564.

Aguirre-Urreta, B., Martinez, M., Schmitz, M., Lescano, M., Omarini, J., Tunik, M., et al., 2019, Interhemispheric radio-astrochronological calibration of the time scales from the Andean and the Tethyan areas in the Valanginian–Hauterivian (Early Cretaceous). *Gondwana Research*, **70**: 104–132.

Algeo, T.J., 1996, Geomagnetic polarity bias patterns through the Phanerozoic. *Journal of Geophysical Research*, **101**: 2785–2814.

Batenburg, S., Sprovieri, M., Gale, A.S., Hilgen, F.J., Lirer, F., and Laskar, J., 2012, Cyclostratigraphy and astronomical tuning of the Maastrichtian at Zumaia (Basque country, northern Spain). *Earth and Planetary Science Letters*, **359**: 264–278.

Beddow, H.M., Liebrand, D., Wilson, D.S., Hilgen, F.J., Sluijs, A., Wade, B.S., et al., 2018, Astronomical tunings of the Oligocene-Miocene transition from Pacific Ocean Site U1334 and implications for the carbon cycle. *Climate of the Past*, **14** (3), 255–270, https://doi.org/10.5194/cp-14-255-2018.

Berggren, W.A., Kent, D.V., Swisher III, C.C., and Aubry, M.-P., 1995, A revised Cenozoic geochronology and chronostratigraphy. *In* Berggren, W.A., Kent, D.V., and Hardenbol, J. (eds), *Geochronology, Time Scales and Global Stratigraphic Correlations: A Unified Temporal Framework for a Historical Geology*. SEPM, Special Volume, 54: 129–212.

Biggin, A.J., Strik, G., and Langereis, C.G., 2008, Evidence for a very-long-term trend in geomagnetic secular variation. *Nature Geosciences*, **1**: 395–398.

Boulila, S., Galbrun, B., Huret, E., Hinnov, L.A., Rouget, I., Gardin, S., et al., 2014, Astronomical calibration of the Toarcian stage: implications for sequence stratigraphy and duration of the early Toarcian OAE. *Earth and Planetary Science Letters*, **386**: 98–111.

Cande, S.C., and Kent, D.V., 1992a, A new geomagnetic polarity time scale for the Late Cretaceous and Cenozoic. *Journal of Geophysical Research*, **97**: 13917–13951.

Cande, S.C., and Kent, D.V., 1992b, Ultrahigh resolution of marine magnetic anomaly profiles: a record of continuous paleointensity variations? *Journal of Geophysical Research*, **97**: 15075–15083.

Cande, S.C., and Kent, D.V., 1995, Revised calibration of the geomagnetic polarity timescale for the Late Cretaceous and Cenozoic. *Journal of Geophysical Research*, **100**: 6093–6095.

Cande, S.C., Larson, R.L., and LaBrecque, J.L., 1978, Magnetic lineations in the Pacific Jurassic Quiet Zone. *Earth and Planetary Science Letters*, **41**: 434–440.

Channell, J.E.T., 2017, Mid-Brunhes magnetic excursions in marine isotope stages 9, 13, 14 and 15 (286, 495, 540 and 590 ka) at North Atlantic IODP Sites U1302/3, U1305 and U1306. *Geochemistry, Geophysics, Geosystems*, **18**: 473–487.

Channell, J.E.T., Erba, E., Nakanishi, M., and Tamaki, K., 1995, Late Jurassic-Early Cretaceous time scales and oceanic magnetic anomaly block models. *In* Berggren, W.A., Kent, D.V., and Hardenbol, J. (eds), *Geochronology, Time Scales and Global Stratigraphic Correlations: A Unified Temporal Framework for a Historical Geology*. SEPM, Special Volume, 54: 51–63.

Channell, J.E.T., Casellato, C.E., Muttoni, G., and Erba, E., 2010, Magnetostratigraphy, nannofossil stratigraphy and apparent polar wander for Adria-Africa in the Jurassic–Cretaceous boundary interval. *Palaeogeography, Palaeoclimatology, Palaeoecology*, **293**: 51–75.

Channell, J.E.T., Harrison, R.J., Lascu, I., McCave, I.N., Hibbert, F.D., and Austin, W.E.N., 2016, Magnetic record of deglaciation using FORC-PCA, sortable-silt grain size, and magnetic excursion at 26 ka, from the Rockall Trough (NE Atlantic). *Geochemistry, Geophysics, Geosystems*, **17**: 1823–1841.

Channell, J.E.T., Singer, B.S., and Jicha, B.R., 2020, Timing of Quaternary geomagnetic reversals and excursions in volcanic and sedimentary archives. *Quaternary Science Reviews*, **228**: 106–114, https://doi.org/10.1016/j.quascirev.2019.106114.

Corfu, F., Polteau, S., Planke, S., Faleide, J.I., Svensen, H., Zayoncheck, A., et al., 2013, U–Pb geochronology of Cretaceous magmatism on Svalbard and Franz Josef Land, Barents Sea large igneous province. *Geological Magazine*, **150**: 1127–1135, https://doi.org/10.1017/S0016756813000162.

Dinarès-Turell, J., Westerhold, T., Pujalte, V., Röhl, U., and Kroon, D., 2014, Astronomical calibration of the Danian stage (Early Paleocene) revisited: Settling chronologies of sedimentary records across the Atlantic and Pacific Oceans. *Earth and Planetary Science Letters*, **405**: 119–131, https://doi.org/10.1016/j.epsl.2014.08.027.

Dinarès-Turell, J., Martinez-Braceras, N., and Payros, A., 2018, High-resolution integrated cyclostratigraphy from the Oyambre Section (Cantabria, N Iberian Peninsula): constraints for orbital tuning and correlation of middle Eocene Atlantic deep-sea records. *Geochemistry Geophysics Geosystems*, **19**: 787–806, https://doi.org/10.1002/2017gc007367.

Drury, A.J., Westerhold, T., Frederichs, T., Tian, J., Wilkens, R., Channell, J.E.T., et al., 2017, Late Miocene climate and time scale reconciliation: accurate orbital calibration from a deep-sea perspective. *Earth and Planetary Science Letters*, **475**: 254–266, https://doi.org/10.1016/j.epsl.2017.07.038.

Francescone, F., Lauretano, V., Bouligand, C., Moretti, M., Sabatino, N., Schrader, C., et al., 2019, A 9 million-year-long astrochronological record of the early-middle Eocene corroborated by seafloor spreading rates. *Geological Society of America Bulletin*, **131**: 499–520, https://doi.org/10.1130/B32050.1.

Gale, A.S., Mutterlose, J., and Batenburg, S., 2020, The Cretaceous Period. *In* Gradstein, F.M., Ogg, J.G., Schmitz, M.D., and Ogg, G.M. (eds), *The Geologic Time Scale 2020*. Elsevier Publ., **Vol. 2** (this book).

Gibbard, P.L., and Head, M., 2020, The Quaternary Period. *In* Gradstein, F.M., Ogg, J.G., Schmitz, M.D., and Ogg, G.M. (eds), *The Geologic Time Scale 2020*. Elsevier Publ., **Vol. 2** (this book).

Gradstein, F.M., Ogg, J.G., and Smith, A.G. (eds), 2004. *A Geologic Time Scale 2004*. Cambridge University Press, Cambridge, pp. 589.

Gradstein, F.M., Ogg, J.G., Schmitz, M.D., and Ogg, G.M. (eds), 2012. *The Geologic Time Scale 2012*. Elsevier Publ., 2 volumes plus chart, 1176 pp.

Hallam, A., Hancock, J.M., LaBreque, J.L., Lowrie, W., and Channell, J.E.T., 1985, Jurassic to Paleogene: Part I. Jurassic and Cretaceous geochronology and Jurassic to Palaeogene magnetostratigraphy. *In* Snelling, N.J. (ed), The Chronology of the Geological Record. *Geological Society of London Memoir*, **10**: 118–140.

Handschumacher, D.W., Sager, W.W., Hilde, T.W.C., and Bracey, D.R., 1988, Pre-Cretaceous evolution of the Pacific plate and extension of the geomagnetic polarity reversal time scale with implications for the origin of the Jurassic "Quiet Zone". *Tectonophysics*, **155**: 365–380.

Harland, W.B., Cox, A.V., Llewellyn, P.G., Pickton, C.A.G., Smith, A.G., and Walters, R., 1982, *A Geologic Time Scale*. Cambridge University Press, Cambridge.

Harland, W.B., Armstrong, R.L., Cox, A.V., Craig, L.A., Smith, A.G., and Smith, A.G., 1990, *A Geologic Time Scale 1989*. Cambridge University Press, Cambridge.

He, H.Y., Deng, C.L., Wang, P.J., Pan, Y.X., and Zhu, R.X., 2012, Toward age determination of the termination of the Cretaceous Normal Superchron. *Geochemistry, Geophysics, Geosystems*, **13** (Q02002), 20, https://doi.org/10.1029/2011GC003901.

Heirtzler, J.R., Dickson, G.O., Herron, E.M., Pitman III, W.C., and LePichon, X., 1968, Marine magnetic anomalies, geomagnetic field reversals, and motions of the ocean floor and continents. *Journal of Geophysical Research*, **73**: 2119–2136.

Hesselbo, S.P., Ogg, J.G., and Ruhl, M., 2020, The Jurassic Period. *In* Gradstein, F.M., Ogg, J.G., Schmitz, M.D., and Ogg, G.M. (eds), *The Geologic Time Scale 2020*. Elsevier Publ., **Vol. 2** (this book).

Hicks, J.F., and Obradovich, J.D., 1995, Isotopic age calibration of the GRTS from C33N to C31N: Late Cretaceous Pierre Shale, Red Bird section, Wyoming, USA. *Geological Society of America, Abstracts with Programs*, **27**: A-174.

Hicks, J.F., Obradovich, J.D., and Tauxe, L., 1995, A new calibration point for the Late Cretaceous time scale: The $^{40}Ar/^{39}Ar$ isotopic age of the C33r/C33n geomagnetic reversal from the Judith River Formation (Upper Cretaceous), Elk Basin, Wyoming, USA. *Journal of Geology*, **103**: 243–256.

Hicks, J.F., Obradovich, J.D., and Tauxe, L., 1999, Magnetostratigraphy, isotopic age calibration and intercontinental correlation of the Red Bird section of the Pierre Shale, Niobrara County, Wyoming, USA. *Cretaceous Research*, **20**: 1–27.

Hilgen, F.J., Kuiper, K.F., and Lourens, L.J., 2010, Evaluation of the astronomical time scale for the Paleocene and earliest Eocene. *Earth and Planetary Science Letters*, **300**: 139–151.

Hounslow, M.W., 2016, Geomagnetic reversal rates following Palaeozoic superchrons have a fast restart mechanism. *Nature Communications*, **7**, http://dx.doi.org/10.1038/ncomms12507.

Hounslow, M.K., and Muttoni, G., 2010, The geomagnetic polarity timescale for the Triassic: linkage to stage boundary definitions. *In* Lucas, S.G. (ed), *The Triassic Time Scale*. The Geological Society, London, Special Publication, **334**: 61–102.

Hounslow, M.W., and Balabanov, Y.P., 2016, A geomagnetic polarity timescale for the Permian, calibrated to stage boundaries. *In* Lucas, S.G., and Shen, S.-Z. (eds), *The Permian Time Scale*. Geological Society, London, **450**: 61–103, http://dx.doi.org/10.1144/SP450.8.

Hounslow, M.K., Domeier, M., and Biggin, A., 2018, Subduction flux modulates the geomagnetic polarity reversal rate. *Tectonophysics*, **742-743**: 34–49.

Huang, C.J., Hesselbo, S.P., and Hinnov, L.A., 2010a, Astrochronology of the late Jurassic Kimmeridgian Clay (Dorset, England) and implications for Earth system processes. *Earth and Planetary Science Letters*, **289**: 242–255.

Huang, C.J., 2018, Astronomical Time Scale for the Mesozoic, *Stratigraphy and Time Scales*, Elsevier, **Vol. 3**: pp. 81–150.

Huang, C.J., Hinnov, L., Fischer, A.G., Grippo, A., and Herbert, T., 2010b, Astronomical tuning of the Aptian stage from Italian reference sections. *Geology*, **38**: 899–902.

Husson, D., Galbrun, B., Laskar, J., Hinnov, L.A., Thibault, N., Gardin, S., et al., 2011, Astronomical calibration of the Maastrichtian. *Earth and Planetary Science Letters*, **305**: 328–340.

International Subcommission on Stratigraphic Classification, 1979, Magnetic polarity units, a supplemental chapter of the International Subcommission on Stratigraphic Classification, International Stratigraphic Guide. *Geology*, **7**: 578–583.

Irving, E., and Pullaiah, G., 1976, Reversals of the geomagnetic field, magnetostratigraphy, and relative magnitude of paleosecular variation in the Phanerozoic. *Earth Science Reviews*, **12**: 35–64.

Kamo, S.L., and Riccardi, A.C., 2009, A new U-Pb zircon age for an ash layer at the Bathonian-Callovian boundary, Argentina. *GFF*, **131**: 177–182.

Kent, D.V., and Olsen, P.E., 1999, Astronomically tuned geomagnetic polarity timescale for the Late Triassic. *Journal of Geophysical Research*, **104**: 12,831–12,841, www.ldeo.columbia.edu/~polsen/nbcp/nbcp.timescale.htm.

Khramov, A.N., 1958, *Palaeomagnetism and Stratigraphic Correlation*. Gostoptechizdat, Leningrad.

Khramov, A.N., and Rodionov, V.P., 1981, The geomagnetic field during Palaeozoic time. *In* McElhinny, M.W., Khramov, A.N., Ozima, M., and Valencio, D.A. (eds), *Global Reconstruction and the Geomagnetic Field During the Palaeozoic*. Center for Academic Publications, Japan, **10**: 99–115.

Kietzmann, D.A., Iglesia Llanos, M.P., and Kohan Martinez, M., 2018, Astronomical calibration of the Upper Jurassic – Lower Cretaceous in the Neuquén Basin, Argentina: a contribution from the Southern Hemisphere to the geologic time scale. *In Stratigraphy and Time Scales*, **Vol. 3**. Elsevier: 327–355.

Kochhann, K.G.D., Holbourn, A., Kunht, W., Channell, J.E.T., Lyle, M. W., Shackford, J.K., et al., 2016, Eccentricity pacing of eastern equatorial Pacific carbonate dissolution cycles during the Miocene Climatic Optimum. *Paleoceanography*, **31** (9), 1176–1192, https://doi.org/10.1002/2016PA002988.

Koppers, A.A.P., Staudigel, H., and Duncan, R.A., 2003, High resolution $^{40}Ar/^{39}Ar$ dating of the oldest oceanic basement basalts in the

Western Pacific Basin. *Geochemistry, Geophysics, Geosystems ("G3")*, **4** (11), 20, https://doi.org/10.1029/2003GC000574.

Laj, C., and Channell, J.E.T., 2007, Geomagnetic excursions. *Treatise on Geophysics*, **5**: 373–416.

Langereis, C.G., Dekkers, M.J., De Lange, G.J., Paterne, M., and Van Santvoort, P., 1997, Magnetostratigraphy and astronomical calibration of the last 1.1 Myr from an eastern Mediterranean piston core and dating of short events in the Brunhes. *Geophysical Journal International*, **129**: 75–94.

Langereis, C.G., Krijgsman, W., Muttoni, G., and Menning, M., 2010, Magnetostratigraphy – concepts, definitions, and applications. *Newsletter on Stratigraphy*, **43**: 207–233.

Larson, R.L., and Hilde, T.W.C., 1975, A revised time scale of magnetic reversals for the Early Cretaceous and Late Jurassic. *Journal of Geophysical Research*, **80**: 2586–2594.

Liebrand, D., Beddow, H.M., Lourens, L.J., Päike, H., Raffi, I., Bohaty, S.M., et al., 2016, Cyclostratigraphy and eccentricity tuning of the early Oligocene through early Miocene (30.1–17.1 Ma): *Cibicides mundulus* stable oxygen and carbon isotope records from Walvis Ridge Site 1264. *Earth and Planetary Science Letters*, **450**: 392–405, http://dx.doi.org/10.1016/j.epsl.2016.06.007.

Lourens, L.J., Hilgen, F.J., Laskar, J., Shackleton, N.J., and Wilson, D., 2004, The Neogene Period. *In* Gradstein, F.M., Ogg, J.G., and Smith, A.G. (eds), *A Geologic Time Scale 2004*. Cambridge University Press, 469–484. 409–440.

Mahoney, J.J., Duncan, R.A., Tejada, M.L.G., Sager, W.W., and Bralower, T.J., 2005, Jurassic-Cretaceous boundary age and mid-ocean-ridge-type mantle source for Shatsky Rise. *Geology*, **33**: 185–188.

Martinez, M., 2018, Mechanisms of preservation of the eccentricity and longer-term Milankovitch cycles in detrital supply and carbonate production in hemipelagig marl-limestone alternations. *Stratigraphy and Time Scales*, Elsevier, **Vol. 3**: pp. 189–218.

Martinez, M., Deconinck, J.F., Pellenard, P., Reboulet, S., and Riquier, L., 2013, Astrochronology of the Valanginian stage from reference sections (Vocontian Basin, France) and palaeoenvironmental implications for the Weissert Event. *Palaeogeography, Palaeoclimatology, Palaeoecology*, **376**: 91–102.

Martinez, M., Deconinck, J.F., Pellenard, P., Riquier, L., Company, M., Reboulet, S., et al., 2015, Astrochronology of the Valanginian–Hauterivian stages (Early Cretaceous): Chronological relationships between the Paraná–Etendeka large igneous province and the Weissert and the Faraoni events. *Cretaceous Research*, **131**: 158–173.

McElhinny, M.W., and McFadden, P.L., 2000, *Paleomagnetism: Continents and Oceans*. (p. 386Academic Press.

Merrill, R.T., McElhinny, M.W., and McFadden, P.L., 1996, *The Magnetic Field of the Earth: Paleomagnetism, the Core, and the Deep Mantle*. Academic Press, San Diego, CA: 531 pp.

Ogg, J.G., 1995, Magnetic polarity time scale of the Phanerozoic. *In* Ahrens, T.J. (ed), *Global Earth Physics: A Handbook of Physics Constants*. American Geophysical Union, Washington, DC, 240–270.

Ogg, J.G., Coe, A.L., Przybylski, P.A., and Wright, J.K., 2010a, Oxfordian magnetostratigraphy of Britain and its correlation to Tethyan regions and Pacific marine magnetic anomalies. *Earth and Planetary Science Letters*, **289**: 433–448, https://doi.org/10.1016/j.epsl.2009.11.031.

Ogg, J.G., Hinnov, L.A., Huang, C., and Przybylski, P.A., 2010b, Late Jurassic time scale: integration of ammonite zones, magnetostratigraphy, astronomical tuning and sequence interpretation for Tethyan, Sub-boreal and Boreal realms. *Earth Science Frontiers*, **17**: 81–82.

Ogg, J.G., Steiner, M.B., Oloriz, F., and Tavera, J.M., 1984, Jurassic magnetostratigraphy, 1. Kimmeridgian–Tithonian of Sierra Gorda and Carcabuey, southern Spain. *Earth and Planetary Science Letters*, **71**: 147–162.

Ogg, J.G., Ogg, G.M., and Gradstein, F.M., 2016, *A Concise Geologic Time Scale 2016*. Elsevier, 234 p.

Opdyke, N.D., and Channell, J.E.T., 1996, *Magnetic Stratigraphy*. Academic Press, San Diego, CA: 346 pp.

Pälike, H., Norris, R.D., Herrie, J.O., Wilson, P.A., Coxall, H.K., Lear, C.H., et al., 2006, The heartbeat of the Oligocene climate system. *Science*, **414**: 1894–1898.

Przybylski, P.A., Ogg, J.G., Wierzbowski, A., Coe, A.L., Hounslow, M.W., Wright, J.K., et al., 2010a, Magnetostratigraphic correlation of the Oxfordian-Kimmeridgian Boundary. *Earth and Planetary Science Letters*, **289**: 256–272, https://doi.org/10.1016/j.epsl.2009.11.014.

Przybylski, P.A., Głowniak, E., Ogg, J.G., Ziółkowski, P., Sidorczuk, M., Gutowski, J., et al., 2010b, Oxfordian magnetostratigraphy of Poland and its Sub-Mediterranean correlations. *Earth and Planetary Science Letters*, **289**: 417–432, https://doi.org/10.1016/j.epsl.2009.11.030.

Raffi, I., Wade, B.S., and Pälicke, H., 2020, The Neogene Period. *In* Gradstein, F.M., Ogg, J.G., Schmitz, M.D., and Ogg, G.M. (eds), *The Geologic Time Scale 2020*. Elsevier Publ., **Vol. 2** (this book).

Ryan, W.B.F., Bolli, H.M., Foss, G.N., Natland, J.H., Hottman, W.E., and Foresman, J.B., 1978, Objectives, principal results, operations, and explanatory notes of Leg 40, South Atlantic. *Initial Reports, Deep Sea Drilling Project*, **40**: 5–20.

Sager, W.W., Fullerton, L.G., Buffler, R.T., and Handschumacher, D.W., 1992, Argo Abyssal Plain magnetic lineations revised: implications for the onset of seafloor spreading and tectonic history of the Eastern Indian Ocean. *Proceedings of the Ocean Drilling Program, Scientific Results*, **123**: 659–669.

Sager, W.W., Weiss, C.J., Tivey, M.A., and Johnson, H.P., 1998, Geomagnetic polarity reversal model of deep-tow profiles from the Pacific Jurassic Quiet Zone. *Journal of Geophysical Research – Solid Earth*, **103**: 5269–5286.

Selby, D., 2007, Direct rhenium-osmium age of the Oxfordian-Kimmeridgian boundary, Staffin Bay, Isle of Skye, UK and the Late Jurassic geologic timescale. *Norwegian Journal of Geology*, **87**: 291–299.

Singer, B.S., 2014, A Quaternary geomagnetic instability time scale. *Quaternary Geochronology*, **21**: 29–52, https://doi.org/10.1016/j.quageo.2013.10.003.

Singer, B.S., Hoffman, K.A., Schnepp, E., and Guillou, H., 2008b, Multiple Brunhes chron excursions in the west Eifel volcanic field: support for long-held mantle control on the non-axial dipole field. *Physics of the Earth and Planetary Interiors*, **169**: 28–40.

Speijer, R.P., Pälicke, H., Hollis, C.J., Hooker, J.J., and Ogg, J.G., 2020, The Paleogene Period. *In* Gradstein, F.M., Ogg, J.G., Schmitz, M.D., and Ogg, G.M. (eds), *The Geologic Time Scale 2020*. Elsevier Publ., **Vol. 2** (this book).

Speranza, F., Satolli, S., Mattioli, E., and Calamita, F., 2005, Magnetic stratigraphy of Kimmeridgian–Aptian sections from Umbria-Marche (Italy): new details on the M-polarity sequence. *Journal of Geophysical Research*, **110**: B12109, https://doi.org/10.1029/2005JB003884.

Strik, G., Blake, T.S., Zegers, T.E., White, S.H., and Langereis, C.G., 2003, Palaeomagnetism of flood basalts in the Pilbara Craton, Western Australia: Late Archaean continental drift and the oldest known reversal of the geomagnetic field. *Journal of Geophysical Research*, **108**: 2551, https://doi.org/10.1029/2003JB002475.

Tamaki, K., and Larson, R.L., 1988, The Mesozoic tectonic history of the Magellan Microplate in the western Central Pacific. *Journal of Geophysical Research*, **93**: 2857–2874.

Tarduno, J.A., 1990, A brief reversed polarity interval during the Cretaceous Normal Polarity Superchron. *Geology*, **18**: 638–686.

Tauxe, L., 2010, *Essentials of Paleomagnetism*(p. 512University of California Press, http://magician.ucsd.edu/Essentials/index.html.

Tauxe, L., Tucker, P., Petersen, N.P., and LaBrecque, J.L., 1984, Magnetostratigraphy of Leg 73 sediments. *Initial Reports, Deep Sea Drilling Project*, **73**: 609–621.

Thibault, N., Husson, D., Harlou, R., Gardin, S., Galbrun, B., Huret, E., et al., 2012, Astronomical calibration of upper Campanian–Maastrichtian carbon isotope events and calcareous plankton biostratigraphy in the Indian Ocean (ODP Hole 762C): implication for the age of the Campanian–Maastrichtian boundary. *Palaeogeography, Palaeoclimatology, Palaeoecology*, **377–378**: 52–71.

Tivey, M.A., Sager, W.W., Lee, S.-M., and Tominaga, M., 2006, Origin of the Pacific Jurassic Quiet Zone. *Geology*, **34**: 789–792.

Tominaga, M., and Sager, W.W., 2010, Revised Pacific M-anomaly geomagnetic polarity timescale. *Geophysical Journal International*, **182**: 203–232, https://doi.org/10.1111/j.1365-246X.2010.04619.x.

Tominaga, M., Sager, W.W., Tivey, M.A., and Lee, S.-M., 2008, Deep-tow magnetic anomaly study of the Pacific Jurassic Quiet Zone and implications for the geomagnetic polarity reversal time scale and geomagnetic field behavior. *Journal of Geophysical Research*, **113**: B07110, 20pp. https://doi.org/10.1029/2007JB005527.

Tominaga, M., Tivey, M.A., and Sager, W.W., 2015, Nature of the Jurassic Magnetic Quiet Zone. *Geophysical Research Letters*, **43**: 8367–8372, https://doi.org/10.1002/2015GL065394.

Vandenberghe, N., Hilgen, F.J., and Speijer, R.P., 2012, The Paleogene Period. *In* Gradstein, F.M., Ogg, J.G., Schmitz, M., and Ogg, G. (eds), *The Geologic Time Scale 2012*. Elsevier Publication, pp. 855–921.

Wang, T.T., Ramezani, J., Wang, C.S., Wu, H.C., He, H.Y., and Bowring, S.A., 2016, High-precision U–Pb geochronologic constraints on the Late Cretaceous terrestrial cyclostratigraphy and geomagnetic polarity from the Songliao Basin, Northeast China. *Earth and Planetary Science Letters*, **446**: 37–44.

Westerhold, T., Röhl, U., Frederichs, T., Agnini, C., Raffi, I., Zachos, J.C., et al., 2017, Astronomical calibration of the Ypresian timescale: implications for seafloor spreading rates and the chaotic behavior of the solar system? *Climate of the Past*, **13**: 1129–1152, https://doi.org/10.5194/cp-13-1129-2017.

Westerhold, T., Röhl, U., Frederichs, T., Bohaty, S.M., and Zachos, J. C., 2015, Astronomical calibration of the geologic timescale: closing the Middle Eocene gap. *Climate of the Past*, **11**: 1181–1195, http://dx.doi.org/10.5194/cp-11-1181-2015, www.clim-past.net/11/1181/2015.

Westerhold, T., Röhl, U., Pälike, H., Wilkens, R., Wilson, P.A., and Acton, G., 2014, Orbitally tuned timescale and astronomical forcing in the middle Eocene to early Oligocene. *Climate of the Past*, **10**: 955–973, http://dx.doi.org/10.5194/cp-10-955-2014.

Wu, H., Hinnov, L.A., Zhang, S., Jiang, G., Chu, R., Yang, T., et al., 2020, Continental geologic evidence for two Solar System chaotic events in the Late Cretaceous. *Proceedings of the National Academy of Sciences of the United States of America*, (in press).

Wu, H.C., Zhang, S.H., Jiang, G.Q., Hinnov, L.A., Yang, T.S., Li, H.Y., et al., 2013, Astrochronology of the Early Turonian–Early Campanian terrestrial succession in the Songliao Basin, northeastern China and its implication for long-period behavior of the Solar System. *Palaeogeography, Palaeoclimatology, Palaeoecology*, **385**: 55–70, https://doi.org/10.1016/j.palaeo.2012.09.004.

Zhang, Y., Ogg, J.G., Minguez, D.A., Hounslow, M., Olaussen, S., Gradstein, F.M., et al., 2019, Magnetostratigraphy of U/Pb-dated boreholes in Svalbard, Norway, implies that the Barremian–Aptian Boundary (beginning of Chron M0r) is 121.2 ± 0.4Ma. *AGU Annual Meeting, San Francisco, CA, 9–13 Dec 2019. #GP44A-06*. <https://agu.confex.com/agu/fm19/meetingapp.cgi/Paper/577991>

M.D. Schmitz, B.S. Singer and A.D. Rooney

Chapter 6

Radioisotope Geochronology

Chapter outline

Abstract

Radioisotope geochronology provides a numerical age framework for the geologic time scale, and within its geologic context is integral to the practice of time scale construction. This chapter highlights the past decade of evolution in practice and interpretation of the U–Pb, $^{40}Ar/^{39}Ar$, and Re–Os radiogenic isotope geochronometers as applied to time scale construction and calibration. Topics include innovations in instrumental analysis and experimental design, the intercalibration of these geochronometers to each other as well as to astrochronology, and progress in the statistical integration of radioisotope geochronology and stratigraphy for age model construction.

6.1 Introduction

The science of radiogenic isotope geochronology, or radioisotopic dating, is an integral partner in the effort to construct the geologic time scale. The Earth's history is recorded in rock sequences deposited in space and time, and its reconstruction thus requires the correlation of temporally equivalent strata across diverse depositional environments in changing tectonic and paleogeographic settings. Correlation of rock sequences, in turn, necessitates the identification and synchronization of a range of physical, chemical, and biological markers preserved in the rock record (Erwin, 2006). Volcanic rocks interstratified with sedimentary successions are geologically instantaneous event beds, and thus when dated provide isochronous timelines that tightly constrain the correlation of their host successions. Radioisotopically dated horizons in stratigraphic successions can be integrated into quantitative biostratigraphic methods for improved correlation and composite section construction (Sadler et al., 2009; Schmitz and Davydov, 2012). Radioisotopic dates embedded within a cyclostratigraphic framework can also anchor floating astrochronologies and associated estimates of the tempo and duration of sedimentary accumulation (Machlus et al., 2015; Meyers et al., 2012). Multiple bracketing radioisotopic ages lend high temporal fidelity to various other bio–chemo-physical markers in the rock record (Baresel et al., 2017; Burgess et al., 2014). Together, these varied uses of radioisotopic ages are integral to the numerical calibration of the geologic time scale and provide an independent temporal framework for testing correlation, assessing causal relationships between processes and phenomena, and establishing the rates of geologic and biologic processes.

Geologic Time Scale 2020. DOI: https://doi.org/10.1016/B978-0-12-824360-2.00006-1

The North American and European EARTHTIME Initiatives for the Calibration of the Earth's History (www.earth-time.org; earthtime-eu.eu), as well as the "GTSNext" European Union Marie Curie Initial Training Network (2008–12), have been notable for fostering not only communication between laboratories and practitioners of geochronology, but also quantitative efforts at interlaboratory and intermethod calibration (Bowring et al., 2004). This effort was spurred in part by the identification of systematic biases between U–Pb and $^{40}Ar/^{39}Ar$ ages for the same rocks (Min et al., 2000, 2001, 2003; Schmitz and Bowring, 2001; Dazé et al., 2003; Kamo et al., 2003; Schoene et al., 2006), as well as the recognition within each methodology that potential systematic errors (and their limitations for age accuracy) could no longer be ignored given improvements in analytical precision (Ludwig, 1998; Renne et al., 1998a; Mattinson, 2000; Villeneuve et al., 2000; Begemann et al., 2001). Specifically, a series of workshops between 2003 and 2019 have brought representatives of many high-precision U–Pb and $^{40}Ar/^{39}Ar$ laboratories together to plan, execute, and assess the results of interlaboratory comparisons using a variety of natural and synthetic standard materials. A comprehensive description of these experiments is beyond the scope of this review (Condon, 2005; Heizler, 2005); however, many of the outcomes of these experiments are highly relevant to time scale calibration (Condon et al., 2010; 2015; Hiess et al., 2012; Jicha et al., 2016; Niespolo et al., 2017; Renne et al., 2010). Next, we summarize the resulting major improvements in radioisotopic dating applied to the construction of the global geologic time scale, first detailing improvements in geochronological practice, and then outlining the consequences of these improvements for the construction of a Geologic Time Scale 2020.

6.2 U–Pb geochronology

Isotope dilution thermal ionization mass spectrometry (ID-TIMS) is the benchmark method for the high-precision (<0.05% relative uncertainty) determination of U and Pb isotope ratios, due to its sensitivity, ion beam stability, low magnitude of instrumental mass bias, and gravimetric metrological basis (Reiners et al., 2017). The geological sciences have seen tremendous growth in application of in situ methods for U–Pb geochronology, including new generations of laser ablation inductively coupled plasma mass spectrometers (LA-ICPMS) and secondary ion mass spectrometers (SIMS). These methods find limited use, however, in time scale geochronology because of their intrinsic precision and accuracy limits of >1% of the relative age (Black et al., 2003; Ireland and Williams, 2003; Kosler and Sylvester, 2003; Chang et al., 2006; Gehrels et al., 2008).

The basic analytical instrumentation and protocols for ID-TIMS have changed little over the past decade. The precision and accuracy required for the measurement of isotope ratios on the picogram quantities of Pb found in single-zircon crystals remain best achieved via single-collector analysis using a discrete dynode electron multiplier or Daly-type conversion dynode photomultiplier detector, which is facilitated by the long-lived, stable ion beams produced by the thermal source. Recent development of higher ohmic resistor amplification circuitry has significantly improved small ion beam analysis of U and to a lesser degree Pb isotope ratios (Quadt et al., 2016; Macdonald et al., 2018). Improvements in analytical blank—the amount of Pb and U added to a sample during the dissolution and processing for ID-TIMS—have been modest but important over the past decade. Several laboratories now report blank levels as low as 0.1 pg of Pb, which allows the analysis of increasingly younger, lower U, and smaller crystal fragments. The vast majority of Pliocene and older zircons can now be analyzed by ID-TIMS with per mil or better precision in clean facilities, and this decrease in sample size also allows the routine analysis of partial zircon crystals previously prepared for cathodoluminescence imaging and/or in situ analysis.

6.2.1 Chemical abrasion

The assumption of closed system behavior in a mineral-isotopic system is a fundamental tenet of geochronology. The preeminence of the U–Pb and $^{40}Ar/^{39}Ar$ methods for precise and accurate geochronology stems in large part from the geochronologists' ability to test and validate this assumption, through intrinsic properties of the isotope systems and/or their analytical methodologies. In U–Pb geochronology the existence of two independent but chemically identical decay chains with differing parent half-lives provides three different radioisotopic ages ($^{206}Pb/^{238}U$, $^{207}Pb/^{235}U$, and the derivative $^{207}Pb/^{206}Pb$) for the assessment of closed system behavior, or "concordance." Concordance between the three isotopic ages provides a particularly robust test for postcrystallization closed system behavior in Precambrian minerals, due to the rapid ingrowth of ^{207}Pb and the strong curvature of the concordia curve early in the Earth's history. Unfortunately, the relative linearity of the concordia curve in the Phanerozoic renders concordance an ineffective tool for assessing Pb-loss or subtle inheritance.

In the 20th century a major limiting factor in the precision and accuracy of U–Pb ages for Phanerozoic time scale calibration, not to mention the efficiency of geochronological studies, was the recognition and mitigation of geological scatter in crystal populations due to Pb-loss and/or subtle inheritance (Bowring and Schmitz, 2003; Davis et al., 2003). The effects of these two forms of open system behavior are particularly troublesome given the two-sided nature of the problem, Pb-loss leading to younger apparent ages, and inheritance biasing analyses to older apparent ages. As highlighted by Mundil et al. (2001), averaging of these effects when analyzing composite fractions of crystals can yield spurious apparent ages. Because of this phenomenon, all time scale quality ages are now obtained on individual crystals or crystal fragments.

In what must be counted among the most influential papers in U–Pb geochronology, Mattinson (2005) elegantly solved the problem of Pb-loss in zircon with the development of the chemical abrasion method. Chemical abrasion thermal ionization mass spectrometry, or "CA-TIMS," combines a high-temperature annealing step with successive partial dissolution in hydrofluoric acid to preferentially remove high U, radiation damaged, and thus more soluble portions of zircon crystals—those domains most likely to have undergone Pb-loss through geologic time (Silver and Deutsch, 1963). In contrast to prior attempts to mitigate Pb-loss through chemical means (Mattinson, 1994a; Corfu, 2000; Davis and Krogh, 2001), CA-TIMS overcomes problems of preferentially leaching of radiogenic daughter products from otherwise undissolved zircon through the high-temperature (800°C–900°C) anneal. This predissolution anneal migrates lattice defects arising from low doses of radiation out of low-U domains in zircon crystals, thus apparently hardening those domains to the detrimental effects of preferential leaching. Solubility contrasts between this recovered crystalline low-U zircon and nonrecoverably damaged high-U zircon are enhanced such that partial dissolution in HF at moderate temperatures ($<200°C$) for short times (<12 hours) can selectively and quantitatively remove Pb-loss domains from zircon crystals at the micron scale. The effectiveness of the CA-TIMS method has been demonstrated in a series of experiments on single- and multigrain fractions of relatively simple igneous zircons lacking inheritance (Mattinson, 2005, 2010b; Huyskens et al., 2016; Widmann et al., 2019). These experiments systematically illustrate the effects of the high-temperature anneal, the preferential dissolution of high-U domains during subsequent chemical abrasion, and the minor volume of these high-U domains in most zircon crystals. In summary, CA-TIMS is now the standard treatment for U–Pb zircon geochronology and by dramatically reducing the degree of geological scatter in zircon data sets is revolutionizing the resolving power and application of ID-TIMS to geochronological problems in time scale calibration and beyond.

6.2.2 Isotope tracers and standards

The systematic uncertainties associated with the gravimetric calibration of the isotope dilution tracer, or "spike," used to calculate U/Pb ratios have been quantified in a successful effort to create and widely distribute mixed tracer and gravimetric standard solutions (Condon et al., 2015; McLean et al., 2015). The desirability of a single set of both mixed tracer solutions and gravimetric standards with which to calibrate existing tracer solutions was highlighted at the EARTHTIME II Workshop in Massachusetts in April of 2004. This task was subsequently spearheaded by a consortium of scientists from the National Isotope Geology Laboratory of the British Geological Survey, the Massachusetts Institute of Technology, and the University of Santa Barbara, resulting in the current availability of three mixed U/Pb gravimetric solutions, two mixed tracer solutions, and three synthetic mixed U/Pb "age" solutions for widespread distribution to the U–Pb geochronological community (www.earth-time.org) (Condon et al., 2007, 2008, 2015). The tracer solutions were mixed from high purity ^{205}Pb, ^{233}U, and ^{235}U; concentrations and ^{205}Pb/^{235}U and ^{233}U/^{235}U ratios were optimized for single-zircon analysis. An aliquot of this tracer was also mixed with ^{202}Pb to yield a double Pb–double U spike for the comprehensive internal correction of instrumental mass bias.

The consistent use of these EARTHTIME tracer and gravimetric standard solutions improves the absolute accuracy of U–Pb geochronological measurements, given their traceability back to fundamental constants, gravimetry, and the benchmark NIST SRMPb982 and SRMU500 standards. Furthermore, time scales constructed upon U–Pb ages derived using these tracers and standards yield relative ages and durations insensitive to uncertainties associated with tracer calibration, thus breaking down a $\sim 0.03\%$ (absolute) age resolution barrier imposed by the systematic tracer calibration uncertainty.

6.2.3 Decay constants and natural ratios

The importance of considering uncertainties in the nominal values of decay constants used by the geochronological community has received increasing attention as the precision of radioisotopic ages has improved (Mattinson, 1987; Ludwig, 1998, 2000; Renne et al., 1998a; Begemann et al., 2001). Difficulties in decay constant determination through direct counting experiments for unenergetic beta or electron capture decay modes have resulted in imprecise estimates, excessive scatter between different apparently precise measurements, and even divergence in the consensus values used in the geological and nuclear physics communities (Min et al., 2000; Begemann et al., 2001; Scherer et al., 2001; Nebel et al., 2011). By contrast the energetic alpha decay modes of ^{235}U and ^{238}U have lent themselves to relatively easier activity measurements, culminating in the experiments of Jaffey et al. (1971), whose decay constants and uncertainties of 0.155125 ± 0.00016 (^{238}U) and $0.98485 \pm 0.00134\ \mathrm{Ga}^{-1}$ (^{235}U) were recommended by Steiger and Jäger (1977) for consensus use in geochronology (all uncertainties in this paper are given at the 2σ or 95% confidence interval).

Oft referred to as the "gold standard" of geochronology, even the ^{238}U and ^{235}U decay constants have been subject to periodic scrutiny (Mattinson, 1987, 1994b, 1997; Renne et al., 1998a; Begemann et al., 2001; Schön et al., 2004). The most definitive treatment of decay constant uncertainties in U–Pb geochronology is that of Ludwig (1998), who derived statistical methodologies for the propagation of decay constant errors on U–Pb, $^{207}Pb/^{206}Pb$, and discordia upper intercept ages (Ludwig, 2000). Several recent studies using geological materials now demand a refinement of the Jaffey et al. (1971) decay constants. Mattinson (2000) first suggested a possible systematic bias in one or both of the U decay constants, from the observation of consistent discordance between $^{206}Pb/^{238}U$ and $^{207}Pb/^{206}Pb$ ages of bulk zircon fractions of Mesozoic granitoids. In a comprehensive study of precise and reproducible single-zircon and xenotime analyses spanning over three billion years in age, Schoene et al. (2006) also highlighted a consistent offset from concordia and calculated a revised ratio of the U decay constants. Mattinson (2010a) reexamined a number of his original Mesozoic granitoids and other widely used high-quality zircon standard materials with the chemical abrasion plateau method, confirming the two earlier studies. The revised decay constant ratio ($\lambda_{235}/\lambda_{238}$) resulting from these studies differs from that of Jaffey et al. (1971) by 0.09% (although within the stated uncertainties of that experiment) and is a factor of five more precise. Both Mattinson (2010a) and Schoene et al. (2006) favored the likelihood of the bias being hosted in the excess scatter of the ^{235}U counting experiments and revised the ^{235}U decay constant with respect to the new decay constant ratio. This revision affects both $^{207}Pb/^{235}U$ and $^{207}Pb/^{206}Pb$ ages (shifting them to younger values) and significantly reduces the propagated uncertainty in $^{207}Pb/^{206}Pb$ and discordia upper intercept ages.

Analytical innovations particularly in the application of multicollector plasma mass spectrometry have led to increased investigation of isotope fractionations in the "heavy" elements, including uranium. A number of recent studies have challenged the canonical value of the $^{238}U/^{235}U$ ratio of 137.88 (Steiger and Jäger, 1977) in a variety of terrestrial and meteoritic materials (Stirling et al., 2005, 2006, 2007; Weyer et al., 2008; Amelin et al., 2009; Bopp et al., 2009; Brennecka et al., 2010b). Richter et al. (2010) and Condon et al. (2010) reported high-precision measurements for a variety of standard reference materials, measured via double-spike ID-TIMS with the gravimetric IRMM-3636 mixed ^{233}U–^{236}U tracer. The results highlighted the dispersion of the U isotopic composition of these materials to values lower than the canonical value; Condon et al. (2010) discussed their implications for the improved calibration of mixed U–Pb tracer solutions.

Several studies have highlighted departures from the canonical U isotope ratio in natural materials, including seawater, carbonates, ferromanganese crusts, anoxic sediments, and uranium ores (Stirling et al., 2007; Weyer et al., 2008; Bopp et al., 2009; Brennecka et al., 2010a). Proposed nuclear volume–dependent (nuclear field shift) isotope fractionation appears to be facilitated by oxidation–reduction reactions in the surficial and near-surface environment (Bigeleisen, 1996; Buchachenko, 2001; Schauble, 2007). Hiess et al. (2012) documented a smaller variance in the U isotope composition of zircon in a variety of igneous samples, with a mean value of 137.818 ± 0.005, slightly lower than the canonical value. This result was recently affirmed and refined by Livermore et al. (2018). These determinations allow a correction and propagation of associated uncertainty in the natural $^{238}U/^{235}U$ (simultaneous with the use of a self-consistent revised ^{235}U decay constant) into the calculation of $^{207}Pb/^{235}U$ and $^{207}Pb/^{206}Pb$ ages (Table 6.1) (Hiess et al., 2012).

It is clear from these studies that care must be taken when comparing the different ages internal to the U–Pb

TABLE 6.1 Decay constants utilized in GTS2012.

Radioisotope	Decay constant (Ga^{-1})	References
^{238}U	0.155125 ± 0.00016	Jaffey et al. (1971)
^{235}U[a]	0.98531 ± 0.00012	Hiess et al. (2012), Mattinson (2010a,b), and Schoene et al. (2006)
^{187}Re	0.01666 ± 0.00005	Smoliar et al. (1996)
^{40}K[b] (λ_{EC})	0.0580 ± 0.0007	Min et al. (2000)
^{40}K[b] (λ_{β})	0.4884 ± 0.049	Min et al. (2000)
^{40}K[b] (λ_{total})	0.5463 ± 0.0054	Min et al. (2000)

[a]*This revised ^{235}U decay constant was calculated by Hiess et al. (2012) using a subset of the closed system zircon ages dated by Schoene et al. (2006) and Mattinson (2010a,b), with respect to the ^{238}U decay constant of Jaffey et al. (1971) and the $^{238}U/^{235}U$ natural ratio = 137.818 ± 0.005 of Hiess et al. (2012).*
[b]*These decay constants are integral to the use of the Kuiper et al. (2008) intercalibration of the $^{40}Ar/^{39}Ar$ and astrochronological clocks.*

system. This issue is particularly relevant to the comparison of Precambrian ages that historically rely upon interpretation of $^{207}Pb/^{206}Pb$ or upper intercept dates (or more rarely $^{207}Pb/^{235}U$ ages for monazites). The Phanerozoic ages of the geologic time scale are, by contrast, predominantly interpreted based upon $^{206}Pb/^{238}U$ ages and thus revision of the ^{235}U decay constant is a very minor concern. Finally, as with systematic tracer calibration uncertainties, the decay constant uncertainties need not be propagated when considering time scales, relative ages, and durations constructed solely upon U−Pb ages. However, decay constant uncertainties must be propagated into ages when comparing them to different radioisotopic, sidereal, or astronomic ages.

6.2.4 Petrochronology

A decade of CA-TIMS geochronology has demonstrated not only the efficient elimination of Pb loss, but the relatively common phenomenon of slightly but resolvably older crystals in the magmatic population, which may derive from one or more processes, including inheritance of xenocrystic cores, crystal recycling from earlier volcanic episodes, or prolonged magma residence prior to eruption (Mundil et al., 2004; Rivera et al., 2013; Wotzlaw et al., 2014a).

The mineral zircon crystallizes within zirconium-saturated silicate magmas of intermediate to felsic composition—a condition that can predate eruption by over 100 degrees of cooling and partial solidification. When combined with the slow kinetics of diffusion through zircon, and dependent upon the cooling rate and thermal longevity of a magmatic system, "autocrystic" zircon crystals can record preeruptive magma chamber dynamics (Barboni and Schoene, 2014; Rivera et al., 2014). Similarly, "antecrystic" zircon crystals that are cannibalized from earlier solidified extrusive and intrusive rocks of the volcanic center and entrained into younger magmas will preserve their earlier history through subsequent magmatic processes (Rivera et al., 2013; Wotzlaw et al., 2014b).

Petrochronology is an integrative approach to studying magmatic systems and processes, which utilizes textural and geochemical information to provide context for the interpretation of geochronological data. Petrochronology is facilitated by the now common application of cathodoluminescence imaging of zircon, which guides in situ SIMS and/or LA-ICPMS geochemical and isotopic analysis followed by chemical abrasion ID-TIMS U−Pb isotope ratio analysis of the same crystal fragments (Rivera et al., 2016; Wotzlaw et al., 2015). Geochemical and isotopic information can also be recovered from the same crystal dissolution through solution ICPMS (Schoene et al., 2010). A petrochronology workflow allows efficient screening of zircon crystal populations for their volcanic component, rejecting inherited or detrital components that can be incorporated into the volcanic ash beds during their magmatic storage and/or eruption (Rooney et al., 2018). Petrochronology also quantifies the uranium contents and correlated Pb-loss phenomena in crystals prior to ID-TIMS analysis, which allows for tuning the conditions of chemical abrasion to eliminate Pb-loss bias (Opluštil et al., 2016). Petrochronology further provides coupled age and geochemical information that can be used to objectively interpret complex single-crystal fragment age spectra (Rivera et al., 2013; Szymanowski et al., 2017).

Petrochronological studies over the past decade have contributed to time scale calibration in numerous ways. Its ability to screen for and avoid crystal inheritance has made time scale geochronological studies more efficient (Aguirre-Urreta et al., 2015). Its ability to differentiate zircon crystals on the basis of their temperature of crystallization and degree of magma evolution has allowed for the objective identification of near-eruption zircon crystallization, which better estimates eruption and deposition (Rivera et al., 2013). And petrochronology has provided new data that place limits on the multimillennial time scales of "magma residence" prior to silicic volcanic eruptions (Rivera et al., 2016; Wotzlaw et al., 2015), in response to earlier questions regarding the fidelity of zircon-based estimates eruption and deposition (Simon et al., 2008). Petrochronology will continue to provide a more informed and objective interpretation of U−Pb zircon isotopic systematics and depositional ages for time scale calibration.

6.3 $^{40}Ar/^{39}Ar$ geochronology

The $^{40}Ar/^{39}Ar$ method is a variant of K−Ar dating that exploits the decay of $^{40}K-^{40}Ar$ via electron capture. The method is powerful in that (1) many rocks and minerals (alkali feldspar, mica, amphibole, and basaltic to rhyolitic lavas) contain sufficient potassium to enable precise measurement, and (2) it is sufficiently sensitive to provide dates from materials spanning from the Holocene to the age of the solar system. The recent review by Reiners et al. (2017) of the K−Ar and $^{40}Ar/^{39}Ar$ systems provides excellent, thoroughly referenced, historical background, as well as highlights regarding accuracy and calibration that are germane to advancing the geologic time scale. Next, we report on innovations and advances in the $^{40}Ar/^{39}Ar$ method aimed at improving its accuracy and precision that have transpired since the publication of GTS2012.

6.3.1 Technical innovations

The most significant advance in $^{40}Ar/^{39}Ar$ geochronology has been the introduction of multicollector mass spectrometers in many laboratories. These spectrometers are mainly of two types that deploy either several ion-counting multipliers to measure the ion beams (e.g., DiMaggio et al., 2015;

Jicha et al., 2016), or multiple faraday cups with high ohm amplifiers, in parallel with an ion-counting multiplier at the low mass position (e.g., Phillips and Matchan, 2013; Phillips et al., 2017; Balbas et al., 2016; Gemignani et al., 2019; Morgan et al., 2019).

The mass spectrometers used by most $^{40}Ar/^{39}Ar$ laboratories from the late 1980s until the 2010s were operated in single-collector (analog multiplier) mode requiring peak-hopping to measure the ^{40}Ar, ^{39}Ar, ^{38}Ar, ^{37}Ar, and ^{36}Ar ion beams. Moreover, these spectrometers typically had a mass resolution incapable of discriminating potential isobaric interferences on the ^{36}Ar beam. Accurate measurement of ^{36}Ar is critical because it is used to correct for atmospheric argon present in the sample, but it is typically a small beam that is challenging to measure in the presence of significant procedural blanks (e.g., Singer, 2014; Singer et al., 2019). Some new-generation $^{40}Ar/^{39}Ar$ multicollector mass spectrometers have sufficient mass-resolving power (herein is defined as $m/\Delta m$, where m is the mass of a peak and Δm is the mass difference at 95% and at 5% of the maximum peak height) to partially or fully separate ^{36}Ar from $H^{35}Cl$ and $3 \cdot {}^{12}C$ interferences (Saxton, 2015; Jicha et al., 2016; Zhang et al., 2016). Coupled with greatly reduced background levels of argon contributed by these mass spectrometers, resulting age determinations are likely more accurate, as well as more precise, relative to older single-collector results (e.g., Jicha et al., 2016; Niespolo et al., 2017; Gemignani et al., 2019; Singer et al., 2019).

In addition to improved mass resolution, and thus accuracy, the current-generation multicollector mass spectrometers are far more sensitive that their single-collector predecessors owing to high ohm amplifiers (10^{12} or 10^{13} Ω) on faraday cups (Balbas et al., 2016; Ware and Jourdan, 2018; Gemignani et al., 2019; Morgan et al., 2019), or ion-counting multipliers to measure all beams simultaneously (Jicha et al., 2016). Coupled with simultaneous collection of the mass spectrum, the improved sensitivity translates into more precise $^{40}Ar/^{39}Ar$ measurements of smaller ion beams, and thus more precise age determinations from ever shrinking sample size (Jicha et al., 2016; Gemignani et al., 2019). For example, although single-crystal laser fusion has become de rigueur to date widespread volcanic fall and flow deposits (e.g., Meyers et al., 2012; Sageman et al., 2014; Reiners et al., 2017), it is now possible to incrementally heat individual sanidine crystals from these deposits to further test for homogeneity and closed system behavior (e.g., Singer et al., 2014; Jicha et al., 2016; Andersen et al., 2017; Giaccio et al., 2017; Morgan et al., 2019). This marked improvement in precision is not without consequences as several studies have begun to reveal isotopic heterogeneity of sanidine standards widely used in $^{40}Ar/^{39}Ar$ chronology (Phillips and Matchan, 2013; Jicha et al., 2016; Phillips et al., 2017). We return to this topic next under the discussion of intercalibration and ongoing challenges.

As noted in GTS2012, beginning in 2003 the EARTHTIME Initiative fostered an intercalibration exercise involving a large fraction of the global $^{40}Ar/^{39}Ar$ community. This exercise prompted many laboratories to undertake introspective evaluation of analytical protocols, including procedural blanks, gas equilibration times between extraction systems and spectrometers, and irradiations (e.g., Singer, 2014; Heizler et al., 2015; Singer et al., 2019). In large part by capitalizing on the improved precision and accuracy afforded by multicollector mass spectrometer technology, the $^{40}Ar/^{39}Ar$ community has made great strides in addressing, and shrinking, interlaboratory calibration biases (Jicha et al., 2016; Niespolo et al., 2017; Reiners et al., 2017; Schaen et al., 2020). Next, we expand upon these advances and their implications for standards and calibration of the $^{40}Ar/^{39}Ar$ system against independent chronometers.

6.3.2 Analytical and systematic sources of uncertainty

As summarized by Reiners et al. (2017) and Schaen et al. (2020) the calibration and accuracy of $^{40}Ar/^{39}Ar$ ages are a function of three components: (1) the precision of the measurement, including corrections for background concentrations, mitigation of isobaric interferences, and mass biases reflecting particular ion sources or detector configurations; (2) nuclear interference corrections required to isolate the radiogenic ^{40}Ar and potassium-derived ^{39}Ar from isotopes generated during irradiation of calcium (produces minor ^{39}Ar) and potassium (produces minor ^{40}Ar) by neutrons; and (3) the ages of fluence monitors (often called "standards") used during irradiation and the ^{40}K decay constants.

Components 1 and 2 contribute to analytical or intralaboratory uncertainty and are appropriate when comparing among $^{40}Ar/^{39}Ar$ dates calibrated using a single-standard age and decay constants. However, when comparing $^{40}Ar/^{39}Ar$ dates to those from other independent chronometers, for example, U–Pb zircon dates, or ^{14}C dates, it is necessary to include the systematic uncertainties contained in abovementioned component 3 and report this as a total uncertainty. A typical way to report these uncertainties is as follows: age $\pm\, \sigma_{\text{analytical}}/\sigma_{\text{total}}$, where the analytical uncertainty includes the uncertainty on the neutron fluence monitor and total uncertainty additionally propagates in the uncertainty on the decay constants (e.g., Meyers et al., 2012; Singer et al., 2014; Sageman et al., 2014). Progress on the quantitation and amelioration of these component 3 uncertainties is summarized next.

TABLE 6.2 Modern ^{40}K decay constants.

Constant	Steiger and Jäger (1977)	Min et al. (2000)	Renne et al. (2011)
λ_{EC}	0.581×10^{-10} year^{-1}	$(0.580 \pm 0.007) \times 10^{-10}$ year^{-1}	$(5.757 \pm 0.016) \times 10^{-11}$ year^{-1}
λ_{β}	4.962×10^{-10} year^{-1}	$(4.884 \pm 0.049) \times 10^{-10}$ year^{-1}	$(4.9548 \pm 0.0134) \times 10^{-10}$ year^{-1}
λ_{total}	5.543×10^{-10} year^{-1}	$(5.463 \pm 0.054) \times 10^{-10}$ year^{-1}	$(5.531 \pm 0.0135) \times 10^{-10}$ year^{-1}

6.3.3 ^{40}K decay constants

Steiger and Jäger (1977) recommended ^{40}K decay constants that were subsequently used for more than three decades. Min et al. (2000) reevaluated the ^{40}K activity data and recommended decay constants that were adopted in GTS2012 (Table 6.2; see Schmitz, 2012 for background). A third set of decay constants is based on the Min et al. (2000) values, combined with the $^{40}Ar^{*}/^{40}K$ of the widely used Fish Canyon sanidine (FCs) standard, and 16 pairs of $^{238}U/^{206}Pb-^{40}Ar/^{39}Ar$ dates for volcanic rocks using a statistical optimization approach (Renne et al., 2011) (Table 6.2).

6.3.4 The isotopic composition and age of standard minerals and their intercalibration

The $^{40}Ar/^{39}Ar$ method requires standards in order to gauge the amount of parent isotope ^{40}K relative to the radiogenic daughter isotope ^{40}Ar in each measurement. Thus as noted by Reiners et al. (2017), standards are partly analogous to the tracer solutions used for isotope dilution measurements. In GTS2012 the astronomically calibrated ages of 28.201 ± 0.023 Ma (1σ) for the widely used FCs standard (Kuiper et al., 2008), calculated with respect to the Min et al. (2000) decay constants of Table 6.2, were adopted (Schmitz, 2012), because these reflected the majority opinion across the $^{40}Ar/^{39}Ar$ community as the most accurate and precise calibration. The optimization approach to calibrating the FCs standard (Renne et al., 2011) yields an $^{40}Ar/^{39}Ar$ age of 28.294 ± 0.036 Ma that is older than the youngest Fish Canyon Tuff zircon dated using the $^{238}U/^{206}Pb$ ID-TIMS method (Wotzlaw et al., 2013). Sageman et al. (2014), Singer et al. (2014), and Andersen et al. (2017) also have found that $^{40}Ar/^{39}Ar$ sanidine dates from several late Cretaceous tuffs, the Quaternary Huckleberry Ridge and Bishop tuffs, would become older than their $^{238}U/^{206}Pb$ ID-TIMS zircon dates if the 28.294 ± 0.036 Ma ages for FCs were used. Given the expectations based on closure temperatures that $^{40}Ar/^{39}Ar$ sanidine dates should be younger than $^{238}U/^{206}Pb$ zircon dates, it appears that the astronomically calibrated age of FCs of 28.201 ± 0.023 Ma is more accurate. To calibrate the $^{40}Ar/^{39}Ar$ dates used in GTS2020, we have used an age of 28.201 ± 0.023 Ma (1σ) for FCs and the intercalibration (R) factors in Table 6.3 for other standards, most of which are the same as in GTS2012 with the exception of the Alder Creek sanidine (ACs), as discussed next [R factors are simply the ratio: $(^{40}Ar^{*}/^{39}Ar_{K})_{unknown}/(^{40}Ar^{*}/^{39}Ar_{K})_{standard}$, where the $^{40}Ar^{*}$ is the radiogenic Ar, and $^{39}Ar_{K}$ denotes the ^{39}Ar derived from ^{39}K during irradiation]. At an EARTHTIME 2 workshop at the Geological Society of America Meeting in Indianapolis in 2018, it was agreed that improving the calibration of FCs and other standards via a new series of $^{238}U/^{206}Pb$ and $^{40}Ar/^{39}Ar$ measurements that can be used in the optimization approach of Renne et al. (2011) is a goal for both the $^{40}Ar/^{39}Ar$ and $^{238}U/^{206}Pb$ communities (see also, Reiners et al., 2017).

Next, we turn to consequences that the improved precision and accuracy afforded by multicollector mass spectrometry have with regard to improving the calibration of $^{40}Ar/^{39}Ar$ standards. The good news is that with respect to the interlaboratory bias issues that arose during the initial EARTHTIME exercise using the ACs standard, there has been a remarkable convergence among several laboratories regarding the age (and thus R value) of ACs relative to FCs (Jicha et al., 2016). This convergence is due to improved analytical procedures (McDougall et al., 2012; Singer, 2014; Giaccio et al., 2017), but more so reflects the deployment of high sensitivity, multicollector mass spectrometry (Rivera et al., 2013; Phillips and Matchan, 2013; Jicha et al., 2016; Niespolo et al., 2017). Recent findings from five laboratories in Denmark (Rivera et al., 2013), Wisconsin (Jicha et al., 2016), Australia (Phillips and Matchan, 2013; Phillips et al., 2017), and California (Coble et al., 2011; Niespolo et al., 2017; Fleck et al., 2019) are in agreement at a level of $\pm 0.07\%$ for the R^{ACs}_{FCs} value (Table 6.4). This represents a two orders of magnitude improvement relative to the initial EARTHTIME intercalibration effort and shifts the age of the ACs standard to an age of 1.1851 ± 0.0004 Ma (Table 6.3) that is $>1\%$ younger than the value reported in GTS2012.

6.3.5 Ongoing challenges and prospects

The progress in calibrating the age of the ACs standard against the FCs standard during the past 15 years reflects several advances enabled by multicollector mass spectrometry and modern gas extraction systems: (1) reduction in

TABLE 6.3 Intercalibration factors (R_{FCs}) for $^{40}Ar/^{39}Ar$ standards utilized in GTS2020.

Standard name	Intercalibration factor (R^{i}_{FCs})	Apparent age[a] (Ma)	References
FCs, FCT-3		28.201 ± 0.046	Kuiper et al. (2008)
MMhb-1	21.4888 ± 0.0380	527.0 ± 0.3	Renne et al. (1998b)
Hb3gr	51.8808 ± 0.1747	1081.5 ± 2.4	Jourdan and Renne (2007) and Jourdan et al. (2006)
TCs	1.0879 ± 0.00078	28.447 ± 0.025	Fleck et al. (2019)
GA-1550	3.5958 ± 0.0087	99.44 ± 0.17	Jourdan and Renne (2007) and Renne et al. (1998b)
ACs	0.041715 ± 0.000029	1.1851 ± 0.0004	Schaen et al. (2020)
GHC-305	3.8549 ± 0.0269	106.4 ± 0.7	Jourdan and Renne (2007); Renne et al. (1998b)
LP-6	4.6652 ± 0.0137	128.0 ± 0.3	Baksi et al. (1996)
Bern 4 Mu	0.6607 ± 0.0107	18.68 ± 0.30	Baksi et al. (1996)
Bern 4 Bi	0.6138 ± 0.0100	17.36 ± 0.28	Baksi et al. (1996)
SB-3	6.0564 ± 0.0510	164.5 ± 1.3	Baksi et al. (1996)

ACs, Alder Creek sanidine; *FCs*, Fish Canyon sanidine; *TCs*, Taylor Creek sanidine.
[a]*All ages are referenced to Fish Canyon Tuff sanidine (FCs) = 28.201 Ma and the decay constants of Min et al. (2000); all errors listed with 2σ uncertainties.*

electronics noise during analysis, (2) mitigation of isobaric interferences on the ^{36}Ar beam, (3) greatly improved counting statistics, (4) remarkably low and stable background levels of argon, and in some cases (5) exceptionally high sensitivity. Nonetheless, however promising the findings in Table 6.4 are, they must be tempered by what has been learned about the isotopic heterogeneity of both the ACs and FCs standards in the studies of Phillips and Matchan (2013), Jicha et al. (2016), Phillips et al. (2017), and Morgan et al. (2019). A key finding in each of these studies is that fusion and plateau dates show significant age dispersion, and plateau ages were only realized from a fraction of the crystals measured, including many saddle-shaped age spectra. The source of dispersion in both ACs and FCs remains unclear, but we consider that the older tail of fusion and plateau dates reflect the presence of antecrysts that retained radiogenic argon ($^{40}Ar^*$) prior to eruption, as has been proposed for numerous, rhyolitic Quaternary tuffs (Singer et al., 2014; Rivera et al., 2014; 2016; Andersen et al., 2017).

TABLE 6.4 *R* values for Alder Creek and Fish Canyon sanidine standards determined using multicollector mass spectrometry.

Reference	$R^{ACs}_{FCs} \pm 2\sigma$
Coble et al. (2011)	0.041805 ± 0.000420
Rivera et al. (2013)	0.041754 ± 0.000030
Phillips and Matchan (2013)	0.041686 ± 0.000049
Jicha et al. (2016)	0.041760 ± 0.000047
Niespolo et al. (2017)	0.041702 ± 0.000028
Phillips et al. (2017)	0.041692 ± 0.000026
Fleck et al. (2019)	0.041714 ± 0.000170
Weighted mean ± 2σ	**0.041715 ± 0.000029, MSWD 2.7**

Note that R^{ACs}_{FCs} of Phillips et al. (2017) is different than what was reported in the original publication due to a calculation error (Phillips, personal communication). *MSWD*, Mean square of weighted deviates.

The question becomes whether the FCs is a suitable standard for precise and accurate $^{40}Ar/^{39}Ar$ geochronology? From the incremental heating experiments conducted by Jicha et al. (2016), Phillips and Matchan (2013), Phillips et al. (2017), and Morgan et al. (2019) on FCs, the integrated ages, essentially equivalent to a K–Ar age, match those of the total fusion ages in the same studies. Thus provided a large enough number of crystals are used to monitor experiments, single crystal fusion measurements of FCs will likely average out the dispersion found in incremental heating experiments, and the astronomically determined age of this standard of 28.201 Ma (Kuiper et al., 2008) remains a useful baseline for GTS2020.

6.3.6 Recalibrating published $^{40}Ar/^{39}Ar$ dates from standard age used in the literature

The myriad of $^{40}Ar/^{39}Ar$ fluence monitors and their ages can be confusing for end users. Fortunately, the equations required to recalibrate $^{40}Ar/^{39}Ar$ ages (using a particular standard and its age, to any other standard, or even a different age for the same monitor), are clearly documented in Reiners et al. (2017) and Schaen et al. (2020). A straightforward approach to recalibrating published $^{40}Ar/^{39}Ar$ dates is the Java-based, internet-accessible, platform ArAR that requires the end user to input the ages and decay constants used for the standards requiring calibration (Mercer and Hodges, 2016).

6.4 Re–Os geochronology

The rhenium–osmium (Re–Os) chronometer is based upon the beta-decay of $^{187}Re–^{187}Os$ with a decay constant of c. 1.666×10^{-11} years and a half-life of c. 42 Ga (Smoliar et al., 1996) (see also Shirey and Walker, 1998 for a comprehensive overview of Re–Os cosmochemistry and high-temperature geochemistry). In addition to displaying siderophilic and chalcophilic behavior, Re and Os also display an affinity for organic matter, resulting in an enrichment in sedimentary rocks deposited under reducing conditions (Koide et al., 1991; Ravizza et al., 1991; Colodner et al., 1993; Crusius and Thomson, 2000; Morford et al., 2005).

Due to relatively large differences in the compatibility of Re and Os during melting of the mantle, crustal materials have an average $^{187}Re/^{188}Os$ of ~50 but can display a spread across three orders of magnitude. With its long half-life and distinct geochemical characteristics, the $^{187}Re–^{187}Os$ system is ideally suited to constraining the rates of key processes over a range of time scales. The $^{187}Re–^{187}Os$ chronometer has been traditionally employed to date ore genesis using sulfide minerals such as molybdenite, pyrite, and arsenopyrite (Stein et al., 2001; Selby and Creaser, 2001; Markey et al., 2007). A focus on the $^{187}Re–^{187}Os$ system in sedimentary rocks has greatly advanced our ability to parse out time in strata of Proterozoic, early Paleozoic and Mesozoic age (Hannah et al., 2004; Selby and Creaser, 2005; Rooney et al., 2011; Sperling et al., 2014; Gibson et al., 2017). Interest in the Snowball Earth events and the evolution of complex life during the Neoproterozoic Era had greatly benefitted from the ability of the $^{187}Re–^{187}Os$ system to directly date the deposition of sedimentary rocks (Kendall et al., 2009; Rooney et al., 2014; 2015; Strauss et al., 2014; Cohen et al., 2017). In addition to chronometry, Os isotopes have shown great potential in tracing changes in the silicate weathering feedback system and the chemical evolution of seawater (see Chapter 8: Osmium Isotope Stratigraphy).

The Re–Os geochronometer utilizes the isochron technique whereby radiogenic isotopes for cogenetic samples are plotted against the parent/daughter ratio (e.g., $^{187}Os/^{188}Os$ vs $^{187}Re/^{188}Os$) forming a best fit line or isochron. The slope of this line is proportional to the age, with the intercept representing the initial Os isotope composition of seawater at the time of deposition. In sedimentary rocks the generation of a geologically meaningful and precise isochron relies upon three crucial requirements: (1) the Re and Os are hydrogenous (i.e., derived from seawater during deposition and are thus authigenic); (2) the samples are cogenetic (i.e., possess a very similar initial $^{187}Os/^{188}Os$ composition at the time of deposition); and (3) the Re–Os system has remained closed since deposition.

Next is an outline of innovations and advances in the Re–Os geochronometer since the publication of GTS 2012 and a discussion of aspects that could benefit from further attention. In particular, the Re–Os system would greatly benefit from the standardization of chemical and analytical techniques, a refinement of λ ^{187}Re, and the development and distribution of gravimetrically calibrated tracer and synthetic reference solutions and reference materials.

6.4.1 Improved chemical extraction and purification techniques

In contrast to sulfide Re–Os geochronology, the sedimentary rock Re–Os chronometer is primarily conducted on powdered splits of a series of whole-rock samples rather than mineral separates. Selby and Creaser (2003) pioneered sedimentary rock digestion using $Cr^{VI}O_3–H_2SO_4$, a technique previously utilized in the meteoritic community. This chemical digestion technique preferentially leaches the hydrogenous Re and Os, thus avoiding incorporation of Re and Os held in the detrital silicate phases. Dates generated by this technique are more accurate than those generated using digestion via inverse aqua regia and the resulting initial Os isotope composition, (the isochron intercept), more accurately reflects seawater at the time of deposition (cf. Burgess and Schafer, 2003; Selby and Creaser, 2003; Kendall et al., 2004). Coupled with advances in mass spectrometry (Creaser et al., 1991; Völkening et al., 1991), tracer-sample equilibration and techniques for the separation and purification of Re and Os, the $Cr^{VI}O_3–H_2SO_4$ technique has greatly expanded the applicability of this chronometer to a range of questions in the geosciences.

6.4.2 Decay constant values

The $^{187}Re–^{187}Os$ ages reported in this volume attempt to follow the procedure recommended by Schoene et al. (2006) whereby age uncertainties are reported as $\pm X/Y/Z$ with X as the internal error in the absence of all systematic errors, Y includes the tracer calibration error, and Z includes the tracer and decay constant errors. As noted next, the sedimentary $^{187}Re–^{187}Os$ system currently lacks community-wide gravimetrically calibrated reference and tracer solutions and thus ages are reported with uncertainties as $\pm X/Z$.

The ^{187}Re decay constant has been calibrated using two approaches, yielding values that are identical within uncertainty. Smoliar et al (1996) analyzed a suite of iron meteorites for Re–Os and combined the slope of these results with the Pb–Pb age of angrites, yielding an ^{187}Re decay constant of $1.666 \pm 0.005 \times 10^{-11}\ a^{-1}$ ($\pm 0.31\%$). Following this work, several studies reported differing decay constants from other approaches (e.g., direct counting experiments). Selby et al. (2007) provided an independent assessment of the decay constant by generating Re–Os ages from magmatic-hosted molybdenite deposits and cross-calibrating with the U–Pb zircon ages of these host bodies, yielding a λ ^{187}Re of $1.6689 \pm 0.0031 \times 10^{-11}\ a^{-1}$ when using the λ ^{235}U of Schoene et al. (2006) and the λ ^{238}U of Jaffey et al. (1971). These studies indicate that the Re–Os chronometer is accurately intercalibrated to the ^{238}U decay constant within the quoted uncertainties, and, as noted by Selby et al. (2007), further refinement of the λ ^{187}Re could be possible given the precision now afforded by the latest U–Pb zircon methodology.

6.4.3 Standardization of reference materials

The U–Pb, Ar–Ar, and U–Th communities have invested time and energy into the development and distribution of tracer solutions, gravimetrically calibrated reference solutions all coupled to cyberinfrastructure plans that homogenized data reduction algorithms and software (Schmitz—this chapter and Singer—this chapter). By combining these approaches with interlaboratory calibration experiments, both communities are now capable of producing highly precise age determinations that can be traced back to SI units, greatly facilitating collaborative science and further integration of geochronological data with large data sets (e.g., EarthChem and Macrostrat).

Highly accurate gravimetrically calibrated reference materials used to calibrate tracers are critical components of isotope dilution geochronology. However, numerous studies have pointed to the lack of a stoichiometric Os reference material resulting in large ($>$%) variations in Os concentrations (Morgan et al., 1995). One promising potential approach to circumvent this issue is the reduction of ammonium hexachloroosmate salts to a pure Os salt under an N_2H_2 atmosphere (Gilchrist, 1932; Selby and Creaser, 2001; Markey et al., 2007).

6.4.4 Re–Os data-reduction procedures

At present, the Microsoft Excel Macro Add-In Isoplot v. 4.15 is most commonly used to generate Re–Os isochrons (Ludwig, 2008). In addition to an age and intercept, the isochron also presents a model classification (1, 2, or 3) and a Mean Square of Weighted Deviates (MSWD) derived from factors related to the uncertainties and errors associated with the measured Re and Os (York, 1969).

A Model 1 age represents a fit of the data to the isochron with the assigned analytical errors representing scatter from a best fit line. A Model 2 age is derived from assigning equal weights and zero-error correlations to each data point on the isochron and avoids weighting the points according to analytical uncertainties when the misfit is larger than predicted from analytical error (cf. Model 1). The Model 3 age assumes scatter on the isochron is due to a combination of assigned analytical uncertainty and a normally distributed uncertainty around the Model 1–based initial isotope ratios (Ludwig, 2003). The MSWD is a measure of fit that quantifies whether the data—within their uncertainty—are consistent with the best fitting line. A poor fit can therefore imply that the data do not fall on a common line (e.g., samples are not cogenetic) or that the assigned uncertainties are inadequate. The Isoplot Macro weighs the deviation for each data point from the best fit line by its uncertainty, which will result in an MSWD of ~ 1 if these deviations are on the order of the uncertainty. The formulation of the MSWD takes the covariance between data into account (McDougall and Harrison, 1999). A calculated MSWD $\gg 1$ suggests that the data are too far away from a best fit line or that the uncertainties prescribed were underestimated. In contrast an MSWD $\ll 1$ means that the data are very close to the best fit line or that the prescribed uncertainties were overestimated. The uncertainty correlation function (rho) is also included because ^{187}Re/^{188}Os and ^{187}Os/^{188}Os uncertainties are also highly correlated (e.g., Cumming, 1969; York, 1969; Ludwig, 1980; Morelli et al., 2005).

Recent work coupling the Re–Os and U–Pb zircon geochronometers highlighted the power of these systems to reconstruct geological histories of Precambrian basins and also presented an assessment of best practices to improve precision in the Re–Os sedimentary rock chronometer (Rooney et al., 2018). Following the approach of Schmitz and Schoene (2007), the study evaluated the magnitude with which sources of uncertainty propagated into the final age uncertainty. Although specific to the data of that particular study, it was found that improved precision of measured Os values led to the most efficient way of reducing uncertainties. Greater precision in the measured Os values could be leveraged via a number of approaches such as increasing the number of measurements per sample, increasing beam stability, or the use of multiple ion counters. The authors also cautioned that any of these changes in Os value precision would not only affect the age uncertainty, but also the age itself (Rooney et al., 2018).

The ^{187}Re–^{187}Os community is still in the nascent stage of efforts to improve absolute precision, the rigor of data reduction techniques (e.g., Li et al., 2018) but with the rise of more labs and research groups utilizing this system, we expect great progress in the coming years.

6.5 Application of radioisotope geochronology in the stratigraphic record

6.5.1 Systematic error propagation

The application of multiple isotope chronometers (e.g., U−Pb, $^{40}Ar/^{39}Ar$, and Re−Os) across the time scale, and the increasingly fine precision of those ages, has only heightened the importance of quantifying systematic uncertainties, in addition to the analytical uncertainties of the radioisotopic ages calibrating the geologic time scale. Following the standards set in GTS2012, a particular emphasis in the treatment of radioisotopic data for the current time scale is the quantitative propagation of systematic errors, including tracer calibration (U−Pb, Re−Os), fluence monitor reproducibility and intercalibration factors ($^{40}Ar/^{39}Ar$), primary monitor standard age ($^{40}Ar/^{39}Ar$), and decay constant uncertainties (all systems). Those systematic errors that can lead to systematic biases between experiments or between laboratories (e.g., tracer calibration and fluence monitor uncertainties) are now quantitatively propagated and reported in Appendix 2, resulting in a robust uncertainty that can be used for comparing data acquired via the same parent−daughter decay chain, regardless of the experiment or laboratory. A second age error is reported in Appendix 2, which additionally propagates uncertainties associated with the decay constants (and the age of the primary monitor standard for $^{40}Ar/^{39}Ar$, FCs). This larger error provides for robust comparison between isotopic systems.

The compilation of radioisotopic ages in GTS2012 rejected the notion of nominal uncertainty assignments in favor of more robust quantitative error propagation drawing upon the original isotope ratios and analytical parameters reported in the literature. In this way, we sought to minimize the potential for bias introduced by inaccurate legacy data masked by nominally large uncertainties. This more rigorous culling of legacy data for GTS2012 highlighted the need to reanalyzed important stratigraphic targets with the modern methodological improvements highlighted earlier in this chapter. This culling is continued in GTS2020, but the commensurate addition of new, more precise, and accurate ages for many of the legacy samples in both GTS2004 and GTS2012 have compensated to a large degree.

6.5.2 Treatment of legacy

For GTS2012, particular attention was paid to the compilation of legacy U−Pb age determinations, in light of both systematic error propagation and the aforementioned reanalysis of the U decay constant ratio ($\lambda_{235}/\lambda_{238}$), which affect the accurate intercomparison of U−Pb ($^{206}Pb/^{238}U$ and $^{207}Pb/^{235}U$) and Pb−Pb ($^{207}Pb/^{206}Pb$) ages. All U−Pb ages were recalculated directly from the radiogenic isotope ratios reported in the primary literature. This compilation and analysis allowed the assessment of data quality, the reinterpretation of age systematics based upon $^{206}Pb/^{238}U$ (or $^{207}Pb/^{235}U$) versus $^{207}Pb/^{206}Pb$ isotope ratios, and the quantitative propagation of systematic uncertainties. Many legacy ages did not meet minimum data and metadata requirements and were culled from the GTS2012 compilation, while others were recalculated to shift interpretation from $^{207}Pb/^{206}Pb$ or upper intercept ages to $^{206}Pb/^{238}U$ ages, or at least maintain interisotopic consistency between ages by using the updated ^{235}U decay constant. In GTS2020, most of these recalculated legacy ages have been superseded by new measurements using EARTHTIME tracers and protocols.

As described in Section 6.3, the $^{40}Ar/^{39}Ar$ method relies on the reproducible analysis of a standard material with a homogeneous $^{40}Ar^{*}/^{40}K$ and known age. A major effort of GTS2004 involved the harmonization of all time scale calibration points to the FCs monitor standard, using published intercalibration factors. In GTS2012, all $^{40}Ar/^{39}Ar$ ages utilized as time scale calibration points were recalculated to the revised age of the FCs monitor standard of 28.201 ± 0.046 Ma (Kuiper et al., 2008), using the total K decay constant, $\lambda_{total} = 0.5463 \pm 0.0107\ Ga^{-1}$ of Min et al. (2000). Both internal (analytical) and external (analytical + systematic) age uncertainties were propagated using published intercalibration factors and error equations (Renne et al., 1998a,b; Kuiper et al., 2008). These same $^{40}Ar/^{39}Ar$ calibration standard values and techniques were used in GTS2020.

6.5.3 Bayesian age models in deep time

Following the lead of the radiocarbon community (Blaauw and Christen, 2005; Parnell et al., 2011; Ramsey, 1997), recent high-precision time scale calibration studies have cast radioisotopic dates within a Bayesian age modeling framework to better interpret suites of depositional ages, and interpolate to the age of boundaries. A number of Bayesian computational algorithms developed for radiocarbon geochronology, including BChron (Haslett and Parnell, 2008), Bacon (Blaauw and Christen, 2005), and Oxcal (Ramsey, 2008), have been applied in these time scale studies of the Permo−Triassic boundary (Baresel et al., 2017) and Early Triassic recovery interval (Ovtcharova et al., 2015), as well as Cenozoic marine and terrestrial records (Sahy et al., 2017; 2015). Trayler et al. (2020) recently adapted the BChron age modeling environment to enhance its utility for deep-time age modeling, while other fit-for-purpose Bayesian algorithms have been applied to flood basalt sequences and their relationship to mass extinction (Schoene et al., 2019; Sprain et al., 2019).

Bayesian statistical methods have been successfully used to combine radioisotopic ages and astrochronology to improve the estimates of stage boundary ages (Meyers et al., 2012). Trayler et al. (2020) have explored the utility of Bayesian age models for finding accurate posterior estimates of depositional age from complex input age likelihoods. And in a work that presages a new era in radioisotopic age interpretation, Keller et al. (2018) have explored the use of Bayesian priors to improve the extraction of eruptive age estimates from complex radioisotopic data. It is clear that Bayesian age modeling will find increasing use in time scale studies (De Vleeschouwer and Parnell, 2014), which promise to achieve increasingly accurate radioisotopic ages, more quantitative integration of the stratigraphic and geochronologic components of the time scale, and stronger ties between stratigraphers and geochronologists.

6.6 Conclusion

In summary the radioisotopic calibration of GTS2020 represents improvements related to (1) the propagation of systematic uncertainties; (2) replacement of legacy U–Pb ages with new measurements using EARTHTIME tracers and protocols; (3) calculation of all $^{40}Ar/^{39}Ar$ data to an age for the FCs monitor standard age of 28.201 ± 0.046 Ma of Kuiper et al. (2008) using the total K decay constant, $\lambda_{total} = 0.5463 \pm 0.0107\ Ga^{-1}$ of Min et al. (2000), which appears to provide the best available intercalibration of $^{40}Ar/^{39}Ar$, $^{206}Pb/^{238}U$, and astronomical clocks; (4) the integration of abundant new Re–Os age constraints on organic-rich shales in Tonian through Ediacaran successions, for Neoproterozoic time scale calibration.

We close with a reminder that the radioisotopic calibration of the geologic time scale is a work in progress, and a caution that while the calibration promulgated in GTS2020 is certainly more accurate where new geochronologic contributions are abundant, there remain significant gaps in those constraints in space and time. Remarkable progress in chronometer integration and the deployment of increasingly sophisticated instrumentation and analytical methods characterize the interval from 2012 to 2020. But it is appropriate that this update to the geological time scale will do as much to highlight its limitations and spur new studies, as demonstrate its utility for understanding the Earth system.

Bibliography

Aguirre-Urreta, B., Lescano, M., Schmitz, M.D., Tunik, M., Concheyro, A., Rawson, P.F., et al., 2015, Filling the gap: new precise Early Cretaceous radioisotopic ages from the Andes. *Geological Magazine*, **152**: 557–564.

Amelin, Y., Connelly, J., Zartman, R.E., Chen, J.H., Goepel, C., Neymark, L.A., et al., 2009, Modern U/Pb chronometry of meteorites; advancing to higher time resolution reveals new problems. *Geochimica et Cosmochimica Acta*, **73**: 5212–5223.

Andersen, N.L., Jicha, B.R., Singer, B.S., and Hildreth, W., 2017, Incremental heating of Bishop Tuff sanidine reveals pre-eruptive radiogenic Ar and rapid remobilization from cold magma storage. *Proceedings of the National Academy of Sciences of the United States of America*, **114**: 12407–12412.

Bachmann, O., and Dungan, M., 2002, Temperature-induced Al-zoning in hornblendes of the Fish Canyon magma, Colorado. *American Mineralogist*, **87**: 1062–1076.

Bachmann, O., Dungan, M., and Lipman, P., 2002, The Fish Canyon magma body, San Juan volcanic field, Colorado: rejuvenation and eruption of an upper-crustal batholith. *Journal of Petrology*, **43**: 1469–1503.

Bachmann, O., Oberli, F., Dungan, M., Meier, M., Mundil, R., and Fischer, H., 2007. $^{40}Ar/^{39}$ and U–Pb dating of the Fish Canyon magmatic system, San Juan Volcanic field, Colorado: evidence for an extended crystallization history. *Chemical Geology*, **236:** 134–166.

Baksi, A.K., Archibald, D.A., and Farrar, E., 1996, Intercalibration of $^{40}Ar/^{39}Ar$ dating standards. *Chemical Geology*, **129**: 307–324.

Balbas, A., Koppers, A.A., Kent, D.V., Konrad, K., and Clark, P.U., 2016, Identification of the short-lived Santa Rosa geomagnetic excursion in lavas on Floreana Island (Galapagos) by $^{40}Ar/^{39}Ar$ geochronology. *Geology*, **44**: 359–362.

Barboni, M., and Schoene, B., 2014, Short eruption window revealed by absolute crystal growth rates in a granitic magma. *Nature Geoscience*, **7**: 524–528.

Baresel, B., Bucher, H., Brosse, M., Cordey, F., Guodun, K., and Schaltegger, U., 2017, Precise age for the Permian–Triassic boundary in South China from high-precision U-Pb geochronology and Bayesian age–depth modeling. *Solid Earth*, **8**: 361–378.

Begemann, F., Ludwig, K., Lugmair, G., Min, K., Nyquist, L., Patchett, P., et al., 2001, Call for an improved set of decay constants for geochronological use. *Geochimica et Cosmochimica Acta*, **65**: 111–121.

Bergström, S.M., Özlem Toprak, F., Huff, W.D., and Mundil, R., 2008, Implications of a new, biostratigraphically well-controlled, radioisotopic age for the lower Telychian Stage of the Llandovery Series (Lower Silurian, Sweden). *Episodes*, **31**: 309–314.

Bigeleisen, J., 1996. Temperature dependence of the isotope chemistry of the heavy elements. *Proceedings of the National Academy of Sciences of the United States of America*, **93**: 9393–9396.

Blaauw, M., and Christen, J.A., 2005, Radiocarbon peat chronologies and environmental change. *Journal of the Royal Statistical Society: Series C (Applied Statistics)*, **54**: 805–816.

Black, L., Kamo, S., Williams, I., Mundil, R., Davis, D., Korsch, R., et al., 2003, The application of SHRIMP to Phanerozoic geochronology; a critical appraisal of four zircon standards. *Chemical Geology*, **200**: 171–188.

Bopp, C.J., Lundstrom, C.C., Johnson, T.M., and Glessner, J.J.G., 2009, Variations in $^{238}U/^{235}U$ in uranium ore deposits: isotopic signatures of the U reduction process? *Geology*, **37**: 611–614.

Bowring, S.A., and Schmitz, M.D., 2003, High-precision U-Pb zircon geochronology and the stratigraphic record. *Reviews in Mineralogy and Geochemistry*, **53**: 305–326.

Bowring, S.A., Erwin, D., Renne, P., 2004. *EARTHTIME; A Community-Based Effort Towards High-Precision Calibration of Earth History.* Abstracts with Programs—Geological Society of America: Boulder, Geological Society of America (GSA): 211.

Brennecka, G.A., Borg, L.E., Hutcheon, I.D., Sharp, M.A., and Anbar, A.D., 2010a, Natural variations in uranium isotope ratios of uranium ore concentrates. Understanding the $^{238}U/^{235}U$ fractionation mechanism. *Earth and Planetary Science Letters*, **291**: 228–233.

Brennecka, G.A., Weyer, S., Wadhwa, M., Janney, E., Zipfel, J., and Anbar, A.D., 2010b, $^{238}U/^{235}U$ variations in meteorites. Extant ^{247}Cm and implications for Pb-Pb dating. *Science*, **327**: 449–451.

Buchachenko, A., 2001, Magnetic isotope effect. Nuclear spin control of chemical reactions. *The Journal of Physical Chemistry A*, **105**: 9995–10011.

Burgess, J.M., and Schaefer, B.F., 2003, Re-Os isotopic age constraints on deposition in the Neoproterozoic Amadeus Basin. implications for the 'Snowball Earth'. *Journal of the Geological Society*, **160**: 825–828.

Burgess, S.D., Bowring, S., and Shen, S.-Z., 2014. High-precision timeline for Earth's most severe extinction. *Proceedings of the National Academy of Sciences of the United States of America*, **111**: 3316–3321.

Chang, Z., Vervoort, J.D., McClelland, W.C., and Knaack, C., 2006, U-Pb dating of zircon by LA-ICP-MS. *Geochemistry, Geophysics, Geosystems*, **7**, 10.1029/2005GC001100.

Coble, M.A., Grove, M., and Calvert, A.T., 2011, Calibration of Nu-Instruments Noblesse multicollector mass spectrometers for argon isotopic measurements using a newly developed reference gas. *Chemical Geology*, **290**: 75–87.

Cohen, P.A., Strauss, J.V., Rooney, A.D., Sharma, M., and Tosca, N., 2017, Controlled hydroxyapatite biomineralization in an ~810 million-year-old unicellular eukaryote. *Science Advances*, **3**: e1700095.

Colodner, D., Sachs, J., Ravizza, G., Turekian, K.K., Edmond, J., and Boyle, E., 1993, The geochemical cycle of rhenium. a reconnaissance. *Earth and Planetary Science Letters*, **117**: 205–221.

Condon, D.J., 2005, Progress report on the U-Pb interlaboratory experiment. *Geochimica et Cosmochimica Acta*, **69**: 319.

Condon, D., Schoene, B., Bowring, S.A., Parrish, R., McLean, N., Noble, S., et al., 2007, *EARTHTIME; Isotopic Tracers and Optimized Solutions for High-Precision U-Pb ID-TIMS Geochronology*. American Geophysical Union, Washington, DC.

Condon, D.J., McLean, N., Schoene, B., Bowring, S., Parrish, R.R., and Noble, S., 2008, Synthetic U-Pb "standard" solutions for ID-TIMS geochronology. *Geochimica et Cosmochimica Acta*, **72**: A175.

Condon, D.J., Mclean, N., Noble, S.R., and Bowring, S.A., 2010, Isotopic composition ($^{238}U/^{235}U$) of some commonly used uranium reference materials. *Geochimica et Cosmochimica Acta*, **74**: 7127–7143.

Condon, D.J., Schoene, B., McLean, N.M., Bowring, S.A., and Parrish, R.R., 2015, Metrology and traceability of U–Pb isotope dilution geochronology (EARTHTIME Tracer Calibration Part I). *Geochimica et Cosmochimica Acta*, **164**: 464–480.

Corfu, F., 2000, Extraction of Pb with artificially too-old ages during stepwise dissolution experiments on Archean zircon. *Lithos*, **53**: 279–291.

Creaser, R.A., Papanastassiou, D.A., and Wasserburg, G.J., 1991, Negative thermal ion mass spectrometry of osmium, rhenium, and iridium. *Geochimica et Cosmochimica Acta*, **55**: 397–401.

Crusius, J., and Thomson, J., 2000, Comparative behavior of authigenic Re, U, and Mo during reoxidation and subsequent long-term burial in marine sediments. *Geochimica et Cosmochimica Acta*, **64**: 2233–2242.

Cumming, G.L., 1969, A recalculation of the age of the solar system. *Canadian Journal of Earth Sciences*, **4**: 719–735.

Davis, D.W., and Krogh, T.E., 2001, Preferential dissolution of ^{234}U and radiogenic Pb from alpha -recoil-damaged lattice sites in zircon; implications for thermal histories and Pb isotopic fractionation in the near surface environment. *Chemical Geology*, **172** (1–2), 41–58.

Davis, D., Williams, I.S., and Krogh, T.E., 2003, Historical development of zircon geochronology. *Reviews in Mineralogy and Geochemistry*, **53**: 145–181.

Dazé, A., Lee, J., and Villeneuve, M., 2003, An intercalibration study of the Fish Canyon sanidine and biotite 40Ar/39Ar standards and some comments on the age of the Fish Canyon Tuff. *Chemical Geology*, **199** (1–2), 111–127.

De Vleeschouwer, D., and Parnell, A.C., 2014, Reducing time-scale uncertainty for the Devonian by integrating astrochronology and Bayesian statistics. *Geology*, **42**: 491–494.

DiMaggio, E.N., Campisano, C.J., Rowan, J., Dupont-Nivet, G., Deino, A.L., Bibi, F., et al., 2015, Late Pliocene fossiliferous sedimentary record and the environmental context of early Homo from Afar, Ethiopia. *Science*, **347**: 1355–1359.

Erwin, D.H., 2006, Dates and rates: temporal resolution in the deep time stratigraphic record. *Annual Review of Earth and Planetary Sciences*, **34**: 569–590.

Fleck, R.J., Calvert, A.T., Coble, M.A., Wooden, J.L., Hodges, K., Hayden, L.A., et al., 2019, Characterization of the rhyolite of Bodie Hills and $^{40}Ar/^{39}Ar$ intercalibration with Ar mineral standards. *Chemical Geology*, **525**: 282–302.

Gehrels, G.E., Valencia, A., and Ruiz, J., 2008, Enhanced precision, accuracy, efficiency, and spatial resolution of U-Pb ages by laser ablation–multicollector–inductively coupled plasma–mass spectrometry. *Geochemistry, Geophysics, Geosystems*, **9**: Q03017.

Gemignani, L., Kuiper, K.F., Wijbrans, J.R., Sun, X., and Santato, A., 2019, Improving the precision of single grain mica $^{40}Ar/^{39}Ar$-dating on smaller and younger muscovite grains. Application to provenance studies. *Chemical Geology*, **511**: 100–111.

Giaccio, B., Hajdas, I., Isaia, R., Deino, A., and Nomade, S., 2017, High-precision ^{14}C and $^{40}Ar/^{39}Ar$ dating of the Campanian Ignimbrite (Y-5) reconciles the time-scales of climatic-cultural processes at 40 ka. *Scientific Reports*, **7**: 45940.

Gibson, T.M., Shih, P.M., Cumming, V.M., Fischer, W.W., Crockford, P.W., Hodgskiss, M.S., et al., 2017, Precise age of *Bangiomorpha pubescens* dates the origin of eukaryotic photosynthesis. *Geology*, **46**: 135–138.

Gilchrist, R., 1932, A new determination of the atomic weight of osmium. *Bureau of Standards Journal of Research*, **9**: 279–290.

Hannah, J.L., Bekker, A., Stein, H.J., Markey, R.J., and Holland, H.D., 2004, Primitive Os and 2316 Ma age for marine shale. implications for Paleoproterozoic glacial events and the rise of atmospheric oxygen. *Earth and Planetary Science Letters*, **225**: 43–52.

Haslett, J., and Parnell, A., 2008, A simple monotone process with application to radiocarbon-dated depth chronologies. *Journal of the Royal Statistical Society: Series C (Applied Statistics)*, **57**: 399–418.

Heizler, M.T., 2005, Evaluating intercomparability amongst several $^{40}Ar/^{39}Ar$ laboratories. *Geochimica et Cosmochimica Acta*, **69**: 318.

Heizler, M.T., Jicha, B., Koppers, A.A.P., and Miggins, D.P., 2015. $^{40}Ar/^{39}Ar$ interlaboratory calibration into the holocene. *AGU Fall Meeting Abstracts*.

Hiess, J., Condon, D.J., McLean, N., and Noble, S.R., 2012, $^{238}U/^{235}U$ systematics in terrestrial uranium-bearing minerals. *Science*, **335**: 1610–1614.

Huyskens, M.H., Zink, S., and Amelin, Y., 2016, Evaluation of temperature-time conditions for the chemical abrasion treatment of single zircons for U–Pb geochronology. *Chemical Geology*, **438**: 25–35.

Ireland, T.R., and Williams, I.S., 2003, Considerations in zircon geochronology by SIMS. *Reviews in Mineralogy and Geochemistry*, **53** (1): 215.

Jaffey, A.H., Flynn, K.F., Glendenin, L.E., Bentley, W.T., and Essling, A.M., 1971, Precision measurement of half-lives and specific activities of U235 and U238. *Physical Review C*, **4**: 1889.

Jicha, B.R., Singer, B.S., and Sobol, P., 2016, Re-evaluation of the ages of $^{40}Ar/^{39}Ar$ sanidine standards and supereruptions in the western U.S. using a Noblesse multi-collector mass spectrometer. *Chemical Geology*, **431**: 54–66.

Jourdan, F., and Renne, P., 2007, Age calibration of the Fish Canyon sanidine 40Ar/39Ar dating standard using primary K–Ar standards. *Geochimica et Cosmochimica Acta*, **71**: 387–402.

Jourdan, F., Verati, C., and Féraud, G., 2006, Intercalibration of the Hb3gr $^{40}Ar/^{39}Ar$ dating standard. *Chemical Geology*, **231** (3): 177–189.

Kamo, S., Czamanske, G., Amelin, Y., Fedorenko, V., Davis, D., and Trofimov, V., 2003, Rapid eruption of Siberian flood-volcanic rocks and evidence for coincidence with the Permian–Triassic boundary and mass extinction at 251 Ma. *Earth and Planetary Science Letters*, **214** (1–2), 75–91.

Keller, C.B., Schoene, B., and Samperton, K.M., 2018, A stochastic sampling approach to zircon eruption age interpretation. *Geochemical Perspectives Letters*, **8**: 31–35.

Kendall, B.S., Creaser, R.A., Ross, G.M., and Selby, D., 2004, Constraints on the timing of Marinoan 'Snowball Earth' glaciation by $^{187}Re-^{187}Os$ dating of a Neoproterozoic post-glacial black shale in Western Canada. *Earth and Planetary Science Letters*, **222**: 729–740.

Kendall, B., Creaser, R.A., Gordon, G.W., and Anbar, A.D., 2009, Re–Os and Mo isotope systematics of black shales from the Middle Proterozoic Velkerri and Wollogorang formations, McArthur Basin, northern Australia. *Geochimica et Cosmochimica Acta*, **73**: 2534–2558.

Koide, M., Goldberg, E.D., Niemeyer, S., Gerlach, D., Hodge, V., Bertine, K.K., et al., 1991, Osmium in marine sediments. *Geochimica et Cosmochimica Acta*, **55**: 1641–1648.

Kosler, J., and Sylvester, J., 2003, Present trends and the future of zircon in geochronology. Laser ablation ICPMS. *Reviews in Mineralogy and Geochemistry*, **53**: 243.

Kuiper, K.F., Deino, A., Hilgen, F.J., Krijgsman, W., Renne, P.R., and Wijbrans, J.R., 2008, Synchronizing rock clocks of Earth history. *Science*, **320**: 500–504.

Li, Y., Zhang, S., Hobbs, R., Caiado, C., Sproson, A.D., Selby, D., et al., 2018, Monte Carlo sampling for error propagation in linear regression and applications in isochron geochronology. *Science Bulletin*, **64**: 189–197.

Livermore, B.D., Connelly, J.N., Moynier, F., and Bizzarro, M., 2018, Evaluating the robustness of a consensus $^{238}U/^{235}U$ value for U-Pb geochronology. *Geochimica et Cosmochimica Acta*, **237**: 171–183.

Ludwig, K.R., 1980, Calculation of uncertainties of U–Pb isotope data. *Earth and Planetary Science Letters*, **46**: 212–220.

Ludwig, K.R., 1998, On the treatment of concordant uranium-lead ages. *Geochimica et Cosmochimica Acta*, **62** (4), 665–676.

Ludwig, K.R., 2000, Decay constant errors in U–Pb concordia-intercept ages. *Chemical Geology*, **166** (3–4), 315–318.

Ludwig, K.R., 2003, Using Isoplot/Ex, Version 2.01: A geochronological toolkit for Microsoft Excel. *Berkeley Geochronology Center Special Publication*. Berkeley Geochronology Center, Berkeley, CA.

Ludwig, K.R., 2008, User's manual for Isoplot 3.70. *Berkeley Geochronology Center Special Publication*, **4**, p.76.

Macdonald, F.A., Schmitz, M.D., Strauss, J.V., Halverson, G.P., Gibson, T.M., Eyster, A., et al., 2018, Cryogenian of Yukon. *Precambrian Research*, **319**: 114–143.

Machlus, M.L., Ramezani, J., Bowring, S.A., Hemming, S.R., Tsukui, K., and Clyde, W.C., 2015, A strategy for cross-calibrating U–Pb chronology and astrochronology of sedimentary sequences. An example from the Green River Formation, Wyoming, USA. *Earth and Planetary Science Letters*, **413**: 70–78.

Markey, R., Stein, H.J., Hannah, J.L., Zimmerman, A., Selby, D., and Creaser, R.A., 2007, Standardizing Re–Os geochronology. a new molybdenite reference material (Henderson, USA) and the stoichiometry of Os salts. *Chemical Geology*, **244**: 74–87.

Mattinson, J.M., 1987, U-Pb ages of zircons; a basic examination of error propagation. *Chemical Geology*, **66** (1–2), 151–162.

Mattinson, J.M., 1994a, A study of complex discordance in zircons using step-wise dissolution techniques. *Contributions to Mineralogy and Petrology*, **116** (1–2), 117–129.

Mattinson, J.M., 1994b, Uranium decay constant uncertainties, and their implications for high-resolution U-Pb geochronology. *Abstracts with Programs—Geological Society of America*, **26**: 221.

Mattinson, J.M., 1997, Decay constants of ^{238}U and ^{235}U; history, present status, future work. *Abstracts with Programs—Geological Society of America*, **29**: 351.

Mattinson, J.M., 2000, Revising the "gold standard", the uranium decay constants of Jaffey et al., 1971. *EOS (Transactions American Geophysical Union)*, **81**: S444.

Mattinson, J.M., 2005, Zircon U-Pb chemical abrasion ("CA-TIMS") method. combined annealing and multi-step partial dissolution analysis for improved precision and accuracy of zircon ages. *Chemical Geology*, **220**: 47–66.

Mattinson, J.M., 2010a, Analysis of the relative decay constants of ^{235}U and ^{238}U by multi-step CA-TIMS measurements of closed-system natural zircon samples. *Chemical Geology*, **275**: 186–198.

Mattinson, J.M., 2010b, Extending the Krogh legacy. development of the CA-TIMS method for zircon U-Pb geochronology. *Canadian Journal of Earth Sciences*, **48** (2), 95–105.

McDougall, I., and Harrison, T.M., 1999. Appendix 4 A.1 Isochron Analysis. In: McDougall I., and Harrison, T.M. (eds), *Geochronology and Thermochronology by the $^{40}Ar/^{39}Ar$ Method*, Oxford University Press, New York: 134–136.

McDougall, I., Brown, F.H., Vasconcelos, P.M., Cohen, B.E., Thiede, D.S., and Buchanan, M.J., 2012, New single crystal $^{40}Ar/^{39}Ar$ ages improve time scale for deposition of the Omo Group, Omo–Turkana Basin, East Africa. *Journal of the Geological Society*, **169** (2), 213–226.

McLean, N.M., Condon, D.J., Schoene, B., and Bowring, S.A., 2015, Evaluating uncertainties in the calibration of isotopic reference materials and multi-element isotopic tracers (EARTHTIME Tracer Calibration Part II). *Geochimica et Cosmochimica Acta*, **164**: 481–501.

Mercer, C.M., and Hodges, K.V., 2016, ArAR—a software tool to promote the robust comparison of K–Ar and $^{40}Ar/^{39}Ar$ dates published using different decay, isotopic, and monitor-age parameters. *Chemical Geology*, **440**: 148–163.

Meyers, S.R., Siewert, S.E., Singer, B.S., Sageman, B.B., Condon, D.J., Obradovich, J.D., et al., 2012, Intercalibration of radioisotopic and astrochronologic time scales for the Cenomanian-Turonian boundary interval, Western Interior Basin, USA. *Geology*, **40**: 7–10.

Min, K., Mundil, R., Renne, P.R., and Ludwig, K.R., 2000, A test for systematic errors in $^{40}Ar/^{39}Ar$ geochronology through comparison with U/Pb analysis of a 1.1-Ga rhyolite. *Geochimica et Cosmochimica Acta*, **64**: 73–98.

Min, K., Renne, P., and Huff, W., 2001, $^{40}Ar/^{39}Ar$ dating of Ordovician K-bentonites in Laurentia and Baltoscandia. *Earth and Planetary Science Letters*, **185** (1–2), 121–134.

Min, K., Farley, K., Renne, P., and Marti, K., 2003, Single grain (U–Th)/He ages from phosphates in Acapulco meteorite and implications for thermal history. *Earth and Planetary Science Letters*, **209** (3–4), 323–336.

Morelli, R.M., Creaser, R.A., Selby, D., Kontak, D.J., and Horne, R.J., 2005, Rhenium-Osmium of Arsenopyrite in Meguma Group gold deposits, Meguma Terrane, Nova Scotia, Canada. Evidence of multiple gold-mineralizing events. *Economic Geology*, **100**: 1229–1241.

Morford, J.L., Emerson, S.R., Breckel, E.J., and Hyun Kim, S., 2005, Diagenesis of oxyanions (V, U, Re and Mo) in pore waters and sediments from a continental margin. *Geochimica et Cosmochimica Acta*, **69**: 5021–5032.

Morgan, J.W., Horan, M.F., Walker, R.J., and Grossman, J., 1995, Rhenium-osmium concentration and isotope systematics in group IIAG iron meteorites. *Geochimica et Cosmochimica Acta*, **59** (11), 2331–2344.

Morgan, L.E., Johnstone, S.A., Gilmer, A.K., Cosca, M.A., and Thompson, R.A., 2019, A supervolcano and its sidekicks. A 100 ka eruptive chronology of the Fish Canyon Tuff and associated units of the La Garita magmatic system, Colorado, USA. *Geology*, **47**: 1–4.

Mundil, R., Metcalfe, I., Ludwig, K., Renne, P., Oberli, F., and Nicoll, R., 2001, Timing of the Permian–Triassic biotic crisis. implications from new zircon U/Pb age data (and their limitations). *Earth and Planetary Science Letters*, **187**: 131–145.

Mundil, R., Ludwig, K., Metcalfe, I., and Renne, P., 2004, Age and timing of the Permian mass extinctions. U/Pb dating of closed-system zircons. *Science*, **305**: 1760–1763.

Nebel, O., Scherer, E.E., and Mezger, K., 2011, Evaluation of the ^{87}Rb decay constant by age comparison against the U-Pb system. *Earth and Planetary Science Letters*, **301**: 1–8.

Niespolo, E.M., Rutte, D., Deino, A.L., and Renne, P.R., 2017, Intercalibration and age of the Alder Creek sanidine $^{40}Ar/^{39}Ar$ standard. *Quaternary Geochronology*, **39**: 205–213.

Opluštil, S., Schmitz, M., Cleal, C.J., and Martínek, K., 2016, A review of the Middle–Late Pennsylvanian west European regional substages and floral biozones, and their correlation to the Geological Time Scale based on new U–Pb ages. *Earth-Science Reviews*, **154**: 301–335.

Ovtcharova, M., Goudemand, N., Hammer, Ø., Guodun, K., Cordey, F., Galfetti, T., et al., 2015, Developing a strategy for accurate definition of a geological boundary through radio-isotopic and biochronological dating. The Early–Middle Triassic boundary (South China). *Earth-Science Reviews*, **146**: 65–76.

Parnell, A.C., Buck, C.E., and Doan, T.K., 2011, A review of statistical chronology models for high-resolution, proxy-based Holocene palaeoenvironmental reconstruction. *Quaternary Science Reviews*, **30**: 2948–2960.

Phillips, D., and Matchan, E.L., 2013, Ultra-high precision $^{40}Ar/^{39}Ar$ ages for Fish Canyon Tuff and Alder Creek Rhyolite sanidine. new dating standards required? *Geochimica et Cosmochimica Acta*, **121**: 229–239.

Phillips, D., Matchan, E.L., Honda, M., and Kuiper, K.F., 2017, Astronomical calibration of $^{40}Ar/^{39}Ar$ reference minerals using high-precision, multi-collector (ARGUSVI) mass spectrometry. *Geochimica et Cosmochimica Acta*, **196**: 351–369.

Quadt, V.A., Wotzlaw, J.-F., Buret, Y., Large, S.J.E., Peytcheva, I., and Trinquier, A., 2016, High-precision zircon U/Pb geochronology by ID-TIMS using new 10 13ohm resistors. *Journal of Analytical Atomic Spectrometry*, **31**: 658–665.

Ramsey, C.B., 1997, Probability and dating. *Radiocarbon*, **40**: 461–474.

Ramsey, C.B., 2008, Deposition models for chronological records. *Quaternary Science Reviews*, **27**: 42–60.

Ravizza, G., Turekian, K.K., and Hay, B.J., 1991, The geochemistry of rhenium and osmium in recent sediments from Black Sea. *Geochimica et Cosmochimica Acta*, **55**: 3741–3752.

Reiners, P.W., Carlson, R.W., Renne, P.R., Cooper, K.M., Granger, D.E., McLean, N.M. et al., 2017. Geochronology and thermochronology, Chapter 9, *The K-Ar and $^{40}Ar/^{39}Ar^{40}Ar/^{39}Ar$ Systems*. John Wiley & Sons. 229–257.

Renne, R., Karner, D.B., and Ludwig, K.R., 1998a, Absolute ages aren't exactly. *Science*, **282**: 1840–1841.

Renne, R., Swisher, C.C., Deino, A.L., Karner, D.B., Owens, T.L., and DePaolo, D.J., 1998b, Intercalibration of standards, absolute ages and uncertainties in $^{40}Ar/^{39}Ar$ dating. *Chemical Geology*, **145**: 117–152.

Renne, P., Mundil, R., Balco, G., Min, K., and Ludwig, K., 2010, Joint determination of ^{40}K decay constants and $^{40}Ar^*/^{40}K$ for the Fish Canyon sanidine standard, and improved accuracy for $^{40}Ar/^{39}Ar$ geochronology. *Geochimica et Cosmochimica Acta*, **74**: 5349–5367.

Renne, P.R., Balco, G., Ludwig, K.R., Mundil, R., and Min, K., 2011, Response to the comment by WH Schwarz et al. on "Joint determination of ^{40}K decay constants and $^{40}Ar^*/^{40}K$ for the Fish Canyon sanidine standard, and improved accuracy for $^{40}Ar/^{39}Ar$ geochronology" by PR Renne et al. (2010). *Geochimica et Cosmochimica Acta*, **75**: 5097–5100.

Richter, S., Eykens, R., Kuhn, H., Aregbe, Y., Verbruggen, A., and Weyer, S., 2010, New average values for the $n(^{238}U)/n(^{235}U)$ isotope ratios of natural uranium standards. *International Journal of Mass Spectrometry*, **295** (1–2), 94–97.

Rivera, T.A., Storey, M., Schmitz, M.D., and Crowley, J.L., 2013, Age intercalibration of $^{40}Ar/^{39}Ar$ sanidine and chemically distinct U/Pb zircon populations from the Alder Creek Rhyolite Quaternary geochronology standard. *Chemical Geology*, **345**: 87–98.

Rivera, T.A., Schmitz, M.D., Crowley, J.L., and Storey, M., 2014, Rapid magma evolution constrained by zircon petrochronology and $^{40}Ar/^{39}Ar$ sanidine ages for the Huckleberry Ridge Tuff, Yellowstone, USA. *Geology*, **42**: 643–646.

Rivera, T.A., Schmitz, M.D., Jicha, B.R., and Crowley, J.L., 2016, Zircon petrochronology and $^{40}Ar/^{39}Ar$ sanidine dates for the Mesa Falls Tuff. Crystal-scale records of magmatic evolution and the short lifespan of a large Yellowstone magma chamber. *Journal of Petrology*, **57**: 1677–1704.

Rooney, A.D., Chew, D.M., and Selby, D., 2011, Re-Os geochronology of the neoproterozoic-cambrian dalradian supergroup of Scotland and Ireland: implications for neoproterozoic stratigraphy, glaciations and Re-Os systematics. *Precambrian Research*, **185** (3-4), 202–214.

Rooney, A.D., Macdonald, F.A., Strauss, J.V., Dudás, F.Ö., Hallmann, C., and Selby, D., 2014, Re-Os geochronology and coupled Os-Sr isotope constraints on the Sturtian snowball Earth. *Proceedings of the National Academy of Sciences of the United States of America*, **111**: 51–56.

Rooney, A.D., Strauss, J.V., Brandon, A.D., and Macdonald, F.A., 2015, A Cryogenian chronology. Two long-lasting synchronous Neoproterozoic glaciations. *Geology*, **43**: 459–462.

Rooney, A.D., Austermann, J., Smith, E.F., Li, Y., Selby, D., Dehler, C.M., et al., 2018, Coupled Re-Os and U-Pb geochronology of the Tonian Chuar Group, Grand Canyon. *The Geological Society of America Bulletin*, **130**: 1085–1098.

Sadler, P., Cooper, R., and Melchin, M., 2009, High-resolution, early Paleozoic (Ordovician-Silurian) time scales. *The Geological Society of America Bulletin*, **121**: 887–906.

Sageman, B.B., Singer, B.S., Meyers, S.R., Siewert, S.R., Walaszczyk, I., Condon, D.J., et al., 2014, Integrating $^{40}Ar/^{39}Ar$, U-Pb, and astronomical clocks in the Cretaceous Niobrara Formation, Western Interior Basin, USA. *The Geological Society of America Bulletin*, **126**: 956–973.

Sahy, D., Condon, D.J., Terry Jr, D.O., Fischer, A.U., and Kuiper, K.F., 2015, Synchronizing terrestrial and marine records of environmental change across the Eocene–Oligocene transition. *Earth and Planetary Science Letters*, **427**: 171–182.

Sahy, D., Condon, D.J., Hilgen, F.J., and Kuiper, K.F., 2017, Reducing disparity in radio-isotopic and astrochronology-based time scales of the late Eocene and Oligocene. *Paleoceanography*, **32**: 1018–1035.

Saxton, J.M., 2015, A method for measurement of ^{36}Ar without $H^{35}Cl$ interference. *Chemical Geology*, **409**: 112–117.

Schaen, A.J., Jicha, B.R., Hodges, K.V., Vermeesch, P., Stelten, M.E., Mercer, C.M., et al., 2020, On the reporting and interpretation of $^{40}Ar/^{39}Ar$ geochronologic data. *Geological Society of America Bulletin*, https://doi.org/10.1130/B35560.1.

Schauble, E.A., 2007, Role of nuclear volume in driving equilibrium stable isotope fractionation of mercury, thallium, and other very heavy elements. *Geochimica et Cosmochimica Acta*, **71**: 2170–2189.

Scherer, E., Munker, C., and Mezger, K., 2001, Calibration of the lutetium-hafnium clock. *Science*, **293**: 683–687.

Schmitz, M.D., 2012, Radiogenic isotope geochronology. *In* Gradstein, F.M., Ogg, J.G., and Schmitz, M.D. (eds), *The Geologic Time Scale 2012*. Elsevier, 115–126.

Schmitz, M., and Bowring, S., 2001, U-Pb zircon and titanite systematics of the Fish Canyon Tuff. an assessment of high-precision U-Pb geochronology and its application to young volcanic rocks. *Geochimica et Cosmochimica Acta*, **65**: 2571–2587.

Schmitz, M.D., and Davydov, V., 2012, Quantitative radiometric and biostratigraphic calibration of the Pennsylvanian–Early Permian (Cisuralian) time scale and pan-Euramerican chronostratigraphic correlation. *The Geological Society of America Bulletin*, **124**: 549–577.

Schmitz, M.D., and Schoene, B., 2007, Derivation of isotope ratios, errors, and error correlations for U–Pb geochronology using ^{205}Pb–^{235}U-(^{233}U)-spiked isotope dilution thermal ionization mass spectrometric data. *Geochemistry, Geophysics, Geosystems*, **8**: Q08006.

Schoene, B., Crowley, J.C., Condon, D.J., Schmitz, M.D., and Bowring, S.A., 2006, Reassessing the uranium decay constants for geochronology using ID-TIMS U–Pb data. *Geochimica et Cosmochimica Acta*, **70**: 426–445.

Schoene, B., Latkoczy, C., Schaltegger, U., and Günther, D., 2010, A new method integrating high-precision U–Pb geochronology with zircon trace element analysis (U–Pb TIMS-TEA). *Geochimica et Cosmochimica Acta*, **74**: 7144–7159.

Schoene, B., Eddy, M.P., Samperton, K.M., Keller, C.B., Keller, G., Adatte, T., et al., 2019, U-Pb constraints on pulsed eruption of the Deccan Traps across the end-Cretaceous mass extinction. *Science*, **363**: 862–866.

Schön, R., Winkler, G., and Kutschera, W., 2004, A critical review of experimental data for the half-lives of the uranium isotopes ^{238}U and ^{235}U. *Applied Radiation and Isotopes*, **60**: 263–273.

Selby, D., and Creaser, R.A., 2001, Re–Os geochronology and systematics in molybdenite from the Endako porphyry molybdenum deposit, British Columbia, Canada. *Economic Geology*, **96**: 197–204.

Selby, D., and Creaser, R.A., 2003, Re–Os geochronology of organic-rich sediments: an evaluation of organic matter analysis. *Chemical Geology*, **200**: 225–240.

Selby, D., and Creaser, R.A., 2005, Direct radiometric dating of the Devonian-Mississippian time-scale boundary using the Re-Os black shale geochronometer. *Geology*, **33**: 545–548.

Selby, D., Creaser, R.A., Stein, H.J., Markey, R.J., and Hannah, J.L., 2007, Assessment of the ^{187}Re decay constant by cross calibration of Re–Os molybdenite and U–Pb zircon chronometers in magmatic ore systems. *Geochimica et Cosmochimica Acta*, **71**: 1999–2013.

Shirey, S.B., and Walker, R.J., 1998, The Re–Os isotope system in cosmochemistry and high temperature geochemistry. *Annual Review of Earth and Planetary Sciences*, **26**: 423–500.

Silver, L.T., and Deutsch, S., 1963, Uranium-lead isotopic variations in zircons; a case study. *The Journal of Geology*, **71** (6): 721–758.

Simon, J.I., Renne, P.R., and Mundil, R., 2008, Implications of pre-eruptive magmatic histories of zircons for U-Pb geochronology of silicic extrusions. *Earth and Planetary Science Letters*, **266**: 182–194.

Singer, B.S., 2014, A Quaternary geomagnetic instability time scale. *Quaternary Geochronology*, **21**: 29–52.

Singer, B.S., Jicha, B.R., Condon, D., Macho, A., Hoffman, K.A., Brown, M., et al., 2014, Precise ages of the Réunion event and Huckleberry Ridge excursion: episodic clustering of geomagnetic instabilities and the dynamics of flow within the outer core. *Earth and Planetary Science Letters*, **405**: 25–38.

Singer, B.S., Jicha, B.R., Mochizuki, N., and Coe, R.S., 2019, Synchronizing volcanic, sedimentary, and ice core records of Earth's last magnetic polarity reversal. *Science Advances*, **5**, http://dx.doi.org/10.1126/sciadv.aaw4621.

Smoliar, M.I., Walker, R.J., and Morgan, J.W., 1996, Re–Os ages of group IIA, IIIA IVA, and IVB iron meteorites. *Science*, **271**: 1099–1102.

Sperling, E.A., Rooney, A.D., Hays, L., Sergeev, V.N., Vorob'eva, N.G., Sergeeva, N.D., et al., 2014, Redox heterogeneity of subsurface waters in the Mesoproterozoic ocean. *Geobiology*, **12**: 373–386.

Sprain, C.J., Renne, P.R., Vanderkluysen, L., Pande, K., Self, S., and Mittal, T., 2019, The eruptive tempo of Deccan volcanism in relation to the Cretaceous-Paleogene boundary. *Science*, **363**: 866–870.

Steiger, R.H., and Jäger, E., 1977, Subcommission on geochronology; convention on the use of decay constants in geo- and cosmochronology. *Earth and Planetary Science Letters*, **36**: 359–362.

Stein, H.J., Markey, R.J., Morgan, J.W., Hannah, J.L., and Scherstén, A., 2001, The remarkable Re–Os chronometer in molybdenite: how and why it works. *Terra Nova*, **13**: 479–486.

Stirling, C., Halliday, A., and Porcell, D., 2005, In search of live ^{247}Cm in the early solar system. *Geochimica et Cosmochimica Acta*, **69**: 1059–1071.

Stirling, C.H., Halliday, A.N., Potter, E.-K., Andersen, M.B., and Zanda, B., 2006, A low initial abundance of ^{247}Cm in the early solar system and implications for r-process nucleosynthesis. *Earth and Planetary Science Letters*, **251** (3–4), 386–397.

Stirling, C.H., Andersen, M.B., Potter, E.-K., and Halliday, A.N., 2007, Low-temperature isotopic fractionation of uranium. *Earth and Planetary Science Letters*, **264**: 208–225.

Strauss, J.V., Rooney, A.D., Macdonald, F.A., Brandon, A.D. and Knoll, A.H., 2014, 740 Ma vase-shaped microfossils from Yukon, Canada: implications for Neoproterozoic chronology and biostratigraphy. *Geology*, 42: 659–662.

Szymanowski, D., Wotzlaw, J.-F., Ellis, B.S., Bachmann, O., Guillong, M., Quadt, et al., 2017, Protracted near-solidus storage and pre-eruptive rejuvenation of large magma reservoirs. *Nature Geoscience*, **10**: 777–782.

Trayler, R.B., Schmitz, M.D., Cuitiño, J.I., Kohn, M.J., Bargo, M.S., Kay, R.F., et al., 2020. An improved approach to age-modeling in deep time: implications for the Santa Cruz Formation, Argentina. *GSA Bulletin*, **132**: 233–244. 10.1130/B35203.1.

Villeneuve, M., Sandeman, H.A., and Davis, W.J., 2000, A method for intercalibration of U-Th-Pb and ^{40}Ar-^{39}Ar ages in the Phanerozoic. *Geochimica et Cosmochimica Acta*, **64**: 4017–4030.

Völkening, J., Walczyk, T., and Heumann, K.G., 1991, Osmium isotope ratio determinations by negative thermal ionization mass spectrometry. *International Journal of Mass Spectrometry and Ion Processes*, **105**: 147–159.

Ware, B., and Jourdan, F., 2018, ^{40}Ar/^{39}Ar geochronology of terrestrial pyroxene. *Geochimica et Cosmochimica Acta*, **230**: 112–136.

Weyer, S., Anbar, A.D., Gerdes, A., Gordon, G.W., Algeo, T.J., and Boyle, E.A., 2008, Natural fractionation of ^{238}U/^{235}U. *Geochimica et Cosmochimica Acta*, **72**: 345–359.

Widmann, P., Davies, J.H.F.L., and Schaltegger, U., 2019, Calibrating chemical abrasion—its effects on zircon crystal structure, chemical composition and UPb age. *Chemical Geology*, **511**: 1–10.

Wotzlaw, J.F., Schaltegger, U., Frick, D.A., Dungan, M.A., Gerdes, A., and Günther, D., 2013, Tracking the evolution of large-volume silicic magma reservoirs from assembly to supereruption. *Geology*, **41** (8), 867–870.

Wotzlaw, J.-F., Hüsing, S.K., Hilgen, F.J., and Schaltegger, U., 2014a, High-precision zircon U–Pb geochronology of astronomically dated volcanic ash beds from the Mediterranean Miocene. *Earth and Planetary Science Letters*, **407**: 19–34.

Wotzlaw, J.F., Bindeman, I.N., Watts, K.E., Schmitt, A.K., Caricchi, L., and Schaltegger, U., 2014b, Linking rapid magma reservoir assembly and eruption trigger mechanisms at evolved Yellowstone-type supervolcanoes. *Geology*, **42**: 807–810.

Wotzlaw, J.-F., Bindeman, I.N., Stern, R.A., D'Abzac, F.-X., and Schaltegger, U., 2015, Rapid heterogeneous assembly of multiple magma reservoirs prior to Yellowstone supereruptions. *Scientific Reports*, **5**: 1–10.

York, D., 1969, Least squares fitting of a straight line with correlated errors. *Earth and Planetary Science Letters*, **5**: 320–324.

Zhang, X., Honda, M., and Hamilton, D., 2016, Performance of the high-resolution, multi-collector Helix MC Plus Noble Gas Mass Spectrometer at the Australian National University. *Journal of the American Society for Mass Spectrometry*, **27**: 1937–1943.

J.M. McArthur, R.J. Howarth, G.A. Shields and Y. Zhou

Chapter 7

Strontium Isotope Stratigraphy

Chapter outline

Abstract

The $^{87}Sr/^{86}Sr$ value of Sr dissolved in the world's oceans has varied through time in a known way. When minerals, such as biogenic calcite, precipitate from seawater, they incorporate Sr from seawater and capture the $^{87}Sr/^{86}Sr$ value for marine-Sr at the time of precipitation. Measurement of the $^{87}Sr/^{86}Sr$ value in fossil precipitates, such as belemnites or foraminifera, can therefore be used to date and to correlate worldwide the marine sedimentary rocks in which the precipitates occur. Here, the theory and practice of the methodology is outlined.

The variation of marine-$^{87}Sr/^{86}Sr$ through time is usually ascribed to changing fluxes of Sr from mid-ocean-ridge volcanism ($^{87}Sr/^{86}Sr \approx 0.703$) coupled with changing $^{87}Sr/^{86}Sr$ and flux through time of riverine inputs to the ocean of Sr with a high ratio (≈ 0.711).

7.1 Introduction

The ability to date and correlate sediments using $^{87}Sr/^{86}Sr$ values in marine minerals, typically biogenic carbonate, relies on the fact that the $^{87}Sr/^{86}Sr$ value of Sr dissolved in the world's oceans has varied through time (Figs. 7.1 and 7.2; for a discussion of this topic, see Peucker-Ehrenbrink and Fiske, 2019). By measuring the $^{87}Sr/^{86}Sr$ value of Sr incorporated into a marine mineral and comparing that value to the calibration curves of Fig. 7.2, or a tabulated version of them, a numerical age can be obtained. The method's utility and accuracy decline with increasing sample age because the method relies on analysis of well-preserved samples that become less common with increasing geologic age.

Correlation, rather than dating, can be accomplished by comparing trends of $^{87}Sr/^{86}Sr$ in minerals profiled through

Geologic Time Scale 2020. DOI: https://doi.org/10.1016/B978-0-12-824360-2.00007-3

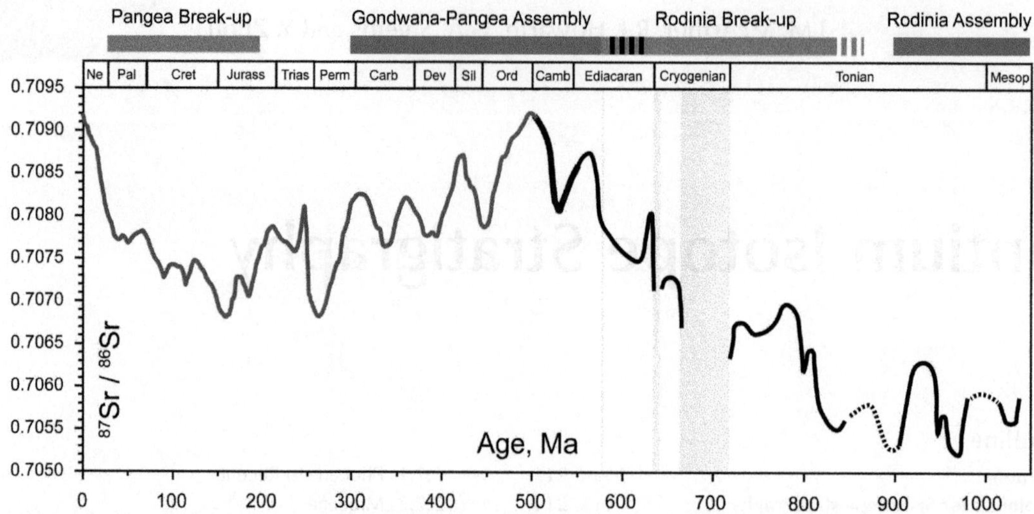

FIGURE 7.1 Variation of marine-$^{87}Sr/^{86}Sr$ through Neoproterozoic and Phanerozoic times. The black line is for the Precambrian, database of G. Shields and Y. Zhou. The red line denotes a post-Cambrian fit to the database of J.M. McArthur and R. Howarth and is accompanied by a LOESS look-up table of values of $^{87}Sr/^{86}Sr$ against time and *vice versa*, available from authors and from ResearchGate.

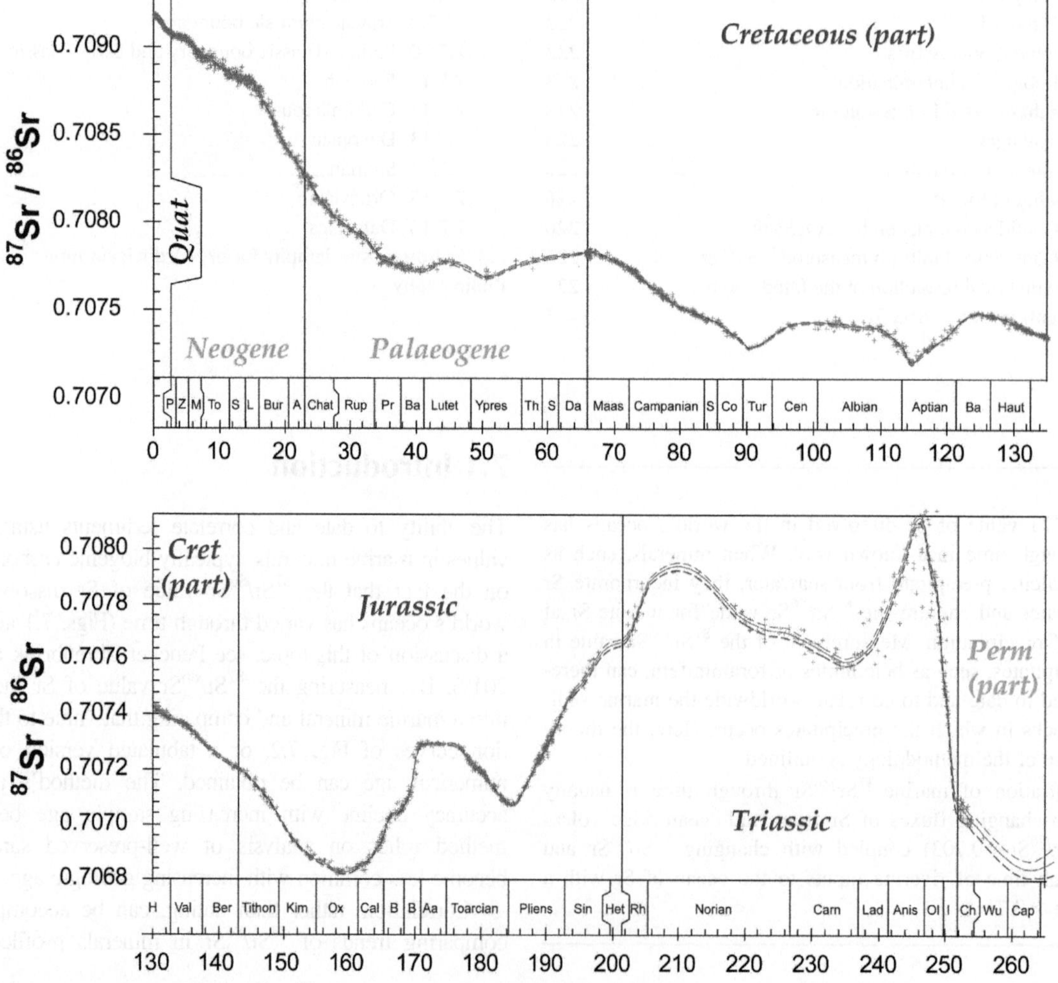

FIGURE 7.2 Details of the variation of $^{87}Sr/^{86}Sr$ through Phanerozoic time, showing the 95% confidence on the fitted curve. See text for a discussion of its parts.

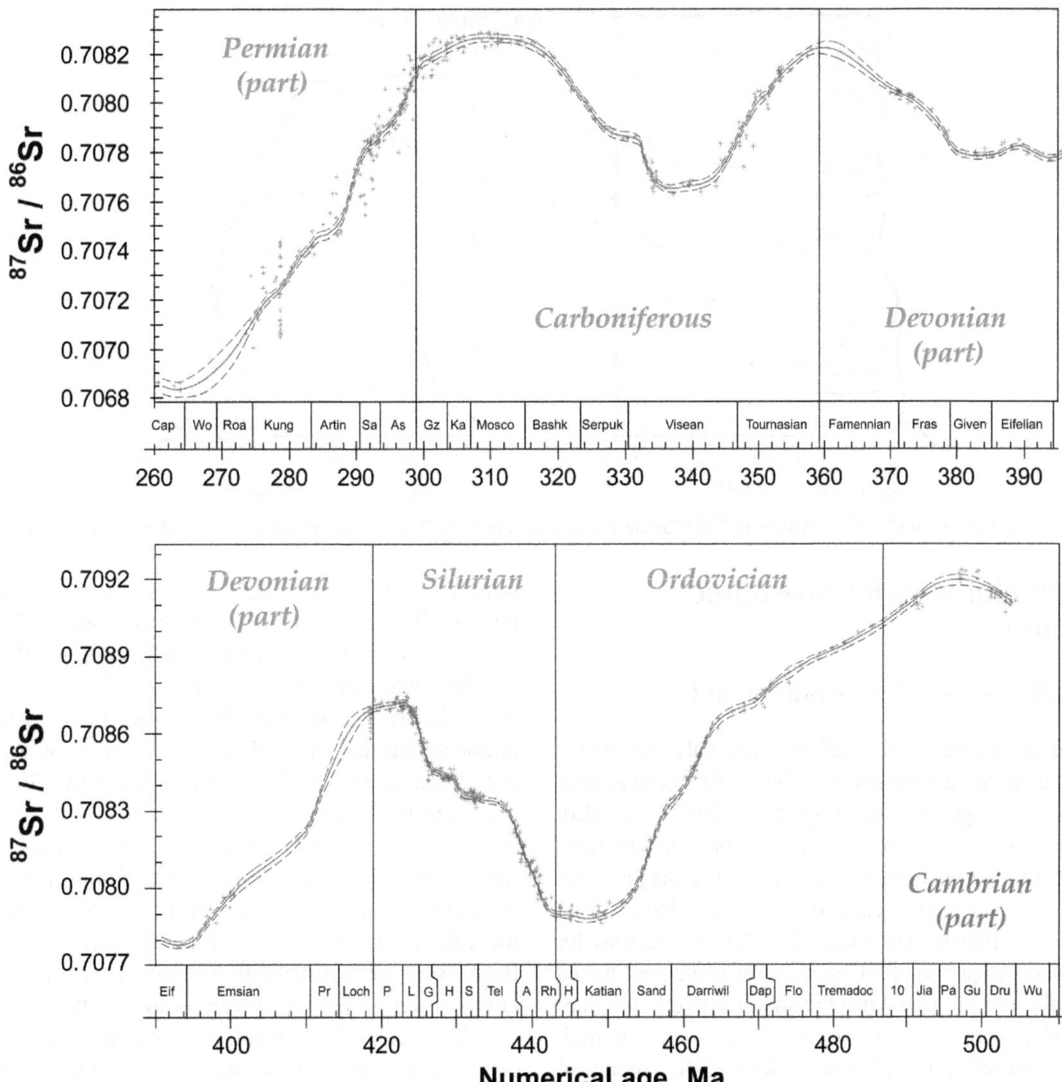

FIGURE 7.2 (Continued)

different sections (Fig. 7.3). Correlation with $^{87}Sr/^{86}Sr$ does not need a time-calibrated reference curve but a glance at such a curve helps one to avoid gross miss-correlation with $^{87}Sr/^{86}Sr$, for example, correlating upper Albian strata to Coniacian strata of similar $^{87}Sr/^{86}Sr$. When proposing to date or correlate with $^{87}Sr/^{86}Sr$, the calibration curve is also useful in order to see when marine-$^{87}Sr/^{86}Sr$ was changing little and so avoid wasting time and money by attempting to use Sr-isotope stratigraphy (SIS) in such intervals, for example, mid-Albian to Cenomanian times (Fig. 7.2).

The principal difficulty in constructing calibration curves of $^{87}Sr/^{86}Sr$ against time is how to derive such profiles (Figs. 7.1 and 7.2) from profiles of $^{87}Sr/^{86}Sr$ through rock sections (Fig. 7.3). That is, how to compensate for the variations in sedimentation rate, and stratigraphic gaps present in any rock section. The problem is outlined in Fig. 7.4, from which it follows that once a trend in time is established, the trend in $^{87}Sr/^{86}Sr$ through any rock section can be interpreted in terms of sedimentation rates (Fig. 7.4).

Under optimum conditions, for example, with well-preserved material and when the rate at which $^{87}Sr/^{86}Sr$ changed with time ($\Delta R/\Delta t$) was high, the precision with which SIS can date and/or correlate marine strata can surpass foraminiferal biostratigraphy in the Cenozoic and ammonite biostratigraphy in the Mesozoic. Profiling $^{87}Sr/^{86}Sr$ through a section (Fig. 7.3) can also reveal stratigraphic gaps and be used to estimate their duration (Miller et al., 1988; Mead and Hodell, 1995; Brasier et al., 1996), reveal diachroneity in biostratigraphic datums (Hess et al., 1989), and reveal relative durations of biozones (McArthur et al., 2000a) and stages (Weedon and Jenkyns, 1999). For a more detailed account of Sr-isotope stratigraphy, the reader is referred to reviews by McArthur (1994) and Veizer et al. (1997, 1999).

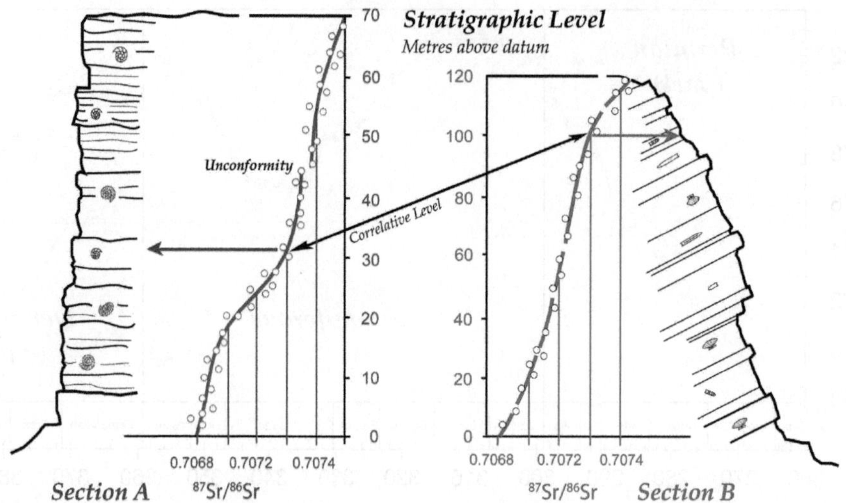

FIGURE 7.3 Correlation with $^{87}Sr/^{86}Sr$. Values of $^{87}Sr/^{86}Sr$ are matched between $^{87}Sr/^{86}Sr$ profiles constructed for independent sections.

7.2 Methodologies for Sr-isotope stratigraphy

7.2.1 Limits to Sr-isotope stratigraphy?

Dating and correlating with $^{87}Sr/^{86}Sr$ work only for marine minerals and on the assumption that the world's oceans have always been homogenous with respect to $^{87}Sr/^{86}Sr$ (modern value 0.709174) at the precision of available measurement. This assumption becomes increasingly suspect as the precision at which $^{87}Sr/^{86}Sr$ can be measured improves. Adopted when precisions were poorer than attainable today, the reasons for the assumption were twofold. First, the oceans are well mixed on time scales ($\approx 10^3$ years) that are short relative to the rates of gain and loss of Sr in the oceans from rivers and mid-ocean-ridge volcanism ($\approx 10^6$ years). Second, the amount of Sr in the sea, which is 7.6 μg/L at salinity 35 psu (equivalent to ‰), is generally 10^2 times higher than the amount in rivers so, when dealing with fully marine faunas, the riverine influence on marine-$^{87}Sr/^{86}Sr$ is assumed to be negligible.

Assessing the effect of riverine dilution on marine-$^{87}Sr/^{86}Sr$, Bryant et al. (1995) showed that, with a few exceptions, dilution of seawater from its usual salinity of around 35‰ to salinities of ~20‰ would be needed before most rivers had a "noticeable effect" on marine-$^{87}Sr/^{86}Sr$. At such a salinity the freshwater influence might be expected to impoverish the marine fauna and so be seen paleontologically. The exceptions made those authors caution against applying SIS except to fully marine faunas.

The "noticeable effect" was set by Bryant et al. (1995) at a difference of ±0.000050 from the seawater value, a difference that was twice the precision of measurement of $^{87}Sr/^{86}Sr$ commonly attainable at that time. The best modern instruments can attain a precision of around ±0.000001 with replication of analyses (Table 7.1). We have therefore updated Bryant et al. (1995) to show, in Fig. 7.5, the salinities at which 252 world rivers can affect marine-$^{87}Sr/^{86}Sr$ at measurement precisions of 1, 2, 5 and 10×10^{-6} (data from Goldstein and Jacobsen, 1987; Palmer and Edmond, 1989; Pearce et al., 2015; Peucker-Ehrenbrink, 2009, 2018; Peucker-Ehrenbrink and Fiske, 2019). It is disconcerting that Fig. 7.5 shows that 87% of world rivers can alter marine-$^{87}Sr/^{86}Sr$ at salinities above 30 psu if the precision of measurement is ±0.000001. At 30 psu and above the minimal freshwater influence would have no impact on the diversity of a marine fauna. It is therefore no surprise that El Meknassi et al. (2018) report nonmarine influences recorded in modern biogenic carbonates from some semirestricted, nearshore, mostly estuarine, environments, echoing Bryant et al. (1995).

This picture is a broad overview that hides important detail, such as the fact that some of the cited river data were collected far upstream of the river mouth and so may not be typical of riverine input to the oceans. For example, the River Avon of Western Australia was sampled by Goldstein and Jacobsen (1987) at Toodyay, on the eastern side of the Darling Scarp some 80 km from the river mouth and before the river is diluted by tributaries draining salt-poor terrain on, and west of, the Darling Scarp. The Avon has both a high $^{87}Sr/^{86}Sr$, of 0.73255, and an exceptionally high Sr concentration of 2.94 μg/mL because it drains salt-rich terrain on Precambrian shield. At the river mouth the Sr concentration and $^{87}Sr/^{86}Sr$ would likely be lower. Furthermore, freshwater influences can be revealed by analysis of $\delta^{18}O$: outside the tropics, freshwater typically has $\delta^{18}O$ more negative than seawater, so unusually negative $\delta^{18}O$ in well-preserved fossils can indicate freshwater influences.

Notwithstanding the previous, Kuznetsov et al. (2012), using multiple analyses in order to lessen uncertainty, proved homogeneity for open-ocean water, a term that here includes the Mediterranean Sea and the Red Sea (pooled mean of 0.709175 ± 0.000001, 2s.e., $n = 49$). Noticeable nonmarine

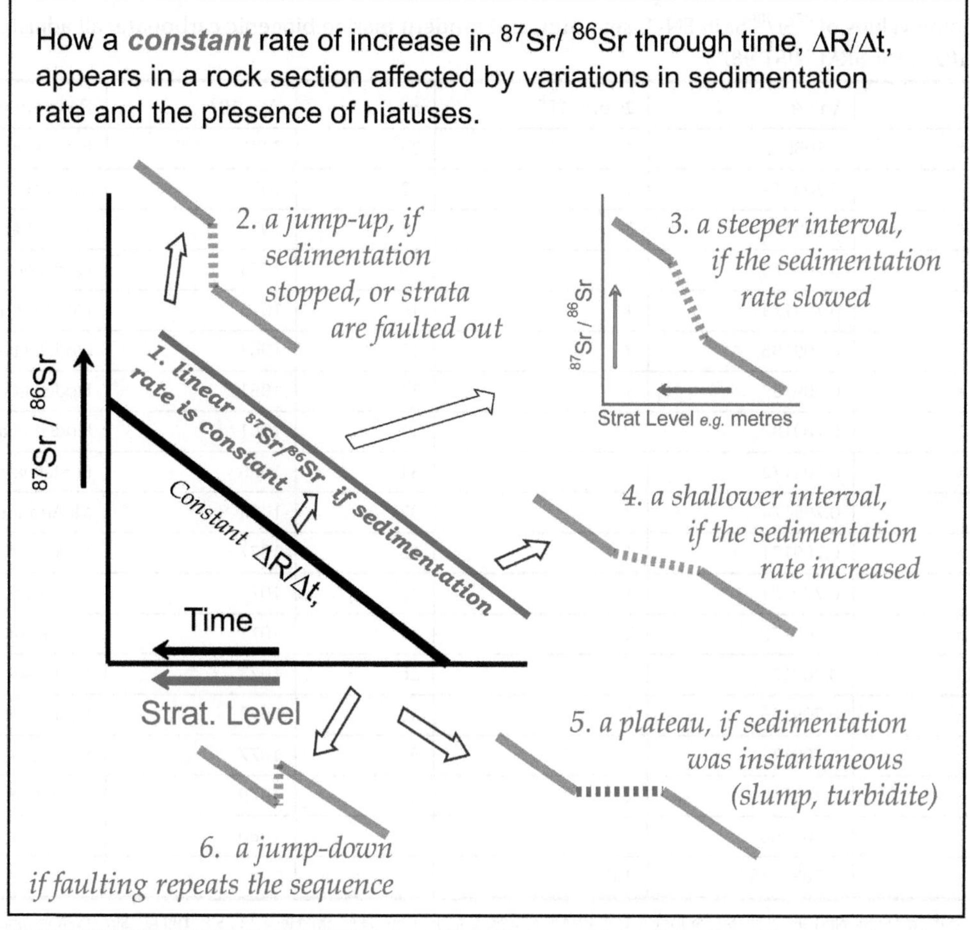
How a *constant* rate of increase in $^{87}Sr/^{86}Sr$ through time, ΔR/Δt, appears in a rock section affected by variations in sedimentation rate and the presence of hiatuses.
2. a jump-up, if sedimentation stopped, or strata are faulted out
3. a steeper interval, if the sedimentation rate slowed
87Sr / 86Sr
Strat Level e.g. metres
1. linear 87Sr/86Sr if sedimentation rate is constant
Constant ΔR/Δt,
4. a shallower interval, if the sedimentation rate increased
Time
Strat. Level
5. a plateau, if sedimentation was instantaneous (slump, turbidite)
6. a jump-down if faulting repeats the sequence

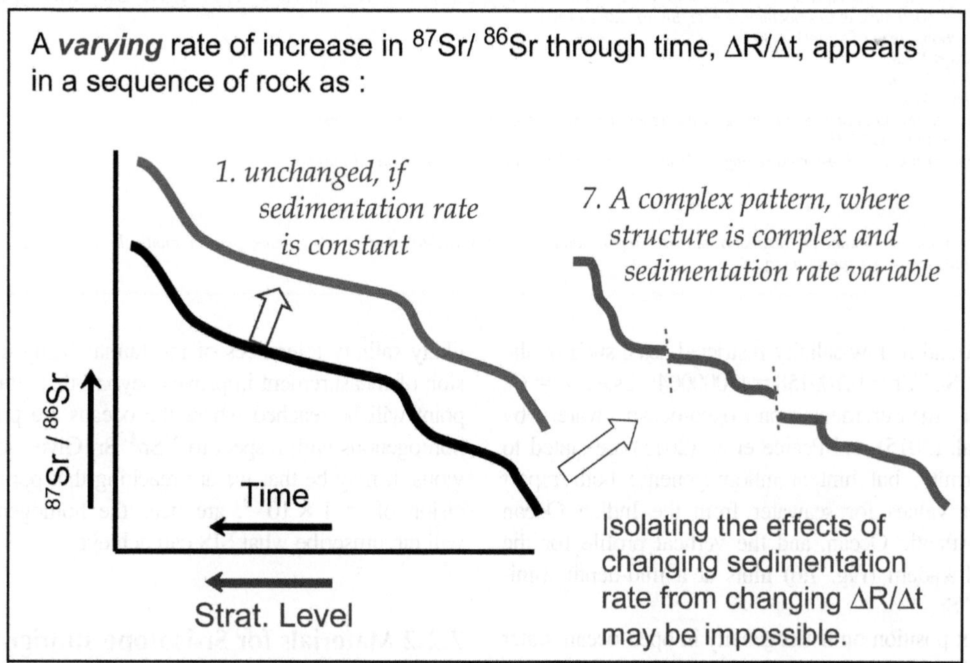
A *varying* rate of increase in $^{87}Sr/^{86}Sr$ through time, ΔR/Δt, appears in a sequence of rock as :
1. unchanged, if sedimentation rate is constant
7. A complex pattern, where structure is complex and sedimentation rate variable
87Sr / 86Sr
Time
Strat. Level
Isolating the effects of changing sedimentation rate from changing ΔR/Δt may be impossible.

FIGURE 7.4 How sedimentation rate alters the profile of $^{87}Sr/^{86}Sr$ in the rocks when it is plotted against stratigraphic level in a section. The rate of change over time of marine-$^{87}Sr/^{86}Sr$ is abbreviated to $\Delta R/\Delta t$.

TABLE 7.1 Some values of $^{87}Sr/^{86}Sr$ in EN-1, seawater, and modern marine biogenic carbonate, all adjusted to a value of 0.710248 for SRM/NIST 987.

Standard	Value	2s.e. $\times 10^6$	*n*	$\Delta \times 10^6$	Reference
E&A	0.708022	4	34	2226	Jones et al. (1994a)
Corals[a]	0.709174	1	42	1074	Ando et al. (2010)
Foraminifera[b]	0.709175	3	12	1073	Ando et al. (2010)
Foraminifera[c]	0.709175	3	8	1073	Farrell et al. (1995)
Foaminifera[d]	0.709173	1	10	1075	Henderson et al. (1994)
EN-1	0.709185	7	11	1063	Hodell et al. (1990)
Foraminifera	0.709187	9	11	1061	Hodell et al. (1990)
Foraminifera	0.709187	9	11	1061	Hodell et al. (1990)
Modern shells[e]	0.709172	1	31	1076	El Meknassi et al. (2018)
EN-1	0.709174	2	37	1074	McArthur (2010)
Seawater	0.709171	1	15	1077	Mokadem et al. (2015)
Foraminifera[f]	0.709171	1	12	1077	Mokadem et al. (2015)
EN-1 (2004/05)	0.709177	2	17	1071	Kuznetsov et al. (2012)
EN-1 (2009/10)	0.709175	1	26	1073	Kuznetsov et al. (2012)
Modern shells[g]	0.709175	1	49	1073	Kuznetsov et al. (2012)
IAPSO SW[h]	0.709171	3	51	1077	Voigt et al. (2015)
IAPSO SW[i]	0.709169	2	5	1079	Voigt et al. (2015)
JCp-1[j]	0.709168	6	10	1080	Voigt et al. (2015)
Mean[k]	0.7091739	1.8			

Source: $\Delta \times 10^6 = (^{87}Sr/^{86}Sr$ for NIST 987$) - (^{87}Sr/^{86}Sr$ for EN-1, or E&A for Jones, C.E., Jenkyns, H.C. and Hesselbo, S.P. 1994a), Strontium isotopes in Early Jurassic seawater. *Geochimica et Cosmochimica Acta*, **58** (4), 1285–1301.

[a] *Ages by radiocarbon, mean of samples <30 ka.*
[b] *Mean of samples <25 ka.*
[c] *Mean of samples <50 ka.*
[d] *Mean of samples <31 ka.*
[e] *Modern biogenic carbonate, unrestricted settings, Atlantic and Pacific coasts, 31 values on 31 samples.*
[f] *Mean of samples <44 ka, ODP Site 758A.*
[g] *Modern biogenic carbonate, unrestricted settings, Atlantic, Pacific, Indian, coasts; 33 values on 25 samples.*
[h] *By ICP-MC-MS.*
[i] *By TIMS.*
[j] *By TIMS.*
[k] *Post-1990 data for modern marine-Sr: mean and standard error weighted by* n. *ICP-MC-MS, Inductively coupled plasma, multicollector, mass spectrometry; TIMS, thermal ionization mass spectrometry.*

effects were found in low-salinity restricted seas, such as the Black Sea ($^{87}Sr/^{86}Sr = 0.709158 \pm 0.000004$; 2s.e., $n = 6$). More limited measurements on open-ocean water by Mokadem et al. (2015) and Pearce et al. (2015) are stated to support uniformity, but hint at inhomogeneity: both report slightly higher values for seawater from the Indian Ocean than for the Atlantic Ocean, and the vertical profile for the Atlantic of Mokadem (Fig. 7.6) hints at a mid-depth minimum in $^{87}Sr/^{86}Sr$.

The present position on heterogeneity in open-ocean water at the limit of measurement is therefore equivocal. What is certain is that with most SIS undertaken on samples from continental margins and epeiric seas, possible nonmarine influences should be evaluated by assessing, for example, the likely salinity tolerances of the faunas being dated. As precision of measurement improves beyond that attainable today, a point will be reached where the oceans are proven not to be homogenous with respect to $^{87}Sr/^{86}Sr$. Given some of the previous, it may be that we are reaching that point and, at a precision of $\pm 1 \times 10^{-6}$, are near the homogeneity limit that will circumscribe what SIS can achieve.

7.2.2 Materials for Sr-isotope stratigraphy

Early workers analyzed macrofossil carbonate (Peterman et al., 1970) or foraminiferal calcite (Dasch and Biscaye, 1971) and most workers have followed this practice. For the

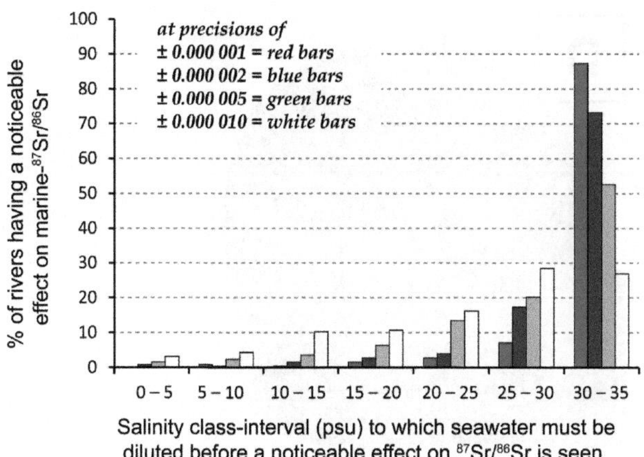

FIGURE 7.5 Dilution of seawater, expressed as salinity class interval in practical salinity units (equivalent to ‰), needed for world rivers to alter marine-$^{87}Sr/^{86}Sr$ at four limiting levels of measurement: 1×10^{-6}, 2×10^{-6}, 5×10^{-6}, and 10×10^{-6}. At a measurement precision of $\pm 1 \times 10^{-6}$, the best currently available utilizing pooled means of replicate analysis, 87% of rivers alter marine-$^{87}Sr/^{86}Sr$ at salinities above 30 psu. Modeled as linear mixing of seawater (35‰, 7.8 ppm Sr, 0.709174) and freshwater (0‰, a range of Sr concentrations and $^{87}Sr/^{86}Sr$).

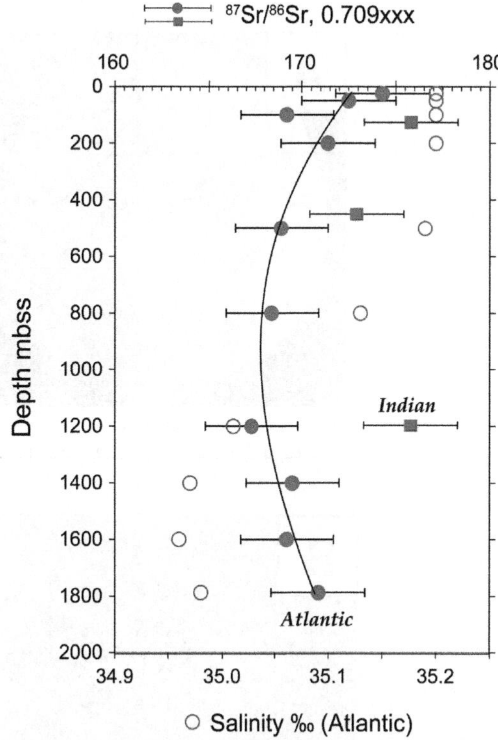

FIGURE 7.6 Vertical profile of $^{87}Sr/^{86}Sr$ in seawater in the northern Atlantic Ocean (62.00°N; 20.00°W, 1800 m water depth; modified from Mokadem et al. 2015). The data show a mid-depth minimum, hinting at non-conservative behavior of $^{87}Sr/^{86}Sr$, although those authors state that the variations are within analytical uncertainty.

Neogene, foraminiferal calcite, largely from DSDP/ODP sites, has underpinned Cenozoic curve construction (see works of Farrell, Hodell, and Miller listed in Table 7.1). For Mesozoic and Paleozoic sediments, the most useful samples have proven to be belemnite guards (Jones et al., 1994a, 1994b; McArthur et al., 2000a) and the inner (secondary) shell of brachiopods (Veizer et al., 1999) because both resist diagenesis well. Inoceramids (Bralower et al., 1997) and atoll carbonates (Jenkyns et al., 1995) have yielded useful data. Early diagenetic marine cements can also be useful (Carpenter et al., 1991) but are rarely used.

Ammonite aragonite gave mostly good data for samples from the Western Interior Seaway of the United States (McArthur et al., 1994) but those authors found that many apparently well-preserved samples gave aberrant results, as others have done when analyzing aragonite (Marcano et al., 2015, and references therein). Given these difficulties, it is probably best to avoid aragonite as a sample medium for SIS. Attempts to use barite have met with mixed success (Paytan et al., 1993; Martin et al., 1995; Mearon et al., 2003) and it has been the same with conodonts (Martin and Macdougall, 1995; Holmden et al., 1996; Ruppel et al., 1996; Ebneth et al., 2001; Korte et al., 2003; Saltzman et al., 2014; Dudás et al., 2017). Trilobite calcite is a little used, but potentially useful, medium for Cambrian studies.

Where no macrofossils or macrofossil debris are available, such as in the Precambrian, bulk carbonate, typically micrite has been used (e.g., Burke et al., 1982; Shields, 1999; Halverson et al., 2007; Cox et al., 2016), although early diagenetic marine calcite cements may have untapped potential (Kaufman et al., 1993; Zhou, in this work). As Peterman et al. (1970) emphasized that dissolution of bulk carbonate may contaminate the Sr from carbonate with Sr from aluminosilicate and diagenetic (secondary) phases so potentially giving erroneous results. Ways to minimize the contribution from contaminant Sr are described in Section 7.2.4.

7.2.3 Assessment of sample quality

Successful SIS requires samples that are well preserved. Descriptors of sample quality are subjective; here, the term "well preserved" means that samples retain their original $^{87}Sr/^{86}Sr$ value. In Figs. 7.7 and 7.8, we provide some examples that illustrate the different states of preservation commonly encountered. The more water-tight the matrix enclosing the sample, the better is the preservation because flowing water promotes alteration. Excellent preservation is often seen in samples from clays, and samples sealed into carbonate rocks by early diagenetic cements.

Preservation should be assessed on a sample-by-sample basis. Methods to assess alteration tend to differ between sample types. For macrofossils, typical chemical methods in widespread use include concentrations of Fe, Mn, Sr, Mg, and stable isotope analysis ($\delta^{18}O$) to identify, and reject, samples that depart from values typical of coeval and modern equivalents of the sample being analyzed. The caveat here is that both the methods are insensitive to small degrees of alteration. Physical methods include

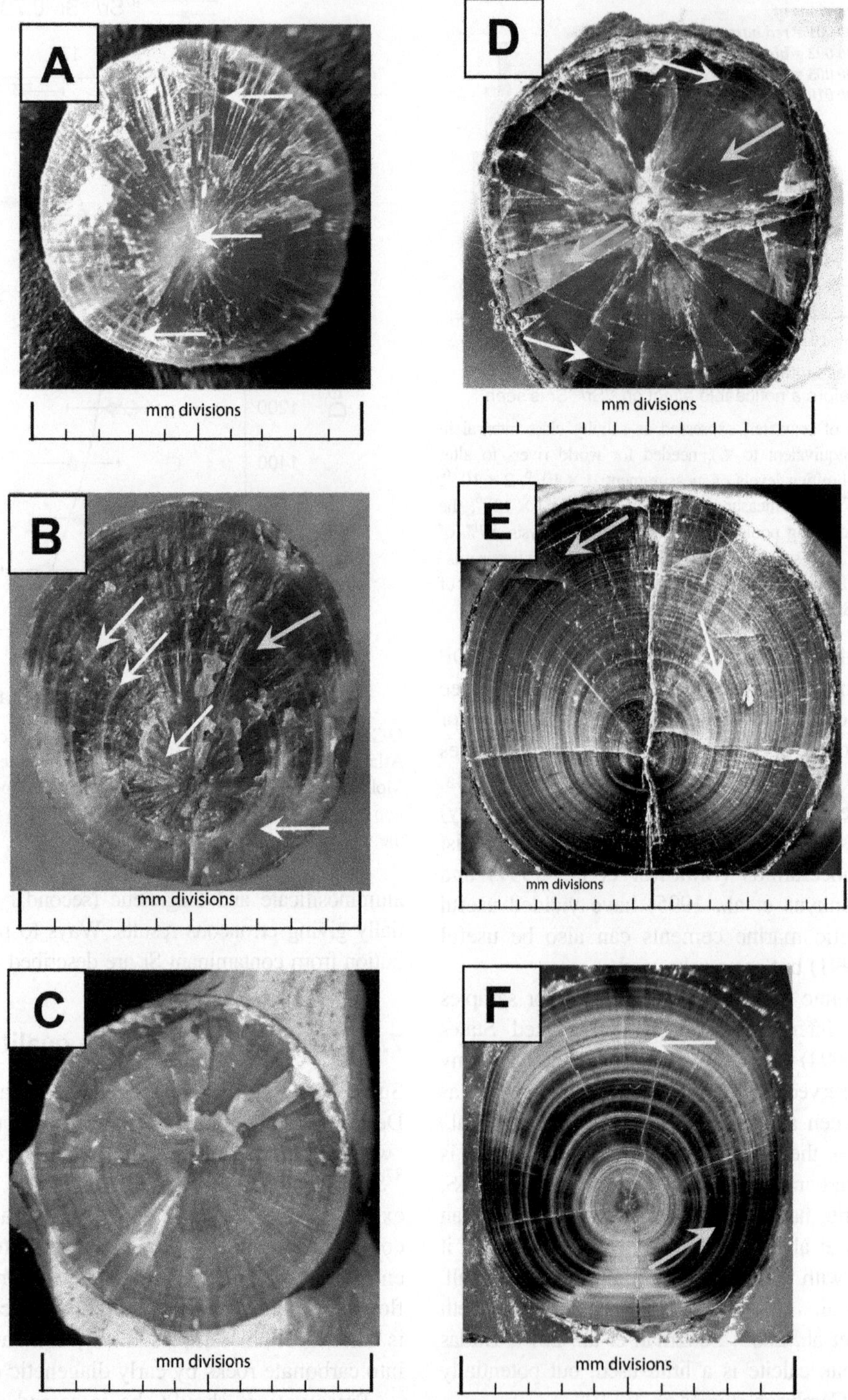

FIGURE 7.7 Preservation in belemnites. Fresh transverse fracture surfaces (A–C) and polished transverse sections (as blocks, D–F) of belemnite showing a range of preservation. Yellow arrows point to well-preserved areas, white arrows point to poorly preserved areas. (A) Good preservation; radial fabric is strong and "growth rings" (in fact, alteration rings) are few; nevertheless, there is alteration around the apical line. (B) Poor-to-middling preservation. Alteration rings are prominent but few. The lowermost 15% of the specimen is bleached from alteration, but patches of well-preserved calcite are still present toward the top of the specimen. (C) The sample is wholly altered and of no value to geochemistry. (D) Slight alteration of outermost millimeter where alteration rings are seen, with excellent preservation of inner portion. (E) Moderate preservation. Good color, much transparency retained, but numerous rings reveal extensive localized alteration. (F) Poor preservation, shown by the abundance of rings, grayish color, and lack of transparency [*cf.* color of (D)]. Nevertheless, some good-quality grains for analysis were found by picking the fragmented sample under the microscope.

FIGURE 7.8 Samples cleaned and fragmented for picking of subsamples for analysis. Background grid has 1 mm divisions. Yellow arrows point to well-preserved areas, white arrows point to poorly preserved areas. (A) Belemnite, good preservation. Color is subdued at this scale; the best fragments are transparent and have a radial fabric. (B) Belemnite, poor preservation [sample (E) of Fig. 7.7]. Most of the fragments are cloudy and altered; a few of the smaller are preserved well enough for analysis. (C) Brachiopod, Aalenian. Among the spar and matrix are abundant well-preserved transparent bundles of acicular calcite crystals from the secondary layer of the shell. (D) Excellent preservation in glassy fragments of *Orbulina universa*, Pliocene, Punta Piccola, Sicily. (E) Frosty globigerinid planktonic foraminifera accompanying glassy *O. universa*, Punta Piccola, Sicily. (F) Disaggregated calcite prisms of a giant inoceramid, Coniacian, Antarctic Peninsula; prisms are either transparent and well-preserved or opaque and altered.

cathodoluminescence, XRD, and examination of ultrastructure under the scanning-electron microscope (SEM). Caveats on cathodoluminescence are that unaltered biogenic carbonate may fluoresce under the cathode (Barbin et al., 1991; Barbin, 2000, 2013) and, that apart, fluorescence identifies only alteration occurring under suboxic conditions. Regarding SEM, ultrastructure can be retained on alteration (cf. silicified wood). Appraisal by SEM is not helped by the wide range of ultrastructures shown by biogenic carbonate; reference to standard texts assists, for example, Taylor et al. (1969, 1973) and Popov (2014) for bivalves, papers in Carter (1990), and Pérez-Huerta et al. (2018) for some other forms. For further information on most of the methods listed here, the reader is referred to McArthur (1994) and the more detailed account in Ullmann and Korte (2015), comparison with which will show the progress made in this regard in the interval between them, while Pérez-Huerta et al. (2018) provide a more detailed examination of some of these methods.

For macrofossils, use of trace element concentrations, $\delta^{18}O$, and XRD, seldom identify alteration before it is visible under the optical microscope and it is optical examination of fragmented specimens and thin sections that are the best way to assess preservation in such specimens, for example, Armendáriz et al. (2003). In thin section, alteration of calcite is indicated by cloudiness; such cloudiness is often visible in hand specimen. For example, four belemnites in Fig. 7.7 show different states of preservation; for belemnites the more rings that are visible and the thicker they are, and the cloudier the sample, the more they are altered. For brachiopods and bivalves, preservation of crystal structure under the optical microscope suggests good preservation (Fig. 7.8): for the prismatic layer of inoceramids, the ability to easily disaggregate individual crystallites is a necessary, but not sufficient, condition of good preservation because cloudy crystals may disaggregate (Fig. 7.8F). The way a brachiopod or bivalve shell fractures is also useful; shells should fragment and flake into multiple pieces with most breakage parallel to the shell surface, rather than breaking cleanly at a high angle to it.

For conodonts the best samples will be those in impermeable host rocks, for example, carbonates in which pore space is filled by early diagenetic cement, locking the conodonts into an impermeable matrix. Such a history may be hidden when assessing sample quality, which should improve as the color alteration index (CAI) of the conodonts decreases. A CAI of 1 is considered optimal. Nevertheless, a careful study of the relation of CAI to $^{87}Sr/^{86}Sr$ by Edwards et al. (2015) concluded that CAI was an unreliable indicator of preservation. Measurement of the F content of the conodont may be a better indicator of sample quality than CAI. Conodonts are made of apatite. Modern biogenic apatite is hydroxyapatite with the approximate composition $Ca_5[PO_4]_3[OH]_2$. In fossil apatite the hydroxyl (OH) group is partially or largely replaced by secondary fluorine (F), proving substantial alteration during burial. It is therefore no surprise that many authors caution that diagenetic alteration of both elemental and isotopic composition of apatite is the norm, not the exception (Holmden et al., 1996; Barrat et al., 2000; Martin and Scher, 2004, and references therein).

In order to assess the validity of conodont analysis, some analyses of enclosing whole rocks are useful in order to indicate which way alteration may have pushed $^{87}Sr/^{86}Sr$; see, for example, Chen et al. (2018) whose whole-rock $^{87}Sr/^{86}Sr$ values were higher than those of enclosed conodonts, thus validating the lower values of $^{87}Sr/^{86}Sr$ in conodonts as the most reliable values. Use of laser-ablation analysis to analyze only the crown portion of conodonts helps one to avoid altered parts of the specimen (Trotter and Eggins, 2006; Song et al., 2015).

Foraminifera are usually assessed visually and by SEM. For the latter, some assistance with assessment is available in *inter alia* (Bolli et al., 1989; Hemleben et al., 2018; Pearson, 2018). Well-preserved foraminifera are glassy and have translucent calcite (Fig. 7.8D). Altered samples are frosty (white and opaque; Fig. 7.8E). Yet frosty samples often preserve a good signal of $^{87}Sr/^{86}Sr$. They do so because the glassy–frosty transition largely occurs on the seafloor or within the uppermost few meters of burial (Pearson et al., 2001; Voigt et al., 2016). In both environments, recrystallization takes place in a fluid with the same $^{87}Sr/^{86}Sr$ as seawater, so exchange during alteration does not alter $^{87}Sr/^{86}Sr$; other chemical signals (e.g., Sr/Ca, Mg/Ca) may not be preserved (Edgar et al., 2015). With deeper burial, alteration continues and exchange with Sr in pore waters, with a different $^{87}Sr/^{86}Sr$, may modify isotopic composition (Richter and DePaolo, 1987; Voigt et al., 2015). Nevertheless, SIS can be done with foraminifera as old as Late Campanian time (Sugarman et al., 1995; Huber et al., 2008).

For bulk carbonate the purer the micrite, and the lower its degree of recrystallization, the better it retains the original $^{87}Sr/^{86}Sr$. Late diagenetic cements are to be avoided but demonstrably early diagenetic cements, typically microspar, may retain a seawater signature. Such factors can be assessed by examination under the optical microscope in thin section, and by SEM identification of diagenetic phases.

The ultimate test of good preservation of the $^{87}Sr/^{86}Sr$ is whether analyses of different parts of an apparently well-preserved sample or, better still, different apparently well-preserved samples from the same stratigraphic level give the same $^{87}Sr/^{86}Sr$. Proxies for diagenetic alteration, such as Mn/Sr ratio cutoff values (Kaufman and Knoll, 1995; Jacobsen and Kaufman, 1999), might apply in cases where systematic differences can be demonstrated between variably altered samples. In addition to such tests, analysis of a few altered samples will indicate the sensitivity of $^{87}Sr/^{86}Sr$ to alteration, which increases $^{87}Sr/^{86}Sr$ when enclosing sediments are of continental origin (e.g., on passive margins) and decreases $^{87}Sr/^{86}Sr$ when the enclosing sediments derive from mantle sources (e.g., active margins, back-arc basins).

7.2.4 Sample preparation

Brachiopod calcite and inoceramid prisms can be flaked from the bulk sample and subsamples picked under the microscope (Fig. 7.8). For belemnites the exterior portion and apical line, both usually altered, can be removed with diamond-cutting tools. The cleaned sample is then fragmented into mm-sized pieces, cleaned of dust by water-washing or brief immersion in dilute acid (e.g., 5 seconds) and the least altered fragments picked under the microscope for analysis. Picking is best done from a dish of alcohol. Preparation by microdrilling allows more precise positioning of a subsample within a bulk sample but, unless done from a thick section, gives samples that are not optically screened and so may yield poorer data than does picking fragments.

Conodonts are picked under the microscope to select (usually) the ones with the least CAI. As the crown area (enamel) of a conodont element is usually preserved best (Trotter and Eggins, 2006), analysis of the crown rather than whole conodonts should improve the quality of data. Cleaning conodonts by leaching in acid prior to analysis may also improve data quality (Holmden et al., 1996).

Foraminifera must be fragmented to allow removal of infillings and then washed ultrasonically in methanol/water (NOT water alone) to remove adhering detritus. The ultrasonification should continue until replenished washings are crystal clear; up to 15 minutes may be needed. Ultrasonification may fragment foraminifera, making cleaning difficult; whether there is a connection between alteration and tendency to fragment is not known. After cleaning, fragments are picked under the microscope to select for analysis the most translucent fragments with the least (or no) overgrowths (Fig. 7.8D).

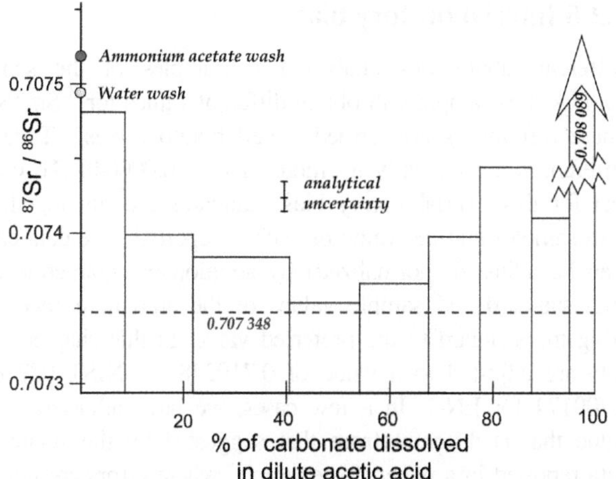

FIGURE 7.9 Effect of successive dissolution steps on measured $^{87}Sr/^{86}Sr$ in a limestone from 1.5 m above the Cenomanian–Turonian boundary at Gubbio. Owing to Sr contamination from noncarbonate phases, all fractions have $^{87}Sr/^{86}Sr$ greater than 0.707348 ± 0.000006, the expected value for a time 0.6 Myr after the C–T boundary. The minimum value of 0.707356 occurs in the fraction of 40.5%–55% dissolved. Water and ammonium acetate refer to leaches with these media alone, which also return elevated $^{87}Sr/^{86}Sr$.

For bulk samples (typically micrite), contributions of Sr from contaminant phases can be minimized, but not removed altogether, by chemically leaching the powdered sample prior to analysis, for example, in ammonium acetate, or in acetic acid. Sequential leaching with a weak acid (the method of Bailey et al., 2000; Fig. 7.9) is one way to minimize contamination in bulk samples (a concentrated weak acid is partially ionized in solution and so is less aggressive than a dilute strong acid such as HNO_3 that is fully ionized in solution). A step-leaching method has been applied to Proterozoic dolostones with qualified success (Liu et al., 2013). Dissolving acid-washed samples using a cation-exchange resin (Kralik, 1984) is the gentlest method but dissolution is slow.

7.2.5 Sample analysis

Natural Sr is composed of the isotopes with masses and approximate abundances as follows: ^{84}Sr, 0.56%; ^{86}Sr, 9.86%; ^{87}Sr, 7.00%; and ^{88}Sr, 82.58%. Abundances are approximate because natural processes fractionate Sr isotopes and alter their relative abundances (e.g., Fietzke and Eisenhauer, 2006). Contributions to the abundance of ^{87}Sr in rocks from the radioactive decay of ^{87}Rb into ^{87}Sr make the relative abundance variations of ^{87}Sr exceed abundance variations for the other isotopes.

Measurement of $^{87}Sr/^{86}Sr$ is made on Sr separated from other elements in the sample by dissolution in acid followed by ion-exchange chromatography. The purified Sr is then dissolved in acid for analysis. The analysis is done using thermal ionization mass spectrometry (TIMS) or by inductively coupled plasma, multicollector, mass spectrometry (ICP-MC-MS). For the latter, both solution mode and laser-ablation mode are available, the former usually being more precise. Using TIMS, isotopic measurements of $^{87}Sr/^{86}Sr$, and other isotopic ratios needed to process the data, are made repeatedly over a period of 1–2 hours in order to accumulate between 100 and 200 measurements and arrive at final values. The uncertainty on the final $^{87}Sr/^{86}Sr$ is then reported as twice the standard error of the mean of the accumulated ratios. Standards are interspersed with samples, typically one standard per 5–10 samples. For ICP-MC-MS, multiple measurements are also made over a period of 10–30 minutes to accumulate sufficient data. Samples are typically bracketed by blanks and standards to correct for machine drift.

Uncertainty of measurement is typically $\geq \pm 0.000020$ for pre-2000 TIMS machines and modern ICP-MC-MS machines in solution mode, as low as ± 0.000004 for modern TIMS machines, and no better than ± 0.000020 for laser-ablation analysis of carbonate (e.g., Burla et al., 2009) or

$\pm$ 0.000050 for analysis of apatite (Müller and Anczkiewicz, 2016; Song et al., 2015).

The separation and analysis of Sr fractionate its isotopes. This fractionation is corrected for by adjusting measured values of $^{87}Sr/^{86}Sr$ so that $^{86}Sr/^{88}Sr$ has a value of 0.1194 when measured at the same time as $^{87}Sr/^{86}Sr$. This process also removes all natural fractionation, leaving values of $^{87}Sr/^{86}Sr$ to reflect only the variation in $^{87}Sr/^{86}Sr$ arising from variations in the abundance of radiogenic ^{87}Sr from the decay of ^{87}Rb.

7.2.6 Sample size

To obtain a precision of analysis useful to SIS, which is usually $< \pm 0.000020$ for the Phanerozoic, the mass of Sr analyzed must exceed a threshold. For TIMS the threshold is about 0.3 μg of Sr. Masses of 1–3 μg are preferred for routine analysis because blank corrections are then typically negligible, and handling these larger amounts is easier than handling smaller samples. For a biogenic calcite containing 1000 μg/g of Sr, a sample mass of 1–3 mg is therefore needed. Since the chromatographic separation of Sr is only 50%–80% efficient (depending on operator), sample sizes around 5 mg are typically used. For a single analysis by solution mode using ICP-MC-MS, concentrations of 50 ng/mL of Sr are typically needed in volumes of 1–2 mL. For both the techniques, smaller samples can be analyzed, but at the expense of worsening precision as sample size decreases below the thresholds.

7.2.7 Standards

Two solid standards are in common use: NIST 987 (also known as SRM 987) is an $SrCO_3$ reference material, assaying at 99.0% $SrCO_3$, sold by the National Institute for Standards Technology of the US Department of Commerce (https://www.nist.gov/). The certified value for $^{87}Sr/^{86}Sr$ is 0.71034 ± 0.00026, but most laboratories report values in the range of 0.710230–0.710260 after normalization to a value of 0.1194 for $^{86}Sr/^{88}Sr$. Reference material EN-1 is a powdered shell of a modern *Tridachna* clam from Enewetak Atoll that is distributed by the US Geological Survey. A third standard, JCp-1, an aragonitic coral, is distributed by the Geological Survey of Japan but is seldom used for SIS. An old solid standard, E&A, now largely exhausted, was an $SrCO_3$ prepared by the Eimer and Amend company of New York (taken over by Fisher Chemical in 1940).

A solution standard, IAPSO seawater is used rarely; it is North East Atlantic seawater distributed by Ocean Scientific International Ltd (OSIL; https://osil.com/) and used primarily by oceanographers for conductivity calibration. Pearce et al. (2015) report a single determination of $^{87}Sr/^{86}Sr$ in IAPSO Seawater that was 0.000005 lower than the value they report for North Atlantic seawater.

For laser-ablation analysis, standards typically used when analyzing carbonates are serendipitously acquired modern shells or modern corals and, when analyzing phosphates, modern fish-teeth (Burla et al., 2009; Müller and Anczkiewicz, 2016).

Which standard is best? The IAPSO seawater is stored in borosilicate glass, which may contain tens of ppm of Sr (Williams et al., 1977). Whether the glass contaminates the sample requires investigation. Being biogenic calcium carbonate, several EN-1 subsamples are processed for analysis along with samples—both are dissolved in acid, and the Sr is isolated and purified with ion-exchange chromatography before being analyzed in the mass spectrometer. In contrast, NIST 987 is a solid $SrCO_3$ that is dissolved in acid to make a dilute solution that is used directly for analysis, thus bypassing ion-chromatography. This difference in preparation, and the fact that, on storage, solutions are easier to contaminate than are solids makes EN-1 the preferred standard. Finally, EN-1 has the advantage of coming from a mid-Pacific atoll and so it is unlikely to incorporate significant crustal-derived detritus (unless atomic-bomb tests at nearby Bikini Atoll released basement rock-dust into the local environment): EN-1 is therefore recommended in preference to the use of shells from a local beach.

There is no accepted value of $^{87}Sr/^{86}Sr$ for any standard: in Table 7.1 are given some reported values, and their uncertainties as twice the standard error (not standard deviation) of the mean of replicate analysis or analysis of multiple equivalent samples, together with the difference ($\Delta \times 10^6$) between measured values of NIST 987/E&A and modern oceanic Sr as represented by EN-1, modern seawater, or modern biogenic carbonate from unrestricted settings.

7.2.8 Interlaboratory bias

Different laboratories analyzing subsamples of the same homogenous sample will obtain different values for $^{87}Sr/^{86}Sr$. These differences are termed "interlaboratory bias." Today, differences are typically no more than $\pm$ 0.000040. To correct for this interlaboratory bias, standards are run together with samples and the value of each is reported. The data can then be adjusted (normalized) by addition or subtraction to both standard and sample values of the amount needed to bring the standard to the preferred value. In this chapter, all data are adjusted to a value of 0.710248 for NIST 987 or 0.709174 for EN-1. In a few cases, we have adjusted to a value that is different from that suggested by the standard data reported in a paper, for example, where errors are noted in reporting of standard data or where alternative normalizers have been specified elsewhere for the same laboratory. Values used for normalizing are given in Table 7.3.

The normalization for TIMS is accomplished in two ways. Most commonly, the standard value used to normalize is the mean value of all standards run over the period during which the samples were analyzed, provided machine performance was stable over than period. If it was not because, for example, collectors were replaced during the period of sample analysis, the periods before and after that machine maintenance would be treated separately because machine reconfiguration may change standard values, albeit by amounts typically ≤ 0.000010. Alternatively, one may normalize to the mean value of the standards run in each batch of samples (each turret, a turret being a batch of 16–20 samples/standards analyzed as a group under vacuum over 2 days). This procedure should be used only when at least five standards are run in a turret in order to minimize statistical uncertainty: the reduction in throughput that this method entails makes its use uncommon. Machine drift is far more serious for ICP-MC-MS analysis, so to correct for this drift, standards, blanks, and samples are typically alternated, for example, blank, standard, blank, sample, blank, standard.

The difference between measured values of $^{87}Sr/^{86}Sr$ for SRM 987 and EN-1 in any laboratory should be invariant over time and should be exactly the same as the difference recorded in any other laboratory. As Table 7.1 shows, this is largely the case for data acquired over the past decade with modern instruments, with a difference ranging from 0.001071 to 0.001077, a range only slightly larger than reported analytical uncertainties at $2\times$ standard errors of the mean. Old instruments gave larger differences: for a fuller comparison of older instruments, see Table 4 in McArthur (1994).

Interlaboratory bias is assumed to represent systematic error and to be correctable by normalizing to a specific value of the chosen standard. Replication of $^{87}Sr/^{86}Sr$ measurement can give mean values precise to $\leq \pm 0.000001$ (Table 7.1), so practitioners should at least attempt to provide standard data to this precision. Not all publications report $^{87}Sr/^{86}Sr$ value of their standards, that is, the mean $^{87}Sr/^{86}Sr$ for replicate runs of both NIST 987 and EN-1, the number of replicates, and the uncertainty of the data at two standard deviations. In such instances, uncertainty over interlaboratory normalization introduces into dating an indeterminate uncertainty that may be as high as the time-equivalent of ± 0.000030 in $^{87}Sr/^{86}Sr$.

A problem when using older data is knowing to which standard data should be normalized where both standards are reported. The better procedure is to normalize to EN-1, not only because it is processed in the same way as a sample but also because its $^{87}Sr/^{86}Sr$ value is nearer the values commonly measured for SIS. We suggest that another standard is needed for low values of $^{87}Sr/^{86}Sr$ because the Phanerozoic minimum in $^{87}Sr/^{86}Sr$ (0.706835 in early Capitanian time) is 0.001574 less than the value for EN-1.

Normalizing to a standard does not always bring data into concordance. Discrepancies of $^{87}Sr/^{86}Sr$ against age in Neogene trends reported by various authors are discussed at length in Oslick et al. (1994), Martin et al. (1999), and Reilly et al. (2002) and remain largely unresolved.

7.2.9 Rubidium contamination

Samples may contain trace Rb incorporated from seawater (biogenic and inorganic precipitates) or in adhering or occluded aluminosilicate detritus, the latter especially in whole rocks. The radioactive isotope of Rb, ^{87}Rb, comprises 27.84% of Rb and it decays to ^{87}Sr. Over time, this added ^{87}Sr may increase the original $^{87}Sr/^{86}Sr$ in the sample. This effect may need correction. Plotting Rb concentration against Al concentration distinguishes these contributions; a good correlation proves Rb is in aluminosilicates (Wierzbowski et al., 2012), a matter that should prompt further cleaning but shows that a correction for Rb in the target phase is not needed.

The correction for radiogenic Sr in target phases precipitated from seawater (e.g., biogenic calcite and apatite) may be small because the amount of Rb in seawater is small (0.12 ppm) and because their structures do not easily accommodate Rb. The more open structure of aragonite not only accommodates Rb more easily than does calcite, but aragonite also incorporates Sr more easily, so the high Sr potentially dilutes the contribution from potentially higher Rb. Kuznetsov et al. (2012) report concentrations mostly in the range of 0.02–0.10 ppm Rb and 1300–2000 ppm Sr for a range of modern gastropods (aragonite) and modern bivalves, which contain both calcite and aragonite. Belemnite rostra (calcite) contain around 800–1200 ppm Sr and brachiopods mostly between 400 and 1200 ppm Sr. Table 7.2 shows how the ^{87}Rb can change $^{87}Sr/^{86}Sr$ over time in biogenic calcite. For bulk rocks the problem of Rb contamination is more serious and should be monitored closely.

7.3 The databases used in this volume

There are several databases available for construction of $^{87}Sr/^{86}Sr$ trends through time. For post-Cambrian time, Table 7.3 lists sources of data used to plot the curves in Figs. 7.1 and 7.2. The data are updated from McArthur et al. (2012). For pre-Ordovician time a version of the Bochum–Ottawa Database (Veizer et al., 1999; Shields and Veizer, 2002; Prokoph et al., 2008), which details over 5000 values of $^{87}Sr/^{86}Sr$ for Phanerozoic and Precambrian times, has been updated using references in McArthur et al. (2012), Cox et al. (2016) and Zhou et al. (2020).

7.4 Numerical ages

The calibration curve given here (Figs. 7.1 and 7.2) uses the time scale of this volume. Where original data were reported to other time scales, the original ages have been converted to the current time scale by linear scaling between the nearest pair of numerically dated stratigraphic tie-points: the tie-points are mostly Period, Epoch, or Stage/Substage boundaries for the Mesozoic and Paleozoic, supplemented by zones boundaries in the Cenozoic. In some instances, where the local or regional stratigraphy has been revised since the publication of

TABLE 7.2 Time in Myr needed to change $^{87}Sr/^{86}Sr$ by a given amount as a function of Sr/Rb mass ratio.

	Precision of measurement of $^{87}Sr/^{86}Sr$				
Sr/Rb (ppm/ppm)	0.5×10^{-6}	1×10^{-6}	2×10^{-6}	5×10^{-6}	10×10^{-6}
	0.0000005	0.000001	0.000002	0.000005	0.000010
	Time for change as a function of Sr/Rb mass ratio				
	Myr	Myr	Myr	Myr	Myr
100	1.21	2.43	4.87	12.2	24.0
500	6.08	12.1	24.3	61	121
1000	12.2	24.3	49	122	242
2000	24.3	49	97	243	485
3000	37	73	146	364	726
4000	49	97	194	485	966
5000	61	122	243	607	1206
6000	73	146	291	726	1445
7000	85	170	340	847	1683
8000	97	194	388	966	1921
9000	109	218	436	1086	2157
10,000	122	243	485	1206	2393
11,000	134	267	533	1325	2627
12,000	146	291	582	1445	2861
13,000	158	316	630	1564	3094
14,000	170	339	678	1683	3327
15,000	182	364	726	1802	3559

TABLE 7.3 Major sources of data for the Phanerozoic interval: 3949 data-pairs. [Bndy or bndy = boundary].

References	Normalizer ($\times 10^6$)	Age range Ma		Interval
Ando et al. (2011): ODP 1120 (new age model)	−2	7	19	Miocene
Azmy et al. (1999)	30	440	442	Silurian
Barrera et al. (1997), Li and Keller (1999) age model	13	69	73	Maastrichtian
Bodin et al. (2015); Vocontian Basin, France	0	107	128	Barremian-Aptian
Bralower et al. (1997): DSDP 511: inoceramids	0	94	115	Aptian and Albian
Bruckschen et al. (1999), ages >334 Ma	31	334	359	Carboniferous
Callomon and Dietl (2000)	0	165.29		Callovian–Bathonian bndy
Carpenter et al. (1991)	−4	373.4		Devonian tie-point
Chen et al. (2018)	−1	298	334	Late Carboniferous–Permian
Clemens et al. (1995) Chain core	−9	0	0.2	Recent
Cramer et al. (2011)	−2	419	442	Silurian
Denison et al. (1993)	102	43	64	Paleogene
Denison et al. (1997) selected data	102	390	409	Devonian
DePaolo and Ingram (1985)	−62	39	64	Paleogene
Dudás et al. (2017)	0	251.6	252.2	Permo–Triassic Bndy

(Continued)

TABLE 7.3 (Continued)

References	Normalizer ($\times 10^6$)	Age range Ma		Interval
M. Engkilde, pers. comm. (1998)	0	146	170	Early Jurassic
Farrell et al. (1995): ODP 758 (most)	−9	0	7	Neogene
Frýda et al. (2002)	1	419		Silurian–Devonian bndy
Gao and Land (1991): updated age model	108	476	493	Cambrian, Early Ordovician
Henderson et al. (1994)	17	0	0.4	Recent
Hesselbo et al. (2000)	0	192.9		Sinemurian–Pliensbachian bndy
Hodell et al. (1991): DSDP 588, 588A	18	7	17	Miocene
Jenkyns et al. (1995)	−12	101	122	Aptian and Albian
Jones et al. (1994a, 1994b): selected data	22	103	202	Jurassic
Koepnick et al. (1990)	102	202	238	Triassic
Korte et al. (2003)	25	203	238	Triassic
Korte et al. (2006)	25	252	299	Permian
Martin et al. (1999): <13.8 Ma. ODP 926 (part)	22	5	14	Miocene
McArthur et al. (1993a, b): Chalk of United Kingdom, Chalk of Germany	0	0	84	Santonian–Campanian
McArthur et al. (1994): US Western Interior	0	73	100	Cenomanian–Campanian
McArthur et al. (1998): Denmark and Antarctica	0	65	69	Cretaceous–Paleogene bndy
McArthur et al. (2000a) and McArthur et al. (unpub data): United Kingdom	0	175	187	Pliensbachian–Toarcian
McArthur et al. (2000b): Skye, United Kingdom	0	170	173	Aalenian–Bajocian bndy
McArthur and Kennedy (unpub. data)	0	0	112	Cenomanian and Albian
McArthur et al. (2006): ODP 758, Sicily, Antarctica.	0	2.6	6.1	Pliocene
McArthur et al. (2004): Speeton, United Kingdom	0	122	133	Hauterivian and Barremian
McArthur et al. (2007): Voccontian Basin, France	0	127	143	Berriasian–Hauterivian
Mead and Hodell (1995): ODP 689B	18	18	45	Cenozoic
Miller et al. (1991): DSDP 608	−17	9	24	Miocene
Montañez et al. (1996)	−6	497	507	Cambrian
Needham (2007)	0	292	311	Carboniferous–Permian
Oslick et al. (1994): ODP 747A >12 Ma	−17	16	24	Miocene
Page et al. (2009)	−3	161.53		Callovian–Oxfordian bndy
Qing et al. (1998): selected data	5	440	442	Silurian
Reilly et al. (2002): DSDP 522	−17	22	35	Mostly Oligocene
Ruppel et al. (1996)	−7	419	442	Silurian
Song et al. (2015)	−35	237	253	Latest Perm.–early Triassic
Sugarman et al. (1995): DSDP 525A; Li and Keller (1999) age model	−17	66	74	Latest Campanian–Maastrichtian
Saltzman et al. (2014)	3	446	486	Ordovician
Sedlacek et al. (2014)	6	244	252	Latest Perm.–early Triassic
Shields et al. (2003) selected data	31	444	450	Ordovician
Tierney (2010); ages >272 Ma	6	275	302	early–mid Permian
Van Geldern et al. (2006)	0	370	415	Devonian
Wang et al. (2018)	−35	275	301	Permian
Wierzbowski et al. (2012)	0	162	168	Bajocian–Callovian
Wierzbowski et al. (2017)	0	140	170	Aalenian–base Cret.
Zachos et al. (1992, 1999)	0	23	43	Paleogene
Zhang et al. (2020); lower bound to data	3	371.1	–	Frasnian-Fammenian bndy

a source of data, we have updated the biostratigraphic and/or numerical age models used in original publications.

The calibration curve shown in Figs. 7.1 and 7.2 is based on measurement of $^{87}Sr/^{86}Sr$ in samples dated mostly by biostratigraphy and magnetostratigraphy, calibrated numerically with radiometric dating, mostly using the U/Pb system. For the Cenozoic, radiometric dating is being superseded by astrochronological calibration of pelagic and hemipelagic sediment that accumulated at a constant rate. For earlier times, where astrochronology is frequently applied to near-shore sediments deposited on shelves and the floors of epeiric seas, the procedures should be considered developmental as they are fraught with uncertainty about the constancy of sedimentation rates, completeness of the section, and other difficulties that are explained well in Bailey and Smith (2008a, 2008b) and Vaughan et al. (2011, 2015).

Assigning numerical ages to sedimentary rocks is not straightforward. The calibration curve in Figs. 7.1 and 7.2, and the accompanying LOESS look-up table for conversion of $^{87}Sr/^{86}Sr$ to age and vice versa are affected by the uncertainties on the original numerical ages for the data used, and the problems inherent in the interpolation, extrapolation, and indirect stratigraphic correlations that are often necessary for age assignment. These include problems of boundary recognition (both bio- and magnetostratigraphic), diachroneity of biostratigraphic datums, and assumptions concerning sedimentation rate, all of which contribute uncertainty to the age models used to generate the calibration line. Whatever method of calibration is used to calibrate tie-points, interpolating ages between tie-points can give a false impression of absolute accuracy; they are no more accurate than bracketing dates.

7.5 Fitting the LOESS database

To obtain a best fit curve for the $^{87}Sr/^{86}Sr$ data as a function of time for post-Cambrian time, we fitted the calibration line to data using the statistical nonparametric regression method LOESS, executed in "R," an open-source statistical software package. The LOESS fit is a derivative of the LOWESS (Cleveland, 1979, 1981; Chambers et al., 1983; Thisted, 1988; Cleveland et al., 1992). Details of the fitting procedure matched closely those given in Howarth and McArthur (1997). Because of the complex shape of the fit, and the very uneven density of data points through time, the curve was optimized by being fitted in overlapping local segments. These were then joined using splines at segment junctions. The resultant fit that predicts $^{87}Sr/^{86}Sr$ from age was then inverted to predict age from $^{87}Sr/^{86}Sr$. Both fit and inversion were turned into a composite table for predicting age from $^{87}Sr/^{86}Sr$ and vice versa, together with 95% confidence intervals (CIs) on predictions. A tabulation of the trend fitted through that data (not the raw data values) is available in electronic from j.mcarthur@ucl.ac.uk and also from the website of "ResearchGate."

7.6 The quality of the fit

7.6.1 Confidence limits on the LOESS fit

In addition to the best fit curve of estimated $^{87}Sr/^{86}Sr$ as a function of age, the LOWESS fitting process also provides a two-sided, 95% CIs on the estimates of age. These CIs are included in Fig. 7.2 but are best seen in Fig. 7.5 as a half-width interval plotted against time. It is important to note that the CIs are a close equivalent to the standard error of a mean ($\pm \sigma/n$) and are not the equivalent of standard deviation ($\pm \sigma$). The width of the CI tells of the confidence with which the mean position of the line is known; it does not describe the distribution of the raw data values about that mean position, although its width reflects their scatter. The distribution of data is described by the standard deviation of the data.

The CI varies with numerical age and is dependent on both the density and spread of the calibration data. Where data are abundant and samples well preserved, for example, 0–7 Ma, the half-width CI is around ± 0.000003. For the rest of the Neogene, and for much of the Mesozoic, values approach ± 0.000005 and are seldom more than ± 0.000010. Where data are few, for example, most of the Permian, the uncertainty is much greater. Well-preserved samples become rarer with increasing age so the uncertainty envelope increases with age as sample quality deteriorates; nevertheless, achieving a precision of ± 0.000015 for the entire Paleozoic is not an unrealistic goal.

Assuming that the half-widths of the upper and lower CIs are about equal, and that U = (upper age CI − estimated age) and L = (estimated age − lower age CI), then the overall uncertainty on an age derived from the curve can be computed by combining the uncertainties on the measurement (s_m) with those of the fitted curve (s_c) as follows:

$$s_{\text{total}} = \left(s_m^2 + s_c^2\right)^{1/2} \tag{7.1}$$

where s_m is the uncertainty of the estimated numerical age of the sample and $s_c = (L + U)/1.96$. If L and U are different enough, then it may be preferable to use upper and lower bounds for s_{total} by replacing s_c with $L/1.96$ and $U/1.96$, respectively.

7.6.2 Confidence limits on measured $^{87}Sr/^{86}Sr$

The uncertainty with which the mean (m) $^{87}Sr/^{86}Sr$ of a sample is known, from n-independent determinations of $^{87}Sr/^{86}Sr$, may be quantified if one assumes that the measurement errors are normally distributed and so a two-sided CI applies:

$$\text{Uncertainty} = \pm t_{1-\alpha/2,n-1}\left(s/n^{1/2}\right) \tag{7.2}$$

where s is the standard deviation of n observed $^{87}Sr/^{86}Sr$ values, and $t_{1-\alpha/2,\, n-1}$ is the 100(1 − α/2)th percentile of the

Student *t*-statistic with $(n-1)$ degrees of freedom; α is the risk (specified as a proportion) that the true (but unknown) value of $^{87}Sr/^{86}Sr$ in the mineral, which is estimated by *m*, will fall outside the specified CI. Thus α is commonly set to 0.05 (5%) in order to obtain two-sided 95% confidence limits on *m*. The *t*-statistic is used for this purpose rather than the $100(1-\alpha/2)$th percentile of the cumulative normal distribution in order to correct for the fact that the number of replicate determinations of $^{87}Sr/^{86}Sr$ is finite. Increasing *n* decreases the uncertainty in *m*. For example, the multipliers for two-sided 95% confidence limits when $n = 2, 3, 4, 5$, and 10 are 12.71, 4.30, 3.18, 2.78, and 2.26, respectively.

It may be possible to obtain only a single determination of $^{87}Sr/^{86}Sr$ (*x*) for a given mineral sample. If, for some reason there exists a *prior* estimate of the expected value of $^{87}Sr/^{86}Sr$ (*a*), for example, from measurements previously made on presumed similar material, or the ratio has been estimated from the $^{87}Sr/^{86}Sr$ curve and a knowledge of the sample's stratigraphic position, then, assuming *x* is the center of a normal distribution, Blachman and Machol (1987) showed that a two-sided $100(1-\alpha)\%$ CI on *x* is given by:

$$x \pm (1 + 0.484/\alpha)|x - a| \tag{7.3}$$

If α is 0.05, the multiplier equals 9.68. Less-conservative bounds are obtained by inverting the prediction interval for a single future observation. This gives:

$$x \pm z_{1+\alpha/2}(1 + 1 \cdot n_0)^{1/2} s_0 \tag{7.4}$$

In this case, s_0 is a *prior* estimate of the standard deviation of the distribution (assumed normal) from which *x* is drawn, for example, the pooled standard deviation based on n_0 sets of previous determinations of similar samples, and $z_{1-\alpha/2}$ is the $100(1-\alpha/2)$th percentile of the cumulative normal distribution. If α is 0.05, the multiplier equals 1.96.

7.6.3 Numerical resolution of the fitted curve

The uncertainty of an estimated numerical age obtained using the calibration curve (Figs. 7.1 and 7.2) depends on (1) the width of the 95% CI on the calibration curve, (2) the uncertainty on the measured $^{87}Sr/^{86}Sr$, and (3) the rate of change of $^{87}Sr/^{86}Sr$ with time ($\Delta dR/\Delta t$). Given that the best defined parts of the calibration curve have half-width CIs no better than ± 0.000003, and that the best attainable precision is ± 0.000001 (Table 7.1), application of Eq. (7.1) results in a minimum uncertainty of ± 0.000003. In the Neogene the slope of the calibration curve (Fig. 7.5) does not exceed a value of 0.000060 per myr, so it follows that the precision in dating in the Neogene with $^{87}Sr/^{86}Sr$ will seldom be better than about ± 0.05 myr and will usually be worse. Correlation with $^{87}Sr/^{86}Sr$ avoids the uncertainty involved in assigning numerical ages and the accuracy with which that can be accomplished.

When correlating with $^{87}Sr/^{86}Sr$, profiles are matched between sections (Fig. 7.3), so to the uncertainty in measurement of $^{87}Sr/^{86}Sr$ must be added the uncertainty on the position of the profile fits. Unless data are closely spaced through a section, the profile may not recognize hiatuses in deposition and points of change in sedimentation rate.

7.7 Comments on the LOESS fit

The post-Cambrian curve presented here is that of McArthur et al. (2012), updated with new numerical ages to GTS2020, and major revisions to the database for three time periods: the Ordovician–Silurian, the mid-to-late Jurassic, and the mid-Carboniferous *sensu lato* to the early Triassic. Details of these updates, and minor revisions to the Neogene curve and other minor updates to the database, are discussed next.

7.7.1 Pliocene to Recent

For the period from 0 to 7 Ma, we rely mostly on the data of Farrell et al. (1995) for ODP Site 758A, except between 2.5 and 6 Ma where their data are moderated with data from McArthur et al. (2006) who reanalyzed some Site 758A levels and cross-checked data by analyses of glassy *Orbulina universa* from the Pliocene type section at Punta Piccola, Sicily, which is astronomically calibrated.

7.7.2 Miocene

The age model for ODP Site 926 (Martin et al., 1999) has been updated to the astrochronological time scales of Zeeden et al. (2013) and Wilkens et al. (2017). Changes are <0.1 Myr down to 213 mbsf (8.1 Ma) and variably older below that by up to 0.4 Myr.

7.7.3 Oligocene/Early Miocene

We use the data of Hodell et al. (1991) for DSDP 588 and 588A. Reilly et al. (2002) supersedes Miller et al. (1988) for Site 522. The data of Ando et al. (2011) for ODP Site 1120 are included revised to a biostratigraphic age model rather than the chemostratigraphic age model of those authors.

7.7.4 Paleogene

The $^{87}Sr/^{86}Sr$ curve for the Paleogene is based on DePaolo and Ingram (1985) with the K/P boundary (0.707830 ± 0.000008) defined by McArthur et al. (1998) and concordant with Sugarman et al. (1995). From the boundary, values of $^{87}Sr/^{86}Sr$ decline to 0.70772 in the Ypresian (51 Ma) before rising to a maximum of 0.70778 in the early Lutetian (47 Ma) and then decline again to a second minimum of 0.70773 in the earliest Bartonian (41 Ma). Thereafter, the ratio increases with decreasing age until modern times. Although low, $\Delta R/\Delta t$ for the

Paleocene (Fig. 7.2) of around 0.000009/Myr may allow dating with a resolution ≈ 0.2 Myr when the curve for the interval is defined better and analysis is replicated to achieve a measurement uncertainty of 0.000001.

7.7.5 Maastrichtian

For the late Maastrichtian interval, we use the data of Sugarman et al. (1995) for DSDP 525A and Barrera et al. (1997) for DSDP Site 463 and 690, all after recalibration to the age model of Li and Keller (1999). The results appear to agree well with an independent assessment of the $^{87}Sr/^{86}Sr$ trend for the Maastrichtian given in Huber et al. (2008).

7.7.6 Campanian–Cenomanian

The trend for Campanian time is defined well data from the Chalk of Germany on both belemnites and acid-leached bulk chalks, moderated by data for leached bulk chalk from England and ammonites from the US Western Interior but excluding anomalous US data for the lowermost middle Campanian (McArthur et al., 2016). The interval Turonian-to-Cenomanian is poorly defined owing to a scarcity of well-preserved samples in this interval, but what data are available suggest that $^{87}Sr/^{86}Sr$ reaches a minimum of 0.707280 in the later part of Turonian time.

7.7.7 Aptian–Albian

Of Bralower et al.'s (1997) data, we use only that for inoceramids. We have adjusted the Albian boundary ages of Bralower et al. (1997) to those in this volume but retain those authors' apportionment of time between them.

7.7.8 Jurassic

The interval is based on data from McArthur et al. (2000a) for the Pliensbachian and Toarcian; McArthur et al. (2000b) for the Aalenian; McArthur et al. (2007) for the Berriasian, Valanginian, and Hauterivian; Wierzbowski et al. (2012, 2017) for the Bajocian to Oxfordian; and Jones et al. (1994a, 1994b) for other intervals. For Hettangian and Sinemurian times, we use the belemnite data of Jones et al. (1994a), updated to the time scale used here. The value of $^{87}Sr/^{86}Sr$ for the Sinemurian/Pliensbachian boundary is from Hesselbo et al. (2000).

7.7.9 Triassic–Jurassic boundary

We use Model B of McArthur et al. (2007) for this interval, omitting the oyster data of Jones et al. (1994a) as it appears to reflect alteration. For Hettangian and Sinemurian times, we use the belemnite data of Jones et al. (1994a) together with those authors' original age models, recomputed to the GTS2020 time scale.

7.7.10 Permo–Triassic boundary and Early Triassic

The Permo–Triassic boundary interval is best defined by Dudás et al. (2017); although the data scatter a good deal, a boundary value of 0.707088 can be determined from their data. Despite the scatter, $^{87}Sr/^{86}Sr$ apparently increased from the early Capitanian minimum, the rate of increase accelerating sharply around 0.1 Myr before the Permo–Triassic boundary, according to Dudás et al. (2017), a conclusion concordant with the data in Brand et al. (2012, their Fig. 14). We refer the reader to these sources for detailed profiles.

The Early Triassic is now revised following Sedlacek et al. (2014), with additional data from Song et al. (2015). Standard data reported in Song et al. (2015) were for solution mode, not laser-ablation mode as implied in that paper (H. Song, pers. comm., 2019), so $^{87}Sr/^{86}Sr$ values have been reduced by 0.000035 to make them concordant with other data. Much of the rest of the data are from Korte et al. (2003), with additions from Koepnick et al. (1990). Two data for Rhaetian time are from Jones et al. (1994a).

The revision shows that the Early Triassic rate of increase of $^{87}Sr/^{86}Sr$ with time, first revealed in Burke et al. (1982) and first quantified in Martin and Macdougall (1995) as 0.000097 per Myr, has apparently increased, making it the fastest $\Delta R/\Delta t$ in the Phanerozoic: 0.000330 per Myr according to Sedlacek et al. (2014) and the time scale used here (Fig. 7.10).

7.7.11 Permian

The Carboniferous–Permian transition is defined by the data of Chen et al. (2018), Tierney (2010), and Bruckschen et al. (1999), with contributions from Triassic data cited previously, and Song et al. (2015) and Brand et al. (2012) for the very latest Permian. A value of 0.707088 is deduced for the Permo–Triassic boundary P/T boundary from the data of Dudás et al. (2017). Additional Permian data are from Needham (2007) and Korte et al. (2006). Finally, we use data from Wang et al. (2018) after correcting to SRM 987 of 0.710248: their data were supposedly reported after normalization to that value but normalizing (subtraction of a further 0.000031) brings them into agreement with other data, so we assume that the reported data were not normalized as stated. Compared to previous LOESS fits, the Capitanian minimum in $^{87}Sr/^{86}Sr$ is revised downward by 0.000022 to a value of 0.706835 on the basis of data in Kani et al. (2018) and Garbelli et al. (2019). For an alternative view

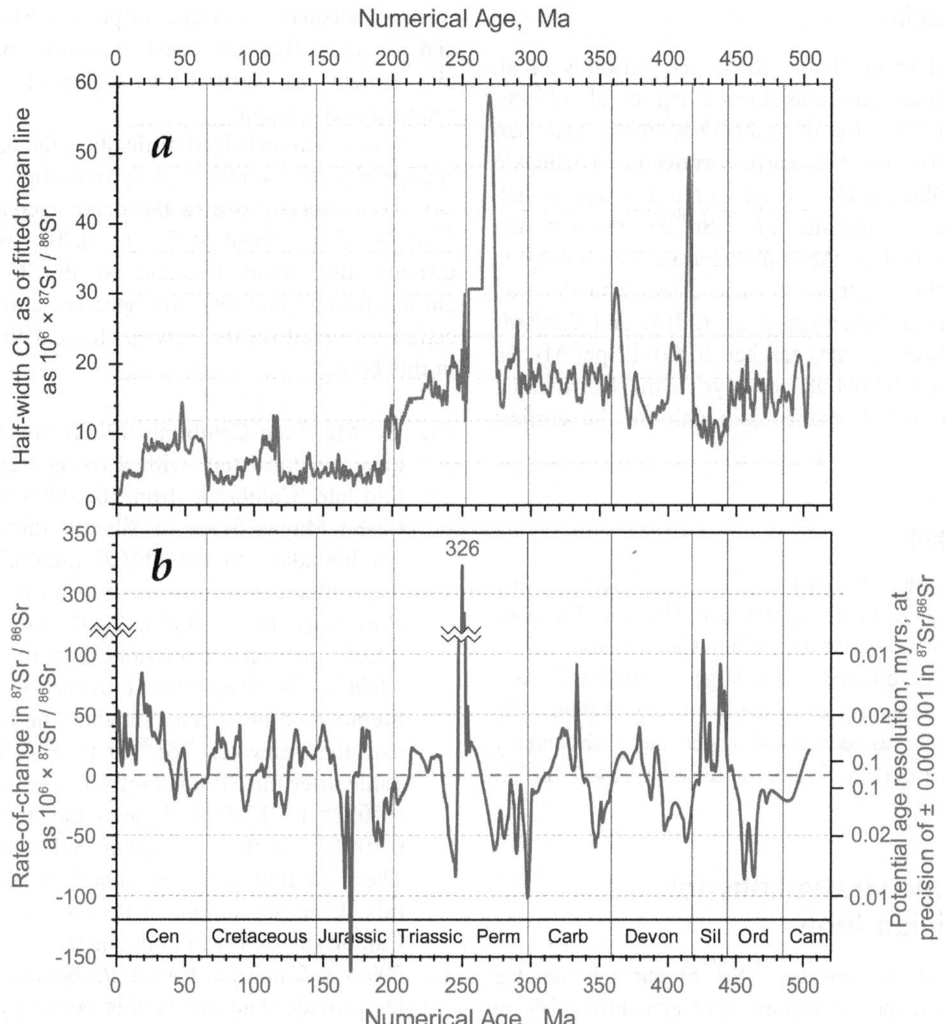

FIGURE 7.10 (A) Half-width of the 95% confidence intervals on the LOESS fit and (B) rate of change with time of $^{87}Sr/^{86}Sr$ over the past 505 Myr with an assessment (right-hand ordinate) of the temporal resolution in dating potentially available when replicate measurement achieves a precision of 0.000001 in the measurement of $^{87}Sr/^{86}Sr$.

of this interval, see Wang et al. (2018) and also Korte and Ullmann (2018).

7.7.12 Carboniferous

The Late Mississippian through the earliest Permian is based on Chen et al. (2018) and Needham (2007). Older Carboniferous data are from Bruckschen et al. (1999) with minor European additions from other authors.

7.7.13 Devonian

The curve for much of the Devonian derives from van Geldern et al. (2006). Their late Devonian data confirm the tie-point provided by Carpenter et al. (1991) for the *Anomoeotes triangularis* conodont zone of the late Devonian carbonate reefs at Golden Spike and Nevis in Alberta, Canada. The Silurian–Devonian boundary interval is fixed by the data of Frýda et al. (2002).

7.7.14 Silurian

The conodont data of Ruppel et al. (1996) agree with later data of Azmy et al. (1999) and Cramer et al. (2011). Successive time scales have shortened the duration of the Gorstian, which has the effect of steepening the $^{87}Sr/^{86}Sr$ curve in that interval, and introducing breaks in slope at the stage boundaries. The original near linear increase through time in $^{87}Sr/^{86}Sr$ reported by Ruppel et al. (1996) is thereby made sinuous. The matter is well explained by Cramer et al. (2011). If the rate of change in $^{87}Sr/^{86}Sr$ with time changes sharply at stage boundaries, then this might indicate a problem with the assignment of numerical ages to stage boundaries.

7.7.15 Ordovician

We rely on Saltzman et al. (2014) and Edwards et al. (2015) with minor additions from Qing et al. (1998), Shields et al. (2003) for the Late Ordovician, and Gao and Land (1991) for the Early Ordovician (Arbuckle Limestone of Oklahoma) updated with a new age model. The high rate of decline of $^{87}Sr/^{86}Sr$ through the Ordovician revealed in these publications has prompted discussions by those authors about its cause (Shields et al. 2003). The data of Saltzman et al. (2014) and Edwards et al. (2015) show the rates reached 0.000112 per Myr in the Sandbian and 0.000098 per Myr in the Darriwilian, rates exceeded in the Phanerozoic only in the earliest Triassic.

7.7.16 Data gaps

Finally, reliable data are not available in sufficient quantity for many intervals of time (e.g., the late Albian to Turonian, the early Devonian, and the Devonian–Carboniferous transition). This lack is reflected in the large (>0.000015) half-width of the CI on the mean for the LOWESS fit (Fig. 7.10) for many intervals; to reduce this uncertainty, substantially will require some three to five accurate and precise $^{87}Sr/^{86}Sr$ values per biozone.

7.8 Sr-isotope stratigraphy for pre-Ordovician time

Reconstruction of the seawater $^{87}Sr/^{86}Sr$ curve before the Ordovician Period must overcome particular difficulties on two fronts: poor age constraints and a lack of suitably well-preserved materials for analysis. Both the relative and absolute ages of older strata remain poorly constrained. Marker fossils of the lower Cambrian tend to be endemic to specific regions and facies, while Precambrian biostratigraphy is in its infancy. The lack of a global stratigraphic framework has necessitated the use of calibration schemes that integrate Sr- and C-isotope trends, geochronology, chemo-oceanographic marker beds, and sequence stratigraphy with the emerging biostratigraphy (Shields, 1999; Robb et al., 2004; Cox et al., 2016).

In the absence of sufficiently large sets of well-constrained $^{87}Sr/^{86}Sr$ data, we approach the reconstruction of the seawater $^{87}Sr/^{86}Sr$ curve by first delimiting seawater $^{87}Sr/^{86}Sr$ at established chronostratigraphic tie-points using the mutual agreement of multiple studies. Longer ranging Sr-isotope studies are then used to trace broad trends between tie-points, primarily using $\delta^{13}C$ features for global calibration in the precambrian. $^{87}Sr/^{86}Sr$ values are generally reported here only to the fifth significant figure in recognition of the poor resolution of the Precambrian and Cambrian $^{87}Sr/^{86}Sr$ record. Until recently, there were no adequate tie-points for pre-800 Ma strata (Shields and Veizer, 2002), but recent data from early marine calcite cements of North China (Zhou et al., 2020) have robust age constraints.

Despite acknowledged difficulties, the use of Sr-isotope stratigraphy to correlate Neoproterozoic and Cambrian strata is promising due to the major increase in seawater $^{87}Sr/^{86}Sr$ from about 0.705 to 0.709, which occurred through the Neoproterozoic to the Cambrian. Next chronostratigraphic tie-point ages are currently accepted estimates based on the new geological time scale given in this book.

1. 497 Ma: Late Cambrian SPICE interval—published data are consistent with a rising trend through the mid-late Cambrian from 0.70893 ± 2 at 502 Ma (latest Mayan Stage in Siberia) through the Epoch 3/4 boundary to the SPICE interval across which least altered values are constrained to 0.70910 ± 1 (Montañez et al., 1996, 2000; Kouchinsky et al., 2008). Internally consistent data for the c. 494 Ma *Elvinia–Taenicephalus* biozone boundary (=the Steptoan–Sunwaptan boundary in Laurentia) indicate that seawater $^{87}Sr/^{86}Sr$ rose to its highest ever value after the SPICE excursion, before falling from 0.70925 to 0.70914 through the upper Steptoan to 0.70910-1 in the Sunwaptan (Saltzman et al., 1995). The conodont study of Ebneth et al. (2001) traces this decrease further to 0.70900 at the c. 487 Ma Cambrian–Ordovician boundary.
2. 509 Ma: Cambrian Epoch 2/3 boundary—three studies provide data across this boundary from Siberia, United States, France, and Spain. Least altered values in Montañez et al. (2000) and Wotte et al. (2007) are mutually consistent, while covariation with high Mg/Ca ratios indicates that the slightly lower values of Derry et al. (1994) arose during dolomitization. Least altered values of 0.70894 ± 3 imply that the $^{87}Sr/^{86}Sr$ rise leveled off during Epoch 3 (Kouchinsky et al., 2008).
3. 539 Ma: Ediacaran–Cambrian boundary—several $^{87}Sr/^{86}Sr$ studies span the Ediacaran–Cambrian boundary, the most comprehensive being that of Brasier et al. (1996). That study and other works (Derry et al., 1994; Kaufman et al., 1996; Nicholas 1996; Valledares et al., 2006; Jiang et al., 2007) constrain latest Ediacaran and earliest Cambrian $^{87}Sr/^{86}Sr$ to c. 0.70845 ± 5. Least altered samples from Mongolia, Siberia, Namibia, and China (Brasier et al., 1996; Kaufman et al., 1993, 1996; Li et al., 2013) define a decreasing trend through Epoch 1 to reach a low of 0.70805 ± 5 by the Stage 2–3 boundary (521 Ma), before rising again through Epoch 2 (Derry et al., 1994).

4. c. 575–c. 550 Ma: Late Ediacaran—a striking feature of the Ediacaran Period is a prolonged, highly negative, likely global $\delta^{13}C$ excursion (=Shuram/Wonoka/DOUNCE anomaly). Several studies (Burns et al., 1994; Pokrovskii et al., 2006; Melezhik et al., 2009) indicate that seawater $^{87}Sr/^{86}Sr$ increased from 0.70802 to 0.70862 during this interval. Although the association with celestite in the most Sr-rich samples hints at a more restricted marine environment, this rise is broadly consistent with 0.70845 ± 3 toward the end of this excursion (Jiang et al., 2007), at a horizon dated at 551 Ma (Condon et al., 2005), and with c. 0.7087 for least altered samples from Oman (Burns et al., 1994; Brasier and Shields, 2000) and Australia (Calver, 2000). It seems likely therefore that seawater $^{87}Sr/^{86}Sr$ reached its Precambrian peak at c. 550 Ma (Cui et al., 2015).
5. c. 625–c. 580 Ma: Early Ediacaran—there are few studies that can be used to constrain the early Ediacaran seawater $^{87}Sr/^{86}Sr$ curve after end-Cryogenian glaciation. High $\delta^{13}C$ values from Siberia are associated with a rise in $^{87}Sr/^{86}Sr$ from 0.7072 to 0.7080 (Pokrovskii et al., 2006). By comparison, sparse $^{87}Sr/^{86}Sr$ data from possibly correlative, early Ediacaran samples of the lower Doushantuo Formation (China) indicate a rise from c. 0.7077–8 to c. 0.7080–1 (Jiang et al., 2007; Xiao and Narbonne, 2020, Ch. 18, The Ediacaran Period, this volume). Studies by Misi and Veizer (1998) and Misi et al. (2007) on Brazilian samples indicate that $^{87}Sr/^{86}Sr$ decreased from about 0.7078 to 0.7074 during the rise to high $\delta^{13}C$, adding complexity to the Ediacaran rise (Fig. 7.1).
6. c. 635 Ma: basal Ediacaran—the base of the Ediacaran System is defined within the postglacial "cap dolostone" of the Nuccaleena Formation in South Australia. Although cap dolostones are not generally suitable for $^{87}Sr/^{86}Sr$ studies (e.g., Yoshioka et al., 2003, but see Liu et al., 2013), immediately overlying limestone units have provided consistent data. For samples from the Hayhook Formation of NW Canada that contain >3000 ppm of Sr, $^{87}Sr/^{86}Sr$ is 0.70714 ± 2 (James et al., 2001) and so consistent with data from postglacial limestones of Namibia (Halverson et al., 2007). In Namibia, least altered $^{87}Sr/^{86}Sr$ values rise subsequently to 0.70748 and then to c. 0.7080 as $\delta^{13}C$ values recover from −4.4‰ to 0‰. High-Sr samples from NW Canada define an increase from 0.70728 to 0.70753, while least altered $^{87}Sr/^{86}Sr$ data from South America consistently indicate a rise from c. 0.7074 to 0.70777 ± 2 during the $\delta^{13}C$ recovery (de Alvarenga et al., 2008; Nogueira et al., 2007). Identical values (c. 0.7077–8) have been reported for basal Ediacaran barite samples of NW Africa at a comparable point in the postglacial $\delta^{13}C$ curve (Shields et al., 2007). Taken together, these data indicate a rise in seawater $^{87}Sr/^{86}Sr$ from c. 0.7071 to c. 0.7077 or higher during the postglacial $\delta^{13}C$ recovery to positive values. The rate of the $^{87}Sr/^{86}Sr$ increase remains unconstrained; however, data are consistent with a rapid rise after the Cryogenian glaciations due to an increased weathering flux and an early Ediacaran peak of between c. 0.7077 and c. 0.7080 (Liu et al., 2018).
7. c. 660–c. 640 Ma: late Cryogenian "Sturtian"–"Marinoan" nonglacial interval—immediately postglacial limestones of the Cryogenian Period reveal a rise in $^{87}Sr/^{86}Sr$ from c. 0.7067 to 0.7071 during the postglacial $\delta^{13}C$ recovery. Four regions of the world provide relevant data: Mongolia from 0.70675 to 0.70709 (Shields et al., 1997; Bold et al., 2016), Namibia from 0.70685 to 0.70699 (Yoshioka et al., 2003), NW Canada from 0.70668 to "unconstrained" (Kaufman et al., 1997), and Australia from "unconstrained" to 0.70706 (McKirdy et al., 2001). Values of $\delta^{13}C$ >10‰ are characteristic of the upper part of this nonglacial interval and are associated with $^{87}Sr/^{86}Sr$ of 0.70713–0.70735 in Mongolia (Shields et al., 2002), 0.70718–0.70742 in NW Canada (Halverson et al., 2007), and 0.70725–0.70735 in Namibia (Halverson et al., 2007). $^{87}Sr/^{86}Sr$ values from Australia are generally higher at this level and indicate the possibility of a peak at c. 0.7076–0.7078 (McKirdy et al., 2001).
8. c. 720 Ma: Tonian–Cryogenian transition interval—it is currently unclear to what extent preglacial carbonate successions can be considered contemporaneous. Nevertheless, $^{87}Sr/^{86}Sr$ typically ranges between 0.7067 and 69 (Halverson et al., 2007; Rooney et al., 2014; Fairchild et al., 2000, 2018) beneath lower Cryogenian glacial units. There is a possibility that seawater $^{87}Sr/^{86}Sr$ fell to 0.7063 before glaciation in Greenland (Fairchild et al., 2000) and it was originally considered that this fall was due to weathering of the c. 720 Ma Franklin large igneous province (Cox et al., 2016). However, more recent age constraints indicate an earlier <c. 735 Ma age for this decrease in seawater $^{87}Sr/^{86}Sr$ (Halverson et al., 2020, Ch. 17, The Tonian and Cryogenian Periods, this volume).
9. c. 802 Ma: Bitter Springs Anomaly—age constraints are particularly poor for the mid-Neoproterozoic. However, a negative $\delta^{13}C$ excursion at c. 810–802 Ma in the Bitter Springs Formation of central Australia may be of global significance based on consistent $^{87}Sr/^{86}Sr$ of 0.7063 at this level in Svalbard, NW Canada, Australia, and possibly Ethiopia, the presence of characteristic acritarchs, and sequence stratigraphy (Halverson et al., 2007; Halverson et al., 2020, Ch. 17,

this volume). Below this level, least-altered $^{87}Sr/^{86}Sr$ ratios are lower, ranging between 0.7052 and 0.7061 in the lower Bitter Springs Formation (Walter et al., 2000), NW Canada (Asmerom et al., 1991; Halverson et al., 2007), Siberia (Gorokhov et al., 1995), and Ethiopia (Miller et al., 2009). The ages of these units are not tightly constrained, but available data suggest that seawater $^{87}Sr/^{86}Sr$ increased during the mid-Neoproterozoic from 0.705 to 0.707 between c. 850 and c. 750 Ma (Halverson et al., 2007).

10. c. 1100–850 Ma: sparse Sr-isotope data covering the late Mesoproterozoic to early Neoproterozoic interval indicate pristine seawater values between 0.7052 and 0.7063 as shown from carbonate successions in Mauritania and Brazil (Veizer et al., 1983; de Alvarenga et al., 2019) as well as poorly age-constrained early Neoproterozoic samples from Siberia and the Urals (Kuznetsov et al., 2006; Kuznetsov et al., 2017). However, studies of thicker, more continuous carbonate platform successions of North China indicate a series of $^{87}Sr/^{86}Sr$ fluctuations across this interval, with deviations to lower values (Zhou et al., 2020; Fig. 7.1), potentially related to the eruption and weathering of large igneous provinces (Cox et al., 2016).

Bibliography

Ando, A., Nakano, T., Hodaka, K., Yokoyama, Y., and Khim, B.-K., 2010, Testing seawater Sr isotopic variability on a glacial interglacial timescale: an application of latest high-precision thermal ionization mass spectrometry. *Geochemical Journal*, **44** (5), 347–357.

Ando, A., Khim, B.-K., Nakano, T., and Takata, H., 2011, Chemostratigraphic documentation of a complete Miocene intermediate-depth section in the Southern Ocean: Ocean Drilling Program Site 1120, Campbell Plateau off New Zealand. *Marine Geology*, **279**: 52–62.

Armendáriz, M., Rosales, I., Bádenas, B., Aurell, M., García-Ramos, J.C., and Piñuela, L., 2003, High-resolution chemostratigraphic records from Lower Pliensbachian belemnites: palaeoclimatic perturbations, organic facies and water mass exchange (Asturian basin, northern Spain). *Palaeogeography, Palaeoclimatology, Palaeoecology*, **333–334**: 178–191.

Asmerom, Y., Jacobsen, S.B., Knoll, A.H., Butterfield, N.J., and Swett, K., 1991, Strontium isotopic variations of Neoproterozoic seawater: implication for crustal evolution. *Geochimica et Cosmochimica Acta*, **55**: 2883–2894.

Azmy, K., Veizer, J., Wenzal, B., Bassett, M., and Cooper, P., 1999, Silurian strontium isotope stratigraphy. *Geological Society of America Bulletin*, **111**: 475–483.

Bailey, R.J., and Smith, D.G., 2008a, Discussion on the Late Palaeocene–Early Eocene and Toarcian (Early Jurassic) carbon isotope excursions: a comparison of their time scales, associated environmental change, causes and consequences. *Journal of the Geological Society of London*, **165**: 875–880.

Bailey, R.J., and Smith, D.G., 2008b, Quantitative tests for stratigraphic cyclicity. *Geological Journal*, **43**: 431–446.

Bailey, T.R., McArthur, J.M., Prince, H., and Thirlwall, M.F., 2000, Dissolution methods for strontium isotope stratigraphy: whole rock analysis. *Chemical Geology*, **167**: 313–319.

Barbin, V., 2000, Cathodoluminescence of carbonate shells: biochemical *vs* diagenetic process. *In* Pagel, M., Barbin, V., Blanc, P., and Ohnenstetter, D. (eds), *Cathodoluminescence in Geosciences*. Springer Verlag, 303–329.

Barbin, V., 2013, Application of cathodoluminescence microscopy to recent and past biological materials: a decade of progress. *Mineralogy and Petrology*, **107**: 353–362.

Barbin, V., Ramseyer, K., Debenay, J.P., Schein, E., Roux, M., and Decrouez, D., 1991, Cathodoluminescence of Recent biogenic carbonates: an envirolunental and ontogenetic fingerprint. *Geological Magazine*, **128**: 19–26.

Barrat, J.A., Taylor, R.N., Andre, J.P., Nesbitt, R.W., and Lecuyer, C., 2000, Strontium isotopes in biogenic phosphates from a Neogene marine formation: implications for palaeoseawater studies. *Chemical Geology*, **168**: 325–332.

Barrera, E., Savin, S., Thomas, E., and Jones, C.E., 1997, Evidence for thermohaline-circulation reversals controlled by sea-level change in the latest Cretaceous. *Geology*, **25**: 715–718.

Blachman, N.M., and Machol, R.E., 1987, Confidence intervals based on one or more observations. *IEEE Transactions on Information Theory*, **33**: 373–382.

Bodin, S., Meissner, P., Janssen, N.M.M., Steuber, T., and Mutterlose, J., 2015. Large igneous provinces and organic carbon burial: Controls on global temperature and continental weathering during the Early Cretaceous. *Global and Planetary Change*, **133**: 238–253.

Bold, U., Smith, E.F., Rooney, A.D., Bowring, S.A., Buchwaldt, R., Dudás, F.Ö., et al., 2016, Neoproterozoic stratigraphy of the Zavkhan Terrane of Mongolia: the backbone for Cryogenian and early Ediacaran chemostratigraphic records. *American Journal of Science*, **315**: 1–63, https://doi.org/10.2475/01.2016.01.

Bolli, H.M., Saunders, J.B., and Perch-Nielsen, K. (eds), 1989. *Plankton Stratigraphy*. Cambridge University Press, Cambridge, **Vol. 1**: planktonic foraminifera, calcareous nannofossils and calpionellids. 599 pp. **Vol. 2**: radiolaria, diatoms, silicoflagellates, dinoflagellates and ichthyoliths, 407 pp.

Bralower, T.J., Fullagar, P.D., Paull, C.K., Dwyer, G.S., and Leckie, R.M., 1997, Mid-Cretaceous strontium-isotope stratigraphy of deep-sea sections. *Geological Society of America Bulletin*, **109**: 1421–1442.

Brand, U., Posenato, R., Came, R., Affek, H., Angiolini, L., Azmy, A., et al., 2012, The end-Permian mass extinction: a rapid volcanic CO_2 and CH_4-climatic catastrophe. *Chemical Geology*, **322–323**: 121–144.

Brasier, M.D., and Shields, G.A., 2000, Neoproterozoic chemostratigraphy and correlation of the Port Askaig glaciation, Dalradian Supergroup of Scotland. *Journal of the Geological Society of London*, **157**: 909–914.

Brasier, M.D., Shields, G.A., Kuleshov, V.N., and Zhegallo, E.A., 1996, Integrated chemo- and biostratigraphic calibration of early animal evolution: Neoproterozoic-early Cambrian of southwest Mongolia. *Geological Magazine*, **133**: 445–485.

Bruckschen, P., Oesmann, S., and Veizer, J., 1999, Isotope stratigraphy of the European Carboniferous: proxy signals for ocean chemistry, climate and tectonics. *Chemical Geology*, **161**: 127–163.

Bryant, J.D., Jones, D.S., and Mueller, P.A., 1995, Influence of freshwater flux on $^{87}Sr/^{86}Sr$ chronostratigraphy in marginal marine environments and dating of vertebrate and invertebrate faunas. *Journal of Paleontology*, **69**: 1–6.

Burke, W.H., Denison, R.E., Hetherington, E.A., Koepnick, R.B., Nelson, H.F., and Otto, J.B., 1982, Variation of $^{87}Sr/^{86}Sr$ throughout Phanerozoic time. *Geology*, **10**: 51–519.

Burla, S., Oberli, F., Heimhofer, U., Wiechert, U., and Weissert, H., 2009, Improved time control on Cretaceous coastal deposits: new results from Sr isotope measurements using laser ablation. *Terra Nova*, **21**: 401–409.

Burns, S.J., Haudenschild, U., and Matter, A., 1994, The strontium isotopic composition of carbonates from the late Precambrian (~560-540 Ma) Huqf Group of Oman. *Chemical Geology*, **111**: 269–282.

Callomon, J., and Dietl, G., 2000, On the proposed basal boundary stratotype (GSSP) of the Middle Jurassic Callovian Stage. *GeoReseach Forum*, **6**: 41–54.

Calver, C.R., 2000, Isotope stratigraphy of the Ediacaran Neoproterozoic (III) of the Adelaide Rift Complex, Australia, and the overprint of water column stratification. *Precambrian Research*, **100**: 121–150.

Carpenter, S.J., Lohmann, K.C., Holden, P., Walter, L.M., Huston, T.J., and Halliday, A.N., 1991, $\delta^{18}O$ values, ^{87}Sr / ^{86}Sr and Sr/Mg ratios of Late Devonian abiotic calcite: implications for the composition of ancient seawater. *Geochimica et Cosmochimica Acta*, **55**: 1991–2010.

Carter, J.G. (ed), 1990. *Skeletal Biomineralization: Pattern, Processes and Evolutionary Trends*. **Vol. I**, 832pp; **Vol. II**. Atlas and Index, 200 plates. Van Nostrand Reinhold, New York, 1990.

Chambers, J.M., Cleveland, W.S., Kleiner, B., and Tukey, P.A., 1983, *Graphical Methods for Data Analysis*. Wadsworth, Belmont, CA, 395 pp.

Chen, J., Montañez, I.P., Qi, Y., Shen, S., and Wang, X., 2018, Strontium and carbon isotopic evidence for decoupling of pCO_2 from continental weathering at the apex of the late Paleozoic glaciation. *Geology*, **46** (5), 395–398.

Clemens, S.C., Gromet, L.P., and Farrell, J.W., 1995, Artefacts in Sr isotope records. *Nature*, **373**: 201.

Cleveland, W.S., 1979, Robust locally weighted regression and smoothing scatterplots. *Journal of the American Statistical Association*, **74**: 829–836.

Cleveland, W.S., 1981, LOWESS—a program for smoothing scatterplots by robust locally weighted regression. *American Statistician*, **35** (1), 54.

Cleveland, W.S., Grosse, E., and Shyu, W.M., 1992, Local regression models. *In* Chambers, J.M., and Hastie, T. (eds), *Statistical Models in S*. Pacific Grove, CA: Wadsworth and Brooks/Cole, pp. 309–376.

Condon, D., Zhu, M., Bowring, S., Jin, Y., Wang, W., and Yang, A., 2005, From the Marinoan glaciation to the oldest bilaterians: U-Pb ages from the Doushantuo Formation, China. *Science*, **308**: 95–98.

Cox, G.M., Halveson, G.P., Stevenson, R.K., Vokary, M., Poirier, A., Kunzmann, M., et al., 2016, Continental flood basalt weathering as a trigger for Neoproterozoic Snowball Earth. *Earth and Planetary Science Letters*, **446**: 89–99.

Cramer, B.D., Munnecke, A., Schofield, D.I., Haase, K.M., and Haase-Schramm, A., 2011, A revised $^{87}Sr/^{86}Sr$ curve for the Silurian: implications for global ocean chemistry and the Silurian timescale. *The Journal of Geology*, **119**: 335–349.

Cui, H., Kaufman, A.J., Xiao, S.H., Zhu, M., Zhou, C., and Liu, X.-M., 2015, Redox architecture of an Ediacaran ocean margin: integrated chemostratigraphic ($\delta^{13}C$-$\delta^{34}S$-$^{87}Sr/^{86}Sr$-Ce/Ce*) correlation of the Doushantuo Formation, South China. *Chemical Geology*, **405**: 48–62.

Dasch, D.J., and Biscaye, P.E., 1971, Isotopic composition of Cretaceous-to-Recent pelagic foraminifera. *Earth and Planetary Science Letters*, **11**: 201–204.

de Alvarenga, C.J.S., de Dardenne, M.A., Santos, R.V., Brod, E.R., Gioia, S.M.C.L., Sial, A.N., et al., 2008, Isotope stratigraphy of Neoproterozoic cap carbonate in the Araras Group, Brazil. *Gondwana Research*, **13**: 469–479.

de Alvarenga, C.J.S., de Oliveira, G.D., Vieira, L.C., Santos, R.V., Baptista, M.C., and Dantas, E.L., 2019, Carbonate chemostratigraphy of the Vazante Group, Brazil: a probable Tonian age. *Precambrian Research*, **331**: 105378.

Denison, R.E., Koepnick, R.B., Fletcher, A., Dahl, D.A., and Baker, M.C., 1993, Re-evaluation of Early Oligocene, Eocene, and Paleocene seawater $^{87}Sr/^{86}Sr$ using outcrop samples from the U.S. Gulf Coast. *Paleoceanography*, **8**: 101–126.

Denison, R.E., Koepnick, R.B., Burke, W.H., Hetherington, E.A., and Fletcher, A., 1997, Construction of the Silurian and Devonian seawater $^{87}Sr/^{86}Sr$ curve. *Chemical Geology*, **140**: 109–121.

DePaolo, D.J., and Ingram, B., 1985, High-resolution stratigraphy with strontium isotopes. *Science*, **227**: 938–941.

Derry, L.A., Brasier, M.D., Corfield, R.M., Rozanov, A.Y., and Zhuravlev, A.Y., 1994, Sr and C isotope in Lower Cambrian carbonates from the Siberian craton: a paleoenvironmental record during the 'Cambrian explosion. *Earth and Planetary Science Letters*, **128**: 671–681.

Dudás, F.Ö., Yuan, D.X., Shen, S.Z., and Bowring, S.A., 2017, A conodont-based revision of the $^{87}Sr/^{86}Sr$ seawater curve across the Permian-Triassic boundary. *Palaeogeography, Palaeoclimatology, Palaeoecology*, **470**: 40–53.

Ebneth, S., Shields, G.A., Veizer, J., Miller, J.F., and Shergold, J.H., 2001, High-resolution strontium isotope stratigraphy across the Cambrian-Ordovician transition. *Geochimica et Cosmochimica Acta*, **14**: 2273–2292.

Edgar, K.M., Anagnostou, E., Pearson, P.N., and Foster, G.L., 2015, Assessing the impact of diagenesis on $\delta^{11}B$, $\delta^{13}C$, $\delta^{18}O$, Sr/Ca and B/Ca values in fossil planktic foraminiferal calcite. *Geochimica et Cosmochimica Acta*, **166**: 189–209.

Edwards, C.T., Saltzman, M.R., Leslie, S.A., Bergström, S.M., Sedlacek, A.R.C., Howard, A., et al., 2015, Strontium isotope ($^{87}Sr/^{86}Sr$) stratigraphy of Ordovician bulk carbonate: implications for preservation of primary seawater values. *Geological Society of America Bulletin*, **127** (9/10), 1275–1289.

El Meknassi, S., Dera, G., Cardone, T., De Rafélis, M., Brahmi, C., and Chavagnac, V., 2018, Sr isotope ratios of modern carbonate shells: good and bad news for chemostratigraphy. *Geology*, **46**: 1003–1006.

Fairchild, I.J., Spiro, B., Herrington, P.M., and Song, T., 2000, Controls on Sr and C isotope compositions of Neoproterozoic Sr-rich limestones of East Greenland and North China. *In* Grotzinger, J., and James, N. (eds), *Carbonate Sedimentation and Diagenesis in an Evolving Precambrian World*. SEPM Special Publication, **67**: 297–313.

Fairchild, I.J., Spencer, A.M., Ali, D.O., Anderson, R.P., Anderton, R., Boomer, I., et al., 2018, Tonian-Cryogenian boundary sections of Argyll, Scotland. *Precambrian Research*, **319**: 1–28.

Farrell, J.W., Clemens, S.C., and Gromet, L.P., 1995, Improved chronostratigraphic reference curve of late Neogene seawater $^{87}Sr/^{86}Sr$. *Geology*, **23**: 403–406.

Fietzke, J., and Eisenhauer, A., 2006, Determination of temperature-dependent stable strontium isotope (Sr-88/Sr-86) fractionation via bracketing standard MC-ICP-MS. *Geochemistry, Geophysics, Geosystems*, **7**: Q08009.

Frýda, J., Hladil, J., and Vokurka, K., 2002, Seawater strontium isotope curve at the Silurian/Devonian boundary: a study of the global Silurian/Devonian boundary stratotype. *Geobios*, **35**: 2–28.

Gao, G., and Land, L.S., 1991, Geochemistry of the Cambro-Ordovician Arbuckle Limestone, Oklahoma: implications for diagenetic $\delta^{18}O$

alteration and secular $\delta^{13}C$ and $^{87}Sr/^{86}Sr$ variation. *Geochimica et Cosmochimica Acta*, **55**: 2911–2920.

Garbelli, C., Shen, S.Z., Immenhauser, I., Brand, U., Buhl, D., Wang, W.Q., et al., 2019, Timing of Early and Middle Permian deglaciation of the southern hemisphere:brachiopod-based $^{87}Sr/^{86}Sr$ calibration. *Earth and Planetary Science Letters*, **516**: 122–135.

Goldstein, S.J., and Jacobsen, S., 1987, The Nd and Sr isotopic systematics of river-water dissolved material: implications for the sources of Nd and Sr in seawater. *Chemical Geology*, **66**: 245–272.

Gorokhov, I.M., Semikhatov, M.A., Baskakov, A.V., Kutyavin, E.P., Melnikov, N.N., Sochava, A.V., et al., 1995, Sr isotopic composition in Riphean, Vendian, and Lower Cambrian carbonates from Siberia. *Stratigraphy and Geological Correlation*, **3** (1), 1–28.

Halverson, G.P., Dudás, F.O., Maloof, A.C., and Bowring, S.A., 2007, Evolution of the $^{87}Sr/^{86}Sr$ composition of Neoproterozoic seawater. *Palaeogeography, Palaeoclimatology, Palaeoecology*, **256**: 103–129.

Halverson, G.P., Porter, S.M., and Shields, G.A., 2020, The Tonian and Cryogenian Periods. *In* Gradstein, F.M., Ogg, J.G., Schmitz, M.D., Ogg, G.M. (eds), *The Geologic Time Scale 2020*. Elsevier Publ., **Vol. 1** (this book).

Hemleben, C., Olsson, R.K., Fucek, V.P., and Kucenjak, M.H., 2018, Chapter 3. Wall textures of Oligocene normal perforate planktonic foraminifera. *In* Wade, et al., (eds), *Atlas of Oligocene Planktonic Foraminifera*. Cushman Foundation Special Publication, **Vol. 46**: 55–78.

Henderson, G.M., Martel, D.J., O'Nions, R.K., and Shackleton, N.J., 1994, Evolution of seawater $^{87}Sr/^{86}Sr$ over the last 400 ka: the absence of glacial/interglacial cycles. *Earth and Planetary Science Letters*, **128**: 643–651.

Hess, J., Stott, L., Bender, M.L., Kennett, J.P., and Schilling, J.-G., 1989, The Oligocene marine microfossil record: age assessments using strontium isotopes. *Paleoceanography*, **4** (6), 655–679.

Hesselbo, S.P., Meister, c, and Gröcke, D.R., 2000, *A potential global stratotype for the Sinemurian–Pliensbachian boundary (Lower Jurassic), Robin Hood's Bay, UK: ammonite faunas and isotope stratigraphy, Geological Magazine*, 137. (pp. 601–607).

Hodell, D.A., Mead, G.A., and Mueller, P.A., 1990, Variation in the strontium isotopic composition of seawater (8 Ma to present): implications for chemical weathering rates and dissolved fluxes to the oceans. *Chemical Geology (Isotope Geoscience Section)*, **80**: 291–307.

Hodell, D.A., Mueller, P.A., and Garrido, J.R., 1991, Variations in the strontium isotopic composition of seawater during the Neogene. *Geology*, **19**: 24–27.

Holmden, C., Creaser, R.A., Muehlenbachs, K., Bergstrom, S.M., and Leslie, S.A., 1996, Isotopic and elemental systematics of Sr and Nd in 454 Ma biogenic apatites: implications for paleoseawater studies. *Earth and Planetary Science Letters*, **142**: 425–437.

Howarth, R.J., and McArthur, J.M., 1997, Statistics for strontium isotope stratigraphy: a robust LOWESS fit to the marine strontium isotope curve for the period 0 to 206 Ma, with look-up table for the derivation of numerical age. *The Journal of Geology*, **105**: 441–456.

Huber, B.T., Macleod, K.G., and Tur, N.A., 2008, Chronostratigraphic framework for Upper Campanian – Maastrichtian sediments on the Blake Nose (subtropical North Atlantic). *Journal of Foraminiferal Research*, **38**: 162–182.

Jacobsen, S.B., and Kaufman, A.J., 1999, The Sr, C and O isotopic evolution of Neoproterozoic seawater. *Chemical Geology*, **161**: 37–57.

James, N.P., Narbonne, G.M., and Kyser, T.K., 2001, Late Neoproterozoic cap carbonates: Mackenzie Mountains, northwestern Canada: precipitation and global glacial meltdown. *Canadian Journal of Earth Sciences*, **38**: 1229–1262.

Jenkyns, H.C., Paull, K., Cummins, D.I., and Fullagar, P.D., 1995, Strontium-isotope stratigraphy of Lower Cretaceous atoll carbonates in the mid Pacific Mountains. *Proceedings of the Ocean Drilling Program, Scientific Results*, **143**: 89–97.

Jiang, G., Kaufman, A.J., Christie-Blick, N., Zhang, S., and Wu, H., 2007, Carbon isotope variability across the Ediacaran Yangtze platform in South China: implications for a large surface-to-deep ocean gradient. *Earth and Planetary Science Letters*, **261**: 303–320.

Jones, C.E., Jenkyns, H.C., and Hesselbo, S.P., 1994a, Strontium isotopes in Early Jurassic seawater. *Geochimica et Cosmochimica Acta*, **58** (4), 1285–1301.

Jones, C.E., Jenkyns, H.C., Coe, A.L., and Hesselbo, S.P., 1994b, Strontium isotope variations in Jurassic and Cretaceous seawater. *Geochimica et Cosmochimica Acta*, **58** (14), 3061–3074.

Kani, T., Isozaki, Y., Hayashi, R., Zakharov, Y., and Popov, A., 2018, Middle Permian (Capitanian) seawater $^{87}Sr/^{86}Sr$ minimum coincided with disappearance of tropical biota and reef collapse in NE Japan and Primorye (Far East Russia). *Palaeogeography, Palaeoclimatology, Palaeoecology*, **499**: 13–21.

Kaufman, A.J., and Knoll, A.H., 1995, Neoproterozoic variations in C-isotopic composition of seawater: stratigraphic and biogeochemical implications. *Precambrian Research*, **73**: 27–49.

Kaufman, A.J., Jacobsen, S.B., and Knoll, A.H., 1993, The Vendian record of Sr and C isotopic variations in seawater: implications for tectonics and paleoclimate. *Earth and Planetary Science Letters*, **120**: 409–430.

Kaufman, A.J., Knoll, A.H., Semikhatov, M.A., Grotzinger, J.P., Jacobsen, S.B., and Adams, W., 1996, Integrated chronostratigraphy of Proterozoic-Cambrian boundary beds in the western Anabar region, northern Siberia. *Geological Magazine*, **133**: 509–533.

Kaufman, A.J., Knoll, A.H., and Narbonne, G.M., 1997, Isotopes, ice ages, and terminal Proterozoic earth history. *Proceedings of the National Academy of Sciences of the United States of America*, **94**: 6600–6605.

Koepnick, R.B., Denison, R.E., Burke, W.H., Hetherington, E.A., and Dahl, D.A., 1990, Construction of the Triassic and Jurassic portion of the Phanerozoic curve of seawater $^{87}Sr/^{86}Sr$. *Chemical Geology*, **80**: 327–349.

Korte, C., and Ullmann, C.V., 2018, Permian strontium isotope stratigraphy. *In* Lucas, S.G., and Shen, S.Z. (eds), *The Permian Timescale. Geological Society*. Geological Society of London Special Publications, **Vol. 450**: 105–118.

Korte, C., Kozur, H.W., Bruckschen, P., and Veizer, J., 2003, Strontium isotope evolution of Late Permian and Triassic seawater. *Geochimica et Cosmochimica Acta*, **67**: 47–62.

Korte, C., Jasper, T., Kozur, H.W., and Veizer, J., 2006, $^{87}Sr/^{86}Sr$ record of Permian seawater. *Palaeogeography, Palaeoclimatology, Palaeoecology*, **240**: 89–107.

Kouchinsky, A., Bengtson, S., Gallet, Y., Korovnikov, I., Pavlov, V., Runnegar, B., et al., 2008, SPICE excursion in Siberia: a combined carbon-oxygen-strontium isotope and magnetostratigraphy study of the upper Middle Cambrian-lowermost Ordovician Kulyumbe river section, northwestern Siberian platform. *Geological Magazine*, **145**: 609–622.

Kralik, K., 1984, Effects of cation-exchange treatment and acid leaching on the Rb-Sr system of illite from Fithian, Illinois. *Geochimica et Cosmochimica Acta*, **48**: 527–533.

Kuznetsov, A.B., Semikhatov, M.A., Maslov, A.V., Gorokhov, I.M., Prasolov, E.M., Krupenin, M.T., et al., 2006, New data on Sr- and C-isotopic chemostratigraphy of the Upper Riphean type section (Southern Urals). *Stratigraphy and Geological Correlation*, **14**: 602–628.

Kuznetsov, A.B., Semikhatov, M.A., and Gorokhov, I.M., 2012, The Sr isotope composition of the world ocean, marginal and inland seas: implications for the Sr isotope stratigraphy. *Stratigraphy and Geological Correlation*, **20** (6), 501–515 ISSN 0869-5938. Translation from the Russian of Stratigrafiya. Geologicheskaya Korrelyatsiya, 20(6): 3–19.

Kuznetsov, A.B., Bekker, A., Ovchinnikova, G.V., Gorokhov, I.M., and Vasilyeva, I.M., 2017, Unradiogenic strontium and moderate-amplitude carbon isotope variations in early Tonian seawater after the assembly of Rodinia and before the Bitter Springs excursion. *Precambrian Research*, **298**: 157–173.

Li, L.-Q., and Keller, G., 1999, Variability in Late cretaceous climate and deep waters: evidence from stable isotopes. *Marine Geology*, **161**: 171–190.

Li, D., Ling, H., Shields-Zhou, G.A., Chen, X., Cremonese, L., Och, L., et al., 2013, Carbon and strontium isotope evolution of seawater across the Ediacaran–Cambrian transition: evidence from the Xiaotan section, NW Yunnan, South China. *Precambrian Research*, **225**: 128–147.

Liu, C., Wang, Z., and Raub, T.D., 2013, Geochemical constraints on the origin of Marinoan cap dolostones from Nuccaleena Formation, South Australia. *Chemical Geology*, **351**: 95–104.

Liu, C., Wang, Z., and Macdonald, F.A., 2018, Sr and Mg isotope geochemistry of the basal Ediacaran cap limestone sequence of Mongolia: implications for carbonate diagenesis, mixing of glacial meltwaters, and seawater chemistry in the aftermath of Snowball Earth. *Chemical Geology*, **491**: 1–13.

Marcano, M.C., Frank, T.D., Mukasa, S.B., Lohmann, K.C., and Taviani, M., 2015, Diagenetic incorporation of Sr into aragonitic bivalve shells: implications for chronostratigraphic and palaeoenvironmental interpretations. *Depositional Record*, **1**: 38–52, https://doi.org/10.1002/dep2.3.

Martin, E.E., and Macdougall, J.D., 1995, Sr and Nd isotopes at the Permian/Triassic boundary: a record of climate change. *Chemical Geology*, **125**: 73–99.

Martin, E.E., and Scher, H.D., 2004, Preservation of seawater Sr and Nd isotopes in fossil fish teeth: bad news and good news. *Earth and Planetary Science Letters*, **220**: 25–39.

Martin, E.E., Macdougall, J.D., Herbert, T.D., Paytan, A., and Kastner, M., 1995, Strontium and neodymium isotopic analyses of marine barite separates. *Geochimica et Cosmochimica Acta*, **59**: 1353–1361.

Martin, E.E., Shackleton, N.J., Zachos, J.C., and Flower, B.P., 1999, Orbitally-tuned Sr isotope chemostratigraphy for the late middle to late Miocene. *Palaeoceanography*, **14**: 74–83.

McArthur, J.M., 1994, Recent trends in strontium isotope stratigraphy. *Terra Nova*, **6**: 331–358.

McArthur, J.M., 2010, Strontium isotope stratigraphy. *In* Ratcliffe, K.T., and Zaitlin, B.A. (eds), *Application of Modern Stratigraphic Techniques: Theory and Case Histories.* No. 94. SEPM (Society for Sedimentary Geology). ISBN 978-1-56576-199-5. 129–142.

McArthur, J.M., Thirlwall, M.F., Gale, A.S., Kennedy, W.J., Burnett, J.A., Mattey, et al., 1993a, Strontium isotope stratigraphy for the Late Cretaceous: a new curve, based on the English Chalk. *Geological Society, London*, **70**: 195–209.

McArthur, J.M., Chen, M., Gale, A.S., Thirlwall, M.F., and Kennedy, W.J., 1993b, Strontium isotope stratigraphy for the Late Cretaceous: age models and intercontinental correlations for the Campanian. *Paleoceanography*, **8**: 859–873.

McArthur, J.M., Kennedy, W.J., Chen, M., Thirlwall, M.F., and Gale, A.S., 1994, Strontium isotope stratigraphy for the Late Cretaceous: direct numerical age calibration of the Sr-isotope curve for the U.S. Western Interior Seaway. *Palaeogeography, Palaeoclimatology, Palaeoecology*, **108**: 95–119.

McArthur, J.M., Thirlwall, M.F., Engkilde, M., Zinsmeister, W.J., and Howarth, R.J., 1998, Strontium isotope profiles across K/T boundaries in Denmark and Antarctica. *Earth and Planetary Science Letters*, **160**: 179–192.

McArthur, J.M., Donovan, D.T., Thirlwall, M.F., Fouke, B.W., and Mattey, D., 2000a, Strontium isotope profile of the Early Toarcian (Jurassic) Oceanic Anoxic Event, the duration of ammonite biozones, and belemnite palaeotemperatures. *Earth and Planetary Science Letters*, **179**: 269–285.

McArthur, J.M., Morton, M., and Thirlwall, M.F., 2000b, Strontium Isotope Stratigraphy of the Aalenian/Bajocian Auxiliary Stratotype Point at Bearreraig, Isle of Skye, NW Scotland. *GeoResearch Forum*, **6**: 137–144.

McArthur, J.M., Rio, D., Massari, F., Castradori, D., Bailey, T.R., Thirlwall, M., et al., 2006, A revised Pliocene record for marine-$^{87}Sr/^{86}Sr$ used to date an interglacial event, Cockburn Island Formation, northern Antarctic Peninsula. *Palaeogeography, Palaeoclimatology, Palaeoecology*, **242**: 126–136.

McArthur, J.M., Janssen, N.M.M., Reboulet, S., Leng, M.J., Thirlwall, M.F., and van de Schootbrugge, B., 2007, Early Cretaceous ice-cap volume, palaeo-temperatures (Mg, $\delta^{18}O$), and isotope stratigraphy ($\delta^{13}C$, $^{87}Sr/^{86}Sr$) from Tethyan belemnites. Palaeogeog. *Palaeogeography, Palaeoclimatology, Palaeoecology*, **248**: 391–430.

McArthur, J.M., Howarth, R.J., and Shields, G.A., 2012, Chapter 7: Strontium isotope stratigraphy. *In* Gradstein, F.M., Ogg, J.G., Schmitz, M.D., and Ogg, G.M. (eds), *The Geologic Time Scale, 2012*. Elsevier, **Vol. 1 of 2**: p. 1144.

McArthur, J.M., Steuber, T., Page, K.N., and Landman, N.H., 2016, Sr-isotope stratigraphy: assigning time in the Campanian, Pliensbachian, Toarcian, and Valanginian. *The Journal of Geology*, **145** (5), 569–586.

McKirdy, D.M., Burgess, J.M., Lemon, N.M., Yu, X., Cooper, A.M., Gostin, V.A., et al., 2001, A chemostratigraphic overview of the late Cryogenian interglacial sequence in the Adelaide Fold-Thrust Belt, South Australia. *Precambrian Research*, **106**: 149–186.

Mead, G.A., and Hodell, D.A., 1995, Controls on the $^{87}Sr/^{86}Sr$ composition of seawater from the middle Eocene to Oligocene: Hole 689B, Maud Rise, Antarctica. *Paleoceanography and Paleoclimatology*, **10**: 327–346.

Mearon, S., Paytan, A., and Bralower, T., 2003, Cretaceous strontium isotope stratigraphy using marine barite. *Geology*, **31**: 15–18.

Melezhik, V.A., Pokrovsky, B.G., Fallick, A.E., Kuznetsov, A.B., and Bujakaite, M.I., 2009, Constraints on the $^{87}Sr/^{86}Sr$ of Late Ediacaran seawater: insights from high-Sr limestones. *The Journal of Geology Society, London*, **166**: 183–191.

Miller, K.G., Feigenson, M.D., Kent, D.V., and Olson, R.K., 1988, Upper Eocene to Oligocene isotope ($^{87}Sr/^{86}Sr$, $\delta^{18}O$, $\delta^{13}C$) standard section, Deep Sea Drilling Project Site 522. *Paleoceanography*, **3**: 223–233.

Miller, K.G., Feigenson, M.D., Wright, J.D., and Clement, B.M., 1991, Miocene isotope reference section, Deep Sea Drilling Project Site

608: an evaluation of isotope and biostratigraphic resolution. *Paleoceanography*, **6**: 33–52.

Miller, N.R., Stern, R.J., Avigad, D., Beyth, M., and Schilman, B., 2009, Cryogenian slate-carbonate sequences of the Tambien Group, northern Ethiopia (1) Pre-"Sturtian" chemostratigraphy and regional correlations. *Precambrian Research*, **170**: 129–156.

Misi, A., and Veizer, J., 1998, *Neoproterozoic carbonate sequences of the Una Group, Irece Basin, Brazil: chemiostratigraphy, age and correlations, Precambrian Research*, 89. (pp. 87–100).

Misi, A., Kaufman, A.J., Veizer, J., Powis, K., Azmy, K., Boggiani, P. C., et al., 2007, Chemostratigraphic correlation of Neoproterozoic successions in South America. *Chemical Geology*, **237**: 161–185.

Mokadem, F., Parkinson, I.J., Hathorne, E.C., Ananda, P., Allen, J.T., and Burton, K.W., 2015, High-precision radiogenic strontium isotope measurements of the modern and glacial ocean: limits on glacial–interglacial variations incontinental weathering. *Earth and Planetary Science Letters*, **415**: 111–120.

Montañez, I.P., Banner, J.L., Osleger, D.A., Borg, L.E., and Bosserman, P. L., 1996, Integrated Sr isotope variations and sea-level history of Middle to Upper Cambrian platform carbonates: implications for the evolution of Cambrian seawater $^{87}Sr/^{86}Sr$. *Geology*, **24** (10), 917–920.

Montañez, I.P., Osleger, D.A., Banner, J.L., Mack, L.E., and Musgrove, M., 2000, Evolution of the Sr and C isotope composition of Cambrian oceans. *GSA Today*, **10**: 1–7.

Müller, W., and Anczkiewicz, R., 2016, Accuracy of laser-ablation (LA)-MC-ICPMS Sr isotope analysis of (bio)apatite – a problem reassessed. *Journal of Analytical Atomic Spectrometry*, **31**: 259–269.

Needham, L., 2007, A High Resolution Pennsylvanian – Early Permian Seawater 87Sr/86Sr Curve. *Unpublished M.Sc. thesis*. Boise State University.

Nicholas, C.J., 1996, The Sr isotopic evolution of the oceans during the 'Cambrian explosion'. *The Journal of Geology Society, London*, **153**: 243–254.

Nogueira, A.C.R., Riccomini, C., Sial, A.N., Moura, C.A.V., Trindade, R.I.F., and Fairchild, T.R., 2007, Carbon and strontium isotope fluctuations and paleoceanographic changes in the late Neoproterozoic Araras carbonate platform, southern Amazon craton, Brazil. *Chemical Geology*, **237**: 191–210.

Oslick, J.S., Miller, K.G., Feigenson, M.D., and Wright, J.D., 1994, Oligocene-Miocene strontium isotopes: stratigraphic revisions and correlations to an inferred glacioeustatic record. *Paleoceanography*, **9**: 427–443.

Page, K.N., Meléndez, G., Hart, M.B., Price, G.D., Wright, J.K., Bown, P.J., et al., 2009, Integrated stratigraphical study of the candidate Oxfordian Global Stratotype Section and Point (GSSP) at Redcliff Point, Weymouth, Dorset, UK. *Volumina Jurassica*, **VII**: 101–111.

Palmer, M.R., and Edmond, J.M., 1989, The strontium isotope budget of the modern ocean. *Earth and Planetary Science Letters*, **92**: 11–26.

Paytan, A., Kastner, M., Martin, E.E., Macdougall, J.D., and Herbert, T., 1993, Marine barite as a monitor of seawater strontium isotope composition. *Nature*, **366**: 445–449.

Pearce, C.R., Parkinson, I.J., Gaillardet, J., Charlier, B.L.A., Mokadem, F., and Burton, K.W., 2015, Reassessing the stable ($\delta^{88/86}Sr$) and radiogenic ($^{87}Sr/^{86}Sr$) strontium isotopic composition of marine inputs. *Geochimica et Cosmochimica Acta*, **157**: 125–146.

Pearson, P.N., 2018, Chapter 15: Wall textures and higher taxonomy of oligocene micro- and medioperforate planktonic foraminifera. *In* Wade, et al., (eds), *Atlas of Oligocene Planktonic Foraminifera*. Cushman Foundation Special Publication, **Vol. 46**: 415–428.

Pearson, P.N., Ditchfield, P.W., Singano, J., Harcourt-Brown, K.G., Nicholas, C.J., Olsson, R.K., et al., 2001, Warm tropical sea surface temperatures in the Late Cretaceous and Eocene epochs. *Nature*, **413**: 481–487.

Pérez-Huerta, A., Coronado, I., and Hegna, T.A., 2018, Understanding biomineralization in the fossil record. *Earth-Science Reviews*, **179**: 95–122.

Peterman, Z.E., Hedge, C.E., and Tourtelot, H.A., 1970, Isotopic composition of strontium in sea water throughout Phanerozoic time. *Geochimica et Cosmochimica Acta*, **34**: 105–120.

Peucker-Ehrenbrink, B., 2009, Land2Sea database of river drainage basin sizes, annual water discharges and suspended sediment fluxes. *Geochemistry, Geophysics, Geosystems*, **10** (6), Q06014, https://doi.org/10.1029/2008GC002356.

Peucker-Ehrenbrink, B., 2018, Land2Sea Database, Version 2.0. *Pangaea*, https://doi.org/10.1594/PANGAEA.892680.

Peucker-Ehrenbrink, B., and Fiske, G.J., 2019, A continental perspective of the seawater $^{87}Sr/^{86}Sr$ record: a review. *Chemical Geology*, **510**: 140–165.

Pokrovskii, B.G., Melezhik, V.A., and Bujakaite, M.I., 2006, Carbon, oxygen, strontium and sulfur isotopic compositions in Late Precambrian rocks of the Patom Complex, Central Siberia: communication. 1. Results, isotope stratigraphy, and dating problems. *Lithology and Mineral Resources*, **41**: 450–474.

Popov, S.V., 2014, Formation of bivalve shells and their microstructure. *Paleontological Journal*, **48** (14), 1519–1531.

Prokoph, A., Shields, G.A., and Veizer, J., 2008, Compilation and time-series analysis of a marine carbonate $\delta^{18}O$, $\delta^{13}C$, $^{87}Sr/^{86}Sr$ and $\delta^{34}S$ database through Earth history. *Earth-Science Reviews*, **87**: 113–133.

Qing, H., Barnes, C.R., Buhl, D., and Veizer, J., 1998, The strontium isotopic composition of Ordovician and Silurian brachiopods and conodonts: relationships to geological events and implications for coeval seawater. *Geochimica et Cosmochimica Acta*, **62**: 1721–1723.

Reilly, T.J., Miller, K.G., and Feigenson, M.D., 2002, Latest Eocene-earliest Miocene Sr isotopic reference section, Site 522, eastern South Atlantic. *Paleoceanography*, **17**: 1046, https://doi.org/10.1029/2001PA000745.

Richter, F.M., and DePaolo, D.J., 1987, Numerical-models for diagenesis and the Neogene Sr isotopic evolution of seawater from DSDP site 590B. *Earth and Planetary Science Letters*, **83** (14), 27–38.

Robb, L., Knoll, A.H., Plumb, K., Shields, G.A., Strauss, H., and Veizer, J., 2004, Chapter 12: The Precambrian. *In* Gradsten, F.M., Ogg, J.G., and Smith, A. (eds), *The 2004 Geological Timescale*. (coordinators). pp. 128–140.

Rooney, A.D., Macdonald, F.A., Strauss, J.V., Dudás, F.Ö., Hallmann, C., and Selby, D., 2014, Re-Os geochronology and coupled Os-Sr isotope constraints on the Sturtian snowball Earth. *Proceedings of the National Academy of Sciences of the United States of America*, **111**: 51–56.

Ruppel, S.C., James, E.W., Barrick, J.E., Nowlan, G., and Uyeno, T.T., 1996, High-resolution $^{87}Sr/^{86}Sr$ chemostratigraphy of the Silurian: implications for event correlation and strontium flux. *Geology*, **24**: 831–834.

Saltzman, M.R., Davidson, J.P., Holden, P., Runnegar, B., and Lohmann, K.C., 1995, Sea-level driven changes in ocean chemistry at an Upper Cambrian extinction horizon. *Geology*, **23**: 893–896.

Saltzman, M.R., Edwards, C.T., Leslie, S.A., Dwyer, G.S., Bauer, J.A., Repetski, J.E., et al., 2014, Calibration of a conodont apatite-based

Ordovician $^{87}Sr/^{86}Sr$ curve to biostratigraphy and geochronology: implications for stratigraphic resolution. *Geological Society of America Bulletin*, **126** (11/12), 1551–1568.

Sedlacek, A.R., Saltzman, M.R., Algeo, T.J., Horacek, M., Brandner, R., Foland, K., et al., 2014, $^{87}Sr/^{86}Sr$ stratigraphy from the Early Triassic of Zal, Iran: linking temperature to weathering rates and the tempo of ecosystem recovery. *Geology*, **42**: 779–782.

Shields, G., and Veizer, J., 2002, Precambrian marine carbonate isotope database: Version 1.1. *Geochemistry, Geophysics, Geosystems*, **3**, https://doi.org/10.1029/2001GC000266.

Shields, G.A., 1999, Working towards a new stratigraphic calibration scheme for the Neoproterozoic-Cambrian. *Eclogae Geologicae Helvitiae*, **92**: 221–233.

Shields, G.A., Stille, P., Brasier, M.D., and Atudorei, N.-V., 1997, Stratified oceans and oxygenation of the late Precambrian. *Terra Nova*, **9**: 218–222.

Shields, G.A., Brasier, M.D., Stille, P., and Dorjnamjaa, D., 2002, Factors contributing to high $\delta^{13}C$ in Cryogenian limestones of western Mongolia. *Earth and Planetary Science Letters*, **196** (3/4), 99–111.

Shields, G.A., Carden, G.A.F., Veizer, J., Meidla, T., Rong, J.-Y., and Li, R.-Y., 2003, Sr, C, and O isotope geochemistry of Ordovician brachiopods: a major isotopic event around the Middle-Late Ordovician transition. *Geochimica et Cosmochimica Acta*, **67** (11), 2005–2025.

Shields, G.A., Deynoux, M., Strauss, H., Paquet, H., and Nahon, D., 2007, Barite-bearing cap carbonates of the Taoudéni Basin, northwest Africa: sedimentary and isotopic evidence for methane seepage from permafrost after a Neoproterozoic glaciation. *Precambrian Research*, **153**: 209–235.

Song, H., Wignall, P.B., Tong, J., Song, H., Chen, J., Chu, D., et al., 2015, Integrated Sr isotope variations and global environmental changes through the Late Permian to early Late Triassic. *Earth and Planetary Science Letters*, **424**: 140–147.

Sugarman, P.J., Miller, K.G., Bukry, D., and Feigenson, M.D., 1995, Uppermost Campanian-Maastrichtian strontium isotopic, biostratigraphic, and sequence stratigraphic framework of the new Jersey Coastal Plain. *Geological Society of America Bulletin*, **107**: 19–37.

Taylor, J.D., Kennedy, W.J., and Hall, A., 1969, The shell structure and mineralogy of the Bivalvia. Introduction. Nuculacea—Trigonacea. *Bulletin of the British Museum (Natural History)*, **3**: 125 pp.

Taylor, J.D., Kennedy, W.J., and Hall, A., 1973, The shell structure of the Bivalvia. II. Lucinacea—Clavageliacea. Conclusions. *Bulletin of the British Museum (Natural History)*, **22** (9), 253–294, London, Zoology Supplement.

Thisted, R.A., 1988, *Elements of Statistical Computing*. Chapman and Hall/CRC; Boca Raton, London, New York, Washington, D.C. 427 pp.

Tierney, K.E., 2010, Carbon and Strontium Isotope Stratigraphy of the Permian From Nevada and China: Implications From an Icehouse to Greenhouse Transition. *Unpublished MSc. thesis*. Ohio State University.

Trotter, J.A., and Eggins, S.M., 2006, Chemical systematics of conodont apatite determined by laser ablation ICPMS. *Chemical Geology*, **233**: 196–216.

Ullmann, C.V., and Korte, c, 2015, Diagenetic alteration in low-Mg calcite from macrofossils: a review. *Geological Quarterly*, **59** (1), 3–20.

Valledares, M.I., Ugidos, J.M., Barba, P., Fallick, A.E., and Ellam, R.M., 2006, Oxygen, carbon and strontium isotope records of Ediacaran carbonates in Central Iberia (Spain). *Precambrian Research*, **147**: 354–365.

van Geldern, R., Joachimski, M.M., Day, J., Jansen, U., Alvarez, F., Yolkin, E.A., et al., 2006, Carbon, oxygen and strontium isotope records of Devonian brachiopod shell calcite. *Palaeogeography, Palaeoclimatology, Palaeoecology*, **240**: 47–67.

Vaughan, S., Bailey, R.J., and Smith, D.G., 2011, Detecting cycles in stratigraphic data: spectral analysis in the presence of red noise. *Paleoceanography*, **26**: PA4211, https://doi.org/10.1029/2011PA002195.

Vaughan, S., Bailey, R.J., Smith, D.G., 2014, Cyclostratigraphy: data filtering as a source of spurious spectral peaks. *In* Smith, D.G., Bailey, R.J., Burgess, P.M., and Fraser, A.J. (eds), 2015. *Strata and Time: Probing the Gaps in Our Understanding*. Geological Society, Special Publications, London, **404**: 151–156. https://doi:10.1144/SP404.11.

Veizer, J., Compston, W., Clauer, N., and Schidlowski, M., 1983, $^{87}Sr/^{86}Sr$ in Late Proterozoic carbonates: evidence for a "mantle" event at ~900 Ma ago. *Geochimica et Cosmochimica Acta*, **47** (2), 295–302.

Veizer, J., Buhl, D., Diener, A., Ebneth, S., Podlaha, O.G., Bruckschen, P., et al., 1997, Strontium isotope stratigraphy: potential resolution and event correlation. *Palaeogeography, Palaeoclimatology, Palaeoecology*, **132**: 65–77.

Veizer, J., Ala, D., Azmy, K., Bruckschen, P., Buhl, D., Bruhn, F., et al., 1999, $^{87}Sr/^{86}Sr$, $\delta^{13}C$ and $\delta^{18}O$ evolution of Phanerozoic seawater. *Chemical Geology*, **161**: 59–88.

Voigt, J., Hathorne, E.C., Frank, M., Vollstaedt, H., and Eisenhauer, A., 2015, Variability of carbonate diagenesis in equatorial Pacific sediments deduced from radiogenic and stable Sr isotopes. *Geochimica et Cosmochimica Acta*, **148**: 360–377.

Voigt, J., Hathorne, E.C., Frank, M., and Holbourn, A., 2016, Minimal influence of recrystallization on middle Miocene benthic foraminiferal stable isotope stratigraphy in the eastern equatorial Pacific. *Paleoceanography*, **31**: 98–114, https://doi.org/10.1002/2015PA002822.

Walter, M.R., Veevers, J.J., Calver, C.R., Gorjan, P., and Hill, A.C., 2000, Dating the 840-544 Ma Neoproterozoic interval by isotopes of strontium, carbon, and sulfur in seawater and some interpretive models. *Precambrian Research*, **100**: 371–433.

Wang, W., Garbelli, C., Zheng, Q.-F., Chen, J., Liu, X.-C., Wang, W., et al., 2018, Permian $^{87}Sr/^{86}Sr$ chemostratigraphy from carbonate sequences in South China. *Palaeogeography, Palaeoclimatology, Palaeoecology*, **500**: 84–94.

Weedon, G.P., and Jenkyns, H.C., 1999, Cyclostratigraphy and the Early Jurassic timescale: data from the Belemnite Marls, southern England. *Geological Society of America Bulletin*, **111**: 1823–1840.

Wierzbowski, H., Anczkiewicz, R., Bazarnik, J., and Pawlak, J., 2012, Strontium isotope variations in Middle Jurassic (Late Bajocian–Callovian) seawater: implications for Earth's tectonic activity and marine environments. *Chemical Geology*, **334**: 171–181.

Wierzbowski, H., Anczkiewicz, R., Pawlak, J., Rogov, M.A., and Kuznetsov, A.B., 2017, Revised Middle–Upper Jurassic strontium isotope stratigraphy. *Chemical Geology*, **466**: 239–255.

Wilkens, R.H., Westerhold, T., Drury, A.J., Lyle, M., Gorgas, T. and Tian, J. 2017. Revisiting the Ceara Rise, equatorial Atlantic Ocean: isotope stratigraphy of ODP Leg 154 from 0 to 5 Ma. Climate of the Past, 13: 779–793. https://doi.org/10.5194/cp-13-779-2017

Williams, J.P., Su, Y.-S., and Wise, W.M., 1977, Trace chemical analysis of high-purity glass. *Mikrochimica Acta [Wien.]*, **II**: 527–536.

Wotte, T., Alvaro, J.-J., Shields, G.A., Brown, B., Brasier, M.D., and Veizer, J., 2007, High resolution C-, O- and Sr-isotope stratigraphy across the Lower-Middle Cambrian transition of the Cantabrian Mountains (Spain) and the Montagne Noire (France), West Gondwana. *Palaeogeography, Palaeoclimatology, Palaeoecology*, **256**: 47–70.

Xiao, S.H., and Narbonne, G.M., 2020, The Ediacaran Period. *In* Gradstein, F.M., Ogg, J.G., Schmitz, M.D., Ogg, G.M. (eds), *The Geologic Time Scale 2020*, Elsevier Publ., **Vol. 1** (this book).

Yoshioka, H., Asahara, Y., Tojo, B., and Kawakami, S., 2003, Systematic variations in C, O, and Sr isotopes and elemental concentrations in Neoproterozoic carbonates in Namibia: implications for glacial to interglacial transition. *Precambrian Research*, **124**: 69–85.

Zachos, J.C., Berggren, W.A., Aubry, M.-P., and Mackensen, A., 1992, Isotopic and trace element geochemistry of Eocene and Oligocene foraminifers from Site 748, Kerguelen Plateau. *Proceedings of the Ocean Drilling Program, Scientific Result*, **120**: 839–854.

Zachos, J.C., Opdyke, B.N., Quinn, T.M., Jones, C.E., and Halliday, A.N., 1999, Early Cenozoic glaciation, Antarctic weathering, and seawater $^{87}Sr/^{86}Sr$: is there a link? *Chemical Geology*, **161**: 165–180.

Zeeden, C., Hilgen, F., Westerhold, T., Lourens, L., Röhl, U., and Bickert, T., 2013, Revised Miocene splice, astronomical tuning and calcareous plankton biochronology of ODP Site 926 between 5 and 14.4 Ma. *Palaeogeography, Palaeoclimatology, Palaeoecology*, **369**: 430–451.

Zhang, L.Y., Chen, D.Z., Huang, T.Y., Yu, H., Zhou, X.Q., and Wang, J.G., 2020, An abrupt oceanic change and frequent climate fluctuations across the Frasnian–Famennian transition of Late Devonian: constraints from conodont Sr isotope. *Geological Journal*, **55**(6): 4479–4492.

Zhou, Y., von Strandmann, P.A.E., Zhu, M.Y., Ling, H.F., Manning, C., Li, D., et al., 2020, Reconstructing Tonian seawater $^{87}Sr/^{86}Sr$ using calcite microspar. *Geology*, **48**: 462–467.

B. Peucker-Ehrenbrink and G.E. Ravizza

Chapter 8

Osmium Isotope Stratigraphy

Chapter outline

Abstract

This chapter presents the currently available $^{187}Os/^{188}Os$ seawater data and emphasizes some of the challenges involved in reconstructing the seawater record from the present to the Precambrian. Radioactive decay of long-lived ^{187}Re to ^{187}Os, large differences in the compatibilities of rhenium (mildly incompatible) and osmium (very compatible) during magmatic differentiation, and various processes that mobilize and transport Os into the ocean shape this seawater record. Differences in magmatic compatibilities of Re and Os have created large isotope contrasts between osmium delivered to seawater from the radiogenic Earth's crust (e.g. rivers, submarine groundwater discharge, aeolian dust) compared to osmium from the unradiogenic mantle (submarine hydrothermal vents) and undifferentiated extraterrestrial matter. Together with the relatively short (10^3-10^4 yr) residence time of osmium in seawater these factors are responsible for the very dynamic isotope evolution of seawater that offers great potential for chemostratigraphic reconstructions. A full assessment of the chemostratigraphic utility of the marine $^{187}Os/^{188}Os$ record requires that it be reconstructed in multiple ocean basins at a temporal resolution approaching the marine residence time of Os. Presently, large time intervals are undersampled. Where high temporal resolution studies have been conducted at widely separated sites, observed $^{187}Os/^{188}Os$ offsets between sites exceed analytical uncertain. It is therefore a possibility that subtle offsets between the $^{187}Os/^{188}Os$ of seawater in different ocean basins could have existed in the past.

8.1 Introduction

This chapter follows reviews of the marine $^{187}Re/^{187}Os$ isotope system by Peucker-Ehrenbrink and Ravizza (2000a) and a previous chapter on osmium isotope stratigraphy in *The Geologic Time Scale 2012* (Peucker-Ehrenbrink and Ravizza, 2012) that summarized our contemporaneous knowledge of the evolution of $^{187}Os/^{188}Os$ in seawater. This chapter builds on these contributions and focuses on some recent advances in the reconstruction of the marine $^{187}Os/^{188}Os$ record, as well as our refined knowledge of the pre-Mesozoic record of seawater that received little attention in previous reviews due to the dearth of data. Many of those reconstructions rely on initial $^{187}Os/^{188}Os$ values that are constrained by $^{187}Re-^{187}Os$ isochrons of organic-rich mudrock (ORM). In addition, we briefly review contributions to the record that are based on analyses of very slowly accumulating hydrogenetic Fe–Mn crusts.

8.2 Untapped potential

The fact that the $^{187}Os/^{188}Os$ composition of global seawater, analyzed directly, is likely homogenous within current analytical uncertainties (Sharma, 2019) yet responds quickly to perturbations indicates that the residence time of Os does not greatly exceed the mixing time of seawater. The challenge associated with adequately characterizing such a seawater record is shown in Fig. 8.1 that plots the existing number of data points with age assignments per time period (age/epoch/period/era) and the fraction of what is needed for adequate characterization if we accept one data point per residence time, here 10,000 years, as a suitable measure for adequate coverage on the right axis. Clearly, only for the Holocene and the Pleistocene do we have adequate knowledge of the record or come close to this goal. Some events (e.g., E/O boundary, K/Pg boundary, some oceanic anoxic events such as OAE 1a) have also been well characterized as shown in Fig. 8.1a (data in red) if the data are

Geologic Time Scale 2020. DOI: https://doi.org/10.1016/B978-0-12-824360-2.00008-5

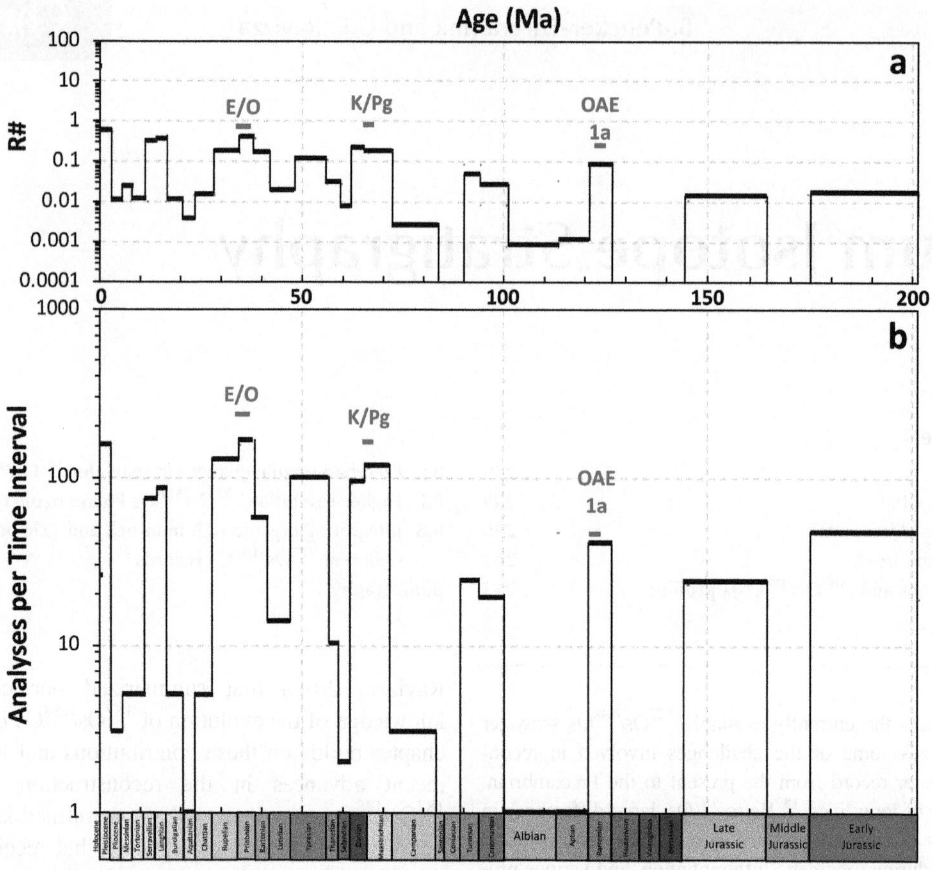

FIGURE 8.1 (a) Required sampling density (*R*#) for at least one data point per 10,000-year time interval (*R* = 1), a realistic measure of the marine residence time (t) of osmium. "*R*," the ratio of existing to required $^{187}Os/^{188}Os$ data per t, scales linearly and inversely with t. (b) Number of $^{187}Os/^{188}Os$ paleoseawater data per time interval. Highlighted in red are narrower time windows for the Eocene/Oligocene (E/O, 3 Myr), the Cretaceous/Paleogene (K/Pg, 2 Myr), and the OAE 1a (2 Myr) boundaries to emphasize clumping of data around stratigraphic boundaries and impact events. The E/O and K/Pg intervals are properly characterized (Fig. 8.1a, $R \sim 0.7-0.9$). Color scale at bottom follows GTS2020 scheme and highlights binning of data for the construction of these diagrams. For some time intervals no data exist. For comparison the average Phanerozoic *R*# for the marine $^{87}Sr/^{86}Sr$ approaches 10.

binned not according to stratigraphic units but instead by the duration of these events. For those well-characterized events the existing $^{187}Os/^{188}Os$ record is uniquely useful to constrain ages of long ferromanganese crust records and slowly accumulating pelagic clays, and for event stratigraphy where large, global excursions in $^{187}Os/^{188}Os$ have been well documented. The fact that adequately sampled time intervals often display systematic offsets in $^{187}Os/^{188}Os$ between geographically separated sites currently precludes using the $^{187}Os/^{188}Os$ record as chemostratigraphic tool analogous to the marine $^{87}Sr/^{86}Sr$ record. Compared to the—for most time periods—superbly reconstructed $^{87}Sr/^{86}Sr$ record of Phanerozoic seawater (McArthur et al., 2020), we are far from adequate characterization of the marine $^{187}Os/^{188}Os$ record (Fig. 8.2).

8.3 Hydrogenic Fe–Mn crusts

While slowly (mm/Myr) accumulating hydrogenous ferromanganese crusts do not allow the temporal resolution needed for adequate reconstruction of this record, they have value in guiding investigators to potentially interesting periods that have not been investigated in greater detail. As not only Os but other trace elements (e.g., Nd: Ling et al., 1997; Pb: Frank et al., 1999; Hf: Lee et al., 1999; Tl: Nielsen et al., 2009, 2011; transition metals such as Fe: Horner et al., 2015) are also enriched in such crusts, multiple isotope records can be established on the same material by either selective leaches or in situ laser ablation analyses. This aids in the interpretation of paleoseawater records. In the following, we therefore briefly review existing records of seawater $^{187}Os/^{188}Os$ of such archives (Fig. 8.3: Burton et al., 1999; Klemm et al., 2005, 2008; Li et al., 2008, Meng et al., 2008; Conrad et al., 2017; Goto et al., 2017; Josso et al., 2019).

Before reliable direct $^{187}Os/^{188}Os$ measurements of seawater could be made (e.g., Sharma, 2019), Os extracted from Os-rich ferromanganese crust surfaces from the main ocean basins showed only small regional variations in $^{187}Os/^{188}Os$ of modern seawater (e.g., 0.03 $^{187}Os/^{188}Os$ units between Pacific and Atlantic ocean crusts; Burton et al., 1999). Since then, $^{187}Os/^{188}Os$ in ferromanganese crusts has been used to establish growth curves for crusts that are otherwise difficult to

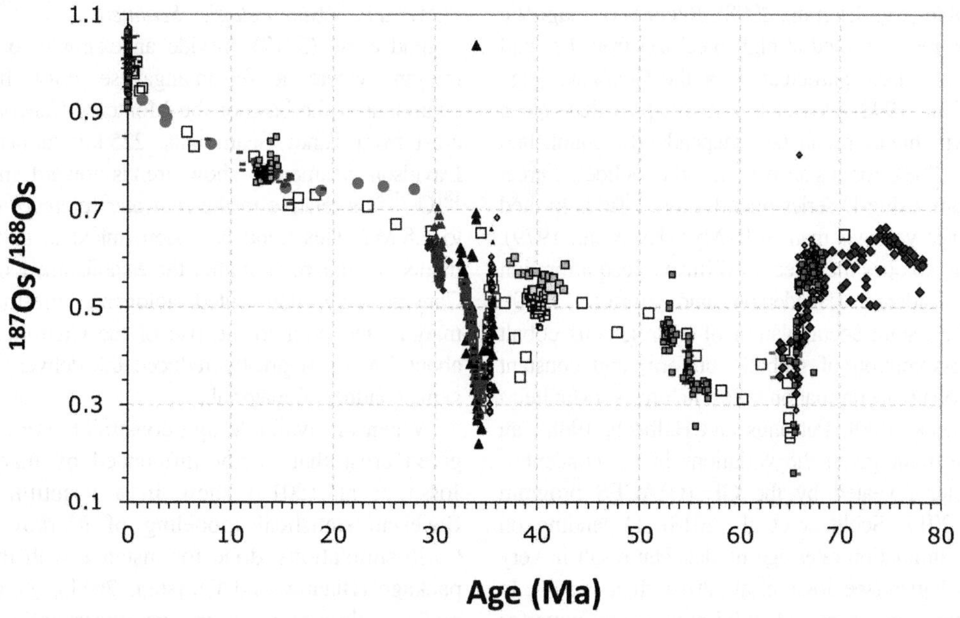

FIGURE 8.2 Compilation of published "best" $^{187}Os/^{188}Os$ data for paleoseawater. Data sources: Ravizza and Turekian (1992); Ravizza (1993); Oxburgh (1998); Reusch et al. (1998); Pegram and Turekian (1999); Peucker-Ehrenbrink and Ravizza (2000b); Ravizza et al. (2001); Ravizza and Peucker-Ehrenbrink (2003); Dalai et al. (2005); Dalai and Ravizza (2006); Oxburgh et al. (2007); Paquay et al. (2008); Robinson et al. (2009); Ravizza and VonderHaar (2012); Peucker-Ehrenbrink and Ravizza (unpublished, see Peucker-Ehrenbrink and Ravizza, 2012); Ravizza et al. (unpublished, see Peucker-Ehrenbrink and Ravizza, 2012); van der Ploeg et al. (2018). See Peucker-Ehrenbrink and Ravizza, GTS2012, for comparison. Note that only samples with seawater $^{187}Os/^{188}Os$ and age rather than depth assignments have been plotted.

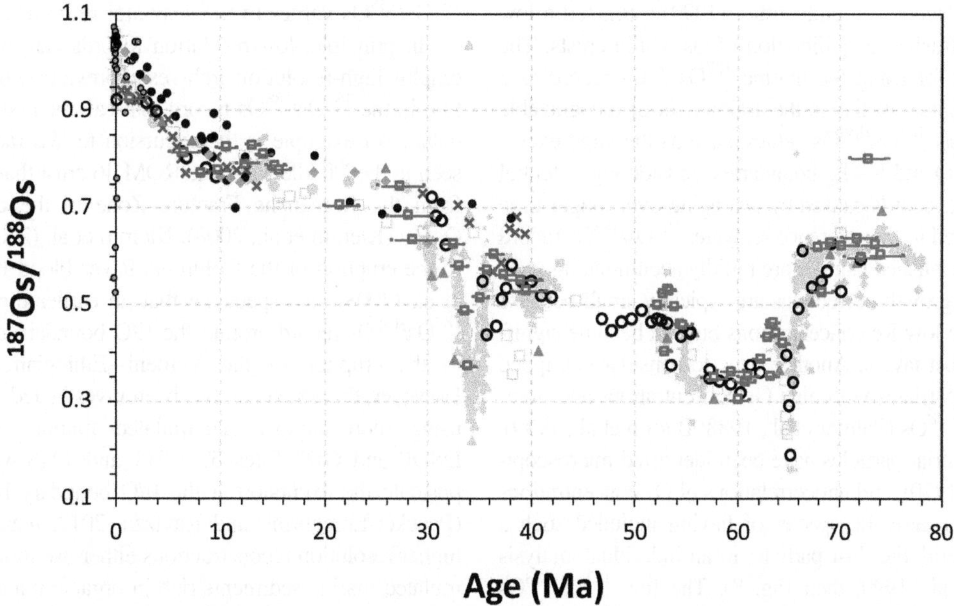

FIGURE 8.3 Compilation of $^{187}Os/^{188}Os$ data for paleoseawater as reconstructed from hydrogenous Fe–Mn crusts. Data shown in Fig. 8.2 are underlain in gray for comparison. Symbols: small black circles with gray fill (Burton et al., 1999, various ocean basins); large circles with black rim (Klemm et al., 2005, central Pacific); small solidly black circles (Klemm et al., 2008, central Atlantic); orange triangles (Li et al., 2008, central Pacific, ages are adjusted to growth hiatuses as shown in their Fig. 4); blue crosses (Meng et al., 2008, central Pacific); green diamonds (Goto et al., 2017, southwestern Atlantic); red open squares with age uncertainties (Josso et al., 2019, eastern central Atlantic). Note that portions of the Paleocene record are currently better characterized by ferromanganese crust data than by more rapidly accumulated sediments.

date. Maximum ages for crusts are given by the substrate age, provided this is accurately known. This age sets the lower bound on chemostratigraphic markers that can be used as tie points for matching the crust record with the marine reference record. The condensed nature of such records makes biostratigraphic approaches based on micro/nannofossils challenging but not impossible (e.g., Li et al., 2008). Records of magnetic reversals can be reconstructed at high precision from Fe- and Ti-rich phases in crusts, particularly for the Cenozoic (e.g., Joshima and Usui, 1998; Oda et al., 2016), provided that a record of growth hiatuses can be independently established (e.g., Li et al., 2008), for instance with radionuclides. Direct radiometric dating using U-series nuclides and ^{10}Be is limited to layers of crusts younger than ~10 Myr (Ku et al., 1979), and for uranium isotopes the effect of diffusive reequilibration has to be considered (Henderson and Burton, 1999). Application of constant accumulation of hydrogenous cobalt relies on the assumption of globally uniform and constant hydrogenous cobalt accumulation rates in crusts (Manheim and Lane-Bostwick, 1988; Puteanus and Halbach, 1988), an astonishing constraint given the variations in Co concentrations in seawater revealed by the GEOTRACES program (Noble et al., 2017; Schlitzer et al., 2018). Depending on assumed Co-accumulation rates age models can result in very different chronologies (see Josso et al., 2019, their Fig. 4). In addition, Co-chronometers provide minimum age estimates as these models cannot quantify growth hiatuses and erosional periods; those have to be established independently. Application of Sr isotope stratigraphy by means of Sr-rich phases in crusts is limited by the availability of such phases.

Osmium isotope chemostratigraphy enriches the tool kit available to date hydrogenous ferromanganese crusts, and it is reassuring that Henderson and Burton (1999) estimated a low potential for diffusive reequilibration of Os within crusts. The main challenge for using the marine $^{187}Os/^{188}Os$ record as a chemostratigraphic tool lies in the assignment of recognizable tie points in crust $^{187}Os/^{188}Os$ values, such as the large excursions at the E−O and K−Pg boundaries, considering potential aliasing of crust records caused by averaging over longer time periods compared to the reference seawater $^{187}Os/^{188}Os$ record that is being established using more rapidly accumulating sediments. ^{187}Re ingrowth corrections are typically small because oxic crusts have low Re concentrations but can become significant for old crust layers. Another issue to consider is trapped extraterrestrial particles with high Os concentrations and unradiogenic $^{187}Os/^{188}Os$ (Palmer et al., 1988; Burton et al., 1999). Such extraterrestrial particles have been identified microscopically (Jedwab, 1970), and anticorrelations of Os concentrations and $^{187}Os/^{188}Os$ raise the specter of having included such a particle, or a peridotite dust particle, in an individual analysis (see Burton et al., 1999, their Fig. 8). The few $^{187}Os/^{188}Os$ values for recent crust surfaces shown in Fig. 8.3 that plot significantly below the seawater reference curve likely represent such unradiogenic inclusions.

It is important to emphasize that ferromanganese crust records, analogous to sedimentary records (e.g., McArthur et al., 2008; Porter et al., 2014; Kuroda et al., 2015; Slack et al., 2015; Marquez et al., 2017; Rooney et al., 2018), may not record fully marine conditions in marginal seas and along ocean margins (see also discussion in Section 8.7: *Higher Resolution $^{187}Os/^{188}Os$ Phanerozoic Records* and *Integrating ORM and Oxic Pelagic Sediment $^{187}Os/^{188}Os$ Records*). Conrad et al. (2017) provide an example for the California margin, where a ferromanganese crust from Davidson Seamount at the base of the Monterey Canyon system and a crust from Taney Seamounts, 225 km farther seaward than Davidson Seamount, show trends toward more radiogenic $^{187}Os/^{188}Os$ relative to the seawater reference curve from 4.5 to 6.8 Ma. This trend has been linked to stronger terrestrial inputs into this margin after the establishment of the Monterey Canyon system that routed radiogenic terrestrial debris to the margin, and prior to the rise of the California Coast Range about 5 Ma that greatly reduced the delivery of such radiogenic continental material.

When all available age constraints are combined for a given crust that is not influenced by margin processes, Josso et al. (2019) show in a beautiful example that Bayesian statistical modeling of Markov Chain Monte Carlo simulations, done for instance with the "rBacon" R package (Blaauw and Christen, 2011), yields a best constrained chronology with age uncertainties for an up to 77 Myr old ferromanganese crust from Tropic Seamount in the eastern Atlantic Ocean. This approach represents a significant advancement in establishing more reliable chronologies with age uncertainties for ferromanganese crusts (red squares in Fig. 8.3) compared to previous approaches that used less quantitative approaches for matching crust $^{187}Os/^{188}Os$ values to the seawater reference curve.

In principle, low-resolution records can guide those who employ high-resolution archives to previously unidentified feature in the $^{187}Os/^{188}Os$ record that can then be investigated in detail. An example is the excursion to less radiogenic values seen in the Middle Miocene ROM 46 crust that was recovered from the Romanche Fracture Zone in the central Atlantic Ocean (Klemm et al., 2008). Klemm et al. (2008) link this dip to the eruption of the Columbia River Flood Basalts. Klemm et al. (2008) also speculate that an earlier dip in the marine $^{187}Os/^{188}Os$ record around the E/O boundary could be linked to the eruption of the Yemeni−Ethiopian Flood Basalts. However, this excursion has been investigated in greater detail using more rapidly accumulated marine sediments from DSDP and ODP Sites 522, 711 and 1218 A and shown to postdate the excursion at the E/O boundary by about 5 Myr (Peucker-Ehrenbrink and Ravizza, 2012, their Fig. 6). Such higher resolution reconstructions either use more rapidly accumulated marine sediments rich in organic matter or oxic sediments with low Re but elevated Os concentrations. Those archives are discussed in Section 8.4.

8.4 Organic-rich mudrock

Many recent articles on the Re−Os system contribute to the reconstruction of the marine $^{187}Os/^{188}Os$ record, especially studies of ORM. These new data and their contribution to our understanding of the marine $^{187}Os/^{188}Os$ record are the focus of this portion of our review. Early work reconstructing $^{187}Os/^{188}Os$ variations of ancient seawater concentrated on Cenozoic pelagic sediments with low Re/Os ratios. Although the potential for using Re–Os data from ORM to reconstruct past variations in seawater $^{187}Os/^{188}Os$ was recognized early on in the study of the marine Os isotope record (Ravizza and Turekian, 1992), several years passed until a Re–Os study of Jurassic ORM (Cohen et al., 1999) demonstrated this approach. Progress in Re–Os ORM research accelerated after Selby and Creaser (2003) presented evidence that Cr(VI)/H_2SO_4 digestion allowed preferential dissolution of authigenic phases, minimizing dissolution of Re and Os from detrital phases. Two decades and dozens of Re–Os isochrons later, nearly all of what we know about the pre-Cenozoic marine Os isotope record is derived from analyses of ORM (Tables 8.1 and 8.2).

Knowledge gained from high temporal resolution, multisite studies of Cenozoic and late Cretaceous marine Os isotope record can inform the interpretation of the rapidly growing data base of initial $^{187}Os/^{188}Os$ ratios, $(^{187}Os/^{188}Os)_0$, determined from analyses of older Mesozoic to Archean ORM. Emerging evidence of secular (long-term) variation in seawater $^{187}Os/^{188}Os$ must be considered in the context of potential geographic variations in seawater $^{187}Os/^{188}Os$ at a given point in time (Poirier and Hillaire-Marcel, 2011; Paquay and Ravizza, 2012; Dickson et al., 2015; Du Vivier et al., 2015; Conrad et al., 2017). Potential challenges posed by temporal aliasing of records also must be considered. Due to the short marine residence time of Os (e.g., Peucker-Ehrenbrink and Ravizza, 1996; Levasseur et al., 1998; Oxburgh, 1998; Oxburgh et al., 2007), $^{187}Os/^{188}Os$ variation can occur on a time/length scale that is short compared to the uncertainties in correlating geographically separated records.

In all efforts to reconstruct the marine $^{187}Os/^{188}Os$ record, there is either an explicit or implicit assumption that $(^{187}Os/^{188}Os)_0$ reflects the Os isotope composition of the waters from which the sediment accumulated. For ORM it has become generally accepted that higher levels of common Os, typically monitored as ^{192}Os or ^{188}Os concentrations, are indicative of greater authigenic Os enrichment, and thus a greater likelihood that nonhydrogenous sources of Os are insignificant. Nevertheless in ORM studies the concern persists that measured $^{187}Os/^{188}Os$ of some samples result from admixtures of hydrogenous/authigenic (seawater-derived) and lithogenic (associated with detrital minerals) Os (Cohen et al., 1999). This concern is particularly important when concentrations of common Os in the ORM under investigation are low enough to approach average crustal concentrations. Efforts to compare results using different Carius tube digestion methods (inverse aqua regia and Cr(VI)/H_2SO_4) are ongoing and become increasingly important as work extends to sediments with low total Re and Os concentrations (Rooney et al., 2011; Kendall et al., 2013) as these are relevant to concerns about partial dissolution of lithogenic phases.

8.5 Re–Os isochrons and $(^{187}Os/^{188}Os)_0$ profiles

Efforts to reconstruct the marine Os isotope record can be divided into two approaches, an isochron approach and a profiling approach (Fig. 8.4). The "isochron" approach involves analyses of closely associated samples to obtain both the time of sediment deposition from the slope of the regression line and $(^{187}Os/^{188}Os)_0$, the *y*-intercept. This approach is elegant, simultaneously providing these two key pieces of information needed to reconstruct the marine Os isotope record. In contrast, the profiling approach requires that age assignments for each sample be based upon an independent age model. Each analysis yields an individual estimate of seawater $^{187}Os/^{188}Os$ at a particular point in time at the site of sediment deposition. Calculation of $(^{187}Os/^{188}Os)_0$ is accomplished using measured $^{187}Re/^{188}Os$ and $^{187}Os/^{188}Os$, with the known age, to correct for in situ decay of ^{187}Re to ^{187}Os, assuming closed system with respect to both elements (Herr et al., 1961; Hirt et al., 1963; Allègre and Luck, 1980). This makes the profiling approach less labor intensive than the isochron approach and, therefore, better suited to high-resolution studies. Though the earliest profiling studies concentrated on oxic sediments in which corrections for in situ ^{187}Re decay were negligible (Pegram et al., 1992; Ravizza, 1993), later work extended this approach to ORM. Early work by Cohen et al. (1999) validated the profiling approach in ORM, integrating multiple individual isochrons with a profile extending from the Triassic–Jurassic boundary well into the Jurassic.

To date there has been tendency for the profiling and isochron approaches to be applied in different parts of the geologic record. The profile method is mainly applied to sediment sequences with good stratigraphic control and a robust age model. The isochron approach is well suited for application to older ORM where age control is poor to absent. As a result most profile studies are conducted in sediments deposited during the Cenozoic to late Cretaceous or across period boundaries where biostratigraphy and/or isotope stratigraphy provide good stratigraphic control and the ability to globally correlate sediment sequences (see next). In contrast, the Re–Os isochron approach has found wider application further back in geologic time, contributing to our knowledge of the accumulation of O_2 in the Earth's atmosphere and oceans (Hannah et al., 2004; Kendall et al., 2015) and the timing of late Proterozoic glaciations (Kendall et al., 2004; Rooney et al., 2015). In addition, the importance of ORM as petroleum source rocks has motived Re–Os studies of some Phanerozoic ORM sequences.

Although the profiling approach should be applicable to sediments throughout the geologic record, applying this approach to very old sediments requires special care. First, care must be taken to propagate errors because

TABLE 8.1 Initial $^{187}Os/^{188}Os$ values from Re–Os organic-rich mudrock isochrons in the order of increasing age plotted in Fig. 8.5.

1st author	Year published	Age (Ma)	Age uncertainty	Initial $^{187}Os/^{188}Os$	Uncertainty
Poirier	2011	36.2	2.2	0.592	0.087
Poirier	2011	36.64	0.74	1.194	0.048
Dickson	2015	53.4	2.5	0.357	0.039
Dickson	2015	55	1.6	0.359	0.007
Selby	2009	91.5	8.6	0.33	0.02
Selby	2009	108.9	6.2	0.68	0.01
Selby	2007	154.1	2.1	0.53	0.02
Cohen	1999	155	4.3	0.59	0.07
Cohen	2004	178.2	5.6	0.4	0.15
Cohen	1999	181	13	0.8	0.07
Cohen	1999	207	12	0.15	0.16
Xu	2014	236.5	3.6	0.732	0.041
Xu	2014	236.61	0.8	0.73	0.003
Xu	2014	237.55	0.8	0.659	0.006
Xu	2014	238.41	1.5	0.791	0.008
Xu	2009	239.3	2.7	0.69	0.02
Xu	2009	241.2	2.2	0.831	0.025
Georgiev	2011	252.1	2.2	0.62	0.11
Georgiev	2011	252.2	1.7	0.56	0.12
Georgiev	2011	252.5	1.3	0.57	0.04
Georgiev	2011	252.9	0.9	0.62	0.04
Tripathy	2015	317	2	0.55	0.02
Turgeon	2007	357	23	0.49	0.24
Harris	2013	357.9	5.3	0.47	0.07
Selby	2005	361.3	2.4	0.42	0.01
Harris	2013	364	13	0.69	0.25
Turgeon	2007	367.7	2.5	0.45	0.02
Harris	2013	371.5	5.8	0.4	0.06
Turgeon	2007	374.2	4	0.47	0.04
Harris	2013	379	7.1	0.29	0.03
Widom	2004	443	34	0.53	0.04
Tripathy	2014	484	16	0.74	0.05
Jiang	2007	535	11	0.8	0.04
Singh	1999	535	11	1.18	0.024
Kendall	2009	543	24	1.26	0.22
Zhu	2013	591.1	5.2	0.874	0.038
Zhu	2013	592	68	0.534	0.057
Kendall	2004	607.8	4.7	0.63	0.03

(Continued)

TABLE 8.1 (Continued)

1st author	Year published	Age (Ma)	Age uncertainty	Initial $^{187}Os/^{188}Os$	Uncertainty
Rooney	2015	632.3	5.9	1.21	0.04
Kendall	2009	640	4.7	1	0.05
Kendall	2006	643	2.4	0.95	0.01
Kendall	2006	657	5.4	0.82	0.03
Rooney	2015	659	4.5	0.6	0.01
Rooney	2011	659.6	9.6	1.04	0.03
Rooney	2011	662.4	3.9	0.54	0.01
Rooney	2015	727.3	4.9	0.35	0.03
Rooney	2011	732.2	3.9	0.15	0.002
Strauss	2014	739.9	6.1	0.61	0.01
Rooney	2015	752.7	5.5	0.33	0.03
van Acken	2013	761	41	0.63	0.05
van Acken	2013	848	49	0.68	0.14
van Acken	2013	892	13	0.64	0.31
Azmay	2008	993	46	0.75	0.16
Bertoni	2014	1002	45	0.252	0.036
Cumming	2013	1054	52	0.81	0.28
Cumming	2013	1078	24	0.49	0.13
Rooney	2010	1105	37	0.31	0.34
Rooney	2010	1107	12	0.28	0.13
Rooney	2010	1109	22	0.31	0.28
Geboy	2013	1112	50	0.51	0.16
Tripathy	2015	1210	52	0.56	0.29
Kendall	2009	1316	21	0.29	0.18
Geboy	2013	1354	88	0.13	0.34
Sperling	2014	1414	40	0.201	0.06
Kendall	2009	1417	29	0.06	0.22
Sperling	2014	1427	43	0.121	0.09
Liu	2016	1447	42	0.93	0.14
Creaser	2007	1541	13	0.51	0.03
Hannah	2004	2316	4.3	0.112	0.0012
Goto	2013	2396	160	0.25	0.42
Kendall	2013	2479	20	0.12	0.01
Kendall	2015	2495	14	0.34	0.19
Kendall	2015	2495	20	0.06	0.09
Yang	2009	2684	16	0.29	0.2
Yang	2009	2695	14	0.15	0.16
Cabral	2013	2710	38	−0.37	0.4

Full publication details are in the References (this chapter). See also supplemental data in Lu et al. (2017).

corrections for in situ production of ^{187}Os can be large depending upon sample ^{187}Re/^{188}Os ratio and age. Fig. 8.4 (Bottom diagram) (sample 4) illustrates the error amplification associated with subtraction of radiogenic Os (^{187}Os*) for a 252 Ma sample with ^{187}Re/^{188}Os of 1750 ± 175 (10% uncertainty). In addition, uncertainties associated with age models are rarely accounted for in error propagation when calculating (^{187}Os/^{188}Os)$_0$. For the Cenozoic and late Cretaceous where calibration of the Geologic Time Scale is quite accurate, the likelihood of significant systematic errors in (^{187}Os/^{188}Os)$_0$ is small. In contrast, the potential for systematic errors in (^{187}Os/^{188}Os)$_0$ due to potential inaccuracy in time scale calibration deserves careful attention when using a profiling approach to reconstruct (^{187}Os/^{188}Os)$_0$ in Paleozoic and Precambrian ORM. Fig. 8.4 (Bottom diagram) (sample 3a–e) illustrates how the isochron and profiling approaches can yield inconsistent results. In this hypothetical example the mismatch between the Re–Os age and the independent age model is set to be small (≈0.2 Myr) for convenience in plotting. In practice, such close age agreement between the two ages is improbable. In older rocks, even quite precise Re–Os ages have an age uncertainty that typically spans the duration of most high-resolution profiles; in the case of Fig. 8.4 where the samples have a nominal age of 252 Ma, an age uncertainty of 0.24% spans the entire 600 kyr duration shown in Fig. 8.4 (Bottom diagram). At this point in time, there are relatively few Re–Os studies that combine both the profiling and the isochron approaches; but in those studies, independent ages control rather than Re–Os isochron ages are typically used when rendering (^{187}Os/^{188}Os)$_0$ profiles.

8.6 Pre-Phanerozoic changes in seawater ^{187}Os/^{188}Os

A compiled record of ^{187}Os/^{188}Os initial ratios from 74 ORM Re–Os isochrons (Fig. 8.5) is suggestive of significant secular changes over the past 2.7 billion years (see also Lu et al., 2017). Although the primary motivation for this type of work is geochronology, interest in initial ^{187}Os/^{188}Os variations as record of ancient seawater chemistry grows as

TABLE 8.2 Osmium isotope records spanning selected geologic events; data sources are listed below.

Event/Boundary	Approximate Age (Ma)	Duration of Os composite record (Myr)	Range in ^{187}Os/^{188}Os[a]	Number of records[b]
Ordovician/Silurian	444	≈1.5	0.28–1.08	1
Permo–Triassic	252	<2	0.20–0.62	1
Triassic–Jurassic	202	≈12	0.12–0.74	2
Toarcian OAE	183	≈3	0.28–1.0	2
OAE 1a	120	≈3	0.15–0.87	3
OAE 2	95	≈2.5	0.12–1.00	8
PETM	56	≈0.5	0.23–0.78	7

[a] *Given range in ^{187}Os/^{188}Os ignores reported initial ratios below the present-day chondrite value.*
[b] *The number of different locations (outcrops and/or cores) included in composites records.*
Source: Refs.: Finlay et al., 2010; Georgiev et al., 2015; Schoepfer et al., 2013; Cohen and Coe, 2002; Kuroda et al., 2010; Cohen et al., 2004; Percival et al., 2016; Bottini et al., 2012; Tejada et al., 2009; Turgeon and Creaser, 2008; Du Vivier et al., 2014, 2015; Ravizza et al., 2001; Schmitz et al., 2004; Wieczorek et al., 2013; Dickson et al., 2015.

FIGURE 8.4 (Top diagram) Illustration of a hypothetical ORM section sampled for both Re–Os geochronology and reconstruction temporal changes in seawater Os isotope composition. Samples 1–4 are spaced "widely," to monitor changes in (^{187}Os/^{188}Os)$_0$ over time. At one depth multiple samples (3a—e) are taken in close spatial proximity with the expectation of homogeneous (^{187}Os/^{188}Os)$_0$, making the sample suite potentially suitable for construction of a Re–Os isochron. (Middle diagram) Measured ^{187}Re/^{188}Os and ^{187}Os/^{188}Os of samples 3a-e yield a Re–Os isochron, providing independent estimates of both the time of sediment deposition and (^{187}Os/^{188}Os)$_0$. In contrast, (^{187}Os/^{188}Os)$_0$ of samples 1, 2, and 4 can only be calculated based on ages derived from a separate age model [see datums in the top diagram]. (Bottom diagram) Schematic plot of (^{187}Os/^{188}Os)$_0$ versus age derived from the graph above. The isochron result displays uncertainties based upon the goodness of fit of sample 3a-e to the regression line. The double-sided arrow indicates that isochron age uncertainty would likely be much larger than the time interval spanned by samples 1–4, and the absolute age from the isochron need not conform to the age model used in the profile approach. For samples 1, 2, and 4, and 3a-e "profiling" (^{187}Os/^{188}Os)$_0$ uncertainty is based upon propagating the uncertainty associated with the subtraction of ^{187}Os produced by in situ ^{187}Re decay, but age uncertainties are not typically included. See text for additional discussion. Although, this figure is schematic, the Permo–Triassic (absolute age ≈252 Ma) results of Georgiev et al. (2011; 2015) guided the construction of the plots.

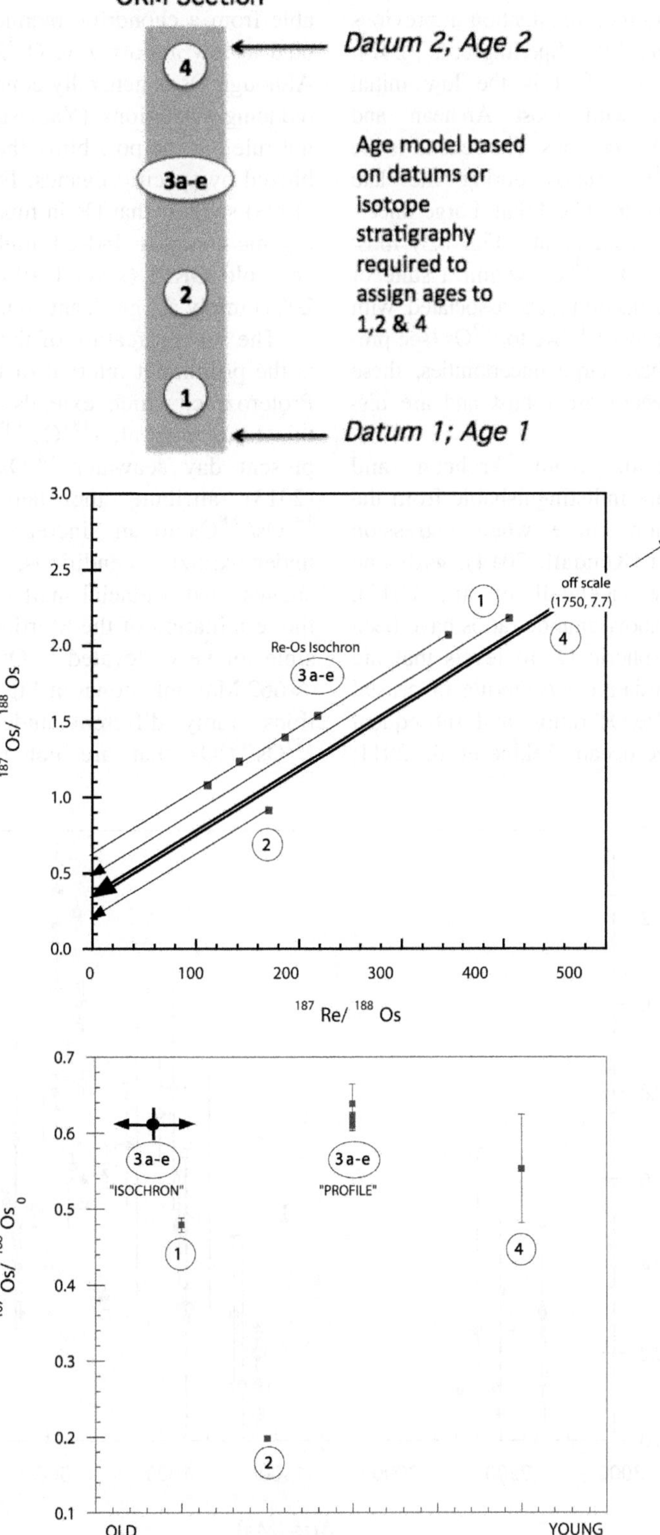
ORM Section
4
3a-e
2
1
Datum 2; Age 2
Datum 1; Age 1
Age model based on datums or isotope stratigraphy required to assign ages to 1,2 & 4
Re-Os Isochron
3a-e
off scale (1750, 7.7)
1
4
2
$^{187}Os/^{188}Os$
$^{187}Re/^{188}Os$
3a-e
"ISOCHRON"
3a-e
"PROFILE"
1
2
4
$^{187}Os/^{188}Os_0$
OLD
YOUNG
Time ≈ 600 kyr

more data become available. Two major features in the pre-Phanerozoic $^{187}Os/^{188}Os$ record receive attention in previous compilations (van Acken et al., 2013; Sperling et al., 2014; Tripathy and Singh, 2015). The first is the low initial $^{187}Os/^{188}Os$ ratio associated with most Archean and Paleoproterozoic ORM Re–Os isochrons. The second is the apparent peak in $^{187}Os/^{188}Os$ ratios during the late Proterozoic, which extends into the Cambrian. Large uncertainties associated with many data points (Fig. 8.5) most commonly result from large $^{187}Re/^{188}Os$ within a suite of samples and the unavoidable uncertainties associated with large corrections for in situ decay of ^{187}Re to ^{187}Os (see previous section). In spite of these large uncertainties, these two major features of the record are robust and are discussed further next.

Initial $^{187}Os/^{188}Os$ ratios from Archean and Paleoproterozoic isochrons are indistinguishable from the $^{187}Os/^{188}Os$ mantle evolution curve when regression uncertainties are considered (Kendall, 2014), with one notable exception to date (Kendall et al., 2015). Deviations to $(^{187}Os/^{188}Os)_0$ above mantle ratios have been attributed to a rise of atmospheric O_2 to levels that are high enough to allow for oxidative weathering of crustal sulfide minerals with high Re/Os ratios, and subsequent transport of soluble Os to the ocean (Sekine et al., 2011; Kendall et al., 2015), while $(^{187}Os/^{188}Os)_0$ indistinguishable from a chondritic mantle evolution curve are attributed to low atmospheric O_2 levels (Hannah et al., 2004). Although Os is generally considered to be insoluble under reducing conditions (Yamashita et al., 2007), this does not rule out the possibility that reduced Os could be solubilized by specific ligands. For example, Levasseur et al. (1998) suggest that Os in modern seawater is stable as an organic complex. Indeed, high Os concentrations in some very old ORM (several 100 pg/g ^{188}Os: Hannah et al., 2004) imply a significant source of authigenic Os.

The second feature of the pre-Phanerozoic Os record is the prominent interval of high $^{187}Os/^{188}Os$ in the late Proterozoic, which extends into the Cambrian. During this time interval, $(^{187}Os/^{188}Os)_0$ of ORM can exceed present day seawater $^{187}Os/^{188}Os$. Van Acken et al. (2013) attribute the late Proterozoic increase in $^{187}Os/^{188}Os$ to an "increase in continental weathering under oxidizing conditions," while Rooney et al. (2014) suggest that a glacial melt water plume associated with the termination of the Sturtian glaciation may be responsible for very elevated $^{187}Os/^{188}Os$ ratios (up to 1.44 at $\approx$662 Ma; not shown in Fig. 8.5). These two interpretations imply different underlying causes of elevated $^{187}Os/^{188}Os$ that are not mutually exclusive. Rising

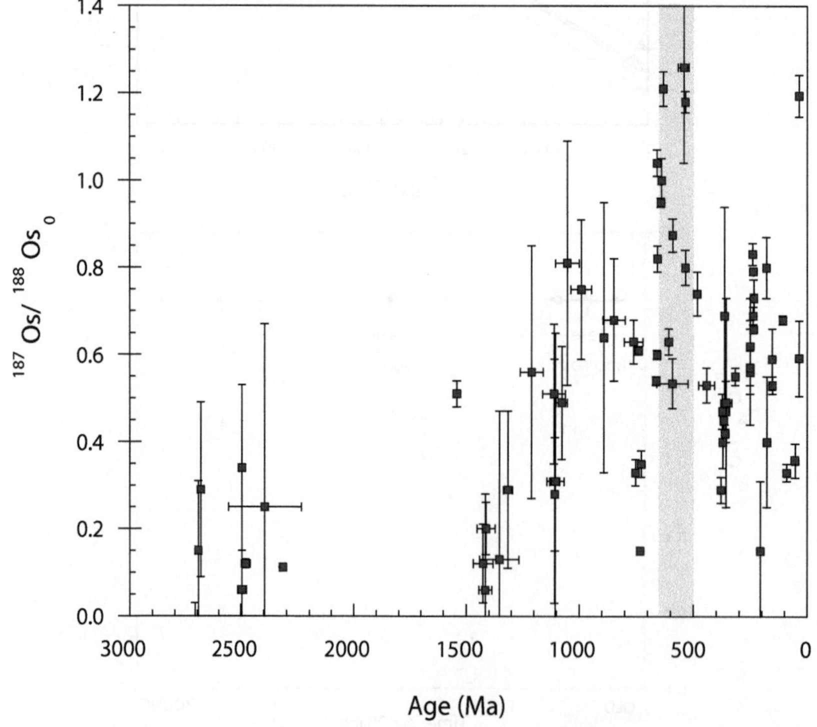

FIGURE 8.5 Compilation of $(^{187}Os/^{188}Os)_0$ and associated ages from published ORM Re–Os isochrons. (See Table 8.1 for data sources). Nearly all samples more than 2 billion years old have $(^{187}Os/^{188}Os)_0$ that is within uncertainty of the mantle evolution curve. The shaded band marks an apparent interval of unusually high $(^{187}Os/^{188}Os)_0$ in the late Proterozoic to the Cambrian. Note that the typical age spacing between data points is many times larger than the "present-day" marine residence time of Os ($\approx 4 \times 10^4$ years). Inferring long-term trends requires caution because of aliasing caused by under sampling of potential high-frequency $(^{187}Os/^{188}Os)_0$ variations.

levels of atmospheric oxygen in the late Proterozoic (Lyons et al., 2014) may allow more complete oxidative weathering of old crustal rocks (Tripathy and Singh, 2015), regardless of glaciation. Alternatively, enhanced physical weathering associated with glaciation may account for elevated $^{187}Os/^{188}Os$ without any need to invoke enhanced oxidation (Peucker-Ehrenbrink and Blum, 1998). Broadly similar Sr and Os isotope variation in the aftermath of the Sturtian glaciation (Rooney et al., 2014) support this later possibility. While the available data do not allow this matter to be resolved, they do provide the basis for formulating testable hypotheses to motivate higher resolution work. Indeed, Sperling et al. (2014) have cautioned against over interpreting a sparse data set.

Occasionally a "profiling approach" (see previous section) has been applied to pre-Phanerozoic rocks; in one case to investigate the oxidative weathering during deglaciation in the Paleoproterozoic (Sekine et al., 2011), and in two others to the late Proterozoic glaciations (Rooney et al., 2015; Peucker-Ehrenbrink et al., 2016). These studies reveal transient deglacial excursions to high $^{187}Os/^{188}Os$ from much lower ratios in sediments likely dominated by hydrogenous (water-derived) Os. The difficulties with globally correlating Precambrian sediment records on these short time scales make this type of Os isotope "event" stratigraphy extremely challenging. However, as outlined next, the Phanerozoic $^{187}Os/^{188}Os$ record reveals numerous examples confirming large amplitude fluctuations in $^{187}Os/^{188}Os$ over short time scales, indicating that caution should be exercised when interpreting low-resolution composite record like the one shown in Fig. 8.5.

8.7 Higher resolution $^{187}Os/^{188}Os$ Phanerozoic records

Working with benefit of biostratigraphic age control and, in some instances, stable isotope stratigraphy, profiles of initial $^{187}Os/^{188}Os$ variations across numerous period and stage boundaries have been derived from Re–Os analyses of ORM (Fig. 8.6). The large and rapid $^{187}Os/^{188}Os$ ratio variations across these boundaries are similar in character to those documented in studies of oxic pelagic sediments across the Eocene–Oligocene transition (Paquay et al., 2014 and reference therein), the Cretaceous–Paleogene boundary (Robinson et al., 2009; Ravizza and VonderHaar, 2012), and the Paleocene–Eocene boundary (Ravizza et al., 2001). Significant variations in the marine $^{187}Os/^{188}Os$ on short time scales that are globally distributed are consistent with a marine residence time on the order of 10^4 years and longer than the mixing time of the global ocean (see earlier).

Not all the profile studies indicated by vertical bars in Fig. 8.6 are equally robust. Some events are extremely well characterized, while other records are best regarded as tentative. For example, Oceanic Anoxic Event (OAE) 1a (Tejada et al., 2009; Bottini et al., 2012) and OAE 2 (Turgeon and Creaser, 2008; Du Vivier et al., 2014, 2015) are characterized at multiple sites yielding globally coherent records of $(^{187}Os/^{188}Os)_0$ variation. In other cases, such as the Triassic–Jurassic boundary (Cohen and Coe, 2002; Kuroda et al., 2010), the Paleocene–Eocene Thermal Maximum (PETM: Wieczorek et al., 2013; Dickson et al., 2015), and the Toarcian OAE (Cohen et al., 2004; Percival et al., 2016), geographically separated records yield Os isotope excursions that are diachronous (Tr–J) or differ in magnitude (Toarcian and PETM). In still other instances such as the Permo–Triassic (Georgiev et al., 2015) and Ordovician–Silurian (Finlay et al., 2010) mass extinction events, records of $(^{187}Os/^{188}Os)_0$ profiles documenting excursions at these important mass extinction events are limited to results from a single sedimentary sequence. The lack of empirical stratigraphic records indicating similar $(^{187}Os/^{188}Os)_0$ variations at multiple sites imparts a significant element of uncertainty to these records. In addition, the Finlay et al. (2010) record is a good example of an instance where low common Os concentrations are correlated with low calculated $(^{187}Os/^{188}Os)_0$, raising the possibility that an unradiogenic detrital component is influencing temporal variations in $(^{187}Os/^{188}Os)_0$. Although it is impractical to discuss these various profiles in detail, we take this opportunity to highlight some features of these records that have not been given much attention in the previous publications, and to speculate about their significance.

The temporal distribution of high-resolution studies of the marine Os isotope record (Fig. 8.6) is biased because studies to date have almost exclusively concentrated on times of environmental perturbation (e.g., mass extinctions, episodes of climate change). Events such as these are obvious targets for Os isotope research because our understanding of the modern Os cycle suggests the marine Os isotope record should be sensitive to changes in riverine flux, hydrothermal activity, and the extraterrestrial influx (e.g., Levasseur et al., 1999; Sharma et al., 1999). Consequently, the marine Os isotope record has been used to infer changes in weathering fluxes (e.g., Ravizza et al., 2001; Cohen et al., 2004; Wieczorek et al., 2013), correlate episodes of basaltic volcanism with the environmental change documented in the marine sediment record (Turgeon and Creaser, 2008), and infer changes in extraterrestrial flux (Dalai et al., 2006; Paquay et al., 2014). A less obvious reason for the concentration of high-resolution Os isotope studies across period and stage boundaries is that these studies rely heavily upon the superior stratigraphic control and age models associated with these better studied intervals of geologic time. Throughout much of the sediment record correlation between widely separated sections cannot be

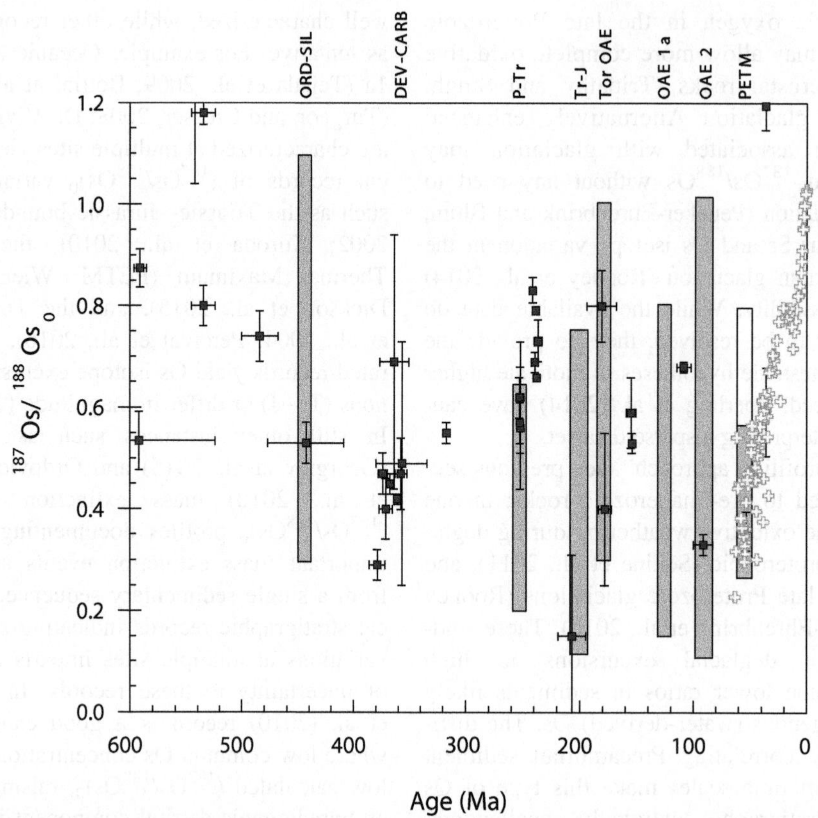

FIGURE 8.6 Expansion of Fig. 8.5 highlighting $(^{187}Os/^{188}Os)_0$ variations during the Phanerozoic. In addition to Re–Os isochron data from Fig. 8.5, this figure represents data from higher resolution ORM "profile" studies as vertical bars, and the Cenozoic D-11 Mn crust record (crosses) of Burton (2006). Note that the majority of these profile studies span period boundaries, stage boundaries, or other recognized episodes of rapid environmental change in the Earth's history. The length of each bar spans the range of $(^{187}Os/^{188}Os)_0$ reported in each study. The open bar indicates more radiogenic values from two Arctic PETM records compared to Tethyian PETM records. Table 8.2 gives sources, numeric ranges, and acronyms for higher resolution studies.

achieved with sufficient precision to confidently compare Os isotope records, unless they are extremely densely sampled. Working on sections where global correlations have already been proposed based on carbon isotope stratigraphy offers one approach to circumventing this problem for some time intervals such as the Cambrian and the early Triassic (Cramer and Jarvis, 2020, Ch.11: Carbon isotope stratigraphy, this volume).

The large amplitude, high-frequency variations revealed in high-resolution studies (Fig. 8.6) could be used to argue that trying to document and interpret secular (million to multimillion year) trends in the marine Os isotope record is a fool's errand, but this claim ignores the bias thus far for investigating Period and Stage boundaries. An alternative but equally viable interpretation is that most of geologic time is characterized by relatively gradual changes in the marine $^{187}Os/^{188}Os$ record and that Fig. 8.6 creates the illusion of extreme variability due to sampling bias. In many respects lower resolution, longer duration Os isotope studies of the Cenozoic pelagic deposits (Pegram et al., 1992; Peucker-Ehrenbrink et al., 1995; Reusch et al., 1998; Pegram and Turekian, 1999) support the notion that over long time scales clear secular trends are apparent. The D-11 Pacific Mn crust record (Burton, 2006) is used to illustrate the coherent overall Cenozoic trend of the marine Os isotope record in Fig. 8.3. In the earliest study (Pegram et al., 1992), the gradual change in $^{187}Os/^{188}Os$ manifest in the Cenozoic record, compared to more recent ORM studies (Fig. 8.6), motivated insightful interpretations that continue to garner attention today. Important examples include the role of organic matter weathering as a source of radiogenic Os to ocean (Dubin and Peucker-Ehrenbrink, 2015; Myrow et al., 2015) and ultramafic weathering as a source of unradiogenic Os to seawater (Reusch, 2011). If these slow, tectonically driven processes influence the Cenozoic Os isotope record, then they are almost certainly important in the earlier record, where they have been largely ignored. While it is premature to draw conclusions about the importance of any specific processes, it is safe to conclude that focusing exclusively on high-resolution Os isotope studies to the exclusion of longer time scale work aimed at discerning secular trends will mislead us in our efforts to identify the underlying processes responsible for variations in the marine Os isotope record.

8.8 Integrating organic-rich mudrock and oxic pelagic sediment $^{187}Os/^{188}Os$ records

Although there are only a handful of overlapping Os isotope records from ORM and oxic pelagic sediments, it is instructive to compare these records because they illustrate unavoidable challenges and new potential applications. Here we concentrate on the Eocene–Oligocene transition because it is perhaps the best characterized interval of the Cenozoic $^{187}Os/^{188}Os$ record, but it should be noted that recent work on the Middle Eocene Climatic Optimum (van der Ploeg et al., 2018) report a careful study integrating reducing ORM data with oxic pelagic sediment record (Fig. 8.2). Although the Os isotope record across this Eocene–Oligocene interval has been studied in numerous cores, we rely on the record of Paquay et al. (2014) because it integrates data from three widely separated pelagic sites, all with excellent stratigraphic control (Fig. 8.7a). Despite

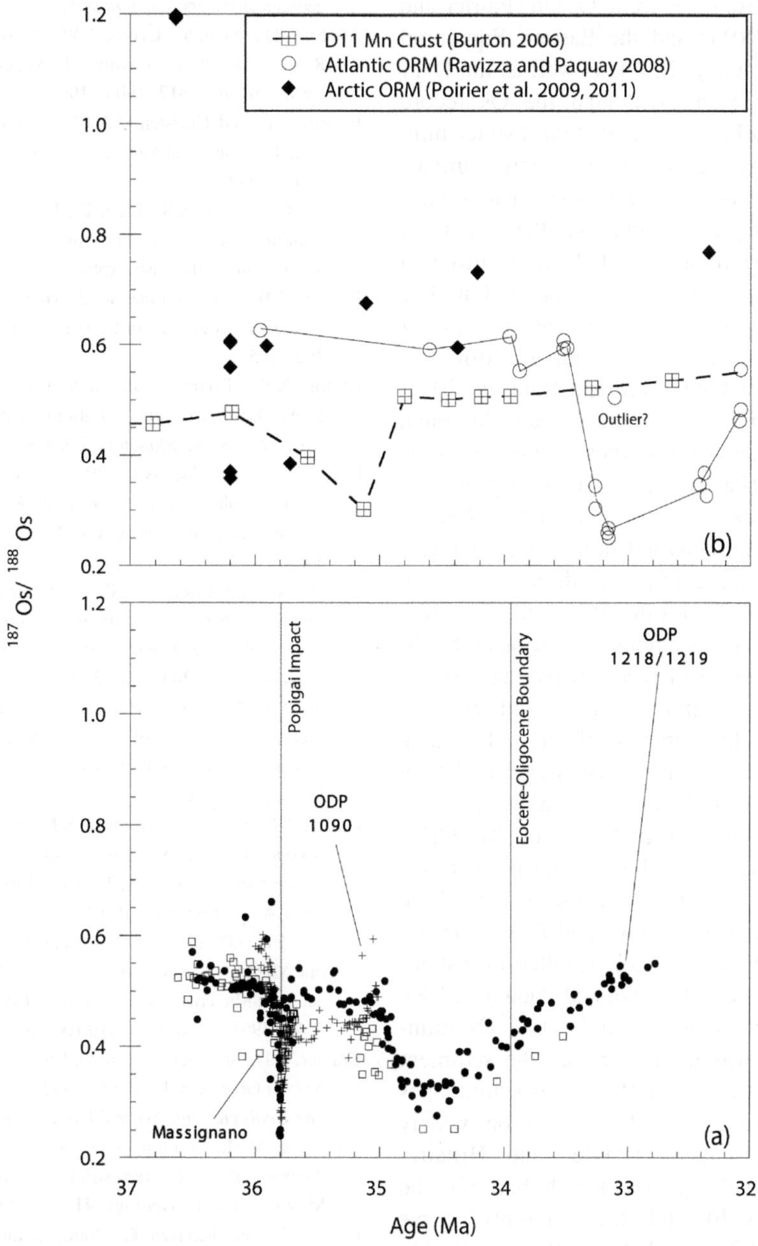

FIGURE 8.7 Late Eocene to early Oligocene marine Os isotope record, integrating data from oxic pelagic carbonate records (bottom panel a: ODP 1218/1219, ODP 1090 and Massignano: Paquay et al., 2014, and references therein), with Pacific Mn Crust, Arctic (ACEX Core) sediment data, including ORM and Atlantic ORM (ODP 959D), all in upper panel (b). The densely sampled carbonate sequences (a) provide the most highly resolve record, documenting variability that is absent from the Mn crust record. The Arctic and Atlantic ORM record are both interpreted to have captured the broad late Eocene minimum in $^{187}Os/^{188}Os$ between 34 and 35 Ma. The apparent age offset in both these ORM records illustrates the difficulty in correlating independent age models. See text for additional discussion. *ORM*, Organic-rich mudrock.

systematic offsets between the various sites the overall coherence of the various records is unambiguous. Unfortunately it remains unclear whether these systematic offsets reflect small (0.1–0.2 $^{187}Os/^{188}Os$ units) variations in seawater Os isotope composition. Alternatively, these offsets between sites could result from the variable influence of lithogenic Os on these records.

In spite of scatter discussed in the preceding paragraph, the composite pelagic carbonate $^{187}Os/^{188}Os$ record (Fig. 8.7a) serves as a valuable point of reference for interpreting ORM data from the Arctic Ocean (Poirier and Hillaire-Marcel, 2009, 2011) and the Eastern Equatorial Atlantic (Ravizza and Paquay, 2008), as well as the D-11 Pacific Mn crust (Fig. 8.7b). Although the Os record derived from pelagic carbonates shows two distinct minima, the older of the two, caused by the Popigai impact event, is extremely short-lived. Capturing such a brief excursion requires sample spacing on the order of $10^3–10^4$ years; consequently it has only been identified at these three sites and is unlikely to be captured in less densely sampled records. In contrast, the later and longer duration (>1 Myr) excursion has been identified in numerous cores (Peucker-Ehrenbrink and Ravizza, 2012) and has value as a chemostratigraphic marker. Although the cause of this excursion is not known with certainty, the most recent works (Paquay et al., 2014) suggest that erosion of ultramafic rocks (Pegram et al., 1992; Reusch, 2011) is more likely than increased influx of extraterrestrial matter (Dalai et al., 2006). All three records in Fig. 8.7b are purported to record this longer duration feature, but there are clear offsets among the various records. In the case of the Mn crust D-11 record where age assignments are based upon correlation to better dated sediment records (Burton, 2006), the apparent offset of less than 1 Myr is simply an artifact of an outdated age model. In addition, the Mn crust record fails to capture all of the fine structure represented in Fig. 8.7a. For the ORM records the offsets are larger (>1 Myr) and have different origins. In the Atlantic record ages are based on widely spaced biostratigraphic datums and linear interpolation between these datums has likely resulted in systematics errors in the age model (Ravizza and Paquay, 2008). In this case, correlation of the broad $^{187}Os/^{188}Os$ minimum between records was used to refine the sediment age model. In the Arctic record Re–Os isochron ages were used to challenge age models based on widely spaced biostratigraphic datums (Poirier and Hillaire-Marcel, 2009, 2011). Although the match between the Arctic record (Fig. 8.7b) and the reference curve (Fig. 8.7a) is poor, the difference between the two prior to ≈ 36.5 Ma is sufficiently large to infer that the Arctic Ocean was isolated from the global ocean prior to this time. In summary, these two examples of Cenozoic ORM Os isotope data demonstrate that Os isotope chemostratigraphy can be used to refine sediment age models provided a well-established reference curve is available. While similar applications may be possible in older portions of the ORM record, the arduous work of empirically determining a reference curve for the open ocean remains to be done.

Bibliography

Allègre, C.J., and Luck, J.M., 1980, Osmium isotopes as petrogenetic and geological tracers. *Earth and Planetary Science Letters*, **48**: 148–154.

Anbar, A.D., Duan, Y., Lyons, T.W., Arnold, G.L., Kendall, B., Creaser, R.A., et al., 2007, A whiff of oxygen before the Great Oxidation Event? *Science*, **317**: 1903–1906.

Blaauw, M., and Christen, J.A., 2011, Flexible paleoclimate age-depth models using an autoregressive gamma process. *Bayesian Analysis*, **6**: 457–474.

Bottini, C., Cohen, A.S., Erba, E., Jenkyns, H.C., and Coe, A.L., 2012, Osmium-isotope evidence for volcanism, weathering, and ocean mixing during the early Aptian OAE 1a. *Geology*, **40** (7): 583–586.

Burton, K.W., 2006, Global weathering variations inferred from marine radiogenic isotope records. *Journal of Geochemical Exploration*, **88**: 262–265.

Burton, K.W., Bourdon, B., Birck, J.-L., Allègre, C.J., and Hein, J.R., 1999, Osmium isotope variations in the oceans recorded by Fe-Mn crusts. *Earth and Planetary Science Letters*, **171**: 185–197.

Cohen, A.S., and Coe, A.L., 2002, New geochemical evidence for the onset of volcanism in the Central Atlantic Magmatic Province and environmental change at the Triassic-Jurassic boundary. *Geology*, **30**: 267–270.

Cohen, A., and Coe, A., 2007, The impact of the Central Atlantic Magmatic Province on climate and on the Sr- and Os-isotope evolution of seawater. *Palaeogeography, Palaeoclimatology, Palaeoecology*, **244**: 374–390.

Cohen, A.S., Coe, A.L., Bartlett, J.M., and Hawkesworth, C.J., 1999, Precise Re-Os ages of organic-rich mudrocks and the Os isotopic composition of Jurassic seawater. *Earth and Planetary Science Letters*, **167**: 159–173.

Cohen, A.S., Coe, A.L., Harding, S.M., and Schwark, L., 2004, Osmium isotope evidence for the regulation of atmospheric CO_2 by continental weathering. *Geology*, **32**: 157–160.

Conrad, T.A., Nielsen, S.G., Peucker-Ehrenbrink, B., Blusztajn, J., Winslow, D., Hein, J.R., et al., 2017, Reconstructing the evolution of the submarine Monterey Canyon system from Os, Nd, and Pb isotopes in hydrogenetic Fe-Mn crusts. *Geochemistry, Geophysics, Geosystems*, **18** (11): 3946–3963, https://doi.org/10.1002/2017GC007071.

Cramer, B.D., and Jarvis, I., 2020, Chapter 11 - Carbon isotope stratigraphy. *In* Gradstein, F.M., Ogg, J.G., Schmitz, M.D., Ogg, G.M. (eds), *The Geologic Time Scale 2020*, Elsevier Publ., **Vol. 1**, this book.

Cumming, V.M., Poulton, S.W., Rooney, A.D., and Selby, D., 2013, Anoxia in the terrestrial environment during the Late Mesoproterozoic. *Geology*, **41**: 583–586.

Dalai, T.K., and Ravizza, G., 2006, Evaluation of osmium isotopes and iridium as paleoflux tracers in pelagic carbonates. *Geochimica et Cosmochimica Acta*, **70**: 3928–3942.

Dalai, T.K., Suzuki, K., Minagawa, M., and Nozaki, Y., 2005, Variations in seawater osmium isotope composition since the last glacial maximum: a case study from the Japan Sea. *Chemical Geology*, **220**: 303–314.

Dalai, T.K., Ravizza, G.E., and Peucker-Ehrenbrink, B., 2006, The late Eocene $^{187}Os/^{188}Os$ excursion, chemostratigraphy, cosmic dust flux and the early Oligocene glaciation. *Earth and Planetary Science Letters*, **241**: 477–492.

Dickson, A.J., Cohen, A.S., Coe, A.L., Davies, M., Shcherbinina, E.A., and Gavrilov, Y.O., 2015, Evidence for weathering and volcanism during the PETM from Arctic Ocean and Peri-Tethys osmium isotope records. *Palaeogeography, Palaeoclimatology, Palaeoecology*, **438**: 300–307.

Doyle, P.S., and Riedel, W.R., 1979, Cretaceous to Neogene ichthyoliths in a giant piston core from the central North Pacific. *Micropaleontology*, **25**: 337–364.

Dubin, A., and Peucker-Ehrenbrink, B., 2015, The importance of organic-rich shales to the geochemical cycles of rhenium and osmium. *Chemical Geology*, **403**: 111–120.

Du Vivier, A.C.C., Selby, D., Sageman, B.B., Jarvis, I., Gröcke, D.R., and Voigt, S., 2014, Marine $^{187}Os/^{188}Os$ isotope stratigraphy reveals the interaction of volcanism and ocean circulation during Oceanic Anoxic Event 2. *Earth and Planetary Science Letters*, **389**: 23–33, https://doi.org/10.1016/j.epsl.2013.12.024.

Du Vivier, A.D.C., Selby, D., Condon, D.J., Takashima, R., and Nishi, H., 2015, Pacific $^{187}Os/^{188}Os$ isotope chemistry and U-Pb geochronology: synchroneity of global Os isotope change across OAE 2. *Earth and Planetary Science Letters*, **428**: 204–216, https://doi.org/10.1016/j.epsl.2015.07.020.

Finlay, A.J., Selby, D., and Gröcke, D.R., 2010, Tracking the Hirnantian glaciation using Os isotopes. *Earth and Planetary Science Letters*, **293**: 339–348.

Frank, M., O'Nions, R.K., Hein, J.R., and Banakar, V.K., 1999, 60 Myr records of major elements and Pb-Nd isotopes from hydrogenous ferromanganese crusts: reconstruction of seawater paleochemistry. *Geochimica et Cosmochimica Acta*, **63** (11–12): 1689–1708.

Fu, Y., Dong, L., Li, C., Qu, W., Pei, H., Qiao, W., et al., 2016, New Re-Os isotopic constrains on the formation of the metalliferous deposits of the Lower Cambrian Niutitang formation. *Journal of Earth Science*, **27** (2): 271–281.

Geboy, N.J., Kaufman, A.J., Walker, R.J., Misi, A., de Oliviera, T.F., Miller, K.E., et al., 2013, Re-Os age constraints and new observations of Proterozoic glacial deposits in the Vazante Group, Brazil. *Precambrian Research*, **238**: 199–213.

Geboy, N.J., Tripathy, G.R., Ruppert, L.F., Eble, C.F., Blake, B.M., Hannah, J.L., et al., 2015, Re-Os age for the Lower-Middle Pennsylvanian boundary and comparison with associated palynoflora. *International Journal of Coal Geology*, **140**: 223–230, https://doi.org/10.1016/j.coal.2015.01.002.

Geogiev, S., Stein, H.J., Hannah, J.L., Bingen, B., Weiss, H.M., and Piasecki, S., 2011, Hot acidic Late Permian seas stifle life in record time. *Earth and Planetary Science Letters*, **310** (3-4): 389–400.

Georgiev, S.V., Stein, H.J., Hannah, J.L., Henderson, C.M., and Algeo, T.J., 2015, Enhanced recycling of organic matter and Os-isotopic evidence for multiple magmatic or meteoritic inputs to the late Permian Panthalassic Ocean, Opal Creek, Canada. *Geochimica et Cosmochimica Acta*, **150**: 192–210, https://doi.org/10.1016/j.gca.2014.11.019.

Gordon, G.W., Rockman, M., Turekian, K.K., and Over, J., 2009, Osmium isotopic evidence against an impact at the Frasnian-Famennian boundary. *American Journal of Science*, **309** (5): 420–430.

Goto, K.T., Sekine, Y., Suzuki, K., Tajika, E., Senda, R., Nozaki, T., et al., 2013, Redox conditions in the atmosphere and shallow-marine environments during the first Huronian deglaciation: Insights from Os isotopes and redox-sensitive elements. *Earth and Planetary Science Letters*, **376**: 145–154.

Goto, K.T., Nozaki, T., Toyofuku, T., Augustin, A.H., Shimoda, G., Chang, Q., et al., 2017, Paleoceanographic conditions on the São Paulo Ridge, SW Atlantic Ocean, for the past 30 million years inferred from Os and Pb isotopes of a hydrogenous ferromanganese crust. *Deep Sea Research Part II: Topical Studies in Oceanography*, **146**: 82–92.

Hannah, J.L., Bekker, A., Stein, H.J., Markey, R.J., and Holland, H.D., 2004, Primitive Os and 2316 Ma age for marine shale: implications for Paleoproterozoic glacial events and the rise of atmospheric oxygen. *Earth and Planetary Science Letters*, **225**: 43–52.

Hannah, J.L., Stein, H.J., Zimmerman, A., Yang, G., Markey, R.J., and Meleshik, V.A., 2006, Precise 2004 ± 9 Ma Re Os age for Pechenga black shale: comparison of sulfides and organic material. *Geochimica et Cosmochimica Acta*, **70** (Suppl), A228.

Harris, N.B., Mnich, C.A., Selby, D., and Korn, D., 2013, Minor and trace element and Re-Os chemistry of the Upper Devonian Woodford Shale, Permian Basin, west Texas: Insights into metal abundance and basin processes. *Chemical Geology*, **365**: 76–93.

Henderson, G.M., and Burton, K.W., 1999, Using ($^{234}U/^{238}U$) to assess diffusion rates of isotope tracers in ferromanganese crusts. *Earth and Planetary Science Letters*, **170**: 169–179.

Herr, W., Hoffmeister, W., Hirt, B., Geiss, J., and Houtermans, F.G., 1961, Versuch zur Datierung von Eisenmeteoriten nach der Rhenium-Osmium Methode. *Zeitschrift fuer Naturforschung*, **16a**: 1053–1058.

Hirt, B., Herr, W., and Hoffmeister, W., 1963, *Age determinations by the rhenium-osmium method. Radioactive Dating*. (pp. 35–44). IAEA.

Horner, T.J., Williams, H.M., Hein, J.R., Saito, M.A., Burton, K.W., Halliday, A.N., et al., 2015, Persistence of deeply sourced iron in the Pacific Ocean. *Proceedings of the National Academy of Sciences of the United States*, **112** (5): 1292–1297, https://doi.org/10.1073/pnas.1420188112.

Jedwab, J., 1970, Les sphérules cosmiques dans les nodules de manganèse. *Geochimica et Cosmochimica Acta*, **34**: 447–457.

Joshima, M., and Usui, A., 1998, Magnetostratigraphy of hydrogenetic manganese crusts from northwestern Pacific seamounts. *Marine Geology*, **146**: 53–62.

Josso, P., Parkinson, I., Horstwood, M., Lusty, P., Chenery, S., and Murton, B., 2019, Improving confidence in ferromanganese crust age models: a composite geochemical approach. *Chemical Geology*, **513**: 108–119.

Kelley, K.D., Selby, D., Falck, H., and Slack, J.F., 2017, Re-Os systematics and age of pyrite associated with stratiform Zn-Pb mineralization in the Howards Pass district, Yukon and Northwest Territories, Canada. *Mineralium Deposita*, **52** (3): 317–335, https://doi.org/10.1007/s00126-016-0663-y.

Kendall, B., 2014, An osmium-based method for assessing the source of dissolved rhenium and molybdenum to Archean seawater. *Chemical Geology*, **385**: 92–103, https://doi.org/10.1016/j.chemgeo.2014.07.021.

Kendall, B., van Acken, D., and Creaser, R.A., 2013, Depositional age of the early Paleoproterozoic Klipputs Member, Nelani Formation (Ghaap Group, Transvaal Supergroup, South Africa) and implications for low-level Re-Os geochronology and Paleoproterozoic global correlations. *Precambrian Research*, **237**: 1–12.

Kendall, B.S., Creaser, R.A., Ross, G.M., and Selby, D., 2004, Constraints on the timing of Marinoan "Snowball Earth" glaciation by ^{187}Re-^{187}Os dating of a Neoproterozoic, post-glacial black shale in Western Canada. *Earth and Planetary Science Letters*, **222**: 729–740.

Kendall, B., Creaser, R.A., and Selby, D., 2006, Re-Os geochronology of post-glacial black shales in Australia: constraints on timing of "Sturtian" glaciation. *Geology*, **34**: 729–732.

Kendall, B., Creaser, R.A., Calver, C.R., Raub, T., and Evans, D.A.D., 2009a, Correlation of Sturtian diamictite successions in southern Australia and northwestern Tasmania by Re-Os black shale geochronology and the ambiguity of "Sturtian"-type diamictite-cap carbonate pairs as chronostratigraphic marker horizons. *Precambrian Research*, **172**: 301–310.

Kendall, B., Creaser, R.A., and Selby, D., 2009b, ^{187}Re-^{187}Os geochronology of Precambrian organic-rich sedimentary rocks. *Geological Society, London, Special Publications*, **326**: 85-107.

Kendall, B., Creaser, R.A., Gordon, G.W., and Anbar, A.D., 2009c, Re-Os and Mo isotope systematics of black shales from the Middle Proterozoic Velkerri and Wollogorang Formations, McArthur Basin, northern Australia. *Geochimica et Cosmochimica Acta*, **73**: 2534–2558.

Kendall, B., Creaser, R.A., Reinhard, C.T., Lyons, T.W., and Anbar, A.D. 2015. Transient episodes of mild environmental oxygenation and oxidative continental weathering during the late Archean. Science Advances **1** (10): article #e1500777: pp. 6. https://doi.org/10.1126/sciadv.1500777.

Klemm, V., Levasseur, S., Frank, M., Hein, J.R., and Halliday, A.N., 2005, Osmium isotope stratigraphy of a marine ferromanganese crust. *Earth and Planetary Science Letters*, **238**: 42–48.

Klemm, V., Frank, M., Levasseur, S., Halliday, A.N., and Hein, J.R., 2008, Seawater osmium isotope evidence for a middle Miocene flood basalt event in ferromanganese crust records. *Earth and Planetary Science Letters*, **273**: 175–183.

Ku, T.L., Omura, A., and Chen, P.S., 1979, ^{10}Be and U-series isotopes in manganese nodules from the central north Pacific. *In* Bishoff, J.L., and Piper, Z. (eds), *Marine Geology and Oceanography of the Pacific Manganese Nodule Province*. Springer, 791–814.

Kuroda, J., Hori, R.S., Suzuki, K., Gröcke, D.R., and Ohkuchi, N., 2010, Marine osmium isotope record across the Triassic-Jurassic boundary from a Pacific pelagic site. *Geology*, **38** (10): 1095–1098.

Kuroda, J., Jiménez-Espejo, F.J., Nozaki, T., Gennari, R., Lugli, S., Manzi, V., et al., 2015, Miocene to Pleistocene osmium isotopic records of the Mediterranean sediments. *Paleoceanography*, **31**: 148–166, https://doi.org/10.1002/2015PA002853.

Lee, D.-C., Halliday, A.N., Hein, J.R., Burton, K.W., Christensen, J.N., and Günther, D., 1999, Hafnium isotope stratigraphy of ferromanganese crusts. *Science*, **285**: 1052–1054.

Levasseur, S., Birck, J.-L., and Allègre, C.J., 1998, Direct measurement of femtomoles of osmium and the ^{187}Os/^{186}Os ratio in seawater. *Science*, **282**: 272–274.

Levasseur, S., Birck, J.-L., and Allègre, C.J., 1999, The osmium riverine flux and the oceanic mass balance of osmium. *Earth and Planetary Science Letters*, **174**: 7–23.

Li, J.S., Fang, N.Q., Qu, W.J., Ding, X., Gao, L.F., Wu, C.H., et al., 2008, Os isotope dating and growth hiatuses of Co-rich crust from central Pacific. *Science in China Series D: Earth Sciences*, **51**: 1452–1459.

Ling, H.F., Burton, K.W., O'Nions, R.K., Kamber, B.S., von Blanckenburg, F., Gibb, A.J., et al., 1997, Evolution of Nd and Pb isotopes in Central Pacific seawater from ferromanganese crusts. *Earth and Planetary Science Letters*, **146** (1–2): 1–12.

Liu, Y., Bagas, L., Nie, F., Jiang, S., and Li, C., 2016, Re-Os system of black schist from the Mesoproterozoic Bayan Obo Group, Central Inner Mongolia, China and its geological implications. *Lithos*, **261**: 296–306, https://doi.org/10.1016/j.lithos.2015.11.023.

Lu, X., Kendall, B., Stein, H.J., and Hannah, J.L., 2017, Temporal record of osmium concentrations and ^{187}Os/^{188}Os in organic-rich mudrocks: implications for the osmium geochemical cycle and the use of osmium as a paleoceanographic tracer. *Geochimica et Cosmochimica Acta*, **216**: 221–241, https://doi.org/10.1016/j.gca.2017.06.046.

Lyons, T.W., Reinhard, C.T., and Planavsky, N.J., 2014, The rise of oxygen in Earth's early ocean and atmosphere. *Nature*, **506**: 307–315.

Manheim, F.T., and Lane-Bostwick, C.M., 1988, Cobalt in ferromanganese crusts as a monitor of hydrothermal discharge on the Pacific sea floor. *Nature*, **335**: 59–62.

Markey, R., Stain, H., Hannah, J., Georgiev, S.V., Pedersen, J.H., and Dons, C., 2017, Re-Os identification of glide faulting and precise ages for correlation from the Upper Jurassic Hekkingen Formation, western Barents Sea. *Palaeogeography, Palaeoclimatology, Palaeoecology*, **466**, https://doi.org/10.1016/j.palaeo.2016.11.032.

Marquez, R.T.C., Tejada, M.L.G., Suzuki, K., Peleo-Alampay, A.M., Goto, K.T., Hyun, S., et al., 2017, The seawater osmium isotope record of South China Sea: implications on its history and evolution. *Marine Geology*, **394**: 98–115.

McArthur, J.M., Algeo, T.J., van de Schrootbrugge, B., Li, Q., and Howarth, R.J., 2008, Basinal restriction, black shales, Re-Os dating and the Early Toarcian (Jurassic) oceanic anoxic event. *Paleoceanography*, **23**: PA4217, https://doi.org/10.1020/2008PA001607.

McArthur, J.M., Howarth, R.J., and Shields, G.A., 2020. Chapter 7: Strontium isotope stratigraphy. *In* Gradstein, F.M., Ogg, J.G., Schmitz, M.D., and Ogg, G.M. (eds), *The Geologic Time Scale 2020*, Elsevier, Oxford, **Vol. 1**, (this book).

Meng, X.W., Liu, Y.G., Qu, W.J., and Shi, X.F., 2008, Osmium isotope of the Co-rich crust from seamount Allison, central Pacific and its use for determination of growth hiatus and growth age. *Science in China Series D: Earth Sciences*, **51**: 1446–1451.

Myrow, P.M., Hughes, N.C., Derry, L.A., McKenzie, N.R., Jiang, G., Webb, A.A.G., et al., 2015, Neogene marine isotopic evolution and the erosion of Lesser Himalayan strata: implications for Cenozoic tectonic history. *Earth and Planetary Science Letters*, **417**: 142–150.

Nielsen, S.G., Mar-Gerrison, S., Gannoun, A., LaRowe, D., Klemm, V., Halliday, A.N., et al., 2009, Thallium isotope evidence for a permanent increase in marine organic carbon export in the early Eocene. *Earth and Planetary Science Letters*, **278**: 297–307.

Nielsen, S.G., Gannoun, A., Marnham, C., Burton, K.W., Halliday, A.N., and Hein, J.R., 2011, New age for ferromanganese crust 109D-C and implications for isotopic records of lead, neodymium, hafnium, and thallium in the Pliocene Indian Ocean. *Paleoceanography*, **26**: PA2213, https://doi.org/10.1029/2010PA002003.

Noble, A.E., Ohnemus, D.C., Hawco, N.J., Lam, P.L., and Saito, M.A., 2017, Coastal sources, sinks and strong organic complexation of dissolved cobalt within the US North Atlantic GEOTRACES transect GA03. *Biogeosciences*, **14**: 2715–2739.

Oda, H., Kawai, J., Miyamoto, M., Miyagi, I., Sato, M., Noguchi, A., et al., 2016, Scanning SQUID microscope system for geological samples: system integration and initial evaluation. *Earth, Planets Space,* **68**: article number 179, pp. 19, https://doi.org/10.1186/s40623-016-0549-3.

Oxburgh, R., 1998, Variations in the osmium isotope composition of sea water over the past 200,000 years. *Earth and Planetary Science Letters*, **159**: 183–191.

Oxburgh, R., Pierson-Wickmann, A.-C., Reisberg, L., and Hemming, S., 2007, Climate-correlated variations in seawater $^{187}Os/^{188}Os$ over the past 200,000 years, evidence from the Cariaco Basin, Venezuela. *Earth and Planetary Science Letters*, **263**: 246–258, https://doi.org/10.1016/j.epsl.2007.08.033.

Palmer, M.R., Kenison Falkner, K., Turekian, K.K., and Calvert, S.E., 1988, Sources of osmium isotopes in manganese nodules. *Geochimica et Cosmochimica Acta*, **52**: 1197–1202.

Paquay, F.S., and Ravizza, G., 2012, Heterogenous seawater $^{187}Os/^{188}Os$ during the Late Pleistocene glaciations. *Earth and Planetary Science Letters*, **349-350**: 126–138, https://doi.org/10.1016/j.epsl.2012.06.051.

Paquay, F.S., Ravizza, G.E., Dalai, T.K., and Peucker-Ehrenbrink, B., 2008, Determining chondritic impactor size from the marine osmium isotope record. *Science*, **320**: 214–218.

Paquay, F.S., Ravizza, G., and Coccioni, R., 2014, The influence of extraterrestrial material on the late Eocene marine Os isotope record. *Geochimica et Cosmochimica Acta*, **144**: 238–257.

Pašava, J., Oszczepalski, S., and Du, A., 2010, Re-Os age of non-mineralized black shale from the Kupferschiefer, Poland, and implications for metal enrichment. *Mineralium Deposita*, **45** (2): 189–199.

Pegram, W.J., and Turekian, K.K., 1999, The osmium isotopic composition change of Cenozoic sea water as inferred from a deep-sea core corrected for meteoritic contributions. *Geochimica et Cosmochimica Acta*, **63**: 4053–4058.

Pegram, W.J., Krishnaswami, S., Ravizza, G.E., and Turekian, K.K., 1992, The record of sea water $^{187}Os/^{186}Os$ variations through the Cenozoic. *Earth and Planetary Science Letters*, **113**: 569–576.

Percival, L.M.E., Cohen, A.S., Davies, M.K., Dickson, A.J., Hesselbo, S.P., Jenkyns, H.C., et al., 2016, Osmium isotope evidence for two pulses of increased continental weathering linked to Early Jurassic volcanism and climate change. *Geology*, **44** (9): 759–762.

Peucker-Ehrenbrink, B., and Blum, J.D., 1998, Re-Os isotope systematics and weathering of Precambrian crustal rocks: implications for the marine Os isotope record. *Geochimica et Cosmochimica Acta*, **62**: 3193–3203.

Peucker-Ehrenbrink, B., and Ravizza, G., 1996, Continental runoff of osmium into the Baltic Sea. *Geology*, **24**: 327–330.

Peucker-Ehrenbrink, B., and Ravizza, G.E., 2000a, The marine Os isotope record. *Terra Nova*, **12**: 205–219.

Peucker-Ehrenbrink, B., and Ravizza, G.E., 2000b, The effects of sampling artifacts on cosmic dust flux estimates: a reevaluation of nonvolatile tracers (Os, Ir). *Geochimica et Cosmochimica Acta*, **64**: 1965–1970.

Peucker-Ehrenbrink, B., and Ravizza, G.E., 2012, Osmium isotope stratigraphy – chapter 8. *In* Gradstein, F.M., Ogg, J.G., Schmitz, M.D., and Ogg, G.M. (eds), *The Geologic Time Scale 2012*. Elsevier, Oxford, **Vol. 1**: 145–166, https://doi.org/10.1016/B978-0-444-59425-9.00008.1.

Peucker-Ehrenbrink, B., Ravizza, G., and Hofmann, A.W., 1995, The marine $^{187}Os/^{186}Os$ record of the past 80 million years. *Earth and Planetary Science Letters*, **130**: 155–167.

Peucker-Ehrenbrink, B., Waters, C.A., Kurz, M.D., and Hoffman, P.F., 2016, No evidence of extraterrestrial noble metal and helium anomalies at Marinoan glacial terminations. *Earth and Planetary Science Letters*, **437**: 76–88, https://doi.org/10.1016/j.epsl.2015.12.040.

Poirier, A., and Hillaire-Marcel, C., 2009, Os-isotope insights into major environmental changes of the Arctic Ocean during the Cenozoic. *Geophysical Research Letters*, **36**: L11602, https://doi.org/10.1029/2009GL037422.

Poirier, A., and Hillaire-Marcel, C., 2011, Improved Os-isotope stratigraphy of the Arctic Ocean. *Geophysical Research Letters*, **38**: L14607, https://doi.org/10.1029/2011GL047953.

Porter, S.J., 2012. *Nickel and osmium isotope and trace element geochemistry of organic-rich sedimentary rocks: The first investigation of Nd isotope systematics in marine sediments*. Ph.D. Thesis, Durham University, U.K.

Porter, S., Selby, D., Suzuki, K., and Gröcke, D., 2013, Opening of a trans-Pangaean marine corridor during the Early Jurassic: Insights from osmium isotopes across the Sinemurian-Pliensbachian GSSP, Robin Hood's bay, UK. *Palaeogeography, Palaeoclimatology, Palaeoecology*, **375**: 50–58.

Porter, S.J., Smith, P.L., Caruthers, A.H., Hou, P., Gröcke, D.R., and Selby, D., 2014, New high resolution geochemistry of Lower Jurassic marine sections in western North America: a global positive carbon isotope excursion in the Sinemurian? *Earth and Planetary Science Letters*, **397**: 19–31, https://doi.org/10.1016/j.epsl.2014.04.023.

Puteanus, D., and Halbach, P., 1988, Correlation of Co concentration and growth rate – a method for age determination of ferromanganese crusts. *Chemical Geology*, **69**: 73–85.

Ravizza, G., 1993, Variations of the $^{187}Os/^{186}Os$ ratio of seawater over the past 28 million years as inferred from metalliferous carbonates. *Earth and Planetary Science Letters*, **118**: 335–348.

Ravizza, G., and Paquay, F., 2008, Os isotope chemostratigraphy applied to organic-rich marine sediments from the Eocene-Oligocene transition on the West African margin (ODP Site 959). *Paleoceanography*, **23**: PA2204, https://doi.org/10.1029/2007PA001460.

Ravizza, G., and Peucker-Ehrenbrink, B., 2003, The marine $^{187}Os/^{188}Os$ record of the Eocene-Oligocene transition: the interplay of weathering and glaciation. *Earth and Planetary Science Letters*, **210**: 151–165.

Ravizza, G., and Turekian, K.K., 1989, Application of the $^{187}Re/^{188}Os$ system to black shale geochronometry. *Geochimica et Cosmochimica Acta*, **53**: 3257–3262.

Ravizza, G., and Turekian, K.K., 1992, The osmium isotopic composition of organic-rich marine sediments. *Earth and Planetary Science Letters*, **110**: 1–6.

Ravizza, G., and VonderHaar, D., 2012, A geochemical clock in earliest Paleogene pelagic carbonates based on the impact-induced Os isotope excursion at the Cretaceous-Paleogene boundary. *Paleoceanography*, **27**: PA3219, https://doi.org/10.1029/2012PA002301.

Ravizza, G., Norris, R.N., Blusztajn, J., and Aubry, M.-P., 2001, An osmium isotope excursion associated with the late Paleocene thermal maximum: evidence of intensified chemical weathering. *Paleoceanography*, **16**: 155–163.

Reinhard, C.T., Raiswell, R., Scott, C., Anbar, A.D., and Lyons, T.W., 2009, A Late Archean sulfidic sea stimulated by early oxidative weathering of the continents. *Science*, **326**: 713–716, https://doi.org/10.1126/science.1176711.

Reusch, D.N., 2011, New Caledonian carbon sinks at the onset of Antarctic glaciation. *Geology*, **39** (9): 807–810.

Reusch, D.N., Ravizza, G., Maasch, K.A., and Wright, J.D., 1998, Miocene seawater $^{187}Os/^{188}Os$ ratios inferred from metalliferous carbonates. *Earth and Planetary Science Letters*, **160**: 163–178.

Robinson, N., Ravizza, G., Coccioni, R., Peucker-Ehrenbrink, B., and Norris, R., 2009, A high-resolution marine osmium isotope record for the late Maastrichtian: distinguishing the chemical fingerprints of Decca and KT impactor. *Earth and Planetary Science Letters*, **281**: 159–168.

Rooney, A.D., Selby, D., Houzay, J.P., and Renne, P.R., 2010, Re-Os geochronology of a Mesoproterozoic sedimentary succession, Taoudeni basin, Mauritania: Implications for basin-wide correlations and Re-Os organic-rich sediments systematics. *Earth and Planetary Science Letters*, **289** (3-4): 486–496.

Rooney, A.D., Chew, D.M., and Selby, D., 2011, Re-Os geochronology of the Neoproterozoic-Cambrian Dalradian Supergroup of Scotland and Ireland: implications for Neoproterozoic stratigraphy, glaciations and Re-Os systematics. *Precambrian Research*, **185**: 202–214.

Rooney, A.D., Macdonald, F.A., Strauss, J.V., Dudás, F.Ö., Hallmann, C., and Selby, D., 2014, Re-Os geochronology and coupled Os-Sr isotope constraints on the Sturtian snowball Earth. *Proceedings of the National Academy of Sciences of the United States*, **111** (1): 51–56, https://doi.org/10.1073/pnas.1317266110.

Rooney, A.D., Strauss, J.V., Brandon, A.D., and Macdonald, F.A., 2015, A Cryogenian chronology: two long-lasting synchronous Neoproterozoic glaciations. *Geology*, **43** (5): 459–462.

Rooney, A.D., Austermann, J., Smith, E.F., Li, Y., Selby, D., Dehler, C. M., et al., 2018, Coupled Re-Os and U-Pb geochronology of the Tonian Chuar Group, Grand Canyon. *Geological Society of America Bulletin*, **130** (7/8): 1085–1098.

Sahoo, S.D., Planavsky, N.J., Kendall, B., Wang, X., Shi, X., Scott, C., et al., 2012, Ocean oxygenation in the wake of the Marinoan glaciation. *Nature*, **489**: 546–549.

Schaefer, B.F., and Burgess, J.M., 2003, Re-Os isotopic age constraints on deposition in the Neoproterozoic Amadeus Basin: implications for the 'Snowball Earth'. *Journal of the Geological Society*, **160** (6): 825–828.

Schlitzer, R., Anderson, R.F., Masferrer Dodas, E., et al., 2018, The GEOTRACES intermediate data product 2017. *Chemical Geology*, **493**: 210–223, https://doi.org/10.1016/j.chemgeo.2018.05.040.

Schmitz, B., Peucker-Ehrenbrink, B., Heilmann-Clausen, C., Åberg, G., Asaro, F., and Lee, C.T.A., 2004, Basaltic explosive volcanism, but no comet impact, at the Paleocene–Eocene boundary: high-resolution chemical and isotopic records from Egypt, Spain and Denmark. *Earth and Planetary Science Letters*, **225**: 1–17.

Schoepfer, S.D., Henderson, C.M., Garrison, G.H., Foriel, J., Ward, P. D., Selby, D., et al., 2013, Termination of a continent-margin upwelling system at the Permian-Triassic boundary (Opal Creek, Canada). *Global and Planetary Change*, **105**: 21–35.

Sekine, Y., Suzuki, K., Senda, R., Goto, K.T., Tajika, E., Tada, R., et al., 2011, Osmium evidence for synchronicity between a rise in atmospheric oxygen and Palaeoproterozoic deglaciation. *Nature Communications*, **2**: 502, https://doi.org/10.1038/ncomms1507.

Selby, D., 2007, Direct Rhenium-Osmium age of the Oxfordian-Kimmeridgian boundary, Staffin Bay, Isle of Skye, UK, and the Late Jurassic time scale. *Norsk Geologisk Tidsskrift*, **87** (3): 291–299.

Selby, D., and Creaser, R.A., 2003, Re-Os geochronology of organic rich sediments: an evaluation of organic matter analysis methods. *Chemical Geology*, **200** (3): 225–240.

Selby, D., and Creaser, R.A., 2005, Direct radiometric dating of the Devonian-Mississippian time-scale boundary using the Re-Os black shale geochronometer. *Geology*, **33**: 545–548.

Selby, D., Mutterlose, J., and Condon, D.J., 2009, U-Pb and Re-Os geochronology of the Aptian/Albian and Cenomanian/Turonian stage boundaries: Implications for timescale calibration, osmium isotope seawater composition and Re-Os systematics in organic-rich sediments. *Chemical Geology*, **265**: 394–409.

Sharma, M., 2019. Platinum group elements and their isotopes in the Ocean. *In* Cochran J.K., Bokuniewicz H.J., Yager P.L. (eds), *Encyclopedia of Ocean Sciences, Volume 1 Marine Biogeochemistry*, third ed., Academic Press, Amsterdam, 174–180, https://doi.org/10.1016/B978-0-12-409548-9.11556-8.

Sharma, M., Wasserburg, G.J., Hofmann, A.W., and Chakrapani, G.J., 1999, Himalayan uplift and osmium isotopes in oceans and rivers. *Geochimica et Cosmochimica Acta*, **63** (23–24): 4005–4012.

Singh, S.K., Trivedi, J.R., and Krishnaswami, S., 1999, Re-Os isotope systematics in black shales from the Lesser Himalaya: Their chronology and role in the $^{187}Os/^{188}Os$ evolution of seawater. *Geochimica et Cosmochimica Acta*, **63** (16): 2381–2392.

Slack, J.F., Selby, D., and Dumoulin, J.A., 2015, Hydrothermal, biogenic, and seawater components in metalliferous black shales of the Brooks Range, Alaska: synsedimentary metal enrichment in a carbonate ramp setting. *Economic Geology*, **110** (3): 653–675, https://doi.org/10.2113/econgeo.110.3.653.

Sperling, E.A., Rooney, A.D., Hays, L., Sergeev, V.N., Vorob'eva, N.G., Sergeeva, N.D., et al., 2014, Redox heterogeneity of subsurface waters in the Mesoproterozoic ocean. *Geobiology*, **12**: 373–386, https://doi.org/10.1111/gbi.12091.

Strauss, J.V., Rooney, A.D., Macdonald, F.A., Brandon, A.D., and Knoll, A.H., 2014, 740 Ma vase-shaped microfossils from Yukon, Canada: Implications for Neoproterozoic chronology and biostratigraphy. *Geology*, **42** (8): 659–662.

Tejada, M.L.G., Suzuki, K., Kuroda, J., Coccioni, R., Mahoney, J.J., Ohkouchi, N., et al., 2009, Ontong Java Plateau eruption as a trigger for the early Aptian oceanic anoxic event. *Geology*, **37**: 855–858.

Tripathy, G.R., and Singh, S.K., 2015, Re-Os depositional age for black shales from the Kaimur Group, Upper Vindhyan, India. *Chemical Geology*, **413**: 63–72, https://doi.org/10.1016/j.chemgeo.2015.08.011.

Tripathy, G.R., Hannah, J.L., Stein, H.J., and Yang, G., 2014, Re-Os age and depositional environment for black shales from the Cambrian-Ordovician boundary, Green Point, western Newfoundland. *Geochemistry, Geophysics, Geosystems*, **15**: 1021–1037, https://doi.org/10.1002/2013GC005217.

Tripathy, G.R., Hannah, J.L., Stein, H.J., Geboy, N.J., and Ruppert, L.F., 2015, Radiometric dating of marine-influenced coal using Re-Os geochronology. *Earth and Planetary Science Letters*, **432**: 13–23.

Turgeon, S.C., and Creaser, R.A., 2008, Cretaceous oceanic anoxic event 2 triggered by a massive magmatic episode. *Nature*, **454**: 323–326, https://doi.org/10.1038/nature07076.

Turgeon, S.C., Creaser, R.A., and Algeo, T.J., 2007, Re-Os depositional ages and seawater Os estimates for the Frasnian-Famennian boundary: Implications for weathering rates, land plant evolution, and extinction mechanisms. *Earth and Planetary Science Letters*, **261**: 649–661.

van Acken, D., Thomson, D., Rainbird, R.H., and Creaser, R.A., 2013, Constraining the depositional history of the Neoproterozoic Shaler Supergroup, Amundsen Basin, NW Canada: Rhenium-osmium dating of black shales from the Wynniatt and Boot Inlet Formations. *Precambrian Research*, **236**: 124–131.

van der Ploeg, R., Selby, D., Cramwinckel, M.J., Li, Y., Bohaty, S.M., Middleburg, J.J., et al., 2018, Middle Eocene greenhouse warming facilitated by diminished weathering feedback. *Nature Communications*, **9**: 2877, https://doi.org/10.1038/s41467-018-05104-9.

Widom, E., Gaddis, S.J., and Wells Jr., N.E., 2004, Re-Os isotope systematics in carbonates from Serpent Mound, Ohio: implications for Re-Os dating of crustal rocks and the osmium isotopic composition of Ordovician seawater. *Geochemistry, Geophysics, Geosystems*, **5** (3): Q03006, https://doi.org/10.1029/2002GC000444.

Wieczorek, R., Fantle, M.S., Kump, L.R., and Ravizza, G., 2013, Geochemical evidence for volcanic activity prior to and enhanced terrestrial weathering during the Paleocene Eocene Thermal Maximum. *Geochimica et Cosmochimica Acta*, **119**: 391–410.

Xu, G., Hannah, J.L., Stein, H.J., Bingen, B., Yang, G., Zimmerman, A., et al., 2009, Re-Os geochronology of Arctic black shales to evaluate the Anisian-Ladinian boundary and global faunal correlations. *Earth and Planetary Science Letters*, **288**: 581–587, https://doi.org/10.1016/j.epsl.2009.10.022.

Xu, G., Hannah, J.L., Stein, H.J., Mørk, A., Vigran, J.O., Bingen, B., et al., 2014, Cause of Upper Triassic climate crisis revealed by Re-Os geochemistry of Boreal black shales. *Palaeogeography, Palaeoclimatology, Palaeoecology*, **395**: 222–232.

Yamashita, Y., Takahashi, Y., Haba, H., Enomoto, S., and Shimizu, H., 2007, Comparison of reductive accumulation of Re and Os in seawater-sediment systems. *Geochimica et Cosmochimica Acta*, **71**: 3458–3475.

Yang, G., Hannah, J.L., Zimmerman, A., Stein, H.J., and Bekker, A., 2009, Re-Os depositional age for Archean carbonaceous slates from the southwestern Superior Province: Challenges and insights. *Earth and Planetary Science Letters*, **280** (1-2): 83–92.

Yang, X., Zhang, Z., Li, C., Duan, S., and Jiang, Z., 2016, Geochemistry and Re-Os geochronology of the organic-rich sedimentary rocks in the Jingtieshan Fe-Cu deposit, North Qilian Mountains, NW China. *Journal of Asian Earth Sciences*, **119**: 65–77, https://doi.org/10.1016/j.jseaes.2016.01.007.

Zhu, B., Becker, H., Jiang, S.-Y., Pi, D.-H., Fischer-Gödde, M., and Yang, J.-H., 2013, Re-Os geochronology of black shales from the Neoproterozoic Doushantuo Formation, Yangtze platform, South China. *Precambrian Research*, **225**: 67–76.

A. Paytan, W. Yao, K.L. Faul and E.T. Gray

Chapter 9

Sulfur Isotope Stratigraphy

Chapter outline

Abstract

The sulfur isotopic composition of dissolved sulfate in seawater has varied through time. Distinct variations and relatively high rates of change characterize certain time intervals. This allows for dating and correlation of sediments using sulfur isotopes. The variation in sulfur isotopes and the potential stratigraphic resolution of this isotope system is discussed and graphically displayed. New data are used to refine the previously published (Geologic Time Scale 2012) for the Paleocene and Eocene.

9.1 Introduction

Sulfur isotope biogeochemistry has broad applications to geological, biological, and environmental studies. Sulfur is an important constituent of the Earth's lithosphere, biosphere, hydrosphere, and atmosphere and occurs as a major constituent or in trace amounts in various components of the Earth system. Many of the characteristics of sulfur isotope geochemistry are analogous to those of carbon and nitrogen, as all three elements occur in reduced and oxidized forms, and undergo an oxidation state change as a result of biological processes.

Sulfur as sulfate (SO_4^{2-}) is the second most abundant anion in modern seawater with an average present-day concentration of 28 mmol/kg. It has a conservative distribution with uniform SO_4^{2-}/salinity ratios in the open ocean and a very long residence time of close to 10 million years (Chiba and Sakai, 1985; Berner and Berner, 1987). Because of the large pool of sulfate in the ocean, it is expected that the rate of change in either concentration or isotopic composition of sulfate will be small, thus reducing the utility of this isotope system as a viable tool for stratigraphic correlation or dating.

However, as seen in Figs. 9.1–9.4, the isotopic record shows distinct variations through time, and at certain intervals, the rate of change and the unique features of the record may yield a reliable numerical age. The features in the record can also be used to correlate between stratigraphic sections and sequences. This is particularly important for sequences dominated by evaporites, where fossils are not abundant or have a restricted distribution range, paramagnetic minerals are rare, and other stratigraphic tools (e.g., oxygen isotopes in carbonates) cannot be utilized.

While the potential for the utility of sulfur isotope stratigraphy exists, this system has not been broadly applied. The examples for the application of S isotopes for stratigraphic correlations predominantly focus on the Neoproterozoic and often employ other methods of correlation such as $^{87}Sr/^{86}Sr$ and $\delta^{13}C$ as well (Misi et al., 2007; Pokrovskii et al., 2006; Walter et al., 2000; Hurtgen et al., 2002; Planavsky et al., 2012; Scott et al., 2014).

It is important to note that the method works only for marine minerals containing sulfate. Moreover, it is crucial that the integrity of the record be confirmed to insure the pristine nature of the record and lack of postdepositional alteration (Kampschulte and Strauss, 2004; Crockford et al., 2019). In the application of sulfur isotopes, it is assumed that the oceans are homogeneous with respect to

Geologic Time Scale 2020. DOI: https://doi.org/10.1016/B978-0-12-824360-2.00009-7

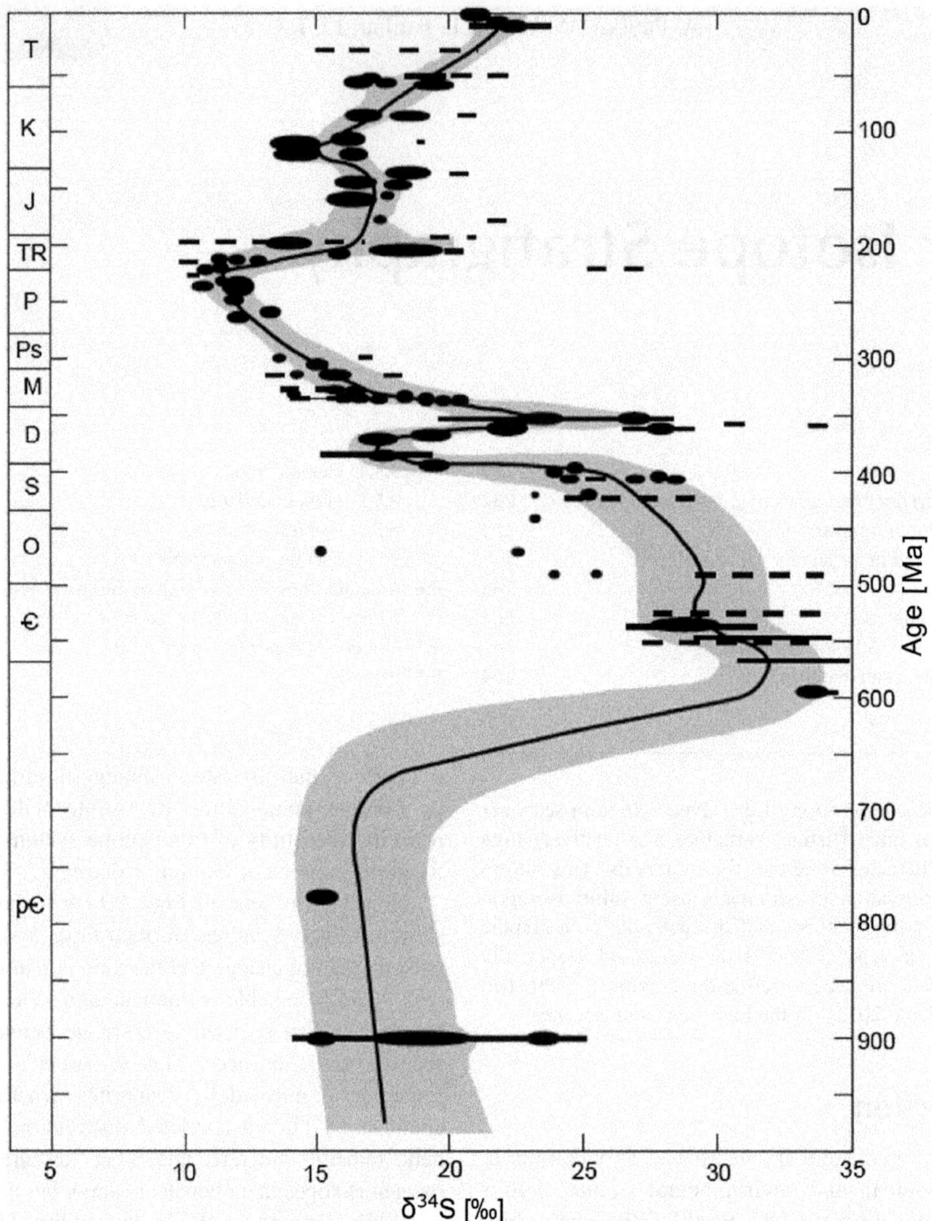

FIGURE 9.1 Evaporite records (Claypool et al., 1980). Solid lines represent data from Claypool et al. and data he compiled from the literature plotted at their most probable age. Dashed lines show the range of all available few analyses for each time interval. The heavy line is the best estimate of $\delta^{34}S$ of the ocean. The shaded area is the uncertainty related to the curve.

sulfur isotopes of dissolved sulfate and that they always were so. As noted, previously, uniformity is expected because of the long residence time of sulfate in the ocean (millions of years) compared to the oceanic mixing time (thousands of years) and because of the high concentration of sulfate in seawater compared to the concentration in major input sources of sulfur to the ocean (rivers, hydrothermal activity, and volcanic activity). Indeed, in the present-day ocean, seawater maintains constant sulfur isotopic composition (at an analytical precision of ~0.2‰) until it is diluted to salinities well below those supportive of fully marine fauna (Crockford et al., 2019) invalidating this assumption and limiting the utility of sulfur isotopes for stratigraphic correlation during such time intervals. The main limitation to the broader application of this isotope system for stratigraphy and correlation is the lack of reliable, high-resolution, globally representative isotope records that could be assigned a numerical age scale. As such records become available the utility of this system could expand considerably.

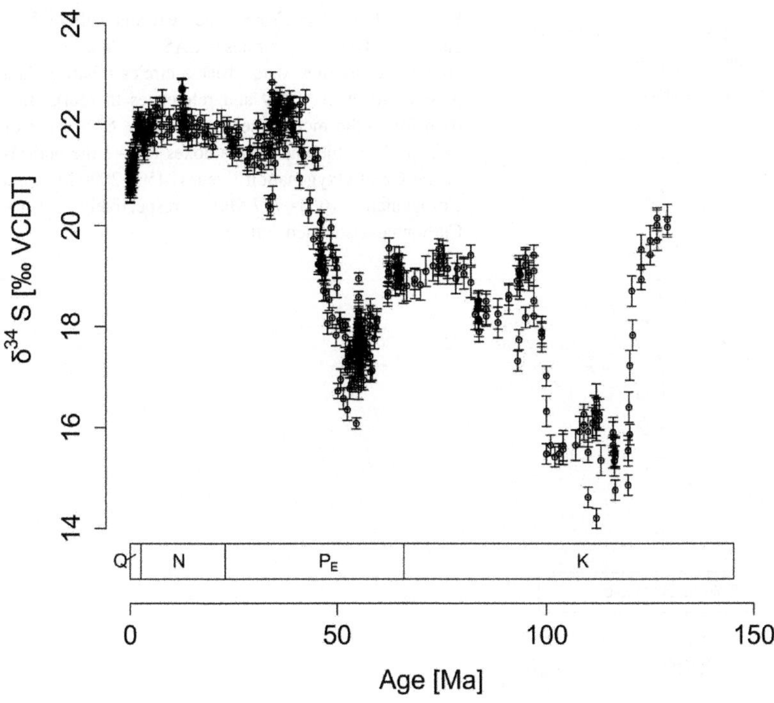

FIGURE 9.2 Seawater sulfate S isotope curve from marine barite for 130 Ma to present. Paytan et al., 1998; Paytan et al., 2004; Turchyn et al., 2009; Markovic et al., 2015; Markovic et al., 2016; Yao et al., 2018; Yao et al., 2020.

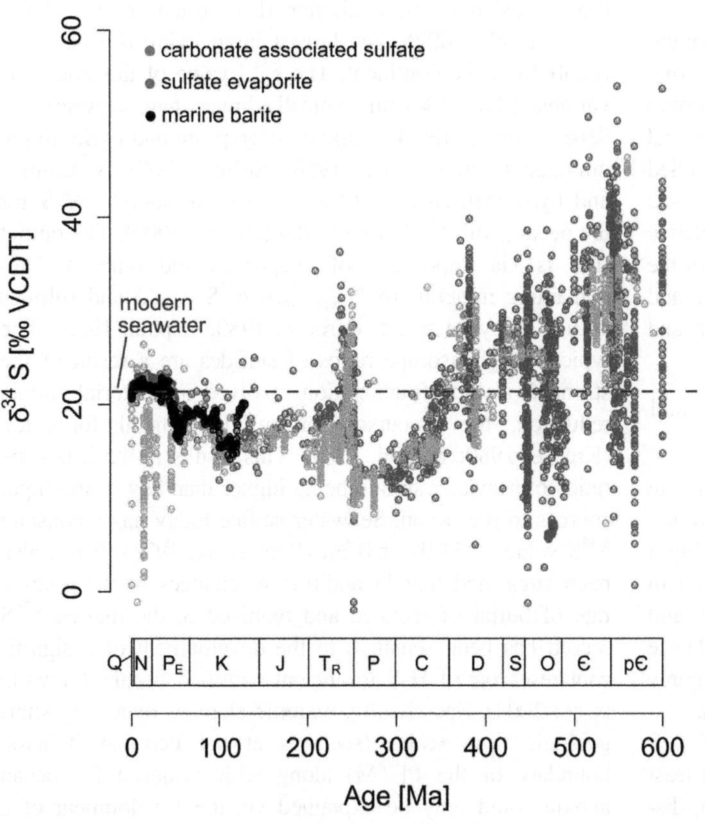

FIGURE 9.3 The Phanerozoic seawater sulfate δ^{34}S record. Green circles = CAS data (Ueda et al., 1987; Strauss, 1993; Kampschulte and Strauss, 2004; Goldberg et al., 2005; Mazumdar and Strauss, 2006; Gill et al., 2007; Hurtgen et al., 2009; Turchyn et al., 2009; Wu et al., 2010, 2014; Thompson and Kah, 2012; Wotte et al., 2012; Present et al., 2015; Sim et al., 2015; Kah et al., 2016; Schobben et al., 2017; Rennie et al., 2018); gray circles = evaporites data (Holser and Kaplan, 1966; Sakai, 1972; Claypool et al., 1980; Cortecci et al., 1981; Pierre and Rouchy, 1986; Das et al., 1990; Rick, 1990; Utrilla et al., 1992; Fox and Videtich, 1997; Strauss, 1997; Worden et al., 1997; Kampschulte et al., 1998; Strauss, 1993; Strauss et al., 2001; Longinelli and Flora, 2007; Orti et al., 2010; Peryt et al., 2005; Surakotra et al., 2018; Crockford et al., 2019); blue dash line = the modern seawater sulfate δ^{34}S value of ~21‰. *CAS*, Carbonate-associated sulfate.

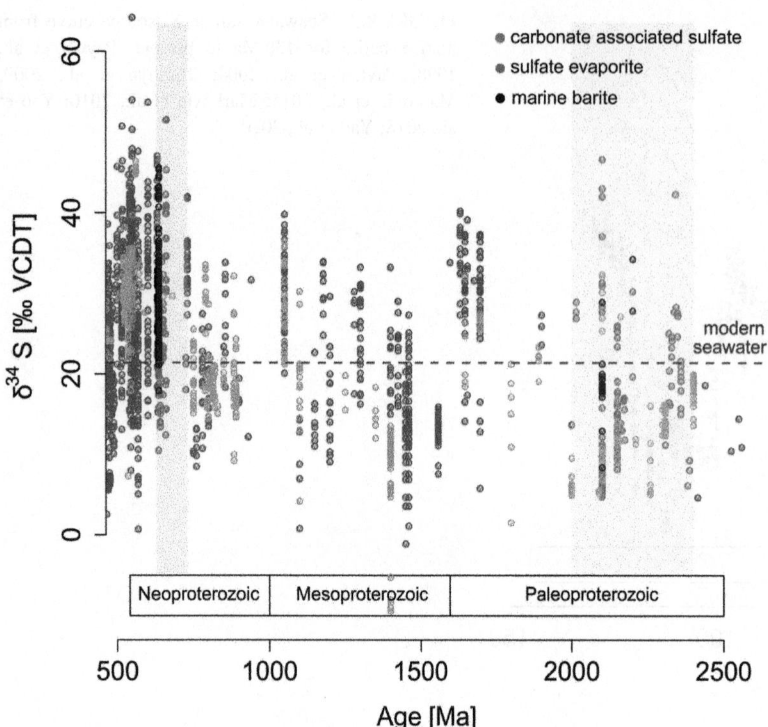

FIGURE 9.4 The Proterozoic seawater sulfate δ^{34}S curve. Green circles = CAS data; gray circles = evaporites data; Black circles = barite data (Crockford et al., 2019 and references therein). Blue dash line = the modern seawater sulfate δ^{34}S value of ~21‰. The blue and purple boxes denote the periods of the Great Oxygenation Event (2450–2000 Ma) and Cryogenian (635–717 Ma), respectively. *CAS*, Carbonate-associated sulfate.

9.2 Mechanisms driving the variation in the S isotope record

The chemical and isotopic composition of the ocean changes over time in response to fluctuations in global weathering rates and riverine loads, volcanic activity, hydrothermal exchange rates, sediment diagenesis, and sedimentation and subduction processes. All of these are ultimately controlled by tectonic and climatic changes. Specifically, the oceanic sulfate δ^{34}S at any given time is controlled by the relative proportion of sulfide and sulfate input and removal from the oceans and their isotopic compositions (e.g., Bottrell and Newton, 2006). S is commonly present in seawater and marine sediments in one of two redox states:

1. in its oxidized state as sulfate and sulfate minerals and
2. in its reduced form as H_2S and sulfide minerals.

The oceanic sulfate δ^{34}S record provides an estimate for the relative partitioning of S between the oxidized and reduced reservoirs through time. Changes in both input and output of sulfur to/from the ocean have occurred in response to changes in the geological, geochemical, and biological processes (Strauss, 1997; Berner, 1999). These changes are recorded in contemporaneous authigenic minerals that precipitate in the oceanic water column.

Seawater contains a large amount of S (~40×10^{18} mol) that is present, as it has been for at least the past 500 million years, predominantly as oxidized, dissolved sulfate (SO_4^{2-}) (Holser et al., 1988; Berner and Canfield, 1989, 1999). Ancient oceans may have at times had lower sulfate concentrations and thus sulfate residence times may have been shorter (Lowenstein et al., 2001; Horita et al., 2002). The largest input today is from river runoff from the continent. The δ^{34}S value of this source is variable (0‰–10‰) but typically lower than seawater and depends on the relative amount of gypsum and pyrite in the drainage basin (Krouse, 1980; Arthur, 2000). Volcanism and hydrothermal activity also are small sources of S for the ocean, with δ^{34}S close to 0‰ (Arthur, 2000). The output flux is via deposition of evaporites and other sulfate-containing minerals ($\delta^{34}S_{evaporite} \approx \delta^{34}S_{seawater}$) and sulfides with δ^{34}S pyrite ≈ 15‰ (Krouse, 1980; Kaplan, 1983). The typically light isotope ratios of sulfides are a result of the strong S isotope fractionation involved in bacterial sulfate reduction, the precursor for sulfide mineral formation (Krouse, 1980; Kaplan, 1983). This results in the S isotope ratios of seawater sulfate being higher than any of the input sources to the ocean. Seawater sulfate today has a constant δ^{34}S value of 21.0‰ ± 0.2‰ (Rees et al., 1978). It has also been suggested that in addition to changes in the relative rate of burial of reduced and oxidized S, the marine δ^{34}S record has been sensitive to the development of a significant reservoir of H_2S in ancient stratified oceans (Newton et al., 2004). Specifically, extreme changes over very short geologic time scales (such as at the Permian–Triassic boundary or the PETM) along with evidence for ocean anoxia could only be explained via the development of a large, relatively short-lived, reservoir of H_2S in the deep oceanic water column followed by oceanic overturning and reoxygenation of the H_2S (Newton et al., 2004; Algeo et al., 2007; Luo et al., 2010; Yao et al., 2018).

The evidence that the S isotopic composition of seawater sulfate has fluctuated considerably over time, until recently, was based on comprehensive, though not continuous, isotope data sets obtained from marine evaporitic sulfate deposits and pyrite (Claypool et al., 1980; Strauss, 1993). More recently, marine barite has been used to construct a continuous, high-resolution *S* curve for the last 130 Ma (Paytan et al., 1998, 2004; Turchyn et al., 2009; Markovic et al., 2015, 2016; Yao et al., 2018, 2020). Methods to analyze the sulfate that is associated with marine carbonate deposits (carbonate-associated sulfate, CAS) have also been developed, and new data sets using these methods are becoming available. Specifically, CAS has been used to reconstruct global change in the sulfur cycle on both long (Kampschulte and Strauss, 2004) and short (Ohkouchi et al., 1999; Kampschulte et al., 2001) time scales. Particularly, CAS data from Foraminifera that is species-adjusted for fractionation offsets can yield high-quality data (Rennie et al., 2018). The new data from barite and from CAS show considerably more detail and fill significant gaps in the former data sets, revealing previously unrecognized structure and increasing the potential for seawater S isotope curves to serve as a tool for stratigraphy and correlation.

9.3 Isotopic fractionation of sulfur

The sulfur isotope fractionation between evaporitic sulfate minerals and dissolved sulfate is approximately 1‰–2‰ (Thode and Monster, 1965). Experiments and analyses of modern evaporites show values 1.1‰ ± 0.9‰ heavier than dissolved ocean sulfate (Holser and Kaplan, 1966). Modern barites measured by the SF_6 method averaged 0.2‰ heavier than dissolved ocean sulfate (Paytan et al., 1998). Carbonates are also expected to have minor fractionation associated with the incorporation of sulfate. The similarity between the $\delta^{34}S$ value of sulfate minerals and dissolved sulfate means that ancient sulfates can be used as a proxy for the $\delta^{34}S$ value of the ocean at the time that the minerals formed.

Reduced S compounds are mostly produced in association with processes of bacterial sulfate reduction. Dissimilatory reduction (converting sulfate to sulfide) is performed by heterotrophic organisms, particularly sulfate-reducing bacteria. Bacterial sulfate reduction is an energy-yielding, anaerobic process that occurs only in reducing environments (Goldhaber and Kaplan, 1974; Canfield, 2001). Measured fractionations associated with sulfate reduction under experimental conditions range from −20‰ to −46‰ at low rates of sulfate reduction to −10‰ at high reduction rates. The $\delta^{34}S$ values of sulfides of modern marine sediments are typically around −40‰; however, a wide range from −40‰ to +3‰ is observed. Sulfate reduction and iron sulfide precipitation continues only as long as:

1. sulfate is available as an oxidant,
2. organic matter is available for sulfate-reducing bacteria, and
3. reactive iron is present to react with H_2S.

In the marine environment, neither sulfate nor iron generally limits the reaction. Instead, it is the abundance of easily metabolized carbon that controls the extent of sulfate reduction. The broad range of $\delta^{34}S$ values observed in sulfides from marine sediments results from variable fractionation associated with the different sedimentary settings and environmental conditions during sulfate reduction (temperature, porosity, diffusion rates, etc.) as well as other processes in the S cycle that involve fractionation such as sulfur disproportionation reactions (Canfield and Thamdrup, 1994; Habicht et al., 1998).

Assimilatory reduction occurs in autotrophic organisms where sulfur is incorporated in proteins, particularly as S_2^- in amino acids. Assimilatory reduction involves a valence change from +6 to −2. The bonding of the product sulfur is similar to the dissolved sulfate ion, and fractionations are small (+0.5‰ to −4.5‰, Kaplan, 1983). The $\delta^{34}S$ value of organic sulfur in extant marine organisms incorporated by assimilatory processes is generally depleted by 0‰ to 5‰ relative to the ocean.

The wide array of environmental conditions that affect the fractionation, together with the broad range of S isotopic values of sulfide minerals at any given time, and post-depositional alteration of assimilatory S into organic matter, limits the utility of sulfites and S in old organic matter as tools for stratigraphy and correlation, since measured values may not be representative of a global oceanic signature.

9.4 Measurement and materials for sulfur isotope stratigraphy

9.4.1 Isotope analyses

There are four stable isotopes of sulfur. The isotopes that are commonly measured are ^{34}S and ^{32}S, as these are the two most abundant of the four. In most but not all samples, the sulfur isotopes are present in constant ratios to each other, thus the others could be easily computed (but see Farquhar et al., 2000). All values are reported as $\delta^{34}S$ relative to the Canõn Diablo Troilite (CDT) standard (Ault and Jensen, 1963) using the accepted delta notation. Due to scarcity of the CDT standard, secondary synthetic argentite (Ag_2S) and other sulfur-bearing standards have been developed, with $\delta^{34}S$ values being defined relative to the accepted CTD value of 0‰. Samples are converted to gas (SO_2 or SF_6) and analyzed on a gas-ratio mass spectrometer. Analytical reproducibility is typically ±0.2‰.

9.4.2 Materials for S isotope analysis

9.4.2.1 Evaporites

Records of oceanic sulfur isotopes through time were originally reconstructed from the analyses of marine evaporitic sulfate minerals (Holser and Kaplan, 1966; Claypool et al., 1980). Evaporites contain abundant sulfate and their formation involves minimal and predictable fractionation, thus they are suitable archives for this analysis. Claypool et al. (1980) presented the first compilation of the secular sulfur isotope record of seawater for the Phanerozoic (Fig. 9.1) and their work provides the basis for our understanding of the sulfur isotope record. However, as a result of the sporadic nature of evaporite formation through geologic time this record is not continuous. Moreover, evaporites are hard to date precisely due to the limited fossil record within these sequences; thus the stratigraphic age control on the evaporitic-based sulfur isotope record is compromised.

9.4.2.2 Barite

Like evaporites, the $\delta^{34}S$ of barite is quite similar to that of sulfate in the solution from which it precipitated. Marine barite precipitates in the oceanic water column and is relatively immune to diagenetic alteration after burial thus it records the changes in the sulfur isotopic composition of seawater through time (Paytan et al., 1998, 2004; Turchyn et al., 2009; Markovic et al., 2015, 2016; Yao et al., 2018, 2020). Moreover, high-resolution, well-dated, and continuous records can be developed as long as barite-containing pelagic marine sediments are available (Paytan et al., 1993). It must be stressed that reliable seawater sulfur isotope records can only be derived from marine (pelagic) barite and not diagenetic or hydrothermal barite deposits (see Eagle et al., 2003 for more details). A sulfur isotope curve was obtained from pelagic marine barites of Cretaceous and Cenozoic ages with unprecedented temporal resolution (Paytan et al., 1998, 2004; Fig. 9.2). The high-resolution curve shows some very rapid changes that could be instrumental for stratigraphic applications.

9.4.2.3 Substituted sulfate in carbonates

Sulfur is a ubiquitous trace element in sedimentary carbonates (e.g., CAS). Concentrations range from several tens of ppm in inorganic carbonates to several thousand ppm in some biogenic carbonates (Burdett et al., 1989; Kampschulte et al., 2001; Lyons et al., 2004). While the mechanism of sulfate incorporation into carbonates is not fully understood, CAS is incorporated with little fractionation thus recording seawater ratios. Carbonates offer an attractive method for refining the secular sulfur curve because of their abundance in the geological record, ease of dating, and relatively high accumulation rates. Indeed, a record for Phanerozoic seawater sulfur isotopes based on CAS has been compiled and published (Kampschulte and Strauss, 2004; Fig. 9.3). Extreme caution must, however, be exercised in extracting CAS from samples and interpreting the sulfur isotope data obtained because carbonates are highly susceptible to postdepositional alteration and secondary mineral precipitation that can obliterate the record. The degree of modification can be assessed by obtaining multiple records from distinct locations (or mineral phases) for the same time interval and construction of secular trends (Kampschulte and Strauss, 2004). Recent work largely overcame these disadvantages by using CAS from single shells of different species of Foraminifera and correcting the data for offsets between species (Rennie et al., 2018).

9.5 A Geologic time scale database

9.5.1 General trends

The current sulfur isotope records include data sets from the Proterozoic to the present (Figs. 9.3–9.5). While the focus of most studies is on shorter time scales and the methods that are used are varied, the overlap among published records and a few long-term studies serve to give a comprehensive view of the sulfur isotope record for the Phanerozoic. Three long-term records have been compiled, two based on evaporites (Claypool et al., 1980; Strauss, 1997) and one based on CAS (Kampschulte and Strauss, 2004). A compilation of data for the Proterozoic was also published (Crockford et al., 2019). Sulfate concentrations in the Proterozoic ocean, however, were much lower than during the Phanerozoic (e.g., Habicht et al., 2002; Kah et al., 2004; Canfield and Farquhar, 2009); hence, it is likely that the oceanic water column was not homogenous with respect to sulfur isotopes limiting the applicability of S isotopes for stratigraphy and correlation.

General trends can be seen in these records. The Proterozoic data show widespread with positive excursions across the Great Oxidation Event and the lower Neoproterozoic. In the Cambrian the average $\delta^{34}S$ value is 34.8±2.8‰ in the CAS record (Kampschulte and Strauss, 2004) and around 30‰ in the evaporite record (Claypool, et al., 1980; Strauss, 1997). These relatively high values are sustained through the Cambrian in the CAS record, ending with anomalously high $\delta^{34}S$ values at the Cambrian/Ordovician boundary. After this point the $\delta^{34}S$ decreases steadily through the remainder of the Paleozoic, reaching a minimum at the Permian/Triassic boundary with an average

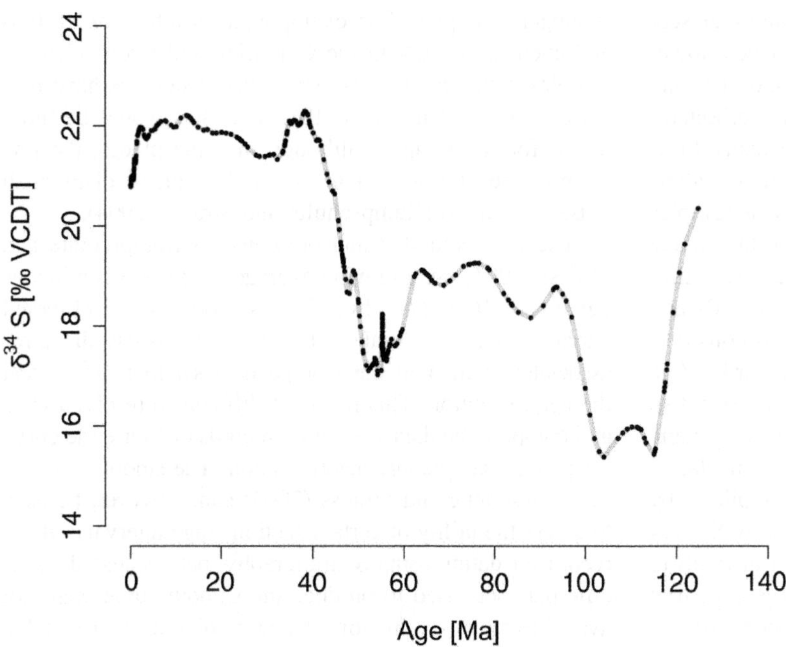

FIGURE 9.5 LOWESS curve for the last 130 million years generated from marine barite data (Paytan et al., 1998, 2004; Turchyn et al., 2009; Markovic et al., 2015, 2016; Yao et al., 2018, 2020); see also Table 9.1.

value of 13.2 ± 2.5‰. A similar but less time-constrained decrease is seen in the evaporite record.

Through the Mesozoic, the δ^{34}S values are generally lower than in the Paleozoic, ranging between 14‰ and 20‰. The δ^{34}S values increase quite rapidly from 13.2 ± 2.5‰ at the Permian/Triassic boundary to 17‰ in the Jurassic and decrease again to about 15‰ in the early Cretaceous (Claypool et al., 1980; Strauss, 1997; Kampschulte and Strauss, 2004). The value at the Cretaceous is about 19‰ but two distinct excursions toward lower values are seen: one at ~120 Ma and the other at ~90 Ma (Paytan et al., 2004). A decrease in δ^{34}S values from ~20‰ to 16‰ is seen in the Paleocene before climbing sharply in the Early to Middle Eocene to the near modern value of 21‰ where it remains steady for the remainder of the Cenozoic (Fig. 9.2).

These broad trends can be useful in obtaining very general stratigraphic information (e.g., typically only at the epoch scale) but are not applicable for age assignments at resolution better than tens of millions of years.

9.5.2 Time boundaries

Strauss (1997) reviewed secular variations in δ^{34}S across time boundaries characterized by profound biological or geological changes. Due to the paucity of evaporite data, all these time boundary studies have used data obtained from sedimentary sulfides. The premise behind the study of S isotope excursions at age boundaries is based on the expected perturbations in the biosphere which may impact sulfate reduction rates. During a catastrophic event, where productivity plunges, the δ^{34}S values of the oceans are expected to decrease because of a reduction in organic matter availability, leading to lower sulfate reduction. The subsequent biological radiations should have the opposite effect. Accordingly, the δ^{34}S values of the oceans should first decrease across a time boundary associated with a catastrophic extinction or major ecosystem reorganization and then increase during the period of recovery. The magnitude of the effect is related to the intensity of the extinction event, the rate of recovery, and the size of the oceanic sulfur reservoir.

Four extinction events have been studied (see Strauss, 1997 for references): the Precambrian–Cambrian, the Frasnian–Famennian, the Permian–Triassic, and the Cretaceous–Tertiary boundaries. Of these, only the Permian–Triassic event shows the expected sulfur trend (Luo et al., 2010). Fluctuations occur at the other boundaries, but no secular (globally concurrent) variations have been observed (see also Newton et al., 2004). In part the reason for the inconsistent results between sections and between extinction events may be related to the inherent problems of analyzing sulfides instead of sulfates and the multitude of controls impacting the isotopic composition of sulfides. Therefore local effects may mask any global sulfur variations. More recent data using CAS Sim et al. (2015) correlated the S isotope record among sections throughout the world representing the Frasnian–Famennian boundary of the Devonian.

9.5.3 Age resolution

Age resolution of the S isotope curve varies with the type of data comprising the record and the specific objectives for the various studies producing the data. The older sections compiled from evaporite and CAS data have a lower resolution because of the scarcity of evaporites and because CAS depends on the integrity of the carbonates and fossils used for reconstruction, which in many locations, are subjected to extensive postdepositional alteration. In addition, large temporal gaps between samples make it difficult to correlate between sites and thus make exact age determinations challenging. Despite these limitations robust records exist for specific time periods and the confidence within each such time interval is considerably improved from the earlier evaporate records. Age resolution of records based on barite is much better but so far barite has been recovered predominantly from pelagic sediments, limiting the applicability to the last 130 Ma.

The Phanerozoic evaporite record, compiled by Claypool et al. (1980) with further work done by Strauss (1997), has several characteristics that make it difficult to use for S stratigraphy. First, the record has large gaps in it that leave long periods of time unaccounted for. In Claypool et al. (1980) a best estimate curve was visually approximated to combine and extrapolate between disparate data sets; however, this eliminates the ability to detect finer fluctuations that may be present. Second, the absolute S isotope values recorded at each time point range considerably, confounding the issue. The range of $\delta^{34}S$ values within each time interval is approximately 5‰ for most of the data sets, which makes pinpointing an age from a stratigraphic perspective difficult since in many cases the broad fluctuations that occur over time are within ±5‰ (Fig. 9.1). Third, the ages used for each sample are approximate due to the scarcity of fossils in sections used to compile the isotope curves. Even in the evaporite record from Strauss (1993) that derives its ages after Harland et al. (1990), the age uncertainty spans more than 10 million years depending on the segment (or specific time range), which makes it difficult to use these data for stratigraphic correlation (Strauss, 1993).

The S isotope record derived from CAS is more robust (Fig. 9.3). The record is consistent with the evaporite data in the broad strokes (Fig. 9.4) but a better constraint on the ages of the samples is possible. The data set presented in Kampschulte and Strauss (2004) and references therein show a record for the Phanerozoic that reduces the uncertainty in age and S isotope values considerably from those associated with evaporites. The CAS samples were taken from stratigraphically well-constrained biogenic calcites (using the time scale of Harland et al., 1990) with a resolution of 1–5 million years within data sets. However, the data sets analyzed are not continuous, leaving gaps, that while not as glaring as those in the evaporite record, still limit the accuracy of a smooth curve and may miss finer details. The CAS data that represent older ages have a wider range of S isotope values than that of more recent (younger) samples. For example, a "scatter" of ±10‰ and even up to 20‰ in the Cambrian and Ordovician for samples with similar ages. More recent samples have narrower ranges, from 5‰ to 10‰, and thus would be more useful for stratigraphy, although in some places, the low temporal resolution still makes it difficult to distinguish noise from trend (Kampschulte and Strauss, 2004).

The data compiled and presented in Kampschulte and Strauss (2004) use a moving average to create a continuous curve (Fig. 9.4). The effect is to smooth out the observed variation that then makes it difficult to assess the error associated with both the isotope data set (e.g., $\delta^{34}S$) and the age resolution. This makes it difficult to resolve trends and compare the data with other records or to use the curve for precise sample age determination. The smoothed curve of Kampschulte and Strauss (2004) can, however, be used to assess the utility of certain sections (age intervals) of the record for dating using S stratigraphy, but because the specific data sets used to produce the smooth curve were not available to us, evaluation of age resolution or a detailed statistical LOWESS fit (McArthur et al., 2001) for derivation of numeric ages using the CAS record cannot be compiled at this time. The analysis of $\delta^{34}S$ hosted in the calcite lattice of single-species foraminifera vastly improved stratigraphy afforded by CAS-based records although corrections for species-specific fractionation must be applied (Rennie et al., 2018). The published Cenozoic foraminifera record agrees well with the barite-derived record (Yao et al., 2020).

The marine barite record presented by Paytan et al. (1998, 2004) is derived from ocean floor sediment. The current record goes back ~130 Ma. The barite-based S isotope curve provides a record with a resolution of less than 1 million years with very few gaps. The age of the samples is constrained by biostratigraphy and Sr isotopes and typically has an error of less than 100,000 years. The continuous and secular (based on data from multiple sites for each time interval) nature and the high resolution of this record illuminate finer features that are missed in the lower resolution evaporite and CAS records. The record also has a narrower range of S isotope values for each time point, further constraining the curve. These features make it the most robust of the three available records thus far and the most useful for stratigraphy, for the periods it covers. This record serves to illustrate the potential use of S isotopes for stratigraphy and as more such detailed high-resolution secular records (e.g., based on coherent data from multiple locations and settings) become available for different geological periods, S isotope stratigraphy can be more widely utilized. At the moment the limited availability of continuous high-resolution secular data and the need for updated and better constrained ages for previously published records are the biggest obstacles to using sulfur isotopes as a stratigraphic tool.

9.5.4 Specific age intervals

While the current S record of the Phanerozoic is not ideal for stratigraphic applications as discussed previously, there is still potential for using S as a stratigraphic tool for certain time intervals. The time periods best suited to dating are those that are distinguished by rapid changes in $\delta^{34}S$. Identifying smaller fluctuations on the "plateaus" of the isotope curve is difficult because of the limited temporal resolution, and the relatively large error in the $\delta^{34}S$ compared to the small fluctuations. These limitations make the potential use of fine features for stratigraphic and correlation purposes impossible at this stage.

At this time the most useful record for S stratigraphy applications is the marine barite curve that extends back to 130 Ma. The distinct features that appear in this high-resolution curve show five time periods with relatively abrupt changes in $\delta^{34}S$ that could lead to precise dating: 130–116, 107–96, 96–86, 83–75, 65–40, and ~2 Ma to the present. Resolving ages during periods of smaller fluctuations is possible but would likely necessitate a much larger data set in order to match multiple points and avoid offsets between data from distinct sites. The plateaus, notably from ~30 Ma to about 2 Ma where the S isotope values do not significantly change, are not useful because there are few features that can be teased out and distinguished from sampling and analytical error.

Next we present the trends in the $\delta^{34}S$ isotope data for each time period and a brief discussion of the utility of the data for stratigraphy is presented. Kampschulte and Strauss (2004) showed that the Phanerozoic CAS record is consistent with and better constrained temporally than the evaporite record. For this reason the trends discussed next will rely on the CAS record from the Cambrian to the Jurassic (Kampschulte and Strauss, 2004, and references therein) and the barite record from Paytan et al., 1998, 2004; Turchyn et al., 2009; Markovic et al., 2015, 2016; and Yao et al., 2018, 2020, from the Cretaceous to the present, unless otherwise specified. Recent studies also showed that multiple sulfur isotopes (^{33}S and ^{36}S) of sulfate in the Proterozoic could be powerful tools for stratigraphy (e.g., Crockford et al., 2019; Farquhar and Wing, 2003; Johnston, 2011 and references therein). However, the use of ^{33}S and ^{36}S has so far been limited and will not be further discussed here.

9.5.4.1 Cambrian

The seawater $\delta^{34}S$ records for the Cambrian are derived from carbonate and evaporite rocks (and a few from barite) in Australia, Canada, China, India, Russia, Spain, and France (Goldberg et al., 2005; Hough et al., 2006; Hurtgen et al., 2009; Mazumdar and Strauss, 2006; Peryt et al., 2005; Wotte et al., 2012). The values recorded represent a wide range. The data show an excursion with a maximum of 50‰ in the lower Cambrian, followed by a systematic >15‰ decrease across the middle–upper Cambrian. The mean value is relatively high (>30‰), although it is unclear if these high values reflect open ocean seawater sulfate or if the integrity of these samples was compromised. The high values and intrabasin variability may partially result from the intrabasin microbial sulfate reduction under sulfate limitation or diagenetic processes as well as euxinic conditions (Goldberg et al., 2005; Mazumdar and Strauss, 2006; Peryt et al., 2005; Hough et al., 2006).

The age resolution that can be theoretically obtained using the moving mean curve is 2.0 Myr from 535 to 525 Ma and 2.8 Myr from 525 to 511 Ma (but note that the curve averages values over 5 Myr) (Kampschulte and Strauss, 2004). When looking at the raw data, one sees that there is a significant age gap between the two time periods sampled that is smoothed over in the moving mean. In addition, while the $\delta^{34}S$ values in both data sets are relatively high (>30‰) and can be used to identify samples of Cambrian age, the range of values is similar for both sets and thus without a larger data set that fills in the gaps, distinguishing between older and younger samples within the Cambrian may be difficult. The global nature of the record should also be verified as sulfate was most likely a nonconservative anion in the Cambrian ocean (Wotte et al., 2012).

9.5.4.2 Ordovician

The CAS record in the Ordovician is composed of 16 samples. The temporal resolution of the record is between 1 and 8 Myr with the older samples dominantly ~4 million years apart and the younger samples 1 million years apart. The $\delta^{34}S$ values were determined from whole rock in 15 of these samples, and for 12 of them brachiopod shells were also used. The record shows a decrease from a moving mean of 30‰ in the Lower Ordovician to 24‰ in the uppermost Ordovician (Kampschulte and Strauss, 2004).

The wide range of the measured $\delta^{34}S$ values (15‰–30‰) throughout the period complicates the picture. Without a higher resolution data set it is impossible to distinguish whether the broad range represents real fluctuations and the lower values (15‰) are a true minimum. Specifically, when considering the time resolution of the record, values of 15‰ and ~30‰ that occur within the same time frame render the use of such records unreliable. However, on a broader scale, the moving average of $\delta^{34}S$ values, which plateaus around 24‰ at ~475 Ma and remain at that level up to the Ordovician/Silurian boundary, can be distinguished from other time periods.

9.5.4.3 Silurian

The Silurian shows a continued trend of decreasing $\delta^{34}S$ values with a range from 35.6‰ to 21.5‰ in the CAS

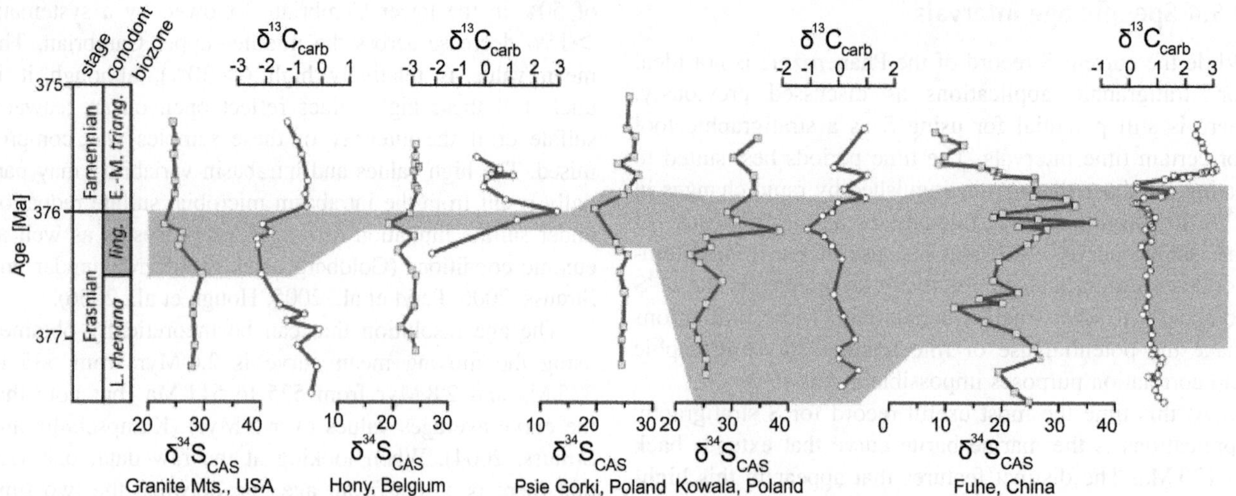

FIGURE 9.6 Sulfur and carbon isotope records across the Frasnian–Famennian boundary. There is a brief $\delta^{34}S$ drop throughout the linguiformis biozone and a positive $\delta^{13}C$ excursion starting in the uppermost part of this biozone. The shaded area denotes the linguiformis conodont biozone. Abbreviations: *L. rhenana*, Late *rhenana*; *ling.*, *linguiformis* E.–M. *triang.*, Early to middle triangularis. Figure after Sim et al. (2015).

record in 15 brachiopod shells and 17 whole rock samples over 30 Myr (Kampschulte and Strauss, 2004). The Ordovician/Silurian boundary exhibits the higher values (30‰–35, which drop by 1‰–2‰ in the Early Silurian. Following is a narrower range of S isotope values from ~24‰ to 28‰ and the moving mean shows a plateau in the record. The running mean seems to smooth away the slight downward trend seen in the raw data. Having the mean at odds with the trend in the raw data makes utility of the curve from this section within the Silurian difficult to use for stratigraphic dating because there is no good method to resolve the inconsistencies without a more complete record. Nevertheless, the range from ~24‰ to 28‰ is distinctive to the Late Ordovician and Silurian.

9.5.4.4 Devonian

A total of 18 samples comprise the record for the Devonian. $\delta^{34}S$ values in the Devonian show a downward trend, decreasing from ~25‰ in the Late Silurian to ~19‰ in the lower Middle Devonian. The steep slope of the curve from 408 to 395 Ma makes it useful for stratigraphy, specifically a 6‰ change over 13 million years and an isotope analytical error of 0.2‰ can yield an age resolution in the range of 0.5 million years. In the second section, from 395 to 381 Ma, the curve plateaus: the moving average remains around 18.8–19.2. The remainder of the Devonian exhibits a distinctive peak with $\delta^{34}S$ increasing from 23‰ in the Frasnian age of the Late Devonian (371 Ma) to a maximum of 26.9‰ (Kampschulte and Strauss, 2004). The age resolution of the data set varies from 1 to 4 Myr with a gap of 8 million years over the Devonian/Carboniferous boundary. The shape of the curve makes this section distinct and thus potentially useful for stratigraphy; however, the moving mean currently smooths the data. It is noteworthy that Sim et al. (2015) correlated the S isotope record among sections throughout the world representing the Frasnian–Famennian boundary, despite relatively low-resolution data available at that time. The generally similar ~5‰ decline in seawater $\delta^{34}S$ has been reported for sections in the United States, Belgium, and Poland, which has the potential for correlation applications as seen in Fig. 9.6 (Sim et al., 2015 and references therein). Moreover, the $\delta^{34}S$ and $\delta^{13}C$ excursions may be linked to the Late Devonian mass extinction (Sim et al., 2015). It is, however, important to obtain more data with better defined ages from diverse sites to verify a global trend.

9.5.4.5 Carboniferous

The Carboniferous is also characterized by a decrease in the CAS data from ~20‰ in the Early Carboniferous (Mississippian) to ~15‰ at 334 Ma where it remains until decreasing to around 12‰ in the Late Carboniferous (Pennsylvanian: Kampschulte et al., 2001; Kampschulte and Strauss, 2004; Surakotra et al., 2018). The age resolution of the record, based on the moving mean, ranges from 5.6 Myr from 362 to 334 Ma in the Mississippian and 3–4 Myr for the remainder of the period. The overall range of values in the raw data is narrower than for other section, which makes distinguishing between noise and trend easier. However, the values plateau from 342.8 to 309.2 Ma and leave only the beginning and end of the period significantly distinguishable for stratigraphic correlation. Thus there is a potential for stratigraphic applications for the Early and Late Carboniferous provided the available data are indeed representative of global trends. The potential age resolution for these time intervals is in the range of about 1 million years (5‰ change over about 20 Myr).

9.5.4.6 Permian

The Permian record maintains the low $\delta^{34}S$ values that characterize the end of the Carboniferous, around 12‰. This value is seen in the 16 samples analyzed for the Permian (Kampschulte and Strauss, 2004). This overall $\delta^{34}S$ value is distinctive for the period and is useful for dating the period as a whole but the plateau in the record does not lend itself to more precise stratigraphic dating or correlation within the Permian.

The Permian/Triassic boundary has been sampled at higher resolution of 1 Myr (Kramm and Wedepohl, 1991; Scholle, 1995; Newton et al., 2004; Algeo et al., 2007; Gorjan et al., 2007) and shows distinct fluctuations that are useful stratigraphically (see next).

9.5.4.7 Triassic

The transition from the Paleozoic to the Mesozoic is characterized by an abrupt increase in the seawater $\delta^{34}S$ value from 12‰ in the upper Permian to a maximum value of ~30‰ across the Permian–Triassic boundary (Cortecci et al., 1981; Worden et al., 1997; Kampschulte and Strauss 2004; Newton et al., 2004; Algeo et al., 2007; Longinelli and Flora, 2007; Luo et al., 2010; Song et al., 2014; Schobben et al., 2017; Bernasconi et al., 2017). This peak value occurs at the top of the Permian–Triassic extinction interval followed by a sharp drop to around a mean of 17‰ in the lower and middle Triassic. These data have been sampled from worldwide locations at a temporal resolution of less than 1 million years (Fig. 9.7), indicating that the striking fluctuation is a predominant and global signal. Previous studies interpreted such extreme changes as evidence for the development of a sizable, relatively short-lived reservoir of reduced sulfur in the deep oceanic water column followed by oceanic overturning and sulfide reoxidation (Newton et al., 2004; Algeo et al., 2007; Luo et al., 2010; Bernasconi et al., 2017). The estimated seawater sulfate concentrations were relatively low for the end Permian and the early Triassic, varying between 2 and 6 mM (Bernasconi et al., 2017). More importantly, the positive excursion of more than 10‰ over a time scale of a few million years or even less allows for robust stratigraphic correlations (e.g., Luo et al., 2010). For the remainder of the Triassic the seawater $\delta^{34}S$ value remains relatively constant at approximately 16‰, followed by short-term fluctuations between 11‰ and 25‰ in the uppermost Triassic. The period of distinct variations is potentially suitable for correlations.

9.5.4.8 Jurassic

The $\delta^{34}S$ data for the Jurassic seawater sulfate cluster between 14‰ and 18.0‰ with two maxima of 23.4‰ in the lower Middle Jurassic (Toarcian) and 20.7‰ in the upper Middle Jurassic (Bathonian) (Claypool et al., 1980; Kampschulte and Strauss, 2004; Williford et al., 2009; Gill et al., 2011; Newton et al., 2011). The positive excursion is attributed to the early Toarcian Oceanic Anoxic Event (183 Ma) with the spread of euxinic (i.e., anoxic and sulfidic) bottom waters and thus increases in pyrite burial (Jenkyns, 1988; Williford et al., 2009; Jenkyns, 2010; Gill et al., 2011; Newton et al., 2011). This drastic change coincides with the widespread extinction of benthic organisms in the Northern Europe (Jenkyns, 1988). The temporal resolution of the evaporite and CAS data for the Toarcian and Pliensbachian is constrained on the sub-million-year scale providing more precise information of seawater $\delta^{34}S$ variations, which could be used for stratigraphy. However, for the rest of the Jurassic the overall age uncertainty is relatively large, and more data are required to show finer $\delta^{34}S$ changes.

9.5.4.9 Cretaceous

The Cretaceous record (Fig. 9.2) derived from marine barite by Paytan et al. (2004) and DeBond et al. (2012) is a continuous record that has a resolution of less than 1 million years. A negative shift from ~20‰ to 15‰ occurs from 130 to 120 Ma, remaining low until 104 Ma when it rises to ~19‰ over 10 million years. There is a small minimum at 88 Ma with a value of 18.3‰, returning to values of 18‰–19‰ at ~80 Ma for the remainder of the period.

These results generally agree with the CAS data from Kampschulte and Strauss (2004). This record and the observed fluctuations further illuminate variations that can be seen when the finer scale not smoothed record is available. The finer detail and the observed changes that occur in the beginning of this period make this record useful for stratigraphy and will be discussed later in the chapter. Specifically, both negative excursions (130–120 and 80–87 Ma) occur on relatively short time scales, likely due to the lower seawater sulfate concentration in the Cretaceous (Horita et al., 2002), which allow for correlation and can provide stratigraphic constraints.

9.5.4.10 Cenozoic

A high-resolution barite curve for the Cenozoic (Fig. 9.2) with an age resolution of <1 Myr shows $\delta^{34}S$ values of ~19‰ at the Cretaceous/Paleogene boundary, which drop precipitously to ~17‰ at the Paleocene/Eocene boundary (Paytan et al., 1998; Markovic et al., 2015; Rennie et al., 2018; Yao et al., 2020). Following this minimum, a relatively rapid rise to ~22‰ in the Early to

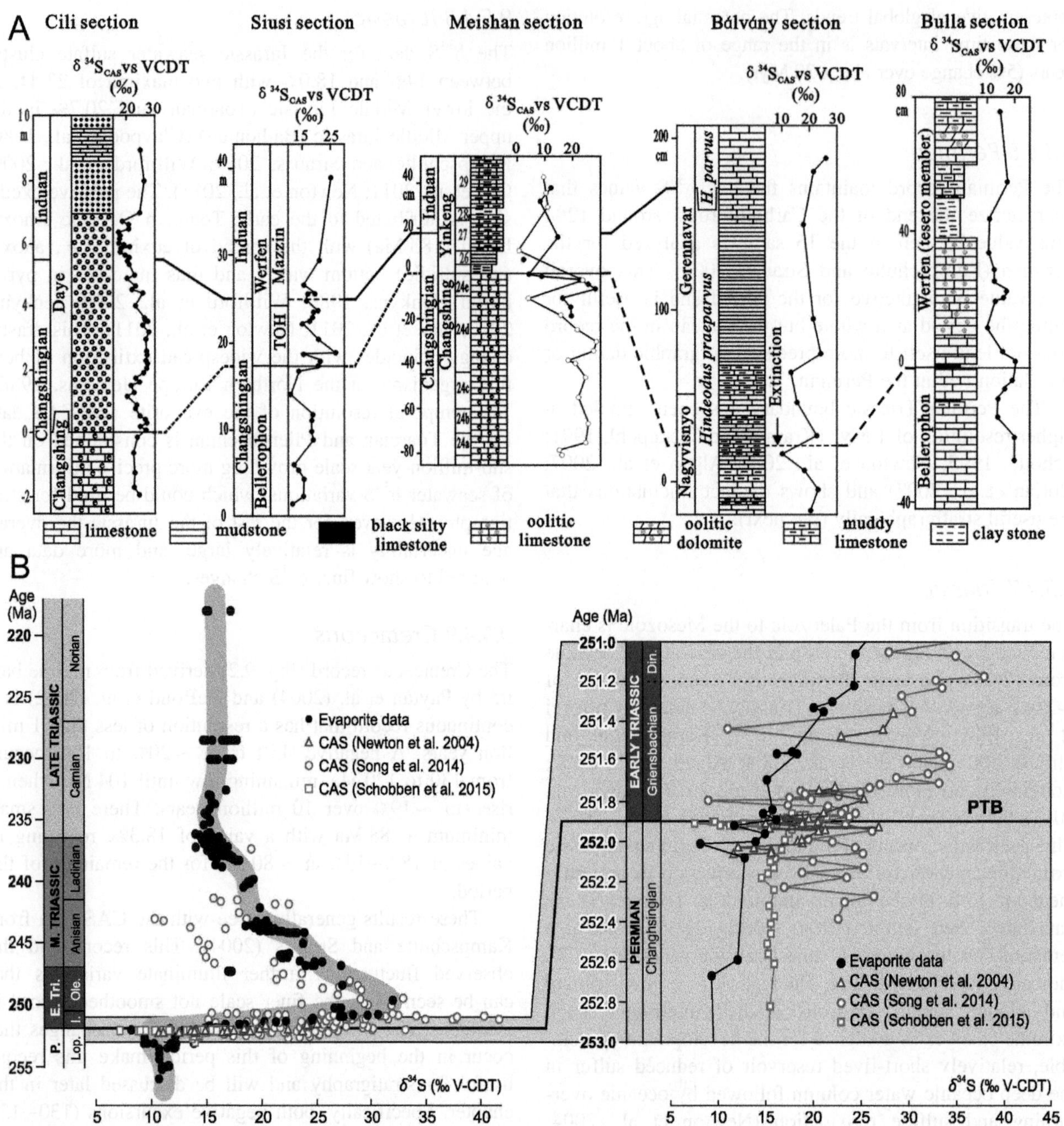

FIGURE 9.7 (A) The CAS-based sulfur isotope records across the Permian–Triassic boundary at different sections from worldwide locations. (B) Comparison of the evaporite-based and CAS-based sulfur isotope records across the Permian–Triassic boundary. *CAS*, Carbonate-associated sulfate. Panel (A): After Luo et al., 2010. Panel (B): After Bernasconi et al., 2017.

Mid-Eocene is observed and this value is maintained until the Pleistocene. The decrease and increase observed between 65 and 40 Ma are useful for stratigraphic purposes (see next). A distinct peak is seen at the PETM (Yao et al., 2018) and a decrease of about 1‰ over the last 2 million years is also evident as reported in Markovic et al. (2015, 2016). In the previous barite record the Eocene rise of seawater $\delta^{34}S$ is defined by only a few samples from Deep Sea Drilling Project Site 366 (Paytan et al., 1998), where the biostratigraphy is not well constrained (Lancelot et al., 1977, 2016). In addition, the decreasing porewater sulfate concentrations with depth, generally higher sedimentation rates (29–41.5 m/Myr), and observable pyrite occurrences at Site 366 throughout the middle to lower Eocene sections (38–56 Ma) imply an organic-rich and reducing environment during this time (Boersma and Shackleton, 1977; Lancelot et al., 1977; Couture et al., 1977), which suggest that the barite in that section could have been diagenetically altered. Taking advantage of more recently retrieved cores and a much improved biostratigraphic framework, Yao et al. (2020) recently evaluated and refined the Eocene $\delta^{34}S$ data with a new high-resolution barite-based $\delta^{34}S$ record between 60 and 30 Ma. They showed anomalously high $^{87}Sr/^{86}Sr$ ratios of Site 366 barites older than 38 Ma, indicating that the local conditions at Site 366 during the Eocene allowed for sulfate reduction and the formation of diagenetic barite.

9.6 A database of S isotope values and their ages for the past 130 Myr using LOWESS regression

At this early stage of development for S isotope stratigraphy, we can see the general trends for the record throughout the Phanerozoic. These trends and values can be used for broad age assignments and correlations at distinct intervals with defined excursions (e.g., the Permian–Triassic Boundary). The goal of developing a LOWESS regression curve for S isotopes and accompanying lookup tables is not yet realized. Currently, the limits to developing such tables include the availability of raw data to construct secular trends, the unknown error associated with age assignments, and gaps in the data sets. The potential for using LOWESS regression, however, can be illustrated by the marine barite data sets over the Cretaceous and Cenozoic (Fig. 9.5). The LOWESS regression curve shown in Fig. 9.5 was produced according to (McArthur et al., 2001).

Based on the LOWESS curve we calculated the age resolution associated with the five age intervals that exhibit abrupt changes in $\delta^{34}S$, 130–116, 107–96, 96–86, 83–75, 65–40, and ~2 Ma to the present. Age resolutions are 0.5, 0.7, 2.6, 2.1, 1.5, and 0.9 Myr, respectively, based on the data and an analytical error of 0.2‰. From this curve we also generated a preliminary lookup table for the data set (Table 9.1).

9.7 Use of S isotopes for correlation

S isotopes have not been widely used as the sole stratigraphic tool for dating samples. The few samples in the literature of S isotopes used for dating and correlation all also use other methods such as $\delta^{13}C$ and $^{87}Sr/^{86}Sr$ at the same time (Walter et al., 2000; Pokrovskii et al., 2006; Misi et al., 2007). Some studies, particularly those focused on the Permian/Triassic Boundary (Scholle, 1995; Kramm and Wedepohl, 1991; Algeo, et al., 2007; Gorjan et al., 2007), use $\delta^{13}C$, $^{87}Sr/^{86}Sr$, biostratigraphy, paleomagnetism, and other methods to correlate the S isotope records and use the S data to investigate the causes and consequences of various biogeochemical cycles across the boundary. Nevertheless, the secular and defined trend in the S isotope record at this time interval could be used for correlation and age determination in the future where methods other than S isotopes are not available or to refine age assignments based on other records.

The utility of using S isotopes for correlation between sites is illustrated in Fig. 9.8 from Yao et al. (2018). This study focuses on the Paleocene Eocene Thermal Maximum at 56 Ma. Ocean Drilling Program Site 1051 is located in the North Atlantic and does not have as distinct a record of the Carbon Isotope Excursion in the $\delta^{13}C$ record that is typically used for correlation purposes of

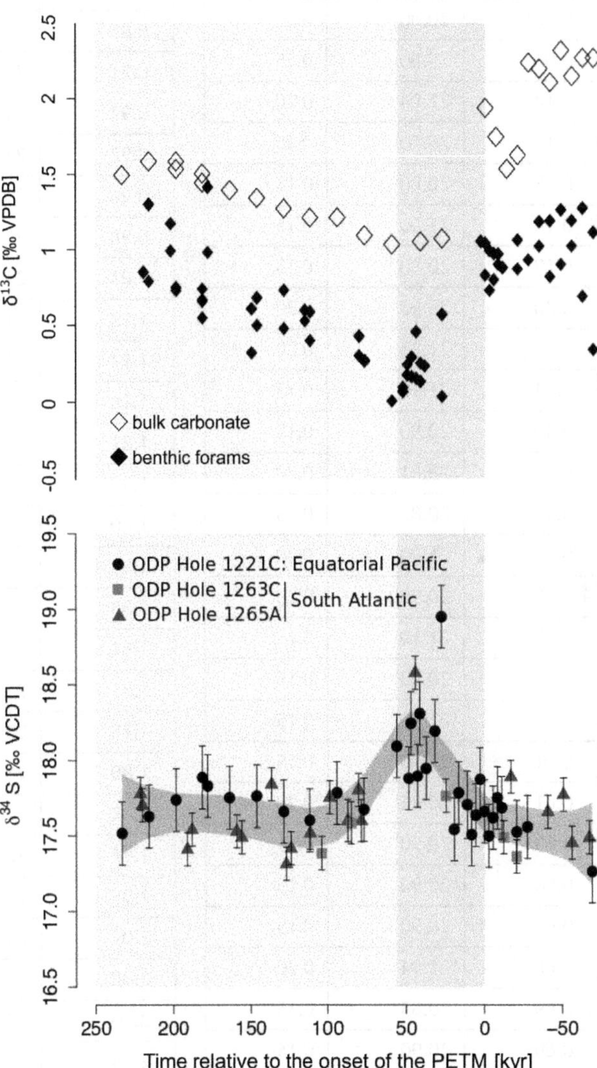

FIGURE 9.8 The sulfur and carbon isotope records across the PETM. Open and solid diamonds denote the $\delta^{13}C$ data derived from bulk carbonate and benthic Foraminifera from ODP Hole 1221A (Nunes and Norris, 2005). Black circles, yellow squares, and red triangles denote the barite-based seawater $\delta^{34}S$ data (1σ) from ODP Hole 1221A, 1263C, and 1265A (Yao et al., 2018). The gray envelope denotes the 95% confidence interval of the LOESS regression for the total $\delta^{34}S$ data. Ages and the PETM stages (*shaded boxes*) as defined by Nunes and Norris (2005).

TABLE 9.1 Preliminary lookup table for the data set of Fig. 9.5.

Age (Ma)	$\delta^{34}S$ Barite	Error (±)
0.00	20.86	0.20
0.00	21.05	0.20
0.02	20.70	0.15
0.03	20.70	0.15
0.05	20.60	0.15
0.07	20.70	0.15
0.08	20.80	0.20
0.08	20.80	0.15
0.12	21.04	0.20
0.16	20.70	0.15
0.17	20.80	0.15
0.18	21.00	0.15
0.19	20.90	0.15
0.20	20.98	0.20
0.24	21.21	0.20
0.24	21.10	0.15
0.30	20.90	0.15
0.31	20.81	0.20
0.38	20.80	0.15
0.39	21.00	0.20
0.40	20.90	0.20
0.42	21.10	0.15
0.48	20.93	0.18
0.53	21.10	0.15
0.61	21.00	0.15
0.61	20.86	0.20
0.62	20.90	0.15
0.66	20.90	0.15
0.66	20.90	0.15
0.68	21.14	0.20
0.69	20.85	0.15
0.69	20.90	0.15
0.71	21.00	0.15
0.72	21.10	0.15
0.74	20.90	0.15
0.76	21.22	0.20

(Continued)

TABLE 9.1 (Continued)

Age (Ma)	$\delta^{34}S$ Barite	Error (±)
0.76	21.08	0.20
0.77	21.10	0.15
0.78	21.10	0.15
0.79	21.20	0.15
0.81	21.30	0.15
0.82	21.30	0.15
0.83	21.30	0.15
0.85	21.40	0.15
0.91	21.34	0.20
0.92	21.30	0.15
0.92	21.20	0.15
0.96	21.20	0.15
0.98	21.20	0.15
1.03	21.35	0.20
1.12	21.30	0.15
1.14	21.10	0.20
1.16	21.40	0.15
1.21	21.45	0.20
1.37	21.80	0.15
1.40	21.70	0.15
1.55	21.80	0.15
1.58	21.80	0.15
1.61	21.80	0.15
1.71	21.80	0.20
1.75	22.00	0.15
1.80	21.80	0.15
1.93	21.80	0.15
1.94	22.05	0.20
1.95	21.90	0.15
2.01	21.90	0.20
2.02	22.10	0.15
2.10	22.00	0.15
2.14	21.90	0.15
2.26	21.90	0.15
2.28	22.02	0.20
2.34	22.00	0.15
2.54	21.80	0.20

(Continued)

TABLE 9.1 (Continued)

Age (Ma)	$\delta^{34}S$ Barite	Error (±)
2.74	22.10	0.15
2.98	21.90	0.15
3.05	21.67	0.20
3.09	21.85	0.20
3.30	21.50	0.20
3.50	21.90	0.20
3.58	21.51	0.20
3.65	21.95	0.20
3.72	21.70	0.20
3.83	21.90	0.20
4.02	21.77	0.20
4.55	22.04	0.20
4.85	21.94	0.20
5.40	21.93	0.20
5.74	21.96	0.20
5.90	21.63	0.20
6.23	22.26	0.20
6.68	22.32	0.20
7.64	21.86	0.20
7.85	22.37	0.20
9.00	21.80	0.20
9.50	22.10	0.20
10.10	21.90	0.20
11.17	22.17	0.20
12.40	22.10	0.20
12.49	21.96	0.20
12.50	21.90	0.20
12.54	22.71	0.20
12.60	21.98	0.24
12.77	22.70	0.20
12.78	22.30	0.20
13.00	22.35	0.22
13.27	22.04	0.20
13.72	22.06	0.20
14.05	21.75	0.22
14.95	22.10	0.20
14.98	21.87	0.20

(Continued)

TABLE 9.1 (Continued)

Age (Ma)	$\delta^{34}S$ Barite	Error (±)
16.20	21.88	0.16
17.04	22.09	0.20
18.13	21.83	0.23
19.00	21.80	0.20
20.14	21.64	0.20
21.08	22.01	0.20
22.20	22.00	0.28
23.47	21.89	0.22
23.97	21.81	0.20
24.36	21.64	0.20
24.52	21.48	0.16
25.26	21.66	0.20
25.83	21.70	0.17
27.68	21.27	0.22
28.38	21.44	0.20
29.61	21.20	0.18
30.50	21.39	0.24
30.60	21.83	0.19
31.48	21.17	0.12
32.30	21.52	0.20
33.44	21.32	0.21
33.49	21.39	0.28
33.58	21.99	0.11
33.90	21.57	0.16
33.92	22.00	0.11
34.00	20.33	0.20
34.10	21.40	0.20
34.39	22.74	0.20
34.44	22.25	0.20
34.49	21.50	0.23
34.93	22.29	0.17
35.02	22.40	0.20
35.10	21.23	0.28
35.17	22.16	0.11
35.37	22.02	0.20
35.49	22.26	0.20
35.76	22.14	0.21

(Continued)

TABLE 9.1 (Continued)

Age (Ma)	$\delta^{34}S$ Barite	Error (±)
35.95	22.05	0.18
35.96	22.39	0.11
36.05	21.60	0.20
36.25	22.52	0.18
36.37	22.03	0.16
36.72	21.78	0.11
36.95	22.17	0.20
37.33	22.31	0.16
37.42	22.14	0.16
37.46	21.52	0.16
37.94	22.36	0.16
38.23	22.32	0.16
38.32	22.20	0.16
38.39	22.36	0.15
38.59	22.51	0.16
38.88	22.00	0.21
38.96	22.37	0.16
39.24	21.91	0.15
39.36	21.98	0.16
39.37	22.36	0.20
39.55	21.80	0.20
40.12	21.71	0.15
40.83	22.19	0.20
40.87	20.94	0.20
40.95	22.39	0.15
41.41	21.66	0.21
41.46	21.47	0.21
41.83	21.38	0.16
42.42	22.49	0.20
43.10	20.25	0.20
43.52	20.50	0.20
44.30	21.48	0.20
44.42	19.73	0.20
44.81	21.30	0.20
45.58	19.23	0.20
45.60	21.33	0.20
45.80	19.24	0.16

(Continued)

TABLE 9.1 (Continued)

Age (Ma)	$\delta^{34}S$ Barite	Error (±)
46.08	19.74	0.11
46.16	19.69	0.20
46.28	19.61	0.20
46.42	19.49	0.16
46.51	19.74	0.18
46.58	19.09	0.20
46.61	19.37	0.20
46.68	19.06	0.16
46.81	19.36	0.16
46.96	18.71	0.21
47.18	19.05	0.20
47.48	19.11	0.20
47.49	18.67	0.15
47.96	18.06	0.21
48.37	18.53	0.21
48.79	19.58	0.21
48.85	19.96	0.16
49.09	18.17	0.20
49.20	19.40	0.20
49.91	19.31	0.20
49.97	17.83	0.21
50.20	18.97	0.21
50.39	16.72	0.15
50.76	18.12	0.16
50.97	18.08	0.20
51.02	16.95	0.21
51.66	16.57	0.21
52.13	17.95	0.14
52.14	17.30	0.21
52.60	16.35	0.21
52.61	17.15	0.11
52.92	17.42	0.17
53.14	16.77	0.21
53.26	17.58	0.15
53.33	17.40	0.21
53.37	17.45	0.11
53.54	16.86	0.11

(Continued)

TABLE 9.1 (Continued)

Age (Ma)	$\delta^{34}S$ Barite	Error (±)
53.78	17.21	0.21
53.90	17.68	0.11
53.96	17.50	0.21
54.13	16.90	0.11
54.19	16.90	0.20
54.67	16.08	0.11
54.98	17.11	0.21
55.03	17.52	0.11
55.05	17.78	0.11
55.05	17.70	0.11
55.05	17.63	0.21
55.07	17.74	0.14
55.07	17.41	0.14
55.08	17.54	0.11
55.08	17.89	0.14
55.09	17.83	0.21
55.09	17.04	0.21
55.10	17.75	0.21
55.11	17.53	0.21
55.11	17.49	0.11
55.12	17.76	0.21
55.13	17.84	0.21
55.13	17.66	0.21
55.14	17.31	0.21
55.14	17.42	0.22
55.15	17.60	0.11
55.15	17.52	0.21
55.16	17.38	0.21
55.16	17.75	0.21
55.17	17.78	0.21
55.17	17.60	0.21
55.18	17.59	0.21
55.18	17.80	0.21
55.18	17.60	0.21
55.18	17.67	0.21
55.21	18.09	0.21
55.21	16.75	0.20

(Continued)

TABLE 9.1 (Continued)

Age (Ma)	$\delta^{34}S$ Barite	Error (±)
55.21	17.88	0.21
55.21	18.25	0.11
55.22	18.58	0.11
55.22	17.90	0.11
55.22	18.31	0.21
55.22	17.95	0.21
55.23	18.19	0.21
55.23	18.95	0.11
55.24	17.77	0.11
55.24	17.54	0.11
55.24	17.78	0.11
55.25	17.71	0.22
55.25	17.51	0.20
55.25	17.64	0.20
55.26	17.87	0.20
55.26	17.66	0.21
55.26	17.50	0.20
55.26	17.62	0.15
55.27	17.75	0.16
55.27	17.68	0.20
55.27	17.49	0.21
55.28	17.89	0.20
55.28	17.36	0.20
55.28	17.53	0.20
55.29	17.56	0.15
55.29	17.21	0.20
55.30	17.66	0.20
55.31	17.77	0.16
55.31	17.45	0.16
55.32	17.49	0.16
55.33	17.26	0.20
55.42	17.63	0.20
55.47	17.42	0.20
55.52	17.19	0.20
55.72	17.34	0.20
55.81	18.05	0.20
55.84	16.99	0.20

(Continued)

TABLE 9.1 (Continued)

Age (Ma)	$\delta^{34}S$ Barite	Error (±)
55.97	17.24	0.20
56.13	17.23	0.20
56.22	17.53	0.20
56.38	16.94	0.20
56.44	17.60	0.20
56.54	17.72	0.20
56.76	18.07	0.20
56.92	17.44	0.20
57.22	17.60	0.20
57.92	17.99	0.20
57.95	17.42	0.20
58.03	18.28	0.20
58.09	17.10	0.20
58.45	17.13	0.20
59.09	17.76	0.20
59.36	17.99	0.20
59.64	18.12	0.20
62.26	18.63	0.20
62.46	19.04	0.20
62.55	19.05	0.20
62.56	19.37	0.20
63.91	19.38	0.20
64.06	19.00	0.20
64.26	18.96	0.20
64.37	19.04	0.20
64.62	19.00	0.20
64.74	19.14	0.20
64.80	18.93	0.20
65.02	19.30	0.20
65.21	18.95	0.30
65.27	18.94	0.30
65.57	19.11	0.30
66.06	18.76	0.30
66.80	18.80	0.30
68.72	18.88	0.27
70.08	18.82	0.30
71.40	19.09	0.30

(Continued)

TABLE 9.1 (Continued)

Age (Ma)	$\delta^{34}S$ Barite	Error (±)
73.09	19.20	0.30
74.27	19.14	0.30
74.48	19.35	0.23
75.40	19.40	0.30
75.69	19.30	0.30
76.49	19.15	0.25
78.45	18.95	0.30
78.79	19.14	0.30
80.35	19.11	0.25
81.98	19.14	0.25
83.01	18.24	0.30
83.62	18.43	0.25
83.68	18.28	0.25
83.83	18.16	0.23
85.16	18.35	0.23
87.93	18.17	0.30
90.72	18.59	0.25
92.91	18.90	0.30

(Continued)

TABLE 9.1 (Continued)

Age (Ma)	$\delta^{34}S$ Barite	Error (±)
93.02	17.32	0.20
93.35	18.42	0.25
93.46	19.04	0.30
93.57	18.84	0.30
93.79	19.02	0.30
95.00	18.92	0.23
95.78	19.04	0.25
97.00	18.81	0.25
98.87	17.86	0.27
100.00	16.27	0.23
101.01	15.65	0.20
102.02	15.42	0.20
103.04	15.48	0.20
104.06	15.61	0.30
107.10	15.65	0.30
108.12	15.92	0.30
109.14	16.16	0.25
110.15	15.35	0.23

(Continued)

TABLE 9.1 (Continued)

Age (Ma)	$\delta^{34}S$ Barite	Error (±)
111.27	16.09	0.30
111.68	16.33	0.30
112.08	16.14	0.30
112.18	15.77	0.28
112.90	16.20	0.25
113.26	15.35	0.30
115.03	15.50	0.30
115.05	15.79	0.27
115.23	15.34	0.30
115.36	15.30	0.25
117.27	15.32	0.23
117.39	16.40	0.30
117.52	16.55	0.25
117.82	18.70	0.30
117.95	17.83	0.30
119.25	19.21	0.27
120.60	19.56	0.25
121.80	19.95	0.23
124.65	20.05	0.25

this time interval making it difficult to correlate to other sites such as Site 1267 in the South Atlantic. At both Sites, however, a minimum in the $\delta^{34}S$ record was recorded and used to align the two records. Ages were determined by biostratigraphy.

S isotopes data are becoming more widely available for many study locations and, as illustrated previously, have the potential to become a more useful tool for stratigraphy and correlation as we refine the global S isotope record. The challenge in the next few years is to expand the data available to produce a reliable, high-resolution, secular data of seawater S isotope values set such that a high-resolution curve like the one currently available for the past 130 Ma could be produced and used for age determination.

Bibliography

Algeo, T.J., Ellwood, B.B., Thoa, N.T.K., Rowe, H., and Maynard, J.B., 2007, The Permian-Triassic boundary at Nhi Tao, Vietnam; evidence for recurrent influx of sulfidic watermasses to a shallow-marine carbonate platform. *Palaeogeography, Palaeoclimatology, Palaeoecology*, **252**: 304–327.

Arthur, M.A., 2000, Volcanic contributions to the carbon and sulfur geochemical cycles and global change. *In* Sigurdsson, H. (ed), *Encyclopedia of Volcanoes*. San Diego, CA: Academic Press, p. 1045–1056.

Ault, W., and Jensen, M.L., 1963, A summary of sulfur isotope standards. *In* Jensen, M.L. (ed), Biogeochemistry of Sulfur Isotopes, National Science Foundation Symposium Proceedings, Yale University, p. 16–29.

Bernasconi, S.M., Meier, I., Wohlwend, S., Brack, P., Hochuli, P.A., Bläsi, H., et al., 2017, An evaporite-based high-resolution sulfur isotope record of Late Permian and Triassic seawater sulfate. *Geochimica et Cosmochimica Acta*, **204**: 331–349.

Berner, R.A., 1999, Atmospheric oxygen over Phanerozoic time. *Proceedings of the National Academy of Sciences of the United States of America*, **96**: 10955–10957.

Berner, E.K., and Berner, R.A., 1987, *The Global Water Cycle; Geochemistry and Environment*. Englewood Cliffs, NJ: Prentice-Hall, pp 397.

Berner, R.A., and Canfield, D.E., 1989, A new model for atmospheric oxygen over Phanerozoic time. *American Journal of Science*, **289**: 333–361.

Berner, R.A., and Canfield, D.E., 1999, Atmospheric oxygen over Phanerozoic time. Proceedings of the National Academy of Sciences of the United States of America, **96**: 10955–10957.

Boersma, A., and Shackleton, N., 1977. *36*. Oxygen and carbon isotope record through the Oligocene, DSDP Site 366, Equatorial Atlantic, *In Initial Reports of the Deep Sea Drilling Project, Vol. 41*. Texas A & M University, Ocean Drilling Program, College Station, TX, pp. 957–962.

Bottrell, S.H., and Newton, R.J., 2006, Reconstruction of changes in global sulfur cycling from marine sulfate isotopes. *Earth-Science Reviews*, **75**: 59–83.

Burdett, J.W., Arthur, M.A., and Richardson, M., 1989, A Neogene seawater sulfur isotope age curve from calcareous pelagic microfossils. *Earth and Planetary Science Letters*, **94**: 189–198.

Canfield, D.E., 2001, Isotope fractionation by natural populations of sulfate-reducing bacteria. *Geochimica et Cosmochimica Acta*, **65**: 1117–1124.

Canfield, D.E., and Farquhar, J., 2009. Animal evolution, bioturbation, and the sulfate concentration of the oceans. Proceedings of the National Academy of Sciences of the United States of America **106**: 8123–8127.

Canfield, D., and Thamdrup, B., 1994, The production of ^{34}S-depleted sulfide during bacterial disproportionation of elemental sulfur. *Science*, **266**: 1973–1975.

Chiba, H., and Sakai, H., 1985, Oxygen isotope exchange rate between dissolved sulfate and water at hydrothermal temperatures. *Geochimica et Cosmochimica Acta*, **49** (4), 993–1000.

Claypool, G.E., Holser, W.T., Kaplan, I.R., Sakai, H., and Zak, I., 1980, The age curves of sulfur and oxygen isotopes in marine sulfate and their mutual interpretation. *Chemical Geology*, **28**: 199–260.

Cortecci, G., Reyes, E., Berti, G., and Casati, P., 1981, Sulfur and oxygen isotopes in Italian marine sulfates of Permian and Triassic ages. *Chemical Geology*, **34**: 65–79.

Couture, R., Miller, R.S., Gieskes, J.M., 1977. 32. Interstitial water and mineralogical studies, Leg 41, *In* Gardner J., Herring J. (Eds.), *Initial Reports of the Deep Sea Drilling Project, Vol. 41*. College Station, TX, pp. 907–914.

Crockford, P.W., et al., 2019, Claypool continued: Extending the isotopic record of sedimentary sulfate. *Chemical Geology*, **513**: 200–225.

Das, N., Horita, J., and Holland, H.D., 1990, Chemistry of fluid inclusions in halite from the Salina Group of the Michigan Basin: implications for Late Silurian Seawater and the origin of sedimentary brines. *Geochimica et Cosmochimica Acta*, **54**: 319–327.

DeBond, N., Oakes, R.L., Paytan, A., and Wortmann, U.G., 2012, Early Aptian carbon and sulphur isotope signatures at ODP Site 765. *Isotopes in Environmental and Health Studies*, **48**: 180–194.

Eagle, M., Paytan, A., Arrigo, K.R., van Dijken, G., and Murray, R.W., 2003, A comparison between excess barium and barite as indicators of carbon export. *Paleoceanography*, **18**: 1–13.

Farquhar, J., and Wing, B., 2003, Multiple sulfur isotopes and the evolution of the Earth's atmosphere. *Earth and Planetary Science Letters*, **213**: 1–13.

Farquhar, J., Bao, H., and Thiemens, M., 2000, Atmospheric influence of Earth's earliest sulfur cycle. *Science*, **289**: 756–758.

Fox, J.S., and Videtich, P.E., 1997, Revised estimate of δ^{34}S for marine sulfates from the Upper Ordovician: data from the Williston Basin, North Dakota, USA. *Applied Geochemistry*, **12**: 97–103.

Gill, B.C., Lyons, T.W., and Saltzman, M.R., 2007, Parallel, high-resolution carbon and sulfur isotope records of the evolving Paleozoic marine sulfur reservoir. *Palaeogeography, Palaeoclimatology, Palaeoecology*, **256**: 156–173.

Gill, B.C., Lyons, T.W., and Jenkyns, H.C., 2011, A global perturbation to the sulfur cycle during the Toarcian Oceanic Anoxic Event. *Earth and Planetary Science Letters*, **312**: 484–496.

Goldberg, T., Poulton, S.W., and Strauss, H., 2005, Sulphur and oxygen isotope signatures of late Neoproterozoic to early Cambrian sulphate, Yangtze Platform, China: diagenetic constraints and seawater evolution. *Precambrian Research*, **137**: 223–241.

Goldhaber, M.B., and Kaplan, I.R., 1974, The sulfur cycle. *In* Goldberg, E.D. (ed), *The Sea. 5. Marine Chemistry*. New York: Wiley, p. 569–655.

Gorjan, P., Kaiho, K., Kakegawa, T., Niitsuma, S., Chen, Z.Q., Kajiwara, Y., et al., 2007, Paleoredox, biotic and sulfur-isotopic changes associated with the end-Permian mass extinction in the western Tethys. *Chemical Geology*, **244**: 483–492.

Habicht, K.S., Canfield, D.E., and Rethmeier, J., 1998, Sulfur isotope fractionation during bacterial reduction and disproportionation of thiosulfate and sulfite. *Geochimica et Cosmochimica Acta*, **62**: 2585–2595.

Habicht, K.S., Gade, M., Thamdrup, B., Berg, P., and Canfield, D.E., 2002, Calibration of Sulfate Levels in the Archean Ocean. *Science*, **298**: 2372–2374.

Harland, W.B., Armstrong, R.L., Cox, A.V., Craig, L.A., Smith, A.G., and Smith, D.G., 1990, *A Geologic Time Scale 1989*. Cambridge: Cambridge University Press, pp 263.

Holser, W.T., and Kaplan, I.R., 1966, Isotope geochemistry of sedimentary sulfates. *Chemical Geology*, **1**: 93–135.

Holser, W.T., Schidlowski, M., Mackenzie, F.T., and Maynard, J.B., 1988, Geochemical cycles of carbon and sulfur. *In* Gregor, C.B., Garrels, R.M., Mackenzie, F.T., and Maynard, J.B. (eds), *Chemical Cycles in the Evolution of the Earth*. New York: Wiley, p. 105–173.

Horita, J., Zimmermann, H., and Holland, H.D., 2002, Chemical evolution of seawater during the Phanerozoic; implications from the record of marine evaporites. *Geochimica et Cosmochimica Acta*, **66**: 3733–3756.

Hough, M.L., Shields, G.A., Evins, L.Z., Strauss, H., Henderson, R.A., and Mackenzie, S., 2006, A major sulphur isotope event at c. 510Ma: a possible anoxia-extinction-volcanism connection during the Early-Middle Cambrian transition? *Terra Nova*, **18**: 257–263.

Hurtgen, M.T., Arthur, M.A., Suits, N.S., and Kaufman, A.J., 2002, The sulfur isotopic composition of Neoproterozoic seawater sulfate: implications for a snowball Earth? *Earth and Planetary Science Letters*, **203**: 413–429.

Hurtgen, M.T., Pruss, S.B., and Knoll, A.H., 2009, Evaluating the relationship between the carbon and sulfur cycles in the later Cambrian ocean: an example from the Port au Port Group, western Newfoundland, Canada. *Earth and Planetary Science Letters*, **281**: 288–297.

Jenkyns, H.C., 1988, The early Toarcian (Jurassic) anoxic event – stratigraphic, sedimentary, and geochemical evidence. *American Journal of Science*, **288**: 101–151.

Jenkyns, H.C., 2010, Geochemistry of oceanic anoxic events. *Geochemistry, Geophysics, Geosystems*, **11**: Q03004.

Johnston, D.T., 2011, Multiple sulfur isotopes and the evolution of Earth's surface sulfur cycle. *Earth-Science Reviews*, **106**: 161–183.

Kah, L.C., Lyons, T.W., and Frank, T.D., 2004, Low marine sulphate and protracted oxygenation of the Proterozoic biospheres. *Nature*, **431**: 834–838.

Kah, L.C., Thompson, C.K., Henderson, M.A., and Zhan, R., 2016, Behavior of marine sulfur in the Ordovician. *Palaeogeography, Palaeoclimatology, Palaeoecology*, **458**: 133–153.

Kampschulte, A., and Strauss, H., 2004, The sulfur isotopic evolution of Phanerozoic sea water based on the analysis of structurally substituted sulfate in carbonates. *Chemical Geology*, **204**: 255–286.

Kampschulte, A., Buhl, D., and Strauss, H., 1998, The sulfur and strontium isotopic compositions of Permian evaporites from the Zechstein basin, northern Germany. *Geologische Rundschau*, **87**: 192–199.

Kampschulte, A., Bruckschen, P., and Strauss, H., 2001, The sulphur isotopic composition of trace sulphates in Carboniferous brachiopods: implications for coeval seawater, correlation with other geochemical cycles and isotope stratigraphy. *Chemical Geology*, **175**: 149–173.

Kaplan, I.R., 1983, Stable isotopes of sulfur, nitrogen and deuterium in recent marine environments. Stable Isotopes in Sedimentary Geology, Chap. 2: 108 pp. *In* Arthur, M.A., Anderson, T.F., Kaplan, I.R., Veizer, J., and Land, L.S. (eds), Stable Isotopes in Sedimentary Geology. *SEPM Short Course Notes*, Vol. 10.

Kaplan, I.R., Emery, K.O., and Rittenberg, S.C., 1963, The distribution and isotopic abundance of sulphur in recent marine sediments off southern California. *Geochimica et Cosmochimica Acta*, **27**: 297–331.

Kramm, U., and Wedepohl, K.H., 1991, The isotopic composition of strontium and sulfur in seawater of Late Permian (Zechstein) age. *Chemical Geology*, **90**: 253–262.

Krouse, H.R., 1980, Sulphur isotopes in our environment. *In* Fritz, P., and Fontes, J.C. (eds), *Handbook of Environmental Isotope Geochemistry*. Amsterdam: Elsevier, p. 435–471.

Lancelot, Y., Seibold, E., Cepek, P., Dean, W.E., Eremeev, V., Gardner, J., et al., 1977. Site 366: Sierra Leone Rise, *In Initial Reports of the Deep Sea Drilling Project, 41*. United States Government Printing Office, Washington, DC, pp. 121–161.

Langton, S.J., Rabideaux, N.M., Borrelli, C., and Katz, M.E., 2016, South-eastern Atlantic deep-water evolution during the late-middle Eocene to earliest Oligocene (Ocean Drilling Program Site 1263 and Deep Sea Drilling Project Site 366). *Geosphere*, **12**: 103–1047.

Longinelli, A., and Flora, O., 2007, Isotopic composition of gypsum samples of Permian and Triassic age from the north-eastern Italian Alps: palaeoenvironmental implications. *Chemical Geology*, **245**: 275–284.

Lowenstein, T.K., Timofeeff, M.N., Brennan, S.T., Hardie, L.A., and Demicco, R.V., 2001, Oscillations in Phanerozoic seawater chemistry; evidence from fluid inclusions. *Science*, **294**: 1086–1088.

Luo, G., Kump, L.R., Wang, Y., Tong, J., Arthur, M.A., Yang, H., et al., 2010, Isotopic evidence for an anomalously low oceanic sulfate concentration following End-Permian Mass Extinction. *Earth and Planetary Science Letters*, **300**: 101–111.

Lyons, T.W., Walter, L.M., Gellatly, A.M., Martini, A.M., and Blake, R. E., 2004, Sites of anomalous organic remineralization in the carbonate sediments of South Florida, USA; the sulfur cycle and carbonate-associated sulfate. *Geological Society of America Special Papers*, **379**: 161–176.

Markovic, S., Paytan, A., and Wortmann, U.G., 2015, Pleistocene sediment offloading and the global sulfur cycle. *Biogeosciences*, **12**: 3043–3060.

Markovic, S., Paytan, A., Li, H., and Wortmann, U.G., 2016, A revised seawater sulfate oxygen isotope record for the last 4Myr. *Geochimica et Cosmochimica Acta*, **175**: 239–251.

Mazumdar, A., and Strauss, H., 2006, Sulfur and strontium isotopic compositions of carbonate and evaporite rocks from the late Neoproterozoic-early Cambrian Bilara Group (Nagaur-Ganganagar Basin, India): constraints on intrabasinal correlation and global sulfur cycle. *Precambrian Research*, **149**: 217–230.

McArthur, J.M., Howarth, R.J., and Bailey, T.R., 2001, Strontium isotope stratigraphy: LOWESS Version 3. Best-fit line to the marine Sr-isotope curve for 0 to 509Ma and accompanying look-up table for deriving numerical age. *Journal of Geology*, **109**: 155–169.

Misi, A., Kaufman, A.J., Veizer, J., Powis, K., Azmy, K., Boggiani, P.C., et al., 2007, Chemostratigraphic correlation of Neoproterozoic successions in South America. *Chemical Geology*, **237**: 143–167.

Newton, R.J., Pevitt, E.L., Wignal, P.B., and Bottrell, S.H., 2004, Large shifts in the isotopic composition of seawater sulphate across the Permo-Triassic boundary in northern Italy. *Earth and Planetary Science Letters*, **218**: 331–345.

Newton, R.J., Reeves, E.P., Kafousia, N., Wignall, P.B., Bottrell, S.H., and Sha, J.-G., 2011, Low marine sulfate concentrations and the isolation of the European epicontinental sea during the Early Jurassic. *Geology*, **39**: 7–10.

Nunes, F., and Norris R.D., 2005, Data report: High-resolution stable isotope records across the Paleocene/Eocene boundary, ODP Sites 1220 and 1221. *In* Wilson, P.A., Lyle, M., Firth, J.V. (eds.), Proceedings of the Ocean Drilling Program, Scientific Results, Vol. 199. College Station, TX, pp. 1–12.

Ohkouchi, N., Kawamura, K., Kajiwara, Y., Wada, E., Okada, M., Kanamatsu, T., et al., 1999, Sulfur isotope records around Livello Bonarelli (Northern Apennines, Italy) black shale at the Cenomanian-Turonian boundary. *Geology*, **27**: 535–538.

Orti, F., Rosell, L., and Anadón, P., 2010, Diagenetic gypsum related to sulfur deposits in evaporites (Libros Gypsum, Miocene, NE Spain). *Sedimentary Geology*, **228**: 304–318.

Paytan, A., Kastner, M., Martin, E.E., Macdougall, J.D., and Herbert, T., 1993, Marine barite as a monitor of seawater strontium isotope composition. *Nature*, **366**: 45–49.

Paytan, A., Kastner, M., Campbell, D., and Thiemens, M.H., 1998, Sulfur isotopic composition of Cenozoic seawater sulfate. *Science*, **282**: 1459–1462.

Paytan, A., Kastner, M., Campbell, D., and Thiemens, M.H., 2004, Seawater sulfur isotope fluctuations in the cretaceous. *Science*, **304**: 1663–1665.

Paytan, A., Gray, E.T., Ma, Z., Erhardt, A., and Faul, A., 2011, Application of sulphur isotopes for stratigraphic correlation. *Isotopes in Environmental and Health Studies*, **48**: 195–206.

Peryt, T.M., Halas, S., Kovalevych, V.M., Petrychenko, Y., and Dzhinoridze, N.M., 2005, The sulphur and oxygen isotopic composition of Lower Cambrian anhydrites in East Siberia. *Geological Quarterly*, **49**: 235–242.

Pierre, C., and Rouchy, J.M., 1986, — Oxygen and sulfur isotopes in anhydrites from Givetian and Visean evaporites of Northern France and Belgium. *Chemical Geology (Isotope Geoscience section)*, **58**: 245–252.

Planavsky, N.J., Bekker, A., Hofmann, A., Owens, J.D., and Lyons, T. W., 2012, Sulfur record of rising and falling marine oxygen and sulfate levels during the Lomagundi event. *Proceedings of the National Academy of Sciences of the United States of America*, **109**: 18300–18305.

Pokrovskii, B.G., Melezhik, V.A., and Bujakaite, M.I., 2006, Carbon, oxygen, strontium, and sulfur isotopic compositions in late Precambrian rocks of the Patom Complex, central Siberia; Communication 2, Nature of carbonates with ultralow and ultrahigh δ^{13}C values. *Lithology and Mineral Resources*, **41**: 576–587.

Present, T.M., Paris, G., Burke, A., Fischer, W.W., and Adkins, J.F., 2015, Large carbonate associated sulfate isotopic variability between brachiopods, micrite, and other sedimentary components in Late Ordovician strata. *Earth and Planetary Science Letters*, **432**: 187–198.

Rees, C.E., Jenkins, W.F., and Monster, J., 1978, The sulphur isotopic composition of ocean water sulphate. *Geochimica et Cosmochimica Acta*, **42**: 377–382.

Rennie, V.C.F., Paris, G., Sessions, A.L., Abramovich, A., Turchyn, A. V., and Adkins, J.F., 2018, Cenozoic record of δ^{34}S in foraminiferal calcite implies an early Eocene shift to deep-ocean sulfide burial. *Nature Geoscience*, **11**: 761–765.

Rick, B., 1990, Sulphur and oxygen isotopic composition of Swiss Gipskeuper (Upper Triassic). *Chemical Geology: Isotope Geoscience Section*, **80**: 243–250.

Sakai, H., 1972, Oxygen isotopic ratios of some evaporites from Precambrian to Recent ages. *Earth and Planetary Science Letters*, **15**: 201–205.

Schobben, M., Stebbins, A., Algeo, T.J., Strauss, H., Leda, L., Haas, J., et al., 2017, Volatile earliest Triassic sulfur cycle: a consequence of persistent low seawater sulfate concentrations and a high sulfur cycle turnover rate? *Palaeogeography, Palaeoclimatology, Palaeoecology*, **486**: 74–85.

Scholle, P.A., 1995, Carbon and sulfur isotope stratigraphy of the Permian and adjacent intervals. *In* Scholle, P.A., Peryt, T.M., and Ulmer-Scholle, D.S. (eds), *The Permian of northern Pangea. Vol. 1*. Berlin: Springer-Verlag, p. 133–149.

Scott, C., Wing, B.A., Bekker, A., Planavsky, N.J., Medvedev, P., Bates, S.M., et al., 2014, Pyrite multiple-sulfur isotope evidence for rapid expansion and contraction of the early Paleoproterozoic seawater sulfate reservoir. *Earth and Planetary Science Letters*, **389**: 95–104.

Sim, M.S., Ono, S., and Hurtgen, M.T., 2015, Sulfur isotope evidence for low and fluctuating sulfate levels in the Late Devonian ocean and the potential link with the mass extinction event. *Earth and Planetary Science Letters*, **419**: 52–62.

Song, H.Y., Tong, J.N., Algeo, T.J., Song, H.J., Qiu, H.O., Zhu, Y.Y., et al., 2014, Early Triassic seawater sulfate drawdown. *Geochimica et Cosmochimica Acta*, **128**: 95–113.

Strauss, H., 1993, The sulfur isotopic record of Precambrian sulfates; new data and a critical evaluation of the existing record. *Precambrian Research*, **63**: 225–246.

Strauss, H., 1997, The isotopic composition of sedimentary sulfur through time. *Palaeogeography, Palaeoclimatology, Palaeoecology*, **132**: 97–118.

Strauss, H., Banerjee, D.M., and Kumar, V., 2001, The sulfur isotopic composition of Neoproterozoic to early Cambrian seawater – evidence from the cyclic Hanseran evaporites, NW India. *Chemical Geology*, **175**: 17–28.

Surakotra, N., Promkotra, S., Charusiri, P., Maruoka, T., and Hisada, K. I., 2018, Sulfur, Strontium, Carbon, and Oxygen Isotopes of Calcium Sulfate Deposits in Late Carboniferous Rocks of the Loei-Wang Saphung (LWS) Area, Loei Province, Thailand. *Geosciences*, **8**: 229–239.

Thode, H.G., and Monster, J., 1965, Sulfur-isotope geochemistry of petroleum, evaporites, and ancient seas. *American Association of Petroleum Geologists Memoir*, **4**: 367–377.

Thompson, C.K., and Kah, L.C., 2012, Sulfur isotope evidence for widespread euxinia and a fluctuating oxycline in Early to Middle Ordovician greenhouse oceans. *Palaeogeography, Palaeoclimatology, Palaeoecology*, **313-314**: 189–214.

Turchyn, A.V., Schrag, D.P., Coccioni, R., and Montanari, A., 2009, Stable isotope analysis of the Cretaceous sulfur cycle. *Earth and Planetary Science Letters*, **285**: 115–123.

Ueda, A., Campbell, F.A., Krouse, H.R., and Spencer, R.J., 1987, ^{34}S/^{32}S variations in trace sulphide and sulphate in carbonate rocks of a Devonian reef, Alberta, Canada, and the Precambrian Siyeh Formation, Montana, USA. *Chemical Geology: Isotope Geoscience Section*, **65**: 383–390.

Utrilla, R., Pierre, C., Orti, F., and Pueyo, J.J., 1992, Oxygen and sulphur isotope compositions as indicators of the origin of Mesozoic and Cenozoic evaporites from Spain. *Chemical Geology*, **102**: 229–244.

Walter, M.R., Veevers, J.J., Calver, C.R., Gorjan, P., and Hill, A.C., 2000, Dating the 840-544 Ma Neoproterozoic interval by isotopes of strontium, carbon, sulfur in seawater, and some interpretative models. *Precambrian Research*, **100**: 371–433.

Williford, K.H., Foriel, J., Ward, P.D., and Steig, E.J., 2009, Major perturbation in sulfur cycling at the Triassic-Jurassic boundary. *Geology*, **37**: 835–838.

Worden, R.H., Smalley, P.C., and Fallick, A.E., 1997, Sulfur cycle in buried evaporites. *Geology*, **25**: 643–646.

Wotte, T., Strauss, H., Fugmann, A., and Garbe-Schönberg, D., 2012, Paired δ^{34}S data from carbonate-associated sulfate and chromium-reducible sulfur across the traditional Lower-Middle Cambrian boundary of W-Gondwana. *Geochimica et Cosmochimica Acta*, **85**: 228–253.

Wu, N.P., Farquhar, J., Strauss, H., Kim, S.-T., and Canfield, D.E., 2010, Evaluating the S-isotope fractionation associated with Phanerozoic pyrite burial. *Geochimica et Cosmochimica Acta*, **74** (7), 2053–2071, https://doi.org/10.1016/j.gca.2009.12.012.

Wu, N.P., Farquhar, J., and Strauss, H., 2014, δ^{34}S and Δ^{33}S records of Paleozoic seawater sulfate based on the analysis of carbonate associated sulfate. *Earth and Planetary Science Letters*, **399**: 44–51, https://doi.org/10.1016/j.epsl.2014. 05.004.

Yao, W.Q., Paytan, A., and Wortmann, U.G., 2018, Large-scale ocean deoxygenation during the Paleocene-Eocene Thermal Maximum. *Science*, **361**: 804–806.

Yao, W.Q., Wortmann, U.G., and Paytan, A., 2019, Sulfur isotopes – Use for stratigraphy during times of rapid perturbations. *Stratigraphy & Timescales*, **4**: 1–33.

Yao, W.Q., Paytan, A., Griffith, E.M., Martínez-Ruiz, F., Markovic, S., and Wortmann, U.G., 2020, A revised seawater sulfate S-isotope curve for the Eocene. *Chemical Geology*, **532**.

E.L. Grossman and M.M. Joachimski

Chapter 10

Oxygen Isotope Stratigraphy

Chapter outline

Abstract

Variations in the $^{18}O/^{16}O$ ratio of marine fossils and microfossils record changes in seawater $^{18}O/^{16}O$ and temperature and provide the basis for global correlation. Based on more than 64,000 measurements, this chapter presents oxygen isotope curves for Phanerozoic foraminifera, mollusks, brachiopods, and conodonts, as well as for Precambrian limestones, dolostones, and cherts. Periodic oxygen isotopic variations in deep-sea foraminifera define marine isotope stages that, when combined with biostratigraphy and astronomical tuning, provide a late Cenozoic chronostratigraphy with a resolution of several thousand years. Oxygen isotope events of late Cenozoic, Mesozoic, and Paleozoic age mark local and global climate change and serve as chemostratigraphic markers for regional and global correlation. Precambrian oxygen isotope stratigraphy is hampered by the lack of unaltered authigenic marine carbonate and phosphate.

10.1 Introduction

Oxygen isotope stratigraphy has revolutionized our understanding of the Earth's paleoclimate. Oxygen isotope measurements ($^{18}O/^{16}O$) of carbonate and phosphate fossils and microfossils have enabled reconstruction of paleotemperatures of Phanerozoic oceans (e.g., Urey et al., 1951; Popp et al., 1986; Luz et al., 1984) and yielded a highly refined Neogene marine stratigraphy (Emiliani, 1955; Shackleton and Opdyke, 1973; Lisiecki and Raymo, 2005). Moreover, oxygen isotopes are being increasingly applied for pre-Neogene stratigraphy as scientists discover new isotopic events related to global climate change. This chapter outlines the principles and pitfalls of oxygen isotope stratigraphy and presents an updated isotopic record of ocean sediments through 3.8 Ga of Earth history. The record is based on more than 64,000 analyses of Phanerozoic fossils and microfossils, including data for benthic foraminifera ($N = 39,675$), planktonic foraminifera ($N = 10,800$), belemnites ($N = 4352$), bivalves ($N = 605$), brachiopods ($N = 4784$), and conodonts and fish teeth ($N = 3898$), as well as 10,080 analyses of Precambrian rocks. This synthesis builds upon compilations by Veizer et al. (1999), Zachos et al. (2001), Shields and Veizer (2002), Knauth (2005), Prokoph et al. (2008), Cramer et al. (2009), Grossman et al. (2008), Grossman (2012a), Veizer and Prokoph (2015), Martinez and Dera (2015), and Ullmann et al. (2016).

To effectively apply oxygen isotope stratigraphy, one must understand and appreciate terminology, standardization, sample provenance, and diagenesis. These topics will be introduced prior to presentation of the oxygen isotope record.

10.2 Methodology

Methodologies for determination of oxygen isotope stratigraphy are discussed in comprehensive publications such as Grossman (1994), Veizer et al. (1999), Zachos et al. (2001), Ravelo and Hillaire-Marcel (2007), Grossman (2012b), and Pearson (2012) for carbonates and MacLeod (2012) for phosphates (conodonts). The guiding principles and relationships used in this chapter are summarized next. Stable isotope analyses of carbonate minerals involve reaction of 0.05 to several milligrams of $CaCO_3$ in phosphoric acid to produce CO_2 that

Geologic Time Scale 2020. DOI: https://doi.org/10.1016/B978-0-12-824360-2.00010-3

is subsequently analyzed on an isotope ratio mass spectrometer. The oxygen isotopic data are reported in delta (δ) notation, such that

$$\delta^{18}O(\text{‰}) = 1000\left(\frac{(^{18}O/^{16}O)_x - (^{18}O/^{16}O)_{std}}{(^{18}O/^{16}O)_{std}}\right)$$

$$= 1000\left(\frac{(^{18}O/^{16}O)_x}{(^{18}O/^{16}O)_{std}} - 1\right)$$

where subscripts x and std refer to the sample and standard, respectively. Oxygen isotope data for carbonate minerals are reported versus PDB (PeeDee Belemnite) or VPDB (Vienna PDB), which entail calibration to PDB using the NBS-19 calcite standard ($\delta^{18}O = -2.20$‰ vs PDB; Gonfiantini, 1984; Coplen et al., 1996). With the declining stocks of NBS-19 the International Atomic Energy Agency (IAEA) has released a new carbonate standard, IAEA-603 ($\delta^{18}O = -2.37$‰), derived from Carrara marble (IAEA, 2016). The precision for oxygen isotope analyses of $CaCO_3$ is typically ±0.05‰ to 0.10‰.

For oxygen isotope analyses of phosphate, the samples (conodonts, fish teeth, and brachiopod shells) are first dissolved in nitric acid then reprecipitated as silver phosphate (Ag_3PO_4). Earlier studies precipitated bismuth phosphate ($BiPO_4$), but the hygroscopic properties of that compound often led to inaccuracies. Silver phosphate (or $BiPO_4$) can be chemically reduced with fluorine gas or bromine pentafluoride, converted to O_2 then CO_2, and analyzed by a conventional dual-inlet isotope ratio mass spectrometry (DI-IRMS); or reduced using glassy carbon in a high-temperature elemental analyzer and analyzed as CO via continuous flow IRMS (CF-IRMS). The precision of the analyses is about ±0.2‰ for TCEA and DI-IRMS. More recently, the $\delta^{18}O$ of biogenic phosphate has been measured using secondary-ion mass spectrometry (SIMS). Whereas DI-IRMS and CF-IRMS use larger amounts of biogenic apatite (0.3 to several mg's) and only measure the $\delta^{18}O$ of phosphate-bound oxygen, SIMS analyzes individual conodont elements but measures the $\delta^{18}O$ of total apatite oxygen (including carbonate- and hydroxyl-bound oxygen). There is an offset in $\delta^{18}O$ between SIMS and IRMS analyses that is not yet well constrained, but based on the comparison of SIMS and IRMS data by Trotter et al. (2016), we applied a correction of −0.6‰ to all published SIMS $\delta^{18}O$ data.

The $\delta^{18}O$ values of phosphate are reported using VSMOW (Vienna Standard Mean Ocean Water; Gonfiantini, 1984; Gröning, 2004), IAEA-produced water that is analytically identical to SMOW (standard mean ocean water). To account for interlaboratory differences, researchers report phosphate $\delta^{18}O$ data along with the value obtained for the phosphorite rock standard NBS120c (Vennemann et al., 2002; Pucéat et al., 2010). Only recently has a consensus been reached for the $\delta^{18}O$ value of NBS120c (21.7‰), with earlier studies reporting different values (e.g., Vennemann et al., 2002; Chenery et al., 2010). In order to account for potential calibration offsets, all $\delta^{18}O$ values in this study were normalized to a value of 21.7‰ for NBS120c.

Numerous equations have been produced to calibrate $CaCO_3$ $\delta^{18}O$ values to paleotemperature (e.g., for calcite: Epstein et al., 1953; O'Neil et al., 1969; Kim and O'Neil, 1997; and for aragonite: Grossman and Ku, 1986; Kim et al., 2007). The equations for calcite differ by less than 1.5°C at temperatures of 20°C–30°C but differ by up to 2.5°C for temperatures near 0°C. In this chapter, we use the equation of Kim and O'Neil (1997) for calcite and Grossman and Ku (1986) for aragonite.

Until recently, oxygen isotopic studies of phosphatic materials used early paleotemperature equations provided by Longinelli and Nuti (1973) and Kolodny et al. (1983). However, these should no longer be applied, because they were determined using hygroscopic $BiPO_4$ as the analyte, giving generally lower $\delta^{18}O$ values compared with analyses based on nonhygroscopic Ag_3PO_4 (Chenery et al., 2010; Pucéat et al., 2003). Newer paleotemperature equations by Pucéat et al. (2010) or Lécuyer et al. (2013) are offset from the previous equations by ~2‰, equating to ~8°C. We apply the equation of Pucéat et al. (2010) because it was produced by the same laboratory at FAU Erlangen-Nuremberg that has produced the majority of oxygen isotope data for Paleozoic conodonts (e.g., Joachimski et al., 2004, 2009; Sun et al., 2012).

The chronology for the data has been updated to the GTS2020 time scale by interpolation from the age information of the original study. For new data, where numerical ages were not given in the original publication, age was estimated from biostratigraphic information and elevation in the stratigraphic section. Regressions of isotopic data were performed using the Locfit package in R (Loader, 2015) with a smoothing factor (α) of 0.05 to 0.25 (see Appendix 4).

Because global oxygen isotope features are ultimately tied to climatic changes, we have assigned climatic-based names (e.g., warm or cold) to $\delta^{18}O$ trends and events [e.g., Givetian–Frasnian Warm Trend (GFWT) and Changhsingian–Olenekian Warm Event (COWE)]. These will aid in future discussions of the $\delta^{18}O$ record and will undoubtedly be modified in character and duration with continued collection of data.

10.3 Application principles and considerations

10.3.1 Principles

Oxygen isotope stratigraphy depends on rapid changes in fossil $\delta^{18}O$ in response to rapid changes in temperature and (or) global seawater $\delta^{18}O$, the latter as a result of changing glacial ice volume. During glacial intervals the storage of ^{18}O-depleted water as glacial ice results in ^{18}O enrichment (higher $\delta^{18}O$) in seawater and consequently in marine authigenic minerals. Lower temperatures during glacial intervals (e.g., Lea et al., 2000) further enrich marine authigenic minerals in ^{18}O. Deglaciation lowers seawater $\delta^{18}O$ and combines with warming to produce lower marine carbonate $\delta^{18}O$ values during interglacial intervals. Glacial–interglacial cyclicity in the $\delta^{18}O$ of marine foraminifera provides a high-definition oxygen isotope stratigraphy for the Neogene (Emiliani, 1955; Shackleton and Opdyke, 1973; Lisiecki and Raymo, 2005; Raffi et al., 2020, Chapter 29, The Neogene Period, this book) and holds promise for a refined Paleogene stratigraphy (Speijer et al., 2020, Chapter 28, The Paleogene Period, this book). Because glacial–interglacial cycles respond predictably to variations in Earth's orbit and tilt (Milankovitch cycles; Hays et al., 1976), their chronology can be tuned to the astronomical time scale. This has led to high-resolution cyclostratigraphy (see later discussion and Laskar, 2020, Chapter 4, Astrochronology, this volume).

The principles used to develop the Neogene oxygen isotope stratigraphy are being applied to older sediments. Although the extension is limited by the availability of precise radioisotope ages, "floating" astronomical time scales (not yet calibrated to an absolute age) exist for the Paleogene and Mesozoic based on $\delta^{18}O$ and other data (Hinnov and Hilgen, 2012; Laskar, 2020, Chapter 4, this volume). As the records reach further back in time, the clarity of the glacial–interglacial $\delta^{18}O$ cycles is reduced by diminishing ice volume and decreased sample resolution and preservation.

The dual dependence of oxygen isotope values on seawater $\delta^{18}O$ and temperature can hinder stratigraphic applications; however, this dual dependence can amplify the isotopic signal as discussed with respect to Neogene marine isotope stratigraphy. The same amplification should apply for studies of other icehouse periods such as the latest Ordovician, Late Carboniferous, and Early Permian. For ice-free periods, global seawater $\delta^{18}O$ will be constant over short (less than tectonic) time scales, simplifying the application of oxygen isotope stratigraphy. However, in marginal marine environments such as epicontinental seas, seawater $\delta^{18}O$ can vary locally and complicate stratigraphic and paleoclimate applications. Nevertheless, advances are being made through the combined application of oxygen isotopes and other paleotemperature proxies such as Mg/Ca (e.g., Lear et al., 2000; McArthur et al., 2007) and clumped isotopes (Ghosh et al., 2006; Came et al., 2007; Henkes et al., 2018).

10.3.2 Sample materials

In selecting material for isotopic study, researchers must consider (1) isotopic fractionation (i.e., equilibrium vs disequilibrium), (2) resistance to diagenesis, (3) geographic and stratigraphic distribution, (4) abundance, (5) habitat, and (6) environmental range. Some organisms precipitate carbonate out of equilibrium with respect to ambient waters. This "vital effect" results from physiological processes. Groups that generally secrete skeletons in oxygen isotopic equilibrium include mollusks, brachiopods (but see later discussion), sclerosponges, and many smaller foraminifera (e.g., González and Lohmann, 1985; Grossman, 1987; Wefer and Berger, 1991; Swart et al., 1998). In contrast, corals, echinoderms, and larger benthic foraminifera precipitate $CaCO_3$ with $\delta^{18}O$ values that can be as much as 3‰ lower than equilibrium values. Fortunately, taxa exhibiting vital effect, such as corals and large foraminifera, often precipitate carbonate with a constant $\delta^{18}O$ offset relative to equilibrium values (e.g., Leder et al., 1996).

Sample preservation is an overriding concern in oxygen isotope stratigraphy and paleothermometry. Oxygen isotopic compositions of carbonate fossils are susceptible to diagenetic alteration because diagenetic waters have an abundant supply of exchangeable oxygen in H_2O. Fossils and microfossils of low-magnesium calcite are preferred for oxygen isotope stratigraphy because of their resistance to diagenesis compared with high-magnesium calcite and aragonite, and thus persist longer in the sedimentary record. Shell size and texture are also important factors in preservation, with thick, dense shells retaining original isotopic chemistry better than thin, and porous shells. Likewise, the more porous tests of planktonic foraminifera are more susceptible to diagenesis than the less porous tests of benthic foraminifera. Phosphate in highly crystalline biogenic apatite (e.g., tooth enamel or conodont crown material) is less susceptible to oxygen exchange than low-Mg calcite and thus retains its oxygen isotope signature longer (e.g., Luz et al., 1984; Wenzel et al., 2000). Application of chert $\delta^{18}O$ stratigraphy, used in studies of the Precambrian (Shields and Veizer, 2002; Knauth, 2005), is complicated because chert is deposited as opal and undergoes dehydration and recrystallization with diagenesis and lithification.

The effect of diagenesis on mineral $\delta^{18}O$ depends on diagenetic environment. Cenozoic planktonic foraminifera can recrystallize on the cold, deep-ocean floor, altering $\delta^{18}O$ to higher values. This process is believed responsible for their recording cool tropical temperatures during warm Cretaceous and Eocene times ("cool tropics paradox"; Schrag, 1999; Pearson et al., 2001). In contrast, recrystallization at great depth below the sediment–water interface (e.g., >500 m) can decrease $\delta^{18}O$ because of higher geothermal temperatures (Miller et al., 1987). Recrystallization of limestones, cherts, and fossils deposited in epicontinental seas usually results in lower $\delta^{18}O$ values, reflecting exchange with ^{18}O-depleted meteoric water and/or higher burial temperatures.

Studies of the Cretaceous and Cenozoic benefit from the deep-sea records provided by piston cores and especially cores collected by the Deep Sea Drilling Project (DSDP),

Ocean Drilling Program (ODP), Integrated Ocean Drilling Program (IODP, later renamed as the International Ocean Discovery Program). These cores permit detailed, continuous isotopic records based on analyses of benthic and planktonic foraminifera (e.g., Emiliani, 1955; Shackleton and Opdyke, 1973; Savin et al., 1975; Miller et al., 1987; Zachos et al., 2001). Because no deep-sea floor older than ~180 Ma is preserved in the ocean today, studies of the Paleozoic and the Mesozoic prior to 110 Ma are restricted to marine sediments from continental margins and epicontinental seas where environments can be influenced by coastal processes such as freshwater influx and restricted circulation. Furthermore, such samples are naturally biased toward periods of high sea level and interglacials during icehouse intervals and are more likely to be exposed to corrosive diagenetic fluids.

Because of their calcitic mineralogy and dense microcrystalline structure, belemnites (e.g., the PDB standard) are the preferred macrofossil for Jurassic and Cretaceous isotopic studies and were used in the first paleotemperature study (Urey et al., 1951). Other Mesozoic isotopic studies have made use of rare occurrences of aragonitic mollusk shells (e.g., Stahl and Jordan, 1969; Anderson et al., 1994; Malchus and Steuber, 2002; Nützel et al., 2010), while studies of the Triassic have relied on brachiopod shells.

Articulate brachiopod shells are the favored carbonate fossil for Paleozoic oxygen isotope records because of their wide stratigraphic distribution (early Cambrian to the Recent), abundance, and resistance to diagenesis, and the tendency for inner shell layers to be precipitated at or near oxygen isotope equilibrium with ambient water (Compston, 1960; Lowenstam, 1961; Veizer et al., 1986; Popp et al., 1986; Carpenter and Lohmann, 1995; Grossman, 1994; Brand et al., 2003). The resistance to diagenesis results from their calcitic mineralogy, low-magnesium content, relatively large size and thickness, and dense microstructure. Because of this diagenetic resistance, brachiopod shells are typically 2‰–3‰ higher in $\delta^{18}O$ than the encasing, diagenetically modified bulk carbonate (Veizer et al., 1999; Mii et al., 1999). While inner brachiopod shell layers appear to be precipitated in oxygen isotope equilibrium, numerous studies have shown that the thin outer primary layer and outer secondary layer of modern punctate brachiopod shells (e.g., terebratulids) can be several per mil depleted in ^{18}O relative to equilibrium (e.g., Carpenter and Lohmann, 1995; Auclair et al., 2003; Cusack et al., 2012; Romanin et al., 2018). Analyses of thicker impunctate shells, however, like the spiriferid shells used in Carboniferous isotopic studies, do not show this tendency, show minimal interspecies $\delta^{18}O$ differences, and thus appear to be precipitated at or near equilibrium (e.g., Grossman et al., 1991; Mii and Grossman, 1994; Roark et al., 2017).

The $\delta^{18}O$ of biogenic apatite is more resistant to diagenetic alteration than that of brachiopod shell calcite (e.g., Wenzel et al., 2000; Joachimski et al., 2004) because of the slow oxygen exchange between phosphate and water at ambient temperatures; rapid exchange can occur, however, with enzyme-catalyzed reactions (Kolodny et al., 1983; Blake et al., 2005). Earlier studies suggested possible alteration of phosphate $\delta^{18}O$ ($\delta^{18}O_{PO_4}$) in phosphorites based on $\delta^{18}O_{PO_4} - \delta^{18}O_{CaCO_3}$ trends and/or low $\delta^{18}O_{PO_4}$ values (Shemesh et al., 1988; McArthur and Herczeg, 1990). However, newer techniques using smaller sample sizes have yielded higher, less variable $\delta^{18}O_{PO_4}$ values for Paleozoic conodonts (e.g., Joachimski et al., 2009). While oxygen isotope exchange is possible at higher temperatures, comparisons between conodont $\delta^{18}O_{PO_4}$ and color alteration index (CAI) show no systematic relation up to CAI of 5 (Joachimski et al., 2009).

Oxygen isotope studies of the Precambrian have utilized sedimentary rocks (cherts, limestones, and dolostones) because of the absence of fossil hard parts. Precambrian cherts are formed from opal precipitates in seawater presumably during early diagenesis. Because of their impermeability, they are believed to strongly resist diagenesis after formation (Knauth, 2005). Fine-grained limestones may also undergo much of their recrystallization during early diagenesis (Veizer and Hoefs, 1976). However, even chalks contain cements that alter the original isotopic composition of the bulk rock (Mitchell et al., 1997). Dolostones are typically a product of diagenetic recrystallization of limestone and are at best a last resort for oxygen isotope stratigraphy.

Understanding the depositional environment and paleoecology of sample materials is essential in oxygen isotope stratigraphy. Since ocean temperatures vary with season, water depth, and latitude, oxygen isotope records will depend on paleogeography, depth habitat, and growth season. Deep-sea benthic foraminifera give higher (colder) $\delta^{18}O$ values than planktonic foraminifera, and shallow-dwelling planktonic foraminifera (*Globigerinoides ruber* and *Globigerina bulloides*) have lower $\delta^{18}O$ values than deeper dwelling species (*Neogloboquadrina pachyderma* and *Globorotalia menardii*; Ravelo and Hillaire-Marcel, 2007). Isotopic studies of nektonic taxa such as belemnites, conodonts, and fishes can be complicated because individuals can live in surface or deep waters and can also accrete skeletal elements far from their ultimate site of deposition. Such issues can be addressed by comparing isotopic trends in nektonic species with those of coeval complementary results for sessile benthic organisms such as bivalves and brachiopods. Seasonal growth can introduce more than 1‰ variability in $\delta^{18}O$ among co-occurring samples. Focusing on low-latitude localities helps to minimize the impact of seasonal variability on isotopic results.

Finally, regional and seasonal variation in seawater $\delta^{18}O$, especially in nearshore environments, also can influence $\delta^{18}O$ records. Open-ocean surface seawater can vary from

−0.2‰ in the Southern Ocean, where glacial meltwater contributes ^{18}O-depleted water, to 1.1‰ within the subtropical high-pressure zone (GEOSECS, 1987; Schmidt et al., 1999). Unusual nearshore environments such as off eastern Greenland (glacial melting) or in the Gulf of Aqaba (evaporation) yield extreme values for surface waters of −2.2‰ and +2.0‰, respectively (GEOSECS, 1987; Al-Rousan et al., 2003). Seasonal discharge from large river systems can have a widespread effect. Because of the lower $\delta^{18}O$ of high-latitude precipitation (Rozanski et al., 1993), high-latitude carbonates tend to be more variable in $\delta^{18}O$ than are low-latitude carbonates (e.g., Tripati et al., 2001). For reasons of signal stability and sample availability, this chapter will focus on tropical and subtropical samples.

10.4 Oxygen isotope stratigraphy

10.4.1 Cenozoic

The oxygen isotope records for Cenozoic surface and bottom waters are based on planktonic and benthic foraminifera from piston cores and DSDP, ODP, and IODP cores. The most successful application of oxygen isotopes as stratigraphic markers is the development of Neogene marine isotope stages based on changes in temperature and seawater $\delta^{18}O$ during glacial–interglacial cycles. First reported in Emiliani's (1955) breakthrough study of planktonic foraminifera from deep-sea piston cores, these isotopic cycles were found to conform to variations in Earth's orbital parameters (Hays et al., 1976) with periodicities corresponding to obliquity (42 kyr), precession (19 and 23 kyr), and eccentricity (100 kyr) (Fig. 10.1; see Laskar, 2020, Chapter 4, Astrochronology, this volume). The last 800–900 kyr of the isotopic record are dominated by high-amplitude fluctuations with 100-kyr periodicity (eccentricity), whereas the early Pleistocene and Pliocene record is dominated by lower frequency variations with a period of 41 kyr (obliquity) (Ruddiman et al., 1986). The 100-kyr eccentricity cycle, along with the 400-kyr eccentricity cycle, has been prevalent during other times in the Cenozoic such as the Paleocene, Oligocene, and Miocene (Zachos et al., 2001; Westerhold et al., 2005, 2008; Pälike et al., 2006).

The discovery of the astronomical periodicity to the Pleistocene climate records led to astronomical tuning of the Pleistocene time scale (SPECMAP; Imbrie et al., 1984; Tiedemann et al., 1994). Fig. 10.1 shows an astronomically tuned $\delta^{18}O$ time scale for the Late Pliocene and Pleistocene based on 38,229 isotopic analyses of benthic foraminifera from 57 globally distributed sites (the "LR04" stack; Lisiecki and Raymo, 2005; see Raffi et al., 2020, Chapter 29, The Neogene Period, this book). The LR04 stack provides a high-resolution geochronology with uncertainty varying from 40 kyr in the oldest section (5.3–5 Ma) to 15 kyr for 4–3 Ma and 4 kyr for 1–0 Ma. To supplement these $\delta^{18}O$-based records, researchers have developed astronomical time scales for earlier in the Cenozoic based primarily on Milankovitch-related sedimentological properties such as magnetic susceptibility and iron content measured by scanning X-ray fluorescence (Hinnov and Ogg, 2007; Westerhold et al., 2008).

The long-term Cenozoic isotope record of benthic foraminifera has been summarized by Savin et al. (1975), Savin (1977), Miller et al. (1987), Zachos et al. (2001, 2008), and Cramer et al. (2009). The record shows the now classic trend of progressive cooling interrupted by warm events in the Early Eocene (E. Eocene Climate Optimum, EECO), late Oligocene, and mid-Miocene (Mid-Miocene Climatic Optimum) (Fig. 10.2, Table 10.1). Many of these pronounced isotopic changes serve as stratigraphic markers of global extent that can be used for correlation (see Speijer et al., 2020, Chapter 28, The Paleogene Period, this book). Relatively constant $\delta^{18}O$ values in the early Paleocene are followed by a middle Paleocene $\delta^{18}O$ maximum. Values then decline through the late Paleocene until interrupted by a negative $\delta^{18}O$ spike near the Paleocene–Eocene boundary (~56 Ma; Kennett and Stott, 1991; Norris and Röhl, 1999; Zachos et al., 2001; Chapter 28: The Paleogene Period). Commonly known as the Paleocene–Eocene Thermal Maximum (PETM), this isotopic event has been attributed to rapid release of oceanic methane hydrates from below the sediment surface (Dickens et al., 1995). However, others have argued for hydrothermal methane release associated with northeast Atlantic volcanism (Svensen et al., 2004) as the cause. A second Eocene thermal maximum (~54 Ma; Fig. 10.2, Table 10.1) has been documented based on oxygen and carbon isotope analyses of carbonate-poor sediments, suggesting additional gas hydrate release events in Earth's past (Lourens et al., 2005). Oxygen isotope values reach a minimum during the Early Eocene climatic optimum (EECO, 52–50 Ma) then increase throughout the Eocene, interrupted by the mid-Eocene climatic optimum at ~40.0 Ma (Bohaty et al., 2009). Cenozoic cooling produced major Antarctic glaciation in the earliest Oligocene, recorded in a sharp 1.0‰–1.5‰ increase at the Eocene–Oligocene boundary (Oi1 glaciation; 33.55 Ma; Miller et al., 1991, 2008). In addition to Oi1, Miller et al. (1991) identified seven other Oligocene–Miocene zones (Oi2 and Mi1–Mi6) where the base of the zone was defined by the maximum $\delta^{18}O$ value. The most distinctive of these is Mi1 at the Miocene–Oligocene boundary, dated at 23.0 Ma (Shackleton et al., 1999; Zachos et al., 2001) and Mi3–Mi4, the sharp Mid-Miocene increase at ~12–14 Ma (Savin et al., 1975; Shackleton and Kennett, 1975; Miller et al., 1991). Through the Pliocene and Pleistocene epochs, $\delta^{18}O$ continued to increase, reflecting expansion of glaciers in the Northern Hemisphere (e.g., Maslin et al., 1998).

While the aforementioned isotopic trends and events are recorded throughout the world ocean, the degree of change

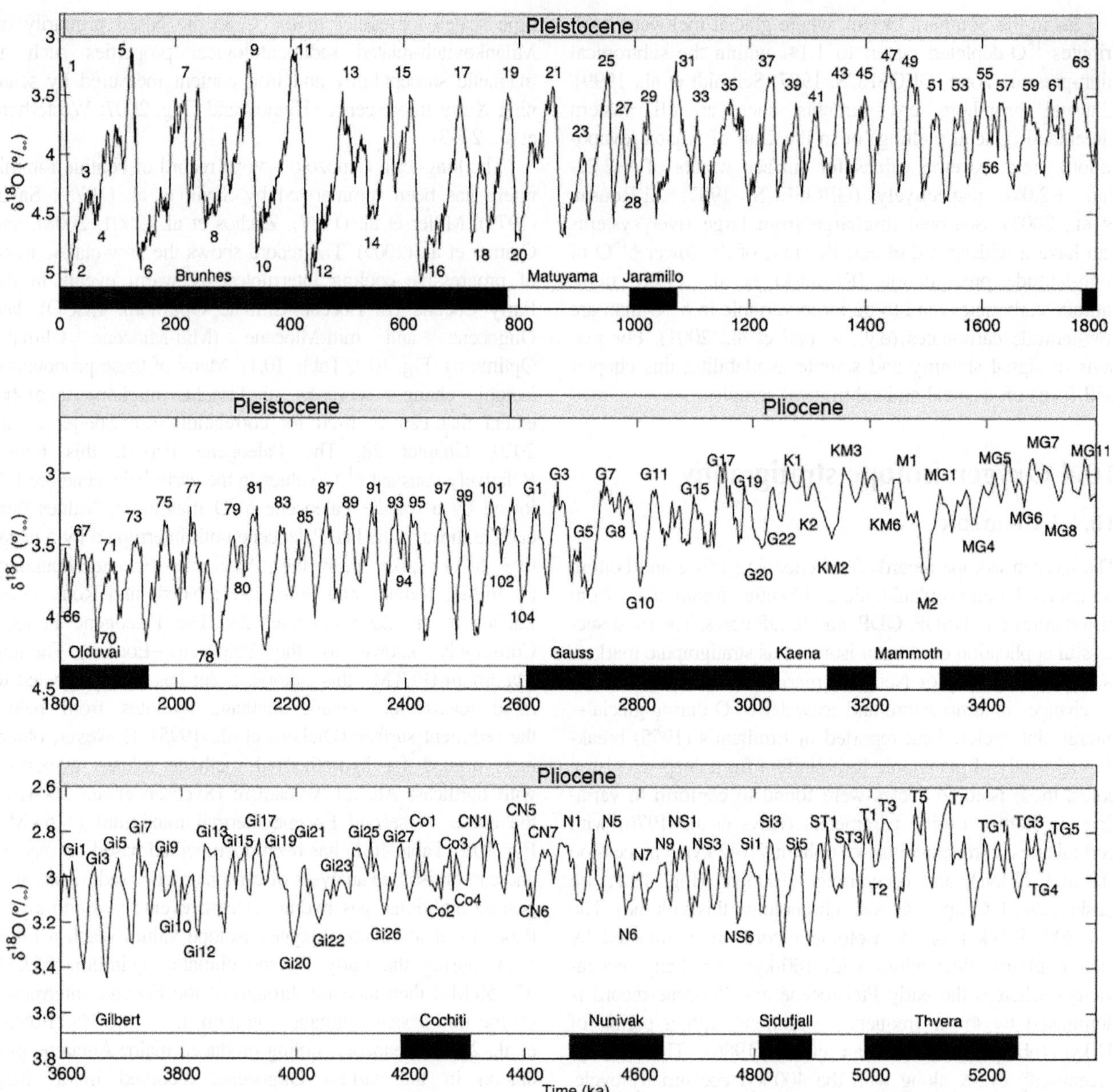

FIGURE 10.1 Marine isotope stage boundaries defined based on the benthic $\delta^{18}O$ stack (LR04) constructed from the graphic correlation of 57 globally distributed late Neogene isotopic records (from Lisiecki and Raymo, 2005). Also shown are geomagnetic chrons. Note that the vertical scale differs between panels and that $\delta^{18}O$ increases downward.

can vary between ocean basins (Cramer et al., 2009), resulting in interbasinal $\delta^{18}O$ gradients that depend on deepwater circulation patterns. Large interbasinal $\delta^{18}O$ gradients (>0.5‰) are seen for the Late Cretaceous and late Paleogene through Neogene, while small gradients (<0.5‰) are characteristic of the early Paleogene ocean (Fig. 10.2; Cramer et al., 2009).

The $\delta^{18}O$ record for Cenozoic planktonic foraminifera is more dispersed than that of the benthic foraminifera because of the geographic and temporal variability of surface water temperature and $\delta^{18}O_w$ (salinity) and the greater susceptibility of planktonic foraminifera to diagenesis. At first glance the tropical–subtropical record shows the same trends as the benthic foraminiferal record, with a Late Cretaceous increase (cooling), early Eocene decrease (warming), and mid-Eocene to Oligocene increase (cooling) (Fig. 10.2; Savin, 1977; Miller et al., 1991; Prokoph et al., 2008; Veizer and Prokoph, 2015). The low-latitude planktonic foraminiferal record, however, shows little evidence of the strong cooling trend seen in the deep sea and high-latitude surface ocean. The trend is tempered by relatively high $\delta^{18}O$ values for planktonic foraminifera, originally

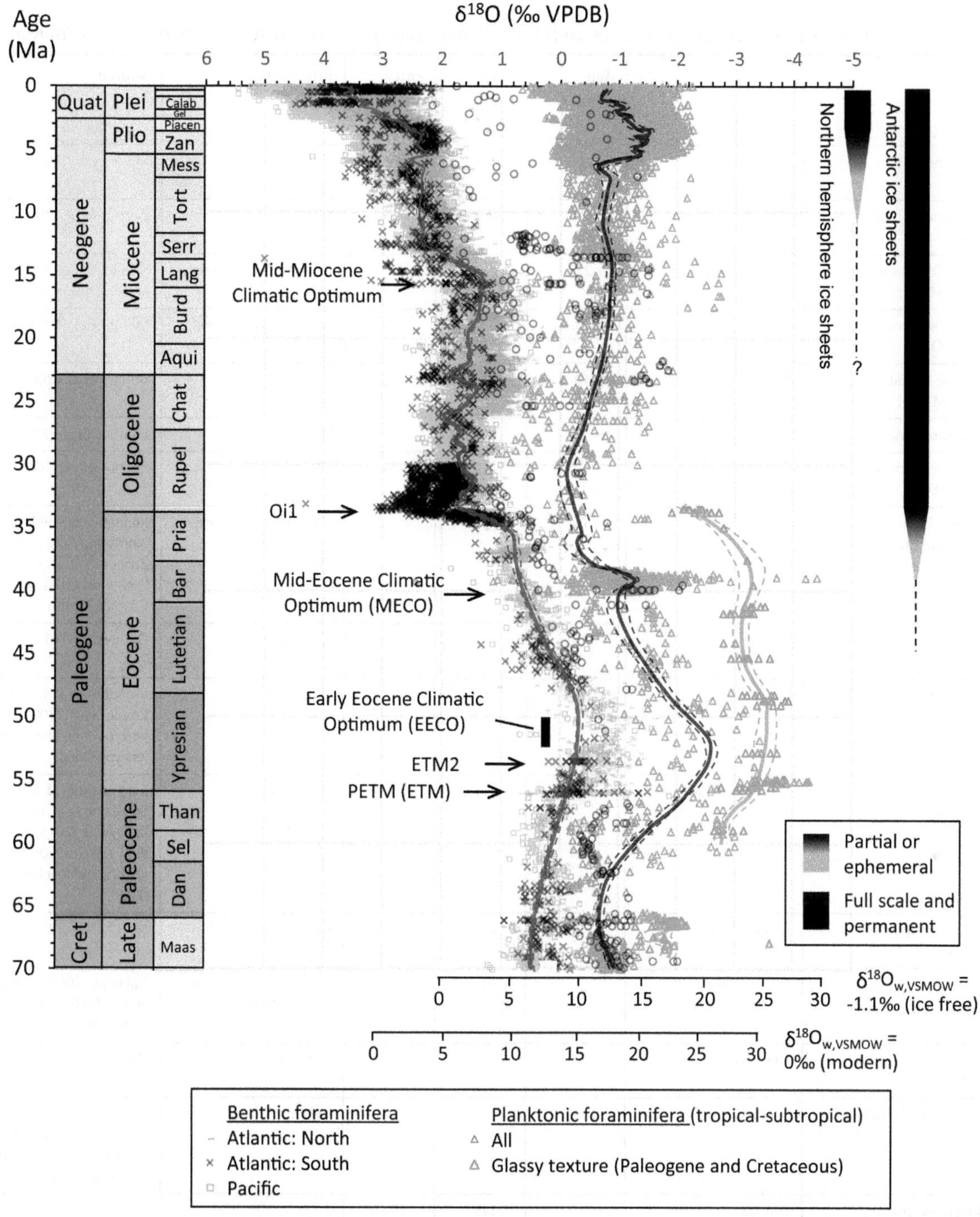

FIGURE 10.2 Oxygen isotopic record for Latest Cretaceous and Cenozoic tropical/subtropical fossils and microfossils. Shown are planktonic foraminiferal data (updated from Veizer and Prokoph, 2015) and deep-sea benthic foraminiferal data (modified from Cramer et al., 2009) based on DSDP, ODP, and IODP cores. Note that $\delta^{18}O$ increases to left in this and subsequent figures. Benthic foraminiferal data are not corrected for genus-specific $\delta^{18}O$ vital effects (e.g., *Cibicidoides* versus *Uvigerina* spp.). Thick and dashed lines show Locfit regressions and their ±95% confidence intervals respectively (Loader, 2015). Regression for benthic foraminifera is based only on data for the Pacific Ocean. The temperature scale in this and subsequent figures is based on Kim and O'Neil (1997) and shows temperatures associated with a seawater $\delta^{18}O$ of a glacier-free world (− 1.1‰ VSMOW; prior to ~35 Ma) and the modern interglacial ocean (0‰ VSMOW). This value is based on isotopic mass balance calculations using updated estimates for glacial ice mass and $\delta^{18}O$, and ocean mass and $\delta^{18}O$ (Poore et al., 2000; L'Homme et al., 2005). Climate events from Zachos et al. (2008) and Cramer et al. (2009); PETM = Paleocene–Eocene Thermal Maximum and ETM = Eocene Thermal Maximum.

TABLE 10.1 Summary of oxygen isotope events useful for stratigraphic purposes in sediments older than 10 Ma.

Event	Period	Age (Ma)	Start age (Ma)	End age (Ma)	Interpretation	Source
Mid-Miocene shift (Mi3–Mi4)	Neogene		~14	~12	Cooling	Miller et al. (1991)
Mid-Miocene Climatic Optimum	Neogene		~16	~15	Warming	Zachos et al. (2001)
Miocene–Oligocene boundary (Mi1)	Paleogene–Neogene	23			Ice volume increase	Shackleton et al. (1999) and Zachos et al. (2001)
Eocene–Oligocene boundary (Oi1)	Paleogene	33.55			Antarctic glaciation	Miller et al. (1991)
Mid-Eocene climatic optimum (MECO)	Paleogene	~40			Warming	Bohaty et al. (2009)
Eocene Thermal Maximum 2	Paleogene	~54			Warming	Lourens et al. (2005)
Early Eocene climatic optimum (EECO)	Paleogene		~52	~50	Warming	Zachos et al. (2001)
Paleocene–Eocene Thermal Maximum (PETM)	Paleogene	~56			Catastrophic release of gas hydrate methane and warming	Kennett and Stott (1991), Norris and Röhl (1999), Zachos et al. (2001), and Speijer et al. (2020, Chapter 28, this book)
Toarcian–Aalenian Cool Event (TACE)	Jurassic	~175			Cooling	Dera et al. (2011)
Toarcian Warm Event (TWE)	Jurassic	~181			Warming	McArthur et al. (2000), Rosales et al. (2001), Jenkyns et al. (2002), and Jenkyns (2003)
Changhsingian–Olenekian Warm Event (COWE)	Permian–Triassic	~252	251.9	251.8	Warming	Joachimski et al. (2012), Schobben et al. (2014), Jiang et al. (2015), Chen et al. (2016a), Sun et al. (2012), and Joachimski et al. (2020)
Serpukhovian–Bashkirian Cool Trend (SBCT)	Carboniferous		323	~319	Cooling, ice buildup	Mii et al. (1999, 2001), and Buggisch et al. (2008)
Tournaisian Cool Trend (TCT)	Carboniferous		359	~347	Cooling, ice buildup, aridification	Mii et al. (1999), Stanton et al. (2002), and Buggisch et al. (2008)
Lochkovian–Emsian Cool Trend (LECT)	Devonian		~414	~400	Cooling	Buggisch et al. (2008)
Ludfordian Cool Event (LCE)	Silurian	~424			Cooling	Samtleben et al. (1996), Wenzel and Joachimski (1996), Bickert et al. (1997), and Brand et al. (2006)
Llandovery Warm Trend (LWT)	Silurian		~443	~437		
Hirnantian Cool Event (HCE)	Ordovician		~444.5	~444.0	Cooling and ice buildup	Marshall and Middleton (1990), Qing and Veizer (1994), and Brenchley et al. (1994)
Ordovician Cool Trend (OCT)	Ordovician		~480	~445	Cooling	Trotter et al. (2008), Bassett et al. (2007), Rosenau et al. (2012), Quinton et al. (2014, 2018), and Shields et al. (2003)

thought to represent cool tropical temperatures during the warm Eocene and Cretaceous intervals. However, these data were later attributed to diagenesis on the cool seafloor (e.g., Schrag et al., 1995; Pearson et al., 2001). Exceptionally well-preserved (glassy) planktonic foraminifera from clay-rich sediments yield lower $\delta^{18}O$ and warmer tropical paleotemperatures during this time (Fig. 10.2; Pearson et al., 2001, 2008; Wilson et al., 2002; Bornemann et al., 2008). Supporting evidence for warm low-latitude temperatures comes from isotopic analyses of gastropods and bivalves (Andreasson and Schmitz, 1998; Kobashi et al., 2001). While the isotopic record from these well-preserved fossils and microfossils from continental shelf and hemipelagic sediments may show greater influence of river influx than that of pelagic specimens (Zachos et al., 2002), this effect accounts for only a small portion of the difference (Pearson et al., 2002).

10.4.2 Mesozoic

The Mesozoic data are updated from Veizer et al. (1999), Prokoph et al. (2008), Grossman (2012a), and Veizer and Prokoph (2015) with additional belemnite (e.g., Dera et al., 2011; Ullmann et al., 2016) and planktonic foraminiferal data (e.g., MacLeod et al., 2013; see Appendices 1 and 2). For the Triassic and Jurassic the best preserved and most complete record comes from analyses of brachiopods and belemnites from Europe (England, Spain, France, Italy, and Poland; e.g., Anderson et al., 1994; Podlaha et al., 1998; Malchus and Steuber, 2002; Jenkyns et al., 2002; Korte et al., 2005b; Dera et al., 2011) and New Zealand (Ullmann et al., 2016). Triassic brachiopods from the tropics and subtropics range in $\delta^{18}O$ from −9‰ to −0.3‰ and show an early Carnian (~225 Ma) increase of 2‰ attributed to cooling and ^{18}O enrichment in seawater due to evaporation (Korte et al., 2005b). Brachiopod $\delta^{18}O$ values for the tropics and subtropics of the latest Triassic average ~ −2‰, similar to $\delta^{18}O$ values for early Jurassic belemnites from northern Europe (Jenkyns et al., 2002).

Fig. 10.3 shows belemnite, brachiopod, and bivalve $\delta^{18}O$ data for tropical/subtropical and temperate climate zones. Oyster data are omitted because of their ability to live in brackish environments. The northward movement of Europe during Triassic to early Jurassic time shifted European samples from tropical/subtropical to temperate latitudes, blurring distinctions. Not surprisingly, the $\delta^{18}O$ values for temperate and tropical/subtropical belemnites are similar on average [-0.9 ± 1.1‰ vs -1.0 ± 0.9‰ ($\pm 1\sigma$)]. Thus these data, along with brachiopod data, are grouped in the regression shown in Fig. 10.3. The temporal trend reveals a $\delta^{18}O$ increase from Early Triassic values averaging less than −3‰ to values of about −1‰ in the Pliensbachian (Jurassic) and then a sharp decrease in the Toarcian (Toarcian Warm Event, TWE; ~181 Ma) to a minimum of about −3‰ (Fig. 10.3). This is followed by a sharp increase (1.4‰) at the Toarcian–Aalenian boundary (Toarcian–Aalenian Cool Event, TACE; ~175 Ma; Dera et al., 2011). The previously identified Callovian–Oxfordian acme at about 165 Ma is not well defined after addition of new data; thus the use of the term is suspended. Nevertheless, $\delta^{18}O$ data for Mid- to early Late Jurassic specimens maintain a broad, irregular maximum, then decline to lower values of −1 to −1.5‰ in the Kimmeridgian and Tithonian (155–153 Ma). These European data are interpreted as changes in global climate, reflecting Toarcian warming (Podlaha et al., 1998; McArthur et al., 2000; Rosales et al., 2001; Jenkyns et al., 2002; Jenkyns, 2003) possibly linked to an oceanic anoxic event (Podlaha et al., 1998; Bailey et al., 2003), followed by a Middle- to early Late Jurassic cool interval (Dromart et al., 2003; Jenkyns, 2003; Dera et al., 2011). Within the Jurassic the TWE and TACE are distinct oxygen isotope events useful for correlation.

Oxygen isotope values of belemnites increase in the Early Cretaceous to a maximum of 0‰–1‰ near the Valanginian–Hauterivian boundary (~136 Ma), interpreted as cooling to a late Valanginian–early Hauterivian temperature minimum (van de Schootbrugge et al., 2000; McArthur et al., 2007). The $\delta^{18}O$ values then sharply decline to a minimum of −2‰ to −1‰ in the middle Barremian (~128 Ma), interpreted as Barremian warming (Mutterlose et al., 2009). Belemnite $\delta^{18}O$ data are sparse after the Barremian but tend to be low in the Aptian then gradually increase to ~0‰ in the Maastrichtian.

High belemnite $\delta^{18}O$ values, sometimes equating to paleotemperatures less than 10°C in the early Middle Jurassic, have been interpreted as indicating nektobenthic habitat (e.g., Dutton et al., 2007; Wierzbowski and Joachimski, 2007). Other evidence for a nektobenthic habitat include (1) $\delta^{18}O$ values similar to benthic foraminiferal values and lower than planktonic foraminiferal values (Dutton et al., 2007), (2) low intraannual variation in $\delta^{18}O$, and (3) $\delta^{18}O$ paleotemperatures similar to those of bivalves and much lower than those of ammonites presumed to dwell in the surface ocean (Wierzbowski and Joachimski, 2007, 2009). An emerging view is that belemnites were pelagic but precipitated calcite ~1.5‰ enriched in ^{18}O relative to other biogenic calcites (Vickers et al., 2020). For the present we assume $\delta^{18}O$ fractionation follows the Kim and O'Neil (1997) equation.

Numerous studies have analyzed fossils from the Cretaceous Western Interior Seaway of North America. However, the results have yielded enigmatic patterns, including anomalously low $\delta^{18}O$ values in shallow-dwelling taxa such as nektonic mollusks and higher $\delta^{18}O$ values in infaunal mollusks versus epifaunal ones (e.g., Wright, 1987; He et al., 2005). Researchers suggest that these patterns reflect a complex, salinity-stratified water column (e.g., Wright, 1987; Hudson and Anderson, 1989;

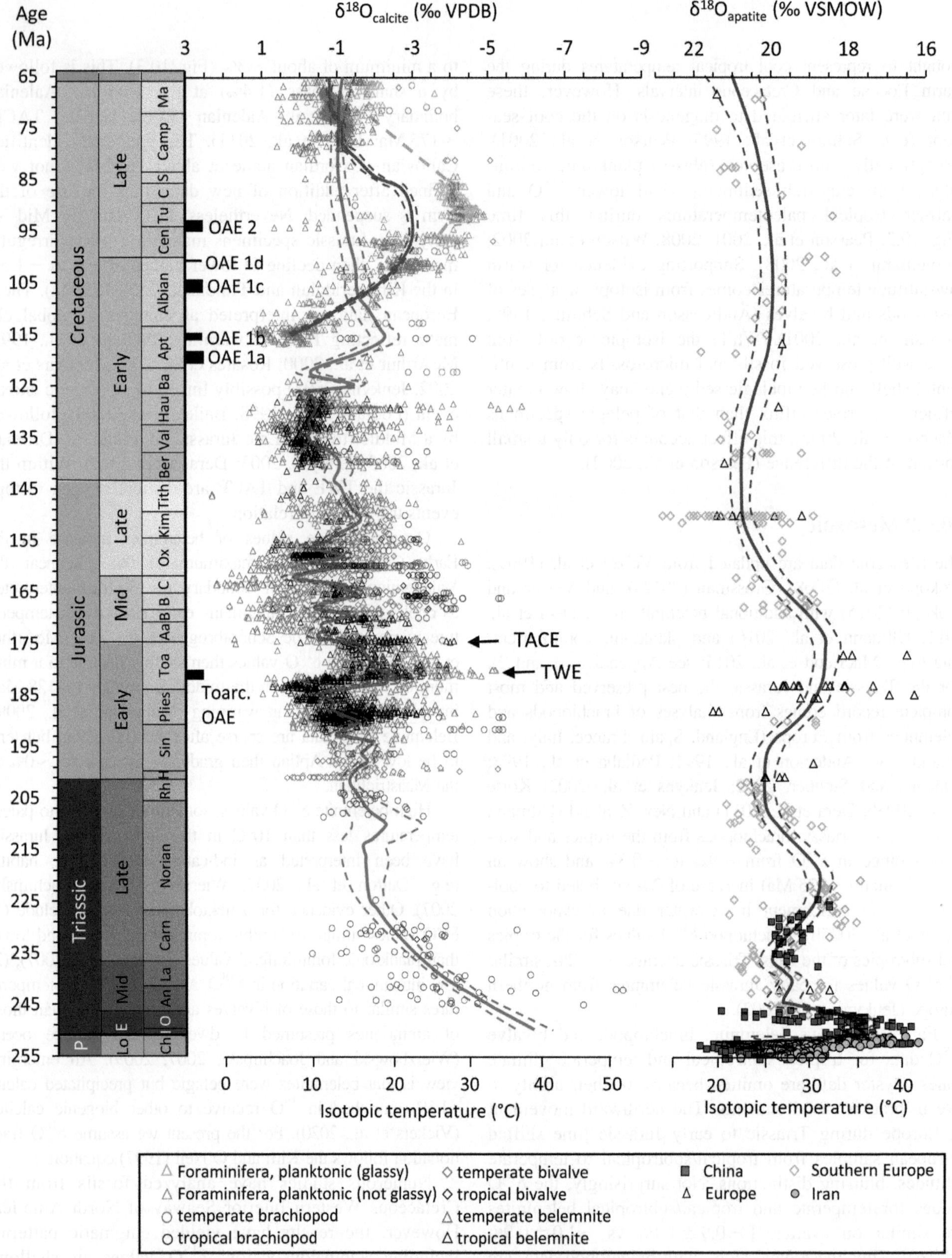

FIGURE 10.3 Oxygen isotope records of tropical/subtropical and temperate fossils and planktonic foraminifera for the Mesozoic. For carbonate macrofossil and phosphate data, heavy lines represent Locfit regression and dashed lines show ±95% confidence interval (Appendix 4). Isotopic temperatures assume "ice-free" conditions ($\delta^{18}O_{seawater} = -1.1‰$ vs. VSMOW). To correct for aragonite−calcite $\delta^{18}O$ differences (Grossman and Ku, 1986), 0.6‰ is subtracted from the $\delta^{18}O$ values of aragonitic taxa. TWE = Toarcian Warm Event, TACE = Toarcian−Aalenian Cool Event, and OAE = oceanic anoxic event (e.g., Jenkyns et al., 2002).

He et al., 2005; Petersen et al., 2016). Because of this complexity, these data are not included in the Mesozoic compilation.

The isotopic record for the middle- and Late Cretaceous is anchored with abundant analyses of foraminifera from DSDP, ODP, and IODP cores (Figs. 10.2 and 10.3). Both planktonic (temperate and tropical/subtropical) and benthic foraminiferal records show a 2‰–3‰ decrease from the Albian (~110 Ma) to the Turonian (~90 Ma) and then a roughly 2‰ increase to a maximum in the late Maastrichtian (~66 Ma; e.g., D'Hondt and Arthur, 1996; Huber et al., 2002; Bornemann et al., 2008; Friedrich et al., 2012). Relatively, high $\delta^{18}O$ values for planktonic foraminifera have been interpreted as representing cool tropical temperatures during warm intervals ("Cool Tropics Paradox"; D'Hondt and Arthur, 1996). However, studies of planktonic foraminifera from Cretaceous oozes and chalks typically used for isotopic studies show textural evidence for significant recrystallization (Pearson et al., 2001), supporting the contention that the higher $\delta^{18}O$ values were caused by diagenesis on the cool seafloor (Schrag, 1999; Pearson et al., 2001). High $\delta^{18}O$ values for Late Cretaceous belemnites from temperate regions support cool, Late Cretaceous temperatures, whereas "glassy" planktonic foraminifera indicate warm temperatures (Pearson et al., 2001). As discussed earlier, belemnites may be nektonic or produce hard parts enriched in ^{18}O relative to other mollusks. Thus the low $\delta^{18}O$ values and warm isotopic temperature from "glassy" foraminifera likely represent the best record of sea-surface conditions of low-latitude oceans during the Late Cretaceous.

Phosphate $\delta^{18}O$ data for the Mesozoic are derived from Triassic conodonts and Jurassic and Cretaceous fish teeth. The conodont $\delta^{18}O$ values are low (<18‰) in the Early Triassic and increase (cooling) in the latest Early Triassic to a plateau of ~20‰ in the Middle- to Late Triassic (e.g., Rigo and Joachimski, 2010; Sun et al., 2012, 2016; Chen et al., 2013, 2016a; Schobben et al., 2014; Trotter et al., 2015). For the Jurassic and Cretaceous, sparse fish teeth data show a poorly defined trend with low values in the Toarcian coincident with low carbonate $\delta^{18}O$, followed by a maximum in the latest Kimmeridgian and a minimum straddling the Albian–Cenomanian boundary coeval with warm signals from planktonic foraminiferal $\delta^{18}O$ (e.g., Pucéat et al., 2003; Billon-Bruyat et al., 2005; Dera et al., 2009).

10.4.3 Paleozoic

10.4.3.1 Brachiopod shells

Ján Veizer and his students and colleagues have led the effort to compile a record of Paleozoic isotope data based on brachiopod shells (Veizer et al., 1999; Fig. 10.4). These data have been updated by Prokoph et al. (2008), Grossman (2012a), and Veizer and Prokoph (2015).

Broadly speaking, brachiopod $\delta^{18}O$ values are generally −10‰ to −4‰ for the Cambrian and Ordovician, −8‰ to −2‰ for the Silurian and Devonian, and −7‰ to 0‰ for the Carboniferous and Permian (Fig. 10.4). The trend toward decreasing $\delta^{18}O$ with increasing age in Paleozoic fossils is also seen in Precambrian carbonate rocks and cherts (see later discussion). The same hypotheses have been proposed to explain both trends: (1) high seawater temperatures (e.g., Knauth and Epstein, 1976; Knauth, 2005) and (or) (2) low seawater $\delta^{18}O$ (Perry, 1967; Veizer and Hoefs, 1976; Veizer et al., 1999; Jaffrés et al., 2007) earlier in Earth history, or (3) the cumulative effects of meteoric diagenesis with progressive age (e.g., Degens and Epstein, 1962; Joachimski et al., 2004).

Sample screening of brachiopod shells and data is critical and contentious. Studies that have focused on thick specimens from localities with excellent fossils preservation, and used plane light and cathodoluminescence petrography (Popp et al., 1986) and microsampling techniques to target the best preserved parts of shells, have generally produced data with reduced scatter (e.g., Grossman et al., 1991, 1993, 2008; Wenzel and Joachimski, 1996; Mii et al., 1999, 2001; Samtleben et al., 2001; Joachimski et al., 2004). Other studies that have (1) flaked or crushed shells, (2) picked and analyzed clear crystals, and (3) used Mn and Sr contents to screen samples, experienced more scatter, though aberrant data are reduced by culling samples with Mn contents greater than 200 or 250 ppm. Samples with highly variable $\delta^{18}O$ may have experienced tectonism and burial. For example, $\delta^{18}O$ values for brachiopods from million-year time slices in the Serpukhovian of the Donets Basin (Ukraine) and Visean of Belgium vary by 9‰ and 11‰, respectively (equivalent to temperature ranges of 45°C and 55°C, respectively), even in samples with low Mn contents (Bruckschen et al., 1997, 1999). In this chapter, we have focused on data from samples evaluated in thin- or thick section with cathodoluminescence and data from shells with Mn and Fe contents < 250 ppm. Note that Mn and Fe contents often do not correlate with $\delta^{18}O$ (e.g., Shields et al., 2003), leading some to choose not to use trace element data to cull samples for diagenesis (Veizer et al., 1999). Data for samples that showed no cathodoluminescence are included in Locfit regressions regardless of $\delta^{18}O$ value except for three analyses of the chonetid *Daviesiella* from the Visean of North Wales, which yielded $\delta^{18}O$ values as low as −11.3‰. Other brachiopod data were excluded from the regression when authors excluded the data from their "best preserved" designation (e.g., Cambrian to mid-Ordovician data of Wadleigh and Veizer, 1992), or when isotopic variability was extreme (e.g., >8‰), such as the Early Carboniferous samples from

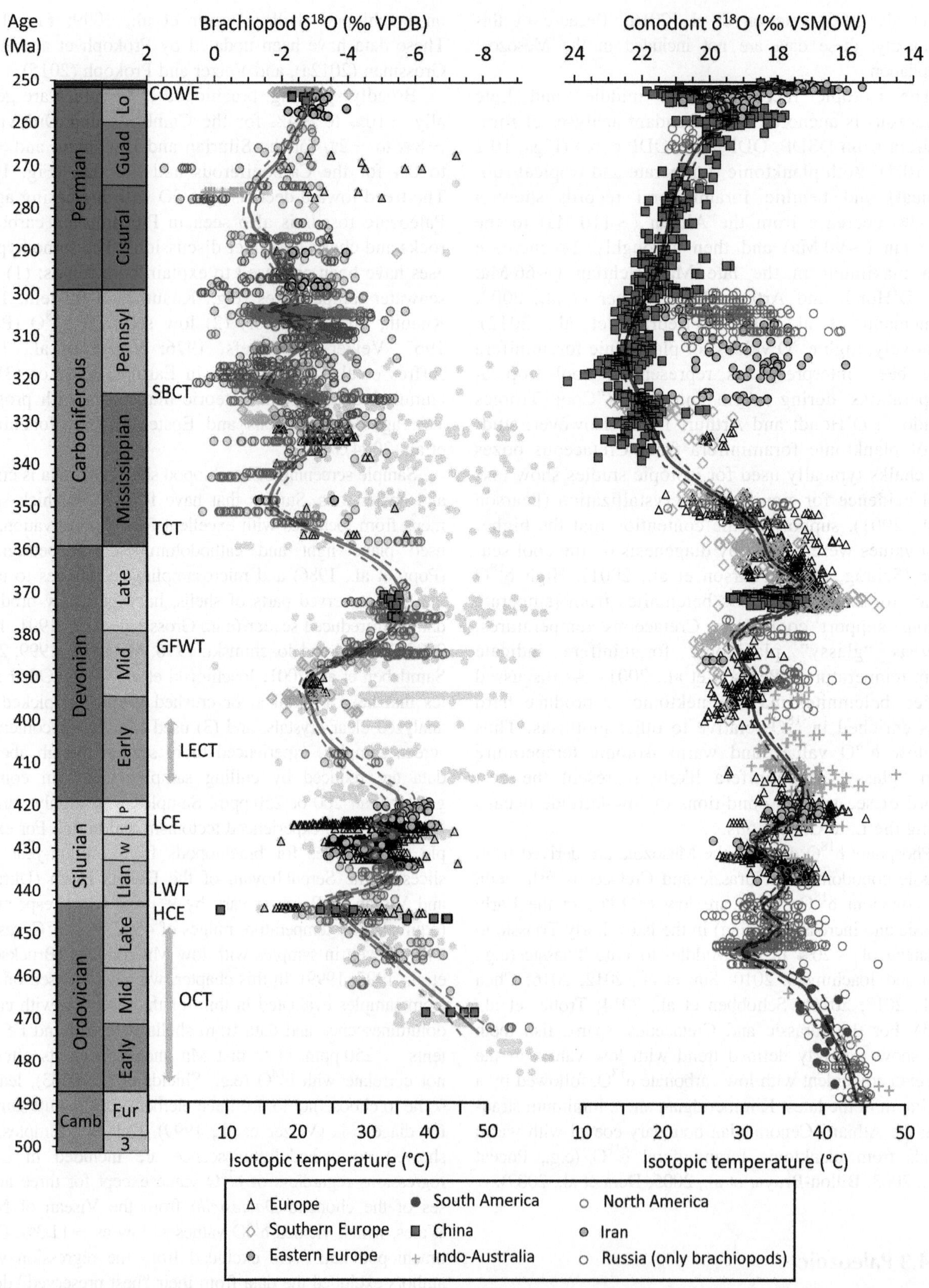

FIGURE 10.4 Oxygen isotopic compositions of tropical/subtropical Paleozoic carbonates (brachiopod calcite) and phosphate (conodonts). Carbonate data satisfying preservation criteria (screening) are shown as darker symbols; all other data are shown as light gray circles and are not used in the Locfit regression. Phosphate data are corrected to an NBS120c value of 21.7‰ (Lécuyer et al., 2003; Pucéat et al., 2010). Only studies for which

Belgium and Ukraine discussed earlier (see Grossman et al., 2008, for details; Appendix 2A).

Brachiopod $\delta^{18}O$ values increase throughout the Ordovician (Ordovician Cool Trend, OCT; ~484–445 Ma), culminating in a well-documented latest Ordovician acme (Hirnantian Cool Event, HCE; ~445 Ma; Figs. 10.4 and 10.5). $\delta^{18}O$ values increase from roughly −5‰ to −4‰ in the Katian (e.g., Wadleigh and Veizer, 1992; Shields et al., 2003) to between −2‰ and 0‰ in the Hirnantian before returning to preshift values (Marshall and Middleton, 1990; Qing and Veizer, 1994; Brenchley et al., 1994). This event of arguably no more than a million-years duration has been recognized in samples from Estonia, Sweden, North America, and Argentina and coincides with sedimentological evidence of Hirnantian glaciation (Brenchley et al., 1995; Marshall et al., 1997). Its glacial nature has been further confirmed by clumped isotopes (Finnegan et al., 2011).

Several studies have provided Silurian isotope stratigraphies based on brachiopods from Gotland (Samtleben et al., 1996; Wenzel and Joachimski, 1996; Bickert et al., 1997; Figs. 10.5 and 10.6). A comprehensive study by Azmy et al. (1998) produced a Silurian isotope record based on samples from Gotland, the Baltics, Scandinavia, Ukraine, Poland, and Canada (Anticosti Island). These data are supplemented with data from the Niagara Gorge area, Canada (Brand et al., 2006). Oxygen isotope values decrease by 2‰ (roughly −3‰ to −5‰) from the Hirnantian maximum to a minimum in the latest Llandovery (Llandovery Warm Trend, LWT; ~444–435 Ma) and then increase to a Late Silurian acme (Ludfordian Cool Event, LCE; ~425 Ma) of as high as −2‰ (Fig. 10.6), before declining. The LCE does not correlate with any known glacial episode. Wenzel and Joachimski (1996) hypothesized that the low preacme $\delta^{18}O$ values were due to sequestration of ^{18}O-rich saline water in the deep ocean.

The brachiopod $\delta^{18}O$ record for the Devonian is based on samples from the United States, Spain, Germany, Morocco, Russia (Siberia), and China (Veizer et al., 1999; van Geldern et al., 2006) (Figs. 10.4 and 10.7). Values rise in the Early Devonian to a Middle Devonian plateau of ~−3‰ (Lochkovian–Emsian Cool Trend, LECT; ~414–400 Ma) then show a rapid Mid- to Late Devonian decline to a minimum of <−6‰ (GFWT; ~388–377 Ma). The $\delta^{18}O$ values remain mostly between −6‰ and −4‰ during the Late Devonian. These trends are interpreted in terms of temperature and seawater $\delta^{18}O$ change, with cool temperatures in the late Early and Middle Devonian and warm temperatures and lower seawater $\delta^{18}O$ in the Late Devonian (van Geldern et al., 2006). Values remain low into the earliest Carboniferous and then increase in the Early Carboniferous (Popp et al., 1986; Veizer et al., 1986; Mii et al., 1999).

The Carboniferous marine isotope record is well expressed on the North American craton and the Russian Platform, which provide long stratigraphic records with well-preserved brachiopod shells. The $\delta^{18}O$ data are mostly between 0‰ and −5‰, yielding paleotemperatures between 10°C and 35°C for a seawater $\delta^{18}O$ of −1.1‰ (VSMOW; Fig. 10.8). In contrast to the North American craton and Russian Platform, many samples from central and western Europe have $\delta^{18}O$ values much less than −5‰ (Fig. 10.8, *gray symbols*; Bruckschen et al., 1999; Veizer et al., 1999) and yield isotopic temperatures often exceeding 50°C (Grossman et al., 2008). As previously discussed, these very low values undoubtedly reflect diagenetic alteration.

US craton data show (1) a 3‰ rise in the Tournaisian to values of −2‰ to 0‰, (2) a Visean decline to −4‰ to −3‰, and (3) a mid-Carboniferous increase of 1‰–2‰ with relatively constant Pennsylvanian values of between −3‰ and −1‰ (Fig. 10.8; Mii et al., 1999). The $\delta^{18}O$ values of brachiopods from the Russian Platform also show a $\delta^{18}O$ increase at the mid-Carboniferous boundary (Bruckschen et al., 2001; Mii et al., 2001; Grossman et al., 2002, 2008) (Fig. 10.8). Mii et al. (1999) attributed the mid-Carboniferous increase to initiation of continental glaciation, which we define as the Serpukhovian–Bashkirian Cool Trend (SBCT, ~323–319 Ma). High-resolution studies of the mid-Carboniferous GSSP section at Arrow Canyon, Nevada do not show the $\delta^{18}O$ increase seen in the US Midcontinent (Brand and Brenckle, 2001; Jones et al., 2003), perhaps because the isotopic shift occurs above or below the boundary section. The greater than −1‰ $\delta^{18}O$ values for late Tournaisian–early Visean brachiopods from the US Midcontinent show the influence of regional aridification and restricted circulation on the isotopic record (Grossman et al., 2008).

Early Permian brachiopods show an Asselian $\delta^{18}O$ maximum in Uralian specimens and a Sakmarian–Artinskian $\delta^{18}O$ decline in Uralian and Australian specimens (Korte

the value of NBS120c is given or determinable are used (see Appendix 2). These include Wenzel et al. (2000), Joachimski et al. (2004, 2006, 2009, 2012), Korte et al. (2004), Kaiser et al. (2006), Bassett et al. (2007), Buggisch et al. (2008), Trotter et al. (2008, 2016), Herrmann et al. (2010), Quinton et al. (2014, 2018), Rosenau et al. (2012), Elrick et al. (2009, 2013), Lehnert et al. (2010), Wenzel et al. (2000), Zigaite et al. (2010), Narkiewicz et al. (2017), Balter et al. (2008), Le Houedec et al. (2013), Huang et al. (2018), Girard et al. (2018), Wallace and Elrick (2014), Chen et al. (2013, 2016b), Barham et al. (2012), Montañez et al. (2018), Elrick and Scott (2010), Rosenau et al. (2014), Joachimski and Lambert (2015), and Schobben et al. (2014). Curves show Locfit regression (*thick lines*) and ±95% confidence intervals (*dashed lines*). Carbonate isotopic temperatures are based on Kim and O'Neil (1997), and phosphate isotopic temperatures are based on Pucéat et al. (2010), assuming seawater $\delta^{18}O$ of −1.1‰ (VSMOW). See Table 10.1 for definitions of isotopic features.

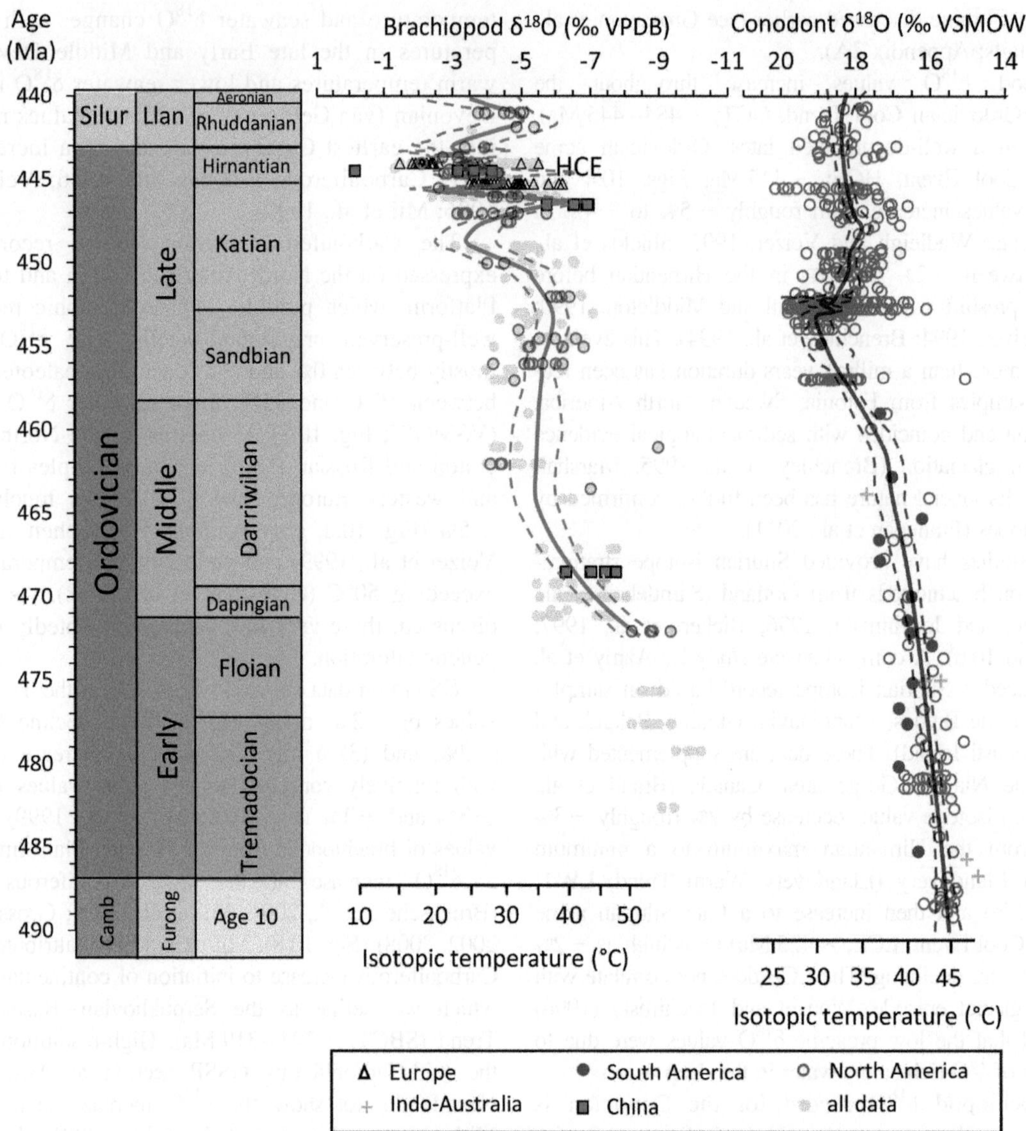

FIGURE 10.5 Isotopic data for brachiopod shells and conodonts showing the HCE in $\delta^{18}O$ and $\delta^{13}C$ (modified from Brenchley et al., 1995). Locfit regression curves (*thick lines*) and ± 95% confidence intervals (*dashed lines*) are defined for data extending above and below the time interval represented by the figure.

et al., 2005a, 2008) (Fig. 10.8). These trends correlate with early Permian glaciation and deglaciation, respectively. However, North American and other Uralian brachiopods fail to show this Asselian $\delta^{18}O$ maximum and Sakmarian–Artinskian decline, instead showing increasing $\delta^{18}O$ values in the Kungurian interpreted as reflecting aridification (Grossman et al., 2008; Noret et al., 2009). Regional differences in Permian and Carboniferous isotopic stratigraphies undoubtedly reflect local to regional variations in seawater temperature and $\delta^{18}O$ (as related to salinity) and highlight the need for understanding the paleoceanographic context in developing a global $\delta^{18}O$ stratigraphy for the Paleozoic.

10.4.3.2 Conodonts

The $\delta^{18}O$ database for Paleozoic and Triassic conodonts is steadily increasing and encompasses almost 3.700 data points (January 2019). In general, conodont apatite $\delta^{18}O$ data are less variable than those even from screened brachiopod shells (Fig. 10.4). As with the brachiopod record, the conodonts show lower $\delta^{18}O$ values for the early Paleozoic (Ordovician–Devonian) compared with the later Paleozoic (Carboniferous–Permian and Triassic). Specifically, conodont $\delta^{18}O$ is on average about 3‰ lower for the Late Ordovician to Devonian (18.3‰) versus the Carboniferous and Early Permian (21.5‰).

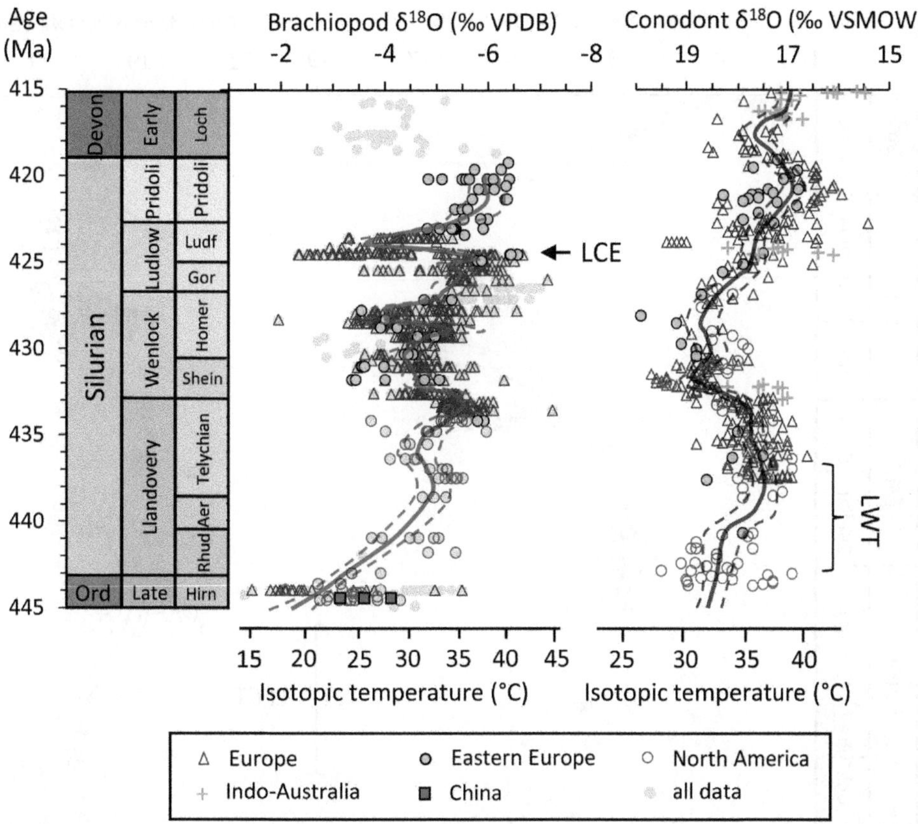

FIGURE 10.6 Oxygen isotope record for Silurian brachiopods and conodonts from tropical and subtropical paleolatitudes showing Llandovery Warm Trend (LWT) and Ludfordian Cool Event (LCE). Data for brachiopod shells are from Gotland, the Baltics, Scandinavia, Ukraine, Poland, the United Kingdom, and Anticosti Island, Canada (Samtleben et al., 1996; Bickert et al., 1997; Azmy et al., 1998; Wenzel et al., 2000; Came et al., 2007). Conodont data are from Wenzel et al. (2000), Joachimski et al. (2009), Lehnert et al. (2010), Zigaite et al. (2010), and Trotter et al. (2016). Curves show Locfit regression (*thick lines*) and ±95% confidence intervals (*dashed lines*).

Many of the key features of the $\delta^{18}O_{PO_4}$ record mimic those of the $\delta^{18}O_{CO3}$ record. Ordovician conodonts show a major increase in $\delta^{18}O$ (from roughly 16‰ to 19‰) from the Tremadocian to Darriwillian interpreted to represent global cooling from very warm Early Ordovician temperatures (>45 °C) to temperatures between 30°C and 35°C in the Late Ordovician (OCT Trotter et al., 2008, Bassett et al., 2007; Rosenau et al., 2012; Quinton and MacLeod, 2014; Quinton et al., 2018). Latest Ordovician conodonts have $\delta^{18}O_{PO_4}$ values around 18‰ and do not show the $\delta^{18}O$ maximum seen in brachiopod shells (HCE). However, the Hirnantian is not well represented in the conodont $\delta^{18}O_{PO_4}$ record due to limited conodont-bearing carbonates deposited during this glacio-eustatic sea level lowstand (Fig. 10.5). Silurian conodonts show a 1‰ decrease in $\delta^{18}O$ during the early- to late Llandovery (LWT) to values around 17.8‰ followed by a 1‰ increase in the late Llandovery to Wenlock (Lehnert et al., 2010; Trotter et al., 2016; Fig. 10.6). From the late Wenlock to Pridoli and Lochkovian, $\delta^{18}O_{PO_4}$ values decrease to 17.1‰, translating into significantly warmer temperatures between 35°C and 40°C compared to the cooler temperatures of 30°C–35°C reconstructed for the Wenlock. $\delta^{18}O_{PO_4}$ values increase during the Early Devonian (LECT) to Middle Devonian with maximum average values of 19.4‰ at the Eifelian to Givetian transition (Joachimski et al., 2009; Elrick et al., 2009; Fig. 10.7). The Late Devonian is characterized by decreasing $\delta^{18}O_{PO_4}$ and thus increasing temperature (GFWT) to a maximum greater than 35°C, with peak temperatures at the Frasnian–Famennian transition. The Frasnian–Famennian transition is marked by two short-term positive excursions in $\delta^{18}O$ of 1‰–1.5‰ related to climate cooling in conjunction with the deposition of the sediment-starved, low-O_2 Kellwasser horizons (Joachimski and Buggisch, 2002; Balter et al., 2008; Le Houedec et al., 2013; Huang et al., 2018). In general, isotopic trends for Devonian brachiopods are similar, with a mid-Devonian maximum (LECT) and mid- to Late Devonian decline (GFWT; Fig. 10.7; Joachimski et al., 2004, 2009); but brachiopods show larger changes in $\delta^{18}O$ translating into significantly larger temperature variations (e.g., Joachimski et al., 2004).

Late Devonian (Famennian) and Early Carboniferous conodonts show a substantial increase in $\delta^{18}O_{PO_4}$ from

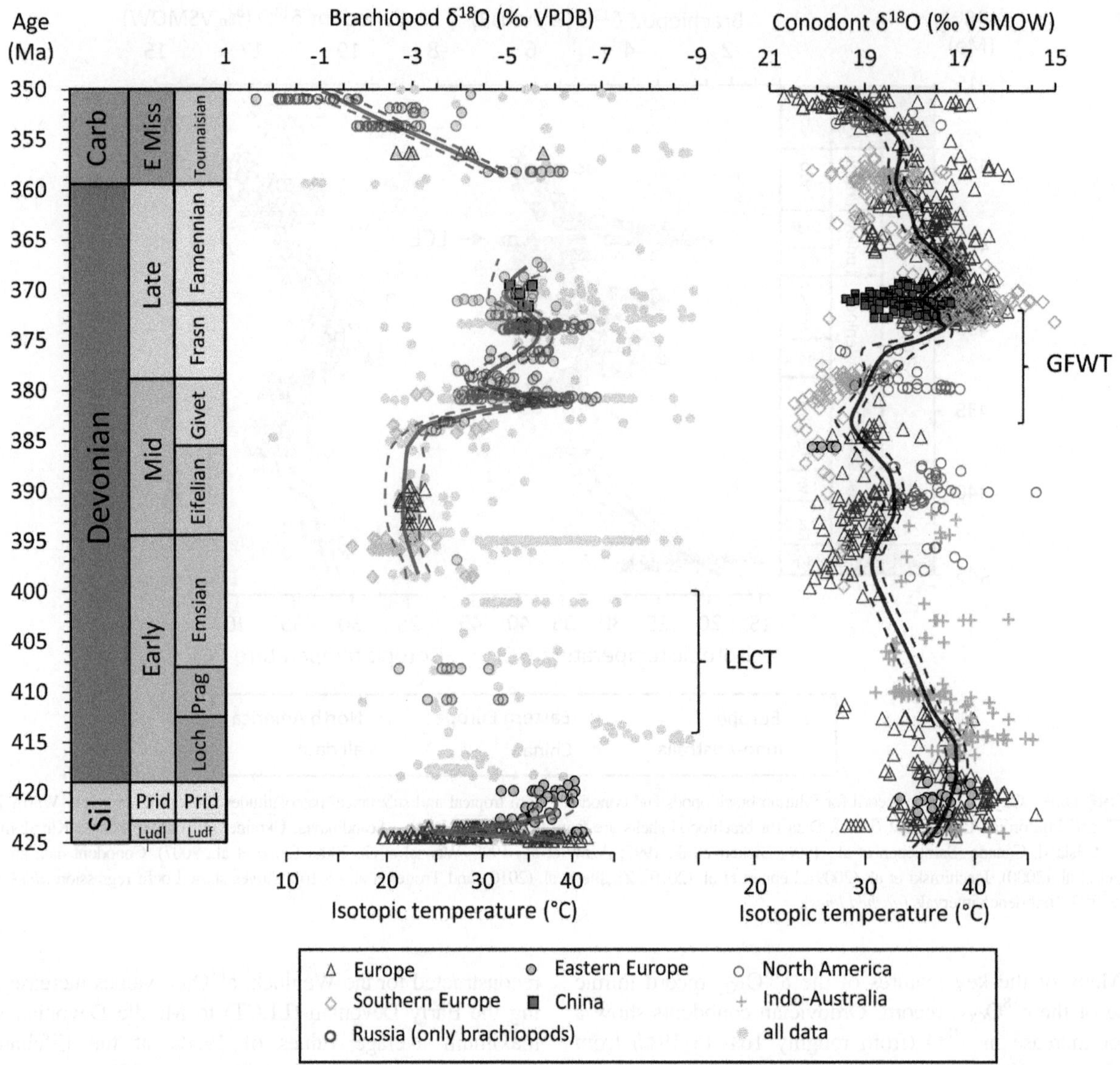

FIGURE 10.7 Oxygen isotope record of Late Silurian, Devonian, and Early Carboniferous brachiopod calcite and conodont apatite from tropical and subtropical paleolatitudes. Curves show Locfit regression (*thick lines*) and ±95% confidence intervals (*dashed lines*). Key features are the Lochkovian-Emsian Cool Trend (LECT) and Givetian-Frasnian Warm Trend (GFWT). Note that the GFWT occurs during the mid-Givetian for brachiopod $\delta^{18}O$ and in the early Frasnian for conodont $\delta^{18}O$. Devonian brachiopod calcite $\delta^{18}O$ dominantly from van Geldern et al. (2006). Conodont $\delta^{18}O$ data from Kaiser et al. (2006), Buggisch et al. (2008), Balter et al. (2008), Joachimski et al. (2009), Elrick et al. (2009), Le Houedec et al. (2013), Narkiewicz et al. (2017), Huang et al. (2018), and Girard et al. (2018).

minimum values of around 18‰ in the Famennian to 21.8‰ during the Serpukhovian to Bashkirian (LCT, SBCT; Joachimski et al., 2009; Girard et al., 2018; Buggisch et al., 2008). This increase in $\delta^{18}O_{PO_4}$ has been related to cooling after the Frasnian–Famennian as well as increasing $\delta^{18}O$ value of seawater as a consequence of the waxing of ice caps of the Late Paleozoic Ice age. The 3.5‰ increase in $\delta^{18}O_{PO_4}$ from the early Tournaisian to Bashkirian could be explained, for example, by a 2‰ increase in seawater $\delta^{18}O$ due the transition from ice-free (early Tournaisian) to ice-house conditions (Bashkirian) as well as cooler climatic conditions (~6°C) (Buggisch et al., 2008). The brachiopod and conodont $\delta^{18}O$ records for the Carboniferous are similar in that both show an increase in the Early Carboniferous (Tournaisian; Fig. 10.8). However, they differ in the late Visean in that brachiopod $\delta^{18}O$ values decrease to about −3‰ (after a $\delta^{18}O$ maximum attributed to aridification; Grossman et al., 2008), whereas conodont values continue to rise through the Mississippian to the Serpukhovian/Bashkirian maximum (Buggisch et al., 2008; Fig. 10.8). This divergence may reflect regional differences in temperature and salinity of ambient water masses.

Pennsylvanian conodonts from the epicontinental seas of the US Midcontinent (Joachimski et al., 2006;

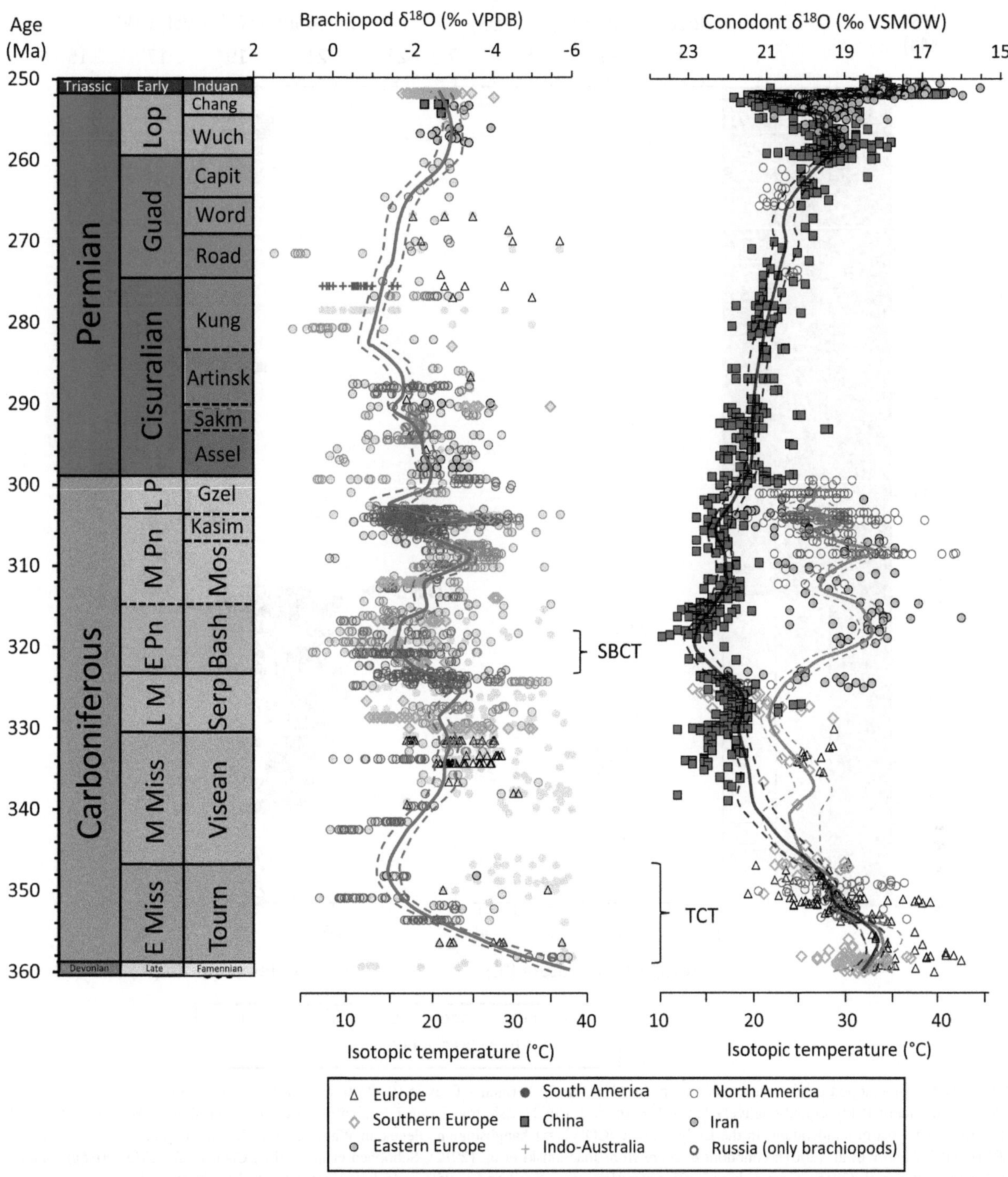

FIGURE 10.8 Oxygen isotopic record for Carboniferous and Permian brachiopod shells and conodonts from tropical and subtropical paleolatitudes. Major sources of brachiopod data include Popp et al. (1986), Grossman et al. (1991, 1993, 2008), Mii et al. (1999, 2001), Bruckschen et al. (1999, 2001), Brand and Brenckle (2001), Stanton et al. (2002), Korte et al. (2005a), Mazzullo et al. (2007), and Armendáriz et al. (2008). Conodont data are from Kaiser et al. (2006), Buggisch et al. (2008), Wallace and Elrick (2014), Chen et al. (2013, 2016a), Barham et al. (2012), Joachimski et al. (2006, 2012), Montañez et al. (2018), Elrick and Scott (2010), Rosenau et al. (2014), Chen et al. (2016b), Joachimski and Lambert (2015), Schobben et al. (2014), Rosenau et al. (2014). Isotopic temperatures assume "ice-free" conditions ($\delta^{18}O_{seawater} = -1.1‰$ vs VSMOW). Features include the Tournaisian Cool Trend (TCT) and the Serpukhovian–Bashkirian Cool Trend (SBCT), though the latter is not well-defined in conodont data. Curves show Locfit regression (*thick lines*) and ±95% confidence intervals (*dashed lines*).

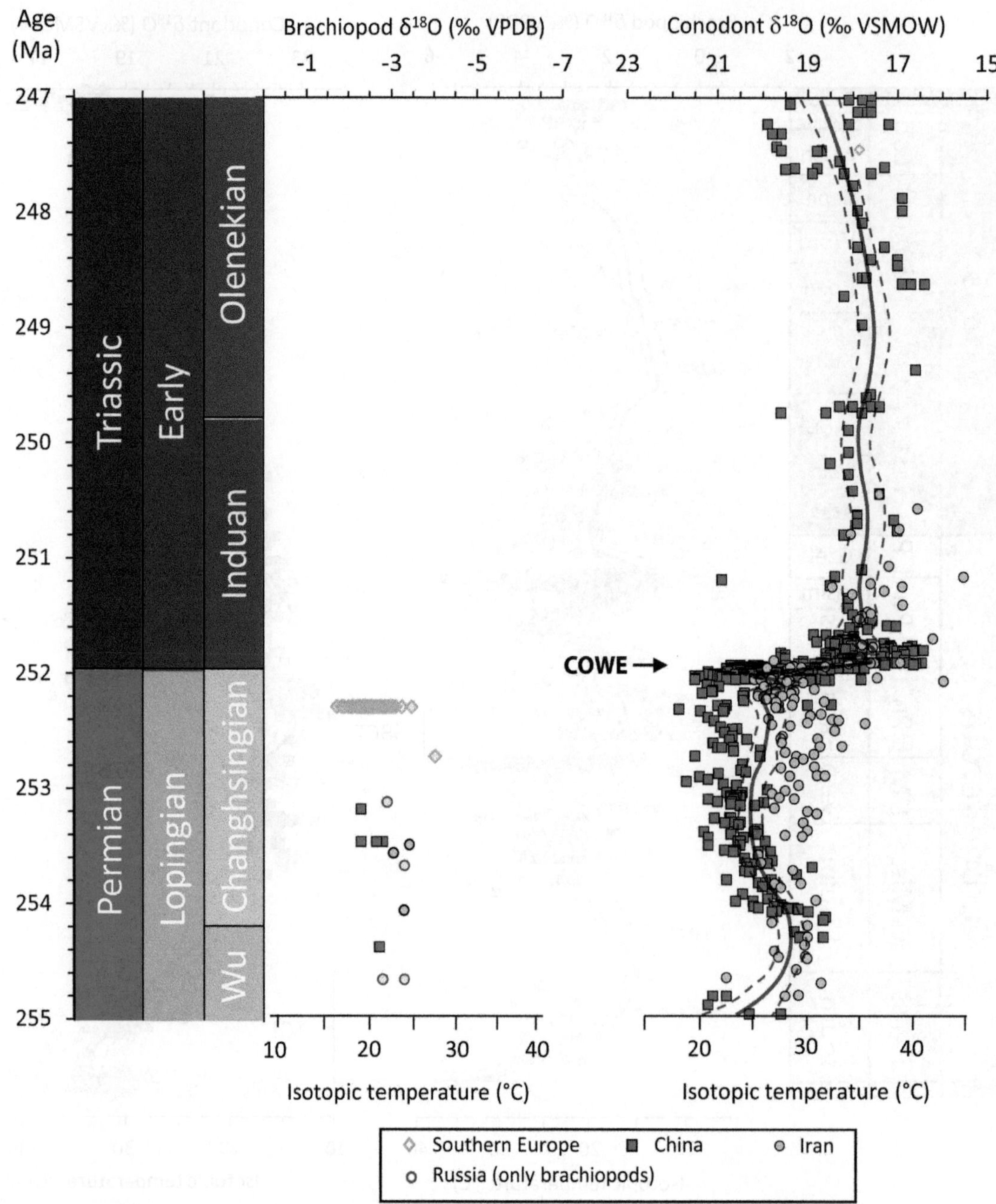

FIGURE 10.9 Brachiopod calcite and conodont apatite $\delta^{18}O$ for the Permian–Triassic (P–T) transition. Conodont $\delta^{18}O$ values show a significant decrease in the latest Permian and relatively low values in the Early Triassic translating into significant climate warming across the P–T boundary and warm to very warm temperatures in the Early Triassic (COWE = Changhsingian-Olenekian Warm Event). Brachiopod data are from Korte et al. (2005a) and Zakharov et al. (2001); conodont data are from Joachimski et al. (2012), Schobben et al. (2014), Chen et al. (2013, 2016a), Sun et al. (2012) and Trotter et al. (2015). Curves show Locfit regression (*thick lines*) and ± 95% confidence intervals (*dashed lines*).

Joachimski and Lambert, 2015; Rosenau et al., 2014) or Donets Basin (Montañez et al., 2018) are considerably lower in $\delta^{18}O_{PO_4}$ values compared to the Bashkirian to Serpukhovian maximum and show a significant variation with values ranging from 17‰ to 21‰ (Fig. 10.8). These variations have been interpreted to reflect the combined effect of interglacial–glacial changes in ice volume, related changes in sea-surface temperature, as well as potential changes in salinity. In contrast, Pennsylvanian $\delta^{18}O_{PO_4}$ values from a deeper, slope setting in South China show generally higher $\delta^{18}O_{PO_4}$ values with less variation (21.8‰–23.2‰; Chen et al., 2016a). This discrepancy can be explained by slightly cooler waters with normal marine salinity in open-ocean settings and potentially minor glacial–interglacial ice volume changes as previously assumed (e.g., Joachimski et al., 2006).

In the Early Permian, $\delta^{18}O_{PO_4}$ values start to decrease from 21.5‰ in the Asselian to 19.2‰ at the Guadalupian–Lopingian transition (Chen et al., 2013). In the latest Permian, conodont $\delta^{18}O_{PO_4}$ shows a significant decrease in $\delta^{18}O_{PO_4}$ from ~20.2‰ to 17.8‰ (COWE; ~252 Ma; Fig. 10.9). This change in $\delta^{18}O_{PO_4}$ was interpreted as a major warming event with low latitudinal temperatures rising in all studied sections from around 24°C–29°C in the late Permian to temperatures between 31°C and 38°C in the Early Triassic (Joachimski et al., 2012; Schobben et al., 2014; Jiang et al., 2015; Chen et al., 2016a). This significant warming is seen as a consequence of Siberian trap volcanism releasing large amounts of CO_2 and CH_4 to the ocean/atmosphere system (e.g., Svensen et al., 2009). The Early Triassic time period is characterized by low $\delta^{18}O_{PO_4}$ values translating into high temperatures (35°C–40°C; Sun et al., 2012; Romano et al., 2012) comparable to Early Paleozoic temperatures. Middle- to Late Triassic low latitudinal temperatures are between 25°C and 30°C and thus comparable to modern equatorial ocean temperatures (Rigo and Joachimski, 2010; Trotter et al., 2015; Sun et al., 2016).

The similar trends in oxygen isotope paleotemperatures for Paleozoic conodonts and brachiopod shells argue for preservation of the original signals and against diagenetic alteration as a cause of the lower $\delta^{18}O$ values for the early Paleozoic. Thus these lower values may reflect 10°C–15°C warmer temperatures or lower seawater $\delta^{18}O$ (e.g., −2‰ VSMOW). A detailed discussion of the arguments for constant versus decreasing seawater $\delta^{18}O$ is beyond the scope of this chapter. However, recent clumped isotope studies of Ordovician and Silurian brachiopods argue for warm tropical temperatures (34°C–37°C) and seawater $\delta^{18}O$ close to that of the modern ocean (−2‰ to −1‰ VSMOW) (Came et al., 2007; Finnegan et al., 2011; Bergmann et al., 2018; Henkes et al., 2018). Thus the assumptions of near-modern seawater $\delta^{18}O$ and retention of original oxygen isotopic compositions in well-preserved brachiopod shells and conodonts appear justified.

10.4.4 Archean and Proterozoic

Compilations by Shields and Veizer (2002) and Knauth (2005) highlight the oxygen isotope trends in Archean and Proterozoic dolostones, limestones, and cherts. The chert data compiled by Knauth (2005) are nearly all based on platform deposits, believed to be chemically stabilized during shallow burial. These represent, at best, early diagenetic conditions. Carbonate rocks also provide at best a record of early diagenetic conditions; note that Paleozoic carbonate sediments typically average 2‰–3‰ lower in $\delta^{18}O$ compared with brachiopod shells (e.g., Mii et al., 1999). Age control is difficult for Precambrian samples because of the paucity of radiogenic isotope ages (Strachan et al., 2020a, Chapter 16, Precambrian, this book). To address this issue, Shields and Veizer (2002) differentiate carbonate data in terms of those with well-constrained ages (known within 50 Myr) and those with poorly constrained ages (>50 Myr).

The isotopic data for Archean and Proterozoic cherts and carbonates are shown in Fig. 10.10. The key features of the Archean-through-Proterozoic chert record are (1) high variability of >10‰ or more within time slices and (2) a roughly 10‰ increase from very low values in the Archean (8‰–22‰ VSMOW) to low values in the Proterozoic (17‰–32‰ VSMOW) (e.g., Perry, 1967; Knauth and Epstein, 1976; Knauth, 2005; Fig. 10.10A). The 10‰ $\delta^{18}O$ change equates to a temperature change of around 50°C. The high variability is attributed to early diagenesis in meteoric waters of variable $\delta^{18}O$ and/or by later diagenesis associated with deep burial and high temperatures (Knauth, 2005).

Archean and Proterozoic dolomites and limestones also show high $\delta^{18}O$ variability (>10‰) and an increase from an average of −17‰ in the early Archean to about −9‰ in the latest Proterozoic (e.g., Veizer and Hoefs, 1976; Shields and Veizer, 2002; Fig. 10.10). As with cherts, variability in carbonate $\delta^{18}O$ is attributed to differing degrees and conditions of diagenetic alteration (Shields and Veizer, 2002). As discussed earlier, the $\delta^{18}O$ trends for Precambrian sedimentary rocks have been interpreted as indicating (1) high Precambrian temperatures (e.g., Knauth and Epstein, 1976; Knauth, 2005), (2) low $\delta^{18}O$ for Precambrian seawater (Perry, 1967; Veizer and Hoefs, 1976; Veizer et al., 1999; Jaffrés et al., 2007), or (3) the cumulative effects of meteoric diagenesis with progressive age (e.g., Degens and Epstein, 1962). Discussion of the merits of each of these hypotheses is beyond the scope of this chapter; however, there is no doubt that diagenesis had a strong influence on the $\delta^{18}O$ of Precambrian sediments. Thus oxygen isotopes presently have limited utility for Archean and Proterozoic chemostratigraphy, compared with strontium, carbon, and sulfur isotopes.

10.5 Summation

The value of oxygen isotopes in stratigraphy increases toward the modern as well-preserved fossils and microfossils increase in availability. The oxygen isotopic record for the Archean and Proterozoic is hampered by the lack of marine sediments unmodified by diagenesis. Values decrease with age and do not show distinct, globally correlatable events. Numerous features in the Phanerozoic isotopic record are potential stratigraphic markers, as summarized in Fig. 10.11 and Table 10.1.

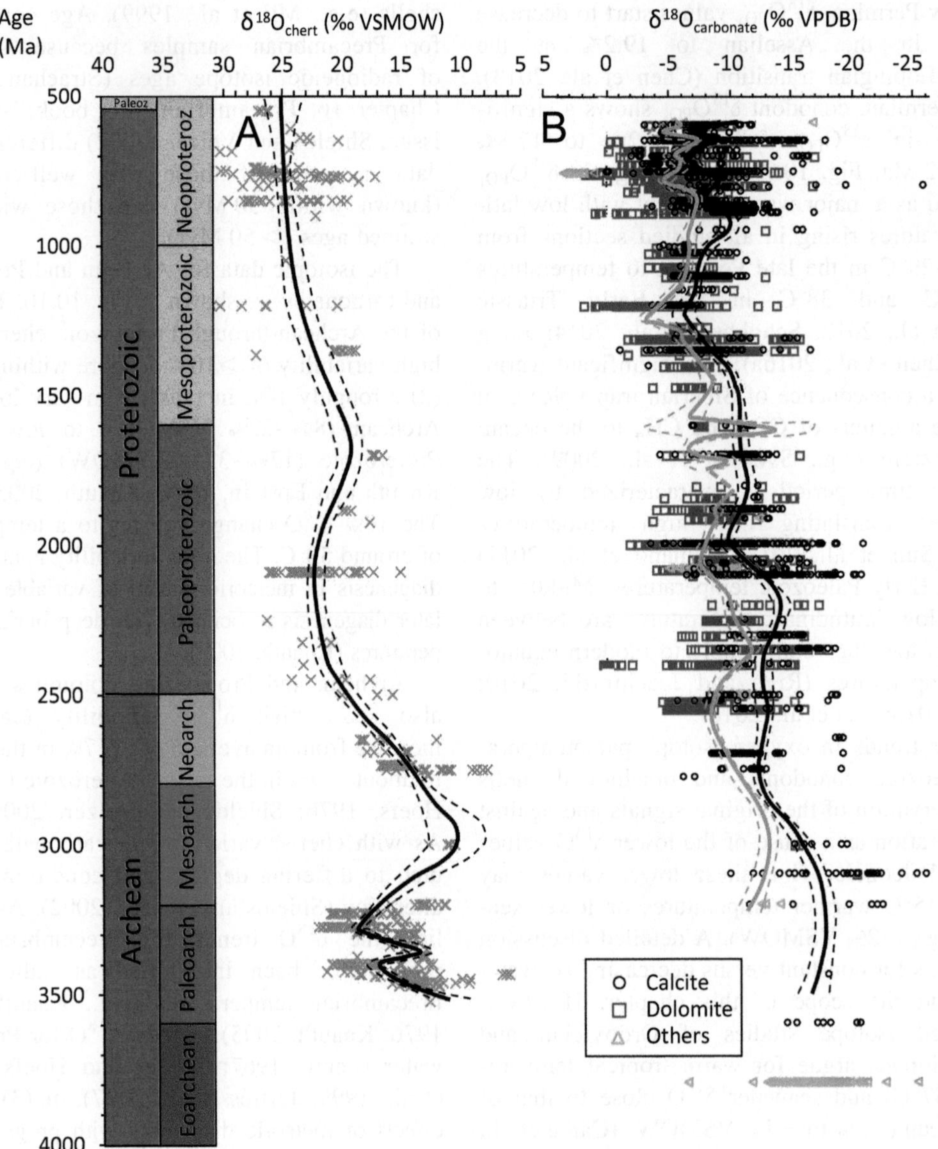

FIGURE 10.10 (A) Oxygen isotopic data for screened Precambrian chert samples from Knauth (2005). All samples are unmetamorphosed except 3800 Ma specimens, which are no higher than greenschist facies. See Knauth (2005) for data sources. (B) Oxygen isotopic compositions of Precambrian carbonate minerals ($N \approx 12{,}000$) from Shields and Veizer (2002). Larger symbols indicate samples with ages constrained to better than 50 million-years. Smaller symbols represent data with poorly constrained ages (>50 Ma). Continuous black line is running mean for calcite data and continuous light blue line is running mean for dolomite data (modified from Fig. 6, Shields and Veizer, 2002). Note that chert $\delta^{18}O$ values are reported versus VSMOW, whereas carbonate values are reported versus VPDB. Silica is enriched in ^{18}O relative to calcite by around 6‰, but the temperature dependences of the mineral-water fractionation are similar. Curves show Locfit regression (*thick lines*) and ±95% confidence intervals (*dashed lines*).

These $\delta^{18}O$ changes are likely recording climatic trends and events. To aid future studies, key features in the carbonate and phosphate $\delta^{18}O$ records have been assigned climate-based names (with C = cool, W = warm, E = event, and T = trend). Paleozoic $\delta^{18}O$ records include an Early- to Late Ordovician rise (OCT), a latest Ordovician acme (HCE), an Early Silurian decline (LWT), a Late Silurian acme (LCE), an Early Devonian increase (LECT), and a Middle- to Late Devonian decline (GFWT). These are followed by $\delta^{18}O$ rises in the Early Carboniferous (TCT) and at the mid-Carboniferous boundary (SBCT), though this latter trend is not well represented in conodont data. The transition from latest Permian to Early Triassic is characterized by a sharp $\delta^{18}O$ decline (COWE).

The carbonate record for the early Mesozoic (Triassic) is based on brachiopods and is as yet too sparse to confidently identify isotopic features. However, conodont $\delta^{18}O$ values decrease from the latest Permian and Early

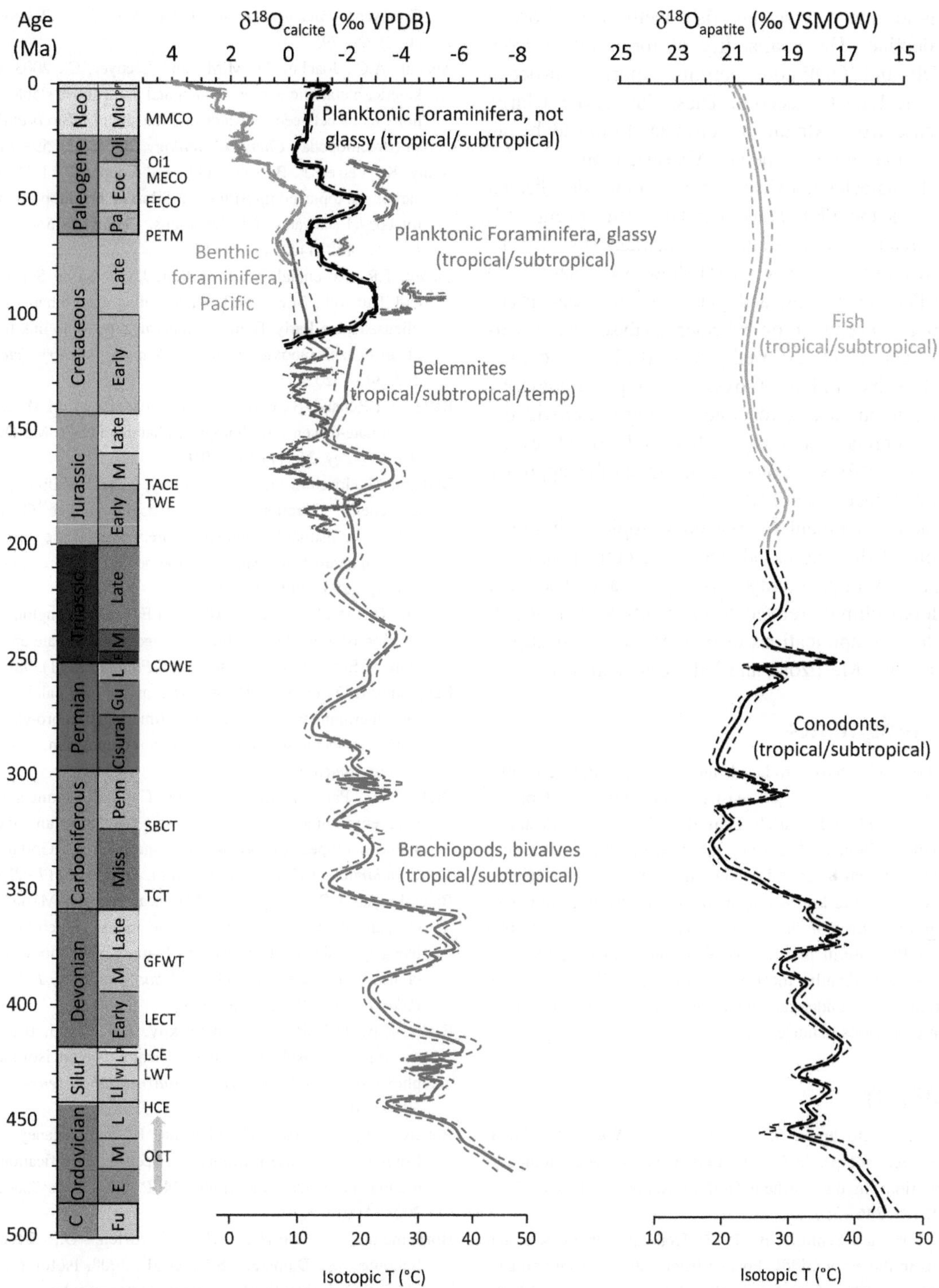

FIGURE 10.11 Oxygen isotopic curves for the Phanerozoic based on carbonate (calcite) and phosphate oxygen from fossils and microfossils. $\delta^{18}O$ values are given in Appendix 4. Isotopic temperatures assume "ice-free" conditions ($\delta^{18}O_{seawater} = -1.1‰$ vs VSMOW. Temperature scales same as in Fig. 10.4). (A) Carbonate (calcite) data and trend lines are from Figs. 10.2 to 10.4. See explanations in those figure captions. (B) Phosphate (apatite) data are from Figs. 10.3 and 10.4, plus Cenozoic data in Appendix 3. Curves show Locfit regression (*thick lines*) and ± 95% confidence intervals (*dashed lines*).

Triassic minimum, indicating extreme warmth, to values representing cooler temperatures in the later Triassic. The Jurassic and Early Cretaceous records based on belemnites show distinct features: (1) a Toarcian decline (TWE) and a sharp Toarcian–Aalenian increase (TACE), (2) an increase in the early Cretaceous to a maximum near the Valanginian–Hauterivian boundary, and (3) a decline to a minimum in the middle Barremian. Sparse phosphate data from Jurassic and Cretaceous fish teeth also show a Toarcian decline. The availability of foraminifera from DSDP, ODP, and IODP cores permits a more open-ocean record for the Late Cretaceous. These data show a large $\delta^{18}O$ decrease from Albian to Turonian, followed by an increase to a maximum in the late Maastrichtian.

The well-characterized Cenozoic record includes distinct events such as the PETM and the Oligocene event Oi1, which are already used as stratigraphic markers (Fig. 10.11). While the deep-sea Cenozoic record shows systematic $\delta^{18}O$ increase reflecting cooling and glaciation, the sea-surface record differs depending on whether analyses were performed on "glassy" or less well-preserved planktonic foraminifera. The integration of oxygen isotope stratigraphy with biostratigraphy and astronomical tuning has provided a late Neogene chronostratigraphy with a resolution of several thousand years. Efforts are ongoing to expand this approach into the early Neogene and Paleogene.

Continued refinement of oxygen isotopic techniques, development of diagenetic indicators and other paleotemperature proxies (e.g., clumped isotopes), and discovery of new global climate-related $\delta^{18}O$ events will undoubtedly lead to new applications of oxygen isotope stratigraphy to Cenozoic, Mesozoic, and Paleozoic sediments.

Acknowledgments

We thank those who have produced and made available compilations that have made our job easier, including Ben Cramer, Guillaume Dera, Oliver Friedrich, Paul Knauth, Andreas Prokoph, Graham Shields, Clemens Ullmann, Ján Veizer, and Jim Zachos. We thank US National Science Foundation and the German Science Foundation for past and future support of oxygen isotope studies of the temperature history of Paleozoic oceans. We also thank John McArthur for his careful review, and Gabi and Jim Ogg for their editorial assistance. Finally, the first author thanks Pam Grossman for her patience and understanding throughout the preparation of this and many previous manuscripts.

Bibliography

Al-Rousan, S., Al-Moghrabi, S., Pätzold, J., and Wefer, G., 2003, Stable oxygen isotopes in *Porites* corals monitor weekly temperature variations in the northern Gulf of Aqaba, Red Sea. *Coral Reefs*, **22** (4), 346–356.

Andreasson, F.P., and Schmitz, B., 1998, Tropical Atlantic seasonal dynamics in the early middle Eocene from stable oxygen and carbon isotope profiles of mollusk shells. *Paleoceanography*, **13** (2), 183–192.

Anderson, T.F., Popp, B.N., Williams, A.C., Ho, L.Z., and Hudson, J.D., 1994, The stable isotopic records of fossils from the Peterborough Member, Oxford Clay Formation (Jurassic), UK – paleoenvironmental implications. *Journal of the Geological Society*, **151**: 125–138.

Armendáriz, M., Rosales, I., and Quesada, C., 2008, Oxygen isotope and Mg/Ca composition of Late Viséan (Mississippian) brachiopod shells from SW Iberia: palaeoclimatic and palaeogeographic implications in northern Gondwana. *Palaeogeography, Palaeoclimatology, Palaeoecology*, **268** (1–2), 65–79.

Auclair, A.C., Joachimski, M.M., and Lécuyer, C., 2003, Deciphering kinetic, metabolic and environmental controls on stable isotope fractionatioéns between seawater and the shell of *Terebratalia transversa* (Brachiopoda). *Chemical Geology*, **202** (1–2), 59–78.

Azmy, K., Veizer, J., Bassett, M.G., and Copper, P., 1998, Oxygen and carbon isotopic composition of Silurian brachiopods: implications for coeval seawater and glaciations. *Geological Society of America Bulletin*, **110** (11), 1499–1512.

Bailey, T.R., Rosenthal, Y., McArthur, J.M., van de Schootbrugge, B., and Thirlwall, M.F., 2003, Paleoceanographic changes of the Late Pliensbachian-Early Toarcian interval: a possible link to the genesis of an oceanic anoxic event. *Earth and Planetary Science Letters*, **212**: 307–320.

Balter, V., Renaud, S., Girard, C., and Joachimski, M.M., 2008, Record of climate-driven morphological changes in 376 Ma Devonian fossils. *Geology*, **36** (11), 907–910.

Barham, M., Joachimski, M.M., Murray, J., and Williams, D.M., 2012, Diagenetic alteration of the structure and $\delta^{18}O$ signature of Palaeozoic fish and conodont apatite: potential use for corrected isotope signatures in palaeoenvironmental interpretation. *Chemical Geology*, **298–299**: 11–19.

Bassett, D., Macleod, K.G., Miller, J.E., and Ethington, R.L., 2007, Oxygen isotopic composition of biogenic phosphate and the temperature of Early Ordovician seawater. *Palaios*, **22** (1), 98–103.

Bergmann, K.D., et al., 2018, A paired apatite and calcite clumped isotope thermometry approach to estimating Cambro-Ordovician seawater temperatures and isotopic composition. *Geochimica et Cosmochimica Acta*, **224**: 18–41.

Bickert, T., Patzold, J., Samtleben, C., and Munnecke, A., 1997, Paleoenvironmental changes in the Silurian indicated by stable isotopes in brachiopod shells from Gotland, Sweden. *Geochimica et Cosmochimica Acta*, **61** (13), 2717–2730.

Billon-Bruyat, J.-P., Lécuyer, C., Martineau, F., and Mazin, J.-M., 2005, Oxygen isotope compositions of Late Jurassic vertebrate remains from lithographic limestones of western Europe: implications for the ecology of fish, turtles, and crocodilians. *Palaeogeography, Palaeoclimatology, Palaeoecology*, **216** (3), 359–375.

Blake, R.E., O'Neil, J.R., and Surkov, A.V., 2005, Biogeochemical cycling of phosphorus: insights from oxygen isotope effects of phosphoenzymes. *American Journal of Science*, **305** (6–8), 596–620.

Bohaty, S.M., Zachos, J.C., Florindo, F., and Delaney, M.L., 2009, Coupled greenhouse warming and deep-sea acidification in the middle Eocene. *Paleoceanography*, **24**: PA2207, https://doi.org/10.1029/2008PA001676.

Bornemann, A., Norris, R.D., Friedrich, O., Beckmann, B., Schouten, S., Damste, J.S.S., et al., 2008, Isotopic evidence for glaciation during the Cretaceous supergreenhouse. *Science*, **319** (5860), 189–192.

Brand, U., and Brenckle, P., 2001, Chemostratigraphy of the mid-Carboniferous boundary global stratotype section and point (GSSP), Bird Spring Formation, Arrow Canyon, Nevada, USA. *Palaeogeography, Palaeoclimatology, Palaeoecology*, **165** (3–4), 321–347.

Brand, U., Logan, A., Hiller, N., and Richardson, J., 2003, Geochemistry of modern brachiopods: applications and implications for oceanography and paleoceanography. *Chemical Geology*, **198** (3–4), 305–334.

Brand, U., Azmy, K., and Veizer, J., 2006, Evaluation of the Salinic I tectonic, Cancaniri glacial and Ireviken biotic events: biochemostratigraphy of the lower Silurian succession in the Niagara Gorge area, Canada and USA. *Palaeogeography, Palaeoclimatology, Palaeoecology*, **241** (2), 192–213.

Brenchley, P.J., Marshall, J.D., Carden, G.A.F., Robertson, D.B.R., Long, D.G.F., Meidla, T., et al., 1994, Bathymetric and isotopic evidence for a short-lived Late Ordovician glaciation in a greenhouse period. *Geology*, **22** (4), 295–298.

Brenchley, P.J., Carden, G.A.F., and Marshall, J.D., 1995, Environmental changes associated with the "first strike" of the late Ordovician mass extinction. *Mod. Geol.*, **20**: 69–82.

Bruckschen, P., and Veizer, J., 1997, Oxygen and carbon isotopic composition of Dinantian brachiopods: paleoenvironmental implications for the Lower Carboniferous of western Europe. *Palaeogeography, Palaeoclimatology, Palaeoecology*, **132** (1–4), 243–264.

Bruckschen, P., Oesmann, S., and Veizer, J., 1999, Isotope stratigraphy of the European Carboniferous: proxy signals for ocean chemistry, climate and tectonics. *Chemical Geology*, **161** (1–3), 127–163.

Bruckschen, P., Veizer, J., Schwark, L., and Leythaeuser, D., 2001, Isotope stratigraphy for the transition from the late Palaeozoic greenhouse in the Permo-Carboniferous icehouse—new results. *Terra Nostra*, **2001/4**: 7–11.

Buggisch, W., Joachimski, M.M., Alekseev, A.S., Sevastopulo, G., and Morrow, J.R., 2008, Mississippian $\delta^{13}C_{carb}$ and conodont apatite $\delta^{18}O$ records – their relation to the late Palaeozoic glaciation. *Palaeogeography, Palaeoclimatology, Palaeoecology*, **268**: 273–292.

Came, R.E., Eiler, J.M., Veizer, J., Azmy, K., Brand, U., and Weidman, C.R., 2007, Coupling of surface temperatures and atmospheric CO_2 concentrations during the Palaeozoic era. *Nature*, **449**: 198–201, https://doi.org/10.1038/nature06085.

Carpenter, S.J., and Lohmann, K.C., 1995, $\delta^{18}O$ and $\delta^{13}C$ values of modern brachiopod shells. *Geochimica et Cosmochimica Acta*, **59**: 3749–3764.

Chen, B., et al., 2013, Permian ice volume and palaeoclimate history: oxygen isotope proxies revisited. *Gondwana Research*, **24** (1), 77–89.

Chen, B., et al., 2016a, Ice volume and paleoclimate history of the late Paleozoic ice age from conodont apatite oxygen isotopes from Naqing (Guizhou, China). *Palaeogeography, Palaeoclimatology, Palaeoecology*, **448**: 151–161.

Chen, J., Shen, S.-Z., Li, X.-H., Xu, Y.-G., Joachimski, M., Bowring, S.A., et al., 2016b, High-resolution SIMS oxygen isotope analysis on conodont apatite from South China and implications for the end-Permian mass extinction. *Palaeogeography, Palaeoclimatology, Palaeoecology*, **448**: 26–38.

Chenery, C., Muldner, G., Evans, J., Eckardt, H., and Lewis, M., 2010, Strontium and stable isotope evidence for diet and mobility in Roman Gloucester, UK. *Journal of Archaeological Science*, **37** (1), 150–163.

Compston, W., 1960, The carbon isotopic composition of certain marine invertebrates and coals from the Australian Permian. *Geochimica et Cosmochimica Acta*, **18**: 1–22.

Coplen, T.B., 1988, Normalization of oxygen and hydrogen isotope data. *Chemical Geology (Isotope Geoscience Section)*, **72**: 293–297.

Coplen, T.B., De Bièvre, P., Krouse, H.R., Vocke Jr., R.D., Gröning, M., and Rozanski, K., 1996, Ratios for light-element isotopes standardized for better interlaboratory comparison. *Eos, Transactions American Geophysical Union*, **77** (27), 255.

Cramer, B.S., Toggweiler, J.R., Wright, J.D., Katz, M.E., and Miller, K.G., 2009, Ocean overturning since the Late Cretaceous: inferences from a new benthic foraminiferal isotope compilation. *Paleoceanography*, **24**: PA4216, https://doi.org/10.1029/2008PA001683.

Cusack, M., Huerta, A.P., and Eimf, 2012, Brachiopods recording seawater temperature—a matter of class or maturation? *Chemical Geology*, **334**: 139–143.

Degens, E.T., and Epstein, S., 1962, Relationship between O^{18}/O^{16} ratios in coexisting carbonates, cherts, and diatomites. *Bulletin of the American Association of Petroleum Geologists*, **46**: 534–542.

Dera, G., et al., 2009, Water mass exchange and variations in seawater temperature in the NW Tethys during the Early Jurassic: evidence from neodymium and oxygen isotopes of fish teeth and belemnites. *Earth and Planetary Science Letters*, **286** (1), 198–207.

Dera, G., et al., 2011, Climatic ups and downs in a disturbed Jurassic world. *Geology*, **39** (3), 215–218.

D'Hondt, S., and Arthur, M.A., 1996, Late Cretaceous oceans and the cool tropic paradox. *Science*, **271** (5257), 1838–1841.

Dickens, G.R., O'Neil, J.R., Rea, D.K., and Owen, R.M., 1995, Dissociation of oceanic methane hydrate as a cause of the carbon-isotope excursion at the end of the Paleocene. *Paleoceanography*, **10** (6), 965–971.

Dromart, G., Garcia, J.-P., Picard, S., Atrops, F., Lécuyer, C., and Sheppard, S.M.F., 2003, Ice age at the Middle-Late Jurassic transition? *Earth and Planetary Science Letters*, **213** (3–4), 205–220.

Dutton, A., Huber, B.T., Lohmann, K.C., and Zinsmeister, W.J., 2007, High-resolution stable isotope profiles of a dimitobelid belemnite: implications for paleodepth habitat and late Maastrichtian climate seasonality. *Palaios*, **22**: 642–650.

Elrick, M., and Scott, L.A., 2010, Carbon and oxygen isotope evidence for high-frequency (10^4-10^5 yr) and My-scale glacio-eustasy in Middle Pennsylvanian cyclic carbonates (Gray Mesa Formation), central New Mexico. *Palaeogeography, Palaeoclimatology, Palaeoecology*, **285** (3–4), 307–320.

Elrick, M., et al., 2009, Stratigraphic and oxygen isotope evidence for My-scale glaciation driving eustasy in the Early–Middle Devonian greenhouse world. *Palaeogeography, Palaeoclimatology, Palaeoecology*, **276** (1–4), 170–181.

Elrick, M., Reardon, D., Labor, W., Martin, J., Desrochers, A., and Pope, M., 2013, Orbital-scale climate change and glacioeustasy during the early Late Ordovician (pre-Hirnantian) determined from $\delta^{18}O$ values in marine apatite. *Geology*, **41**: 775–778.

Emiliani, C., 1955, Pleistocene temperatures. *The Journal of Geology*, **63** (6), 538–578.

Epstein, S., Buchsbaum, R., Lowenstam, H.A., and Urey, H.C., 1953, Revised carbonate-water isotopic temperature scale. *Geological Society of America Bulletin*, **64** (11), 1315–1325.

Finnegan, S., Bergmann, K., Eiler, J.M., Jones, D.S., Fike, D.A., Eisenman, I., et al., 2011, The magnitude and duration of Late Ordovician–Early Silurian glaciation. *Science*, **331**: 903–906.

Friedrich, O., Norris, R.D., and Erbacher, J., 2012, Evolution of middle to Late Cretaceous oceans—a 55 m.y. record of Earth's temperature and carbon cycle. *Geology*, **40** (2), 107–110.

GEOSECS, 1987, *GEOSECS Atlantic, Pacific, and Indian Ocean Expeditions*, **Vol. 7**, *Shorebased Data and Graphics*. National Science Foundation, Washington, DC, 200 p.

Ghosh, P., et al., 2006, $^{13}C-^{18}O$ bonds in carbonate minerals: a new kind of paleothermometer. *Geochimica et Cosmochimica Acta*, **70** (6), 1439–1456.

Girard C., Cornée J.J., Joachimski M.M., Charruault, A.L., Dufour, A.B., Renaud, S., 2018, Paleogeographic differences in temperature, water depth and conodont biofacies during the Late Devonian. *Online-Palaeogeography, Palaeoclimatology, Palaeoecology*, article #108852: 12 pp. https://doi.org/10.1016/j.palaeo.2018.06.046

Gonfiantini, R., 1984, Advisory group meeting on stable isotope reference samples for geochemical and hydrological investigations. *International Atomic Energy Agency, Vienna, 19–21 September 1983, Report to the Director General, 77 p.*

González, L.A., and Lohmann, K.C., 1985, Carbon and oxygen isotopic composition of Holocene reefal carbonates. *Geology*, **13** (11), 811–814.

Gröning, M., 2004, International stable isotope reference materials. *In* de Groot, P.A. (ed), Handbook of Stable Isotope Analytical Techniques. *Elsevier*, Amsterdam, **Vol. 1**: Amsterdam: Elsevier, 874–906.

Grossman, E.L., 1984, Stable isotope fractionation in live benthic foraminifera from the Southern California borderland. *Palaeogeography, Palaeoclimatology, Palaeoecology*, **47** (3–4), 301–327.

Grossman, E.L., 1987, Stable isotopes in modern benthic foraminifera – a study of vital effect. *Journal of Foraminiferal Research*, **17** (1), 48–61.

Grossman, E.L., 1994, The carbon and oxygen isotopic record during the evolution of Pangea: Carboniferous to Triassic. *In* Klein, G.D. (ed), Pangea: Paleoclimate, Tectonics, and Sedimentation during Accretion, Zenith, and Breakup of a Supercontinent. *Geological Society of America Special Paper*, **288**: 207–228.

Grossman, E.L., 2012a, Chapter 10 – Oxygen isotope stratigraphy. *In* Gradstein, F.M., Ogg, J.G., Schmitz, M.D., and Ogg, G.M. (eds), *The Geologic Time Scale*. Elsevier, Boston, MA, 181–206.

Grossman, E.L., 2012b, Applying oxygen isotope paleothermometry in deep time. *The Paleontological Society Papers*, **18**: 39–68.

Grossman, E.L., and Ku, T.L., 1986, Oxygen and carbon isotope fractionation in biogenic aragonite – temperature effects. *Chemical Geology*, **59** (1), 59–74.

Grossman, E.L., Zhang, C.L., and Yancey, T.E., 1991, Stable isotope stratigraphy of brachiopods from Pennsylvanian shales in Texas. *Geological Society of America Bulletin*, **103** (7), 953–965.

Grossman, E.L., Mii, H.S., and Yancey, T.E., 1993, Stable isotopes in Late Pennsylvanian brachiopods from the United States – implications for Carboniferous paleoceanography. *Geological Society of America Bulletin*, **105** (10), 1284–1296.

Grossman, E.L., Bruckschen, P., Mii, H.-S., Chuvashov, B.I., Yancey, T.E., and Veizer, J., 2002, *Carboniferous paleoclimate and global change: isotopic evidence from the Russian Platform. Carboniferous Stratigraphy and Paleogeography in Eurasia*. (pp. 61–71). Institute of Geology and Geochemistry, Russian Academy of Sciences, Urals Branch.

Grossman, E.L., Yancey, T.E., Jones, T.E., Chuvashov, B., Mazzullo, S.J., and Mii, H.-S., 2008, Glaciation, aridification, and carbon sequestration in the Permo-Carboniferous: the isotopic record for low latitudes. *Palaeogeography, Palaeoclimatology, Palaeoecology*, **268**: 222–233.

Hays, J.D., Imbrie, J., and Shackleton, N.J., 1976, Variations in Earth's orbit – pacemaker of ice ages. *Science*, **194** (4270), 1121–1132.

He, S., Kyser, T.K., and Caldwell, W.G.E., 2005, Paleoenvironment of the Western Interior Seaway inferred from $\delta^{18}O$ and $\delta^{13}C$ values of molluscs from the Cretaceous Bearpaw marine cyclothem. *Palaeogeography, Palaeoclimatology, Palaeoecology*, **217** (1–2), 67–85.

Henkes, G.A., et al., 2018, Temperature evolution and the oxygen isotope composition of Phanerozoic oceans from carbonate clumped isotope thermometry. *Earth and Planetary Science Letters*, **490**: 40–50.

Herrmann, A.D., MacLeod, K.G., and Leslie, S.A., 2010, Did a volcanic mega-eruption cause global cooling during the Late Ordovician? *Palaios*, **25** (12), 831–836.

Hinnov, L.A., and Ogg, J.G., 2007, Cyclostratigraphy and the astronomical time scale. *Stratigraphy*, **4** (2/3), 239–251.

Hinnov, L.A., and Hilgen, F.J., 2012, Ch. 4: Earth's orbital parameters and cycle stratigraphy. *In* Gradstein, F.M., Ogg, J.G., Schmitz, M., and Ogg, G.M. (eds), (coordinators). *A Geologic Time Scale 2012*. Cambridge Press, Cambridge.

Huang, C., Joachimski, M.M., and Gong, Y., 2018, Did climate changes trigger the Late Devonian Kellwasser Crisis? Evidence from a high-resolution conodont $\delta^{18}O_{PO4}$ record from South China. *Earth and Planetary Science Letters*, **495**: 174–184.

Huber, B.T., Norris, R.D., and MacLeod, K.G., 2002, Deep-sea paleotemperature record of extreme warmth during the Cretaceous. *Geology*, **30** (2), 123–126.

Hudson, J.D., and Anderson, T.F., 1989, Ocean temperatures and isotopic compositions through time. *Transactions of the Royal Society of Edinburgh Earth Sciences*, **80**: 183–192.

IAEA, 2016, *Reference Sheet for IAEA-603*. International Atomic Energy Agency, Vienna, 7 pp. https://nucleus.iaea.org/rpst/ReferenceProducts/ReferenceMaterials/Stable_Isotopes/13C18and7Li/IAEA-603.htm.

Imbrie, J., Hays, J.D., Martinson, D.G., McIntyre, A., Mix, A.C., Morley, J.J., et al., 1984, The orbital theory of Pleistocene climate: support from a revised chronology of the marine $\delta^{18}O$ record. *In* Berger, A. (ed), Milankovitch and Climate, *Part 1*. Hingham, MA: D. Reidel, 269–305.

Jaffrés, J.B.D., Shields, G.A., and Wallmann, K., 2007, The oxygen isotope evolution of seawater: a critical review of a long-standing controversy and an improved geological water cycle model for the past 3.4 billion years. *Earth-Science Reviews*, **83** (1–2), 83–122.

Jenkyns, H.C., 2003, Evidence for rapid climate change in the Mesozoic–Palaeogene greenhouse world. *Philosophical Transactions of the Royal Society of London, Series A: Mathematical, Physical and Engineering Sciences*, **361** (1810), 1885.

Jenkyns, H.C., Jones, C.E., Gröcke, D.R., Hesselbo, S.P., and Parkinson, D.N., 2002, Chemostratigraphy of the Jurassic System: applications, limitations and implications for palaeoceanography. *Journal of the Geological Society*, **159**: 351–378.

Jiang, H., Joachimski, M.M., Wignall, P.B., Zhang, M., and Lai, X., 2015, A delayed end-Permian extinction in deep-water locations and its relationship to temperature trends (Bianyang, Guizhou Province, South China). *Palaeogeography, Palaeoclimatology, Palaeoecology*, **440**: 690–695.

Joachimski, M.M., and Buggisch, W., 2002, Conodont apatite $\delta^{18}O$ signatures indicate climatic cooling as a trigger of the Late Devonian mass extinction. *Geology*, **30** (8), 711–714.

Joachimski, M.M., and Lambert, L.L., 2015, Salinity contrast in the US Midcontinent Sea during Pennsylvanian glacio-eustatic highstands: evidence from conodont apatite $\delta^{18}O$. *Palaeogeography, Palaeoclimatology, Palaeoecology*, **433**: 71–80.

Joachimski, M.M., van Geldern, R., Breisig, S., Buggisch, W., and Day, J., 2004, Oxygen isotope evolution of biogenic calcite and apatite during the Middle and Late Devonian. *International Journal of Earth Sciences*, **93** (4), 542–553.

Joachimski, M.M., von Bitter, P.H., and Buggisch, W., 2006, Constraints on Pennsylvanian glacioeustatic sea-level changes using oxygen isotopes of conodont apatite. *Geology*, **34** (4), 277–280.

Joachimski, M.M., Breisig, S., Buggisch, W., Talent, J.A., Mawson, R., Gereke, M., et al., 2009, Devonian climate and reef evolution: insights from oxygen isotopes in apatite. *Earth and Planetary Science Letters*, **284**: 599–609.

Joachimski, M.M., Lai, X.L., Shen, S.Z., Jiang, H.S., Luo, G.M., Chen, B., et al., 2012, Climate warming in the latest Permian and the Permian-Triassic mass extinction. *Geology*, **40** (3), 195–198.

Joachimski, M., Alekseev, A.S., Grigoryan, A., and Gatovsky, Y.A., 2020, Siberian Trap volcanism, global warming and the Permian-Triassic mass extinction: New insights from Armenian Permian-Triassic sections. *Geological Society of America Bulletin*, **132**: 427–443.

Jones, T.E., Grossman, E.L., and Yancey, T.E., 2003, Exploring the stable isotope record of global change and paleoclimate: the mid-Carboniferous GSSP (Arrow Canyon, Nevada) and the Ural Mountains, Russia. *Abstracts With Programs—Geological Society of America*, **5**: 254.

Kaiser, S.I., Steuber, T., Becker, R.T., and Joachimski, M.M., 2006, Geochemical evidence for major environmental change at the Devonian-Carboniferous boundary in the Carnic Alps and the Rhenish Massif. *Palaeogeography, Palaeoclimatology, Palaeoecology*, **240** (1–2), 146–160.

Kennett, J.P., and Stott, L.D., 1991, Abrupt deep-sea warming, palaeoceanographic changes and benthic extinctions at the end of the Paleocene. *Nature*, **353** (6341), 225–229.

Kim, S.T., and O'Neil, J.R., 1997, Equilibrium and nonequilibrium oxygen isotope effects in synthetic carbonates. *Geochimica et Cosmochimica Acta*, **61** (16), 3461–3475.

Kim, S.T., O'Neil, J.R., Hillaire-Marcel, C., and Mucci, A., 2007, Oxygen isotope fractionation between synthetic aragonite and water: influence of temperature and Mg^{2+} concentration. *Geochimica et Cosmochimica Acta*, **71** (19), 4704–4715.

Knauth, L.P., 2005, Temperature and salinity history of the Precambrian ocean: implications for the course of microbial evolution. *Palaeogeography, Palaeoclimatology, Palaeoecology*, **219** (1–2), 53–69.

Knauth, L.P., and Epstein, S., 1976, Hydrogen and oxygen isotope ratios in nodular and bedded cherts. *Geochimica et Cosmochimica Acta*, **40** (9), 1095–1108.

Kobashi, T., Grossman, E.L., Yancey, T.E., and Dockery, D.T., 2001, Reevaluation of conflicting Eocene tropical temperature estimates: molluskan oxygen isotope evidence for warm low latitudes. *Geology*, **29** (11), 983–986.

Kolodny, Y., Luz, B., and Navon, O., 1983, Oxygen isotope variations in phosphate of biogenic apatites. 1. Fish bone apatite – rechecking the rules of the game. *Earth and Planetary Science Letters*, **64** (3), 398–404.

Korte, C., Kozur, H.W., Joachimski, M.M., Strauss, H., Veizer, J., and Schwark, L., 2004, Carbon, sulfur, oxygen and strontium isotope records, organic geochemistry and biostratigraphy across the Permian/Triassic boundary in Abadeh, Iran. *International Journal of Earth Sciences (Geologische Rundschau)*, **93**: 565–581.

Korte, C., Jasper, T., Kozur, H.W., and Veizer, J., 2005a, $\delta^{18}O$ and $\delta^{13}C$ of Permian brachiopods: a record of seawater evolution and continental glaciation. *Palaeogeography, Palaeoclimatology, Palaeoecology*, **224** (4), 333–351.

Korte, C., Kozur, H.W., and Veizer, J., 2005b, $\delta^{13}C$ and $\delta^{18}O$ values of Triassic brachiopods and carbonate rocks as proxies for coeval seawater and palaeotemperature. *Palaeogeography, Palaeoclimatology, Palaeoecology*, **226** (3–4), 287–306.

Korte, C., Jones, P.J., Brand, U., Mertmann, D., and Veizer, J., 2008, Oxygen isotope values from high-latitudes: clues for Permian sea-surface temperature gradients and late Palaeozoic deglaciation. *Palaeogeography, Palaeoclimatology, Palaeoecology*, **269** (1–2), 1–16.

Laskar, J., 2020, Chapter 4 – Astrochronology. *In* Gradstein, F.M., Ogg, J.G., Schmitz, M.D., and Ogg, G.M. (eds), *The Geologic Time Scale 2020*. Elsevier, Boston, MA. **Vol. 1** (this book).

Lea, D.W., Pak, D.K., and Spero, H.J., 2000, Climate impact of late Quaternary equatorial Pacific sea surface temperature variations. *Science*, **289** (5485), 1719–1724.

Lear, C.H., Elderfield, H., and Wilson, P.A., 2000, Cenozoic deep-sea temperatures and global ice volumes from Mg/Ca in benthic foraminiferal calcite. *Science*, **287**: 269–272.

Lécuyer, C., Picard, S., Garcia, J.-P., Sheppard, S., Grandjean, P., and Dromart, G., 2003, Thermal evolution of Tethyan surface waters during the Middle–Late Jurassic: evidence from $\delta^{18}O$ values of marine fish teeth. *Paleoceanography*, **18** (3), 1076.

Lécuyer, C., Amiot, R., Touzeau, A., and Trotter, J., 2013, Calibration of the phosphate $\delta^{18}O$ thermometer with carbonate–water oxygen isotope fractionation equations. *Chemical Geology*, **347** (Suppl. C), 217–226.

Leder, J.J., Swart, P.K., Szmant, A.M., and Dodge, R.E., 1996, The origin of variations in the isotopic record of scleractinian corals: 1. Oxygen. *Geochimica et Cosmochimica Acta*, **60** (15), 2857–2870.

Lehnert, O., Mannik, P., Joachimski, M.M., Calner, M., and Fryda, J., 2010, Palaeoclimate perturbations before the Sheinwoodian glaciation: a trigger for extinctions during the 'Ireviken Event'. *Palaeogeography, Palaeoclimatology, Palaeoecology*, **296** (3–4), 320–331.

L'Homme, N., Clarke, G.K.C., and Ritz, C., 2005, Global budget of water isotopes inferred from polar ice sheets. *Geophysical Research Letters*, **32**, no. L20502, https://doi.org/10.1029/2005GL023774.

Le Houedec, S., Girard, C., and Balter, V., 2013, Conodont Sr/Ca and $\delta^{18}O$ record seawater changes at the Frasnian-Famennian boundary. *Palaeogeography, Palaeoclimatology, Palaeoecology*, **376**: 114–121.

Lisiecki, L.E., and Raymo, M.E., 2005, A Pliocene-Pleistocene stack of 57 globally distributed benthic $\delta^{18}O$ records. *Paleoceanography*, **20** (1), PA1003, https://doi.org/10.1029/2004PA001071.

Loader, C., 2015. *Package "Locfit"*. https://cran.r-project.org/web/packages/locfit/locfit.pdf.

Longinelli, A., and Nuti, S., 1973, Revised phosphate-water isotopic temperature scale. *Earth and Planetary Science Letters*, **19** (3), 373–376.

Lourens, L.J., Sluijs, A., Kroon, D., Zachos, J.C., Thomas, E., Rohl, U., Bowles, J., and Raffi, I., 2005, Astronomical pacing of late Palaeocene to early Eocene global warming events. *Nature*, **435** (7045), 1083–1087.

Lowenstam, H.A., 1961, Mineralogy, O^{18}/O^{16} ratios, and strontium and magnesium contents of recent and fossil brachiopods and their bearing on the history of the oceans. *The Journal of Geology*, **69**: 241–260.

Luz, B., Kolodny, Y., and Kovach, J., 1984, Oxygen isotope variations in phosphate of biogenic apatites. 3. Conodonts. *Earth and Planetary Science Letters*, **69** (2), 255–262.

MacLeod, K.G., 2012, Conodonts and the paleoclimatological and paleoecological applications of phosphate $\delta^{18}O$ measurements. *In* Ivany, L.C., and Huber, B.T. (eds), *Reconstructing Earth's Deep-Time Climate – The State of the Art in 2012*. The Paleontology Society Papers, **Vol. 18**. 69–84.

MacLeod, K.G., Huber, B.T., Berrocoso, Á.J., and Wendler, I., 2013, A stable and hot Turonian without glacial $\delta^{18}O$ excursions is indicated by exquisitely preserved Tanzanian foraminifera. *Geology*, **41** (10), 1083–1086.

Malchus, N., and Steuber, T., 2002, Stable isotope records (O, C) of Jurassic aragonitic shells from England and NW Poland: palaeoecologic and environmental implications. *Geobios*, **35** (1), 29–39.

Marshall, J.D., and Middleton, P.D., 1990, Changes in marine isotopic composition and late Ordovician glaciation. *Journal of the Geological Society, London*, **147**: 1–4.

Marshall, J.D., Brenchley, P.J., Mason, P., Wolff, G.A., Astini, R.A., Hints, L., et al., 1997, Global carbon isotopic events associated with mass extinction and glaciation in the late Ordovician. *Palaeogeography, Palaeoclimatology, Palaeoecology*, **132** (1–4), 195–210.

Martinez, M., and Dera, G., 2015, Orbital pacing of carbon fluxes by a ~9-My eccentricity cycle during the Mesozoic. *Proceedings of the National Academy of Sciences of the United States of America*, **112** (41), 12604–12609.

Maslin, M.A., Li, X.S., Loutre, M.F., and Berger, A., 1998, The contribution of orbital forcing to the progressive intensification of Northern Hemisphere glaciation. *Quaternary Science Reviews*, **17** (4–5), 411–426.

Mazzullo, S.J., Boardman, D.R., Grossman, E.L., and Dimmick-Wells, K., 2007, Oxygen-carbon isotope stratigraphy of upper Carboniferous to lower Permian marine deposits in midcontinent USA (Kansas and NE Oklahoma): implications for sea water chemistry and depositional cyclicity. *Carbonates and Evaporites*, **22** (1), 55–72.

McArthur, J.M., and Herczeg, A., 1990, Diagenetic stability of the isotopic composition of phosphate oxygen: palaeoenvironmental implications. *In* Notholt, A., and Jarvis, I. (eds), *Phosphorite Research and Development*. Geological Society, London, Special Publications. **Vol. 52**. 119–124.

McArthur, J.M., Donovan, D.T., Thirlwall, M.F., Fouke, B.W., and Mattey, D., 2000, Strontium isotope profile of the early Toarcian (Jurassic) oceanic anoxic event, the duration of ammonite biozones, and belemnite palaeotemperatures. *Earth and Planetary Science Letters*, **179** (2), 269–285.

McArthur, J.M., Janssen, N.M.M., Reboulet, S., Leng, M.J., Thirlwall, M.F., and van de Schootbrugge, B., 2007, Palaeotemperatures, polar ice-volume, and isotope stratigraphy (Mg/Ca, $\delta^{18}O$, $\delta^{13}C$, $^{87}Sr/^{86}Sr$): the Early Cretaceous (Berriasian, Valanginian, Hauterivian). *Palaeogeography, Palaeoclimatology, Palaeoecology*, **248** (3–4), 391–430.

Mii, H.S., and Grossman, E.L., 1994, Late Pennsylvanian seasonality reflected in the ^{18}O and elemental composition of a brachiopod shell. *Geology*, **22** (7), 661–664.

Mii, H.S., Grossman, E.L., and Yancey, T.E., 1999, Carboniferous isotope stratigraphies of North America: implications for Carboniferous paleoceanography and Mississippian glaciation. *Geological Society of America Bulletin*, **111** (7), 960–973.

Mii, H.S., Grossman, E.L., Yancey, T.E., Chuvashov, B., and Egorov, A., 2001, Isotopic records of brachiopod shells from the Russian Platform – evidence for the onset of mid-Carboniferous glaciation. *Chemical Geology*, **175** (1–2), 133–147.

Miller, K.G., Fairbanks, R.G., and Mountain, G.S., 1987, Tertiary oxygen isotope synthesis, sea level history, and continental margin erosion. *Paleoceanography*, **2**: 1–19.

Miller, K.G., Wright, J.D., and Fairbanks, R.G., 1991, Unlocking the ice house – Oligocene-Miocene oxygen isotopes, eustasy, and margin erosion. *Journal of Geophysical Research: Solid Earth Planets*, **96** (B4), 6829–6848.

Miller, K.G., Browning, J.V., Aubry, M.P., Wade, B.S., Katz, M.E., Kulpecz, A.A., et al., 2008, Eocene-Oligocene global climate and sea-level changes: St. Stephens Quarry, Alabama. *Geological Society of America Bulletin*, **120** (1–2), 34–53.

Mitchell, S.F., Ball, J.D., Crowley, S.F., Marshall, J.D., Paul, C.R.C., Veltkamp, C.J., et al., 1997, Isotope data from Cretaceous chalks and foraminifera: environmental or diagenetic signals? *Geology*, **25** (8), 691–694.

Montañez, I.P., et al., 2018, Carboniferous climate teleconnections archived in coupled bioapatite $\delta^{18}O_{PO4}$ and $^{87}Sr/^{86}Sr$ records from the epicontinental Donets Basin, Ukraine. *Earth and Planetary Science Letters*, **492**: 89–101.

Mutterlose, J., Pauly, S., and Steuber, T., 2009, Temperature controlled deposition of early Cretaceous (Barremian-early Aptian) black shales in an epicontinental sea. *Palaeogeography, Palaeoclimatology, Palaeoecology*, **273**: 330–345.

Narkiewicz, M., Narkiewicz, K., Krzemińska, E.W.A., and Kruchek, S.A., 2017, Oxygen isotopic composition of conodont apatite in the equatorial epeiric Belarussian Basin (Eifelian) – relationship to fluctuating seawater salinity and temperature. *Palaios*, **32** (7), 439–447.

Noret, J.R., Grossman, E.L., Yancey, T.E., and Chuvashov, B.I., 2009, Global climatic and ecological correlations during the Early Permian (Cisuralian). *South-Central GSA Abstracts with Programs*.

Norris, R.D., and Röhl, U., 1999, Carbon cycling and chronology of climate warming during the Palaeocene/Eocene transition. *Nature*, **401** (6755), 775–778.

Nützel, A., Joachimski, M., and López Correa, M., 2010, Seasonal climatic fluctuations in the Late Triassic tropics—high-resolution oxygen isotope records from aragonitic bivalve shells (Cassian Formation, Northern Italy). *Palaeogeography, Palaeoclimatology, Palaeoecology*, **285**: 194–204.

O'Neil, J.R., Clayton, R.N., and Mayeda, T.K., 1969, Oxygen isotope fractionation in divalent metal carbonates. *The Journal of Chemical Physics*, **51** (12), 5547–5558.

Pälike, H., Frazier, J., and Zachos, J.C., 2006, Extended orbitally forced palaeoclimatic records from the equatorial Atlantic Ceara Rise. *Quaternary Science Reviews*, **25** (23–24), 3138–3149.

Pearson, P.N., 2012, Oxygen isotopes in foraminifera: overview and historical review. *Paleontological Society Papers*, **18**: 1–38.

Pearson, P.N., Ditchfield, P.W., Singano, J., Harcourt-Brown, K.G., Nicholas, C.J., Olsson, R.K., et al., 2001, Warm tropical sea surface temperatures in the Late Cretaceous and Eocene epochs. *Nature*, **413** (6855), 481–487.

Pearson, P.N., Ditchfield, P., and Shackleton, N.J., 2002, Palaeoclimatology – tropical temperatures in greenhouse episodes – reply. *Nature*, **419** (6910), 898.

Pearson, P.N., McMillan, I.K., Wade, B.S., Dunkley Jones, T., Coxall, H.K., Bown, P.R., et al., 2008, Extinction and environmental change across the Eocene-Oligocene boundary in Tanzania. *Geology*, **36** (2), 179–182.

Perry, E.C., 1967, Oxygen isotope chemistry of ancient cherts. *Earth and Planetary Science Letters*, **3**: 62–66.

Petersen, S.V., et al., 2016, Temperature and salinity of the Late Cretaceous Western Interior Seaway. *Geology*, **44** (11), 903–906.

Podlaha, O.G., Mutterlose, J., and Veizer, J., 1998, Preservation of $\delta^{18}O$ and $\delta^{13}C$ in belemnite rostra from the Jurassic Early Cretaceous successions. *American Journal of Science*, **298** (4), 324–347.

Poore, R. Z., Williams, R. S., Jr., and Tracey, C., 2000, Sea level and climate. *U.S. Geological Survey Fact Sheet* 002–00, **2018**: https://pubs.usgs.gov/fs/fs2-00/, USGS.

Popp, B.N., Anderson, T.F., and Sandberg, P.A., 1986, Brachiopods as indicators of original isotopic compositions in some Paleozoic limestones. *Geological Society of America Bulletin*, **97** (10), 1262–1269.

Prokoph, A., Shields, G.A., and Veizer, J., 2008, Compilation and time-series analysis of a marine carbonate $\delta^{18}O$, $\delta^{13}C$, $^{87}Sr/^{86}Sr$ and $\delta^{34}S$ database through Earth history. *Earth-Science Reviews*, **87** (3–4), 113–133.

Pucéat, E., et al., 2003, Thermal evolution of Cretaceous Tethyan marine waters inferred from oxygen isotope composition of fish tooth enamels. *Paleoceanography*, **18** (2), https://doi.org/10.1029/2002PA000823.

Pucéat, E., Joachimski, M.M., Bouilloux, A., Monna, F., Bonin, A., Motreuil, S., et al., 2010, Revised phosphate-water fractionation equation reassessing paleotemperatures derived from biogenic apatite. *Earth and Planetary Science Letters*, **298**: 135–142.

Qing, H.R., and Veizer, J., 1994, Oxygen and carbon isotopic composition of Ordovician brachiopods – implications for coeval seawater. *Geochimica et Cosmochimica Acta*, **58** (20), 4429–4442.

Quinton, P.C., and MacLeod, K.G., 2014, Oxygen isotopes from conodont apatite of the midcontinent, US: implications for Late Ordovician climate evolution. *Palaeogeography, Palaeoclimatology, Palaeoecology*, **404**: 57–66.

Quinton, P.C., Speir, L., Miller, J., Ethington, R.G., and MacLeod, K.G., 2018, Testing the early Late Ordovician cool-water hypothesis with oxygen isotopes from conodont apatite. *Geological Magazine*, **155** (8), 1727–1741.

Raffi, I., Pälike, H., and Wade, B., 2020, Chapter 29 – The Neogene Period. *In* Gradstein, F.M., Ogg, J.G., Schmitz, M.D., and Ogg, G.M. (eds), *The Geologic Time Scale 2020.* Elsevier, Boston, MA, **Vol. 2** (this book).

Ravelo, A.C., and Hillaire-Marcel, C., 2007, The use of oxygen and carbon isotopes of foraminifera in paleoceanography. *In* Hillaire-Marcel, C., and De Vernal, A. (eds), *Proxies in Late Cenozoic Paleoceanography*. Amsterdam: Elsevier, 735–764.

Rigo, M., and Joachimski, M.M., 2010, Palaeoecology of Late Triassic conodonts: constraints from oxygen isotopes in biogenic apatite. *Acta Palaeontologica Polonica*, **55** (3), 471–478.

Roark, A., Flake, R., Grossman, E.L., Olszewski, T., Lebold, J., Thomas, D., et al., 2017, Brachiopod geochemical records from across the Carboniferous seas of North America: Evidence for salinity gradients, stratification, and circulation patterns. *Palaeogeography, Palaeoclimatology, Palaeoecology*, **485**: 136–153.

Romanin, M., et al., 2018, A sampling strategy for Recent and fossil brachiopods: selecting the optimal shell segment for geochemical analyses. *The Rivista Italiana di Paleontologia e Stratigrafia*, **124** (2), 343–359.

Romano, C., Goudemand, N., Vennemann, T.W., Ware, D., Schneebeli-Hermann, E., Hochuli, P.A., et al., 2012, Climatic and biotic upheavals following the Permian-Triassic mass extinction. *Nature Geoscience*, **6**: 57–60.

Rosales, I., Quesada, S., and Robles, S., 2001, Primary and diagenetic isotopic signals in fossils and hemipelagic carbonates: the Lower Jurassic of northern Spain. *Sedimentology*, **48** (5), 1149–1169.

Rosenau, N.A., Herrmann, A.D., and Leslie, S.A., 2012, Conodont apatite $\delta^{18}O$ values from a platform margin setting, Oklahoma, USA: implications for initiation of Late Ordovician icehouse conditions. *Palaeogeography, Palaeoclimatology, Palaeoecology*, **315–316**: 172–180.

Rosenau, N.A., Tabor, N.J., and Herrmann, A.D., 2014, Assessing the paleoenvironmental significance of Middle-Late Pennsylvanian conodont apatite $\delta^{18}O$ values in the Illinois Basin. *Palaios*, **29** (6), 250–265.

Rozanski, K., Araguás-Araguás, L., and Gonfiantini, R., 1993, Isotopic patterns in modern global precipitation, Geophysical Monograph. *In* Swart, P.K., Lohmann, K.C., McKenzie, J., and Savin, S. (eds), *Climate Change in Continental Isotopic Records*. American Geophysical Union, Washington, DC. **78**: p. 1–36.

Ruddiman, W.F., Raymo, M., and McIntyre, A., 1986, Matuyama 41,000-year cycles – North-Atlantic ocean and northern-hemisphere ice sheets. *Earth and Planetary Science Letters*, **80** (1–2), 117–129.

Samtleben, C., Munnecke, A., Bickert, T., and Pätzold, J., 1996, The Silurian of Gotland (Sweden): facies interpretation based on stable isotopes in brachiopod shells. *Geologische Rundschau*, **85** (2), 278–292.

Samtleben, C., Munnecke, A., Bickert, T., and Pätzold, J., 2001, Shell succession, assemblage and species dependent effects on the C/O-isotopic composition of brachiopods – examples from the Silurian of Gotland. *Chemical Geology*, **175** (1–2), 61–107.

Savin, S.M., 1977, The history of the Earth's surface temperature during the past 100 million years. *Annual Review of Earth and Planetary Sciences*, **5**: 319–355.

Savin, S.M., Douglas, R.G., and Stehli, F.G., 1975, Tertiary marine paleotemperatures. *Geological Society of America Bulletin*, **86** (11), 1499–1510.

Schmidt, G.A., Bigg, G.R., and Rohling, E.J., 1999. *Global Seawater Oxygen-18 Database*. http://data.giss.nasa.gov/o18data/.

Schobben, M., Joachimski, M.M., Korn, D., Leda, L., and Korte, C., 2014, Palaeotethys seawater temperature rise and an intensified hydrological cycle following the end-Permian mass extinction. *Gondwana Research*, **26** (2), 675–683.

Schrag, D.P., 1999, Effects of diagenesis on the isotopic record of late Paleogene tropical sea surface temperatures. *Chemical Geology*, **161** (1–3), 215–224.

Schrag, D.P., Depaolo, D.J., and Richter, F.M., 1995, Reconstructing past sea-surface temperatures-correcting for diagenesis of bulk marine carbonate. *Geochimica et Cosmochimica Acta*, **59** (11), 2265–2278.

Shackleton, N.J., and Kennett, J.P., 1975, Paleotemperature history of the Cenozoic and the initiation of Antarctic glaciation: oxygen and carbon isotope analyses in DSDP Sites 277, 279, and 281. *Initial Reports of the Deep Sea Drilling Project*, **29**: 743–755.

Shackleton, N.J., and Opdyke, N.D., 1973, Oxygen isotope and palaeomagnetic stratigraphy of equatorial Pacific core V28-238: oxygen isotope temperatures and ice volumes on a 10^5 year and 10^6 year scale. *Quaternary Research*, **3**: 39–55.

Shackleton, N.J., Crowhurst, S.J., Weedon, G.P., and Laskar, J., 1999, Astronomical calibration of Oligocene-Miocene time. *Philosophical Transactions of the Royal Society of London, Series A: Mathematical, Physical and Engineering Sciences*, **357** (1757), 1907–1929.

Shemesh, A., Kolodny, Y., and Luz, B., 1988, Isotope geochemistry of oxygen and carbon in phosphate and carbonate of phosphate francolite. *Geochimica et Cosmochimica Acta*, **52** (11), 2565–2572.

Shields, G., and Veizer, J., 2002, Precambrian marine carbonate isotope database: Version 1.1. *Geochemistry, Geophysics, Geosystems*, **3** (6), https://doi.org/10.1029/2001GC000266.

Shields, G.A., et al., 2003, Sr, C, and O isotope geochemistry of Ordovician brachiopods: a major isotopic event around the Middle-Late Ordovician transition. *Geochimica et Cosmochimica Acta*, **67** (11), 2005–2025.

Speijer, R.P., Pälike, H., Hollis, C.J., Hooker, J.J., and Ogg, J.G., 2020, Chapter 28 – The Paleogene Period. *In* Gradstein, F.M., Ogg, J.G., Schmitz, M.D., and Ogg, G.M. (eds), *The Geologic Time Scale 2020.* Elsevier, Boston, MA. **Vol. 2** (this book).

Stahl, W., and Jordan, R., 1969, General considerations on isotopic paleotemperature determinations and analyses on Jurassic ammonites. *Earth and Planetary Science Letters*, **6**: 173–178.

Stanton, J.R.J., Jeffery, D.L., and Ahr, W.M., 2002, Early Mississippian climate based on oxygen isotope compositions of brachiopods, Alamogordo Member of the Lake Valley Formation, south-central New Mexico. *Geological Society of America Bulletin*, **114** (1), 4–11.

Strachan, R., Darling, J., Storey, C., and Murphy, B., 2020a, Chapter 16 – The Hadean and the Archean and Proterozoic Eons. *In* Gradstein, F.M., Ogg, J.G., Schmitz, M.D., and Ogg, G.M. (eds), *The Geologic Time Scale 2020.* Elsevier, Boston, MA. (this book).

Strachan, R., Murphy, J.B., Darling, J., Storey, C., Shields, G.A., 2020b, Precambrian (4.56 Ga to 1 Ga). *In* Gradstein, F.M., Ogg, J.G., Schmitz, M.D., Ogg, G.M. (eds), *The Geologic Time Scale 2020*, Elsevier Publ. **Vol. 2** (this book).

Sun, Y.D., et al., 2012, Lethally hot temperatures during the Early Triassic greenhouse. *Science*, **338** (6105), 366–370.

Sun, Y.D., et al., 2016, Climate warming, euxinia and carbon isotope perturbations during the Carnian (Triassic) Crisis in South China. *Earth and Planetary Science Letters*, **444**: 88–100.

Svensen, H., Planke, S., Malthe-Sorenssen, A., Jamtveit, B., Myklebust, R., Eidem, T.R., and Rey, S.S., 2004, Release of methane from a volcanic basin as a mechanism for initial Eocene global warming. *Nature*, **429** (6991), 542–545.

Svensen, H., Planke, S., Polozov, A., Schmidbauer, N., Corfu, F., Podladchikov, Y., et al., 2009, Siberian gas venting and the end-Permian environmental crisis. *Earth and Planetary Science Letters*, **277**: 490–500.

Swart, P.K., Moore, M., Charles, C., and Bohm, F., 1998, Sclerosponges may hold new keys to marine paleoclimate. *Eos*, **636**: 633.

Tiedemann, R., Sarnthein, M., and Shackleton, N.J., 1994, Astronomic timescale for the Pliocene Atlantic $\delta^{18}O$ and dust flux records of Ocean Drilling Program Site 659. *Paleoceanography*, **9** (4), 619–638.

Tripati, A., Zachos, J., Marincovich, L., and Bice, K., 2001, Late Paleocene Arctic coastal climate inferred from molluscan stable and radiogenic isotope ratios. *Palaeogeography, Palaeoclimatology, Palaeoecology*, **170** (1–2), 101–113.

Trotter, J.A., Williams, I.S., Barnes, C.R., Lécuyer, C., and Nicoll, R.S., 2008, Did cooling oceans trigger Ordovician biodiversification? Evidence from conodont thermometry. *Science*, **321** (5888), 550–554.

Trotter, J.A., Williams, I.S., Nicora, A., Mazza, M., and Rigo, M., 2015, Long-term cycles of Triassic climate change: a new delta ^{18}O record from conodont apatite. *Earth and Planetary Science Letters*, **415**: 165–174.

Trotter, J.A., Williams, I.S., Barnes, C.R., Männik, P., and Simpson, A., 2016, New conodont $\delta^{18}O$ records of Silurian climate change: implications for environmental and biological events. *Palaeogeography, Palaeoclimatology, Palaeoecology*, **443**: 34–48.

Ullmann, C.V., Campbell, H.J., Frei, R., and Korte, C., 2016, Oxygen and carbon isotope and Sr/Ca signatures of high-latitude Permian to Jurassic calcite fossils from New Zealand and New Caledonia. *Gondwana Research*, **38**: 60–73.

Urey, H.C., Lowenstam, H.A., Epstein, S., and McKinney, C.R., 1951, Measurement of paleotemperatures and temperatures of the upper Cretaceous of England, Denmark, and the southeastern United States. *Geological Society of America Bulletin*, **62**: 399–416.

van de Schootbrugge, B., Follmi, K.B., Bulot, L.G., and Burns, S.J., 2000, Paleoceanographic changes during the early Cretaceous (Valanginian-Hauterivian): evidence from oxygen and carbon stable isotopes. *Earth and Planetary Science Letters*, **181** (1–2), 15–31.

van Geldern, R., Joachimski, M.M., Day, J., Jansen, U., Alvarez, F., Yolkin, E.A., et al., 2006, Carbon, oxygen and strontium isotope records of Devonian brachiopod shell calcite. *Palaeogeography, Palaeoclimatology, Palaeoecology*, **240** (1–2), 47–67.

Veizer, J., and Hoefs, J., 1976, The nature of O^{18}/O^{16} and C^{13}/C^{12} secular trends in sedimentary carbonate rocks. *Geochimica et Cosmochimica Acta*, **40**: 1387–1395.

Veizer, J., and Prokoph, A., 2015, Temperatures and oxygen isotopic composition of Phanerozoic oceans. *Earth-Science Reviews*, **146**: 92–104.

Veizer, J., Fritz, P., and Jones, B., 1986, Geochemistry of brachiopods – oxygen and carbon isotopic records of Paleozoic oceans. *Geochimica et Cosmochimica Acta*, **50** (8), 1679–1696.

Veizer, J., Ala, D., Azmy, K., Bruckschen, P., Buhl, D., Bruhn, F., et al., 1999, $^{87}Sr/^{86}Sr$, $\delta^{13}C$ and $\delta^{18}O$ evolution of Phanerozoic seawater. *Chemical Geology*, **161** (1–3), 59–88.

Vennemann, T.W., Hegner, E., Cliff, G., and Benz, G.W., 2001, Isotopic composition of recent shark teeth as a proxy for environmental conditions. *Geochimica et Cosmochimica Acta*, **65** (10), 1583–1599.

Vennemann, T.W., Fricke, H.C., Blake, R.E., O'Neil, J.R., and Colman, A., 2002, Oxygen isotope analysis of phosphates: a comparison of techniques for analysis of Ag_3PO_4. *Chemical Geology*, **185** (3–4), 321–336.

Vickers, M. L., Fernandez, A., Hesselbo, S. P., Price, G. D., Bernasconi, S. M., Lode, S., et al., 2020, Unravelling Middle to Late Jurassic palaeoceanographic and palaeoclimatic signals in the Hebrides Basin using belemnite clumped isotope thermometry. *Earth and Planetary Science Letters*, **546**, no. 116401.

Wadleigh, M.A., and Veizer, J., 1992, $^{18}O/^{16}O$ and $^{13}C/^{12}C$ in Lower Paleozoic articulate brachiopods – implications for the isotopic composition of seawater. *Geochimica et Cosmochimica Acta*, **56** (1), 431–443.

Wallace, Z.A., and Elrick, M., 2014, Early Mississippian orbital-scale glacio-eustasy detected from high-resolution oxygen isotopes of marine apatite (conodonts). *Journal of Sedimentary Research*, **84** (10), 816–824.

Wefer, G., and Berger, W.H., 1991, Isotope paleontology – growth and composition of extant calcareous species. *Marine Geology*, **100** (1–4), 207–248.

Wenzel, B., and Joachimski, M.M., 1996, Carbon and oxygen isotopic composition of Silurian brachiopods (Gotland/Sweden): palaeoceanographic implications. *Palaeogeography, Palaeoclimatology, Palaeoecology*, **122** (1–4), 143–166.

Wenzel, B., Lécuyer, C., and Joachimski, M.M., 2000, Comparing oxygen isotope records of Silurian calcite and phosphate – $\delta^{18}O$ compositions of brachiopods and conodonts. *Geochimica et Cosmochimica Acta*, **64** (11), 1859–1872.

Westerhold, T., Bickert, T., and Röhl, U., 2005, Middle to late Miocene oxygen isotope stratigraphy of ODP site 1085 (SE Atlantic): new constrains on Miocene climate variability and sea-level fluctuations. *Palaeogeography, Palaeoclimatology, Palaeoecology*, **217** (3–4), 205–222.

Westerhold, T., Röhl, U., Raffi, I., Fornaciari, E., Monechi, S., Reale, V., et al., 2008, Astronomical calibration of the Paleocene time. *Palaeogeography, Palaeoclimatology, Palaeoecology*, **257** (4), 377–403.

Wierzbowski, H., and Joachimski, M.M., 2007, Reconstruction of late Bajocian-Bathonian marine palaeoenvironments using carbon and oxygen isotope ratios of calcareous fossils from the Polish Jura Chain (central Poland). *Palaeogeography, Palaeoclimatology, Palaeoecology*, **254** (3–4), 523–540.

Wierzbowski, H., and Joachimski, M.M., 2009, Stable isotopes, elemental distribution, and growth rings of belemnopsid belemnite rostra: proxies for belemnite life habitat. *Palaios*, **25** (5–6), 377–386.

Wilson, P.A., Norris, R.D., and Cooper, M.J., 2002, Testing the Cretaceous greenhouse hypothesis using glassy foraminiferal calcite from the core of the Turonian tropics on Demerara Rise. *Geology*, **30** (7), 607–610.

Wright, E.K., 1987, Stratification and paleocirculation of the Late Cretaceous Western Interior Seaway of North America. *Geological Society of America Bulletin*, **99** (4), 480–490.

Yamamoto, K., Asami, R., and Iryu, Y., 2010, Carbon and oxygen isotopic compositions of modern brachiopod shells from a warm-temperate shelf environment, Sagami Bay, central Japan. *Palaeogeography, Palaeoclimatology, Palaeoecology*, **291** (3–4), 348–359.

Zachos, J., Pagani, M., Sloan, L., Thomas, E., and Billups, K., 2001, Trends, rhythms, and aberrations in global climate 65 Ma to present. *Science*, **292** (5517), 686–693.

Zachos, J.C., Arthur, M.A., Bralower, T.J., and Spero, H.J., 2002, Palaeoclimatology – tropical temperatures in greenhouse episodes. *Nature*, **419** (6910), 897–898.

Zachos, J.C., Dickens, G.R., and Zeebe, R.E., 2008, An early Cenozoic perspective on greenhouse warming and carbon-cycle dynamics. *Nature*, **451** (7176), 279–283.

Zakharov, Y.D., Ignatiev, A.V., Boriskina, T.A., Velivetskaya, T.A., Smyshlyaeva, O.P., Tanabe, K., et al., 2001, Palaeozoic and Mesozoic carbon-isotopic macrorhythms and macrocycles of solar activity. *Albertiana*, **25**: 28–35.

Zeebe, R.E., 1999, An explanation of the effect of seawater carbonate concentration on foraminiferal oxygen isotopes. *Geochimica et Cosmochimica Acta*, **63** (13–14), 2001–2007.

Zigaite, Z., Joachimski, M.M., Lehnert, O., and Brazauskas, A., 2010, $\delta^{18}O$ composition of conodont apatite indicates climatic cooling during the Middle Pridoli. *Palaeogeography, Palaeoclimatology, Palaeoecology*, **294** (3–4), 242–247.

Appendices

(see https://issues.pangaea.de/browse/PDI-24621).

Appendix 1. References for data, including those cited previously in Prokoph et al. (2008; Prokoph_2008_ESR_f.xls; "P"), Grossman (2012a), and Veizer and Prokoph (2015).

Appendix 2A. Oxygen isotope data for calcium carbonate macrofossils updated from Prokoph et al.'s (2008, Appendix A, supplementary data) and Grossman (2012a).

Appendix 2B. Oxygen isotope data compiled for foraminifera from Cramer et al. (2009), Friedrich et al. (2012), Veizer and Prokoph (2015), and this study.

Appendix 3. Oxygen isotope data for phosphate minerals.

Appendix 4. Compilation of values for Locfit regression and ± 95% confidence interval curves.

B.D. Cramer and I. Jarvis

Carbon Isotope Stratigraphy

Chapter outline

Abstract

The $^{13}C/^{12}C$ value of dissolved inorganic carbon (DIC) in the ocean has varied through time and can be determined from the marine carbonate record as changes in $\delta^{13}C_{carb}$. These variations provide insight into global carbon cycle dynamics, as well as relative age information (chronostratigraphy) that can be used to correlate sedimentary successions globally. The global carbon cycle includes both short- and long-term components, and their interactions dominate the isotopic record presented in this chapter. The partitioning and sequestration of carbon between organic and carbonate rock reservoirs, and their fluxes to and from the ocean–atmosphere–biosphere system, drive secular changes in the $\delta^{13}C$ of DIC in the oceans that are ultimately recovered from the stratigraphic record. The pre-Cenozoic data presented here utilize bulk carbonate data for compilation, but a wide range of materials has been analyzed in the literature to produce previous composites. Care must be taken to consider what materials have been analyzed in comparing global carbon isotope records from the literature.

11.1 Introduction

Carbon isotope stratigraphy is central to our understanding of the connections within the ocean–atmosphere–biosphere–geosphere Earth system. The ratio of $^{13}C/^{12}C$ in the ocean, reported in delta notation as $\delta^{13}C$, and its change through time are pivotal to Earth system modeling of the development of an oxygenated atmosphere. The ratio is fundamental to the causes and consequences of climate transitions (e.g., icehouse to greenhouse), and the overall state of the global carbon cycle (e.g., Kump and Garrels, 1986; Berner, 1987, 2006, 2009; Gruber et al., 1999; Anbar and Knoll, 2002; Falkowski, 2003; Bartley and Kah, 2004; Sundquist and Visser, 2004; Saltzman, 2005; Ridgwell and Zeebe, 2005; Zachos and Kump, 2005; Holland, 2006; Canfield et al., 2013; Caves et al., 2016; Bachan et al., 2017; Schachat et al., 2018). In addition to their use in global climate studies and Earth system modeling, carbon isotope data and their detailed integration with biostratigraphy have revolutionized global chronostratigraphic correlation over the past two decades. Increasingly higher resolution data become available each year for all parts of the time scale with the greatest increases in data density coming from older portions of the time scale. The carbon isotope record presented in this chapter is based on 59,641 analyses [29,036 Cenozoic (average of 2,273 years/sample); 14,214 Mesozoic (average of 13,122 years/sample); 9,236 Paleozoic (average of 31,063 years/sample); 2,611 Neoproterozoic (average of 176,637 years/sample); and 4,544 latest Archean through Mesoproterozoic (average of 341,109 years/sample)], dramatically increasing the resolution of previous composites. The decreased sample resolution toward older portions of the geologic time scale (GTS) is not only a product of both the availability of strata with respect to geologic age, but also the number of

Geologic Time Scale 2020. DOI: https://doi.org/10.1016/B978-0-12-824360-2.00011-5

geologists per interval of the Earth's history (i.e., research hours/million years). New data not available in 2012 are combined with recalibrations of data utilized in prior compilations to produce the composite presented next.

11.2 Methodology

11.2.1 Analytical methodology

Seminal publications on carbon isotope stratigraphy (e.g., Craig, 1953; Scholle and Arthur, 1980; Shackleton, 1987; Berner, 1990, 2004, 2006; Gale et al., 1993; Hayes et al., 1999; Kump and Arthur, 1999; Zachos et al., 2001; Sundquist and Visser, 2004) provide much of the modern foundation of the discipline. The underlying principles and methodologies utilized in this chapter are outlined later, including laboratory procedures, sample selection and preparation, stratigraphic procedures and community standards, as well as analytical caveats and assumptions.

Stable isotope analysis of carbon can be carried out by analyzing either carbonate minerals or organic matter, as $\delta^{13}C_{carb}$ or $\delta^{13}C_{org}$, respectively. Whereas both sets of analyses are ultimately aimed at measuring changes in the global carbon cycle, the pathways and reservoirs from which each set of analyses draw are different. Therefore the two sets of data provide similar, albeit unique, insights into the distribution of carbon in the combined ocean–atmosphere–biosphere–geosphere Earth system. In either case, CO_2 is produced from carbonate minerals or organic molecules and analyzed in an isotope ratio mass spectrometer. The resultant data are reported in delta notation (δ) via the following formula:

$$\delta^{13}C = 1000\left[\frac{(^{13}C/^{12}C)_X - (^{13}C/^{12}C)_{std}}{(^{13}C/^{12}C)_{std}}\right] = 1000\left[\frac{(^{13}C/^{12}C)_X}{(^{13}C/^{12}C)_{std}} - 1\right]$$

where subscripts X and std refer to sample and standard, respectively. Carbon isotope data are reported versus PDB (Peedee Belemnite) or, more commonly, VPDB (Vienna PDB) via calibration of international standards to PDB. Most laboratories run multiple standards, both internal and external, during each analytical run. NBS-18, NBS-19, and IAEA-603 are typically used as carbonate standards and NBS-22 and IAEA-600 are typically used as organic carbon standards. A host of national standards exist as well as internal standards utilized by a single laboratory or group of laboratories. Typically, two to five standards will be utilized in the quality control and calibration process with all values eventually reported following calibration to PDB or VPDB. Precision for carbon isotope analyses is typically better than $\pm 0.10‰$ for both carbonate and organic carbon isotope samples.

Methods of CO_2 generation for analysis in a mass spectrometer necessarily vary between carbonate and organic carbon. Carbonate powder is reacted with 100% phosphoric acid with density >1.9 (Wachter and Hayes, 1985) to generate CO_2. Some laboratories roast the sample powders under vacuum at 380°C to remove volatiles (e.g., Cramer and Saltzman, 2005); however, this does not appear to be a consistent treatment across all laboratories or at least is not consistently reported in the literature. The process of CO_2 generation from organic samples is less consistent across laboratories as described in the literature; however, all $\delta^{13}C_{org}$ data are ultimately generated via combustion of powder and the resultant CO_2 analyzed for $\delta^{13}C$. The major differences in methodology lie primarily in the temperature and time of combustion between laboratories, any purification processes utilizing organic-free cupric oxide, and/or cryogenic separation of water or noncondensable by-products of combustion. Additional significant differences in sample preparation at the decarbonatization step are discussed in Section 11.2.2.

11.2.2 Carbonate carbon versus organic carbon

Carbonate carbon data are far more numerous across the geologic time scale than are organic carbon. This is due primarily to the substantial additional time required for sample preparation of organic carbon isotope samples. Based upon lithology alone however, one might expect organic carbon isotope data to be more prevalent given the fact that there is often enough organic carbon even in very carbonate-rich limestones to generate $\delta^{13}C_{org}$ data (samples with total organic carbon (TOC) values below 0.1% are routinely analyzed for $\delta^{13}C_{org}$). Typically, carbonate carbon samples are ready for analysis after generating powder, with the caveat that some laboratories take the additional step of roasting under vacuum. Organic carbon samples must first have all carbonate carbon removed (be decarbonatized) before further analytical steps may proceed. It is at this point that a wide range of practices has developed and there appears to be little consensus in the literature as to best practices for organic carbon sample preparation. HCl is most commonly used to accomplish the decarbonatization process; however, the strength of acid and manner of introduction to the sample vary widely. Ten percent HCl at 40°C for a few hours, 6N HCl left overnight, and 0.5N HCl introduced in four separate 20 mL washes each less than 30 minutes have all been reported in the literature. All acid washes are followed by rinsing in DI water, drying, and pulverization prior to further analysis. Drying temperatures as low as 40°C and as high as 85°C have been reported. Concentrated acid digestion of carbonate has the potential to degrade organic compounds and therefore the treatment of samples with less concentrated HCl is now recommended by many laboratories.

Both carbonate and organic carbon isotope chemostratigraphy are useful tools for chronostratigraphic correlation. Carbonate carbon isotope data are overwhelmingly more common than organic carbon data in the literature. A comparatively complete $\delta^{13}C_{carb}$ record has been developed for the most recent 900 Myr of the Earth's history, and a nearly complete record of $\delta^{13}C_{carb}$ extends well beyond 2.5 Ga into the Archean. By comparison a detailed $\delta^{13}C_{org}$ record of the Cenozoic Era alone is not available in the literature, and large gaps of 10 million years or more are typical of many parts of the Paleozoic. Coverage of $\delta^{13}C_{org}$ throughout the Proterozoic and older portions of the time scale is unsurprisingly even more spotty. As a result of this difference of coverage, and due to the focus of this chapter on chronostratigraphic correlation rather than the workings of the global carbon cycle throughout the Earth's history, we spend the remainder of this chapter on the carbonate carbon isotope ($\delta^{13}C_{carb}$) record.

All data shown in this chapter, and when used in other chapters throughout this book, are calibrated to the updated chronology of GTS2020. This was accomplished by interpolation of the original data from literature into the chronology of GTS2020 via biostratigraphy and elevation in section. When original publications included radioisotopic information, those dates were utilized for placement within the new chronology for temporal calibration of $\delta^{13}C_{carb}$ data.

11.3 Application principles and considerations

11.3.1 Principles

Partitioning of carbon between organic and carbonate reservoirs in the lithosphere, combined with the strongly preferential uptake of ^{12}C via photosynthetic fractionation, results in large variations in the $^{13}C/^{12}C$ ratio of the ocean and atmosphere over time (e.g., Shackleton, 1987; Berner, 1990, 2004; Hayes et al., 1999; Kump and Arthur, 1999; Falkowski, 2003; Sundquist and Visser, 2004). Both biologically mediated and inorganically precipitated marine carbonates ultimately derive their carbon for CO_3 from the marine dissolved inorganic carbon (DIC) reservoir. Changes to the carbon isotopic composition of marine carbonates are therefore an indirect measure of changes in the $\delta^{13}C_{carb}$ value of the DIC reservoir through time. This is the underlying principle of carbon isotope stratigraphy.

A large negative fractionation occurs during photosynthetic fixation of CO_2 such that all organic carbon molecules are strongly enriched in ^{12}C relative to atmospheric CO_2 and therefore carry a comparatively negative $\delta^{13}C$ signature (e.g., Maslin and Thomas, 2003). The magnitude of fractionation varies by organism and metabolic pathway; however, the overall range of organic carbon isotope values in primary organic carbon appears to be −9‰ to −33‰, with average marine values between −17‰ and −22‰ (Hayes et al., 1999; Maslin and Thomas, 2003). The $\delta^{13}C$ values of most Recent land plants that utilize the C3 photosynthetic pathway are between −23‰ and −33‰, whereas those that utilize the C4 pathways, including tropical and salt water grasses, have substantially less ^{12}C-enriched values of −9‰ to −16‰ (Maslin and Thomas, 2003). Regardless of organismal pathway, all photosynthesis enriches organic matter in ^{12}C, providing the mechanism by which partitioning of organic matter into different reservoirs can change the overall carbon isotopic composition of the oceans.

Variations in $\delta^{13}C_{carb}$ of the DIC reservoir are the result of redistribution of carbon, particularly organic carbon, among the surficial carbon reservoirs (atmosphere, oceans, biosphere, soils, etc.) and the lithosphere reservoirs (carbonate and organic carbon rocks, including oil and gas). Fig. 11.1 illustrates the average isotopic composition and generalized fluxes between carbon stored in the surficial and lithosphere reservoirs. Partitioning and redistribution of carbon within and among the surficial carbon reservoirs drive the short-term carbon cycle and are largely responsible for changes in the $\delta^{13}C$ value of the DIC reservoir on time scales of tens of thousands of years or less (e.g., Sundquist and Visser, 2004; Berner, 2006). On longer time scales of hundreds of thousands to millions of years, changes in the exchange fluxes between the surficial carbon reservoirs and the lithosphere reservoirs of carbonate and organic carbon drive changes in $\delta^{13}C$ of DIC (Kump and Arthur, 1999; Sundquist and Visser, 2004; Berner, 2006). Specifically, the relative rates of addition and/or removal of organic carbon compared to carbonate carbon to and from the lithosphere reservoirs dominate the long-term carbon cycle. In the present ocean, roughly 20% of all carbon removed from the surficial reservoir into the lithosphere is organic carbon (Shackleton 1984, 1987). Any increase or decrease in the relative amount of organic carbon removed or added to the surficial reservoir compared to carbonate carbon will drive a change in the $\delta^{13}C$ value of DIC in the global ocean (Shackleton, 1987; Berner, 1990; Derry et al., 1992; Des Marais et al., 1992; Hayes et al., 1999; Kump and Arthur, 1999; Sundquist and Visser, 2004). As a result, any net increase in organic carbon burial globally will increase the $\delta^{13}C$ value of DIC in the global ocean and any net increase in oxidation of organic matter will decrease the $\delta^{13}C$ value of DIC in the global ocean.

11.3.2 Spatial heterogeneity of dissolved inorganic carbon

The oceans are not homogenous with respect to $\delta^{13}C$ and the equilibration fractionation between dissolved $CO_{2(aq)}$

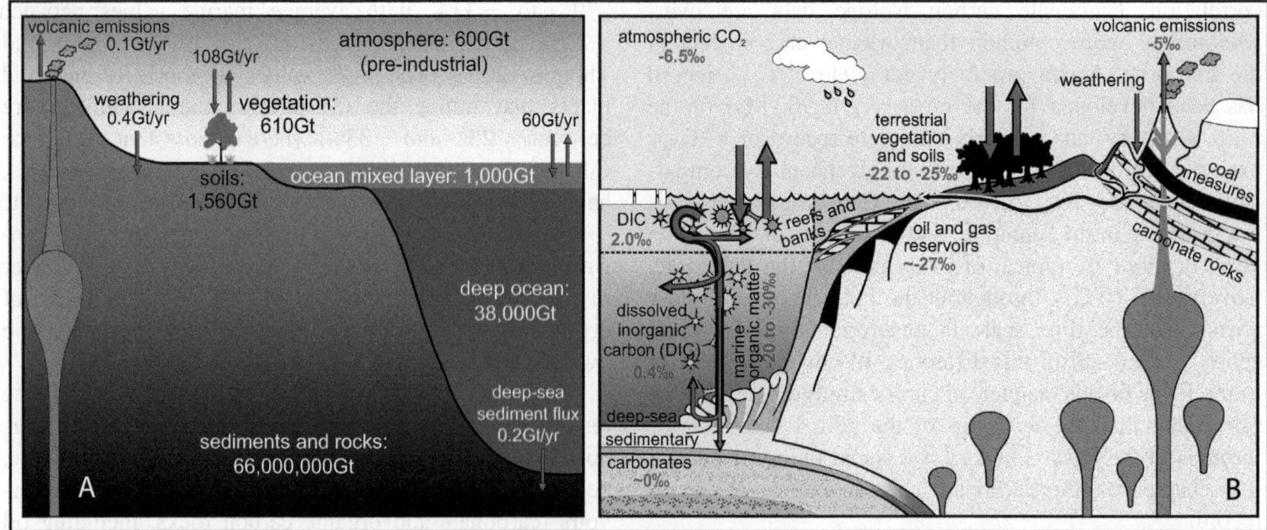

FIGURE 11.1 (A) Reservoir and generalized flux sizes, modified from Ruddiman (2014) and Ciais et al. (2013). The sediment and rock reservoir holds approximately 1580 times more carbon in the long-term carbon cycle than all of the short-term reservoirs (vegetation, soil, atmosphere, oceans) combined. Sizes of fluxes are approximated and averaged preindustrial values shown here to illustrate the general orders of magnitudes of each of the fluxes compared to the sizes of the reservoirs. Several additional fluxes included in Ciais et al. (2013) are not shown in panel (A) and the reader should refer to their report for additional information. (B) Isotopic composition of each of the reservoirs, modified from Saltzman and Thomas (2012), which was originally modified from Dunkley-Jones et al. (2010).

and bicarbonate in any given part of the ocean (as DIC or ΣCO_2) is dependent on an array of factors, including temperature, oceanography, local riverine flux, local productivity, oxygenation, and remineralization (e.g., Kroopnick, 1985; Gruber et al., 1999). Whereas the equilibration fractionation changes by approximately 0.1‰ per °C such that the $\delta^{13}C$ of cold water is higher than that of warmer waters (e.g., Lynch-Stieglitz, 2003), this "solubility pump" of higher $\delta^{13}C$ values to deep water is rarely encountered in the modern ocean. In most parts of the modern ocean, surface waters are +2‰ to +3‰ heavier than deep waters due to primary productivity removing ^{12}C from surface waters (the "biological pump" of Raven and Falkowski, 1999, see also Hotinski et al., 2004; Meyer et al., 2016), while the average global ocean value of DIC is within 1‰ of the average deep water value of 0‰ (Kroopnick, 1985; Gruber et al., 1999; Sarmiento and Gruber, 2006).

Lower $\delta^{13}C$ values below the photic zone are the result of shuttling ^{12}C in the form of organic matter that sinks to lower depths where it is remineralized and lowers the overall $\delta^{13}C$ value of the deeper part of the water column. Simultaneously, the removal of that ^{12}C from the photic zone during photosynthesis has the effect of increasing the $\delta^{13}C$ value of surface waters. The gradient and magnitude of this biological pump is dependent upon total productivity, the transport flux of organic carbon from surface to deep, and the oxygenation state of the water column below the photic zone. In the modern ocean the largest gradient is approximately 3‰ (Sarmiento and Gruber, 2006); however, this value may have been considerably larger during the Proterozoic when the reservoir of dissolved and particulate organic carbon may have been much larger than the present-day oxygenated deep ocean allows (Rothman et al., 2003; Fike et al., 2006; Swanson-Hysell et al., 2010; Luo et al., 2014).

Local to regional decreases in the $\delta^{13}C$ value of DIC are most often the result of remineralization of organic carbon and/or increasing the time ("aging" a water mass) during which a given water mass has not been in contact with the atmosphere (e.g., Kroopnick, 1985; Patterson and Walter, 1994; Immenhauser et al., 2002; Lynch-Stieglitz, 2003; Ravizza and Zachos, 2003; Sarmiento and Gruber, 2006). This is especially true in the modern ocean in coastal waters, either near major rivers where CO_2 derived from the remineralization of terrestrial organic carbon delivered via the riverine flux of dissolved organic carbon is a major contributor to DIC or where stratification of the water column develops and seasonal oxidation of phytoplankton blooms contributes isotopically light (^{12}C-enriched) carbon to the local/regional DIC reservoir (Thomas et al., 2000; Diz et al., 2009).

11.3.3 Global versus local water mass signals

Whereas the $\delta^{13}C$ record of carbonates is utilized as a proxy for changes in the global isotopic composition of DIC in the ocean, the previous discussion highlights the fact that care must be taken when interpreting $\delta^{13}C$ data to differentiate truly global signals from potential local overprinting of any given isotopic record. This is particularly true for the pre-Mesozoic portion of the Earth's history where the overwhelming majority of $\delta^{13}C$ data come from epicontinental carbonates. The lack of unrestricted circulation to the open ocean, the greater propensity to include a range of carbonate minerals (low-Mg calcite, high-Mg calcite, and aragonite, all of which have different fractionation coefficients, Romanek et al., 1992), and the increased likelihood of later development of regionally extensive exposure surfaces all have the potential to impact $\delta^{13}C_{carb}$ values obtained from epicontinental carbonates (Patterson and Walter, 1994; Holmden et al., 1998; Immenhauser et al., 2002; Railsback et al., 2003; Swart and Eberli, 2005; Panchuk et al., 2005; Gischler et al., 2009; Swart and Oehlert, 2018). This combination of effects is likely responsible for the fact that pelagic $\delta^{13}C$ curves generally show lower variability and attenuated magnitudes compared to records from epicontinental carbonates (e.g., Falkowski, 2003).

A number of publications addressed the significance of carbon cycling in epicontinental seas on the ability to utilize $\delta^{13}C$ records for either chronostratigraphic correlation or investigation of the global carbon cycle (e.g., Grötsch et al., 1998; Holmden et al., 1998; Swart and Eberli, 2005; Panchuk et al., 2005; Swart, 2008; Swart and Oehlert, 2018), and indeed local controls on the $\delta^{13}C$ of DIC in epicontinental settings must be considered when evaluating any $\delta^{13}C_{carb}$ curve. These concerns are particularly important when the total magnitude of variation in the $\delta^{13}C$ curve is low (<1‰–2‰). However, the general pattern of epicontinental versus pelagic $\delta^{13}C$ that has been demonstrated repeatedly throughout the Earth's history is that the magnitude of variation in epicontinental settings is simply amplified compared to coeval pelagic settings (e.g., Mutti et al., 2006; Amodio et al., 2008), but both records faithfully record the same sense of change (positive vs negative trends and excursions). Global compilations of any given major carbonate carbon isotope excursion (those >2‰), particularly those that are well constrained biostratigraphically, illustrate that they are extremely useful chronostratigraphic tools and even though the absolute magnitude of the record may vary, they are responding to some underlying mechanism of change within the global carbon cycle (e.g., Frýda and Manda, 2013; Hillbun et al., 2015). When major excursions in the $\delta^{13}C$ record are illustrated from a variety of water depths, depositional settings, continents, and latitudes globally, it is exceptionally difficult to attribute the entirety of the $\delta^{13}C$ excursion to diagenetic or local carbon cycling effects. As a general guideline, a margin of uncertainty of approximately 1‰ is typically assumed for bulk epicontinental carbonates (e.g., Halverson et al., 2005) and a more narrow value of approximately 0.5‰ for species-specific curves from the Cenozoic (Katz et al., 2003; Zachos et al., 2008; Cramer et al., 2009). Hence why the greatest emphasis for correlation potential has been placed on major excursions with absolute magnitude shifts from a preceding baseline of greater than 1‰–2‰.

11.4 Materials and methods

11.4.1 Bulk versus component

Any carbonate-bearing mineral may be sampled for $\delta^{13}C_{carb}$, including biologically precipitated, biologically mediated, and purely abiotic materials. Comparison of the $\delta^{13}C_{carb}$ value of pelagic calcifying organisms with time-equivalent benthic calcifying organisms allows researchers to measure isotopic gradients with depth as well as the overall spatial heterogeneity of $\delta^{13}C$ in the global ocean (e.g., Vincent and Berger, 1985; Ravizza and Zachos, 2003). The use of individual species, or groups of species, for $\delta^{13}C$ analyses is complicated by the fact that biocalcification can impart a fractionation (vital effect) on the $\delta^{13}C$ of the resultant carbonate mineral and mask the original marine DIC $\delta^{13}C$ value (e.g., Rohling and Cooke, 1999; Katz et al., 2003, 2005; McCelland et al., 2017). Foraminiferal calcite is the most commonly sampled material for $\delta^{13}C$ from Cenozoic sediments, and even single species analyses of foraminifera extend into the Mesozoic (e.g., Wilson and Norris, 2001; Huber et al., 2018). Unfortunately, the separation of single specimens becomes increasingly difficult with age of increased lithification of strata, and the majority of Mesozoic records are now produced using bulk carbonate samples (see Section 11.5.3).

Paleozoic $\delta^{13}C$ stratigraphy began with a focus on brachiopods composed of low-Mg calcite (Brand, 1982; Popp et al., 1986; Veizer et al., 1986, 1999; Grossman et al., 1991; Banner and Kaufman, 1994; Wenzel and Joachimski, 1996; Mii et al., 1999). Three major drawbacks to the reliance on brachiopod calcite to generate $\delta^{13}C_{carb}$ data are issues with variable preservation (Carpenter and Lohmann, 1995; Veizer et al., 1999; Wenzel, 2000; Grossman et al., 2008), species-specific variations (vital effects) in fractionation from the DIC reservoir during calcification of brachiopods as well (e.g., Mii et al., 1999; Batt et al., 2007), and most importantly, the limitations on stratigraphic resolution imposed by the limited presence of brachiopods in any given stratigraphic interval. Primarily in an effort to improve stratigraphic, and therefore temporal, resolution, Paleozoic $\delta^{13}C$ studies have become almost exclusively focused on bulk carbonate over the past decade. This transition in sampling medium is supported by studies that illustrate bulk carbonate and brachiopod data from identical sections show broadly similar $\delta^{13}C_{carb}$ values (e.g., Cramer et al., 2010a). Of course most of the Precambrian stratigraphic record lacks skeletal carbonate components altogether and bulk carbonate must be used for analysis (e.g., Schidlowski et al., 1975; Knoll et al., 1982; Kaufman et al., 1991; Derry et al., 1992; Buick et al., 1995; Hoffman et al., 1998; Halverson et al., 2005; Swanson-Hysell et al., 2010; Hodgskiss et al., 2019).

Bulk sampling can be accomplished in a disk mill or ball mill to generate large volumes of powder (10–100 g) and this is typically only done to generate enough material to analyze other isotope proxies such as strontium, sulfur, or organic carbon from the same sample powder. The major drawback to this method is the inability to target specific carbonate components. Most bulk carbonate sampling targets fine-grained, primarily micritic, carbonate with extreme care taken to avoid secondary calcite veins or void infill. Microdrilling a small amount of powder (0.5–5 mg) with a handheld microdrill or dental drill helps to isolate the specific carbonate type and generates enough material to provide a homogeneous sample. No studies have shown a systematic impact of drill or ball mill material (ceramic, tool steel, titanium, or tungsten carbide) on $\delta^{13}C$ values and all of these materials appear to be appropriate for $\delta^{13}C$ sample preparation.

11.4.2 Diagenesis

The role of diagenesis in $\delta^{13}C_{carb}$ stratigraphy is primarily focused on the incorporation of isotopically light carbon (^{12}C) from oxidized organic material into preexisting carbonate minerals that recorded the original $\delta^{13}C$ signature of DIC at the time of their formation. This is of particular importance in carbonates collected from outcrops (as opposed to oceanic or continental drill cores) where meteoric waters containing ^{12}C-enriched DIC from the oxidation of organic carbon have the potential to alter the original $\delta^{13}C$ value of the carbonate. Such meteoric diagenesis has the effect of lowering the $\delta^{13}C_{carb}$ value of the carbonate (e.g., Allan and Matthews, 1982; Lohmann, 1988; Marshall, 1992; Algeo et al., 1992) but will also typically lower the $\delta^{18}O$ value of the carbonate as well (Banner and Hanson, 1990; Knauth and Kennedy, 2009; Cochran et al., 2010). Therefore positive covariance between $\delta^{13}C$ and $\delta^{18}O$ is often a first-order demonstration of alteration of the original $\delta^{13}C$ signal by meteoric diagenesis.

Additional mechanisms can introduce ^{12}C from organic carbon into carbonates and have a similar effect of lowering $\delta^{13}C$ values. In particular, remineralization of organic carbon, either locally or in situ, can introduce light carbon (^{12}C) during diagenetic stabilization and/or cementation, which can lower the analyzed $\delta^{13}C$ value of the carbonate (Scholle and Arthur, 1980; Zachos and Kump, 2005; Weissert et al., 2008). Such remineralization effects are most likely where sediments have low carbonate content and high organic content and a general guideline of a >7:1 ratio of carbonate to organic carbon in the original sediment has been suggested as a reliable boundary (Scholle and Arthur, 1980). The typical directionality of diagenesis toward lower $\delta^{13}C$ (more ^{12}C-enriched) values highlights the fact that negative $\delta^{13}C_{carb}$ excursions require the incorporation of ^{12}C through diagenesis to be ruled out before they can be interpreted as primary signals.

11.5 Chronostratigraphic correlation and excursions

11.5.1 Chronostratigraphic procedures

Stable isotope stratigraphy is a central component of the GTS and tuning the $\delta^{18}O$ record to astronomical periodicity is the most significant example of the chronostratigraphic utility of stable isotope stratigraphy (see Laskar, 2020, Chapter 4, Astrochronology, this volume; Grossman and Joachimski, 2020, Chapter 10, Oxygen Isotope Stratigraphy, this volume; Raffi et al., 2020, Chapter 29, The Neogene Period, this book). The importance of $\delta^{18}O$ Marine Isotope Stages (MIS) to the Neogene community demonstrates the potential of stable isotope stratigraphy as a chronostratigraphic tool, and for the pre-Cenozoic portion of the GTS, $\delta^{13}C$ stratigraphy has become the primary stable isotopic tool for chronostratigraphic correlation (e.g., Weissert et al., 2008; Saltzman and Thomas, 2012, but also see Derry, 2010). $\delta^{13}C_{carb}$ has begun to be utilized for astronomical tuning in the pre-Cenozoic portion of the time scale (e.g., Sageman et al., 2006) and carbon isotope stages have been introduced as far back as the Ordovician (Ainsaar et al., 2010; Bergström et al., 2016). The marriage of $\delta^{13}C$ stratigraphy with numerical stratigraphic techniques such as CONOP (CONstrained OPtimization) (e.g., Sadler, 2012; and see Goldman et al., 2020, Chapter 20, The Ordovician Period, this book) and the development of new seriation and data modeling methods for stable isotope stratigraphy (e.g., Lisiecki and Lisiecki, 2002; Meyers and Sageman, 2007; Lisiecki and Herbert, 2007; Lin et al., 2014; Martinez et al., 2016; Schmittner et al., 2017; Ahn et al., 2017; Hay et al., 2019) provide the analytical tools required to resolve the stable isotopic record of the pre-Cenozoic portion of the GTS to within time scales of tens of thousands of years or less (i.e., well within the astronomical band).

Outside of astronomical tuning, the primary function of $\delta^{13}C$ stratigraphy to the GTS is the identification and correlation of positive and negative excursions in the $\delta^{13}C$ record. These are large (typically >2‰), transient variations from a pre- and post-excursion baseline that have been identified globally (e.g., Weissert et al., 2008; Saltzman and Thomas, 2012). These excursions persist for 10's of Myr to <1 Myr and can be verified to be globally significant chronostratigraphic markers through integration with biostratigraphy, magnetostratigraphy, or some other chronostratigraphic tool, or through direct integration with radioisotopic data. A general trend of larger magnitude and longer duration $\delta^{13}C$ excursions during the Precambrian gave way to progressively smaller magnitude and shorter duration $\delta^{13}C$ excursions (Figs. 11.2–11.13) and a variety of explanations have been provided for the attenuation of the $\delta^{13}C$ signal throughout the Earth's history (e.g., Hayes et al., 1999; Rothman et al., 2003; Bartley and Kah, 2004; Weissert et al., 2008; Saltzman and Thomas, 2012; Bachan et al., 2017). Most of the major $\delta^{13}C$ excursions have been named and demonstrated globally, but comparison of the GTS2012 compilation (Saltzman and Thomas, 2012) with Figs. 11.2–11.13 herein illustrates that new features and excursions are still being discovered.

Community consensus regarding the procedures to define the precise onset, duration, and termination of $\delta^{13}C$ excursions has yet to be accomplished. Each stratigraphic community developed their own practices and standards throughout the time scale and, as a result, it is difficult to apply one single set of standard terminology or definitions across the GTS for $\delta^{13}C$ excursions. Railsback et al. (2015) provided an excellent overview of several approaches to define chronostratigraphic intervals from a stable isotope curve, but for most of the pre-Cenozoic portion of the GTS, there is a wide range of nomenclatural procedures and temporal points of consideration. Most communities have adopted the inflection point at the onset of major $\delta^{13}C$ excursions to be the point of highest chronostratigraphic significance, although even that is a vexingly difficult position to define precisely (e.g., Cramer et al., 2010a, 2015). The position of "peak" values has become less significant, particularly for positive $\delta^{13}C$ excursions, as higher resolution studies have demonstrated throughout the pre-Cenozoic that major $\delta^{13}C$ excursions typically have a plateau of elevated values (e.g., Cramer et al., 2006; Frýda and Manda, 2013; Stolfus et al., submitted). Utilizing points of inflection (e.g., Weissert et al., 2008; Railsback et al., 2015) in $\delta^{13}C$ curves instead of absolute magnitudes helps to avoid many of the potential local and/or diagenetic factors outlined in Sections 11.3 and 11.4.

11.5.2 Integration with biostratigraphy

The integration of $\delta^{13}C$ stratigraphy with biostratigraphy has likely been the most revolutionary aspect of $\delta^{13}C$ stratigraphy to the GTS, providing not only improved global chronostratigraphic correlation, but also a new avenue of research by providing a nonbiostratigraphic, chronostratigraphic tool against which multiple biostratigraphic tools can be compared and cross-calibrated (see discussions in Cramer et al., 2010a,b, 2015; Kaljo et al., 2015). For most of the history of stratigraphy, biostratigraphy was the primary, and often only, chronostratigraphic tool used for global correlation. Until recently, the deep-time stratigraphic record was rarely asked to produce data on time scales where stratigraphic uncertainty (e.g., Cramer et al., 2015; Martinez et al., 2016) and the temporal consequences of paleobiogeographic diachroneity were likely to cause problems. In the past decade however, as global stratigraphic correlation within the Milankovitch Band (i.e., within 100 kyr or less) has become an increasingly common requirement for Earth system modeling, the reliance (perhaps overreliance) on biostratigraphy alone has begun to require reevaluation.

The chronostratigraphic utility of stable isotope stratigraphy has long been understood by the Cenozoic community, and the Neogene MIS are demonstration of this fact (see Raffi et al., 2020, Chapter 29, The Neogene Period, this book). As discussed previously, $\delta^{13}C$ stratigraphy has become the primary chronostratigraphic tool for the pre-Cenozoic portion of the Earth's history but the embrace of its potential has been less widespread (e.g., Gale et al., 1993; Weissert et al., 2008). Integration of $\delta^{13}C$ with biostratigraphy offers the potential to cross-calibrate biostratigraphic zonations of fossil groups that do not occur in the same lithologies or environments and offers a way to test paleobiogeographic diachroneity and dispersal (e.g., Cramer et al., 2010a,b, 2015; Kaljo et al., 2015). Unfortunately, many stratigraphic workers, particularly those in older parts of the Phanerozoic, continue to utilize biostratigraphy as a temporal "magic bullet" (e.g., Hillbun et al., 2015).

Ocean mixing times are typically on the order of 1000 years or less, even during times of unfavorable paleogeography or poor ventilation (e.g., Kiehl and Shields, 2005). Biological speciation and migration, combined with the likelihood of actually sampling the true first or last appearance of a given species in a given section, can limit the temporal precision of biostratigraphy to tens to hundreds of thousands of years (e.g., Gale et al., 1993; Ma and Day, 2003; Barrick and Männik, 2005; Cody et al., 2008). From a perspective of first principles, large global $\delta^{13}C$ excursions are more likely to be temporally precise chronostratigraphic tools than is biostratigraphy alone (Cramer et al., 2015) and certainly more precise than purely lithostratigraphic correlation (e.g., Danielsen et al., 2019). That being said however, $\delta^{13}C$ stratigraphy in isolation is little more than wiggle matching. The future of both biostratigraphy and $\delta^{13}C$ stratigraphy lies in their integration, particularly for the Mesozoic and Paleozoic portions of the GTS.

11.5.3 The $\delta^{13}C$ composite

Paleo- and Mesoproterozoic: The $\delta^{13}C_{carb}$ record of the latest Archean through Mesoproterozoic plotted in Fig. 11.2 builds

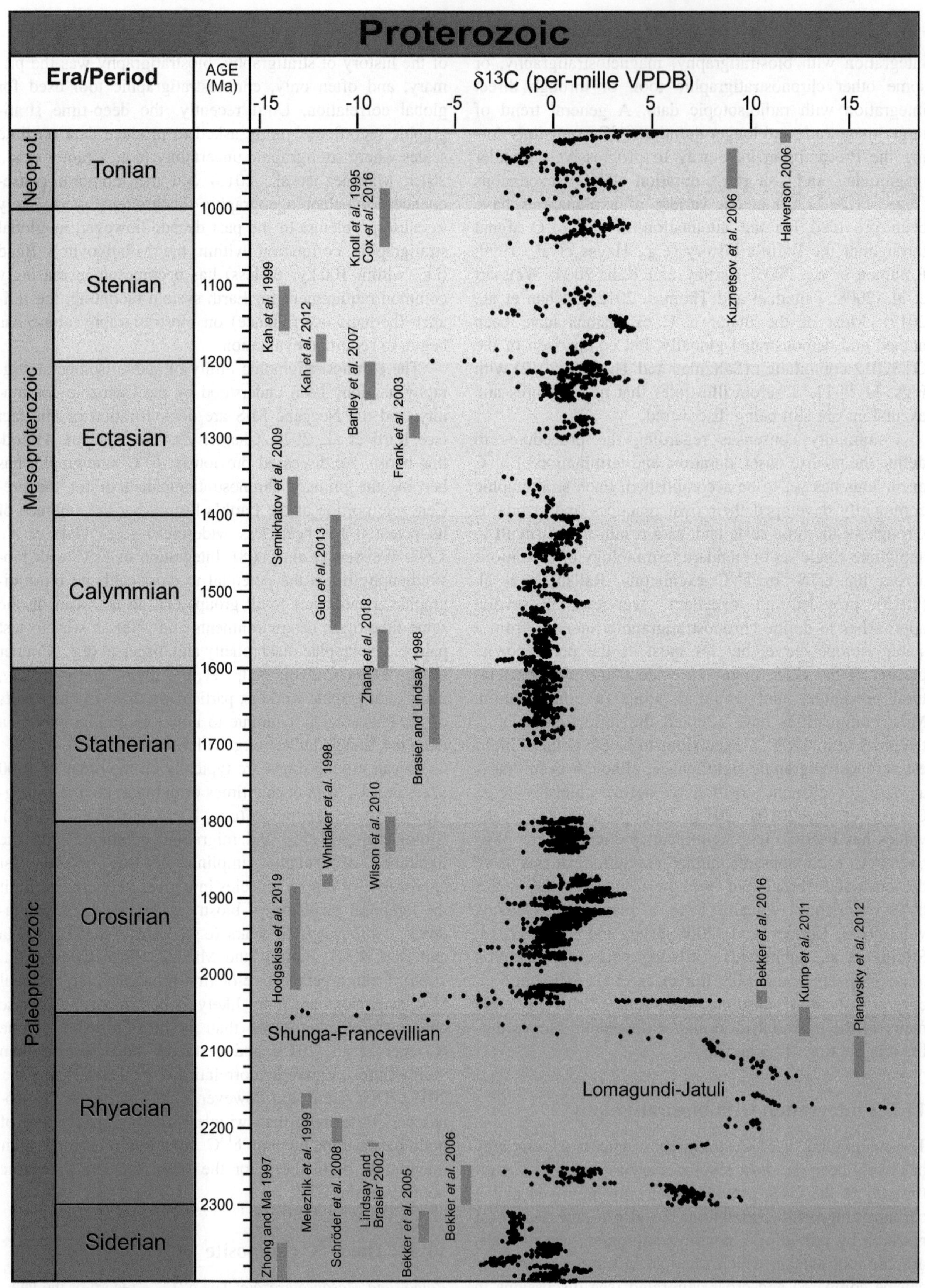

FIGURE 11.2 Variation in $\delta^{13}C_{carb}$ through the Paleo- and Mesoproterozoic. Data sources are indicated by vertical bars showing chronostratigraphic interval. Please see Section 11.5.3 and the corresponding interval chapter later in this book for a more detailed discussion of the data. *PTBE*, Permian-Triassic Boundary Event.

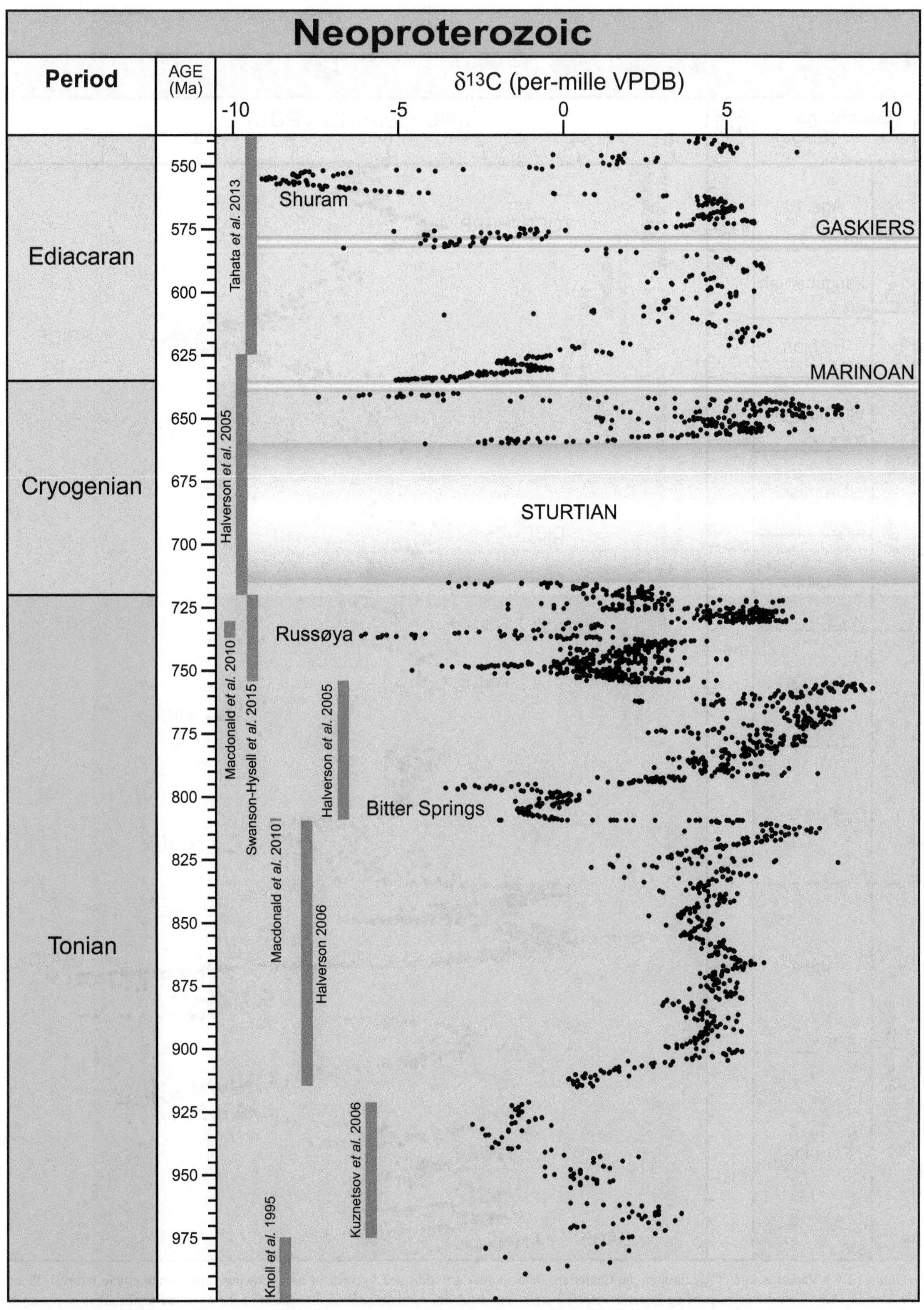

FIGURE 11.3 Variation in $\delta^{13}C_{carb}$ through the Neoproterozoic. Data sources are indicated by vertical bars showing chronostratigraphic interval. Please see Section 11.5.3 and the corresponding interval chapter later in this book for a more detailed discussion of the data.

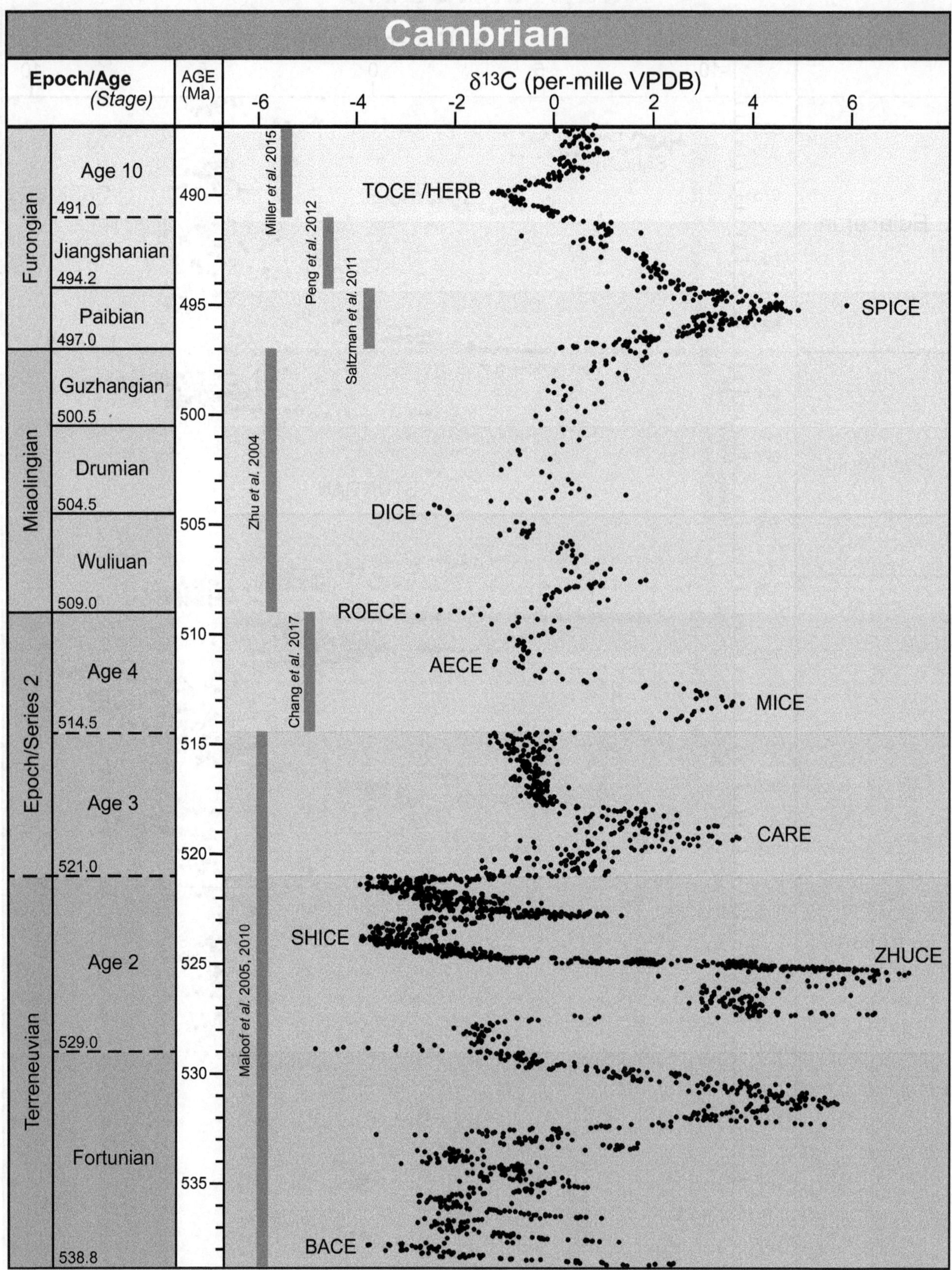

FIGURE 11.4 Variation in $\delta^{13}C_{carb}$ through the Cambrian. Data sources are indicated by vertical bars showing chronostratigraphic interval. Please see Section 11.5.3 and the corresponding interval chapter later in this book for a more detailed discussion of the data and explanation of acronyms used to identify events.

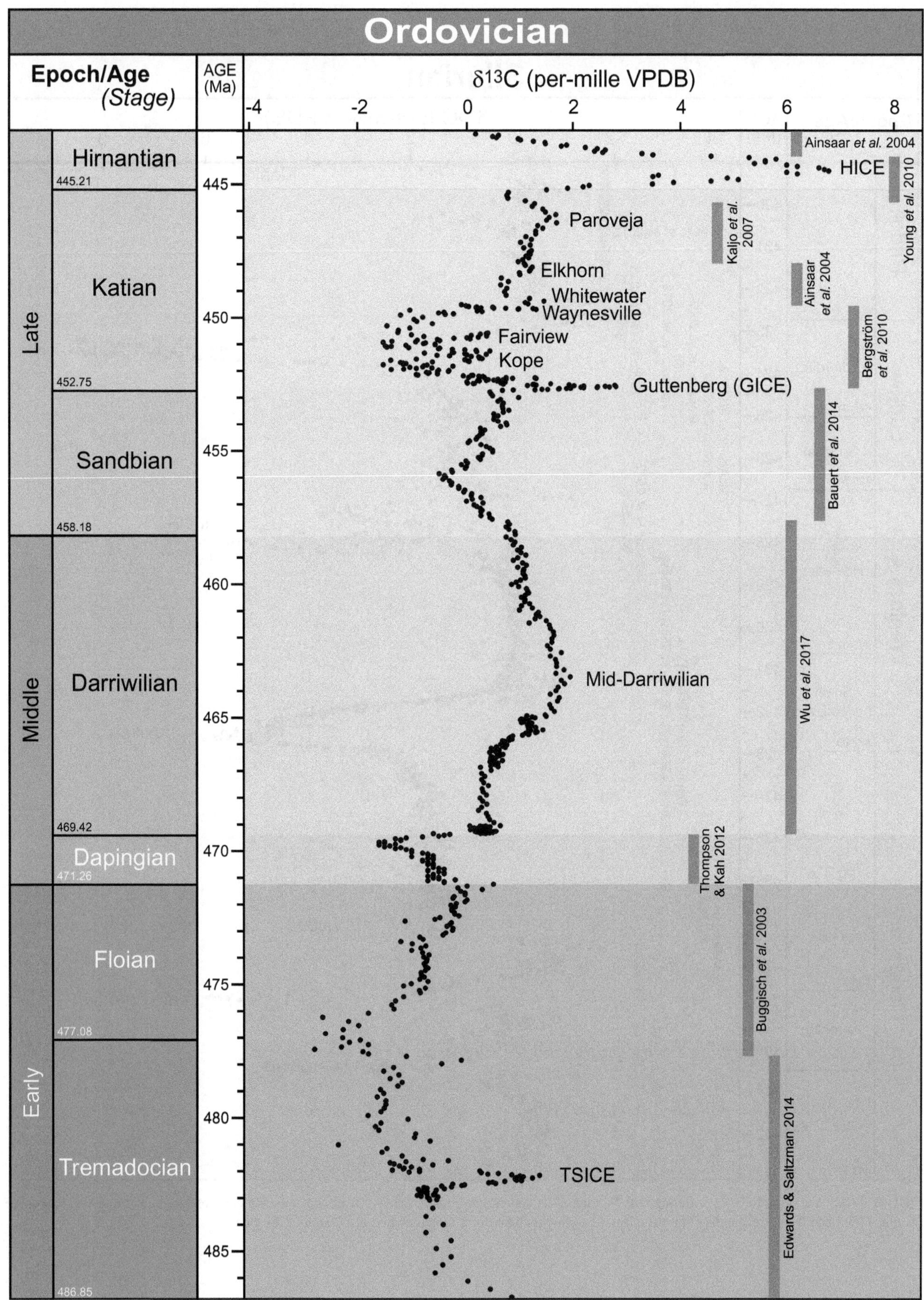

FIGURE 11.5 Variation in $\delta^{13}C_{carb}$ through the Ordovician. Data sources are indicated by vertical bars showing chronostratigraphic interval. Please see Section 11.5.3 and the corresponding interval chapter later in this book for a more detailed discussion of the data and explanation of acronyms used to identify events.

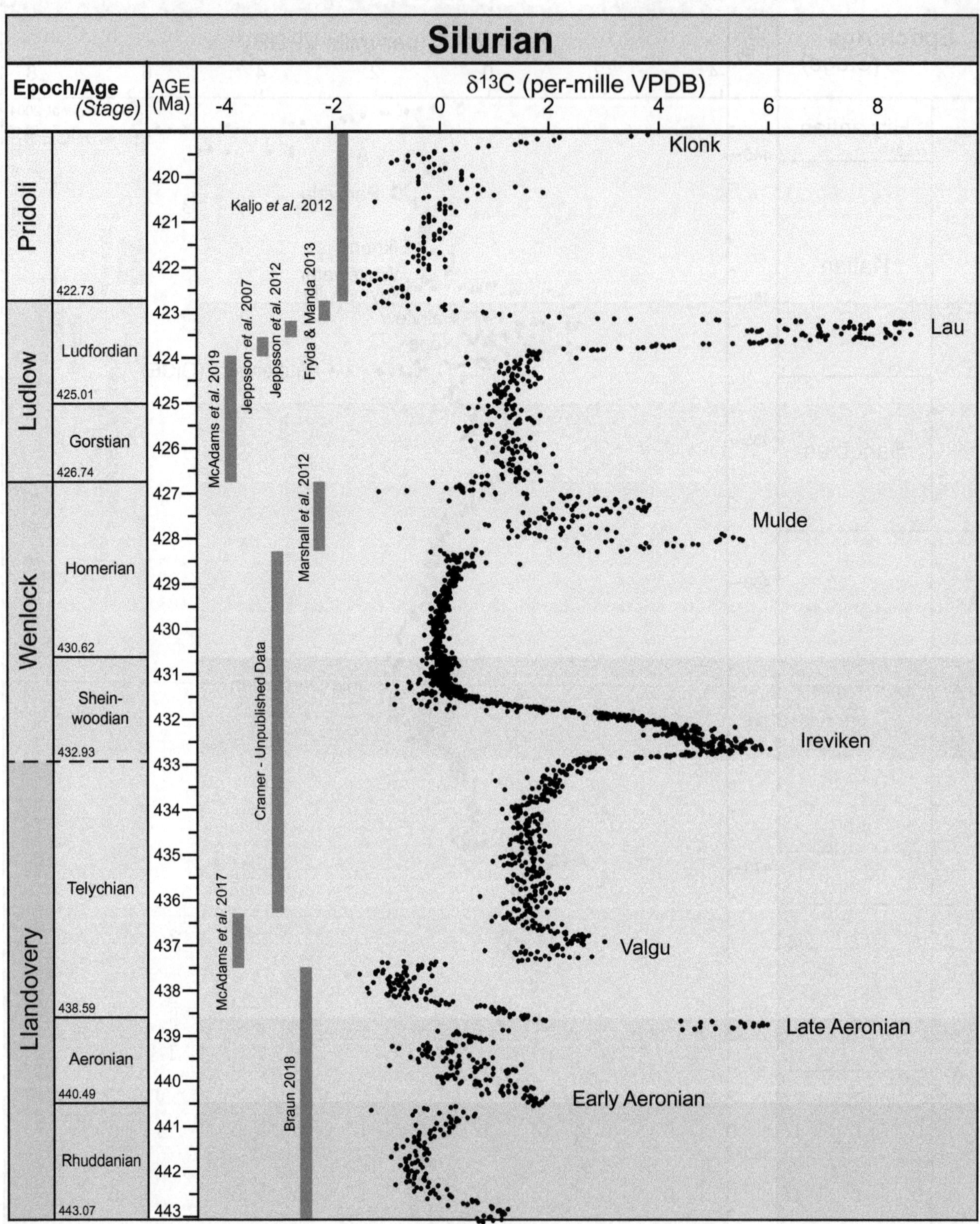

FIGURE 11.6 Variation in $\delta^{13}C_{carb}$ through the Silurian. Data sources are indicated by vertical bars showing chronostratigraphic interval. Please see Section 11.5.3 and the corresponding interval chapter later in this book for a more detailed discussion of the data.

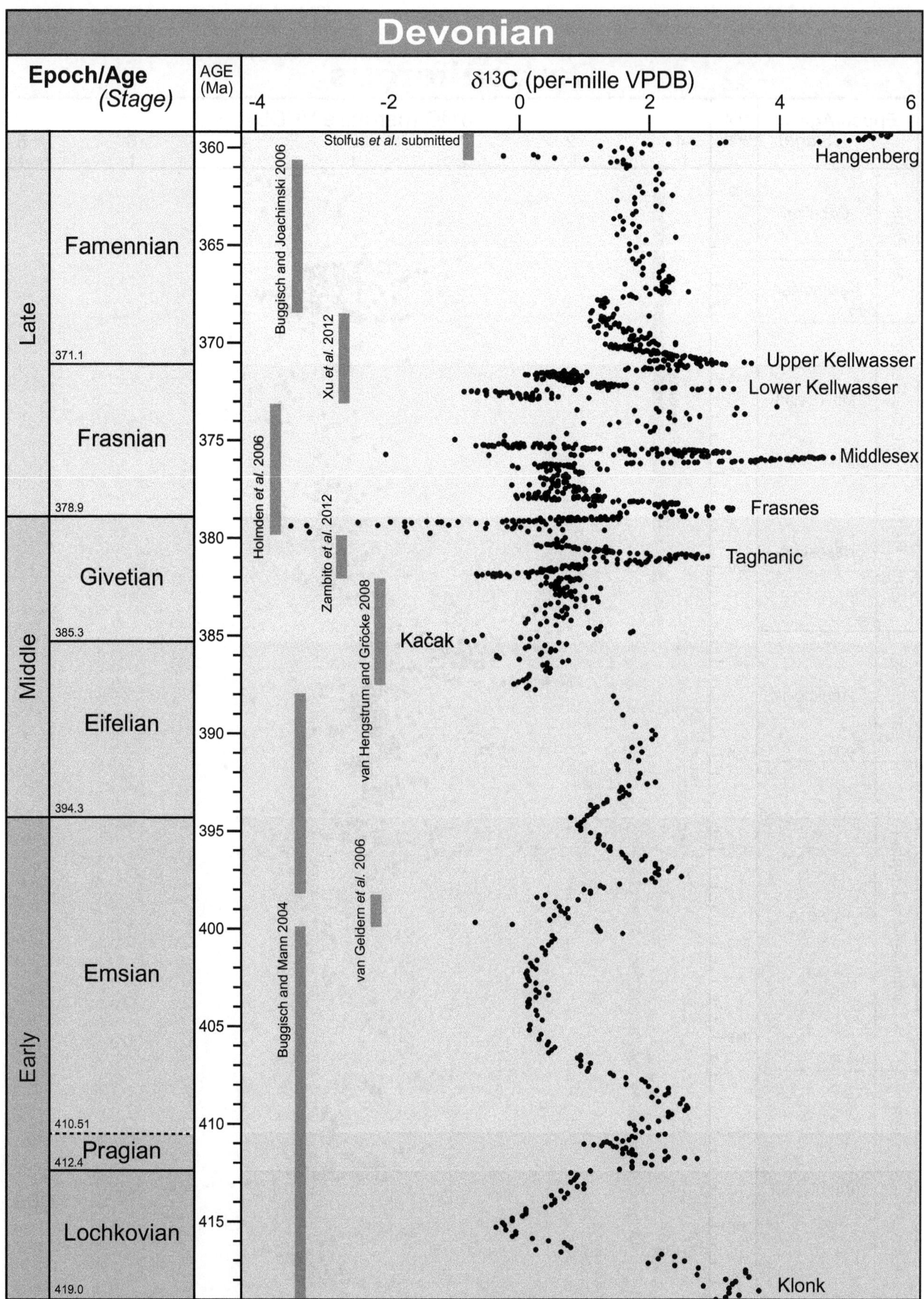

FIGURE 11.7 Variation in $\delta^{13}C_{carb}$ through the Devonian. Data sources are indicated by vertical bars showing chronostratigraphic interval. Please see Section 11.5.3 and the corresponding interval chapter later in this book for a more detailed discussion of the data.

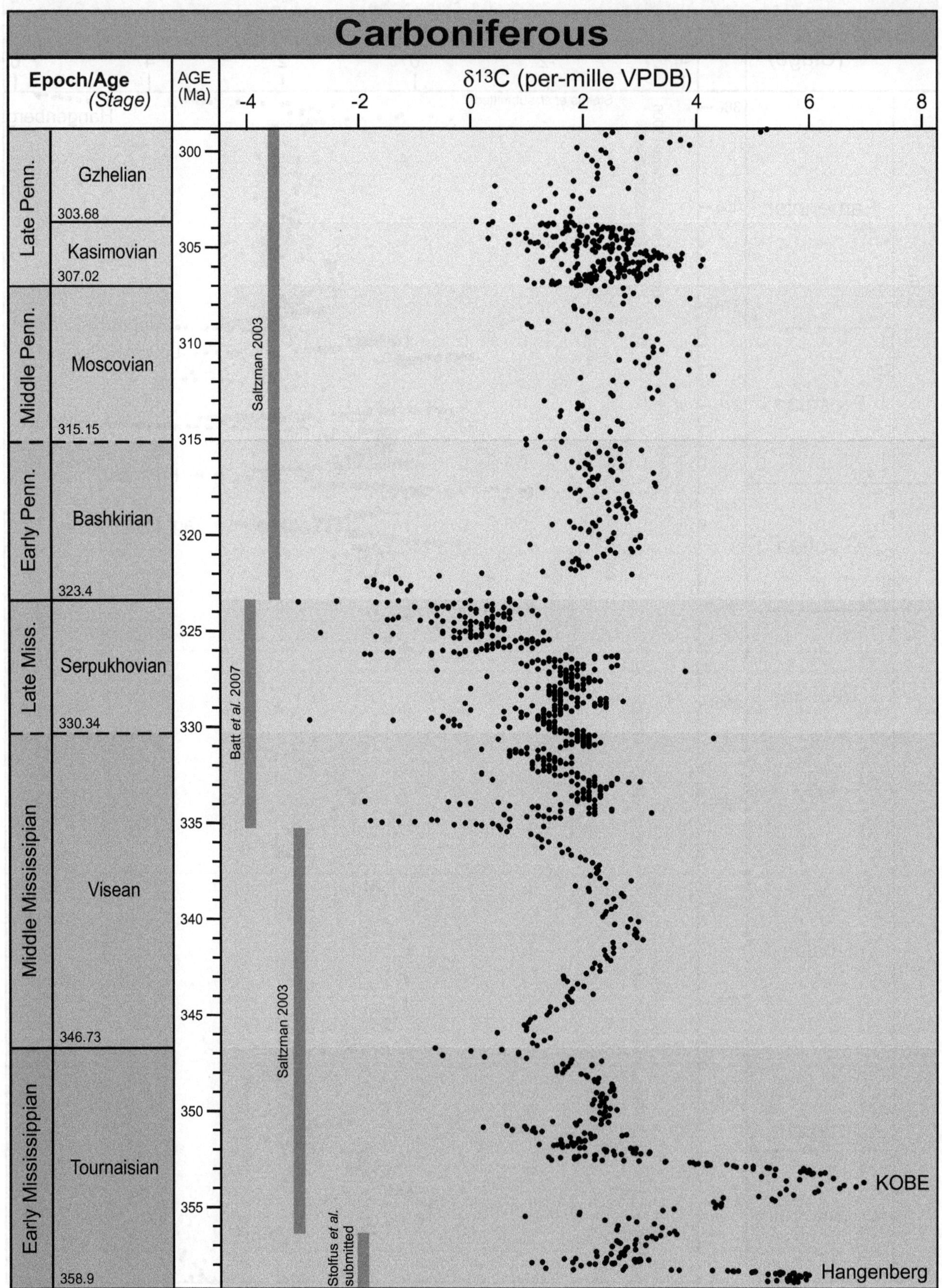

FIGURE 11.8 Variation in $\delta^{13}C_{carb}$ through the Carboniferous. Data sources are indicated by vertical bars showing chronostratigraphic interval. Please see Section 11.5.3 and the corresponding interval chapter later in this book for a more detailed discussion of the data. *KOBE*, Kinderhookian–Osagean Boundary Excursion.

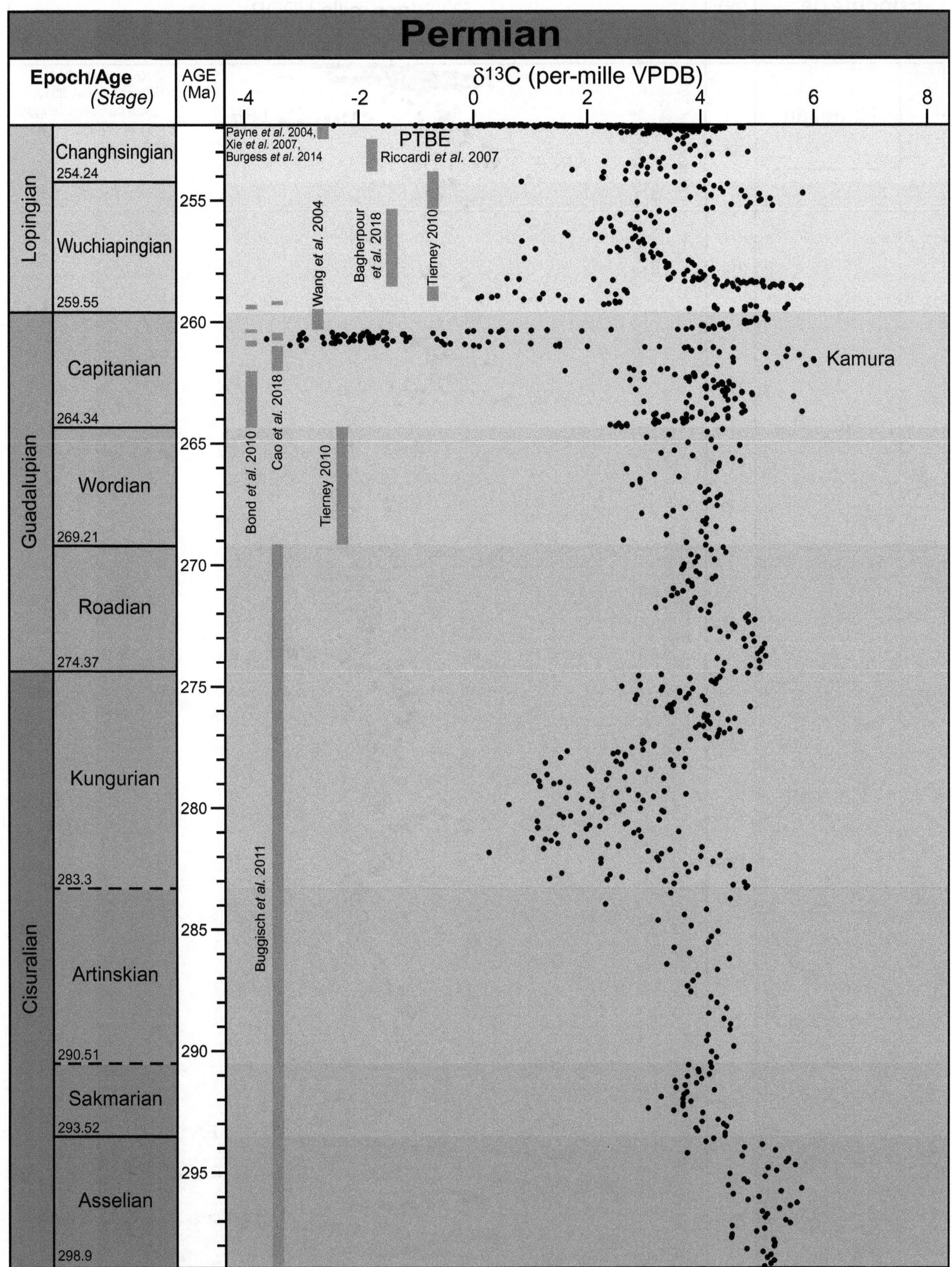

FIGURE 11.9 Variation in $\delta^{13}C_{carb}$ through the Permian. Data sources are indicated by vertical bars showing chronostratigraphic interval. Please see Section 11.5.3 and the corresponding interval chapter later in this book for a more detailed discussion of the data. *PTBE*, Permian-Triassic Boundary Event.

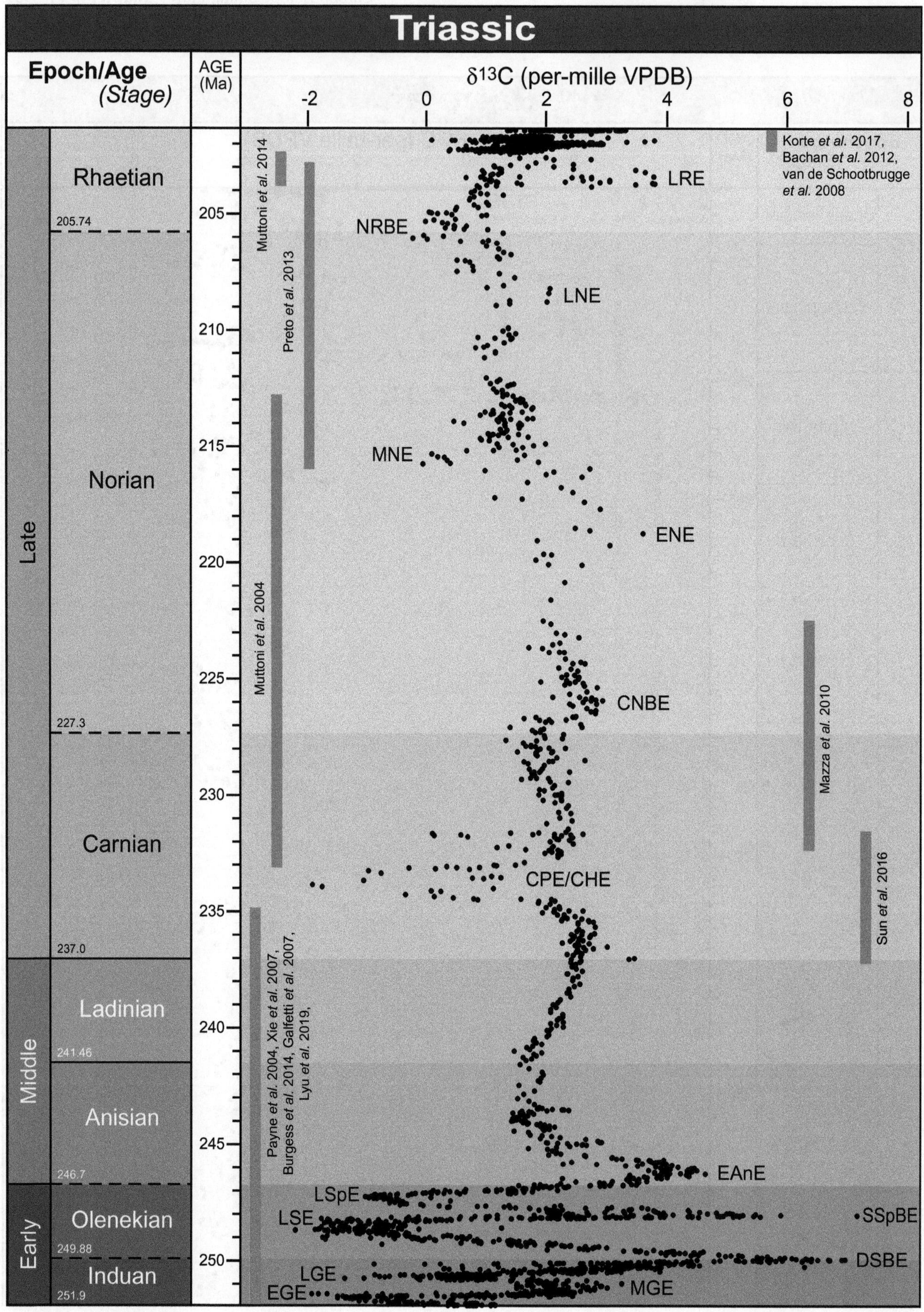

FIGURE 11.10 Variation in $\delta^{13}C_{carb}$ through the Triassic. Data sources are indicated by vertical bars showing chronostratigraphic interval. Please see Section 11.5.3 and the corresponding interval chapter later in this book for a more detailed discussion of the data and explanation of acronyms used to identify events.

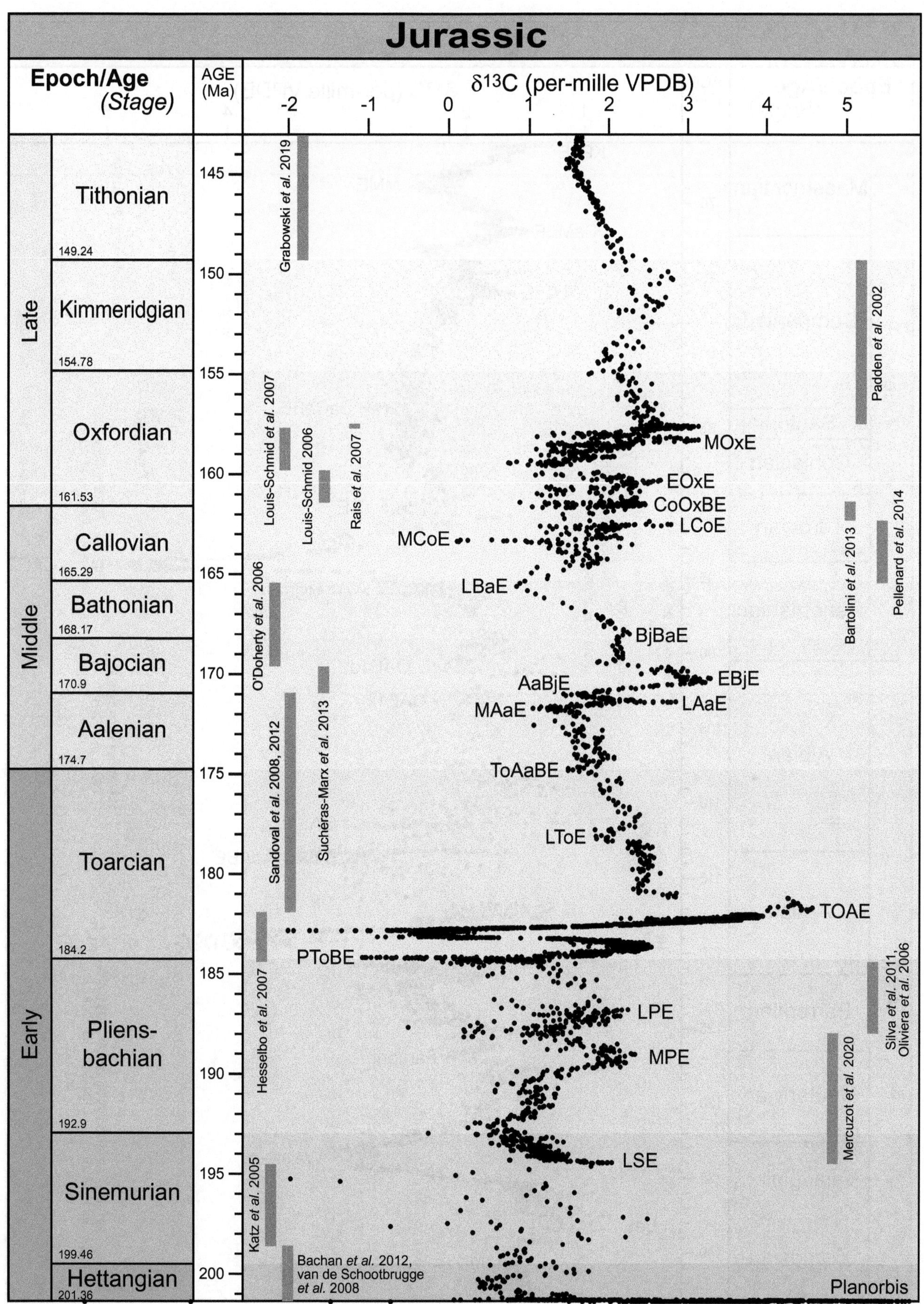

FIGURE 11.11 Variation in $\delta^{13}C_{carb}$ through the Jurassic. Data sources are indicated by vertical bars showing chronostratigraphic interval. Please see Section 11.5.3 and the corresponding interval chapter later in this book for a more detailed discussion of the data and explanation of acronyms used to identify events.

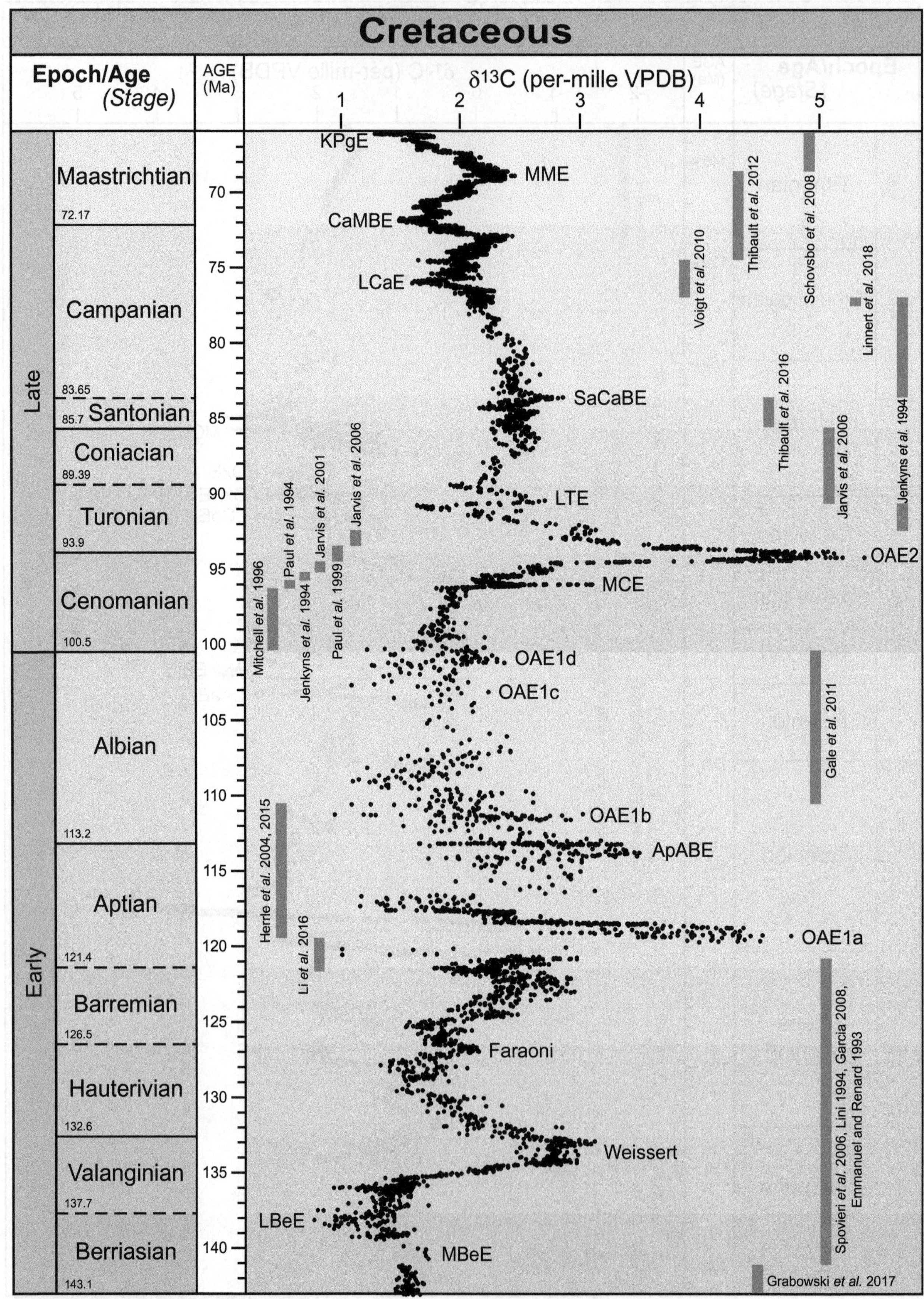

FIGURE 11.12 Variation in $\delta^{13}C_{carb}$ through the Cretaceous. Data sources are indicated by vertical bars showing chronostratigraphic interval. Please see Section 11.5.3 and the corresponding interval chapter later in this book for a more detailed discussion of the data and explanation of acronyms used to identify events.

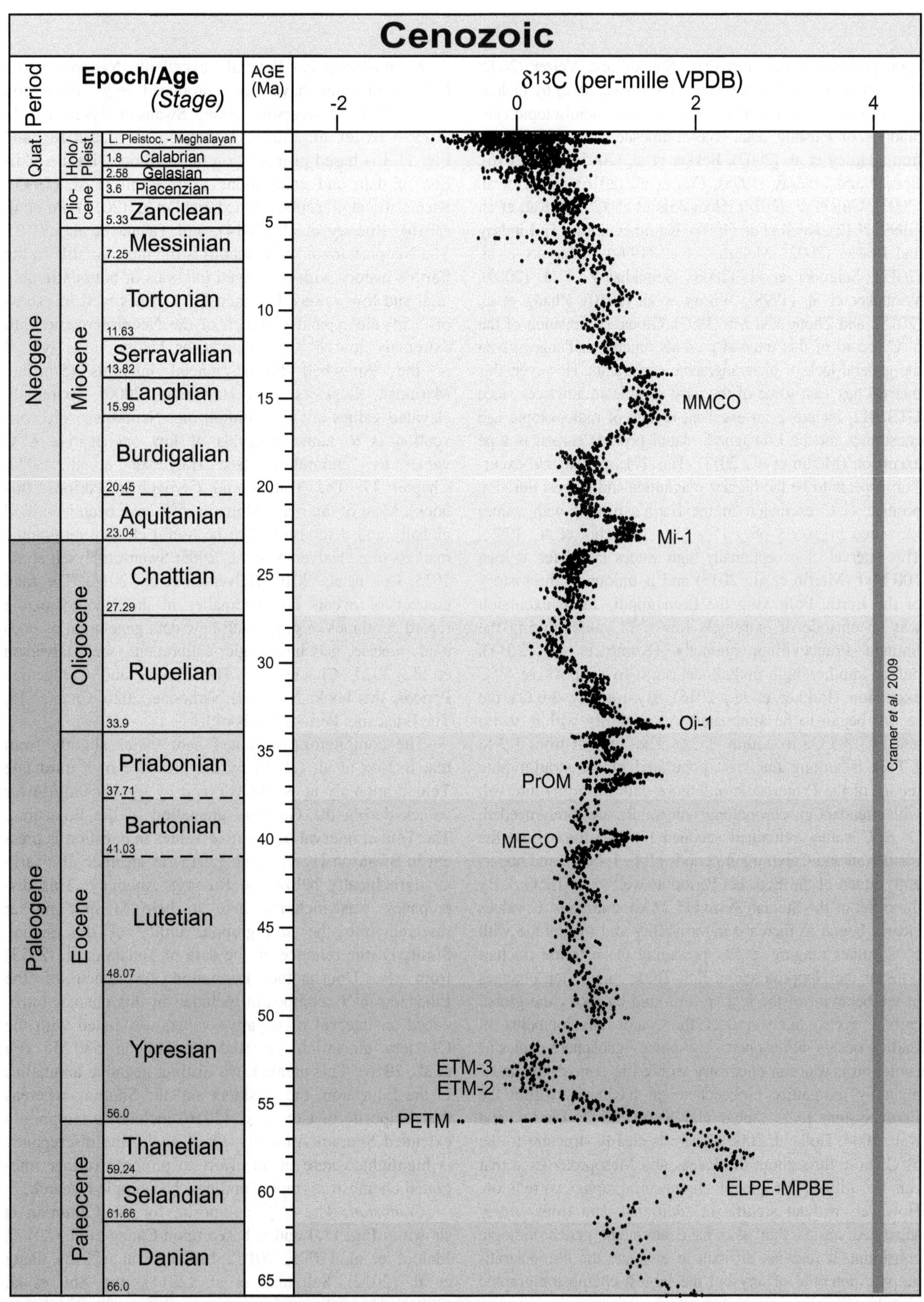

FIGURE 11.13 Variation in $\delta^{13}C_{carb}$ through the Cenozoic. Data sources are indicated by vertical bars showing chronostratigraphic interval. Please see Section 11.5.3 and the corresponding interval chapters later in this book for a more detailed discussion of the data and explanation of acronyms used to identify events. *PETM*: Paleocene-Eocene Thermal Maximum.

upon previous composites (e.g., Shields and Veizer, 2002; Prokoph et al., 2008; Saltzman and Thomas, 2012) by including both new carbon isotope data and new radioisotopic calibrations of existing data. The composite presented here is from Bartley et al. (2007), Bekker et al. (2005, 2006, 2016), Brasier and Lindsay (1998), Cox et al. (2016), Frank et al. (2003), Guo et al. (2013), Hodgskiss et al. (2019), Kah et al. (1999, 2012), Knoll et al. (1995), Kump et al. (2011), Lindsay and Brasier (2002), Melezhik et al. (1999), Planavsky et al. (2012), Schröder et al. (2008), Semikhatov et al. (2009), Whittaker et al. (1998), Wilson et al. (2010), Zhang et al. (2018), and Zhong and Ma (1997). Global compilation of the $\delta^{13}C$ record of this interval presents unique challenges given the general lack of biostratigraphic constraints. However, this interval has seen some of the most significant advances since GTS2012, including an excellent review of radioisotopic age constraints for the Lomagundi–Jatuli positive carbon isotope excursion (Martin et al., 2013). This Paleoproterozoic excursion appears to be the highest magnitude and longest duration positive $\delta^{13}C$ excursion in the Earth's history with values recovered in excess of +15‰ (e.g., Melezhik et al., 1999). This interval of exceptionally high values lasted for at least 100 Myr (Martin et al., 2013) and is unique in the history of the Earth. Following the Lomagundi–Jatuli excursion was an episode of extremely low $\delta^{13}C$ values during the Shunga–Francevillian anomaly (Kump et al., 2011), before another high-magnitude, short-lived, positive $\delta^{13}C$ excursion (Bekker et al., 2016). By roughly 2.0 Ga the record began to be attenuated to variability within ±4‰ and by 1.85 Ga to within ±2‰. The interval from 1.9 to 1.7 Ga is among the least populated in the stratigraphic record of the Proterozoic and more data from this interval, with attendant geochronologic constraints, are sorely needed.

$\delta^{13}C$ values remained subdued (±2‰) throughout the Statherian and Calymmian periods (1.8–1.4 Ga), and apparently much of the Ectasian Period as well (1.4–1.2 Ga). By the onset of the Stenian Period (1.2 Ga), marine $\delta^{13}C$ values clearly began to increase in variability and magnitude with $\delta^{13}C$ values ranging ±5‰, presaging the extreme fluctuations of the Neoproterozoic Era. These major step changes in the behavior of the $\delta^{13}C$ record, and by proxy the global carbon cycle, likely reflect the major developments in Earth's ocean–atmosphere–biosphere–geosphere cycles as evolution and ocean chemistry worked in concert to fundamentally reorganize biogeochemical feedbacks within the Earth system (e.g., Anbar and Knoll, 2002; Bartley and Kah, 2004; Holland, 2006). There is clearly structure to the $\delta^{13}C$ curve throughout the Paleo- and Mesoproterozoic that can be utilized for global chronostratigraphic correlation. However, without significant additional data from widely separated basins that also have attendant geochronologic constraint, it remains difficult to evaluate the chronostratigraphic potential of any but the largest chemostratigraphic signals.

Neoproterozoic: Several excellent Neoproterozoic $\delta^{13}C$ composites have been produced (e.g., Halverson et al., 2005; Halverson, 2006; Swanson-Hysell et al., 2015; Cox et al., 2016; Halverson et al., 2018) and Fig. 11.3 is based primarily on these works with the addition of data and calibrations from Knoll et al. (1995), Kuznetsov et al. (2006), Macdonald et al. (2010), Pu et al. (2016), Rooney et al. (2014), and Tahata et al. (2013). The Neoproterozoic $\delta^{13}C$ record is the most volatile in the Earth's history with prolonged intervals of both extremely high and low values. Elevated $\delta^{13}C$ values well in excess of +5‰ are typical of much of the Neoproterozoic with extremely low $\delta^{13}C$ values at or below −5‰ typical of the "Snowball Earth" glacial intervals (Sturtian, Marinoan, Gaskiers, e.g., Halverson, 2006). Extremely elevated values are so common that Neoproterozoic convention is to name intervals of low or negative $\delta^{13}C$ values as "anomalies" (see Halverson et al., 2020, Chapter 17, The Tonian and Cryogenian Periods, this book). Most of the major shifts in $\delta^{13}C$ have been identified globally and demonstrated to be useful chronostratigraphic markers (e.g., Halverson et al., 2005; Swanson-Hysell et al., 2015; Cox et al., 2016; Halverson et al., 2018). The total number of events and anomalies in the Neoproterozoic record continues to grow with new data generation as does their precise geochronologic calibration (see Halverson et al., 2020, Chapter 17, The Tonian and Cryogenian Periods, this book; Xiao and Narbonne, 2020, Chapter 18, The Ediacaran Period, this book).

The compilation presented here varies slightly from that in Cox et al. (2016) by the presence of a third late Tonian anomaly at ~748 Ma, and by significantly lower values during the Gaskiers glaciation of the Ediacaran. The Tonian interval of negative values in question is present in Swanson-Hysell et al. (2015) as an interval clearly stratigraphically below the Russøya Anomaly. This discrepancy was included here to help to spur further research into the stratigraphic utility of this signal. Similarly, the reliance on the data of Tahata et al. (2013) from the Doushantuo Formation for much of the Ediacaran $\delta^{13}C$ composite included in this chapter introduced an interval of negative values associated with the Gaskiers glaciation centered roughly on 580 Ma (Pu et al., 2016). This created two distinct negative anomalies in the Ediacaran, the Gaskiers and the Shuram, whereas the composite of Cox et al. (2016) includes a temporally extended Shuram Anomaly. Once again, the discrepancy is highlighted here in an effort to promote further integrated chemostratigraphic and geochronologic research.

Cambrian: The $\delta^{13}C$ composite for the Cambrian is shown in Fig. 11.4 and is based upon Chang et al. (2017), Maloof et al. (2005, 2010), Miller et al. (2015), Peng et al. (2012), Saltzman et al. (2011), and Zhu et al. (2004). The details of the curve are broadly similar to previous compilations by Zhu et al. (2004, 2006) and Saltzman and Thomas (2012), with the addition of significant new detail in the Terreneuvian. Many of the large shifts in $\delta^{13}C$ have been given names (e.g., ZHUCE for ZHUjiaqing Carbon isotope Excursion, and SPICE for Steptoean PositIve Carbon isotope Excursion) and their utility in global correlation has been widely recognized. The International Subcommission on Cambrian Stratigraphy has integrated $\delta^{13}C$ stratigraphy into their discussions and decision-making process more heavily than most other Paleozoic subcommissions, and $\delta^{13}C$ has begun to play an increasingly larger role in Cambrian global correlation. Of course this is also a by-product of the presence of large variations in the Cambrian record that increase the utility of $\delta^{13}C$ as well.

The Cambrian $\delta^{13}C$ record is clearly the transition from that of the Neoproterozoic, with long-lived high-amplitude positive and negative shifts, to the more quiescent record of the lower to middle Paleozoic, with baselines near zero and discreet excursions that rarely last more than 1 or 2 million years. The two major excursions of the Terreneuvian (ZHUCE and unnamed excursion in the Fortunian) appear to be the longest duration excursions within the Paleozoic $\delta^{13}C$ record. Similarly, the apparently cyclical $\delta^{13}C$ signal in the lower half of the Fortunian appears to be unique for the Paleozoic, at least until the Late Paleozoic Ice Age of the Pennsylvanian and Permian. These Fortunian features in the $\delta^{13}C$ record are only now beginning to be utilized for global correlation and are yet to be demonstrated globally. By contrast, the SPICE Event of the Paibian was one of the first major Paleozoic $\delta^{13}C$ excursions to be globally documented.

Ordovician: The Ordovician $\delta^{13}C$ composite includes data from Ainsaar et al. (2004), Bauert et al. (2014), Bergström et al. (2010), Buggisch et al. (2003), Edwards and Saltzman (2014), Kaljo et al. (2007), Thompson and Kah (2012), Wu et al. (2017), and Young et al. (2010). Generally stable $\delta^{13}C$ values persist for much of the Ordovician with discreet excursions away from baseline. Several of the major positive $\delta^{13}C$ excursions (e.g., GICE for Guttenberg carbon isotope excursion, and HICE for Hirnantian carbon isotope excursion) have been recognized globally for more than a decade, whereas other excursions such as the Tremadocian TSICE (Top Skullrockian Isotopic Carbon Excursion) are only now beginning to be identified. The $\delta^{13}C$ curve presented in Fig. 11.5 differs little from GTS2012 (Saltzman and Thomas, 2012) with the exception of a significant low in the Dapingian recognized by Thompson and Kah (2012), and the addition of new names for events within the Katian. Of note is the lower baseline shown in the lower half of the Katian (nearly −2‰) compared to the rest of the Katian (nearly +1‰). This is the result of compositing the US Midcontinent data of Bergström et al. (2010) with the Baltic data of Ainsaar et al. (2004) and Kaljo et al. (2007). The US Midcontinent data are consistently shifted to lighter (more negative) values, and as such the "excursions" originally named and recognized from there (Kope, Fairview, Waynesville, Whitewater, Elkhorn) have not been straightforward to identify in other basins worldwide. Ainsaar et al. (2010) introduced isotope zones for the Middle and Upper Ordovician based upon the Baltoscandian $\delta^{13}C$ record and Bergström et al. (2015) integrated these zones with existing names of Katian events identified in the US Midcontinent. As pointed out in Goldman et al. (2020, Chapter 20, The Ordovician Period, this book), the precise global correlation and chronostratigraphic utility of some of the smaller Katian events remain in flux.

The Ordovician $\delta^{13}C$ record demonstrates a step change in the ocean−atmosphere−biosphere−geosphere Earth system at approximately the base of the Katian Stage (e.g., Cooper et al., 2014). Prior to the Katian, the $\delta^{13}C$ record is generally subdued with limited variability, the TSICE and Dapingian notwithstanding. From the Katian onward, through the Lower Devonian, the $\delta^{13}C$ record enters an interval of episodic, very large-magnitude positive $\delta^{13}C$ excursions, often in excess of +5‰. The largest magnitude positive $\delta^{13}C$ excursion of the Ordovician coincides with the Hirnantian glaciation marking the acme of the Early Paleozoic Ice Age (e.g., Ghienne et al., 2014). The base of the Katian also marks a shift in diversity patterns among graptolites (Cooper et al., 2014) and a major step change in extinction regime (Crampton et al., 2016). These integrated analyses of the graptolite clade with the $\delta^{13}C$ record are among the most detailed integrations of paleontology and $\delta^{13}C$ in the Paleozoic and demonstrate the utility of $\delta^{13}C$ stratigraphy in unraveling the biological history of the Earth.

Silurian: The Silurian $\delta^{13}C$ composite shown in Fig. 11.6 includes data from Braun (2018), Frýda and Manda (2013), Jeppsson et al. (2007, 2012), Kaljo et al. (2012), Marshall et al. (2012), McAdams et al. (2017, 2019), and unpublished data of B.D. Cramer. Previous composites of Silurian $\delta^{13}C$ were presented by Saltzman and Thomas (2012) and stylized general $\delta^{13}C$ curves were presented in Cramer et al. (2011) and updated in McAdams et al. (2019). Very high-amplitude positive excursions departing from intervals of stable baseline characterize the Silurian $\delta^{13}C$ record, including what may be the highest amplitude excursion of the Phanerozoic (Lau excursion) during the Ludfordian with values typically in excess of +8‰ (Baltica, Perunica, and Gondwana, Frýda and Manda, 2013). Saltzman (2005) identified the interval from the Late Ordovician to Early Devonian as a time of rapid, large-magnitude fluctuations in the global marine $\delta^{13}C$ record, and the composites presented here still largely bear this out. The step change at the base of the Katian (Cooper et al., 2014; Crampton et al., 2016) that ushered in more frequent and larger positive $\delta^{13}C$ excursions in the Ordovician continued throughout the Silurian only coming to an end with the Klonk Excursion at the Silurian–Devonian Boundary. The ~40 Myr interval of general $\delta^{13}C$ quiescence from the SPICE Event of the Cambrian to the GICE Event of the Ordovician marks the earlier step, whereas the ~37 Myr interval from the GICE Event to the Klonk Event marks the more active interval during the Late Ordovician and Silurian. Such short-duration, high-magnitude variability in the $\delta^{13}C$ record returns later in the Middle Devonian, but after more than 30 Myr of generally attenuated variability.

Most of the Silurian $\delta^{13}C$ excursions shown in Fig. 11.6 are named after biotic events identified in the conodont record of the Baltic Basin (Jeppsson, 1987; Männik, 2007), with the exceptions being the Klonk, named for the Global Boundary Stratotype Section for the base of the Devonian, and the two Aeronian excursions currently given chronostratigraphic designations. Even with the exceptional resolution and long history of study of the Silurian $\delta^{13}C$ record, new features are still being identified. For example, the Late Aeronian excursion has only recently begun to be recovered as a large-magnitude excursion in $\delta^{13}C_{carb}$ (e.g., McAdams et al., 2017; Braun, 2018), there remains no consensus regarding the global nature of a mid-Pridoli event and positive $\delta^{13}C$ excursion (e.g., Kaljo et al., 2012, 2015), and the early-Homerian excursion of Hughes and Ray (2016) has yet to be demonstrated globally.

Devonian: The Devonian $\delta^{13}C$ composite shown in Fig. 11.7 includes data from Buggisch and Joachimski (2006), Buggisch and Mann (2004), Holmden et al. (2006), Stolfus et al. (submitted), van Geldern et al. (2006), van Hengstum and Gröcke (2008), Xu et al. (2012), and Zambito et al. (2016). Many of the major positive $\delta^{13}C$ excursions of the Devonian have been well documented, and the Frasnian–Famennian Boundary Event (Kellwasser) was among the first major Paleozoic excursion to be demonstrated globally (e.g., Joachimski and Buggisch, 1993). The Middle and Upper Devonian are much better represented in the literature and the Lower Devonian represents one of the remaining frontiers for $\delta^{13}C$ development within the Paleozoic. Fig. 11.7 demonstrates the variable resolution available for Devonian $\delta^{13}C$ data as well as the "jumps" in values where one data set was stitched onto the next (e.g., ~387.5 Ma). This is due in large part to the limited data available from certain intervals of the Devonian. Major positive $\delta^{13}C$ excursions coincide with the Taghanic, Frasnes, Middlesex, Kellwasser, and Hangenberg global anoxic and/or biocrisis events.

The Lower Devonian through Eifelian $\delta^{13}C$ record appears to be one of general quiescence; however, the limited resolution of data available may be more responsible for this appearance than the actual record itself. What events do appear in the Emsian and Eifelian have limited total magnitude change from baseline and lack the abrupt and extreme variability seen higher in the Devonian. Following the end of the Klonk Event, and notwithstanding the small perturbations in the Emsian and Eifelian, it is more than 35 Myr before the Taghanic Crisis ushers in another interval of rapid, high-magnitude variation in $\delta^{13}C$ that persists into the Carboniferous. The well-known anoxic intervals of the Devonian are sometimes correlative with positive $\delta^{13}C$ excursions (e.g., the F–F Boundary Event) and sometimes immediately precede major positive $\delta^{13}C$ excursions (e.g., the Hangenberg Event) ending during the rising limb of the excursion. Major Devonian $\delta^{13}C$ features have been demonstrated globally and are extremely useful for chronostratigraphic correlation. For some of the better known Devonian events, there are sufficient global data to use $\delta^{13}C$ to identify biostratigraphic diachroneity resulting from paleobiogeographic migration.

Carboniferous: The Carboniferous $\delta^{13}C$ composite is based upon Batt et al. (2007), Saltzman (2003), and Stolfus et al. (submitted) and is shown in Fig. 11.8. Two major positive $\delta^{13}C$ excursions (Hangenberg and Kinderhookian–Osagean Boundary Excursion = KOBE) occur within the Tournaisian and the majority of the Visean shows a slow broad trend of change up until roughly 335 Ma. From this point forward the remainder of the Carboniferous $\delta^{13}C$ composite shows very rapid fluctuations as $\delta^{13}C$ begins to mirror the cyclical nature of the upper Carboniferous stratigraphic record. Following a significant low at the Mississippian–Pennsylvanian Boundary, the Pennsylvanian curve remains generally elevated around approximately +2‰, while continuing the trend of rapid fluctuations. It is likely that the record of cyclothemic deposition is superimposed on this interval of the $\delta^{13}C$ composite (e.g., Tierney-Cramer and Bostic, 2015); however, no complete and systematic, cyclothem-scale, $\delta^{13}C$ composite has been produced for the Pennsylvanian. Until such a composite is available, there will remain little utility in global correlation of the Pennsylvanian $\delta^{13}C$ record on a fine temporal scale.

The two major positive $\delta^{13}C$ excursions of the Tournaisian (Hangenberg and KOBE) have been demonstrated globally and are among the last of the major Paleozoic positive $\delta^{13}C$ excursions that have total magnitude changes away from baseline in excess of +5‰. Elevated values in excess of +4‰ are common throughout much of the Permian; however, the baseline rarely reaches back down to zero and "excursions" do not appear to have the same total magnitude deviation from their starting point. The KOBE marks the end of the Middle Devonian–Mississippian interval of rapid, large-magnitude positive excursions in $\delta^{13}C_{carb}$. Similarly rapid positive excursions of equal magnitude do not appear to return until the Early Triassic.

Permian: The Permian $\delta^{13}C$ composite includes data from Bagherpour et al. (2018), Bond et al. (2010), Buggisch et al. (2011), Cao et al. (2018), Jin et al. (2000), Riccardi et al. (2007), Tierney (2010), and Wang et al. (2004). Fig. 11.9 demonstrates that the Permian $\delta^{13}C$ record is among the most poorly resolved intervals of the Phanerozoic and significant new high-resolution $\delta^{13}C$ data are badly needed for most of the Permian. The degree of provincialism in conodont fauna (e.g., Mei and Henderson, 2001) has also hindered the development of a global $\delta^{13}C$ composite for the Permian and direct integration of new biostratigraphic data with new chemostratigraphic data will be required. Most of the Permian $\delta^{13}C$ record is one of elevated values that show broad trends in variation centered around +4‰. The Kungurian $\delta^{13}C$ record appears to be more closely centered around +2‰ and stands out among the rest of the Cisuralian record. The elevated values in the middle to late Capitanian approaching +6‰ have been identified as the Kamura Event (Isozaki et al., 2007; Cao et al., 2018) and immediately precede an extreme negative excursion in $\delta^{13}C$ during the late Capitanian. $\delta^{13}C$ values recover backup to above +5‰ and there appears to be a small-magnitude total change positive excursion in the late Wuchiapingian but this has yet to be demonstrated to be of global chronostratigraphic significance. The Permian $\delta^{13}C$ record ends with the extremely low $\delta^{13}C$ values that have been best documented at the base Triassic GSSP in Meishan, China (e.g., Payne et al., 2004; Xie et al., 2007; Burgess et al., 2014).

Triassic: The Triassic $\delta^{13}C$ composite in Fig. 11.10 includes data from Bachan et al. (2012), Burgess et al. (2014), Galfetti et al. (2007), Korte et al. (2017), Lyu et al. (2019), Mazza et al. (2010), Muttoni et al. (2004, 2014), Payne et al. (2004), Preto et al. (2013), Shen et al. (2016), Sun et al. (2016), van de Schootbrugge et al. (2008), and Xie et al. (2007). There are several excursions and boundary events (BE) within the Triassic (Fig. 11.10) with additional "N" and "P" designations by Song et al. (2013): PTBE Permian-Triassic Boundary Event; EGE, MGE, LGE are Early (N1), Mid- (P1) and Late (N2) Griesbachian events; DSBE Dienarian-Smithian BE (P2); LSE Late Smithian Event (N3); SSpBE Smithian-Spathian BE (P3); LSpE Late Spathian (N4), EAnE Early Anisian (P4); CPE/CHE Carnian Pluvial/Humid Event; CNBE Carnian-Norian BE; ENE, MNE, LNE, Early, Mid-, Late Norian; NRBE Norian-Rhaetian BE; and LRE Late Rhaetian event. The Early Triassic $\delta^{13}C$ record of large rapid swings from −2‰ to >6‰ is dramatically different from the remainder of the Triassic record, which is generally quiescent with values between +1‰ and +2‰. The exceptions to this general trend are the early Anisian positive $\delta^{13}C$ excursion and the lower values during the Carnian Pluvial/Humid Event (e.g., Sun et al., 2016). The trend toward decreasing baseline values and the return to baseline levels approaching +1‰ represents the first time in more than 100 Myr that baseline values had been at that level (Late Mississippian, Figs. 11.8−11.10). The interval from the Middle Triassic to the base of the Jurassic is another roughly 40 Myr interval with limited variability in the $\delta^{13}C$ record of marine DIC, similar to the patterns that were so common in the lower to middle Paleozoic $\delta^{13}C$ record.

Jurassic: The Jurassic $\delta^{13}C$ composite shown in Fig. 11.11 is from Bartolini et al. (2013), Grabowski et al. (2019), Hesselbo et al. (2007), Katz et al. (2005), Louis-Schmid (2006), Louis-Schmid et al. (2007), Mercuzot et al. (2020), O'Dogherty et al. (2006), Oliveira et al. (2006), Padden et al. (2002), Pellenard et al. (2014a,b), Rais et al. (2007), Sandoval et al. (2008, 2012), Silva et al. (2011), Sucheras-Marx et al. (2013), and Weissert and Channell (1989). Excursions and boundary events (BE) within the Jurassic (Fig. 11.11) include: LSE Late Sinemurian Event; MPE, LPE Mid-, Late Pliensbachian events; PToBE Pliensbachian-Toarcian BE; TOAE Toarcian Oceanic Anoxic Event; LToE Late Toarcian; ToAaBE Toarcian-Aalenian BE; MAaE, LAaE Mid- and Late Aalenian; AaBjBE Aalenian-Bajocian BE; EBjE Early Bajocian; BjBaBE Bajocian-Bathonian BE; LBaE Late Bathonian; MCoE, LCoE Mid-, Late Collovian; CoOxBE Collovian-Oxfordian BE; and EOxE, MOxE Early, and Mid-Oxfordian events. Two major positive $\delta^{13}C$ excursions dominate the record, one at the base of the Jurassic (Planorbis Event, > +5‰) and the other within the early Toarcian (Toarcian Oceanic Anoxic Event, TOAE, > +4‰). The Triassic−Jurassic Boundary Planorbis Event also includes a preceding negative $\delta^{13}C$ excursion. Here, data points are shown well to the left of the rest of the graph at the base of Fig. 11.11. This was done to allow enlargement of the remainder of the data set to maximize the appearance of excursions; however, we still wanted to show the total range of data through the Planorbis Event. Whereas most of the rest of the Jurassic has variability of lower magnitude, the record is clearly not one of stability and high-frequency variability in the range of 1−2 per mille is the general theme throughout the interval. The TOAE is the first named oceanic anoxic event (OAE) we have come to in the compilation, and this relationship between OAEs and major positive $\delta^{13}C$ excursions continues into the Cretaceous.

Cretaceous: The Cretaceous $\delta^{13}C$ record is compiled from Emmanuel and Renard (1993), Gale et al. (2011), Garcia (2008), Grabowski et al. (2019), Herrle et al. (2004, 2015), Jarvis et al. (2001, 2006), Jenkyns et al. (1994), Li et al. (2016), Lini (1994), Linnert et al. (2018), Mitchell et al. (1996), Paul et al. (1994, 1999), Schovsbo et al. (2008), Sprovieri et al. (2006), Thibault et al. (2012, 2016), and Voigt et al. (2010). The curve shown in Fig. 11.12

includes more than 6000 data points and is the most data-dense period curve illustrated in this chapter. Many of the large events in the Cretaceous $\delta^{13}C$ record have been known for four decades (e.g., Scholle and Arthur, 1980), but the push to extend astrochronology into the Cretaceous (e.g., Sageman et al., 2006; Sageman et al., 2014; Locklair and Sageman, 2008; Ma et al., 2017; Huang, 2018) has been a driving factor behind the tremendous increase in data production. Named excursions or boundary events (BE) within the Jurassic (Fig. 11.12) include: MBeE, LBeE Mid-, Late Berriasian events; OAE1a-d and OAE2 suite of Oceanic Anoxic Events; ApABE Aptian-Albian BE; MCE Mid-Cenomanian Event; LTE Late Turonian Event (Hitch Wood); SaCaBE Santonian-Campanian BE; LCaE: Late Campanian; CaMBE Campanian-Maastrichtian BE; MME Mid-Maastrichtian; and the KPgE Cretaceous-Paleogene event. This is particularly obvious in the Maastrichtian and upper Campanian portions of the curve. The two largest positive $\delta^{13}C$ excursions are associated with major oceanic anoxic events (OAE1a and OAE2); however, additional positive and negative shifts in $\delta^{13}C$ are clearly global features of the Cretaceous that have been demonstrated to be useful for stratigraphic correlation. OAE2, at approximately 93 Ma, was the last major positive $\delta^{13}C$ excursion, and global marine $\delta^{13}C$ values have never returned to such elevated values since that time.

Cenozoic: The Cenozoic composite presented in Fig. 11.13 is from Cramer et al. (2009) and is a modified version of the same curve presented in Saltzman and Thomas (2012) with the scaling updated to the GTS2020 time scale. The curve is based on 29,036 data points; however, Fig. 11.13 illustrates a synthetic version of that data set showing only every 10th data point of a 9-point moving average. The purpose of this graphical representation is to provide a more direct comparison with the other $\delta^{13}C$ curves shown in this chapter. At 66 Myr in duration, the Cenozoic Era is roughly the same length of time as many periods of the Phanerozoic Eon. Therefore we find it instructive to illustrate the entire Cenozoic record for direct comparison with the rest of the Phanerozoic periods illustrated in this chapter. For example, the broad trends of the Paleocene and lower Eocene are overprinted by multiple very rapid and transient features of great climatic significance such as the Paleocene–Eocene Thermal Maximum (PETM) that is recorded as a dramatic decrease in $\delta^{13}C$ (e.g., Zachos et al., 2010; Turner and Ridgwell, 2016). In addition to the PETM, other major carbon isotope excursions during the Cenozoic (Fig. 11.13) are informally named after the simultaneous climate excursions recognized by oxygen isotope stratigraphy, including: ELPE-MPBE, Early Late Paleocene Event – Mid-Paleocene Biotic Event; ETM-2 and ETM-3, early Eocene Thermal Maximums; MECO, Mid-Eocene Climatic Optimum; PrOM, Priabonian Oxygen isotopic Maximum; Oi-1, first Oligocene oxygen isotopic maximum; Mi-1, first Miocene oxygen isotopic maximum; and MMCO, Mid-Miocene Climatic Optimum. It is informative to consider comparison of this feature in Fig. 11.13 with other $\delta^{13}C$ features throughout this chapter in consideration of identifying similar features in pre-Cenozoic portions of the Earth's history. For higher resolution views of the carbon isotope curve and a more thorough discussion of the Cenozoic $\delta^{13}C$ record, please see Speijer et al. (2020, Chapter 28, The Paleogene Period, this book) and Raffi et al. (2020, Chapter 29, The Neogene Period, this book) for the Paleogene and Neogene records, respectively.

11.6 Causes of carbon isotope excursions

A detailed discussion of all possible causes of both positive and negative $\delta^{13}C$ excursions is far beyond the scope of this chapter; however, some general principles are helpful to discuss. Kump and Arthur (1999) remains one of the most useful general overviews of mechanisms that can drive secular changes in the $\delta^{13}C$ record and the reader is strongly encouraged to start there for a basic discussion of $\delta^{13}C$ excursions. At their most simple, $\delta^{13}C$ excursions must result from removal or addition of either ^{12}C or ^{13}C from the environment being sampled. For example, an imbalance in the removal of ^{12}C from surface waters as primary biomass that results in an increase in burial of ^{12}C as sedimentary organic carbon would have the effect of increasing $^{13}C/^{12}C$ in the water column and therefore producing an increase in $\delta^{13}C$. Conversely, the injection of a large amount of methane, a hydrocarbon with a very negative $\delta^{13}C$ value (e.g., Fig. 11.1), into the ocean–atmosphere system would decrease $\delta^{13}C$ as a result of the large addition of ^{12}C to the short-term carbon system (e.g., Zachos et al., 2010; Turner and Ridgwell, 2016).

A modern example of the addition of ^{12}C into the ocean–atmosphere system has been well documented as the change in $\delta^{13}C$ of atmospheric CO_2 that has resulted from the burning of fossil fuels (Keeling et al., 1979, 2017; Bauska et al., 2015). Known as the Suess effect (Keeling, 1979), the addition of $^{12}CO_2$ to the atmosphere resulting from the burning of fossil fuels has dramatically decreased $\delta^{13}C$ values of the atmosphere. Preindustrial $\delta^{13}C$ of atmospheric CO_2 was roughly −6.5‰, and as of 2014 the average atmosphere CO_2 value was roughly −8.4‰ (e.g., Bauska et al., 2015; Keeling et al., 2017). This relationship between increasing atmospheric CO_2 concentrations and decreasing $\delta^{13}C$ values of atmospheric CO_2 is among the clearest evidence that burning hydrocarbons is a major contributor to the current rise in atmospheric CO_2. Furthermore, this relationship underscores the significance of carbon isotope stratigraphy to our understanding of Earth system dynamics and the nature of modern global change.

11.7 Conclusion

Carbon isotope stratigraphy can be used as tool to unravel the complex web of interactions within the Earth system and explore global carbon cycle dynamics. In addition, the carbon isotope record of the Earth's history can be utilized as a tool for stratigraphic correlation. It is to this later aspect that the majority of this chapter has been devoted. The ability to provide a nonbiostratigraphic, chronostratigraphic tool has begun to revolutionize our ability to tell relative time in the rock record, and the proliferation of carbon isotope stratigraphy in the Proterozoic has likely been the greatest advancement in this arena in the past 20 years. The general lack of biostratigraphy for the majority of the Earth's history had traditionally limited the potential for detailed analysis of early the Earth's history, and the addition of $\delta^{13}C$ stratigraphy has changed the entire landscape of Proterozoic marine and Earth system research. The $\delta^{13}C$ composites presented here represent the work of hundreds of scientists over the past 20–30 years and are a tremendous advancement over previous global time scale composites of the past 2.5 Gyr. However, these composites should not be construed as demonstration that we have identified all of the events in the $\delta^{13}C$ record of the Earth's history. Significant $\delta^{13}C$ features are still being discovered throughout the time scale, and this is more true the farther back in time one looks. Portions of the Proterozoic still have little-to-no data available and some entire periods of the Phanerozoic still do not even have a generalized $\delta^{13}C$ composite that can be considered a global "standard" (e.g., the Permian). There is still considerable research to complete and the direct integration of $\delta^{13}C$, biostratigraphy, and radioisotopic dating will provide even better $\delta^{13}C$ composites in the future.

Acknowledgments

The authors thank Ethan Grossman, Michael Joachimski, Ben Cramer, Galen Halverson, Alan Rooney, Matt Braun, Brittany Stolfus, Emma Hartke, Ellie Biebesheimer, Daniel Goldman, Stephen Leslie, Michael Melchin, Peter Sadler, and Stephen Hesselbo for access to data, early copies of chapters in this book, and useful discussions that benefitted this document. This work was partially supported by the US National Science Foundation grant no. CAREER-1455030 to B.D. Cramer.

References

Ahn, S., Khider, D., Lisiecki, L.E., and Lawrence, C.E., 2017, A probabilistic Pliocene-Pleistocene stack of benthic $\delta^{18}O$ using a profile hidden Markov model. *Dynamics and Statistics of the Climate System*, **2**: 1–6, https://dx.doi.org/10.1093/climsys/dzx002.

Ainsaar, L., Meidla, T., and Tinn, O., 2004, Middle and Upper Ordovician stable isotope stratigraphy across the facies belts in the East Baltic. *In* Hints, O., and Ainsaar, L. (eds), *WOGOGOB-2004 Conference Materials*. Tartu University Press, Tartu, Estonia, pp. 11–12.

Ainsaar, L., Kaljo, D., Martma, T., Meidla, T., Männik, P., Nõlvak, J., et al., 2010, Middle and Upper Ordovician carbon isotope chemostratigraphy in Baltoscandia: a correlation standard and clues to environmental history. *Palaeogeography, Palaeoclimatology, Palaeoecology*, **294**: 189–201, https://dx.doi.org/10.1016/j.palaeo. 2010.01.003.

Algeo, T.J., Wilkinson, B.H., and Lohmann, K.C., 1992, Meteoric-burial diagenesis of Middle Pennsylvanian limestones in the Orogrande Basin, New Mexico: water/rock interactions and basin geothermics. *Journal of Sedimentary Petrology*, **62**: 652–670, https://dx.doi.org/10.1306/D426797E-2B26-11D7-8648000102C1865D.

Allan, J.R., and Matthews, R.K., 1982, Isotope signatures associated with early meteoric diagenesis. *Sedimentology*, **29**: 797–817, https://dx.doi.org/10.1111/j.1365-3091.1982tb00085.x.

Amodio, S., Ferreri, V., d'Argenio, B., Weissert, H., and Sprovieri, M., 2008, Carbon-isotope stratigraphy and cyclostratigraphy of shallow-marine carbonates: the case of San Lorenzell, Lower Cretaceous of Southern Italy. *Cretaceous Research*, **29**: 803–813, https://dx.doi. org/10.1016/j.cretres.2008.05.022.

Anbar, A.D., and Knoll, A.H., 2002, Proterozoic ocean chemistry and evolution: a bioinorganic bridge. *Science*, **297**: 1137–1142, https:// dx.doi.org/10.1126/science.1069651.

Bachan, A., van de Schootbrugge, B., Fiebig, J., McRoberts, C.A., Ciarapica, G., and Payne, J.L., 2012, Carbon cycle dynamics following the end-Triassic mass extinction: constraints from paired $\delta^{13}C_{carb}$ and $\delta^{13}C_{org}$ records. *Geochemistry, Geophysics, Geosystems*, **13**: Q09008, https://dx.doi.org/10.1029/2012GC004150.

Bachan, A., Lau, K.V., Saltzman, M.R., Thomas, E.T., Kump, L.R., and Payne, J.L., 2017, A model for the decrease in amplitude of carbon isotope excursions across the Phanerozoic. *American Journal of Science*, **317**: 641–676, https://dx.doi.org/10.2475/06.2017.01.

Bagherpour, B., Bucher, H., Schneebeli-Hermann, E., Vennemann, T., Chiaradia, M., and Shen, Sz, 2018, Early Late Permian coupled carbon and strontium isotope chemostratigraphy from South China: extended Emeishan volcanism? *Gondwana Research*, **58**: 58–70, https://dx.doi.org/10.1016/j.gr.2018.01.011.

Banner, J.L., and Hanson, G.N., 1990, Calculation of simultaneous isotopic and trace element variations during water-rock interaction with applications to carbonate diagenesis. *Geochimica et Cosmochimica Acta*, **54**: 3123–3137, https://dx.doi.org/10.1016/0016-7037(90) 90128-8.

Banner, J.L., and Kaufman, J., 1994, The isotopic record of ocean chemistry and diagenesis in non-luminescent brachiopods from Mississippian carbonate rocks, Illinois and Missouri. *Geological Society of America Bulletin*, **106**: 1074–1082, https://doi.org/ 10.1130/0016-7606(1994)106 < 1074:TIROOC > 2.3.CO;2.

Barrick, J.E., Männik, P., 2005. Silurian conodont biostratigraphy and palaeobiology in stratigraphic sequences. *In* Purnell, M.A., Donoghue, P.C.J., (eds). *Conodont Biology and Phylogeny – Interpreting the Fossil Record.* The Palaeontological Association Special Papers in Palaeontology, 73, 103–116.

Bartley, J.K., and Kah, L.C., 2004, Marine carbon reservoir, C_{org}-C_{carb} coupling, and the evolution of the Proterozoic carbon cycle. *Geology*, **32**: 129–132, https://dx.doi.org/10.1130/G19939.1.

Bartley, J.K., Kah, L.C., McWilliams, J.L., and Stagner, A.F., 2007, Carbon isotope chemostratigraphy of the Middle Riphean type section (Avzyan Formation, Southern Urals, Russia): signal recovery in a fold-and-thrust belt. *Chemical Geology*, **237**: 211–232, https://dx.doi.org/10.1016/j.chemgeo.2006.06.018.

Bartolini, A., Bonnot, A., Chateau-Smith, C., Collin, P.-Y., Enay, R., Fortwengler, D., et al., 2013, Integrated stratigraphy of some key Callovian-Oxfordian boundary sections in South-East France. Contribution to the choice of the Global Boundary Stratotype Section and Point (GSSP) of the Oxfordian Stage. *Field guide 2013 – Oxfordian GSSP Workshop 30th September–2nd October 2013. Groupe Français d'Etude du Jurassique, 79 pp.*

Batt, L.S., Pope, M.C., Isaacson, P.E., Montañez, I.M., and Abplanalp, J., 2007, Multi-carbonate component reconstruction of mid-carboniferous (Chesterian) seawater $\delta^{13}C$. *Palaeogeography, Palaeoclimatology, Palaeoecology*, **256**: 298–318, https://dx.doi.org/10.1016/j.palaeo.2007.02.049.

Bauert, H., Ainsaar, L., Põldsaar, K., and Sepp, S., 2014, $\delta^{13}C$ chemostratigraphy of the Middle and Upper Ordovician succession in the Tartu-453 drillcore, southern Estonia, and the significance of the HICE. *The Estonian Journal of Earth Sciences*, **63**: 195–200, https://dx.doi.org/10.3176/earth.2014.18.

Bauska, T.K., Joos, F., Mix, A.C., Roth, R., Ahn, J., and Brook, E.J., 2015, Links between atmospheric carbon dioxide, the land carbon reservoir and climate over the past millennium. *Nature Geoscience*, **8**: 383–387, https://dx.doi.org/10.1038/NGEO2422.

Bekker, A., Kaufman, A.J., Karhu, J.A., and Eriksson, K.A., 2005, Evidence for Paleoproterozoic cap carbonates in North America. *Precambrian Research*, **137**: 167–206, https://dx.doi.org/10.1016/j.precamres.2005.03.009.

Bekker, A., Karhu, J.A., and Kaufman, A.J., 2006, Carbon isotope record for the onset of the Lomagundi carbon isotope excursion in the Great Lakes area, North America. *Precambrian Research*, **148**: 145–180, https://dx.doi.org/10.1016/j.precamres.2006.03.008.

Bekker, A., Krapež, B., Müller, S.G., and Karhu, J.A., 2016, A short-term, post-Lomagundi positive C isotope excursion at *c.* 2.03 Ga recorded by the Wooly Dolomite, Western Australia. *Journal of the Geological Society*, **173**: 689–700, https://dx.doi.org/10.1144/jgs2015-152.

Bergström, S.M., Young, S.A., and Schmitz, B., 2010, Katian (Upper Ordovician) $\delta^{13}C$ chemostratigraphy and sequence stratigraphy in the United States and Baltoscandia: a regional comparison. *Palaeogeography, Palaeoclimatology, Palaeoecology*, **296**: 217–234, https://dx.doi.org/10.1016/j.palaeo.2010.02.035.

Bergström, S.M., Saltzman, M.R., Leslie, S.A., Ferretti, A., and Young, S.A., 2015, Trans-Atlantic application of the Baltic Middle and Upper Ordovician isotope zonation.. *The Estonian Journal of Earth Sciences*, **64**: 8–12, https://dx.doi.org/10.3176/earth.2015.02.

Bergström, S.M., Eriksson, M.E., Schmitz, B., Young, S.A., and Ahlberg, P., 2016, Upper Ordovician $\delta^{13}C_{org}$ chemostratigraphy, K-bentonite stratigraphy, and biostratigraphy in southern Scandinavia: a reappraisal. *Palaeogeography, Palaeoclimatology, Palaeoecology*, **454**: 175–188.

Berner, R.A., 1987, Models for carbon and sulfur cycles and atmospheric oxygen: application to Paleozoic history. *American Journal of Science*, **287**: 397–437, https://dx.doi.org/10.2475/ajs.287.3.177.

Berner, R.A., 1990, Atmospheric carbon dioxide levels over Phanerozoic time. *Science*, **249**: 1382–1386, https://dx.doi.org/10.1126/science.249.4975.1382.

Berner, R.A., 2004, The Phanerozoic Carbon Cycle: CO_2 and O_2. 150 pp. Oxford University Press.

Berner, R.A., 2006, GEOCARBSULF: a combined model for Phanerozoic atmospheric O_2 and CO_2. *Geochimica et Cosmochimica Acta*, **70**: 5653–5664, https://dx.doi.org/10.2475/05.2006.01.

Berner, R.A., 2009, Phanerozoic atmospheric oxygen: new results using the GEOCARBSULF model. *American Journal of Science*, **309**: 603–606, https://dx.doi.org/10.2475/07.2009.03.

Bond, D.P.G., Wignall, P.B., Wang, W., Izon, G., Jiang, Hs, Lai, Xl, et al., 2010, The mid-Capitanian (Middle Permian) mass extinction and carbon isotope record of South China. *Palaeogeography, Palaeoclimatology, Palaeoecology*, **292**: 282–294, https://dx.doi.org/10.1016/j.palaeo.2010.03.056.

Brand, U., 1982, The oxygen and carbon isotope composition of carboniferous fossil components: sea-water effects. *Sedimentology*, **29**: 139–147, https://dx.doi.org/10.1111/j.1365-3091.1982.tb01715.x.

Brasier, M.D., and Lindsay, J.F., 1998, A billion years of environmental stability and the emergence of eukaryotes: new data from northern Australia. *Geology*, **26**: 555–558, https://doi.org/10.1130/0091-7613(1998)026 < 0555:ABYOES > 2.3.CO;2.

Braun, M., 2018, High resolution chemostratigraphy and cyclostratigraphy of lower Silurian neritic carbonates from Anticosti Island, Quebec, Canada. *Unpublished M.Sc. thesis*. University of Ottawa, Ottawa, Canada, 114 pp.

Buggisch, W., and Joachimski, M.M., 2006, Carbon isotope stratigraphy of the Devonian of Central and Southern Europe. *Palaeogeography, Palaeoclimatology, Palaeoecology*, **240**: 68–88, https://dx.doi.org/10.1016/j.palaeo.2006.03.046.

Buggisch, W., and Mann, U., 2004, Carbon isotope stratigraphy of Lochkovian to Eifelian limestones from the Devonian of central and southern Europe. *The International Journal of Earth Sciences (Geologische Rundschau)*, **93**: 521–541, https://dx.doi.org/10.1007/s00531-004-0407-6.

Buggisch, W., Keller, M., and Lehnert, O., 2003, Carbon isotope record of Late Cambrian to Early Ordovician carbonates of the Argentine Precordillera. *Palaeogeography, Palaeoclimatology, Palaeoecology*, **195**: 357–373, https://dx.doi.org/10.1016/S0031-0182(03)00365-1.

Buggisch, W., Wang, Xd, Alekseev, A.S., and Joachimski, M.M., 2011, Carboniferous-Permian carbon isotope stratigraphy of successions from China (Yangtze platform), USA (Kansas) and Russia (Moscow Basin and Urals). *Palaeogeography, Palaeoclimatology, Palaeoecology*, **301**: 18–38, https://dx.doi.org/10.1016/j.palaeo.2010.12.015.

Buick, R., Des Marais, D., and Knoll, A.H., 1995, Stable isotopic compositions of carbonate from the Mesoproterozoic Bangemall Group, Northwestern Australia. *Chemical Geology*, **123**: 153–171, https://dx.doi.org/10.1016/0009-2541(95)00049-R.

Burgess, S.D., Bowring, S., and Shen, S.Z., 2014, High-precision timeline for Earth's most severe extinction. *Proceedings of the National Academy of Sciences of the United States of America*, **111**: 3316–3321, https://dx.doi.org/10.1073/pnas.1317692111.

Canfield, D.E., Ngombi-Pemba, L., Hammarlund, E.U., Bengston, S., Chaussidon, M., Gauthier-Lafaye, F., et al., 2013, Oxygen dynamics in the aftermath of the Great Oxidation of Earth's atmosphere. *Proceedings of the National Academy of Sciences of the United States of America*, **110**: 16736–16741, https://dx.doi.org/10.1073/pnas.1315570110.

Cao, C.Q., Cui, C., Chen, J., Summons, R.E., Shen, S.Z., and Zhang, H., 2018, A positive C-isotope excursion induced by sea-level fall in the middle Capitanian of South China. *Palaeogeography, Palaeoclimatology, Palaeoecology*, **505**: 305–316, https://dx.doi.org/10.1016/j.palaeo.2018.06.010.

Carpenter, S.J., and Lohmann, K.C., 1995, $\delta^{18}O$ and $\delta^{13}C$ values of modern brachiopod shells. *Geochimica et Cosmochimica Acta*, **59**: 3749–3764, https://dx.doi.org/10.1016/0016-7037(95)00291-7.

Caves, J.K., Jost, A.B., Lau, K.V., and Maher, K., 2016, Cenozoic carbon cycle imbalances and a variable weathering feedback. *Earth and Planetary Science Letters*, **450**: 152–163, https://dx.doi.org/10.1016/j.epsl.2016.06.035.

Chang, C., Hu, W.Z., Wang, X.L., Yu, H., Yang, A.H., Cao, J., et al., 2017, Carbon isotope stratigraphy of the lower to middle Cambrian on the eastern Yangtze Platform, South China. *Palaeogeography, Palaeoclimatology, Palaeoecology*, **479**: 90–101, https://dx.doi.org/10.1016/j.palaeo.2017.04.019.

Ciais, P., Sabine, C., Bala, G., Bopp, L., Brovkin, V., Canadell, J., et al., 2013, Carbon and other biogeochemical cycles. *In* Stocker, T.F., Qin, D., Plattner, G.K., Tignor, M., Allen, S.K., Boschung, J., Nauels, A., Xia, Y., Bex, V., and Midgley, P.M. (eds), *Climate Change 2013: The Physical Science Basis.* Contribution of Working Group I to the Fifth Assessment Report of the Intergovernmental Panel on Climate Change. Cambridge, United Kingdom: Cambridge University Press, pp. 465–570.

Cochran, J.K., Kallenberg, K., Landman, N.H., Harries, P.J., Weinreb, D., Turekian, K.K., et al., 2010, Effect of diagenesis on the Sr, O, and C isotope composition of Late Cretaceous mollusks from the Western Interior Seaway of North America. *American Journal of Science*, **310**: 69–88, https://doi.org/10.2475/02.2010.01.

Cody, R.D., Levy, R.H., Harwood, D.M., and Sadler, P.M., 2008, Thinking outside the zone: high-resolution quantitative diatom biochronology for the Antarctic Neogene. *Palaeogeography, Palaeoclimatology, Palaeoecology*, **260**: 92–121, https://dx.doi.org/10.1016/j.palaeo.2007.08.020.

Cooper, R.A., Sadler, P.M., Munnecke, A., and Crampton, J.S., 2014, Graptoloid evolutionary rates track Ordovician-Silurian global climate change. *Geological Magazine*, **151**: 349–364, https://dx.doi.org/10.1017/S0016756813000198.

Cox, G.M., Halverson, G.P., Stevenson, R.K., Vokaty, M., Poirier, A., Kunzmann, M., et al., 2016, Continental flood basalt weathering as a trigger for Neoproterozoic Snowball Earth. *Earth and Planetary Science Letters*, **446**: 89–99, https://dx.doi.org/10.1016/j.epsl.2016.04.016.

Craig, H., 1953, The geochemistry of the stable carbon isotopes. *Geochimica et Cosmochimica Acta*, **3**: 53–92, https://dx.doi.org/10.1016/0016-7037(53)90001-5.

Cramer, B.D., and Saltzman, M.R., 2005, Sequestration of ^{12}C in the deep ocean during the early Wenlock (Silurian) positive carbon isotope excursion. *Palaeogeography, Palaeoclimatology, Palaeoecology*, **219**: 333–349, https://dx.doi.org/10.1016/j.palaeo.2005.01.009.

Cramer, B.D., Saltzman, M.R., and Kleffner, M.A., 2006, Spatial and temporal variability in organic carbon burial during global positive carbon isotope excursions: new insight from high resolution $\delta^{13}C_{carb}$ stratigraphy from the type area of the Niagaran (Silurian) Provincial Series. *Stratigraphy*, **2**: 327–340.

Cramer, B.S., Toggweiler, J.R., Wright, J.D., Katz, M.E., and Miller, K.G., 2009, Ocean overturning since the Late Cretaceous: inferences from a new benthic foraminiferal compilation. *Paleoceanography*, **24**: PA4216, https://dx.doi.org/10.1029/2008PA001683.

Cramer, B.D., Loydell, D.K., Samtleben, C., Munnecke, A., Kaljo, D., Männik, P., et al., 2010a, Testing the limits of paleozoic chronostratigraphic correlation via high-resolution (<500 k.y.) integrated conodont, graptolite, and carbon isotope ($\delta^{13}C_{carb}$) biochemostratigraphy across the Llandovery-Wenlock (Silurian) boundary: is a unified Phanerozoic time scale achievable? *Geological Society of America Bulletin*, **122**: 1700–1716, https://dx.doi.org/10.1130/B26602.1.

Cramer, B.D., Kleffner, M.A., Brett, C.E., McLaughlin, P.I., Jeppsson, L., Munnecke, A., et al., 2010b, Paleobiogeography, high-resolution stratigraphy, and the future of paleozoic biostratigraphy: fine-scale diachroneity of the Wenlock (Silurian) conodont *Kockelella walliseri*. *Palaeogeography, Palaeoclimatology, Palaeoecology*, **294**: 232–241, https://dx.doi.org/10.1016/j.palaeo.2010.01.002.

Cramer, B.D., Brett, C.E., Melchin, M.J., Männik, P., Kleffner, M.A., McLaughlin, P.I., et al., 2011, Revised correlation of Silurian Provincial Series of North America with global and regional chronostratigraphic units and $\delta^{13}C_{carb}$ chemostratigraphy. *Lethaia*, **44**: 185–202, https://dx.doi.org/10.1111/j.1502-3931.2010.00234.x.

Cramer, B.D., Vandenbroucke, T.R.A., and Ludvigson, G.A., 2015, High-Resolution Event Stratigraphy (HiRES) and the quantification of stratigraphic uncertainty: Silurian examples of the quest for precision in stratigraphy. *Earth-Science Reviews*, **141**: 136–153, https://doi.org/10.1016/j.earscirev.2014.11.011.

Crampton, J.S., Cooper, R.A., Sadler, P.M., and Foote, M., 2016, Greenhouse-icehouse transition in the Late Ordovician marks a step change in extinction regime in the marine plankton. *Proceedings of the National Academy of Sciences of the United States of America*, **113**: 1498–1503, https://dx.doi.org/10.1073/pnas.1519092113.

Danielsen, E.M., Cramer, B.D., and Kleffner, M.A., 2019, Identification of a global sequence boundary within the upper Homerian (Silurian) Mulde Event: high-resolution chronostratigraphic correlation of the midcontinent United States with Sweden and the United Kingdom. *Geosphere*, **15**: 839–855, https://dx.doi.org/10.1130/GES01685.1.

Derry, L., 2010, On the significance of $\delta^{13}C$ correlations in ancient sediments. *Earth and Planetary Science Letters*, **296**: 497–501, https://dx.doi.org/10.1016/j.epsl.2010.05.035.

Derry, L.A., Kaufman, A.J., and Jacobsen, S.B., 1992, Sedimentary cycling and environmental change in the Late Proterozoic: evidence from stable and radiogenic isotopes. *Geochimica et Cosmochimica Acta*, **56**: 1317–1329, https://dx.doi.org/10.1016/0016-7037(92)90064-P.

Des Marais, D.J., Strauss, H., Summons, R.E., and Hayes, J.M., 1992, Carbon isotope evidence for stepwise oxidation of the Proterozoic environment. *Nature*, **359**: 604–609, https://dx.doi.org/10.1038/359605a0.

Diz, P., Jorissen, F.J., Reochart, G.J., Poulain, C., Dehairs, F., Leorri, E., et al., 2009, Interpretation of benthic foraminiferal stable isotopes in subtidal estuarine environments. *Biogeosciences*, **6**: 2549–2560, https://dx.doi.org/10.5194/bg-6-2549-2009.

Dunkley-Jones, T., Ridgwell, A., Lunt, D.J., Maslin, M.A., Schmidt, D. N., and Valdez, P.J., 2010, A Palaeogene perspective on climate sensitivity and methane hydrate instability. *Philosophical Transactions of the Royal Society, A*, **368**: 2395–2415, https://dx.doi.org/10.1098/rsta.2010.0053.

Edwards, C.T., and Saltzman, M.R., 2014, Carbon isotope ($\delta^{13}C_{carb}$) stratigraphy of the Lower-Middle Ordovician (Tremadocian-Darriwilian) in the Great Basin, western United States: implications for global correlation. *Palaeogeography, Palaeoclimatology, Palaeoecology*, **399**: 1–20, https://dx.doi.org/10.1016/j.palaeo.2014.02.005.

Emmanuel, L., and Renard, M., 1993, Carbonate geochemistry (Mn, $\delta^{13}C$, $\delta^{18}O$) of the Late Tithonian – Berriasian pelagic limestones of the Vocontian Trough (SE France). *Bulletin des Centres de Recherches Exploration—Production Elf-Aquitaine*, **17**: 205–221.

Falkowski, P., 2003, Biogeochemistry of primary production in the sea. *Treatise on Geochemistry*, **8**: 185–213, https://dx.doi.org/10.1016/B0-08-043751-6/08129-9.

Fike, D.A., Grotzinger, J.P., Pratt, L.M., and Summons, R.E., 2006, Oxidation of the Ediacaran Ocean. *Nature*, **444**: 744–747, https://dx.doi.org/10.1038/nature05345.

Frank, T.D., Kah, L.C., and Lyons, T.W., 2003, Changes in organic matter production and accumulation as a mechanism for isotopic evolution in the Mesoproterozoic ocean. *Geological Magazine*, **140**: 397–420, https://dx.doi.org/10.1017/S0016756803007830.

Frýda, J., and Manda, Š., 2013, A long-lasting steady period of isotopically heavy carbon in the late Silurian ocean: evolution of the $\delta^{13}C$ record and its significance for an integrated $\delta^{13}C$, graptolite and conodont stratigraphy. *Bulletin of Geosciences*, **88**: 463–482, https://dx.doi.org/10.3140/bull.geosci.1436.

Gale, A.S., Jenkyns, H.C., Kennedy, W.J., and Corfield, R.M., 1993, Chemostratigraphy versus biostratigraphy: data from around the Cenomanian-Turonian boundary. *Journal of the Geological Society*, **150**: 29–32, https://dx.doi.org/10.1144/gsjgs.150.1.0029.

Gale, A.S., Bown, P., Caron, M., Crampton, J., Crowhurst, S.J., Kennedy, W.J., et al., 2011, The uppermost Middle and Upper Albian succession at the Col de Palluel, Hautes-Alpes, France: an integrated study (ammonites, inoceramid bivalves, planktonic *Foraminifera*, nannofossils, geochemistry, stable oxygen and carbon isotopes, cyclostratigraphy). *Cretaceous Research*, **32**: 59–130.

Galfetti, T., Bucher, H., Brayard, A., Hochuli, P.A., Weissert, H., Guodun, K., et al., 2007, Late Early Triassic climate change: insights from carbonate carbon isotopes, sedimentary evolution and ammonoid paleobiogeography. *Palaeogeography, Palaeoclimatology, Palaeoecology*, **243**: 394–411, https://dx.doi.org/10.1016/j.palaeo.2006.08.014.

Garcia, T.I., 2008, *The Valanginian Oceanic Anoxic Event: A Comparison Study Between the Austroalpine, the Southern Alps and the Lusitanian Basin*. 185 pp. ETH Swiss Federal Institute of Technology.

Ghienne, J.F., Desrochers, A., Vandenbroucke, T.R.A., Achab, A., Asselin, E., Dabard, M.P., et al., 2014, A Cenozoic-style scenario for the end-Ordovician glaciation. *Nature Communications*, **5**: 4485, https://dx.doi.org/10.1038/ncomms5485.

Gischler, E., Swart, P.K., and Lomando, A.J., 2009, Stable isotopes of carbon and oxygen in modern sediments of carbonate platforms, barrier reefs, atolls, and ramps: patterns and implications. *International Association of Sedimentologists Special Publication*, **41**: 61–74, https://dx.doi.org/10.1002/9781444312065.ch5.

Goldman, D., Sadler, P.M., and Leslie, S.A., 2020, The Ordovician Period. *In* Gradstein, F.M., Ogg, J.G., Schmitz, M.D., and Ogg, G.M. (eds), *The Geologic Time Scale 2020*. Elsevier Publ., **Vol. 2**.

Grabowski, J., Bakhmutov, V., Kdýr, S., Krobicki, M., Pruner, P., Reháková, D., et al., 2019, Integrated stratigraphy and palaeoenvironmental interpretation of the Upper Kimmeridgian to Lower Berriasian pelagic sequences of the Velykyi Kamianets section (Pieniny Klippen Belt, Ukraine). *Palaeogeography, Palaeoclimatology, Palaeoecology*, **532**: 109216, https://dx.doi.org/10.1016/j.palaeo.2019.05.038.

Grossman, E.L., Mii, H.S., and Yancey, T.E., 1991, Stable isotope stratigraphy of brachiopods from Pennsylvanian shales in Texas. *Geological Society of America Bulletin*, **103**: 953–965, https://dx.doi.org/10.1130/0016-7606(1991)103 < 0953:SISOBF > 2.3.CO;2.

Grossman, E.L., Yancey, T.E., Jones, T.E., Bruckschen, P., Chuvashov, B., Mazzullo, S.J., et al., 2008, Glaciation, aridification, and carbon sequestration in the Permo-Carboniferous: the isotopic record from low-latitudes. *Palaeogeography, Palaeoclimatology, Palaeoecology*, **268**: 222–233, https://dx.doi.org/10.1016/j.palaeo.2008.03.053.

Grossman, E.L., and Joachimski, M.M., 2020, Oxygen isotope stratigraphy. *In* Gradstein, F.M., Ogg, J.G., Schmitz, M.D., and Ogg, G.M. (eds), *The Geologic Time Scale 2020*. Elsevier Publ., **Vol. 1**.

Grötsch, J., Billing, I., and Vahrenkamp, V., 1998, Carbon-isotope stratigraphy in shallow-water carbonates: implications for Cretaceous black-shale deposition. *Sedimentology*, **45**: 623–634, https://dx.doi.org/10.1046/j.1365-3091.1998.00158.x.

Gruber, N., Keeling, C.D., Bacastow, R.B., Guenther, P.R., Lueker, T.J., Wahlen, M., et al., 1999, Spatio-temporal patterns of carbon-13 in the global surface oceans and the oceanic Suess effect. *Global Biogeochemical Cycles*, **13**: 307–335, https://dx.doi.org/10.1029/1999GB900019.

Guo, H., Du, Ys, Kah, L.C., Huang, Jh, Hu, C.Y., Huang, H., et al., 2013, *Isotopic composition of organic and inorganic carbon from the Mesoproterozoic Jixian Group, North China: implications for biological and oceanic evolution, Precambrian Research*, 224. (pp. 169–183)., https://dx.doi.org/10.1016/j.precamres.2012.09.023.

Halverson, G.P., 2006, Chapter 8: A Neoproterozoic chronology. *In* Xiao, S., and Kaufman, A.J. (eds), *Neoproterozoic Geobiology and Paleobiology*. Springer, 231–271, https://dx.doi.org/10.1007/1-4020-5202-2.

Halverson, G.P., Hoffman, P.F., Schrag, D.P., Maloof, A.C., and Rice, H.N., 2005, Toward a Neoproterozoic composite carbon-isotope record. *Geological Society of America Bulletin*, **117**: 1181–1207, https://dx.doi.org/10.1130/B25630.1.

Halverson, G.P., Porter, S.M., and Gibson, T.M., 2018, Dating the late Proterozoic stratigraphic record. *Emerging Topics in Life Science*, **2**: 137–147.

Halverson, G., Porter, S., and Shields, G.A., 2020, The Tonian and Cryogenian Periods.

Hay, C.C., Creveling, J.R., Hagen, C.J., Maloof, A.C., and Huybers, P., 2019, A library of early Cambrian chemostratigraphic correlations from a reproducible algorithm. *Geology*, **47**: 457–460, https://dx.doi.org/10.1130/G46019.1.

Hayes, J.M., Strauss, H., and Kaufman, A.J., 1999, The abundance of ^{13}C in marine organic matter and isotopic fractionation in the global biogeochemical cycle of carbon during the past 800Ma. *Chemical Geology*, **161**: 103–125, https://dx.doi.org/10.1016/S0009-2541(99)00083-2.

Herrle, J.O., Kossler, P., Friedrich, O., Erlenkeuser, H., and Hemleben, C., 2004, High-resolution carbon isotope records of the Aptian to Lower Albian from SE France and the Mazagan Plateau (DSDP Site 545): a stratigraphic tool for paleoceanographic and paleobiologic reconstruction. *Earth and Planetary Science Letters*, **218**: 149–161.

Herrle, J.O., Schroder-Adams, C.J., Davis, W., Pugh, A.T., Galloway, J.M., and Fath, J., 2015, Mid-Cretaceous High Arctic stratigraphy, climate, and Oceanic Anoxic Events. *Geology*, **43**: 403–406.

Hesselbo, S.P., Jenkyns, H.C., Duarte, L.V., and Oliveira, L.C.V., 2007, Carbon-isotope record of the Early Jurassic (Toarcian) Oceanic Anoxic Event from fossil wood and marine carbonate (Lusitanian Basin, Portugal). *Earth and Planetary Science Letters*, **253**: 455–470, https://dx.doi.org/10.1016/j.epsl.2006.11.009.

Hillbun, K., Playton, T.E., Tohver, E., Ratcliffe, K., Trinajstic, K., Roelofs, B., et al., 2015, Upper Kellwasser carbon isotope excursion pre-dates the F-F boundary in the Upper Devonian Lennard Shelf carbonate system, Canning Basin, Western Australia. *Palaeogeography, Palaeoclimatology, Palaeoecology*, **438**: 180–190, https://dx.doi.org/10.1016/j.palaeo.2015.07.035.

Hodgskiss, M.S.W., Dagnaud, O.M.J., Frost, J.L., Halverson, G.P., Schmitz, M.D., Swanson-Hysell, N.L., et al., 2019, New insights on the Orosirian carbon cycle, early Cyanobacteria, and the assembly of Laurentia from the Paleoproterozoic Belcher Group. *Earth and Planetary Science Letters*, **520**: 141–152, https://dx.doi.org/10.1016/j.epsl.2019.05.023.

Hoffman, P.F., Kaufman, A.J., Halverson, G.P., and Schrag, D.P., 1998, A Neoproterozoic snowball earth. *Science*, **281**: 1342–1346, https://dx.doi.org/10.1126/science.281.5381.1342.

Holland, H.D., 2006, The oxygenation of the atmosphere and oceans. *Philosophical Transactions of the Royal Society, B*, **361**: 903–915, https://dx.doi.org/10.1098/rstb.2006.1838.

Holmden, C., Creaser, R.A., Muehlenbachs, K., Leslie, S.A., and Bergström, S.M., 1998, Isotopic evidence for geochemical decoupling between ancient epeiric seas and bordering oceans: implications for secular curves. *Geology*, **26**: 567–570, https://dx.doi.org/10.1130/0097-7613(1998)026 < 0567:IEFGDB > 2.3.CO;2.

Holmden, C., Braun, W.K., Patterson, W.P., Eglington, B.M., Prokopiuk, T.C., and Whittaker, S., 2006, Carbon isotope chemostratigraphy of Frasnian Sequences in Western Canada. In: *Summary of Investigations 2006, Volume 1, Saskatchewan Geological Survey, Saskatchewan Industry Resources, Miscellaneous Report 2006-4.1, CD-ROM, Paper A-8.* 6pp.

Hotinski, R.M., Kump, L.R., and Arthur, M.A., 2004, The effectiveness of the Paleoproterozoic biological pump: a $\delta^{13}C$ gradient from platform carbonates of the Pethei Group (Great Slave Lake Supergroup, NWT). *Geological Society of America Bulletin*, **116**: 539–554, https://dx.doi.org/10.1130/B25272.1.

Huang, C., 2018, Chapter 2: Astronomical time scale for the Mesozoic. *Stratigraphy Timescales*, **3**: 81–150, https://dx.doi.org/10.1016/bs.sats.2018.08.005.

Huber, B.T., MacLeod, K.G., Watkins, D.K., and Coffin, M.F., 2018, The rise and fall of the Cretaceous Hot Greenhouse climate. *Global and Planetary Change*, **167**: 1–23, https://dx.doi.org/10.1016/j.gloplacha.2018.04.004.

Hughes, H.E., and Ray, D.C., 2016, The carbon isotope and sequence stratigraphic record of the Sheinwoodian and lower Homerian stages (Silurian) of the Midland Platform, UK. *Palaeogeography, Palaeoclimatology, Palaeoecology*, **445**: 97–114, https://dx.doi.org/10.1016/j.palaeo.2015.12.022.

Immenhauser, A., Kenter, J.A.M., Ganssen, G., Bahamonde, J.R., Van Vliet, A., and Saher, M.H., 2002, Origin and significance of isotope shifts in Pennsylvanian carbonates (Asturias, northwest Spain). *Journal of Sedimentary Research*, **72**: 82–94, https://dx.doi.org/10.1306/051701720082.

Isozaki, Y., Kawahata, H., and Ota, A., 2007, A unique carbon isotope record across the Guadalupian-Lopingian (Middle Upper Permian) boundary in mid-oceanic paleo-atoll carbonates: the high-productivity "Kamura Event" and its collapse in Panthalassa. *Global and Planetary Change*, **55**: 21–38, https://dx.doi.org/10.1016/j.gloplacha.2006.06.006.

Jarvis, I., Murphy, A.M., and Gale, A.S., 2001, Geochemistry of pelagic and hemipelagic carbonates: criteria for identifying systems tracts and sea-level change. *Journal of the Geological Society*, **158**: 685–696.

Jarvis, I., Gale, A.S., Jenkyns, H.C., and Pearce, M.A., 2006, Secular variation in Late Cretaceous carbon isotopes: a new $\delta^{13}C$ carbonate reference curve for the Cenomanian-Campanian (99.6-70.6Ma). *Geological Magazine*, **143**: 561–608.

Jenkyns, H.C., Gale, A.S., and Corfield, R.M., 1994, Carbon- and oxygen-isotope stratigraphy of the English Chalk and Italian Scaglia and its palaeoclimatic significance. *Geological Magazine*, **131**: 1–34.

Jeppsson, L., 1987, Lithological and conodont distributional evidence for episodes of anomalous oceanic conditions during the Silurian. *In* Aldridge, R.J. (ed), *Paleobiology of Conodonts*. Ellis Horwood, Chichester, UK, 129–145.

Jeppsson, L., Talent, J.A., Mawson, R., Simpson, A.J., Andrew, A.S., Calner, M., et al., 2007, High-resolution Late Silurian correlations between Gotland, Sweden, and the Broken River region, NE Australia: lithologies, conodonts and isotopes. *Palaeogeography, Palaeoclimatology, Palaeoecology*, **245**: 115–137, https://dx.doi.org/10.1016/j.palaeo.2006.02.032.

Jeppsson, L., Talent, J.A., Mawson, R., Andrew, A., Corradini, C., Simpson, A.J., et al., 2012, Late Ludfordian correlations and the Lau Event. *In* Talent, J.A. (ed), *Earth and Life*. Springer, 653–675, https://dx.doi.org/10.1007/978-90-481-3428-1_21.

Jin, Y.G., Wang, Y., Wang, W., Shang, Q.H., Cao, C.Q., and Erwin, D. H., 2000, Pattern of marine mass extinction near the Permian-Triassic Boundary in South China. *Science*, **289**: 432–436, https://dx.doi.org/10.1126/science.289.5478.432.

Joachimski, M.M., and Buggisch, W., 1993, Anoxic events in the Late Frasnian – causes of the Frasnian-Famennian faunal crisis. *Geology*, **21**: 675–678, https://dx.doi.org/10.1130/0091-7613(1993)021 < 0675:AEITLF > 2.3.CO;s.

Kah, L.C., Sherman, A.G., Narbonne, G.M., Knoll, A.H., and Kaufman, A.J., 1999, $\delta^{13}C$ stratigraphy of the Proterozoic Bylot Supergroup, Baffin Island, Canada: implications for regional lithostratigraphic correlations. *Canadian Journal of Earth Sciences*, **36**: 313–332, https://dx.doi.org/10.1139/e98-100.

Kah, L.C., Bartley, J.K., and Teal, D.A., 2012, Chemostratigraphy of the Late Mesoproterozoic Atar Group, Taoudeni Basin, Mauritania: muted isotopic variability, facies correlation, and global isotopic trends. *Precambrian Research*, **200–203**: 82–103, https://dx.doi.org/10.1016/j.precamres.2012.01.011.

Kaljo, D., Martma, T., and Saadre, T., 2007, Post-Hunnebergian Ordovician carbon isotope trend in Baltoscandia, its environmental implications and some similarities with that of Nevada. *Palaeogeography, Palaeoclimatology, Palaeoecology*, **245**: 138–155, https://dx.doi.org/10.1016/j.palaeo.2006.02.020.

Kaljo, D., Martma, T., Grytsenko, V., Brazauskas, A., and Kaminskas, D., 2012, Přidoli carbon isotope trend and upper Silurian to lowermost Devonian chemostratigraphy based on sections in Podolia (Ukraine) and the East Baltic area. *The Estonian*

Journal of Earth Sciences, **61**: 162–180, https://dx.doi.org/10.3176/earth.2012.3.03.

Kaljo, D., Einasto, R., Martma, T., Märss, T., Nestor, V., and Viira, V., 2015, A bio-chemostratigraphical test of the synchronicity of biozones in the upper Silurian of Estonia and Latvia with some implications for practical stratigraphy. *The Estonian Journal of Earth Sciences*, **64**: 267–283, https://dx.doi.org/10.3176/earth.2015.33.

Katz, M.E., Wright, J.D., Katz, D.R., Miller, K.G., Pak, D.K., Shackleton, N.J., et al., 2003, Earth Cenozoic benthic foraminiferal isotopes: species reliability and interspecies correction factors. *Paleoceanography*, **18**: 1024, https://dx.doi.org/10.1029/2002PA000798.

Katz, M.E., Wright, J.D., Miller, K.G., Cramer, B.S., Fennel, K., and Falkowski, P.G., 2005, Biological overprint of the geological carbon cycle. *Marine Geology*, **217**: 323–338, https://dx.doi.org/10.1016/j.margeo.2004.08.005.

Kaufman, A.J., Hayes, J.M., Knoll, A.H., and Germs, G.J.B., 1991, Isotopic compositions of carbonate and organic carbon from Upper Proterozoic succession in Namibia: stratigraphic variation and the effects of diagenesis and metamorphism. *Precambrian Research*, **49**: 301–327, https://dx.doi.org/10.1016/0301-9268(91)90039-D.

Keeling, C.D., 1979, The Suess effect: ^{13}Carbon-^{14}Carbon interrelations. *Environment International*, **2**: 229–300.

Keeling, C.D., Mook, W.G., and Tans, P.P., 1979, Recent trends in the $^{13}C/^{12}C$ ratio of atmospheric carbon dioxide. *Nature*, **277**: 121–123, https://dx.doi.org/10.1038/277121a0.

Keeling, R.F., Graven, H.D., Welp, L.R., Resplandy, L., Bi, J., Piper, S.C., et al., 2017, Atmospheric evidence for a global secular increase in carbon isotopic discrimination of land photosynthesis. *Proceedings of the National Academy of Sciences of the United States of America*, **114**: 10361–10366, https://dx.doi.org/10.1073/pnas.1619240114.

Kiehl, J.T., and Shields, C.A., 2005, Climate simulations of the latest Permian: implications for mass extinction. *Geology*, **33**: 757–760, https://dx.doi.org/10.1130/G21654.1.

Knauth, L.P., and Kennedy, M.J., 2009, The late Precambrian greening of the Earth. *Nature*, **460**: 728–732, https://dx.doi.org/10.1038/nature08213.

Knoll, A.H., Hayes, J.M., Kaufman, A.J., Swett, K., and Lambert, I.B., 1982, Secular variation in carbon isotope ratios from Upper Proterozoic successions in Svalbard and East Greenland. *Nature*, **321**: 832–838, https://dx.doi.org/10.1038/321832a0.

Knoll, A.H., Kaufman, A.J., and Semikhatov, M.A., 1995, The carbon-isotopic composition of Proterozoic carbonate: Riphean successions from northwestern Siberia (Anabar Massif, Turukhansk Uplift). *American Journal of Science*, **295**: 823–850, https://dx.doi.org/10.2475/ajs.295.7.823.

Korte, C., Thibault, N., Ullmann, C.V., Clemence, M.E., Mette, W., Olsen, T.K., et al., 2017, Brachiopod biogeochemistry and isotope stratigraphy from the Rhaetian Eiberg section in Austria: potentials and limitations. *Neues Jahrbuch für Geologie und Paläontologie, Abhandlungen*, **284**: 117–138, https://dx.doi.org/10.1127/njgpa/2017/0651.

Kroopnick, P.M., 1985, The distribution of ^{13}C of ΣCO_2 in the world oceans. *Deep Sea Research*, **32**: 57–84, https://dx.doi.org/10.1016/0198-0149(85)90017-2.

Kump, L.R., and Arthur, M.A., 1999, Interpreting carbon-isotope excursions: carbonates and organic matter. *Chemical Geology*, **161**: 181–198, https://dx.doi.org/10.1016/S0009-2541(99)00086-8.

Kump, L.R., and Garrels, R.M., 1986, Modeling atmospheric O_2 in the global sedimentary redox cycle. *American Journal of Science*, **286**: 337–360, https://dx.doi.org/10.2475/ajs.286.5.337.

Kump, L.R., Junium, C., Arthur, M.A., Brasier, A., Fallick, A., Melezhik, V., et al., 2011, Isotopic evidence for massive oxidation of organic matter following the great oxidation event. *Science*, **334**: 1694–1696, https://dx.doi.org/10.1126/science.1213999.

Kuznetsov, A.B., Semikhatov, M.A., Maslov, A.V., Gorokhov, I.M., Prasolov, E.M., Krupenin, M.T., et al., 2006, New data on Sr- and C-Isotopic chemostratigraphy of the Upper Riphean type section (southern Urals). *Stratigraphy and Geological Correlation*, **14**: 602–628, https://dx.doi.org/10.1134/S0869593806060025.

Laskar, J., 2020, Astrochronology. *In* Gradstein, F.M., Ogg, J.G., Schmitz, M.D., and Ogg, G.M. (eds), *The Geologic Time Scale 2020*. Elsevier Publ., **Vol. 1**.

Li, J., Hu, X.M., Zhao, K.D., Cai, Y.F., and Sun, T., 2016, Paleoceanographic evolution and chronostratigraphy of the Aptian Oceanic Anoxic Event 1a (OAE1a) to oceanic red bed 1 (ORB1) in the Gorgo a Cerbara section (central Italy). *Cretaceous Research*, **66**: 115–128.

Lin, L., Khider, D., Lisiecki, L.E., and Lawrence, C.E., 2014, Probabilistic sequence alignment of stratigraphic records. *Paleoceanography*, **29**: 976–989, https://dx.doi.org/10.1002/2014PA002713.

Lindsay, J.F., and Brasier, M.D., 2002, Did global tectonics drive early biosphere evolution? Carbon isotope record from 2.6 to 1.9 Ga carbonates of Western Australian basins. *Precambrian Research*, **114**: 1–34, https://dx.doi.org/10.1016/S0301-9268(01)00219-4.

Lini, A., 1994, *Early Cretaceous Carbon Isotope Stratigraphy of the Maiolica Formation, Southern Alps (Northern Italy and Southern Switzerland) Stratigraphic and Paleoenvironmental Significance*. ETH Swiss Federal Institute of Technology, Zürich.

Linnert, C., Robinson, S.A., Lees, J.A., Perez-Rodriguez, I., Jenkyns, H. C., Petrizzo, M.R., et al., 2018, Did Late Cretaceous cooling trigger the Campanian-Maastrichtian Boundary Event? *Newsletters on Stratigraphy*, **51**: 145–166.

Lisiecki, L.E., and Herbert, T.D., 2007, Automated composite depth scale construction and estimates of sediment core extension. *Paleoceanography*, **22**: PA4213, https://dx.doi.org/10.1029/2006PA001401.

Lisiecki, L.E., and Lisiecki, P.A., 2002, Application of dynamic programming to the correlation of paleoclimate records. *Paleoceanography*, **17** (D4), 1049, https://dx.doi.org/10.1029/2001PA000733.

Locklair, R.E., and Sageman, B.B., 2008, Cyclostratigraphy of the Upper Cretaceous Niobrara Formation, Western Interior, U.S.A.: a Coniacian-Santonian orbital time scale. *Earth and Planetary Science Letters*, **269**: 540–553.

Lohmann, K.C., 1988, Geochemical patters of meteoric diagenetic systems and their application to studies of paleokarst. *In* James, N.P., and Choquette, P.W. (eds), *Paleokarst*. Springer-Verlag, Berlin, pp. 58–80.

Louis-Schmid, B., 2006, Feedback mechanisms between carbon cycling, climate and oceanography: a combined geochemical, sedimentological and modeling approach. *Ph.D. doctoral thesis*. ETH Swiss Federal Institute of Technology, Zürich, 132pp. https://doi.org/10.3929/ethz-a-005358592

Louis-Schmid, B., Rais, P., Bernasconi, S.M., Pellenard, P., Collin, P.Y., and Weissert, H., 2007, Detailed record of the mid-Oxfordian (Late Jurassic) positive carbon-isotope excursion in two hemipelagic sections (France and Switzerland): a plate tectonic trigger? *Palaeogeography, Palaeoclimatology, Palaeoecology*, **248**: 459–472, https://dx.doi.org/10.1016/j.palaeo.2007.01.001.

Luo, Gm, Junium, C.K., Kump, L.R., Huang, Jh, Li, C., Feng, Ql, et al., 2014, Shallow stratification prevailed for ~1700 to ~1300Ma ocean: evidence from organic carbon isotope in the North China Craton. *Earth and Planetary Science Letters*, **400**: 219–232, https://dx.doi.org/10.1016/j.epsl.2014.05.020.

Lynch-Stieglitz, J., 2003, Tracers of past ocean circulation. *Treatise on Geochemistry*, **6**: 433–451, https://dx.doi.org/10.1016/B0-08-043751-6/06117-X.

Lyu, Z.Y., Zhang, L., Algeo, T.J., Zhao, L.S., Chen, Z.Q., Li, C., et al., 2019, Global-ocean circulation changes during the Smithian-Spathian transition inferred from carbon-sulfur cycle records. *Earth-Science Reviews*, **195**: 114–132, https://dx.doi.org/10.1016/j.earscirev.2019.01.010.

Ma, X., and Day, J.E., 2003, Revision of selected North American and Eurasian Late Devonian (Frasnian) species of *Cryptospirifer* and *Regelia* (Brachiopoda). *Journal of Paleontology*, **77**: 267–292, https://dx.doi.org/10.1666/0022-3360(2003)007 < 0267:ROSNAA > 2.0.CO;2.

Ma, C., Meyers, S.R., and Sageman, B.B., 2017, Theory of chaotic orbital variations confirmed by Cretaceous geological evidence. *Nature*, **542**: 468–470.

Macdonald, F.A., Schmitz, M.D., Crowley, J.L., Roots, C.F., Jones, D.S., Maloof, A.C., et al., 2010, Calibrating the Cryogenian. *Science*, **327**: 1241–1243, https://dx.doi.org/10.1126/science.1183325.

Maloof, A.C., Schrag, D.P., Crowley, J.L., and Bowring, S.A., 2005, An expanded record of Early Cambrian carbon cycling from the Anti-Atlas Margin, Morocco. *Canadian Journal of Earth Sciences*, **42**: 2195–2216, https://dx.doi.org/10.1139/E05-062.

Maloof, A.C., Ramezani, J., Bowring, S.A., Fike, D.A., Porter, S.M., and Mazouad, M., 2010, Constraints on early Cambrian carbon cycling from the duration of the Nemakit-Daldynian-Tommotian boundary $\delta^{13}C$ shift, Morocco. *Geology*, **38**: 623–626, https://dx.doi.org/10.1130/G30726.1.

Männik, P., 2007, Some comments on the Telychian-Early Sheinwoodian conodont faunas, event and stratigraphy. *Acta Palaeontologica Sinica*, **46**: 305–310.

Marshall, J.D., 1992, Climatic and oceanographic isotopic signals from the carbonate rock record and their preservation. *Geological Magazine*, **129**: 143–160, https://dx.doi.org/10.1017/S0016756800008244.

Marshall, C., Thomas, A.T., Boomer, I., and Ray, D.C., 2012, High resolution $\delta^{13}C$ stratigraphy of the Homerian (Wenlock) of the English Midlands and Wenlock Edge. *Bulletin of Geosciences*, **87**: 669–679, https://dx.doi.org/10.3140/bull.geosci.1306.

Martin, A.P., Condon, D.J., Prave, A.R., and Lepland, A., 2013, A review of temporal constraints for the Palaeoproterozoic large, positive carbonate carbon isotope excursion (the Lomagundi-Jatuli Event). *Earth-Science Reviews*, **127**: 242–261, https://dx.doi.org/10.1016/j.earscirev.2013.10.006.

Martinez, M., Kotov, S., De Vleeschouwer, D., Pas, D., and Pälike, H., 2016, Testing the impact of stratigraphic uncertainty on spectral analyses of sedimentary series. *Climate of the Past*, **12**: 1765–1783, https://dx.doi.org/10.5194/cp-12-1765-2016.

Maslin, M.A., and Thomas, E., 2003, Balancing the deglacial global carbon budget: the hydrate factor. *Quaternary Science Reviews*, **22**: 1729–1736, https://dx.doi.org/10.1016/S0277-3791(03)00135-5.

Mazza, M., Furin, S., Spotl, C., and Rigo, M., 2010, Generic turnovers of Carnian/Norian conodonts: climatic control or competition? *Palaeogeography, Palaeoclimatology, Palaeoecology*, **290**: 120–137, https://dx.doi.org/10.1016/j.palaeo.2009.07.006.

McAdams, N.E.B., Bancroft, A.M., Cramer, B.D., and Witzke, B.J., 2017, Integrated carbon isotope and conodont biochemostratigraphy of the Silurian (Aeronian-Telychian) of the East-Central Iowa Basin, Iowa, USA. *Newsletters on Stratigraphy*, **50**: 391–416, https://dx.doi.org/10.1127/nos/2017/0375.

McAdams, N.E.B., Cramer, B.D., Bancroft, A.M., Melchin, M.J., Devera, J.A., and Day, J.E., 2019, Integrated $\delta^{13}C_{carb}$, conodont, and graptolite biochemostratigraphy of the Silurian from the Illinois Basin and stratigraphic revision of the Bainbridge Group. *Geological Society of America Bulletin*, **131**: 335–352, https://dx.doi.org/10.1130/B32033.1.

McCelland, H.L.O., Bruggeman, J., Hermoso, M., and Rickaby, R.E.M., 2017, The origin of carbon isotope vital effects in coccolith calcite. *Nature Communications*, **8**: 14511, https://dx.doi.org/10.1038/ncomms14511.

Mei, Sl, and Henderson, C.M., 2001, Evolution of Permian conodont provincialism and its significance in global correlation and paleoclimate implications. *Palaeogeography, Palaeoclimatology, Palaeoecology*, **170**: 237–260, https://dx.doi.org/10.1016/S0031-0182(01)00258-9.

Melezhik, V.A., Fallick, A.E., Medvedev, P.V., and Makarikhin, V.V., 1999, Extreme $^{13}C_{carb}$ enrichment in ca. 2.0 Ga magnesite-stromatolite-dolomite-'red beds' association in a global context: a case for the world-wide signal enhanced by a local environment. *Earth-Science Reviews*, **48**: 71–120, https://dx.doi.org/10.1016/S0012-8252(99)00044-6.

Mercuzot, M., Pellenard, P., Durlet, C., Bougeault, C., Meister, C., Dommergues, J.L., et al., 2020, Carbon-isotope events during the Pliensbachian (Lower Jurassic) on the African and European margins of the NW Tethyan Realm. *Newsletters on Stratigraphy*, **53**: 41–69, https://dx.doi.org/10.1127/nos/2019/0502.

Meyer, K.M., Ridgwell, A., and Payne, J.L., 2016, The influence of the biological pump on ocean chemistry: implications for long-term trends in marine redox chemistry, the global carbon cycle, and the evolution of marine animal ecosystems. *Geobiology*, **14**: 207–219, https://dx.doi.org/10.1111/gbi.12176.

Meyers, S.R., and Sageman, B.B., 2007, Quantification of deep-time orbital forcing by average spectral misfit. *American Journal of Science*, **307**: 773–792, https://dx.doi.org/10.2475/05.2007.01.

Mii, H.S., Grossman, E.L., and Yancey, T.E., 1999, Carboniferous isotope stratigraphies of North America: implications for Carboniferous paleoceanography and Mississippian glaciation. *Geological Society of America Bulletin*, **111**: 960–973, https://dx.doi.org/10.1130/0016-7606(1999)111 < 0960:CISONA > 2.3.CO;2.

Miller, J.F., Ripperdan, R.L., Loch, J.D., Freeman, R.L., Evans, K.R., Taylor, J.F., et al., 2015, Proposed GSSP for the base of Cambrian Stage 10 at the lowest occurrence of *Eoconodontus notchpeakensis* in the House Range, Utah, USA. *Annales de Paléontologie*, **101**: 199–211, https://dx.doi.org/10.1016/j.annpal.2015.04.008.

Mitchell, S.F., Paul, C.R.C., and Gale, A.S., 1996, Carbon isotopes and sequence stratigraphy. *In* Howell, J.A., and Aitken, J.F. (eds), *High*

Resolution Sequence Stratigraphy: Innovations and Applications. Geological Society of London Special Publication. The Geological Society, Bath, pp. 11–24.

Mutti, M., John, C.M., and Kroech, A., 2006, Chemostratigraphy in Miocene heterozoan carbonate settings: applications, limitations, and perspectives. *Geological Society, London, Special Publications*, **255**: 307–322, https://dx.doi.org/10.1144/GSL.SP.2006.255.01.18.

Muttoni, G., Kent, D.V., Olsen, P.E., Di Stefano, P., Lowrie, W., Bernasconi, S.M., et al., 2004, Tethyan magnetostratigraphy from Pizzo Mondello (Sicily) and correlation to the Late Triassic Newark astrochronological polarity time scale. *Geological Society of America Bulletin*, **116**: 1043–1058, https://dx.doi.org/10.1130/B25326.1.

Muttoni, G., Mazza, M., Mosher, D., Katz, M.E., Kent, D.V., and Balini, M., 2014, A Middle-Late Triassic (Ladinian-Rhaetian) carbon and oxygen isotope record from the Tethyan Ocean. *Palaeogeography, Palaeoclimatology, Palaeoecology*, **399**: 246–259, https://dx.doi.org/10.1016/j.palaeo.2014.01.018.

O'Dogherty, L., Sandoval, J., Bartolini, A., Bruchez, S., Bill, M., and Guex, J., 2006, Carbon-isotope stratigraphy and ammonite faunal turnover for the Middle Jurassic in the Southern Iberian palaeomargin. *Palaeogeography, Palaeoclimatology, Palaeoecology*, **239**: 311–333, https://dx.doi.org/10.1016/j.palaeo.2006.01.018.

Oliveira, L.C.V., Rodriguez, R., Duarte, L.V., and Lemos, V.B., 2006, Avaliação do potencial gerador de petróleo e interpretação paleoambiental com base em biomarcadores e isótopos estáveis de carbono da seção Pliensbaquiano – Toarciano inferior (Jurássico Inferior) da região de Peniche (Bacia Lusitânica, Portugal). *Boletim de Geociencias - Petrobras*, **14**: 207–234.

Padden, M., Weissert, H., Funk, H., Schneider, S., and Gansner, C., 2002, Late Jurassic lithological evolution and carbon-isotope stratigraphy of the western Tethys. *Eclogae Geologicae Helvetiae*, **95**: 333–346, https://dx.doi.org/10.5169/seals-168964.

Panchuk, K.M., Holmden, C., and Kump, L.R., 2005, Sensitivity of the epeiric sea carbon isotope record to local-scale carbon cycle processes: tales from the Mohawkian sea. *Palaeogeography, Palaeoclimatology, Palaeoecology*, **228**: 320–337, https://dx.doi.org/10.1016/j.palaeo.2005.06.019.

Patterson, W.P., and Walter, L.M., 1994, Depletion of ^{13}C in seawater ΣCO_2 on modern carbonate platforms: significance for the carbon isotope record of carbonates. *Geology*, **22**: 885–888, https://doi.org/10.1130/0091-7613(1994)022%3C0885:DOCISC%3E2.3.CO;2.

Paul, C.R.C., Mitchell, S.F., Marshall, J.D., Leary, P.N., Gale, A.S., Duane, A.M., et al., 1994, Palaeoceanographic events in the Middle Cenomanian of Northwest Europe. *Cretaceous Research*, **15**: 707–738.

Paul, C.R.C., Lamolda, M.A., Mitchell, S.F., Vaziri, M.R., Gorostidi, A., and Marshall, J.D., 1999, The Cenomanian-Turonian boundary at Eastbourne (Sussex, UK): a proposed European reference section. *Palaeogeography, Palaeoclimatology, Palaeoecology*, **150**: 83–121.

Payne, J.L., Lehrmann, D.J., Wei, J., Orchard, M.J., Schrag, D.P., and Knoll, A.H., 2004, Large perturbations of the carbon cycle during recovery from the end-Permian extinction. *Science*, **305**: 506–509, https://dx.doi.org/10.1126/science.1097023.

Pellenard, P., Fortwengler, D., Marchand, D., Thierry, J., Bartolini, A., Boulila, S., et al., 2014a, Integrated stratigraphy of the Oxfordian global stratotype section and point (GSSP) candidate in the Subalpine Basin (SE France). *Volumina Jurassica*, **12**: 1–44.

Pellenard, P., Tramoy, R., Puceat, E., Huret, E., Martinez, M., Bruneau, L., et al., 2014b, Carbon cycle and sea-water palaeotemperature evolution at the Middle-Late Jurassic transition, eastern Paris Basin (France). *Marine and Petroleum Geology*, **53**: 30–43, https://dx.doi.org/10.1016/j.marpetgeo.2013.07.002.

Peng, S.c., Babcock, L.E., Zuo, J.x., Zhu, X.j., Lin, H.l., Yang, X.f., et al., 2012, Global Standard Stratotype-Section and Point (GSSP) for the Base of the Jiangshanian Stage (Cambrian: Furongian) at Duibian, Jiangshan, Zhejiang, Southeast China. *Episodes*, **35**: 462–477, https://dx.doi.org/10.18814/epiiugs/2012/v35i4/002.

Planavsky, N.J., Bekker, A., Hofmann, A., Owens, J.D., and Lyons, T.W., 2012, Sulfur record of rising and falling marine oxygen and sulfate levels during the Lomagundi Event. *Proceedings of the National Academy of Sciences of the United States of America*, **109**: 18300–18305, https://doi.org/10.1073/pnas.1120387109.

Popp, B.N., Anderson, T.F., and Sandberg, P.A., 1986, Brachiopods as indicators of original isotopic compositions in some Paleozoic limestones. *Geological Society of America Bulletin*, **97**: 1262–1269, https://doi.org/10.1130/0016-7606(1986)97 < 1262:BAIOOI > 2.0.CO;2.

Preto, N., Agnini, C., Rigo, M., Sprovieri, M., and Westphal, H., 2013, The calcareous nannofossil Prinsiosphaera achieved rock-forming abundances in the latest Triassic of western Tethys: consequences for the $\delta^{13}C$ of bulk carbonate. *Biogeosciences*, **10**: 6053–6068, https://dx.doi.org/10.5194/bg-10-6053-2013.

Prokoph, A., Shields, G.A., and Veizer, J., 2008, Compilation and time-series analysis of a marine carbonate $\delta^{18}O$, $\delta^{13}C$, $^{87}Sr/^{86}Sr$, and $\delta^{34}S$ database through Earth history. *Earth-Science Reviews*, **87**: 113–133, https://dx.doi.org/10.1016/j.earscirev.2007.12.003.

Pu, J.P., Bowring, S.A., Ramezani, J., Myrow, P., Raub, T.D., Landing, E., et al., 2016, Dodging snowballs: geochronology of the Gaskiers glaciation and the first appearance of the Ediacaran biota. *Geology*, **44**: 955–958, https://dx.doi.org/10.1130/G38284.1.

Raffi, I., Wade, B.S., and Pälicke, H., 2020, The Neogene Period. *In* Gradstein, F.M., Ogg, J.G., Schmitz, M.D., and Ogg, G.M. (eds), *The Geologic Time Scale 2020.* Elsevier Publ., **Vol. 2**.

Railsback, L.B., Holland, S.M., Hunter, D.M., Jordan, M.E., Diaz, J.R., and Crowe, D.E., 2003, Controls on geochemical expression of subaerial exposure in Ordovician limestones from the Nashville Dome, Tennessee, U.S.A. *Journal of Sedimentary Research*, **73**: 790–805, https://dx.doi.org/10.1306/020503730790.

Railsback, L.B., Gibbard, P.L., Head, M.J., Voarintsoa, N.R.G., and Toucanne, S., 2015, An optimized scheme of lettered marine isotope substages for the last 1.0 million years, and the climatostratigraphic nature of isotope stages and substages. *Quaternary Science Reviews*, **111**: 94–106, https://dx.doi.org/10.1016/j.quascirev.2015.01.012.

Rais, P., Louis-Schmid, B., Bernasconi, S.M., and Weissert, H., 2007, Palaeoceanographic and palaeoclimatic reorganization around the Middle-Late Jurassic transition. *Palaeogeography, Palaeoclimatology, Palaeoecology*, **251**: 527–546, https://dx.doi.org/10.1016/j.palaeo.2007.05.008.

Raven, J.A., and Falkowski, P.G., 1999, Oceanic sinks for atmospheric CO_2. *Plant, Cell & Environment*, **22**: 741–755, https://dx.doi.org/10.1046/j.1365-3040.1999.00419.x.

Ravizza, G.E., and Zachos, J.C., 2003, Records of Cenozoic Ocean Chemistry. *Treatise on Geochemistry*, **6**: 551–581, https://dx.doi.org/10.1016/B0-08-043751-6/06121-1.

Riccardi, A., Kump, L.R., Arthur, M.A., and D'Hondt, S., 2007, Carbon isotopic evidence for chemocline upward excursions during the end-Permian Event. *Palaeogeography, Palaeoclimatology, Palaeoecology*, **248**: 73–81, https://dx.doi.org/10.1016/j.palaeo.2006.11.010.

Ridgwell, A., and Zeebe, R.E., 2005, The role of the global carbonate cycle in the regulation and evolution of the Earth System. *Earth and Planetary Science Letters*, **234**: 299–315, https://dx.doi.org/10.1016/j.epsl.2005.03.006.

Rohling, E.J., and Cooke, S., 1999, Stable oxygen and carbon isotopes in foraminiferal carbonate shells. *In* Sen Gupta, B.K. (ed), *Modern Foraminifera*. Kluwer Academic Publishers, UK, pp. 239–258.

Romanek, C.S., Grossman, E.L., and Morse, J.W., 1992, Carbon isotopic fractionation in synthetic aragonite and calcite: effects of temperature and precipitation rate. *Geochimica et Cosmochimica Acta*, **56**: 419–430, https://dx.doi.org/10.1016/0016-7037(92)90142-6.

Rooney, A.D., Macdonald, F.A., Strauss, J.V., Dudás, F.Ö., Hallmann, C., and Selby, D., 2014, Re-Os geochronology and coupled Os-Sr isotope constraints on the Sturtian snowball Earth. *Proceedings of the National Academy of Sciences of the United States of America*, **111**: 51–56, https://dx.doi.org/10.1073/10.1073/pnas.1317266110.

Rothman, D.H., Hayes, J.M., and Summons, R.E., 2003, Dynamics of the Neoproterozoic carbon cycle. *Proceedings of the National Academy of Sciences of the United States of America*, **100**: 8124–8129, https://doi.org/10.1073/pnas.0832439100.

Ruddiman, W.F., 2014, *Earth's Climate Past and Future*, 3rd Ed., W.H. Freeman and Company, New York, p. 465.

Sadler, P.M., 2012, Integrating carbon isotope excursions into automated stratigraphic correlations: an example from the Silurian of Baltica. *Bulletin of Geosciences*, **84**: 681–694, https://doi.org/10.3140/bull.geosci.1307.

Sageman, B.B., Meyers, S.R., and Arthur, M.A., 2006, Orbital time scale and new C-isotope record for Cenomanian-Turonian boundary stratotype. *Geology*, **34**: 125–128, https://doi.org/10.1130/G22074.1.

Sageman, B.B., Singer, B.S., Meyers, S.R., Siewert, S.E., Walaszczyk, I., Condon, D.J., et al., 2014, Integrating $^{40}Ar/^{39}Ar$, U–Pb, and astronomical clocks in the Cretaceous Niobrara Formation, Western Interior Basin. *Geological Society of America Bulletin*, **126** (7–8): 956–973.

Saltzman, M.R., 2003, Late Paleozoic ice age: oceanic gateway or pCO_2. *Geology*, **31**: 151–154, https://doi.org/10.1130/0091-7613(2003)031 < 0151:LPIAOG > 2.0.CO;2.

Saltzman, M.R., 2005, Phosphorus, nitrogen, and the redox evolution of the Paleozoic oceans. *Geology*, **33**: 573–576, https://doi.org/10.1130/G21535.1.

Saltzman, M.R., and Thomas, E., 2012, Chapter 11: Carbon isotope stratigraphy. *In* Gradstein, F.M., Ogg, J.G., Schmitz, M., and Ogg, G. (eds), *The Geologic Time Scale 2012*. Elsevier Publisher. 207–233. (Coordinators), https://doi.org/10.1016/B978-0-444-59425-9.00011-1.

Saltzman, M.R., Young, S.A., Kump, L.R., Gill, B.C., Lyons, T.W., and Runnegar, B., 2011, Pulse of atmospheric oxygen during the late Cambrian. *Proceedings of the National Academy of Sciences of the United States of America*, **108**: 3876–3881, https://doi.org/10.1073/pnas.1011836108.

Sandoval, J., O'Dogherty, L., Aguado, R., Bartolini, A., Bruchez, S., and Bill, M., 2008, Aalenian carbon-isotope stratigraphy: calibration with ammonite, radiolarian and nannofossil events in the Western Tethys. *Palaeogeography, Palaeoclimatology, Palaeoecology*, **267**: 115–137, https://doi.org/10.1016/j.palaeo.2008.06.013.

Sandoval, J., Bill, M., Aguado, R., O'Dogherty, L., Rivas, P., Morard, A., et al., 2012, The Toarcian in the Subbetic basin (southern Spain): bio-events (ammonite and calcareous nannofossils) and carbon-isotope stratigraphy. *Palaeogeography, Palaeoclimatology, Palaeoecology*, **342**: 40–63, https://doi.org/10.1016/j.palaeo.2012.04.028.

Sarmiento, J.L., and Gruber, N., 2006, *Ocean Biogeochemical Dynamics*. 503 pp. Princeton University Press.

Schachat, S.R., Labandeira, C.C., Saltzman, M.R., Cramer, B.D., Payne, J.L., and Boyce, C.K., 2018, Phanerozoic pO_2 and the early evolution of terrestrial animals. *Proceedings of the Royal Society, B*, **285**: 20172631, https://doi.org/10.1098/rspb.2017.2631.

Schidlowski, M., Eichmann, R., and Junge, C.E., 1975, Precambrian sedimentary carbonates: carbon and oxygen isotope geochemistry and implications for the terrestrial oxygen budget. *Precambrian Research*, **2**: 1–69, https://doi.org/10.1016/0301-9268(75)90018-2.

Schmittner, A., Bostock, H.C., Cartapanis, O., Curry, W.B., Filipsson, H.L., Galbraith, E.D., et al., 2017, Calibration of the carbon isotopic composition ($\delta^{13}C$) of epibenthic *Foraminifera*. *Paleoceanography*, **32**: 512–530, https://doi.org/10.1002/2016PA003072.

Scholle, P.A., and Arthur, M.A., 1980, Carbon isotope fluctuations in Cretaceous pelagic limestones: potential stratigraphic and petroleum exploration tool. *The American Association of Petroleum Geologists*, **64**: 67–87, https://doi.org/10.1306/2F91892D-16CE-11D7-8645000102C1865D.

Schovsbo, N.H., Rasmussen, S.L., Sheldon, E., and Stemmerik, L., 2008, Correlation of carbon isotope events in the Danish Upper Cretaceous chalk. *Geological Survey of Denmark and Greenland Bulletin*, **15**: 13–16.

Schröder, S., Bekker, A., Beukes, N.J., Strauss, H., and van Niekerk, H.S., 2008, Rise in seawater sulphate concentration associated with the Paleoproterozoic positive carbon isotope excursion: evidence from sulphate evaporates in the ~2.2-2.1Gyr shallow-marine Lucknow Formation, South Africa. *Terra Nova*, **20**: 108–117, https://doi.org/10.1111/j.1365-3121.2008.00795.x.

Semikhatov, M.A., Kuznetsov, A.B., Maslov, A.V., Gorokhov, I.M., and Ovchinnikova, G.V., 2009, Stratotype of the Lower Riphean, the Burzyan Group of the Southern Urals: lithostratigraphy, paleontology, geochronology, Sr- and C-Isotopic characteristics of its carbonate rocks. *Stratigraphy Correlation*, **17**: 574–601, https://doi.org/10.1134/S0869593809060021.

Shackleton, N.J., 1984, Carbon isotope data from Leg 74 sediments. *Initial Reports of the Deep Sea Drilling Project*, **74**: 613–619, https://doi.org/10.2973/dsdp.proc.74.116.1984.

Shackleton, N.J., 1987. The carbon isotope record of the Cenozoic: history of organic carbon burial and of oxygen in the ocean and atmosphere. *In* Brooks, J., Fleet, A.J., (eds), *Marine Petroleum Source Rocks*, Geological Society of London, Special Publication **26**, pp. 423–434. https://doi.org/10.1144/GSL.SP.1987.026.01.27

Shen, J., Feng, Q.L., Algeo, T.J., Li, C., Planaysky, N.J., Zhou, L., et al., 2016, Two pulses of oceanic environmental disturbance during the Permian-Triassic boundary crisis. *Earth and Planetary Science Letters*, **443**: 139–152. https://doi.org/j.epsl.2016.03.030.

Shields, G., and Veizer, J., 2002, Precambrian marine carbonate isotope database: version 1.1. *Geochemistry, Geophysics, Geosystems*, **3** (6): 12, http://g-cubed.org/gc2002/2001GC000266.

Silva, R.L., Duarte, L.V., Comas-Rengifo, M.J., Mendonça Filho, J.G., and Azerêdo, A.C., 2011, Update of the carbon and oxygen isotopic records of the Early–Late Pliensbachian (Early Jurassic, ~187 Ma): insights from the organic-rich hemipelagic series of the Lusitanian Basin (Portugal). *Chemical Geology*, **283**: 177–184, https://doi.org/10.1016/j.chemgeo.2011.01.010.

Song, H.Y., Tong, J.N., Algeo, T.J., Horacek, M., Qiu, H., Song, H.J., Tian, L., and Chen, Z.Q., 2013, Large vertical $\delta^{13}C_{DIC}$ gradients in Early Triassic seas of the South China craton: Implications for oceanographic changes related to Siberian Traps volcanism. *Global and Planetary Change*, **105**: 7–20, https://doi.org/10.1016/j.gloplacha.2012.10.023.

Speijer, R.P., Pälicke, H., Hollis, C.J., Hooker, J.J., and Ogg, J.G., 2020, The Paleogene Period. *In* Gradstein, F.M., Ogg, J.G., Schmitz, M.D., and Ogg, G.M. (eds), *The Geologic Time Scale 2020*. Elsevier Publ., **Vol. 2**.

Sprovieri, M., Coccioni, R., Lirer, F., Pelosi, N., and Lozar, F., 2006, Orbital tuning of a lower Cretaceous composite record (Maiolica Formation, central Italy). *Paleoceanography*, **21**: PA4212.

Stolfus, B.M., Cramer, B.D., Clark, R.J., Hogancamp, N.J., Day, J.E., Tassier-Surine, S.A., et al., submitted, An expanded stratigraphic record of the Devonian-Carboniferous Boundary Hangenberg biogeochemical event from southeast Iowa. *Bulletin of Geosciences*.

Sucheras-Marx, B., Giraud, F., Fernandez, V., Pittet, B., Lecuyer, C., Olivero, D., et al., 2013, Duration of the Early Bajocian and the associated $\delta^{13}C$ positive excursion based on cyclostratigraphy. *Journal of the Geological Society*, **170**: 107–118, https://doi.org/10.1144/jgs2011-133.

Sun, Y.D., Wignall, P.B., Joachimski, M.M., Bond, D.P.G., Grasby, S.E., Lai, X.L., et al., 2016, Climate warming, euxinia and carbon isotope perturbations during the Carnian (Triassic) Crisis in South China. *Earth and Planetary Science Letters*, **444**: 88–100, https://doi.org/10.1016/j.epsl.2016.03.037.

Sundquist, E.T., and Visser, K., 2004, The geologic history of the carbon cycle. *Treatise on Geochemistry*, **8**: 425–472, https://doi.org/10.1016/B0-08-043751-6/08133-0.

Swanson-Hysell, N.L., Rose, C.V., Calmet, C.C., Halverson, G.P., Hurtgen, M.T., and Maloof, A.C., 2010, Cryogenian glaciation and the onset of carbon-isotope decoupling. *Science*, **328**: 608–611, https://doi.org/10.1126/science.1184508.

Swanson-Hysell, N.L., Maloof, A.C., Condon, D.J., Jenkin, G.R.T., Alene, M., Tremblay, M.M., et al., 2015, Stratigraphy and geochronology of the Tambien Group, Ethiopia: evidence for globally synchronous carbon isotope change in the Neoproterozoic. *Geology*, **43**: 323–326, https://doi.org/10.1130/G36347.1.

Swart, P.K., 2008, Global synchronous changes in the carbon isotopic composition of carbonate sediments unrelated to changes in the global carbon cycle. *Proceedings of the National Academy of Sciences of the United States of America*, **105**: 13741–13745, https://doi.org/10.1073/pnas.0802841105.

Swart, P.K., and Eberli, G., 2005, The nature of the $\delta^{13}C$ of periplatform sediments: implications for stratigraphy and the global carbon cycle. *Sedimentary Geology*, **175**: 115–129, https://doi.org/10.1016/j.sedgeo.2004.12.029.

Swart, P.K., and Oehlert, A.M., 2018, Revised interpretations of stable C and O patterns in carbonate rocks resulting from meteoric diagenesis. *Sedimentary Geology*, **364**: 14–23, https://doi.org/10.1016/j.sedgeo.2017.12.005.

Tahata, M., Ueno, Y., Ishikawa, T., Sawaki, Y., Murakami, K., Han, J., et al., 2013, Carbon and oxygen isotope chemostratigraphies of the Yangtze platform, South China: decoding temperature and environmental changes through the Ediacaran. *Gondwana Research*, **23**: 333–353, https://doi.org/10.1016/j.gr.2012.04.005.

Thibault, N., Harlou, R., Schovsbo, N., Schioler, P., Minoletti, F., Galbrun, B., et al., 2012, Upper Campanian-Maastrichtian nannofossil biostratigraphy and high-resolution carbon-isotope stratigraphy of the Danish Basin: towards a standard $\delta^{13}C$ curve for the Boreal Realm. *Cretaceous Research*, **33**: 72–90.

Thibault, N., Jarvis, I., Voigt, S., Gale, A.S., Attree, K., and Jenkyns, H.C., 2016, Astronomical calibration and global correlation of the Santonian (Cretaceous) based on the marine carbon isotope record. *Paleoceanography*, **31**: 847–865.

Thomas, E., Gapotchenko, T., Varenkamp, J.C., Mecray, E.L., and Buchholtz ten Brink, M.R., 2000, Benthic *Foraminifera* and environmental changes in Long Island Sound. *The Journal of Coastal Research*, **16**: 641–655.

Thompson, C.K., and Kah, L.C., 2012, Sulfur isotope evidence for widespread euxinia and a fluctuating oxycline in Early to Middle Ordovician greenhouse oceans. *Palaeogeography, Palaeoclimatology, Palaeoecology*, **313–314**: 189–214, https://doi.org/10.1016/j.palaeo.2011.10.020.

Tierney, K.E., 2010, Permian carbon and strontium isotope stratigraphy in Nevada and China: implications for a greenhouse-icehouse transition. *Unpublished Ph.D. dissertation*. The Ohio State University, Columbus, OH.

Tierney-Cramer, K., and Bostic, M., 2015, High-resolution carbon isotope ($\delta^{13}C_{carb}$) chemostratigraphy of the lower Permian from the U. S. midcontinent: checking the pulse of the late Paleozoic ice age. *Geological Society of America Bulletin*, **127**: 584–595, https://doi.org/10.1130/B31024.1.

Turner, S.K., and Ridgwell, A., 2016, Development of a novel empirical framework for interpreting geological carbon isotope excursions, with implications for the rate of carbon injection across the PETM. *Earth and Planetary Science Letters*, **435**: 1–13, https://doi.org/10.1016/j.epsl.2015.11.027.

van de Schootbrugge, B., Payne, J.L., Tomasovych, A., Pross, J., Fiebig, J., Benbrahim, M., et al., 2008, Carbon cycle perturbation and stabilization in the wake of the Triassic-Jurassic boundary mass-extinction event. *Geochemistry, Geophysics, Geosystems*, **9**: Q04028, https://doi.org/10.1029/2007GC001914.

van Geldern, R., Joachimski, M.M., Day, J., Jansen, U., Alvarez, F., Yolkin, E.A., et al., 2006, Carbon, oxygen and strontium isotope records of Devonian brachiopod shell calcite. *Palaeogeography, Palaeoclimatology, Palaeoecology*, **240**: 47–67, https://doi.org/10.1016/j.palaeo.2006.03.045.

van Hengstum, P.J., and Gröcke, D.R., 2008, Stable isotope record of the Eifelian-Givetian boundary Kačák-*otomari* Event (Middle Devonian) from Hungry Hollow, Ontario, Canada. *Canadian Journal of Earth Sciences*, **45**: 353–366, https://doi.org/10.1139/E08-005.

Veizer, J., Ala, D., Azmy, K., Bruckschen, P., Buhl, D., Bruhn, F., et al., 1999, $^{87}Sr/^{86}Sr$, $\delta^{13}C$ and $\delta^{18}O$ evolution of Phanerozoic seawater. *Chemical Geology*, **161**: 59–88, https://doi.org/10.1016/S0009-2541(99)00081-9.

Veizer, J., Fritz, P., and Jones, B., 1986, Geochemistry of brachiopods: oxygen and carbon isotopic records of Paleozoic oceans.

Geochimica et Cosmochimica Acta, **50**: 1679–1696, https://doi.org/10.1016/0016-7037(86)90130-4.

Vincent, E., and Berger, W.H., 1985, Carbon dioxide and polar cooling in the Miocene: the Monterey hypothesis. *In* Sundquist, E.T., and Broecker, W.S. (eds), *The Carbon Cycle and Atmospheric* CO_2*: Natural Variations Archean to Present*. American Geophysical Union, Washington, DC, pp. 455–468.

Voigt, S., Friedrich, O., Norris, R.D., and Schoenfeld, J., 2010, Campanian–Maastrichtian carbon isotope stratigraphy: shelf-ocean correlation between the European shelf sea and the tropical Pacific Ocean. *Newsletters on Stratigraphy*, **44**: 57–72.

Wachter, E.A., and Hayes, J.M., 1985, Exchange of oxygen isotope in carbon dioxide-phosphoric acid systems. *Chemical Geology*, **52**, https://doi.org/10.1016/0168-9622(85)90046-6.

Wang, C.Y., Wang, P., and Li, W.G., 2004, Conodonts from the Permian Jisu Honguer (Zhesi) Formation of Inner Mongolia, China. *Geobios*, **37**: 471–480, https://doi.org/10.1016/j.geobios.2003.06.003.

Weissert, H., and Channell, J.E.T., 1989, Tethyan carbonate carbon isotope stratigraphy across the Jurassic-Cretaceous boundary: an indicator of decelerated global carbon cycling? *Paleoceanography*, **4**: 483–494, https://doi.org/10.1029/PA004i004p00483.

Weissert, H., Joachimski, M., and Sarnthein, M., 2008, Chemostratigraphy. *Newsletters on Stratigraphy*, **42**: 145–179, https://doi.org/10.1127/0078-0421/2008/0042-0145.

Wenzel, B., 2000, Differential preservation of primary isotopic signatures in Silurian brachiopods from northern Europe. *Journal of Sedimentary Research*, **70**: 194–209, https://doi.org/10.1306/2DC4090A-0E47-11D7-8643000102C1865D.

Wenzel, B., and Joachimski, M.M., 1996, Carbon and oxygen isotopic composition of Silurian brachiopods (Gotland/Sweden). *Palaeogeography, Palaeoclimatology, Palaeoecology*, **122**: 143–166, https://doi.org/10.1016/0031-0182(95)00094-1.

Whittaker, S.G., Sami, T.T., Kyser, T.K., and James, N.P., 1998, Petrogenesis of 1.9 Ga limestones and dolostones and their record of Paleoproterozoic environments. *Precambrian Research*, **90**: 187–202, https://doi.org/10.1016/S0301-9268(98)00048-5.

Wilson, P.A., and Norris, R.D., 2001, Warm tropical ocean surface and global anoxia during the mid-Cretaceous period. *Nature*, **412**: 425–429, https://doi.org/10.1038/35086553.

Wilson, J.P., Woodward, W.F., Johnston, D.T., Knoll, A.H., Grotzinger, J. P., Walter, M.R., et al., 2010, Geobiology of the late Paleoproterozoic Duck Creek Formation, Western Australia. *Precambrian Research*, **179**: 135–149, https://doi.org/10.1016/j.precamres.2010.02.019.

Wu, R., Calner, M., and Lehnert, O., 2017, Integrated conodont biostratigraphy and carbon isotope chemostratigraphy in the Lower-Middle Ordovician of southern Sweden reveals a complete record of the MDICE. *Geological Magazine*, **154**: 334–353, https://doi.org/10.1017/S0016756816000017.

Xiao, S.H., and Narbonne, G.M., 2020, The Ediacaran Period. *In* Gradstein, F.M., Ogg, J.G., Schmitz, M.D., and Ogg, G.M. (eds), *The Geologic Time Scale 2020*. Elsevier Publ., **Vol. 2**.

Xie, S.C., Pancost, R.D., Huang, J.H., Wignall, P.B., Yu, J.X., Tang, X.Y., et al., 2007, Changes in the global carbon cycle occurred as two episodes during the Permian-Triassic crisis. *Geology*, **35**: 1083–1086, https://doi.org/10.1130/G24224A.1.

Xu, B., Gu, X.Y., Wang, C.Y., Hao, Q.Z., Han, J.T., Liu, Q., et al., 2012, Carbon isotopic evidence for the associations of decreasing CO_2 level with the Frasnian-Famennian mass extinction. *Journal of Geophysical Research*, **117**: G01032, https://doi.org/10.1029/2011JG001847.

Young, S.A., Saltzman, M.R., Ausich, W.I., Desrochers, A., and Kaljo, D., 2010, Did changes in atmospheric CO_2 coincide with latest Ordovician glacial-interglacial cycles? *Palaeogeography, Palaeoclimatology, Palaeoecology*, **296**: 376–388, https://doi.org/10.1016/j.palaeo.2010.02.033.

Zachos, J.C., Pagani, M., Sloan, L., Thomas, E., and Billups, K., 2001, Trends, rhythms, and aberrations in global climate 65Ma to present. *Science*, **292**: 686–693, https://doi.org/10.1126/science.1059412.

Zachos, J.C., and Kump, L.R., 2005, Carbon cycle feedbacks and the initiation of Antarctic glaciation in the earliest Oligocene. *Global and Planetary Change*, **47**: 51–66, https://doi.org/10.1016/j.gloplacha.2005.01.001.

Zachos, J.C., Dickens, G.R., and Zeebe, R.E., 2008, An early Cenozoic perspective on greenhouse warming and carbon cycle dynamics. *Nature*, **451**: 279–283, https://doi.org/10.1038/nature06588.

Zachos, J.C., McCarren, H., Murphy, B., Röhl, U., and Westerhold, T., 2010, Tempo and scale of late Paleocene and early Eocene carbon isotope cycles: implications for the origin of hyperthermals. *Earth and Planetary Science Letters*, **299**: 242–249, https://doi.org/10.1016/j.epsl.2010.09.004.

Zambito, J.J., Joachimski, M.M., Brett, C.E., Baird, G.C., Aboussalam, Z.S., 2016. A carbonate carbon isotope record for the late Givetian (Middle Devonian) Global Taghanic Biocrisis in the type region (northern Appalachian Basin). *In* Becker, R.T., Königshoff, P., Brett, C.E., (eds). *Devonian Climate, Sea Level and Evolutionary Events*, Geological Society, London, Special Publications **423**, 223–233. https://doi.org/10.1144/SP423.7

Zhang, K., Zhu, Xk, Wood, R.A., Shi, Y., Gao, Zf, and Poulton, S.W., 2018, Oxygenation of the Mesoproterozoic ocean and the evolution of complex eukaryotes. *Nature Geoscience*, **11**: 345–350, https://doi.org/10.1038/s41561-018-0111-y.

Zhong, H., and Ma, Ys, 1997, Carbon isotope stratigraphy of dolomites in the early Proterozoic succession, north China. *Geological Magazine*, **134**: 763–770, https://doi.org/10.1017/S0016756897007577.

Zhu, M.Y., Zhang, J.M., Li, G.X., and Yang, A.H., 2004, Evolution of C isotopes in the Cambrian of China: implications for Cambrian subdivisions and trilobite mass extinctions. *Geobios*, **37**: 287–301, https://doi.org/10.1016/j.geobios.2003.06.001.

Zhu, M.Y., Babcock, L.E., and Peng, S.C., 2006, Advances in Cambrian stratigraphy and paleontology: integrating correlation techniques, paleobiology, taphonomy and paleoenvironmental reconstruction. *Palaeoworld*, **15**: 217–222.

R.E. Ernst, D.P.G. Bond and S.H. Zhang

Chapter 12

Influence of Large Igneous Provinces

Chapter outline

Abstract

Owing to their large volume (up to millions of km^3) and short duration of emplacement (often less than a few million years) Large Igneous Provinces (LIPs) and associated Silicic LIPs (SLIPs) can have a dramatic effect on global environments. Postulated effects include warming, cooling, acid rain and ocean acidification, ozone depletion and increased UV-B radiation, marine anoxia, mercury poisoning, and sea level changes, many of which are evidenced by, for example, stable isotopic excursions and changes in sedimentary composition (e.g., black shales). Major environmental changes linked to LIPs have resulted in biotic crises, including several mass extinctions. With increasing precision of U–Pb dating of LIPs resulting in age uncertainties that can be of <50,000 years, an increasing number of Phanerozoic chronostratigraphic boundaries that mark biotic crises can be correlated with LIP events. This relationship extends into the Precambrian, for which existing chronostratigraphic boundaries are represented by approximate numbers (mostly rounded to the nearest 100 Myr). We propose that specific LIPs should define these boundaries. The context is that while LIPs have a regional magmatic extent (often more than 1 Mkm^3 in volume) their often major, global environmental effects are preserved in sedimentary archives. Thus LIPs are not "golden spikes" in themselves, but their sedimentary signatures are potential proxies for golden spikes in the sedimentary record. There is a need for a more integrated and detailed correlation of LIPs and sedimentary records in order to (1) identify LIPs with significant environmental effects, as well as those with only minor or even no recognizable environmental effects, and (2) lead to a full evaluation of the causal relationship between LIPs and sudden environmental change in comparison with other drivers of sudden change such as bolide impact, orogenic weathering, and biological evolution. Key to this progress is expanded high-precision dating of LIPs and the identification and analysis of time-correlative portions of the sedimentary record.

12.1 Large Igneous Provinces

Large Igneous Provinces (LIPs) are voluminous (>0.1 Mkm^3; frequently above 1 Mkm^3), mainly mafic (–ultramafic) magmatic events of intraplate affinity (based on tectonic setting and/or geochemistry) that occur in both continental and oceanic settings, and are typically either of short duration (<5 Myr; often <2 Myr) or consist of multiple short pulses over a maximum of a few tens of Myr (e.g., Coffin and Eldholm, 1994; Courtillot and Renne, 2003; Bryan and Ernst, 2008; Bryan and Ferrari, 2013; Ernst, 2014; Ernst and Youbi, 2017; Buchan and Ernst, 2019). LIPs consist of volcanic packages (flood basalts) and a plumbing system of regional dyke swarms (linear, radiating, and a newly identified circumferential type), sill complexes, layered mafic–ultramafic (M–UM) intrusions, and crustal magmatic underplates (Ernst et al., 2019). Continental LIPs can also be associated with major silicic magmatic events termed Silicic LIPs (SLIPs) (Bryan and Ferrari, 2013; Ernst, 2014), as well as carbonatites and kimberlites (Ernst and Bell, 2010; Ernst et al., 2018). Oceanic LIPs comprise oceanic plateaus and ocean basin flood basalts (e.g., Coffin and Eldholm, 1994; Kerr, 2005, 2014); however, oceanic LIPs are poorly preserved during ocean closure (Coffin and Eldholm, 2001; Dilek and Ernst, 2008; Ernst, 2014). Continental LIPs have occurred on average (but irregularly) every 30 million years throughout the

Geologic Time Scale 2020. DOI: https://doi.org/10.1016/B978-0-12-824360-2.00012-7

Proterozoic. The oceanic LIP record is similar for the past 200 Myr, while for earlier times it is incompletely preserved in ophiolite fragments in orogenic belts (Coffin and Eldholm, 2001; Dilek and Ernst, 2008; Doucet et al., 2020). The rate of LIPs (combined continental and oceanic) in the Archean is more difficult to define due to the paucity of their record. This chapter focuses on the record of Phanerozoic and Proterozoic LIPs.

12.2 Influence on environment

LIPs (and SLIPs) have long been linked with rapid environmental changes and with mass extinction events (e.g., Rampino and Stothers, 1988; Courtillot, 1994, 1999; Wignall, 2001, 2005; White and Saunders, 2005; Kravchinsky, 2012; Courtillot et al., 2015; Bond and Grasby, 2017; Ernst and Youbi, 2017; Svensen et al., 2017; Clapham and Renne, 2019; Grasby et al., 2019; Jones et al., 2019; Kasbohm et al., 2020). Perhaps the most deleterious effect on climate is global warming due to greenhouse gases generated and released during LIP emplacement (Fig. 12.1). Conversely, subsequent cooling (and even global glaciations) might be caused by CO_2 drawdown through weathering of LIP basalts, increases in oceanic productivity through eroded LIP nutrients, associated silicic magmatism, and/or by sulfate aerosols released into the atmosphere during the eruptions themselves. Additional LIP-driven extinction mechanisms include oceanic anoxia (a function of warming), ocean acidification, sea level changes, and toxic metal input, often intertwined in a complex web of catastrophic environmental effects.

In the sedimentary record these effects often manifest as lithological and compositional changes. Sudden

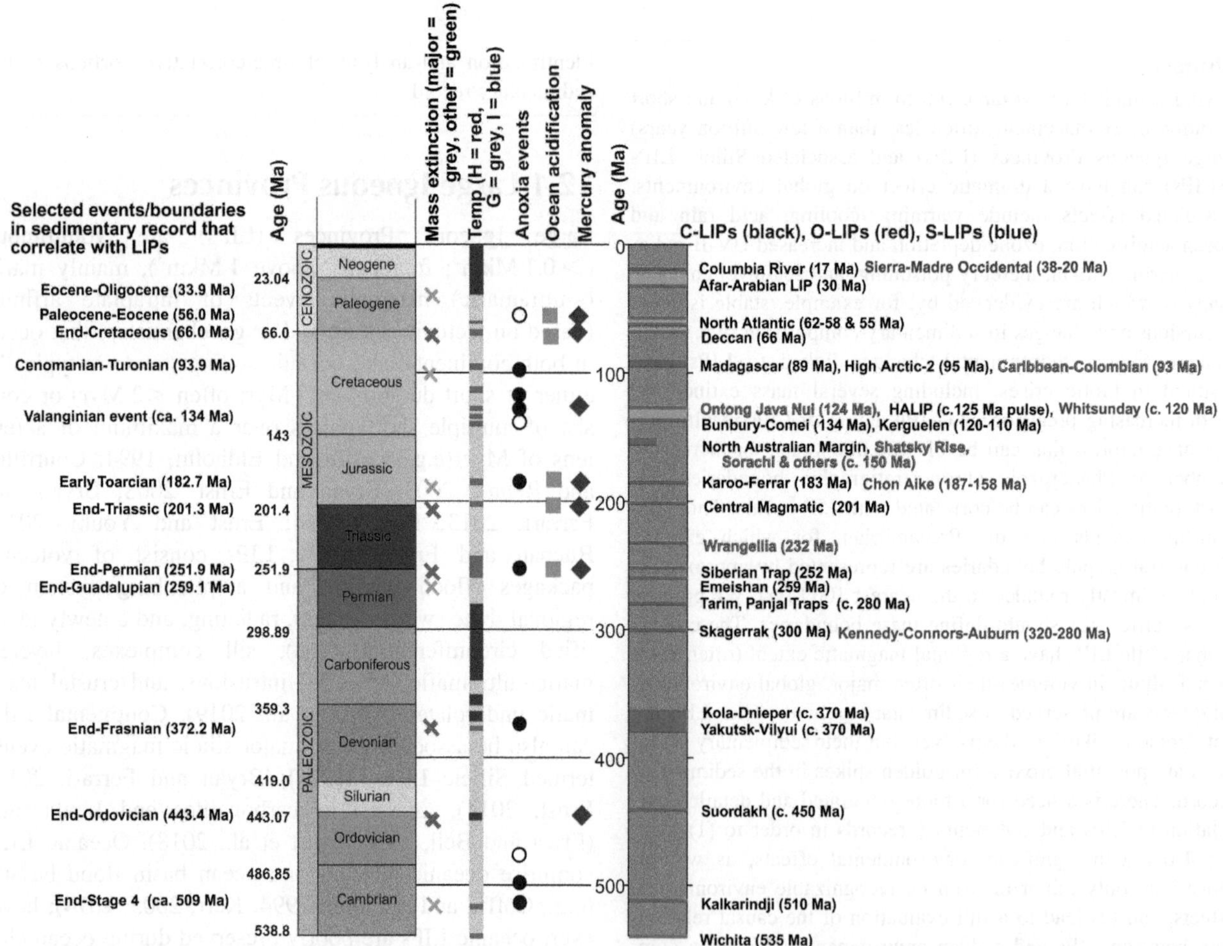

FIGURE 12.1 Phanerozoic record of mass extinctions, climate state, oceanic anoxic events, and mercury/TOC anomalies, in comparison with the Phanerozoic LIP record (C-LIPs = continental, O-LIPs = oceanic, and S-LIPs = silicic; note some continental LIPs have oceanic portions and vice versa). Climate states (H = hothouse; G = greenhouse; I = icehouse) based on Kidder and Worsley (2010). Filled circles represent anoxic events. Open circles record carbon isotope excursions and/or black shale events that are not recognized as an OAE. LIP main pulses are marked by red bars, and associated smaller volume pulses, by pink bars. After Ernst and Youbi (2017) and building on an earlier diagram of Percival (2015).

lithological changes have been temporally linked with LIPs, including deposition of black shales (a common feature of extinction events) (e.g., Zhang et al., 2018), diamictites (glacial events; Youbi et al., 2020a), and iron formations (associated with oceanic plateaus) (Bekker and Ernst, 2017). Other potential signs of LIP events in the sedimentary record include major changes in the stable isotopic composition of rocks (sensitive to temperature, carbon fixing, mafic sedimentary input, pH, oxidized/reduced level) and their trace element contents (e.g., Hg).

12.3 Correlation with Phanerozoic time scale boundaries

With the improving record of high-precision U–Pb dating of LIPs (e.g., summary in Kasbohm et al., 2020), their correlation with mass extinctions and selected biostratigraphic boundaries has become robust. High-precision U–Pb dating over the past decade has revealed an unexpectedly short duration for many LIPs (approximately 1 Myr or less) and confirmed a precise temporal coincidence with several mass extinction events. Key examples (Table 12.1) are the links between the 252 Ma Siberian Traps LIP and the end-Permian extinction (Burgess et al., 2015), the 201 Ma CAMP (Central Atlantic Magmatic Province) and the end-Triassic mass extinction (Blackburn et al., 2013; Davies et al., 2017), and the 66 Ma Deccan LIP and the end-Cretaceous extinction (Schoene et al., 2019; see also high-precision Ar–Ar dating of Sprain et al., 2019).

The precision of these correlations strongly implies a causal relationship. While it is true that meteorite impacts can also drive major environmental change, the only extinction event to precisely coincide with an impact is the end-Cretaceous extinction (e.g., Schoene et al., 2019; Sprain et al., 2019), in which case the combined effects of the Deccan LIP and the Chicxulub meteorite was a “one-two punch.” Another possible instance of a combined

TABLE 12.1 Phanerozoic Large Igneous Provinces (LIPs) with precise links to major environmental changes and current chronostratigraphic boundaries (GTS2020).

LIP (location) and age [minimum areal extent (in millions of km^2, Mkm^2)]	Environmental impact (age)	Key Reference—A: for LIP, B: for precise LIP age, C: for precise chronostratigraphic age [if not ICS (2019) and GTS2020], D: for link between LIP and chronostratigraphic boundary
Columbia River (North America) 16.7 and 15.9 Ma (=95% of volume) [0.68 Mkm^2]	Burdigalian–Langhian (15.97 Ma) mid-Miocene climate optimum (MMCO) (~16 Ma)	A, B, D: Kasbohm and Schoene (2018)
Second pulse NAIP (Europe, Greenland) begins ~56 Ma [1.10 Mkm^2 for both pulses]	Paleocene–Eocene (Thanetian–Ypresian) Thermal Maximum (PETM) (55.8 Ma)	A: Wilkinson et al. (2016) D: Jones et al. (2019) B: Charles et al. (2011). D: Schaller et al. (2019)
Deccan (India) 66.3–65.5 Ma [1.85 Mkm^2]	Cretaceous–Paleogene (66.016 ± 0.050 Ma)	A, C, D: Schoene et al. (2019) See also Sprain et al. (2019)
Karoo–Ferrar (southern Africa, Antarctica): Karoo: 183.0 ± 0.5 to 182.3 ± 0.6 Ma [2.12 Mkm^2] Ferrar: 182.779 ± 0.033 Ma [0.18 Mkm^2]	Pliensbachian–Toarcian (182.7 ± 0.7 Ma)	A, B, D: Svensen et al. (2012), Burgess et al. (2015)
CAMP (continents bordering the Atlantic ocean) 201.635 ± 0.029 to 201.111 ± 0.071 Ma [11.29 Mkm^2]	Triassic–Jurassic (201.564 ± 0.015 Ma)	A, B, C, D: Davies et al. (2017) See also: Blackburn et al. (2013)
Siberian Traps (Siberia) Intrusive age range ~251.9 and ~251.4 Ma [3.47 Mkm^2]	Permian–Triassic Between 251.941 ± 0.037 and 251.880 ± 0.031 Ma	A, B, D Burgess and Bowring (2015) C: Burgess et al. (2014)

Notes: Areal extent estimates are from unpublished LIPs ArcGIS database of Ernst. Only CA-IDTIMS ages on zircons are specifically mentioned in the table because of their high precision and importance in demonstrating robust correlations. Additional LIPs have close relationships (Table 1 in Ernst et al., 2020), but need increased dating precision for confirmation.

LIP-impact event is the Paleocene–Eocene Thermal Maximum (PETM), which is associated with the second pulse of the North Atlantic LIP and the onset of opening of the North Atlantic (Jones et al., 2019) and is also coeval with a tektite event (Schaller et al., 2016).

Other precisely dated LIPs are associated with smaller extinction events: the 183 Ma Karoo–Ferrar LIP coincides with the Pliensbachian–Toarcian transition and the 16 Ma Columbia River LIP coincides with the mid-Miocene thermal maximum (Kasbohm and Schoene, 2018).

Another tool for precise relative dating and unit correlation within LIPs, potentially at the scale of a few hundred years, is provided through paleomagnetic secular variation (Pavlov et al., 2019).

12.4 Implications for natural boundaries in the Precambrian

While the Phanerozoic time scale is based on bio-magneto-cyclo stratigraphy (which is increasingly well constrained), the Proterozoic chronostratigraphic time scale is currently divided into broad periods of geodynamic significance but with boundaries refined to the nearest 100 − 50 Myr (ICS, 2019; GTS2020). In pursuit of natural Precambrian boundaries (van Kranendonk et al., 2012) we offer well-dated major LIPs as proxies for natural boundaries following Ernst and Youbi (2017).

Ideally boundaries should be placed at key events or transitions in the stratigraphic record (to establish "golden spikes") (e.g., Gradstein et al., 2012a,b; Van Kranendonk et al., 2012; Ogg et al., 2016). Given their potential to drive major global environmental changes, as known for Phanerozoic time (Section 12.3), LIPs can represent proxies for such "golden spikes." This is based on the idea that while LIPs have a regional extent (up to millions of km^3) their environmental effects can be global. Therefore, while they do not define golden spikes in themselves, their effects are most likely expressed in the global sedimentary record. An example is provided by 1380 Ma black shales in the North China craton and Northern Australian cratons that are coeval with c. 1390–1375 Ma LIPs found in multiple crustal blocks around the world (Zhang et al., 2018). Other correlations between black shales and LIPs are known from the Meso-proterozoic at c. 1650–1620 and 1110 Ma (Zhang et al., 2020). Furthermore, the 2055 Ma Bushveld LIP and coeval Baltic LIPs are correlated with the termination of the major Lomagundi–Jatuli positive isotope excursion (see next).

As a contribution toward the identification of appropriate natural boundaries, the current Proterozoic LIP record (Ernst, 2014) was canvassed for candidates to mark such boundaries. LIPs at 2500–2450, 2100, 2060, 1880, 1790–1750, 1525–1500, 1460, 1380, 1270, 1110, 825, 720, 615–560, and 510 Ma are of particular significance both for their scale and extent and are thus predicted to have significant environmental effects and to potentially represent natural Precambrian boundaries. However, we focus on a subset of these LIPs that approximately correlate with boundaries in the currently defined Proterozoic chronostratigraphic scheme (Fig. 12.2).

In particular, LIPs at 2510, 2056, 1790, 1380, and 720 Ma are close in age to currently defined Proterozoic boundaries (Table 12.2; Fig. 12.2). Notably, the 720 Ma Tonian–Cryogenian boundary that is now defined by the start of the Sturtian glaciation is now robustly linked to the Franklin LIP of northern Laurentia (Macdonald and Wordsworth, 2017; Ernst and Youbi, 2017) plus additional coeval LIPs fragments: Irkutsk LIP (Siberia), Mutare–Fingeren event (Kalahari craton and reconstructed Grunehogna terrane of Antarctica) (Ernst et al., 2016; Gumsley et al., 2019).

The c. 1400 Ma Calymmian–Ectasian boundary can be redefined to match 1390–1375 Ma LIPs on many crustal blocks, associated with final breakup of the Nuna (Columbia) supercontinent and marked by black shales (Zhang et al., 2018). The most precise age for this global event(s) are CA-IDTIMS dates of 1382.15 ± 0.39 and 1382.14 ± 0.36 Ma on Hart River sills of NW Laurentia (Verbaas et al., 2018). This age matches the peak of U–Pb ages on both LIPs (1382 Ma) and black shales (1384 Ma) in Zhang et al. (2018).

The 1790 Ma LIP magmatism is present on several crustal blocks (Fig. 12.2) and can be linked to the c. 1800 Ma Orosirian–Statherian boundary. Possibly associated black shales are suggested in Zhang et al. (2020).

The 2050 Ma Rhyacian–Orosirian boundary is linked to the 2056 Ma Bushveld LIP (Kaapvaal craton), and the coeval Kevitsa LIP (Karelian craton). Notably, these magmatic events are also coeval with the end of the Lomagundi–Jatuli positive isotope excursion (e.g., Bekker, 2015) at 2056.6 ± 0.8 Ma (Martin et al., 2013), which was time-correlated with the Bushveld LIP (Ernst, 2014, Section 14.3.10) and coeval magmatism in Baltica (Melezhik et al., 2007). Since many LIP events are linked to negative carbon isotope excursions, it is plausible to consider that these magmatic events at c. 2056 Ma could cause the negative shift in carbon isotopes that resulted in the termination of the strongly positive carbon isotope values associated with the Lomagundi–Jatuli event.

More speculatively, the Archean–Proterozoic boundary at 2500 Ma could be linked to 2510 Ma LIPs: Mistassini of eastern Laurentia and BLIP-1 of formerly attached Baltica. Furthermore, 2510 Ma represents the start of a major burst of multiple LIPs at 2510, 2460, 2410, and 2370 Ma that collectively could contribute to changes across the Archean–Proterozoic boundary.

The boundaries of 1000 Ma (Stenian–Tonian), 1200 Ma (Ectasian–Stenian), and 2300 Ma Siderian–Rhyacian (Table 12.2) are much more speculatively correlated with the 1005 Ma Sette Daban LIP (eastern Siberian craton), the 1205 Ma Marnda Moorn LIP (Yilgarn craton, Australia), and the 2330–2320 Ma Kuito-Taivalkovsiki LIP (Karelia craton), respectively. However, these LIPs are small (Table 12.2) and unless further precise dating identifies additional units belonging to the events and thus increasing their extents, they are unlikely to have had sufficient global

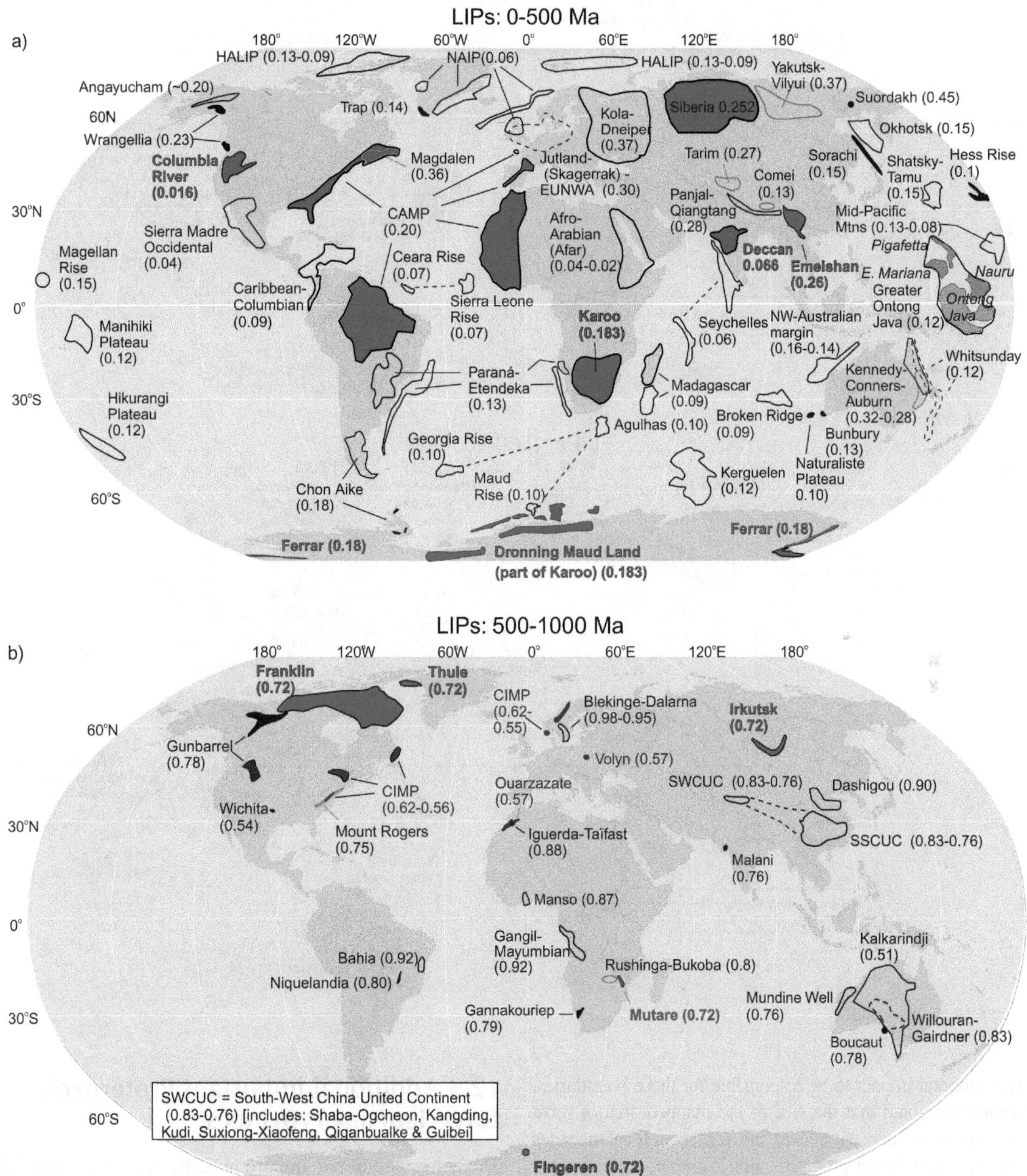

FIGURE 12.2 Distribution of Phanerozoic and Proterozoic LIPs updated and modified after Ernst and Youbi (2017) and Ernst (2014). Numbers in parentheses are emplacement ages in Ga. Those LIPs discussed in Tables 12.1 and 12.2 are in colors other than black. Maps are in Robinson Projection.

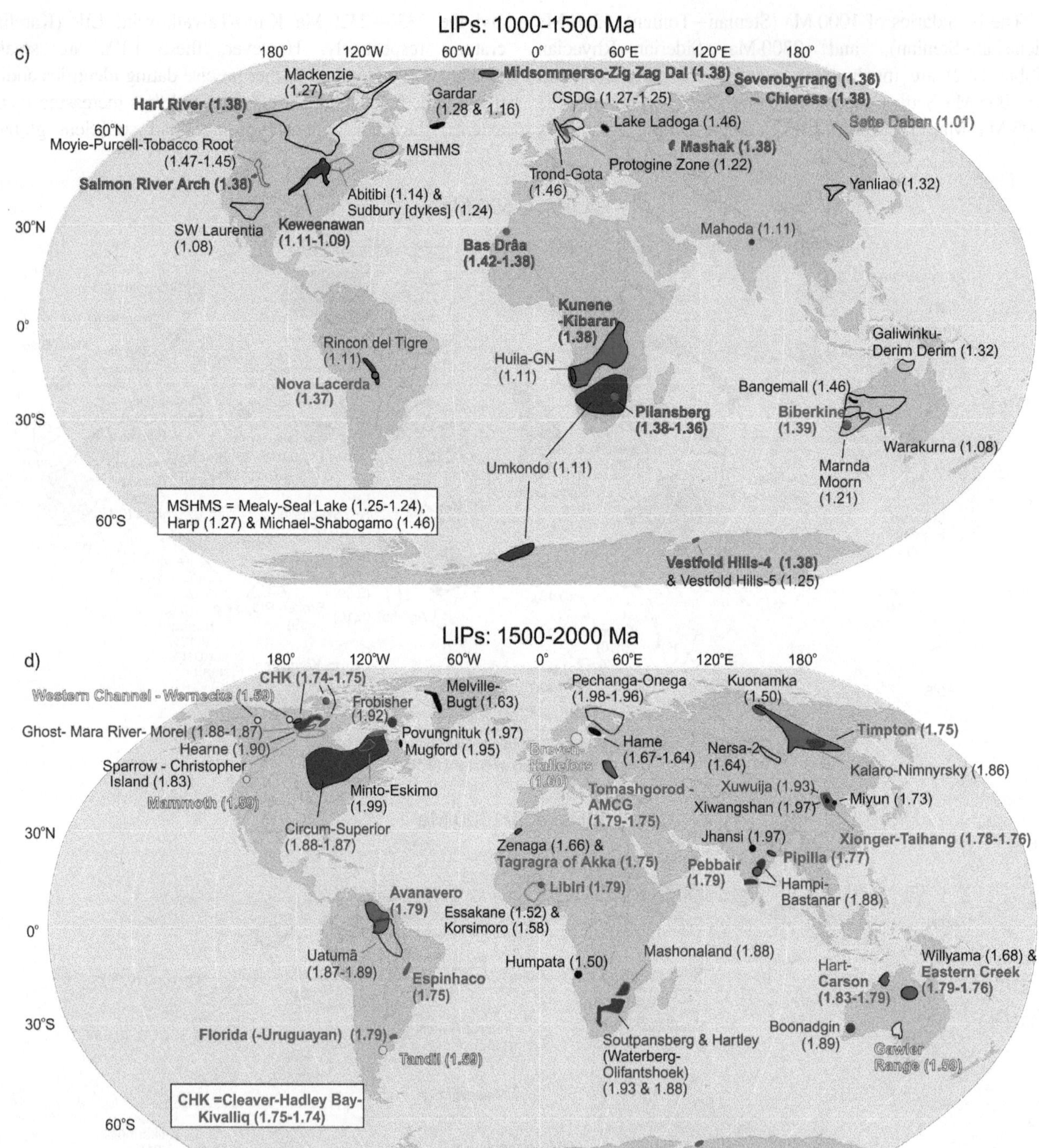

FIGURE 12.2 (Continued)

environmental impact to be responsible for these boundaries. It should be noted that the size of the mapped area of most LIPs has been increasing over the past couple of decades with expanded dating programs. For example, the estimated volume of the Siberian Traps LIP doubled in extent after Ar–Ar dating of rift volcanics within the West Siberian sedimentary basin (e.g., Reichow et al., 2002).

12.5 Additional important Proterozoic Large Igneous Provinces

There are additional important LIPs with ages that fall inside Precambrian chronostratigraphic boundaries; their environmental significance needs to be investigated along with their potential to define further chronostratigraphic

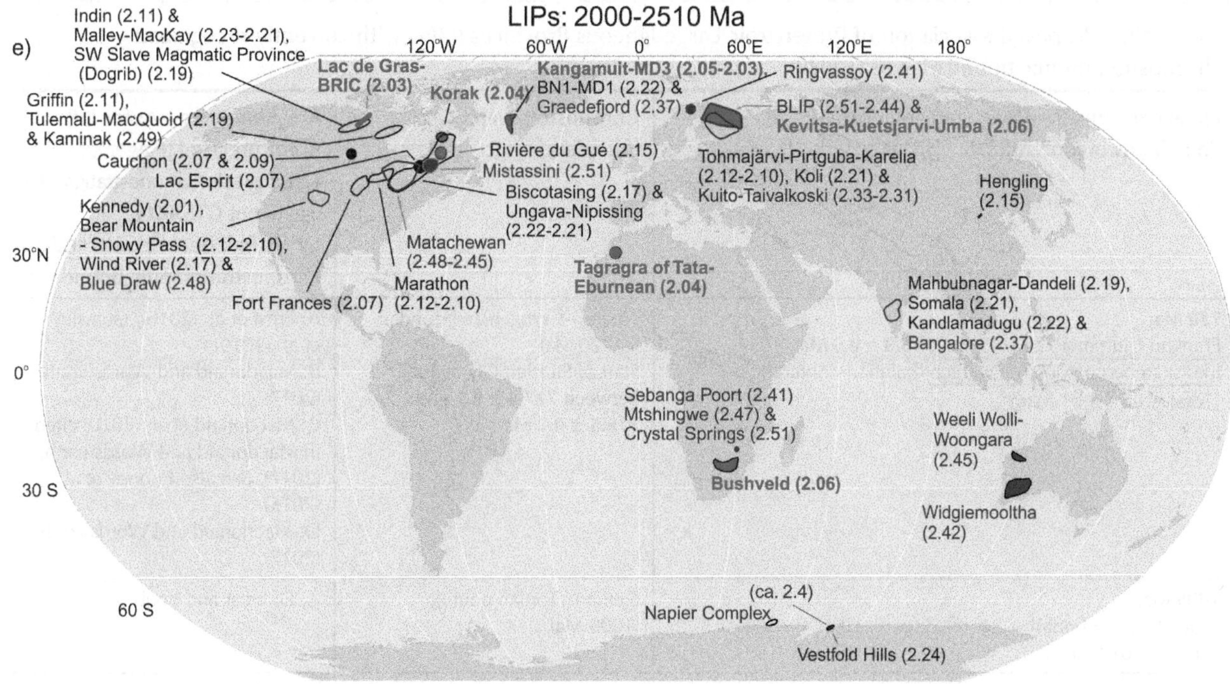

FIGURE 12.2 (Continued)

subdivisions (Table 1 in Ernst and Youbi, 2017). These LIPs include the following (with ages marking single and multiple pulsed LIPs, and the minimum areal extent also included): 615–560 Ma (0.75 Mkm^2), 780 Ma (2.00 Mkm^2), 825 Ma (2.65 Mkm^2), 920–900 Ma (0.99 Mkm^2), 1110 Ma (2.47 Mkm^2), 1270 Ma (3.09 Mkm^2), 1501 Ma (0.25 Mkm^2), 1520 Ma (0.01 Mkm^2), 1750 Ma (0.74 Mkm^2), 1890–1860 Ma (1.65 Mkm^2), 1980–1970 Ma (0.83 Mkm^2), 1998 Ma (0.45 Mkm^2), 2125–2100 Ma (0.47 Mkm^2), 2170–2150 Ma (0.84 Mkm^2), 2190–2180 Ma (0.01 Mkm^2), 2220–2210 Ma (1.03 Mkm^2), 2250 Ma (0.31 Mkm^2), 2420–2370 Ma (0.78 Mkm^2), and 2460–2450 Ma (0.25 Mkm^2).

As an example of potential environmental significance, the c. 580 Ma pulse of the Central Iapetus Magmatic Province (615–560 Ma) has been tentatively correlated with the Gaskiers glaciation (Youbi et al., 2020a,b).

12.6 Large Igneous Provinces volume and extent of environmental effects

The volume of an LIP is an important but not sole control on its environmental impact as originally emphasized by Wignall (2001). Other factors are also important such as the rate of effusion, the abundance of LIP-produced pyroclastic material, and the volatile fluxes that reach the stratosphere. While flood basalt degassing (CO_2, SO_2, halogens) is important (and is also from associated silicic volcanism), a significant amount of these gases are released from volatile-rich sedimentary rocks (e.g., evaporites and coal horizons) heated by the intrusive component of LIPs (Svensen et al., 2009, 2018; Heimdal et al., 2018). Feedbacks are important, such as global warming leading to destabilization of clathrates, consequent release of additional greenhouse gases, and greater global warming. In the broadest sense LIPs can affect (or even induce) shifts between Icehouse, Greenhouse, and Hothouse climatic states. However, the specific effects, their severity, and their time sequencing are specific to each LIP. In general, oceanic LIPs have a smaller environmental effect despite being generally larger in size. For instance, the largest known LIP, the nearly 80 Mkm^3 combined c. 122 Ma Ontong Java–Manihiki–Hikurangi oceanic plateau event is associated only with the Selli oceanic anoxic event (OAE 1a) and not a mass extinction event, clearly illustrating the role of seawater in buffering the environmental effect of oceanic LIPs in comparison to continental LIPs.

LIP volume is difficult to estimate since it requires not only an understanding of the original extent of the volcanics, but also the scale and distribution of the plumbing system that includes the potentially huge magmatic underplate (e.g., Ernst et al., 2019). An imperfect but useful proxy for the volume of LIPs is their areal extent and this parameter is used in Fig. 12.3. Phanerozoic LIPs (marked by blue dots in Fig. 12.3) are precisely linked to major climate change, including mass extinctions. The 201 CAMP 251 Ma Siberian Traps LIPs are associated with mass extinctions and the 183 Ma Karoo–Ferrar LIP with

TABLE 12.2 Proposed association of Proterozoic Large Igneous Provinces (LIPs) with currently recognized chronostratigraphic boundaries (GTS2020).

LIP events (location), age, and areal extent [in millions of km^2, Mkm^2]	Chronostratigraphic boundary	Key Reference—A: for LIP, B: for precise LIP age, C: for precise chronostratigraphic age (if not GTS2020), D: for link between LIP and chronostratigraphic boundary
720 Ma: Franklin Laurentia 725–715 Ma, **716.3 ± 0.5 Ma** Irkutsk (Siberia), Mutare-Finergen (Kalahari–Antarctica) [Total Area = 3.01 Mkm^2]	Tonian–Cryogenian boundary (c. 720 Ma) Start of Sturtian Glaciation **between 717.4 ± 0.1 and 716.5 ± 0.2 Ma**	A: Ernst et al. (2016), Gumsley et al. (2019) B: Macdonald and Wordsworth (2017) C: Macdonald et al. (2010) cited in Macdonald and Wordsworth. (2017). See also Rooney et al. (2015) D: Macdonald and Wordsworth. (2017)
1005 Ma: Sette Daban (Siberia) [Area = 0.01 Mkm^2]	Stenian–Tonian boundary (1000 Ma)	A, D: Ernst and Youbi (2017)
1205 Ma: Marnda Moorn (Yilgarn) [Area = 0.71 Mkm^2]	Ectasian–Stenian boundary (1200 Ma)	A: Pirajno and Hoatson (2012) D: Ernst and Youbi (2017)
1375–1390 Ma: Midsommerso–Zig-Zag Dal (Laurentia) Chieress–Severobyrrang (Siberia) Hart-sills-Salmon River Arch (Laurentia) **(1382.15 ± 0.39 and 1382.14 ± 0.36 Ma)**, Mashak (Baltica), Kunene–Kibaran (Congo), Vestfold Hills-4 (Antarctica). [Total Area = 2.33 Mkm^2]	Calymmian–Ectasian boundary (1400 Ma)	A: Ernst et al. (2008), Zhang et al. (2018) (supplementary files) B: Verbaas et al. (2018) D: Zhang et al. (2018)
1590 Ma: Gawler Range/Olympic Dam (Gawler) Western Channel—Wernecke—Mammoth (western Laurentia) Tandil (Rio de la Plata) craton [Total Area = 0.57 Mkm^2]	Statherian–Calymmian boundary (1600 Ma)	A: Hamilton and Buchan (2010), Teixeira et al. (2013), Rogers et al. (2018) D: Ernst and Youbi (2017)
1790–1780 Ma: Avanavero (Amazonia) Florida (Rio de la Plata) Tomashgorod–AMCG (Sarmatia) Libiri (WAC) Xiong'er–Taihang (North China) [Total Area = 4.66 Mkm^2]	Orosirian–Statherian boundary (1800 Ma)	A: Ernst et al. (2008), Reis et al. (2013), Baratoux et al. (2019), Shumlyanskyy et al. (2016), Chaves and Rezende (2019) D: Ernst and Youbi (2017)
2055 Ma: Bushveld (Kaapvaal) Rustenburg layered suite **(2056.28 ± 0.15 and 2055.54 ± 0.27 Ma)**; Kevitsa-Kuetsjarvi-Umba (Karelia) [Total Area = 0.40 Mkm^2]	Rhyacian–Orosirian boundary (2050 Ma) End Lomagundi Carbon Isotope Excursion (2056.6 ± 0.8 Ma; Martin et al., 2013)	A: Rajesh et al. (2013) B: Mungall et al. (2016) C: Martin et al. (2013) D: Melezhik et al. (2007), Ernst (2014), (Section 14.3.10)
2330–2320 Ma: Kuito-Taivalkovsiki (Karelia) [Area = 0.02 Mkm^2]	Siderian–Rhyacian boundary (2300 Ma)	A: Stepanova et al. (2015). D: Ernst and Youbi (2017)

Notes: Areal extent estimates from unpublished LIPs ArcGIS database of Ernst. Only CA-IDTIMS ages on zircons are specifically mentioned in the table (bolded) because of their high precision and importance in demonstrating robust correlations. The full cataloging of the additional U–Pb ages with typical uncertainties of several Myr is available in the listed references.

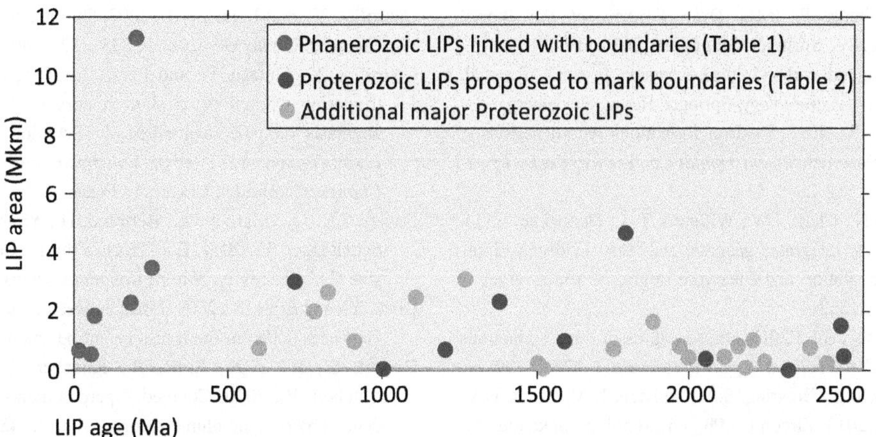

FIGURE 12.3 Areal extent of LIP event with: Blue dots = those that are robustly correlated with Phanerozoic chronostratigraphic boundaries in Table 12.1; Red dots = those proposed to define natural boundaries in Proterozoic time in Table 12.2; and Green dots = those major LIPs with ages falling inside the formal Proterozoic chronostratigraphic boundaries and proposed to mark additional natural chronostratigraphic subdivisions.

a major anoxic event, and the 16 Ma Columbia River LIP with the mid-Miocene thermal maximum and the second pulse of the North Atlantic Igneous Province with the 55.8 Ma PETM. Each of these Phanerozoic LIPs also corresponds with stage/period/age boundary as described in Table 12.1. The comparison with the selected Proterozoic LIPs in Fig. 12.3 (*blue and green dots*) is revealing.

First of all, the older LIPs (2000–2500 Ma) are mostly smaller in size and that likely reflects poorer and more incomplete preservation back through time. However, the Neoproterozoic LIPs (2000–700 Ma) are mostly comparable in size with Phanerozoic continental LIPs (*blue dots*; in Fig. 12.3; see Fig. 12.1). This similarity in scale indicates that these Neo- and Meso-Proterozoic continental LIPs could be reasonably expected to have environmental changes similar in style and magnitude to those of Phanerozoic LIPs. On this basis it is plausible to use Neo- and Meso-Proterozoic LIPs (red dots) to define natural boundaries for the currently approximately defined chronostratigraphic boundaries (Table 12.2). On this basis it is also plausible to suggest that important Proterozoic LIPs (*green dots* in Fig. 12.3), which have a timing that falls inside chronostratigraphic system boundaries could also have driven major environmental effects and therefore represent potential second order Proterozoic chronostratigraphic boundaries.

12.7 Future work

There is a need for a more integrated and detailed comparison of LIPs and sedimentary records in order to (1) identify those LIPs that induced major environmental changes, as well as those that had minor, or no observable effects; (2) lead to better characterization of the specific factors of LIPs that cause sudden environmental change; and (3) allow proper integration of LIPs with other drivers of rapid environmental change such as bolide impacts (Alvarez et al., 1980; Richards et al., 2015), orogenic weathering (Macdonald et al., 2019; Park et al., 2020a), and biological evolution (Algeo and Scheckler, 1998; see also Esmeray-Senlet, 2020, Chapter 3L, Three Major Mass Extinctions and Evolutionary Radiations in Their Aftermath, this volume). Key to this progress is a sustained high-precision dating program of LIPs and time-correlative portions of the sedimentary record. Another research frontier is considering the linkage of Archean and Proterozoic LIP events to evolutionary steps since 3.9 Ga as revealed by genomic and fossil evidence (Betts et al., 2018).

Acknowledgments

REE partially supported by Canadian NSERC grant CRDPJ 523131-17 and Russian grants: RSF grant 18-17-00240 and Mega-Grant 14.Y26.31.0012. We acknowledge valued discussions with Steve Grasby, Nasser Youbi, Ken Buchan, and Andrey Bekker, and excellent feedback on the manuscript from Felix Gradstein.

Bibliography

Algeo, T.J., and Scheckler, S.E., 1998, Terrestrial-marine teleconnections in the Devonian: links between the evolution of land plants, weathering processes, and marine anoxic events, *Philosophical Transactions (B): Biological Sciences*, 353. Royal Society of London, pp. 113–130.

Alvarez, L.W., Alvarez, W., Asaro, F., and Michel, H.V., 1980, Extraterrestrial cause for the Cretaceous-Tertiary extinction. *Science*, **208** (4448), 1095–1108.

Baratoux, L., Söderlund, U., Ernst, R.E., De Roever, E., Jessell, M.W., Kamo, S., et al., 2019, New U–PB baddeleyite ages of mafic dyke swarms of the west African and Amazonian cratons: Implication for their configuration in supercontinents through time. *In* Srivastava, R.K.,

Ernst, R.E., and Peng, P. (eds), *Dyke Swarms of the World: A Modern Perspective*. Springer, Singapore, 263–314.

Bekker, A., 2015, Lomagundi carbon isotope excursion. *In* Amils, R., et al., (eds), *Encyclopedia of Astrobiology*. Springer, Berlin, Heidelberg.

Bekker, A., and Ernst, R., 2017, Do iron formations record periods of ocean plateau emplacement? *Goldschmidt Conference, Paris, 13–18 August 2017*.

Betts, H.C., Puttick, M.N., Clark, J.W., Williams, T.A., Donoghue, P.C.J., and Pisani, D., 2018, Integrated genomic and fossil evidence illuminates life's early evolution and eukaryote origin. *Nature Ecology & Evolution*, **2**: 1556–1562.

Bond, D.P.G., and Grasby, S.E., 2017, On the causes of mass extinctions. *Palaeogeography, Palaeoclimatology, Palaeoecology*, **478**: 3–29.

Blackburn, T.J., Olsen, P.E., Bowring, S.A., McLean, N.M., Kent, D.V., Puffer, J.H., et al., 2013, Zircon U–Pb geochronology links the end-Triassic extinction with the Central Atlantic Magmatic Province. *Science*, **340**: 941–945.

Bryan, S., and Ernst, R.E., 2008, Revised definition of large igneous provinces (LIPs). *Earth-Science Reviews*, **86**: 175–202.

Bryan, S.E., and Ferrari, L., 2013, Large igneous provinces and silicic large igneous provinces: progress in our understanding over the last 25 years. *Geological Society of America Bulletin*, **125**: 1053–1078.

Buchan, K.L., and Ernst, R.E., 2019, Giant circumferential dyke swarms: catalogue and characteristics. *In* Srivastava, R.K., Ernst, R.E., and Peng (eds), *Dyke Swarms of the World – A Modern Perspective*. Springer, 1–44.

Burgess, S.D., and Bowring, S.A., 2015, High-precision geochronology confirms voluminous magmatism before, during and after Earth's most severe extinction. *Science Advances*, **1** (7), e1500470, http://dx.doi.org/10.1126/sciadv.1500470.

Burgess, S.D., Bowring, S., and Shen, S.-Z., 2014, High-precision timeline for Earth's most severe extinction. *Proceedings of the National Academy of Sciences of the United States of America*, **111**: 3316–3321 [correction 2014, 111: 5050].

Burgess, S.D., Bowring, S.A., Fleming, T.H., and Elliot, D.H., 2015, High-precision geochronology links the Ferrar large igneous province with early-Jurassic ocean anoxia and biotic crisis. *Earth and Planetary Science Letters*, **415**: 90–99.

Charles, A., Condon, D., Harding, I., Pälike, H., Marshall, J., Cui, Y., et al., 2011, Constraints on the numerical age of the Palaeocene-Eocene boundary. *Geochemistry Geophysics Geosystems*, **12**: Q0AA17, https://doi.org/10.1029/2010GC003426.

Chaves, A.O., and Rezende, C.R., 2019, Fragments of 1.79-1.75 Ga large igneous provinces in reconstructing Columbia (Nuna): a Statherian supercontinent-superplume coupling? *Episodes*, **42**: 55–67.

Clapham, E., and Renne, P.R., 2019, Flood basalts and mass extinctions. *Annual Review of Earth and Planetary Sciences*, **47**: 275–303.

Coffin, M.F., and Eldholm, O., 1994, Large igneous provinces: crustal structure, dimensions, and external consequences. *Reviews of Geophysics*, **32**: 1–36.

Coffin, M.F., and Eldholm, O., 2001, Large igneous provinces: progenitors of some ophiolites? *In* Ernst, R.E., and Buchan, K.L. (eds), *Mantle Plumes: Their Identification Through Time*. Geological Society of America Special Paper, **352**: 59–70.

Courtillot, Y., 1994, Mass extinctions in the last 300 million years: one impact and seven flood basalts. *Israel Journal of Earth Sciences*, **43**: 255–266.

Courtillot, Y., 1999, *Evolutionary Catastrophes: The Science of Mass Extinctions*. Cambridge University Press, Cambridge.

Courtillot, Y., and Renne, P.R., 2003, On the ages of flood basalt events. *Comptes Rendus Geoscience*, **335**: 113–140.

Courtillot, Y., Fluteau, F., and Besse, J., 2015, Evidence for volcanism triggering extinctions: a short history of IPGP contributions with emphasis on paleomagnetism. *In* Schmidt, A., Fristad, K.E., and Elkins-Tanton, L.T. (eds), *Volcanism and Global Environmental Change*. Cambridge University Press.

Davies, J.H.F.L., Marzoli, A., Bertrand, H., Youbi, N., Ernesto, M., and Schaltegger, U., 2017, End-Triassic mass extinction started by intrusive CAMP activity. *Nature Communications*, **8**: art. no. 15596.

Dilek, Y., and Ernst, R., 2008, Links between ophiolites and Large Igneous Provinces (LIPs) in Earth history: introduction. *Lithos*, **100** (1), 1–13.

Doucet, L., Li, Z.-X., Ernst, R., Kirscher, U., el Dien, H.G., and Mitchell, R., 2020, Coupled supercontinent-superplume events evidenced by oceanic plume record. *Geology*, **48**: 159–163.

Ernst, R.E., 2014, *Large Igneous Provinces*. Cambridge University Press, 653 pp.

Ernst, R.E., and Bell, K., 2010, Large igneous provinces (LIPs) and carbonatites. *Mineralogy and Petrology*, **98** (1-4), 55–76.

Ernst, R.E., and Jowitt, S.M., 2013, Large igneous provinces (LIPs) and metallogeny. *In* Colpron, M., Bissig, T., Rusk, B.G., and Thompson, J.F.H. (eds), *Tectonics, Metallogeny, and Discovery: The North American Cordillera and Similar Accretionary Settings*. Society of Economic Geologists Special Publication, **17**: 17–51.

Ernst, R.E., and Youbi, N., 2017, How large igneous provinces affect global climate, sometimes cause mass extinctions, and represent natural markers in the geological record. *Palaeogeography, Palaeoclimatology, Palaeoecology*, **478**: 30–52.

Ernst, R.E., Wingate, M.T.D., Buchan, K.L., and Li, Z.X., 2008, Global record of 1600–700 Ma large igneous provinces (LIPs): implications for the reconstruction of the proposed Nuna (Columbia) and Rodinia supercontinents. *Precambrian Research*, **160**: 159–178.

Ernst, R.E., Hamilton, M.A., Söderlund, U., Hanes, J.A., Gladkochub, D.P., Okrugin, A.V., et al., 2016, Long-lived connection between southern Siberia and northern Laurentia in the Proterozoic. *Nature Geoscience*, **9**: 464–469.

Ernst, R.E., Davies, D.R., Jowitt, S.M., and Campbell, I.H., 2018, When do mantle plumes destroy diamonds? *Earth and Planetary Science Letters*, **502**: 244–252.

Ernst, R.E., Liikane, D.A., Jowitt, S.M., Buchan, K.L., and Blanchard, J.A., 2019, A new plumbing system framework for mantle plume-related continental large igneous provinces and their mafic-ultramafic intrusions. *Journal of Volcanology and Geothermal Research*, **384**: 75–84.

Ernst, R.E., Bond, D.P.G., Zhang, S.H., Buchan, K.L., Grasby, S.E., Youbi, N., et al., 2020, Large Igneous Province record through time and implications for secular environmental changes and Geological Time-Scale boundaries. *In* Ernst, R.E., Dickson, A.J., and Bekker, A. (eds), *Large Igneous Provinces: A Driver of Global Environmental and Biotic Changes*. AGU Geophysical Monograph, **255**: (in press).

Ernst, R.E., Dickson, A.J., Bekker, A. (eds.) *Large Igneous Provinces: A Driver of Global Environmental and Biotic Changes*. AGU Geophysical Monograph, **255** (in press).

Esmeray-Senlet, S., 2020, Three major mass extinctions and their evolutionary radiations in their aftermath. *In* Gradstein, F.M., Ogg, J.G., Schmitz, M.D., and Ogg, G.M. (eds), *The Geologic Time Scale 2020*. Elsevier Publ., **Vol. 1**: (this book).

Gradstein, F.M., Ogg, J.G., Schmitz, M.D., Ogg, G.M., Agterberg, F.P., Anthonissen, D.E., et al., 2012a, *The Geologic Time Scale 2012*. Elsevier, Boston, MA.

Gradstein, F.M., Ogg, J.G., and Hilgen, F.J., 2012b, On the geologic time scale. *Newsletters on Stratigraphy*, **45** (2), 171–188, http://dx.doi.org/10.1127/0078-0421/2012/0020.

Grasby, S.E., Them, T.R., Chen, Z.-H., Yin, R.-S., and Ardakani, O.H., 2019, Mercury as a proxy for volcanic emissions in the geologic record. *Earth-Science Reviews*, **196**, https://doi.org/10.1016/j.earscirev.2019.102880.

Gumsley, A., Sałacińska, A., Knoper, M., Mamuse, A., Chew, D., Söderlund, U., et al., 2019, The Kalahari craton in the fiery heart of Rodinia. *Abstract for Goldschmidt 2019, Barcelona, Spain, 18–23 August.*

Hamilton, M.A., and Buchan, K.L., 2010, U–Pb geochronology of the Western Channel Diabase, northwestern Laurentia: implications for a large 1.59 Ga magmatic province, Laurentia's APWP and paleocontinental reconstructions of Laurentia, Baltica and Gawler craton of southern Australia. *Precambrian Research*, **183** (3): 463–473.

Heimdal, T.H., Svensen, H.H., Ramezani, J., Iver, K., Pereira, E., Rodriques, R., et al., 2018, Large-scale sill emplacement in Brazil as a trigger for the end-Triassic crisis. *Scientific Reports*, **8**, Article number: 141.

ICS, 2019. *International Commission on Stratigraphy (ICS) Timescale, Version 2019/5.* http://www.stratigraphy.org/index.php/ics-chart-timescale.

Jones, M.T., Percival, L.M.E., Stokke, E.W., Frieling, J., Mather, T.A., Riber, L., et al., 2019, Mercury anomalies across the Palaeocene–Eocene Thermal Maximum. *Climate of the Past*, **15**: 217–236.

Kasbohm, J., and Schoene, B., 2018, Rapid eruption of the Columbia River flood basalt and correlation with the mid-Miocene climate optimum. *Science Advances*, **4**: eaat8223.

Kasbohm, J., Schoene, B., and Burgess, S., 2020, Radiometric constraints on the timing, tempo, and effects of large igneous province emplacement. *In* Ernst, R.E., Dickson, A.J., and Bekker, A. (eds), *Large Igneous Provinces: A Driver of Global Environmental and Biotic Changes.* AGU Geophysical Monograph, **255**: (in press).

Kerr, A.C., 2005, Oceanic LIPs: the kiss of death. *Elements*, **1**: 289–292.

Kerr, A.C., 2014, Oceanic plateaus. *In* Rudnick, R. (ed), *The Crust* (Treatise on Geochemistry, 2nd ed.). Elsevier, Amsterdam.

Kidder, D.L., and Worsley, T.R., 2010, Phanerozoic large igneous provinces (LIPs), HEATT (haline euxinic acidic thermal transgression) episodes, and mass extinctions. *Palaeogeography, Palaeoclimatology, Palaeoecology*, **295** (1-2), 162–191.

Kravchinsky, A., 2012, Paleozoic large igneous provinces of Northern Eurasia: correlation with mass extinction events. *Global and Planetary Change*, **86–87**: 31–36.

Linnemann, U., Ovtcharova, M., Schaltegger, U., Gärtner, A., Hautmann, M., Geyer, G., et al., 2018, New high-resolution age data from the Ediacaran–Cambrian boundary indicate rapid, ecologically driven onset of the Cambrian explosion. *Terra Nova*, https://doi.org/10.1111/ter.12368.

Macdonald, F.A., and Wordsworth, R., 2017, Initiation of Snowball Earth with volcanic sulfur aerosol emissions. *Geophysical Research Letters*, **44**: 1938–1946.

Macdonald, F.A., Schmitz, M.D., Crowley, J.L., Roots, C.F., Jones, D.S., Maloof, A.C., et al., 2010, Calibrating the Cryogenian. *Science*, **327**: 1241–1243.

Macdonald, F.A., Swanson-Hysell, N.L., Park, Y., Lisiecki, L., and Jagoutz, O., 2019, Arc-continent collisions in the tropics set Earth's climate state. *Science*, **364**: 181–184, https://doi.org/10.1126/science.aav5300.

Martin, A.P., Condon, D.J., Prave, A.R., et al., 2013, Dating the termination of the Palaeoproterozoic Lomagundi-Jatuli carbon isotopic event in the North Transfennoscandian Greenstone Belt. *Precambrian Research*, **224**: 160–168.

Melezhik, A., Huhma, H., Condon, D.J., Fallick, A.E., and Whitehouse, M.J., 2007, Temporal constraints on the Paleoproterozoic Lomagundi–Jatuli carbon isotopic event. *Geology*, **35**: 655–658.

Mungall, J.E., Kamo, S.L., and McQuade, S., 2016, U–Pb geochronology documents out-of-sequence emplacement of ultramafic layers in the Bushveld Igneous Complex of South Africa. *Nature Communications*, **7**: 13385, https://doi.org/10.1038/ncomms13385.

Ogg, J.G., Ogg, G.M., and Gradstein, F.M., 2016, *A Concise Geologic Time Scale 2016.* Elsevier, 243 pp. http://dx.doi.org/10.1016/B978-0-444-59467-9.00008-X.

Park, Y., Swanson-Hysell, N.L., Lisiecki, L.E., and Macdonald, F.A., 2020a, Evaluating the relationship between the area and latitude of large igneous provinces and Earth's long-term climate state. *In* Ernst, R.E., Bekker, A., and Dickson, A. (eds), *Environmental Change and Large Igneous Provinces: The Deadly Kiss of LIPs.* AGU book. (accepted).

Park, Y., Swanson-Hysell, N.L., Lisiecki, L.E., and Macdonald, F.A., 2020b, Evaluating the relationship between the area and latitude of large igneous provinces and Earth's long-term climate state. *In* Ernst, R.E., Dickson, A.J., and Bekker, A. (eds), *Large Igneous Provinces: A Driver of Global Environmental and Biotic Changes.* AGU Geophysical Monograph, **255**: (in press).

Pavlov, V.E., Gallet, Y., and Petrov, P.Y., 2019, A new Siberian record of the ~1.0 Gyr-old Maya superchron. *Precambrian Research*, **320**: 350–370.

Percival, L.M.E., Witt, M.L.I., Mather, T.A., Hermoso, M., Jenkyns, H.C., Hesselbo, S.P., et al., 2015, Globally enhanced mercury deposition during the end-Pliensbachian extinction and Toarcian OAE: a link to the Karoo-Ferrar Large Igneous Province. *Earth and Planetary Science Letters*, **428**: 267–280.

Percival, et al., 2020, Mercury as a tracer of Large Igneous Province volcanism. *In* Ernst, R.E., Dickson, A.J., and Bekker, A. (eds), *Large Igneous Provinces: A Driver of Global Environmental and Biotic Changes.* AGU Geophysical Monograph, **255**: (in press).

Pirajno, F., and Hoatson, D.M., 2012, A review of Australia's large igneous provinces and associated mineral systems: implications for mantle dynamics through geological time. *Ore Geology Reviews*, **48**: 2–54.

Rajesh, H.M., Chisonga, B.C., Shindo, K., Beukes, N.J., and Armstrong, R.A., 2013, Petrographic, geochemical and SHRIMPU–Pb titanite age characterization of the Thabazimbi mafic sills: extended time frame and a unifying petrogenetic model for the Bushveld Large Igneous Province. *Precambrian Research*, **230**: 79–102.

Rampino, M.R., and Caldeira, K., 1993, Major episodes of geologic change: correlations, time structure and possible causes. *Earth and Planetary Science Letters*, **114**: 215–227.

Rampino, M.R., and Stothers, R.B., 1988, Flood basalt volcanism during the past 250 million years. *Science*, **241**: 663–668, https://doi.org/10.1126/science.241.4866.663.

Reichow, M.K., Saunders, A.D., White, R.V., et al., 2002, 40Ar/39Ar dates from the West Siberian basin: Siberian flood basalt province doubled. *Science*, **296**: 1846–1849.

Reis, N.J., Teixeira, W., Hamilton, M.A., et al., 2013, Avanavero mafic magmatism, a late Paleoproterozoic LIP in the Guiana Shield, Amazonian Craton: U–Pb IDTIMS baddeleyite, geochemical and paleomagnetic evidence. *Lithos*, **174**: 175–195.

Richards, M.A., Alvarez, W., Self, S., Karlstrom, L., Renne, P.R., Manga, M., et al., 2015, Triggering of the largest Deccan eruptions by the Chicxulub impact. *Geological Society of America Bulletin*, **127** (11–12), 1507–1520, http://dx.doi.org/10.1130/B31167.1.

Rogers, C., Kamo, S.L., Soderlund, U., Hamilton, M.A., Ernst, R.E., Cousens, B., et al., 2018, Geochemistry and U-Pb geochronology of 1590 and 1550 Ma mafic dyke swarms of Western Laurentia: mantle plume magmatism shared with Australia. *Lithos*, **314–315**: 216–235.

Rooney, A.D., Strauss, J., Brandon, A.D., and Macdonald, F.A., 2015, A Cryogenian chronology: two long-lasting, synchronous Neoproterozoic Snowball Earth glaciations. *Geology*, **43**: 459–462.

Schaller, M.F., Fung, M.K., Wright, J.D., Katz, M.E., and Kent, D.V., 2016, Impact ejecta at the Paleocene-Eocene boundary. *Science*, **354**: 225–229.

Schaller, M.F., Turrin, B.D., Fung, M.K., Katz, M.E., and Swisher, C.C., 2019, Initial ^{40}Ar-^{39}Ar ages of the Paleocene-Eocene boundary impact spherules. *Geophysical Research Letters*, **46** (15): 9091–9102.

Schoene, B., Eddy, M.P., Samperton, K.M., Keller, C.B., Keller, G., Adatte, T., et al., 2019, U-Pb constraints on pulsed eruption of the Deccan Traps across the end-Cretaceous mass extinction. *Science*, **363**: 862–866.

Shumlyanskyy, L., Mitrokhin, O., Billström, K., Ernst, R., Vishnevska, E., Tsymbal, S., et al., 2016, The ca. 1.8 Ga mantle plume related magmatism of the central part of the Ukrainian shield. *GFF*, **138** (1), 86–101.

Sprain, C.J., Renne, P.R., Vanderkluysen, L., Pande, K., Self, S., and Mittal, T., 2019, The eruptive tempo of Deccan volcanism in relation to the Cretaceous-Paleogene boundary. *Science*, **363** (6429), 866–870.

Stark, J.C., Wang, X.-C., Li, Z.-X., Denyszyn, S.W., Rasmussen, B., and Zi, J.-W., 2018, 1.39 Ga mafic dyke swarm in southwestern Yilgarn Craton marks Nuna to Rodinia transition in the West Australian Craton. *Precambrian Research*, **316**: 291–304.

Stepanova, A.V., Salnikova, E.B., Samsonov, A.V., Egorova, S.V., Larionova, Y.O., and Stepanov, S., 2015, The 2.31 Ga mafic dykes in the Karelian Craton, eastern Fennoscandian shield: U–Pb age, source characteristics and implications for continental break-up processes. *Precambrian Research*, **259**: 43–57.

Svensen, H., Planke, S., Polozov, A.G., Schmidbauer, N., Corfu, F., Podladchikov, Y.Y., et al., 2009, Siberian gas venting and the end-Permian environmental crisis. *Earth and Planetary Science Letters*, **277**: 490–500.

Svensen, H., Corfu, F., Polteau, S., Hammer, Ø., and Planke, S., 2012, Rapid magma emplacement in the Karoo large igneous province. *Earth and Planetary Science Letters*, **325–326**: 1–9, http://dx.doi.org/10.1016/j.epsl.2012.01.015.

Svensen, H.H., Torsvik, T.H., Callegaro, S., Augland, L., Heimdal, T.H., Jerram, D.A., et al., 2017, Gondwana large igneous provinces: plate reconstructions, volcanic basins and sill volumes. *Geological Society, London, Special Publications*, **463**: 17–40, https://dx.doi.org/10.1144/SP463.7.

Svensen, H.H., Planke, S., Neumann, E.-R., Aarnes, I., Marsh, J.S., Polteau, S., et al., 2018, Sub-volcanic intrusions and the link to global climatic and environmental change. *In* Breitkreuz, C., and Rocchi, S. (eds), *Physical Geology of Shallow Magmatic Systems: Dykes, Sills and Laccoliths*. Springer, pp. 249–272.

Teixeira, W., D'Agrella-Filho, M.S., Ernst, R.E., Hamilton, M.A., Girardi, A.V., Mazzucchelli, M., et al., 2013, U-Pb (ID-TIMS) baddeleyite ages and paleomagnetism of 1.79 and 1.50 Ga tholeiitic dyke swarms, and position of the Rio de la Plata craton within the Columbia supercontinent. *Lithos*, **174**: 157–174.

Van Kranendonk, M.J., Altermann, W., Beard, B.L., Hoffman, P.F., Johnson, C.M., Kasting, J.F., et al., 2012, A chronostratigraphic division of the Precambrian: possibilities and challenges. *In* Gradstein, F. M., Ogg, J.G., and Schmitz, M. (eds), *The Geologic Time Scale 2012*: 299–392, http://dx.doi.org/10.1016/B978-0-444-59425-9.00016-0.

Verbaas, J., Thorkelson, D.J., Milidragovic, D., Crowley, J.L., Foster, D., Gibson, H.D., et al., 2018, Rifting of western Laurentia at 1.38 Ga: the Hart River sills of Yukon, Canada. *Lithos*, **316–317**: 243–260.

White, R.V., and Saunders, A.D., 2005, Volcanism, impact and mass extinctions: incredible or credible coincidences? *Lithos*, **79**: 299–316, https://doi.org/10.1016/j.lithos.2004.09.016.

Wignall, P.B., 2001, Large igneous provinces and mass extinctions. *Earth-Science Reviews*, **53**: 1–33.

Wignall, P.B., 2005, The link between large igneous province eruptions and mass extinctions. *Elements*, **1**: 293–297.

Wilkinson, C., Ganerød, M., Hendriks, B., and Eide, E., 2016, Compilation and appraisal of geochronological data from the North Atlantic Igneous Province (NAIP). *In* Péron-Pinvidic, G., Hopper, J. R., Stoker, M.S., Gaina, C., Doornenbal, J.C., Funck, T., and Árting, U.E. (eds), *The NE Atlantic Region: A Reappraisal of Crustal Structure, Tectonostratigraphy and Magmatic Evolution*. Geological Society, Special Publications, **447**: 69–103, https://doi.org/10.1144/SP447.10.

Youbi, N., Ernst, R.E., Söderlund, U., Boumehdi, M.A., Ait Lahna, A., Tassinari, C.C.G., et al., 2020a, The Central Iapetus magmatic province: An updated review and link with the ca. 580 Ma Gaskiers glaciation. *In* Adatte T., Bond, D.P.G., and Keller, G. (eds), *Mass Extinctions, Volcanism, and Impacts: New Developments*. Geological Society of America Special Paper, **544**, https://doi.org/10.1130/2020.2544(02).

Youbi, N., Ernst, R.E., Mitchell, R., Boumehdi, M.A., El Moume, W., Ait Lahna, A., et al., 2020b, Large Igneous Provinces as a potential trigger for glaciations with special reference to the Neoproterozoic Era and the Phanerozoic Eon. *In* Ernst, R.E., Dickson, A.J., and Bekker, A. (eds), *Large Igneous Provinces: A Driver of Global Environmental and Biotic Changes*. AGU Geophysical Monograph, **255**: (in press).

Zhang, S.-H., Ernst, R.E., Pei, J.-L., Zhao, Y., Zhou, M.-F., and Hu, G.-H., 2018, A temporal and causal link between ~1380 Ma large igneous provinces and black shales: implications for the Mesoproterozoic time-scale and paleoenvironment. *Geology*, **46**: 963–966.

Zhang, S.-H., Ernst, R.E., Pei, J.-L., Zhao, Y., and Hu, G.-H., 2020, LIPs (large igneous provinces) and anoxia events in 'the Boring Billion'. *In* Ernst, R.E., Dickson, A.J., and Bekker, A. (eds), *Large Igneous Provinces: A Driver of Global Environmental and Biotic Changes*. AGU Geophysical Monograph, **255**: (in press).

M.D. Simmons, K.G. Miller, D.C. Ray, A. Davies, F.S.P. van Buchem and B. Gréselle

Chapter 13

Phanerozoic Eustasy

Chapter outline

Abstract

Isolation of the eustatic signal from the sedimentary record remains challenging, yet much progress is being made toward understanding the timing, magnitude, and rate of eustasy on both long-term (10^7-10^8 years) and short-term (10^5-10^6 years) scales throughout the Phanerozoic. Long-term eustasy is primarily driven by a number of factors relating to plate tectonics. The magnitude and rate of short-term eustatic change strongly suggests glacio-eustasy as the key driving mechanism, even in episodes of the Earth's history often typified as having "greenhouse" climates. This notion is, in turn, supported by a growing body of both direct and proxy evidence for relatively substantial polar glaciation in many periods of the Earth's history (with the possible exception of the Triassic). An understanding of eustasy is important for the development of the geologic time scale because it contributes to the sequence stratigraphic organization of sedimentary successions (including chronostratigraphic reference sections) and helps to understand the often incomplete nature of the geologic record. The integration of eustasy with our evolving knowledge of the Earth systems science (e.g., paleoclimate evolution, orbital forcing of sedimentary systems, geochemical evolution of the oceans, and biological evolutions and extinctions) will help to provide the tools to develop a context for the subdivisions of the geologic time scale.

13.1 Introduction

Ever since the great Austrian geologist Suess (1888, 1906) introduced the term "eustatic movements" to describe globally recognizable and synchronous transgressions and regressions in the geological past, geoscientists have sought to better understand eustasy and its expression in the rock record. The early 20th century pioneers, such as Chamberlin (1909) and Grabau (1936a,b, 1940), argued for a "rhythm of the ages," the global signature of eustasy in the rock record (Johnson, 1992; Pemberton et al., 2016; Simmons, 2018).

The study of eustasy became somewhat neglected in the 1950s and 1960s, with the attention of many geologists focused on the development of the plate tectonics paradigm [although see Hallam (1963) for an early example of the integration of eustasy with the developments in marine geology that would shape plate tectonics]. Eustasy returned to the forefront of thinking in sedimentary geology in the late 1970s with the publication of the seminal paper on eustasy and its relationship to the concepts of sequence stratigraphy by Vail et al. (1977) at Exxon Production Research (EPR). Vail et al. published a much cited Phanerozoic global sea-level curve that would continue to be substantially revised in later years (Haq et al., 1987, 1988; Hardenbol et al., 1998; Haq and Schutter, 2008; Haq, 2014, 2017, 2018).

Much of the original work by Vail, Haq, and the EPR team was based on subsurface geology: the perceived expression of eustasy in biostratigraphically calibrated seismic and wire line log data. Because confidentiality restrictions prevented much of this data from being published, the proofs of the early eustatic models from this team were not available, which was a cause of significant criticism

Geologic Time Scale 2020. DOI: https://doi.org/10.1016/B978-0-12-824360-2.00013-9

(e.g., Miall, 1991, 1992; Miall and Miall, 2001). This uncertainty led many other stratigraphers worldwide to seek supporting evidence of the EPR models, or to develop alternative models, often based on outcrop geology (e.g., Embry, 1988, 1997; Hallam, 1992, 2001; Sahagian et al., 1996; House and Ziegler, 1997; Johnson et al., 1998; Izart et al., 2003; Miller et al., 2005a; Simmons et al., 2007; and see Section 13.4).

Eustasy refers to global sea level that is independent of local factors, namely, the position of the sea surface with reference to a fixed datum (Myers and Milton, 1996) (Fig. 13.1). Because such a datum level is often lacking or equivocal, geologists who use the term eustasy are often referring to global mean sea level (GMSL) (Gregory et al., 2019; Miller et al., 2020). Nonetheless, the terms eustasy, eustatic sea level, and eustatic change are persistent in the geological literature (Rovere et al., 2016) and are maintained here.

Geoscientists continue to seek to understand the timing, magnitude, pace, and drivers of eustasy in the rock record. Beyond simple scientific curiosity, there are practical reasons for this. For example, identifying the eustatic component of sequence stratigraphic models enhances their use by improving the ability to predict the likely lateral and vertical variation in sedimentary facies with the framework of stacking patterns (van Buchem and Simmons, 2017) and aids correlation. These factors have value in the search for hydrocarbon source rocks and reservoirs, which is why the study of eustasy has resonated with industry geologists. However, the application of eustasy is not without its challenges. For example, assuming eustasy as a basis for correlation can become a self-fulfilling prophecy; consequently, there is a danger of circular reasoning (see Miall, 2010 and references therein). Nonetheless, *if* a eustatic signal can be isolated in the rock record and constrained using biostratigraphy and other chronostratigraphic proxy techniques, then it can be used as a *guide* to the correlation of transgressive and regressive sedimentary successions (bearing in mind the controls of tectonics and sediment supply on the nature of local sedimentary successions).

Within the context of the geologic time scale an understanding of eustasy is important because it emphasizes the typically incomplete nature of the stratigraphic record, especially in facies deposited from alluvial plains to continental shelves and epicontinental seas (Barrell, 1917; Ager, 1981, 1993). High-amplitude eustatic changes will drive the presence of widespread unconformities and attendant hiatuses and assist in understanding whether or not chronostratigraphic reference sections [Global Boundary Stratotype Sections and Points (GSSPs)] are likely to contain continuous stratigraphy. An understanding of whether such sections are placed in transgressive or regressive settings can also help to facilitate their correlation. Furthermore, as understanding of eustasy evolves, it can assist in the placement of chronostratigraphic boundaries by relating them to widely correlatable events in the rock record that can have a distinctive expression (Simmons, 2012). Peter Vail's comment "using global cycles with their natural and significant boundaries, an international system of geochronology can be developed on a rational basis" (Vail et al., 1977) has failed to find much favor with the chronostratigraphic community, mainly because the expression of eustasy in the rock record is variable in time and space, and thus continues to be debated. Nonetheless, as Phanerozoic eustatic models become stable,

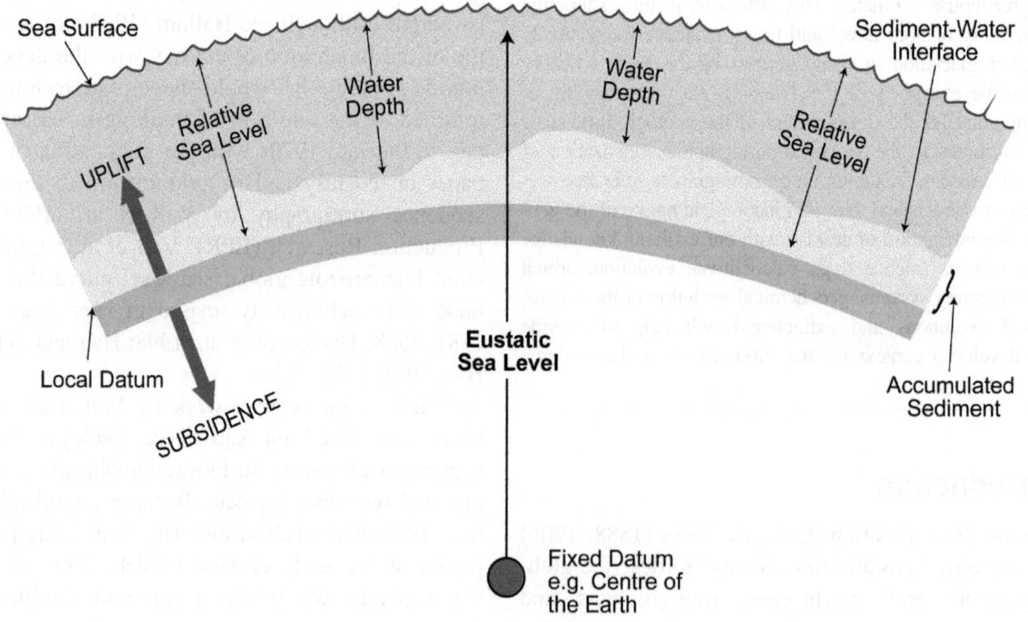

FIGURE 13.1 Illustration of eustasy, relative sea level, and water depth. After Myers and Milton (1996).

then eustasy can provide a clear guide to the formal subdivision of geologic time.

Indeed, there is an increasing integration of eustasy with chronostratigraphic definitions. For example, Babcock et al. (2015) noted that the first appearance datums of agnostoid trilobites, which are the primary correlation events for the bases of the Drumian, Guzhangian, Pabian, and Jiangshanian stages of the Cambrian, are associated with eustatic rises, and with oceanographic and climatic cycles. Such holistic approaches to chronostratigraphic definition that integrate GSSPs with various aspects of the Earth system science (including eustasy) are to be applauded: the proposed GSSP for the base of the Lopingian (Permian) stage is a further example (Jin et al., 2006), whereas Triassic stages have long been linked to eustatic cycles (Embry, 1997).

Identifying eustasy in the rock record is not easy. Major challenges exist to prove synchroneity, magnitude, and pace. Driving mechanisms are much debated outside of the well-established episodes of major polar glaciation that Chamberlin (1899) first recognized as a driver of sea-level change. Entire books (e.g., Miall, 2010) have been published justly emphasizing how difficult these challenges are. Although much work is still needed to improve our understanding of Phanerozoic eustasy, here we hope to demonstrate that knowledge of the timing, magnitude, duration, and drivers of eustasy is evolving, at least in the sense of what Johnson et al. (1991) termed "practical eustasy," and that this can provide insight into the development of the stratigraphic record and geologic time scale.

13.2 The sequence stratigraphy paradigm and eustasy

13.2.1 Sequence stratigraphy

The recognition of eustasy in the rock record is possible through an understanding of the principles of sequence stratigraphy. Sequence stratigraphy relies on recognizing changes in the space available for sediments to accumulate (accommodation), of which eustasy is but one driver, versus sediment supply. The technique builds upon the long-established geologic concept that the sedimentary rock record displays cycles that can be linked to water depth changes (e.g., Barrell, 1917). It enables the identification of packages of strata that were deposited during similar conditions of accommodation change (stationary, increasing, or decreasing) in relation to sediment supply, and the key stratigraphic surfaces that bound them.

Changes in accommodation relate to the interplay of various independent factors. In the marine realm, accommodation relates to relative sea level (RSL) that, in turn, is primarily controlled by tectonism (subsidence or uplift, including the effects of thermal subsidence, sediment loading, flexure, isostasy, and dynamic topography); changes in the height of the geoid driven by the changing distribution of ice and ocean mass; and short-term (10- to 1000-year scale) oceanographic effects and eustasy. Sediment supply also has a large effect on depositional architecture because changes in sedimentation affect how accommodation is filled. For example, the modern Mississippi delta is currently entering a phase of retrogradation in response to a 50% reduction in the sediment load of the river resulting from the construction of numerous dams (Maloney et al., 2018). These factors control the sequence stratigraphic architecture in every sedimentary basin (Catuneanu, 2019a, 2019b). Consequently, when making a sequence stratigraphic interpretation, it is necessary to consider changes in both the rate of accommodation (A) change (creation or destruction) and changes in the sediment supply (S). Therefore the A:S relationship is critical in determining stratigraphic architecture.

RSL is defined as a change in accommodation (vertical space) relative to the crust, determined by rates of sea-level change and subsidence/uplift (Jervey, 1988; Posamentier and Vail, 1988), although it can be defined more precisely as the difference in height between the sea surface and the solid Earth (Milne et al., 2009; Gregory et al., 2019) (Fig. 13.1). RSL is important because it is the local/region expression of sea-level change, from which the eustatic component must be extracted to develop a view on the timing, magnitude, and rate of eustasy. Subsequent subsections discuss the complexities of this undertaking. However, local sequence stratigraphic models are effectively built from knowledge of change in RSL.

The organization of the stratigraphic record is multiscale. The genetic unit, or parasequence, is the basic building block. Facies distribution within parasequences and how parasequences stack can differ. The characteristic stratal stacking patterns resulting from changes in accommodation and sediment supply are classified as (Fig. 13.2):

- "Aggradational," when sediments of the same facies stack broadly vertically. Here, the creation of accommodation and sediment supply are broadly in balance ($A = S$).
- "Retrogradational,"' when facies belts display a landward movement. Here, accommodation creation exceeds sediment supply ($A > S$). This can often occur during RSL rise.
- "Progradational," when facies belts display a basinward movement. Here, sediment supply exceeds accommodation creation ($A < S$) and can often occur when RSL is stationary. "Forced progradation" is a type of progradation related to the active destruction of accommodation (by a drop in RSL), when sediments are forced to prograde, irrespective of sediment supply.

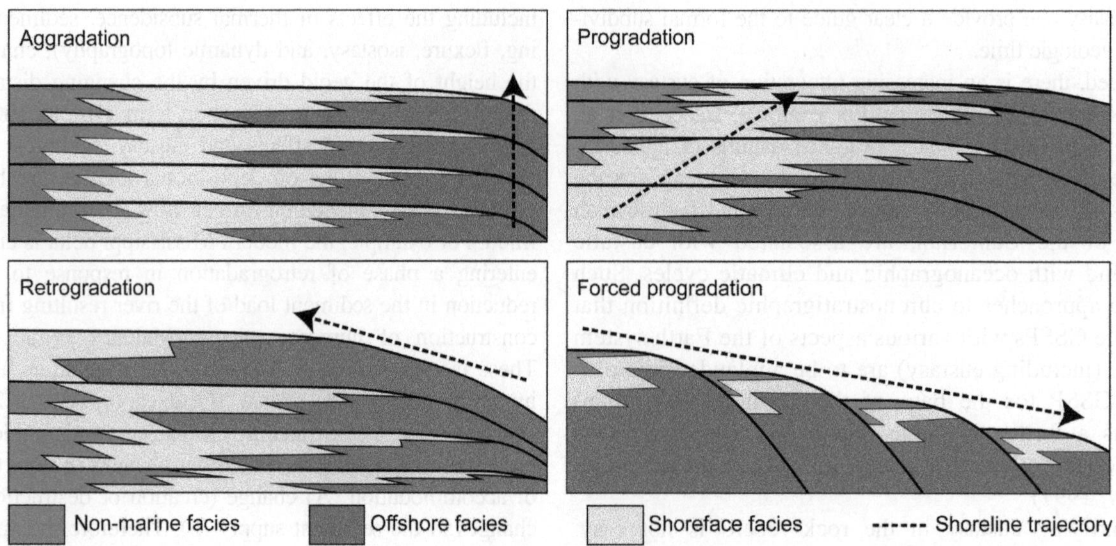

FIGURE 13.2 Stratal stacking patterns relating to the evolution of accommodation versus sedimentation rate over time. Modified after Van Wagoner et al. (1988).

A systems tract (Vail, 1987) represents a series of linked contemporaneous facies, deposited during a particular regime of accommodation creation or reduction (and consequently very often a particular state of RSL change). It is important to note that depositional systems will react differently to accommodation change and will produce and/or transport sediment in different ways. A key distinction can be made between clastic and carbonate systems because carbonates can grow rapidly in situ (Schlager, 2005). Similarly, evaporite systems react distinctively to variations in A/S. However, many of the basic principles are common and can be summarized as follows (Fig. 13.3):

- *Transgressive systems tract (TST)*. When the creation of accommodation outpaces sediment supply, such as during periods of rapid sea-level rise or when sediment supply is dramatically reduced, stratal stacking patterns display a retrogradation pattern. Sediments deposited under these conditions are grouped into a TST. TST deposits display a rising shoreline trajectory (the path taken by the shoreline as it changes position in response to accommodation change; see Fig. 13.3) as the shoreface transgresses toward the land. The top of the TST is marked by a maximum flooding surface (MFS) that represents the most landward migration of the shoreline and the maximum amount of accommodation creation. In carbonate systems, different types of response are possible to RSL rise (e.g., Schlager, 2005), one of which is the development of isolated carbonate buildups during the TST that may be drowned, if the creation of accommodation is sufficiently rapid.
- *Highstand systems tract* (HST). Above the TST, sediments occur that comprise the HST. They are characterized by initial aggradation, reflecting a balance between accommodation creation and sediment supply, and later by progradation, as sediment supply outpaces any new accommodation creation. In the marine realm, HST sediments record the slowing of RSL rise. HST sediments display a rising, followed by flat, shoreline trajectory.
- *Lowstand systems tract (LST) and falling stage systems tract (FSST)*. The top of the HST is marked by the sequence boundary (SB), which reflects the onset of the active destruction of accommodation, resulting from a drop in RSL. Sediments deposited under these conditions are forced to prograde, irrespective of sediment supply, and display a falling shoreline trajectory. They may form part of the LST or be classified into a discrete FSST. After baselevel fall has ceased, sediment supply may outpace accommodation creation, so that sediments continue to prograde. Sediments deposited under these conditions form part of the LST and display a rising shoreline trajectory. The top of the LST is marked by a maximum regression surface (MRS) or transgressive surface (TS), representing the most basinward migration of the shoreline. Although the MRS or TS is locally erosional, it can be usually distinguished from the SB by its local distribution and stacking patterns; in the absence of LSTs, MRS merge with SB.

At the larger scale, when several sequences are stacked together, the same descriptive terminology as defined previously (Fig. 13.2) can be used to describe the sequence stacking pattern. This notion of scale is important because the application of the principle of systems tracts applies at different scales. Although the expression of changing accommodation versus sediment supply is well understood, the exact means of classifying the different systems tracts

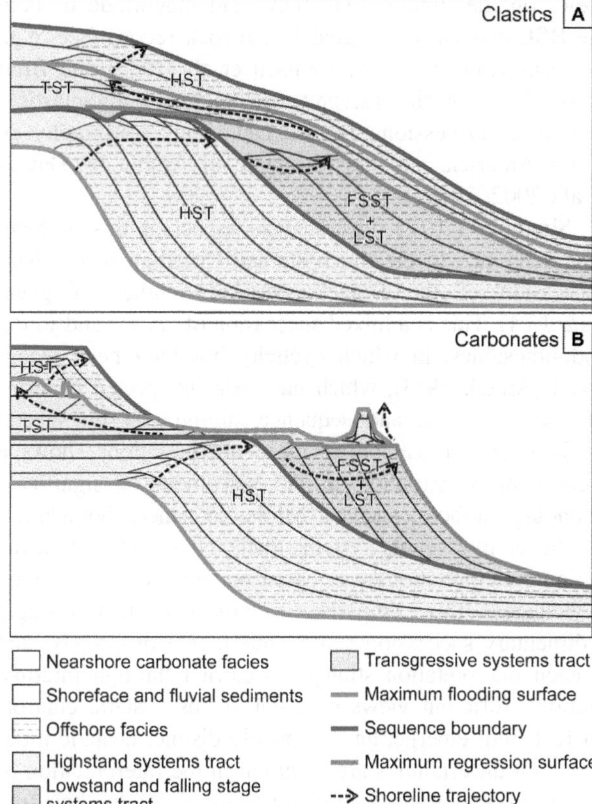

FIGURE 13.3 The typical response of a clastic depositional system (A), and one of the possible responses of a carbonate depositional system (B) to changes in accommodation. Stratal stacking patterns and shoreline trajectory help define three systems tracts (the FSST has been grouped into the LST) and their bounding stratal surfaces. Note the potential to form isolated carbonate buildups during transgression. *FSST*, falling stage systems tract; *HST*, highstand systems tract; *LST*, lowstand systems tract; *TST*, transgressive systems tract.

and stratal surfaces remains a subject of preference and debate (see Catuneanu et al., 2009; Donovan et al., 2010; Catuneanu, 2017, 2019a,b; Miller et al., 2018 and discussion in Simmons, 2012). For example, some authors do not recognize an FSST, and others place the SB at the top of the FSST. The identification of systems tracts and key stratal surfaces in various data types (outcrops, seismic, well logs) and the relationship of these features to position on a RSL curve can vary between different schools of thought, as recently reviewed by Neal and Abreu (2009), Miller et al. (2018), and Catuneanu (2019a). One commonality is the salience and pervasive nature of the MFS, which has led some to propose defining "sequences" not on SBs (unconformities) but on MFS ("genetic stratigraphy"; Galloway, 1989). Previous studies have shown that these approaches are useful on longer time scales and larger spatial scales for regional basin scale stratigraphy (e.g., Sharland et al., 2001) but lack the resolution for reservoir-scale interpretations (Miller et al., 2018).

13.2.2 Synchronous sea-level change

As previously noted, eustasy is one of several factors that control sequence stratigraphic organization of a sedimentary succession. The ongoing challenge is to disentangle eustatic influences from the various local controls to demonstrate that synchronous sequence stratigraphic surfaces exist in multiple sedimentary basins worldwide. Therefore a key challenge to recognizing eustasy in the rock record is the ability to confirm the synchroneity of changes in sea level through chronostratigraphically significant calibration, typically using biostratigraphy (Armentrout, 2019). Such techniques have inherent limitations. These include:

- Do biozones offer sufficient precision to unequivocally confirm synchroneity? For many biozonation schemes based on planktonic fossils, individual biozones can be of a duration of 500,000 years or less, but this is variable. In well-studied basins, such as the Neogene Gulf of Mexico, biostratigraphic resolution approaches that of cyclostratigraphy with average biozonal duration being 144,000 years (Bergen et al., 2019). Although the recognition of biozones defined by bioevents (typically extinctions and inceptions of taxa) remains the default method of conducting biostratigraphy, other approaches, including quantitative and semiquantitative methods, consider the whole fossil assemblage present, rather than the presence or absence of marker species. Such techniques include graphic correlation (e.g., Edwards, 1989) and constrained optimization (CONOP; Sadler, 2004). Such techniques, where applicable, provide a much higher temporal resolution for correlation than traditional biostratigraphy (Cooper et al., 2001).
- How well-calibrated are different biozonation schemes and bioevents to one another and to the geologic time scale? The correlation of RSL events in multiple sections around the globe often requires the use of a variety of biozonation schemes and fossil groups. For example, nearshore successions will contain different fossil assemblages to basinal successions; consequently, the correlation between them requires the calibration of different biozonation schemes. At a global scale, endemism may complicate calibration. Although the calibration of biozonal schemes against one another and the geologic time scale has progressed greatly in recent years (see, e.g., the charts within this book), inherent uncertainties exist (e.g., Luber et al., 2019 provides an example of calibration uncertainty between Cretaceous ammonites, planktonic foraminifera, and the subdivisions of the Aptian stage).
- Issues around reworking, caving (in well-based samples), identification of fossils, and knowledge of their stratigraphic range.

Put simply, the use of fossils for precise correlation and age calibration is not straightforward (Simmons, 2015).

Nonetheless, numerous examples exist in which biostratigraphy can provide high-resolution correlation within astronomically calibrated time scales in the order of 10^5 years (e.g., Gale et al., 2002, 2008).

The use of stable isotopes (e.g., $\delta^{13}C$ and $\delta^{18}O$) holds great promise for precise correlation (Saltzman and Thomas, 2012; Grossman, 2012; Jarvis et al., 2006; Bergström et al., 2008; Cramer et al., 2010a,b), but trends in the variation of these isotopes may be nonunique and can be subject to diagenetic alteration. As a result, they tend to be supported by biostratigraphy and require a good understanding of sedimentology and diagenesis. The $^{86}Sr/^{87}Sr$ ratios of sedimentary rocks, especially carbonates, are another potential correlation technique (McArthur et al., 2012). Again, the values are nonunique and, for some parts of the geologic record, the values remain constant for periods of significant duration. In other intervals, such as the Miocene, the $^{86}Sr/^{87}Sr$ ratio values change significantly through time, and the methodology has been applied to great effect for age determination and correlation (Ehrenberg et al., 2007; van Buchem et al., 2010a).

Despite these limitations, meaningful correlations of sections can be made with the overlap of the age range of an event in different sections pointing toward its precise timing (Sharland et al., 2001; Armentrout, 2019). Even in undated sequences (e.g., barren of fossils), superposition between well-dated sequences can provide resolution of a fraction of a biozone (e.g., Browning et al., 2013). Error bars will always exist, but within the current limitations of correlation techniques, many sea-level events in the Phanerozoic appear to be synchronous, being tied to a single, reasonably short-duration biozone or isotopic excursion event (see, e.g., worked examples from the Paleozoic in Simmons et al., 2007 and Simmons, 2012; and from the Mesozoic in Gale et al., 2002, 2008; Simmons, 2012).

13.2.3 Challenges in recognizing sea-level change and the eustatic signal

Interpretations of the sedimentary record in terms of changing depositional environments (that in a marine setting, we would relate to changing water depth) date back to the early history of geoscience (e.g., Cuvier and Brongniart, 1811). Nonetheless, the interpretation of a succession of facies can be challenging and requires an interpretation strategy. This strategy must be used consistently if multiple successions are to be studied and commonality recognized. Such an approach is a prerequisite to isolating the eustatic signal that also requires high-resolution chronostratigraphic calibration. Differences in interpretation strategy of facies successions and of chronostratigraphic proxies can ultimately lead to different views on the timing, frequency, and magnitude of both the RSL and eustatic signal in the rock record (see, e.g., the contrasting views of Johnson et al. (1985) and Brett et al. (2011) on the interpretation of mixed siliciclastic–carbonate successions in the Devonian stratigraphy of North America, and the Mesozoic of Arabia by Davies et al., 2002, 2019b).

Simmons (2012) illustrated an aspect of this problem with reference to the much studied Corallian (Oxfordian) succession of the Dorset coast of southern England (Fig. 13.4). This is a mixed succession of clays, sandstones, and limestones, in which cyclicity has long been recognized (Arkell, 1933), which has been interpreted in terms of changing RSL and sequence stratigraphy by several workers. A comparison of these interpretations shows a great deal of variation in the placement of significant bounding surfaces, such as MFSs, sequences boundaries, and hence intervening systems tracts. No doubt each of the various interpretations was based on thoughtful reasoning. Nonetheless, this comparison demonstrates that a single sedimentary succession can be interpreted differently, and if each interpretation strategy is carried through multiple sections, different views on local versus eustatic controls on RSL will emerge, and ultimately distinct eustatic models. Such uncertainties are common in the interpretation of geologic data because geoscientists are biased by their specialist skills and experience (Bond et al., 2007).

The recognition of RSL change in good resolution seismic data at an appropriate scale is arguably less contentious (Christie-Blick et al., 1990; Catuneanu, 2006; Neal and Abreu, 2009; Miller et al., 2018). This is because seismic data demonstrates the geometrical relationship of sedimentary systems within two-dimensional transects or within three-dimensional volumes. In other words, the progradational, aggradational, or retrogradational response of sediments to changes in accommodation and sedimentation is clear from the geometries visible within the seismic data. More importantly, the shelf-edge and shoreface trajectories can be recognized, providing clear insights into RSL and sediment supply.

In addition, the stratal geometries visible within seismic data can be replicated in flume tank experiments, computer models, and observed in large-scale outcrops, allowing a straightforward interpretation of RSL change (Miller et al., 2018). Indeed, it was the assessment of large amounts of seismic data that first led Peter Vail and his coworkers at EPR to develop the modern sequence stratigraphy paradigm (Vail, 1992).

However, the timing of the changes observed can be less easy to determine because it requires biostratigraphic calibration from well data that intersects the seismic lines. This may be of variable resolution depending, for example, on the quality of samples (e.g., cuttings versus cores) and the types of microfossil used. Nonetheless, where there is

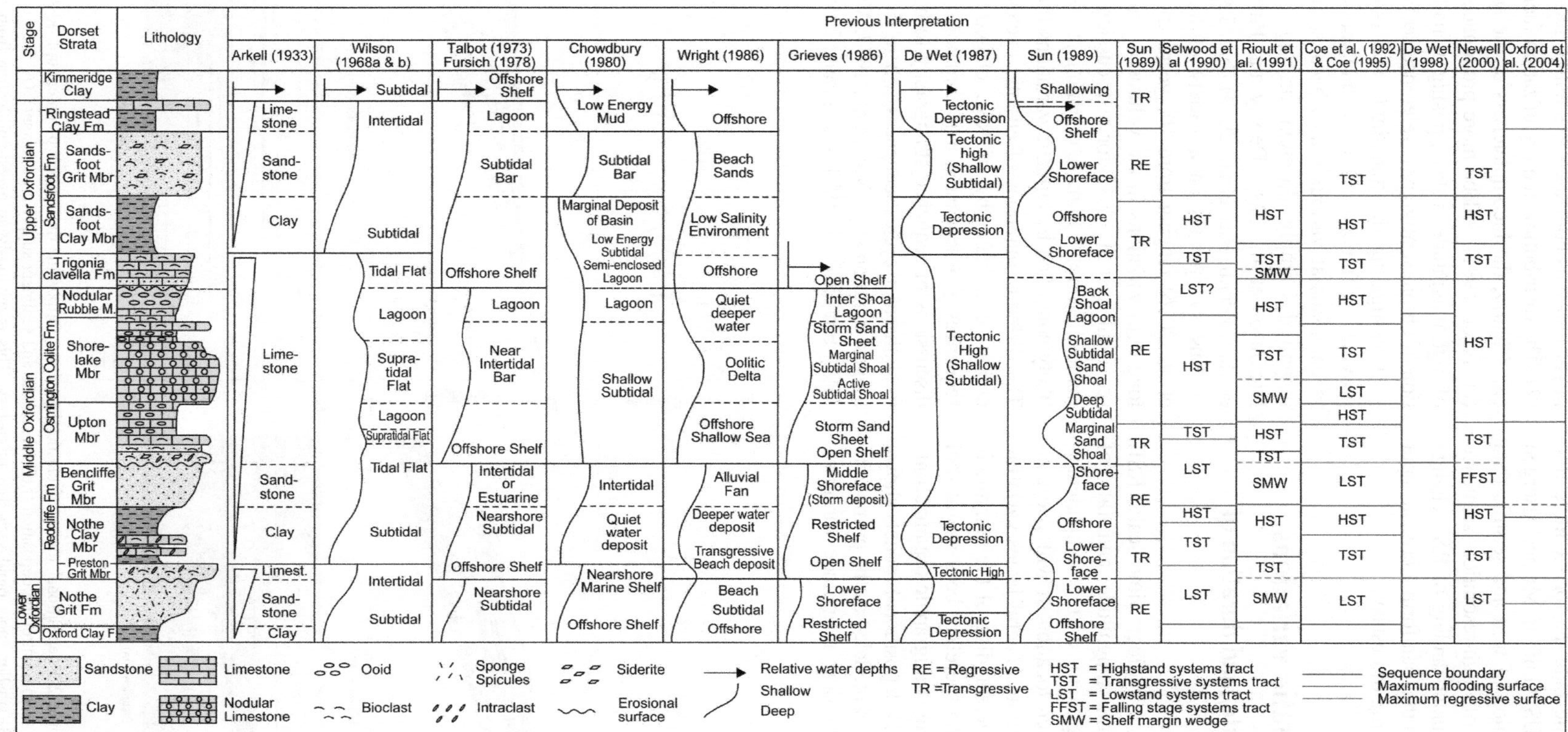

FIGURE 13.4 Comparison of different interpretations of the Corallian (Oxfordian) succession of the Dorset coast, southern England (following earlier comparisons by Sun, 1989; Newell, 2000; Oxford et al., 2004). Different strategies can exist for the interpretation of sea-level variation in the same succession of facies. An internally consistent and robust strategy needs to be developed when attempting to develop a global model of eustasy from a compilation of individual synchronous stratigraphic sections. Differences in interpretation strategy can explain differences between global sea-level curves. After Simmons (2012).

abundant, high-quality, and precisely chronostratigraphically calibrated biostratigraphic data, as for example, the Cenozoic sediments of the US Gulf of Mexico (Bergen et al., 2019), then the integration of well and seismic data can lead to the generation of high-resolution sequence stratigraphic models and an understanding of RSL change (e.g., Armentrout, 1996, 2019) that can form a critical input into developing an understanding of eustasy.

13.3 Anatomy of eustatic variations

13.3.1 The magnitude, rate, and duration of eustatic cycles

In the context of developing a geologic time scale, RSL change (as influenced by the magnitude and rate of eustasy) will be a controlling factor on the completeness of the rock record at any given location. It will also control the stratal stacking pattern and lateral facies variation within systems tracts. An understanding of the magnitude and rate of eustatic cycles can therefore be a useful tool for those engaged in predicting stratigraphic organization.

Consider the two simple 2D depositional models shown in Fig. 13.5, in which eustasy is modeled as the prime control on RSL. Large, relatively slow magnitude variations (1) produce more stratigraphically incomplete sections over larger areas, as compared to smaller, more rapid variations (2). The distribution and organization facies are also different. Clearly, the incompleteness of the stratigraphic record (cf. Ager, 1981) will be more pronounced during episodes of high-magnitude eustasy, posing a challenge to the selection of chronostratigraphic reference sections.

Investigating the magnitude and rate of eustasy also provides a crucial step to understanding its driving mechanisms at various scales because different rates and magnitudes imply different driving mechanisms (e.g., Dickinson et al., 1994; Dewey and Pitman, 1998; Miller et al., 2005a,b; Ray et al., 2019) (Fig. 13.6).

Eustasy operates on a variety of time scales (Rovere et al., 2016) ranging from 10^8 years, mostly controlled by long-term variations in the volume of the oceans (although see Boulila et al., 2018 for a discussion of possible astronomical controls), to those operating at 10^4-10^5 years, most likely controlled by climatic variations (Guillocheau, 1995). The differing durations of eustatic cycles contribute to the notion of a hierarchy of RSL change and the resulting sequences. Consequently, it is common in the literature for discussions of sequence stratigraphy to be in terms of first- to sixth-order cycles/sequences, where first order are of the longest duration (e.g., Vail et al., 1977; Van Wagoner et al., 1990; Einsele et al., 1991; Catuneanu, 2019b). Short-duration

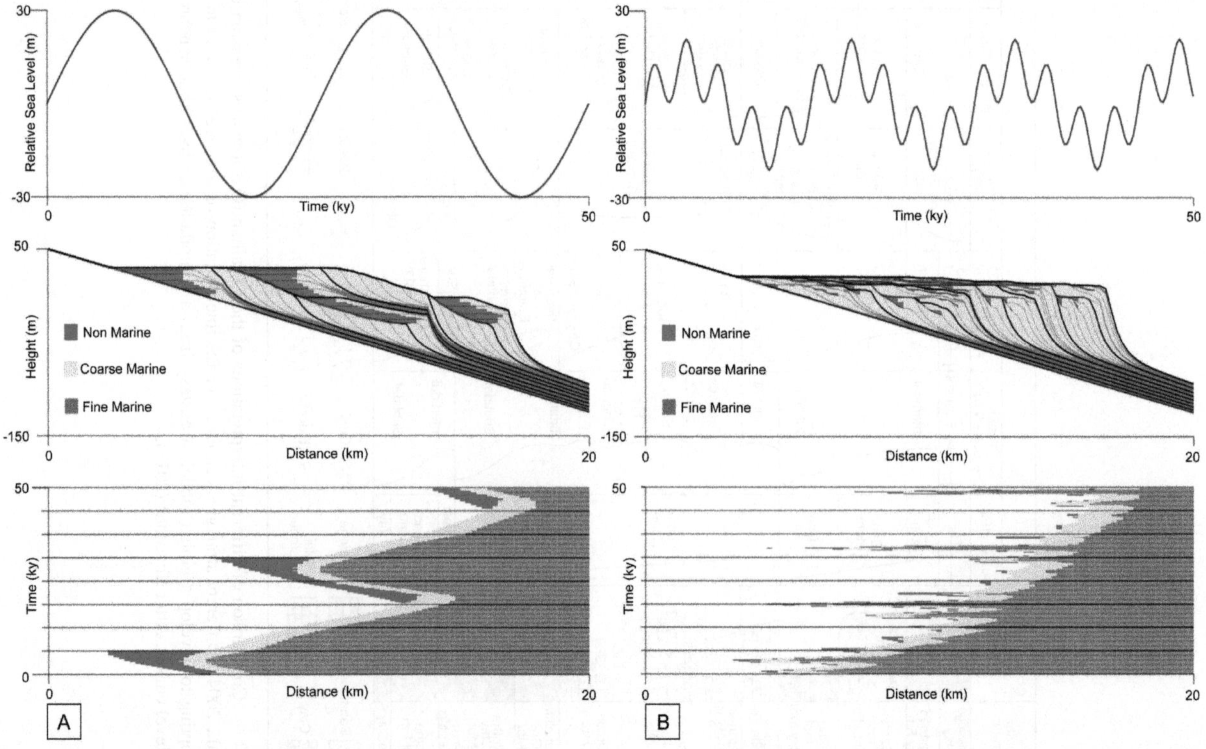

FIGURE 13.5 Outputs from a simple 2D depositional model of clastic deposition (http://nm2.rhul.ac.uk/wp-content/uploads/2015/03/DeltaModel3.html), where eustasy is the dominant factor controlling deposition (i.e., subsidence and sediment supply are constant). (A) Large, relatively slow magnitude variations of eustasy; versus (B) smaller, more rapid variations in eustasy. This is obviously an oversimplification from what controls the rock record in reality but is useful to demonstrate the influence magnitude and rate of eustasy can have on depositional completeness and facies distribution.

fifth- and sixth-order cycles can also be termed parasequences and will be strongly controlled by variations in sediment supply. Carter et al. (1991), Drummond and Wilkinson (1996), Schlager (2004, 2010), Allen (2017), and others have pointed out that the sedimentary record shows the characteristics of scale invariance (i.e., is fractal), and moreover, that ordering or ranking sequences by duration shows significant inconsistency in application within the scientific community. This is in part related to differences in sediment supply, which can result in the thickness of fifth- or sixth-order sequences greatly exceeding that of "typical" third-order sequences. In contrast, Miller et al. (2018) concluded that the stratigraphic record of sea-level changes largely reflects composites of sea-level cycles nested together. The bundling together of sea-level cycles controlled by c. 100- and 405-kyr orbital forcing yields a predictable packaging of

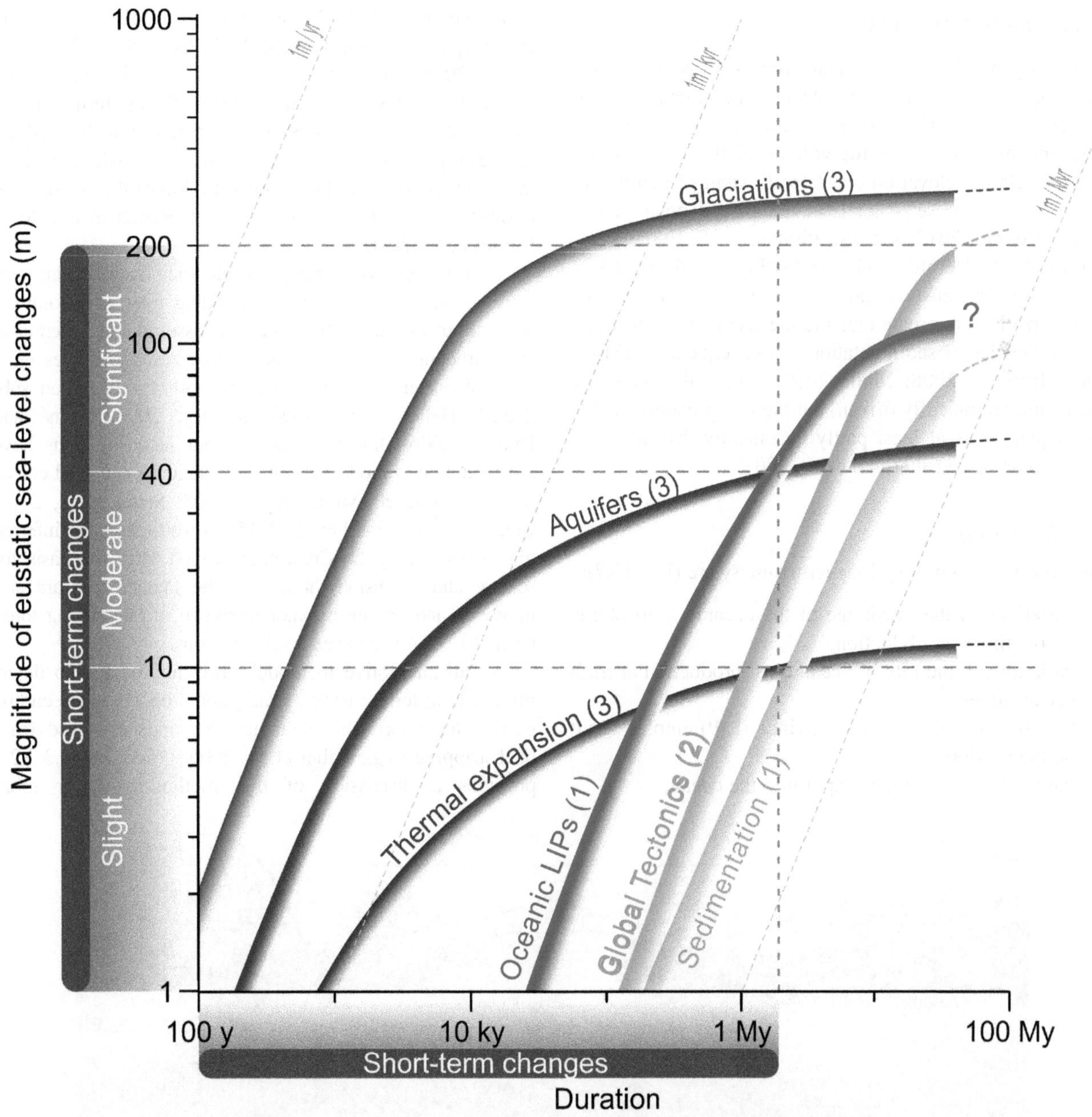

FIGURE 13.6 A schematic representation of the duration, magnitude, and rate of known drivers of eustatic changes, created from data within Emery and Aubrey (1991), Jacobs and Sahagian (1993), Immenhauser and Matthews (2004), Miller et al. (2011), Cloetingh and Haq (2015), Sames et al. (2016), and Wendler and Wendler (2016). The curves reflect the upper limits of durations, magnitudes, and rates that are reflective of the drivers of eustasy. Note that because of the different nature of the drivers, they can cause (1) sea-level rise; (2) sea-level rises and falls; and (3) regular, high-frequency, cyclic sea-level rises and falls. The "?" shown for LIPs represent the upper duration limit of continuous activity for a LIP. For an updated view on the magnitude of aquifer-eustasy see Davies et al. (2020). *LIPs*, Large igneous provinces. After Ray et al. (2019).

longer term sequences on the Myr scale. Given these uncertainties, we simplify our consideration of the magnitude and rate of eustasy to that operating on long-term time scales (10^8 years, largely forced by tectonics) and short-term time scales (10^5-10^6 years, largely controlled by astronomical forcing) (see also Sames et al., 2016), although make mention of ordering when citing from previous studies that use that terminology.

13.3.2 Long-term eustasy

There is general consensus that processes operating on a scale of 10^8 years can generate eustatic fluctuations on the scale of c. 100–300 m. These processes include mechanisms that change the volume of the ocean basins and the relative elevation and lateral extent of continents, or the volume of seawater (e.g., long-lived polar glaciations) (Conrad, 2013; see also Pitman, 1978; Burgess and Gurnis, 1995; Vérard et al., 2015) (Figs. 13.6 and 13.7). Such long-term eustasy can interact with major tectonic reorganizations to create tectonic megasequences or major cratonic cycles of sedimentation (Sloss sequences) (Sloss, 1963; Burgess, 2008; Miall, 2010), where the bounding events are tectonically driven, but the onlap pattern within the sequences is at least partly eustatically driven, as on the Arabian Plate (Sharland et al., 2001).

13.3.2.1 Drivers

The processes controlling long-term eustasy are (Fig. 13.7):

1. variations in the mean age of the oceanic lithosphere, accounting for subduction;
2. variations in the rate of ocean crust production at mid-ocean ridges;
3. the size of large igneous province (LIP) emplacement on the seafloor;
4. the volume of sediment input into the ocean;
5. dynamic topographic considerations;
6. the long-term creation and destruction of polar ice sheets; and
7. long-term variations in groundwater storage.

Of these, Conrad (2013) concluded that ocean ridge spreading volume was the most important (Fig. 13.8). Geodynamic (plate reconstruction) models can therefore be powerful tools for determining the likely timing, rate, and magnitude of long-term eustatic change (e.g., Cogné et al., 2006; Xu et al., 2006; Müller et al., 2008; Kirschner et al., 2010; Spasojevic and Gurnis, 2012; Conrad, 2013; Vérard et al., 2015; van der Meer et al., 2017; Karlsen et al., 2019). Estimates of the magnitude of long-term eustasy using plate reconstructions are hampered by a diminishing record of preserved oceanic crust with time, which leads to large uncertainties in the age distribution of the ocean floor (Rowley, 2002; Torsvik et al., 2010; Ruban et al., 2010, Müller et al., 2016).

Even for relatively young periods, such as the Cretaceous, there are disputes concerning spreading rates and volumes. Several authors have challenged the assumptions inherent in reconstructing fast Cretaceous seafloor spreading rates (e.g., half the ocean crust older than 50–60 Myr has been subducted: Heller et al., 1996; Rowley, 2002; Cogné and Humler, 2006); however, most recent reconstructions have affirmed at least moderately higher spreading rates and consequently sea level (Müller et al., 2008; Seton et al., 2009; Conrad, 2013; Vérard et al., 2015). Nevertheless, the inferred high rates during the Cretaceous, which form the basis for scaling and extension throughout the Phanerozoic are still unproven and remain a major unknown in interpreting long-term (10^7-10^8 years) sea-level variations.

As an alternative to model-based approaches to determining long-term eustasy, stratigraphic observations can be used. Such approaches can include trends observed from backstripping (e.g., Miller et al., 2005a) (Section 13.3.3.2.1 provides a discussion of this methodology) or more

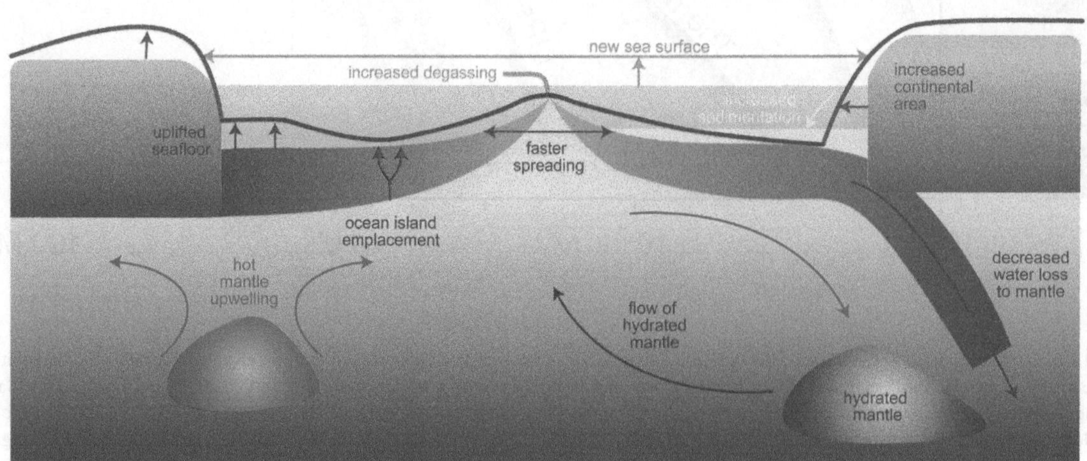

FIGURE 13.7 Compilation of factors contributing to long-term eustatic change and its magnitude. After Conrad (2013).

qualitative estimates based on the extent of flooding of paleocontinents and long-term patterns of coastal onlap [e.g., Hallam, 1992; Snedden and Liu, 2010 (after Hardenbol et al., 1998; Haq and Al-Qahtani, 2005; Haq and Schutter, 2008)]. Fig. 13.9 shows a compilation of some long-term eustatic curves derived using both geodynamic modeling and stratigraphic observations. Guillaume et al. (2016) produced an averaged long-term eustatic curve

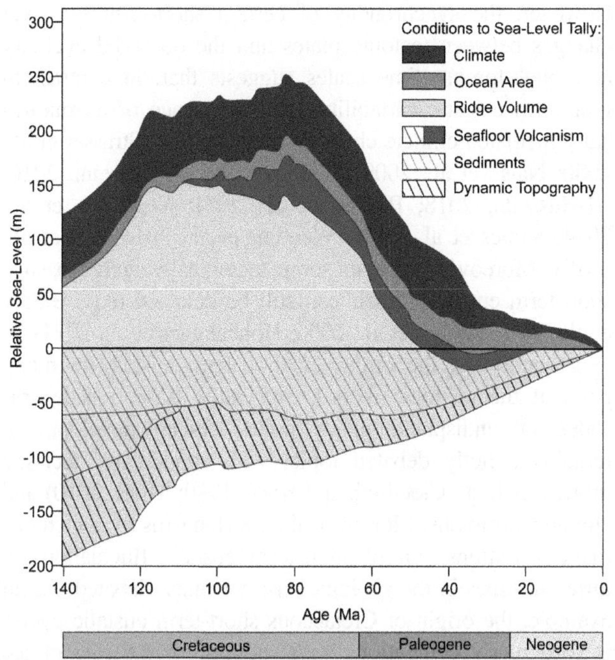

FIGURE 13.8 Relative importance of contributors to long-term term eustasy. After Conrad (2013).

for the Phanerozoic using a variety of papers, including some older, more qualitative attempts at estimating long-term eustatic magnitudes (Vail et al., 1977; Hallam, 1992; Haq and Al-Qahtani, 2005; Haq and Schutter, 2008).

Papers that include the entire Phanerozoic typically show eustatic peaks in the Late Ordovician and Late Cretaceous (although precise timing and magnitude varies) and a broad low around the Paleozoic–Mesozoic transition. This long-term periodicity has been related to tectonic supercycles of plate reorganization (Wilson Cycles) (e.g., Worsley et al., 1986; Veevers, 1990; Algeo and Seslavinsky, 1995; Miall, 2010; Nance and Murphy, 2013). Conceptually, during continental assembly remaining oceans were likely old and therefore deep leading to low sea-level. In comparison, times of continental breakup lead to new ridge formation, spreading and therefore shallower oceans and hence higher sea-level.

Karlsen et al. (2019) suggested that an imbalance between water fluxes from the mantle at ridges and into the mantle at trenches may have contributed to sea-level change since the breakup of Pangea. Thus faster slab subduction during Pangea breakup transported extra water to the mantle that may have contributed up to c. 130 m of gradual sea-level fall since 230 Ma. Cloetingh and Haq (2015) have suggested that water exchange with the mantle may also play a role in creating short-term eustatic cycles.

13.3.2.2 Magnitude

As shown in Fig. 13.9, although some broad consensus exists regarding the general timing of long-term eustatic highs and lows, estimates of magnitudes (and rates) of

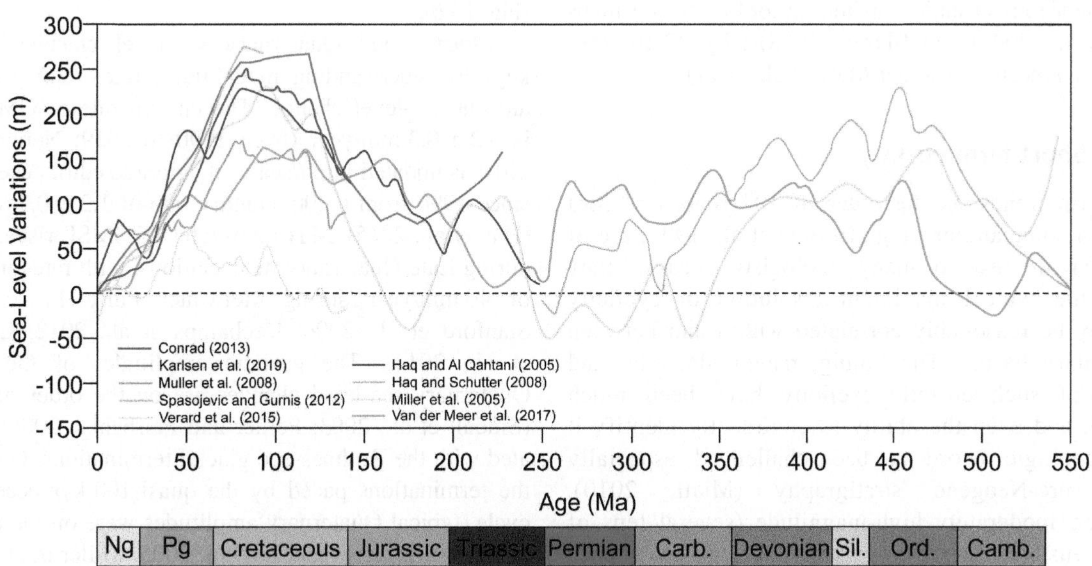

FIGURE 13.9 Long-term Phanerozoic eustatic fluctuations, as determined by geodynamic methods (Müller et al., 2008; Conrad, 2013; Spasojevic and Gurnis, 2012; Vérard et al., 2015; Karlsen et al., 2019), strontium isotope ratios as a proxy for geodynamic methods (van der Meer et al., 2017), and stratigraphic interpretations (Miller et al., 2005a; Haq and Al-Qahtani, 2005; Haq and Schutter, 2008).

change vary quite markedly; this variance occurs between model and data-driven interpretations and within each type of approach.

The magnitude of the Late Cretaceous long-term eustatic high appears to be a point of particular contention, with values estimated to be as much as c. 286 m above present-day levels by Spasojevic and Gurnis (2012) and less than 100 m by Miller et al. (2005a). Conrad (2013) argued that ridge volumes have decreased since the mid-Cretaceous, in response to a ~50% slowdown in seafloor spreading rate, resulting in a contribution of ~150 m to a total ~250 m of sea-level fall (Figs. 13.8 and 13.9). However, as elegantly demonstrated by Xu et al. (2006), differences in plate models can have a profound effect on calculations of the magnitudes of long-term eustasy. They noted that the use of the Hall (2002) Cenozoic plate model, which despite having only a c. 20% reduction in oceanic lithospheric production rates as compared to the Gordon and Jurdy (1986) plate model, resulted in halving the resultant modeled eustatic change (i.e., a fall of 125 vs 250 m for the Cenozoic).

Studies of continental flooding suggest that a Late Cretaceous peak occurred on the order of 135 ± 55 (Bond, 1979) or 150 m (Harrison, 1990), although more recent estimates have suggested only a c. 100 m peak (Rowley, 2013). McDonough and Cross (1991) calculated a Late Cenomanian sea-level elevation of 269 ± 87 m above present sea level from a backstripped shoreline in the Western Interior Seaway, although compensation for glacial isostatic effects of the last ice age may significantly reduce this estimate. Intriguingly, a sea-level rise of c. 250 m from today's mean sea level would be required to flood cratons to the extent mapped during Late Cretaceous eustatic maxima, according to the maps of Golonka (2007) and Blakey (2008) (Fig. 13.10) (see also the synthesis of van der Meer et al., 2017).

13.3.3 Short-term eustasy

Short-term trends on the order of 10^6 years (="third order" of some authors, e.g., Einsele et al., 1991) are of particular interest to many geologists because they reflect the typical maximum resolution of cyclicity that may be reasonably correlated within and between sedimentary basins. The timing, magnitude, rate, and drivers of such eustatic cyclicity have been much debated, and even the ability to confidently identify it in the geologic record has been challenged, especially within pre-Neogene stratigraphy (Miall, 2010). However, moderately high-magnitude (several tens of meters) eustatic changes occurring at or within the pace of orbital forcing (hundreds of thousands to millions of years) appear to be a prevalent feature of Phanerozoic geologic history (Miller et al., 2005a, 2011) and require appeal to driving mechanisms that occur at suitable rates (Fig. 13.6).

13.3.3.1 Drivers

Tectonics (e.g., intraplate deformation, mantle upwelling) have been viewed as an important control on short-term RSL changes (Cloetingh et al., 1985, 2013; Vakarelov et al., 2006; Petersen et al., 2010; Lovell, 2010; Miall, 2010). However, the synchroneity of certain short-term sea-level changes between tectonic plates and the observed cyclicity at orbital forcing time scales suggests that, in contrast to long-term eustatic variability, the importance of astronomically mediated climate changes is paramount (Strasser et al., 2000; Naish et al., 2009; Matthews and Al-Husseini, 2010; Al-Husseini, 2018; Boulila et al., 2011; Wagreich et al., 2014; Sames et al., 2016; Wendler et al., 2014; Liu et al., 2019). Moreover, even in some tectonically active basins, short-term eustatic signals can still be detected (e.g., Bartek et al., 1991; Strauss et al., 2006; Hohenegger et al., 2014).

Nonetheless, the origin of short-term eustasy in many parts of the geologic record, especially those outside episodes of undisputed major polar ice-cap development, remains a hotly debated topic, with support for tectonic influences (e.g., Cloetingh and Kooi, 1990; Miall, 2010) and climatic variations. Moreover, the mechanisms by which climatic variations control short-term eustatic fluctuations at different times in the geologic past are much debated. As an example, the origin of Cretaceous short-term eustatic cycles is particularly contentious with support for the role of ice sheets (glacio-eustasy) and groundwater storage (aquifer-eustasy) (e.g., Wagreich et al., 2014; Sames et al., 2016; Ray et al., 2019; Laurin et al., 2019; Davies et al., 2020) (Fig. 13.6).

Modern and Quaternary sea-level changes provide keys to understanding magnitudes, rates, and drivers of ancient sea-level change. The current rate of GMSL rise is 3.2 ± 0.3 mm/year (from 1990 to 2019; Nerem et al., 2010 as updated http://sealevel.colorado.edu), accelerating since 1990 from a 20th century rate of 1.2 ± 0.2 mm/year (Hay et al., 2015). Maximum rates of GMSL rise occurred during Late Quaternary deglaciations, with rates in excess of 40 mm/year during Meltwater Pulse 1a (c. 14 ka; Stanford et al., 2006; Dechamps et al., 2012; Lambeck et al., 2014). The eustatic amplitudes of the largest Quaternary sea-level changes are on the order of 130 m (Siddall et al., 2003; Peltier and Fairbanks, 2006) associated with the Bruhnes-age glacial terminations. Outside of the terminations paced by the quasi-100-kyr eccentricity cycle, typical Quaternary amplitudes were on the order of 50–60 m (Lisiecki and Raymo, 2005; Miller et al., 2011).

Throughout the Oligocene–Quaternary interval, short-term eustasy operated with large (more than 50 m) magnitude and often a rapid pace (over 40 mm/year = 40 m/kyr)

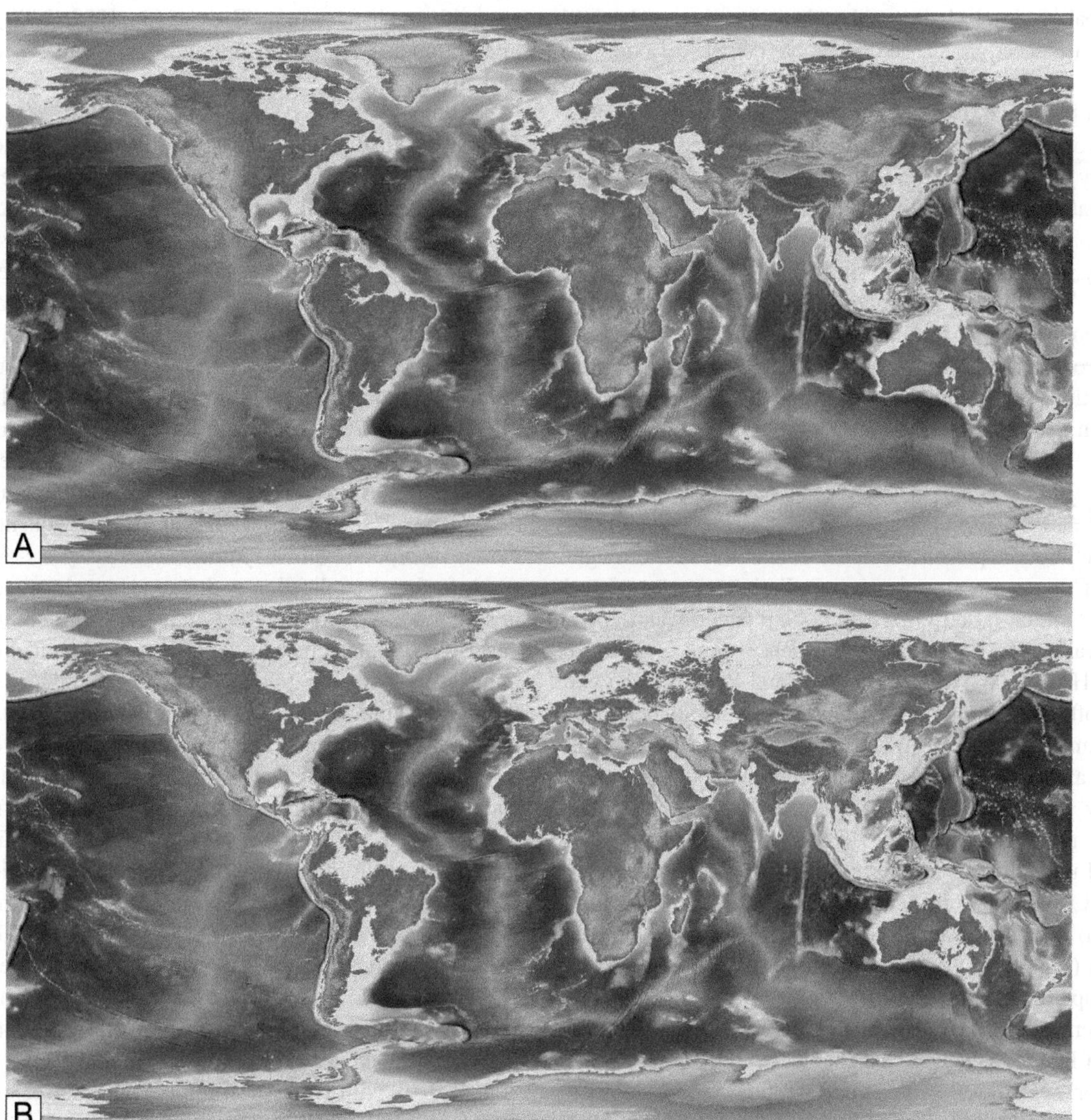

FIGURE 13.10 (A) The effect of a global sea-level rise 100 m above present-day levels on coastal inundation; (B) the effect of a global sea-level rise of 300 m above present-day levels on coastal inundation. (B) more closely matches modeled levels of Late Cretaceous inundation (Golonka, 2007; Blakey, 2008).

(Miller et al., 2020) with the c. 1.2 Myr obliquity orbital forcing cycle determining major glacial episodes (Zachos et al., 2001; Wade and Pälike, 2004; Pälike et al., 2006) and prominent eustatic cyclicity. Higher frequency orbitally forced glacio-eustasy is also evident (Miller et al., 2020). Consequently, changes in sea level were driven by changes in continental ice volume, particularly northern hemisphere (the ice ages) during the Quaternary (last 2.55 Myr) and Antarctic ice volume in the Cenozoic (Miller et al., 2005a).

Therefore our understanding of the relatively recent geologic past demonstrates that the signature of short-term glacio-eustasy is relatively large magnitude (tens—200 m) changes operating on short-term cyclicities controlled by the astronomical forcing of climate (Miller et al., 2005a,b, 2011, 2020; Naish et al., 2009). In subsequent subsections, we review our knowledge of the magnitude and duration of short-term eustasy for pre-Oligocene stratigraphy, but there seems to be little dispute that, within the Phanerozoic, glacio-eustasy was operating within the Late Paleozoic (Visean–Middle Permian) (e.g., Heckel, 1986; Dickinson et al., 1994; Wright and Vanstone, 2001; Eros et al., 2012a,b; Giles, 2009; Rygel et al., 2008; Fielding et al, 2008; Bishop et al., 2009; Horton and Poulsen, 2009; Fang et al., 2015; van Hinsbergen et al., 2015; Buso et al., 2019; Chen et al., 2019), and the latest Ordovician–Early Silurian (e.g., Hambrey, 1985; Sutcliffe et al., 2000; Finnegan et al., 2011; Ghienne, 2011; Ghienne et al., 2014; Davies et al., 2016). For these periods, glacio-eustasy has been regularly implicated as a major driver of global sea-level change, although the precise mechanisms driving ice sheet growth and retreat are complex (Horton and Poulsen, 2009).

Could glacio-eustasy have been operating during other Phanerozoic periods, especially those that are characterized by warm or hot (greenhouse) climates? Or does an explanation for short-term eustasy during these times require other processes to dominate, such as aquifer-eustasy, or tectonic drivers, such as intraplate stress variations? To answer these questions an assessment is required of the magnitude and duration of short-term Phanerozoic eustasy, which we address in the subsequent subsections of this chapter, drawing together our conclusions in Section 13.3.3.4.

13.3.3.2 Magnitudes

A contentious topic has been the estimation of the magnitude of short-term eustatic change. Early estimates of such changes, often based on seismic onlap patterns and apparently failing to account for subsidence (e.g., Vail et al., 1977; Haq et al., 1987, 1988; Ross and Ross, 1987), were high, often in excess of 100 m per event, and quickly drew criticism (e.g., Christie-Blick, 1990; Miall, 1992; Christie-Blick and Driscoll, 1995; Miller and Mountain, 1996; Dewey and Pitman, 1998). More recent estimates have tended to revise magnitudes downward. Even so, a great deal of uncertainty exists, as exemplified by the differences in the Cretaceous short-term eustatic curves of Miller et al. (2005a) and Sahagian et al. (1996), as compared to Haq (2014) (Fig. 13.11) or the estimates of Rygel et al. (2008) as compared to Ross and Ross (1987).

There are several methodologies by which the magnitude of RSL change can be estimated within any given outcrop or subsurface sedimentary section. These methods include simple approaches involving determining likely water depth changes from facies juxtapositions and fossil assemblage changes (e.g., Brett et al., 1993, 2009; Banner and Simmons, 1994), to the study of seismic geometries and the identification of erosional and depositional relief (e.g., Johnson et al., 1991; Miall, 2010; Ray et al., 2019). Estimating RSL magnitudes from the stratigraphic record has inherent limitations (Burton et al., 1987; Immenhauser, 2009; Sames et al., 2016) arising from the complex effect of several processes, including subsidence/uplift, sediment input, compaction, and isostasy, and inherent uncertainties (e.g., estimating palaeowater depth). As a result, many published eustatic curves are unscaled and show relative magnitudes because of uncertainties in assigning numerical values in terms of magnitude (e.g., Brett et al., 2011; Nielsen, 2004, 2011; Babcock et al., 2015; see also Davies et al., 2016 for a discussion of this issue with respect to Silurian eustasy). Likewise, many local/regional RSL curves are presented unscaled and are consequently difficult to incorporate into a synthesis of eustasy.

A further complication is that a sea-level estimate from a single location or transect may not be dominated by eustasy. The interaction of controls on sedimentation operating at a variety of frequencies and magnitudes develop the local stratigraphic record (e.g., Guillocheau, 1995). Although the effect of local subsidence/uplift rates has long been acknowledged, the effects of dynamic topography (the surface expression of mantle flow originating from the upper thermal boundary of mantle convection) (Fig. 13.7) have become an increasingly important consideration (e.g., Burgess and Gurnis, 1995; Burgess, 2008; Kominz et al., 2008, Conrad and Husson, 2009; Miall, 2010, 2016; Spasojevic and Gurnis, 2012; Conrad, 2013; Rowley, 2013; Guillaume et al., 2016). However, it is worth emphasizing that dynamic topography operates on time scales typically 2 to more than 10 Myr (Moucha et al., 2008; Petersen et al., 2010), with its greatest impact on time scales greater than 5 Myr (Cloetingh and Haq, 2015). Therefore, although an important factor in considering the magnitude of long-term

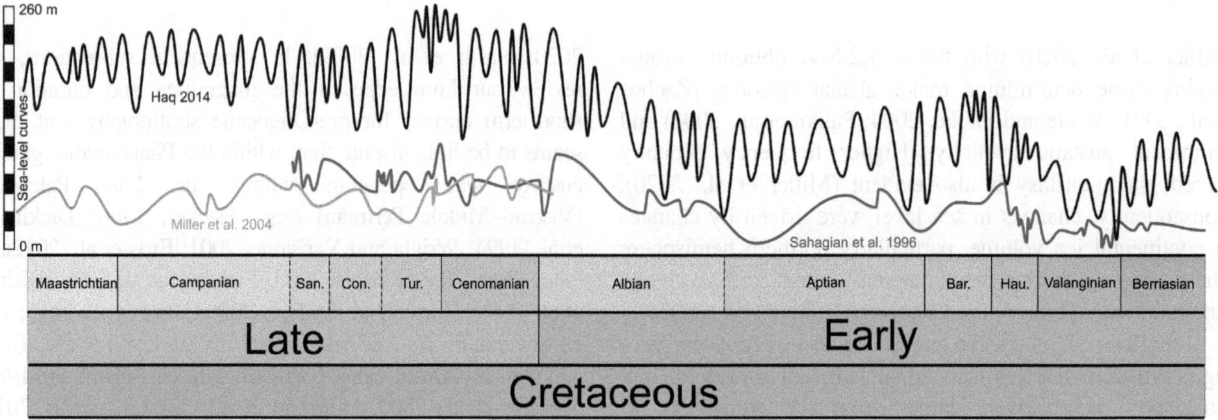

FIGURE 13.11 A comparison of the eustatic sea-level changes of Sahagian et al. (1996), Miller et al. (2004) and Haq (2014) illustrating the marked difference in magnitude estimates. From Ray et al. (2019).

eustasy, it has a reduced impact on assessing the magnitude of short-term eustatic events.

Sea-level curves produced from an assessment of local stratigraphy will effectively reflect local water depth changes (Holland and Patzkowsky, 1998; Loi et al., 2010). Three approaches can be undertaken to extract the eustatic magnitude given such circumstances: (1) backstripping; (2) use of the $\delta^{18}O$ record from foraminifera combined with an independent temperature proxy (for sediments Late Cretaceous and younger); and (3) a global synthesis of empirical estimates of eustatic sea-level change based on different types of geological observations, and incorporating data from (1) and (2) as appropriate, followed by a demonstration of synchroneity. These approaches are each discussed in turn.

13.3.3.2.1 Backstripping

Backstripping can be employed to progressively account for the effects of sediment compaction, sediment loading, and thermal subsidence (e.g., Miller et al., 2005a; Kominz et al., 2008, 2016). The residual in backstripping modeling is attributable to eustasy and nonthermal subsidence (R2 of Kominz et al., 2008, 2016) and can provide magnitude estimates for both long-term and short-term eustasy.

The sediments from the New Jersey margin of eastern North America are ideal for backstripping because sedimentation rates are well understood, and porosity-depth data provides reliable estimates of sediment compaction. This has enabled several workers (Miller et al., 2003a,b, 2004, 2005a; Kominz et al., 2003, 2008, 2016; Van Sickel et al., 2004) to show that short-term eustatic changes were in the range of 15–80 m during the Late Cretaceous to Miocene, with Cretaceous estimates on the low end of this range (15–40 m). Similar studies by Sahagian and Jones (1993) and Sahagian et al. (1996) on Middle Jurassic to Late Cretaceous sediments from the Russian Platform suggested comparable magnitudes of sea-level change to the work of the Miller-led team, indicating that estimates of short-term eustatic change as much as 160 m for same geologic time periods of study (Haq et al., 1987, 1988) or 400 m (Vail et al., 1977) are unlikely. Long-term trends can also be contrasted. Miller et al. (2005a) and Kominz et al. (2008) suggest that sea levels have fallen by c. 75–110 m from a Late Cretaceous maximum; Haq et al. (1987), however, have suggested that long-term sea level has fallen by c. 250 m during the same time period, although their long-term sea-level estimates were based entirely on those derived from the seafloor reconstructions of Pitman (1978) and Pitman and Golovchenko (1983).

It has been argued (e.g., Müller et al, 2008; Spasojevic et al., 2008; Spasojevic and Gurnis, 2012; Rowley, 2013; Haq, 2014) that the estimates of the magnitude of Late Cretaceous–Cenozoic eustatic change at all scales by Miller and his coworkers are underestimates because they have failed to account for the influence of dynamic topography, especially those related to the migration of North America over the subducted and negatively buoyant Fallon Plate during the last 70 Myr. Nonetheless, the potential effects of dynamic topography were considered by Kominz et al. (2008, 2016), which still produced eustatic magnitude estimates markedly lower than those of Haq et al. (1987), Haq (2014), and Müller et al. (2008). Backstripping estimates for eustatic changes from the Miocene of the Marion Plateau (east Australian margin) are also on the order of 50–60 m (John et al., 2004, 2011).

Loi et al. (2010) and Dabard et al. (2015) have successfully applied backstripping to Ordovician sediments in elegant studies from the North African Gondwana margin and the Armorican Massif. In their study of the Late Ordovician of the Bou Ingarf succession in Morocco, Loi et al. (2010) demonstrated that third-order (c. 1–3 Myr) eustatic magnitudes were greater than 40 m, and a fall in association with the growth of the Hirnantian ice sheet was estimated as more than 70 m (Fig. 13.12). Superimposed on these third-order magnitudes are fourth-order (400 kyr) cycles with eustatic magnitudes in the range 10–30 m. These interpretations were used to suggest that glacio-eustasy operated throughout the Katian and Hirnantian, supporting the notion of pre-Hirnantian Gondwanan ice sheets.

Dabard et al. (2015) extended this analysis into Darriwilian and Sandbian (Middle to Late Ordovician) strata through study of the Crozon Peninsula succession in Armorica, western France. Second-, third-, and fourth-order eustatic cycles were recognized. The second- and third-order cycles have magnitudes of more than 50 m, occasionally more than 80 m, whereas fourth-order cycles have magnitudes primarily in the range of 10–30 m. The authors interpret such magnitudes/periodicities as evidence for glacio-eustasy. Interestingly, the backstripping analysis in this case study highlights the effects that high subsidence rates can have on amplifying sea-level magnitudes. From the depositional model, amplitudes of fourth-order RSL change are high (c. 60 m), but backstripping suggests the eustatic component is only 30 m.

13.3.3.2.2 Oxygen isotope records

Oxygen isotope ($\delta^{18}O$) records from benthic foraminifera comprise two dominant signals: ambient temperature and $\delta^{18}O$ of seawater (Pearson, 2012). The latter parameter is affected by continental ice volume and changes attributable to fractionation from evaporation and precipitation often expressed as salinity (Miller, 2002). Therefore $\delta^{18}O$ measurements can be a useful proxy for reconstructing past ocean temperatures (Emiliani, 1955) and ice volumes (Shackleton, 1967) and, in turn, the magnitude of eustatic change driven by ice volume changes (e.g., Miller et al., 1987, 1991). As noted by Haq (2014), if the Pleistocene sea

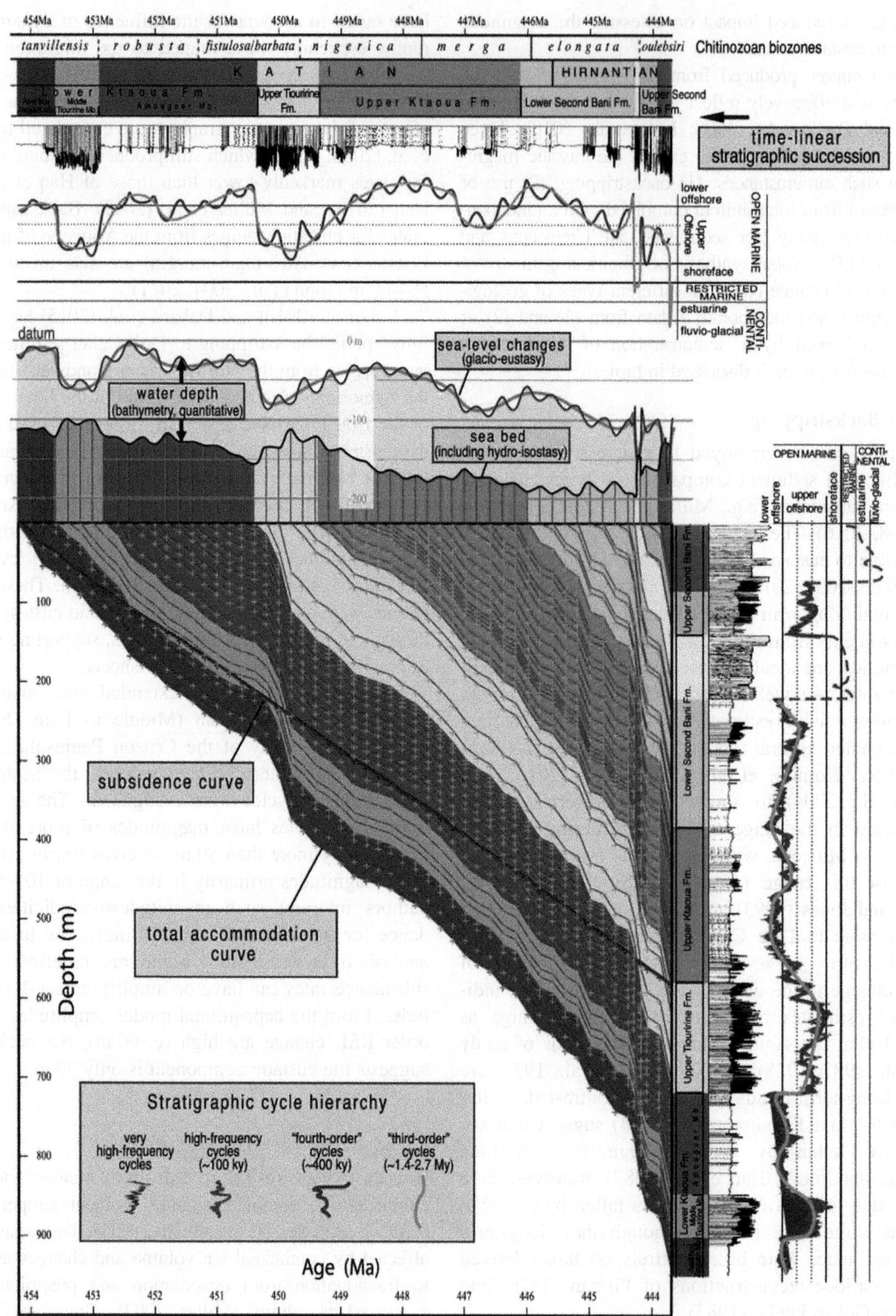

FIGURE 13.12 Example of backstripping used to calculate Late Ordovician eustatic magnitudes based on data from Morocco. After Loi et al. (2010).

level: $\delta^{18}O$ slope can be assumed to be similar across all geologic time, it may be possible to estimate the magnitude of eustatic variations using this proxy (Cramer et al., 2011 provide a comprehensive discussion of this technique). However, several problems limit this application (e.g., Wendler and Wendler, 2016). First, it is necessary to remove temperature and the local hydrological factors through the study of Mg:Ca ratios of the same samples to derive $\delta^{18}O$ of seawater ($\delta^{18}O_{sw}$) (Billups and Schrag, 2002). This carries a great deal of uncertainty for pre-Cenozoic sediments. The organic biomarker-based TEX_{86} proxy, alkenones, or clumped isotope techniques can also be used to calculate temperature (Hollis et al., 2019). Second, ice sheets become progressively depleted in ^{18}O as ice sheet elevation increases and temperatures decrease, thereby increasing $\delta^{18}O_{sw}$ by varying amounts. Third, "vital effects," the effect of the organism on changing the isotopic ratio as it metabolizes and constructs its shell, may distort values. Finally, pH variations and diagenesis can influence the $\delta^{18}O$ signal, detracting from its application in sediments older than late Mesozoic (Haq and Schutter, 2008).

Nonetheless, several workers (e.g., Stoll and Schrag, 2000; Miller et al., 1991, 2005a, 2011) have used variations in $\delta^{18}O$ to assess past ice volume and eustatic magnitudes. Combining backstripped estimates of eustatic change with those derived from $\delta^{18}O$ records, were both records are well age calibrated, can provide powerful insight into the magnitude of short-term eustatic change (e.g., Pekar et al., 2002; John et al., 2004, 2011).

Cramer et al. (2011) reconciled onshore New Jersey backstripped sea-level estimates with those obtained from deep-sea benthic foraminiferal $\delta^{18}O$ and Mg/Ca records. Because of limitations in the data, this approach, as illustrated in Fig. 13.13, was restricted to periods longer than 2 Myr and shows similar changes from both methods. It was judged to be most reliable for sediments younger than 45 Ma because of data limitations and uncertainties (especially the Mg/Ca ratio of seawater), although Miller et al. (2005a) documented specific intra–Late Cretaceous $\delta^{18}O$ increases that could be used to calculate the magnitude of specific short-term Cretaceous eustatic falls.

Ongoing studies (Fig. 13.14) are using higher resolution $\delta^{18}O$ records to compare Cenozoic changes on the Myr scale, calibrated by Milankovitch cyclicity (Miller et al., 2020). These results can be favorably compared to the backstripping results from New Jersey margin and help develop a model of variable Cenozoic Antarctic ice sheet growth and decay creating short-term eustatic changes with magnitudes most in the range 15–30 m in the Eocene, increasing to ~50 m in the Oligocene to Early Miocene (with a c. 60 m fall around the Eocene/Oligocene boundary). During the Miocene Climate Optimum (c. 17–15 Ma), magnitudes were reduced to less than 20 m as a result of greatly diminished ice sheets. Short-term eustatic magnitudes returned to c. 20–30 m during the Late Middle to late Miocene and Pliocene. Large sea-level changes with lowering of 60–120 m below present were restricted to the past 2.7 Myr, linked to full-scale continental ice sheet development in the Northern Hemisphere. Even considering the large (± 10 to ± 20 m) errors in magnitudes, $\delta^{18}O$ records provide a useful constraint. Moreover, the timing of eustatic events can be constrained by this method when the $\delta^{18}O$ record is linked to high-resolution biostratigraphy or other chronostratigraphic proxies (see Section 13.2.2).

13.3.3.2.3 Geological synthesis

For any given time period a useful approach to estimating the magnitude limits is to make a comparative synthesis of magnitude records from local and regional studies where (1) the sea-level change is deemed to be eustatic (because of relatively tectonically stable location and the short duration of the event) and (2) the magnitude estimates are derived by clearly documented reliable means. These include, in addition to backstripping and $\delta^{18}O$ analysis, sedimentological and paleontological observations, such as erosional and depositional relief, facies juxtaposition, fossil assemblages, and seismic and stratigraphic geometries. Rygel et al. (2008) pioneered this methodology for the study of Late Paleozoic eustasy; more recently, Ray et al. (2019) followed a similar approach to determine Cretaceous eustatic magnitude limits, supported by a data sensitivity analysis.

A similar but apparently more qualitative approach was undertaken by Haq and Schutter (2008) and Haq (2014), who derive eustatic magnitude estimates by averaging local measurements from the stratigraphic sections used to build the eustatic model (see also Haq, 2017, 2018). Haq (2014) has acknowledged that such measurements will be approximations, but it is intriguing that the magnitudes of eustatic change suggested by Haq and Schutter (2008) and by Haq (2014) greatly exceed those of Rygel et al. (2008) and Ray et al. (2019), respectively, or estimates purely from backstripping (e.g., Kominz et al., 2008). Johnson (2010) noted that the largest changes suggested in the Silurian short-term eustatic curve of Johnson (2006) are only half the magnitude suggested by Haq and Schutter (2008). Many of the sea-level changes documented by Johnson (2006) are determined from the extent of transgression and regression measured against topographic relief. A simple conclusion may be that the magnitude of local water depth change in the sections selected by Haq and Schutter (2008) and Haq (2014) has been overestimated, leading to a high-value average.

Rygel et al. (2008) synthesized more than 100 papers that had documented Late Paleozoic eustatic magnitudes based mostly on physical observations (e.g., erosion and depositional relief, facies juxtapositions, and cycle thickness) in the rock record from specific successions with short temporal durations (Fig. 13.15). By doing so, they sought to

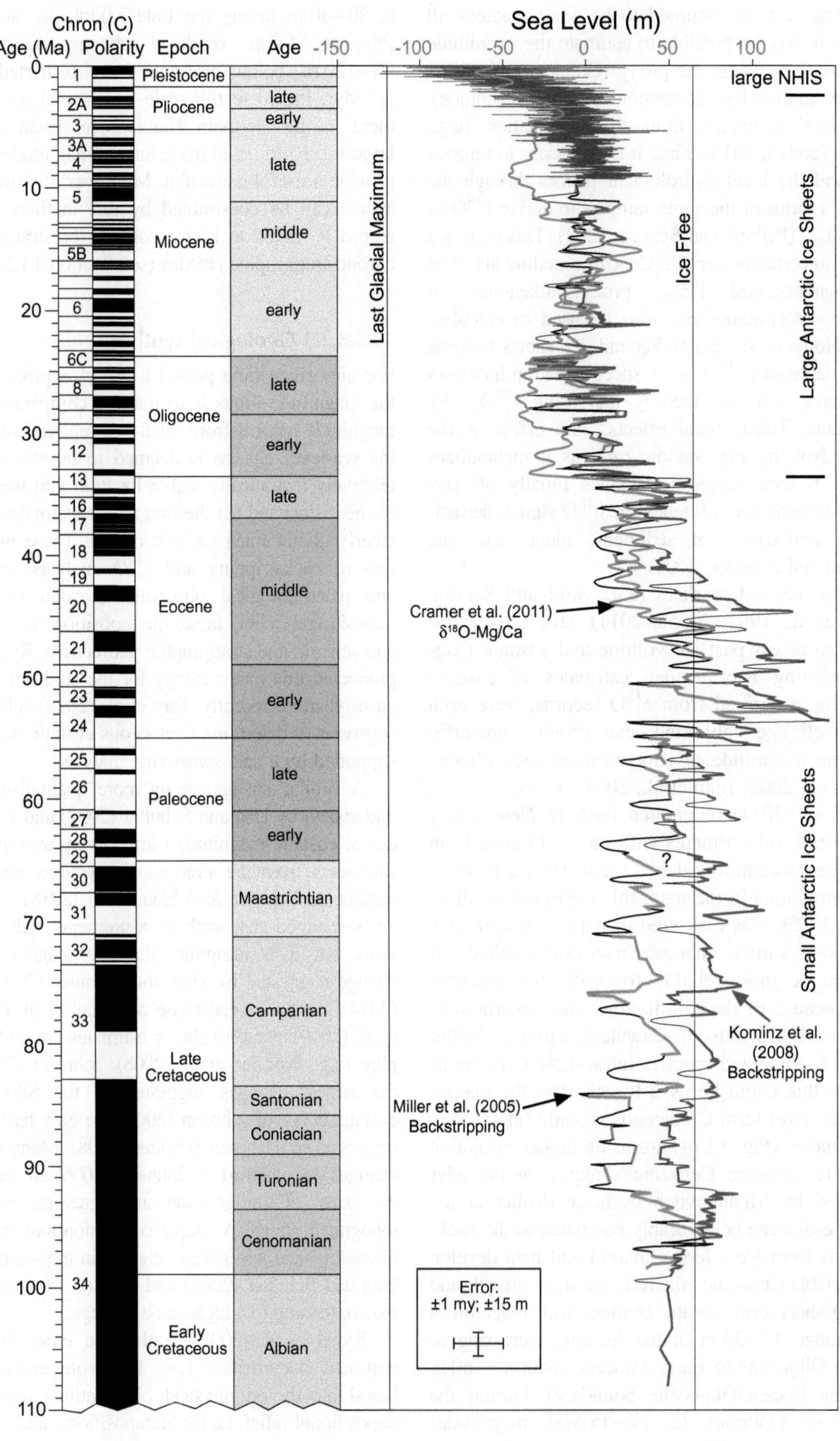
Chron (C)
Age (Ma)
Polarity
Epoch
Age
Sea Level (m)
-150
-100
-50
0
50
100
Pleistocene
Pliocene
Miocene
Oligocene
Eocene
Paleocene
Late Cretaceous
Early Cretaceous
late
early
middle
Maastrichtian
Campanian
Santonian
Coniacian
Turonian
Cenomanian
Albian
Last Glacial Maximum
Ice Free
large NHIS
Large Antarctic Ice Sheets
Small Antarctic Ice Sheets
Cramer et al. (2011)
δ18O-Mg/Ca
Kominz et al. (2008)
Backstripping
Miller et al. (2005)
Backstripping
Error:
±1 my; ±15 m

overcome the caveats and assumptions associated with each method of calculating eustatic magnitude and remove local and regional biases from the data.

They noted that at least eight intervals could each be characterized by specific magnitudes of eustasy. This supports the views of Isbell et al. (2003) and Fielding et al. (2008) that Late Paleozoic Gondwana ice sheets were dynamic and waxed and waned throughout much of the Carboniferous and Permian. Eustatic fluctuations of 20–25 m, and occasionally as much as 60 m, occurred throughout the Early Mississippian (Tournaisian), a widely recognized glacial period. Middle Mississippian (mid-Chadian–Holkerian) eustatic changes were 10–25 m, a decrease that matches a paucity of coeval glacial deposits. Late Viséan fluctuations of 10–50 m record the initial phases of ice accumulation ahead of the widespread mid-Carboniferous glacial event. The latest Mississippian–earliest Pennsylvanian was a time of widespread glaciation and eustatic magnitudes in the range of 40–100 m. A reduction in magnitudes of less than 40 m occurred in the middle Pennsylvanian, followed by an increase to 100–120 m in the late Pennsylvanian–earliest Permian; the latter corresponds to growth of Gondwanan ice sheets and the presence of northern hemisphere ice. Early–middle Permian magnitudes of 30–70 m reflect the waning stages of major glaciation. Finally, eustatic fluctuations of 10–60 m in the Late Permian reflect the late-stage glaciation, although the modest magnitude of some events may imply other driving mechanisms.

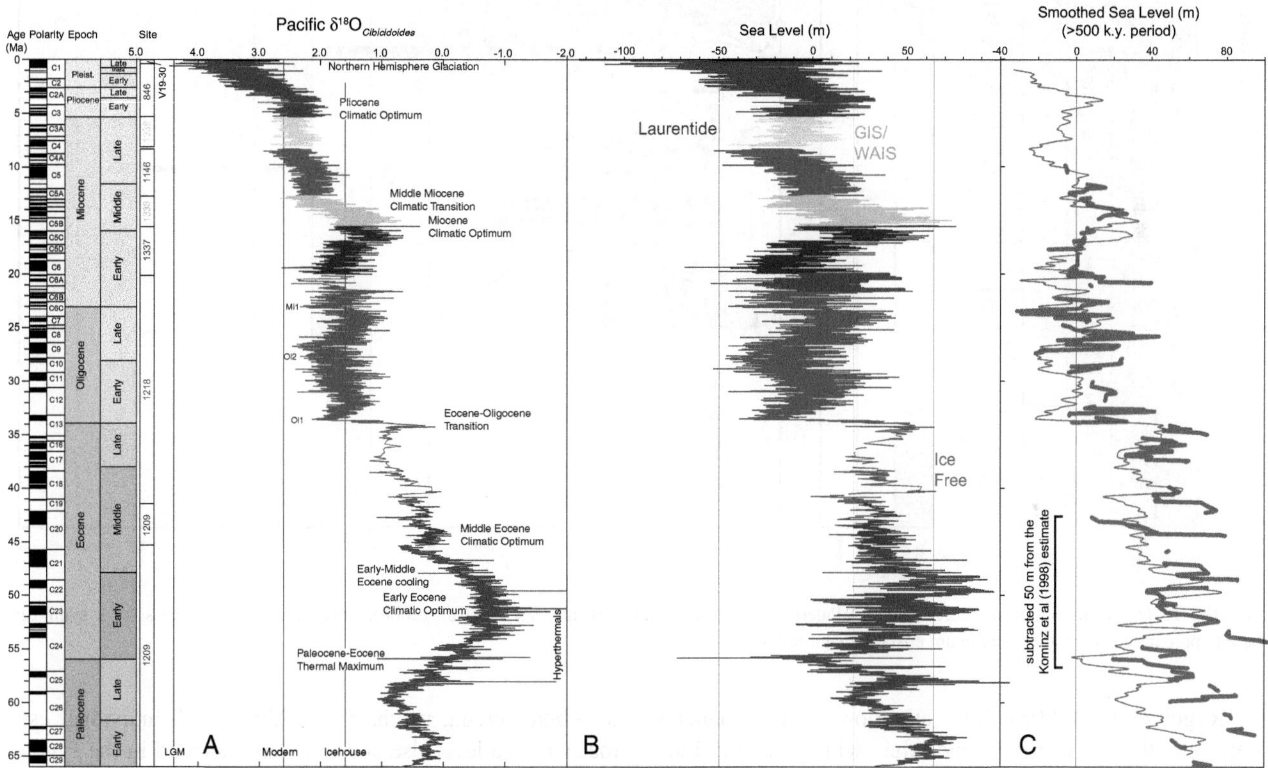

FIGURE 13.14 Summary of Cenozoic benthic foraminiferal $\delta^{18}O$, sea level, and CO_2 records. Panel (A) Benthic foraminiferal $\delta^{18}O$ splice reported to *Cibicidoides* spp. Modern is the core top value for $\delta^{18}O_{Cibicidoides}$; the Icehouse line is placed at 1.8‰ in *Cibicidoides*, with values greater requiring major ice sheets. Panel (B) Sea level obtained using a new benthic foraminiferal $\delta^{18}O$ splice and $\delta^{18}O_{seawater}$ from Mg/Ca; ice-free line (*magenta*) drawn 64 m above present, GIS-WAIS (Greenland ice sheet and West Antarctic ice sheet; *light blue*) drawn at +12 m above present; Laurentide (*dark blue*) drawn at −50 m. Panel (C) Comparison of smoothed sea-level estimates from $\delta^{18}O$ and Mg/Ca (*blue*; obtained by interpolating to 20-kyr intervals and using a 49-point Gaussian convolution filter, removing periods shorter than 490 kyr) with backstripped NJ estimates (*red*; Kominz et al., 2008, 2016). The NJ estimates for the Early to Middle Eocene were shifted by −50 m. See Miller et al. (2020) for further details.

FIGURE 13.13 Comparison of Cenozoic sea-level curves relative to modern (=0 m) using two methods: backstripping of New Jersey onshore sequences (*blue*, Miller et al., 2005a; *brown*, update of Kominz et al., 2008 using slightly different initial subsidence conditions) and $\delta^{18}O$-Mg/Ca method to extract temperature from $\delta^{18}O_{benthic}$ records (Cramer et al., 2011), with the residual $\delta^{18}O_{seawater}$ assumed to be global mean sea level as a result of ice-volume fluctuations. The Cramer record was smoothed to remove periods shorter than 2 Myr; it is truncated at 48 Ma because of uncertainties in the Mg/Ca record described by Cramer et al. (2011). The "ice-free line" is set at 64 m, the uncompensated change in water volume stored in continental ice sheets and glaciers (Fretwell et al., 2013). The Last Glacial Maximum (LGM) is set at 120 m below modern (Fairbanks, 1989). Error bars in age sea level are for backstripped estimates (Miller et al., 2005a; Kominz et al., 2008). Ice volume history and figure layout modified after Miller et al. (2011) and presented to the GTS2004, including geomagnetic polarity chrons. *NHIS*, Northern Hemisphere ice sheets.

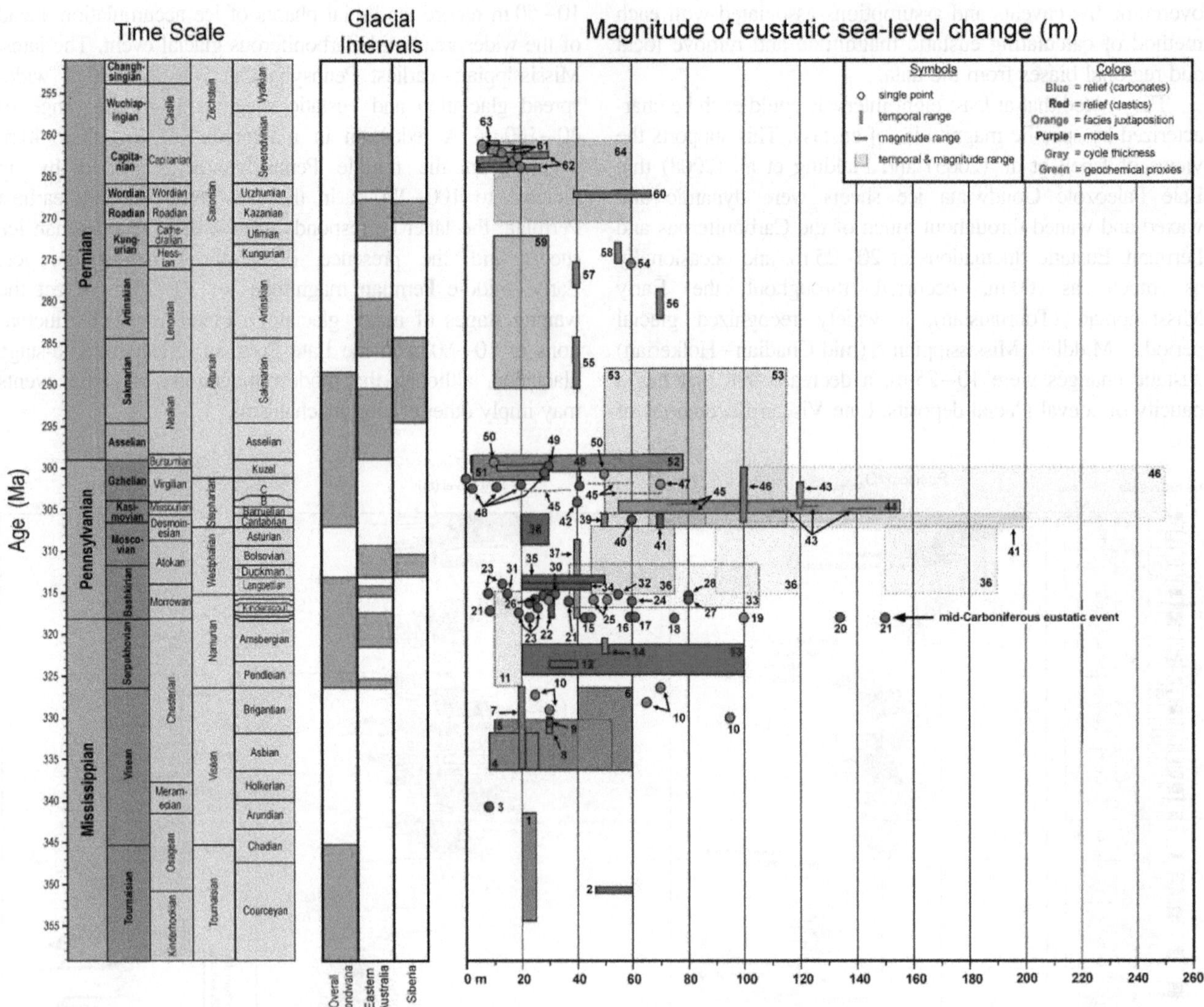

FIGURE 13.15 Compilation of short-term Late Paleozoic eustatic magnitudes after Rygel et al. (2008). This data forms the basis for a synthesis-based approach to calculating maximum eustatic magnitudes.

Rygel et al. (2008) draw attention to discrepancies between their synthesis and the widely cited Late Paleozoic sea-level curve of Ross and Ross (1985, 1987). First, Ross and Ross (1987) illustrate frequent eustatic magnitudes in excess of 100 m throughout the Late Paleozoic, a conclusion not substantiated by the Rygel et al. (2008) synthesis. Second, the timing of the highest magnitudes on the Ross and Ross (1987) curve correspond to periods of low magnitudes on the Rygel et al. (2008) synthesis and vice versa. Consequently, long-term highstands of eustasy on the Ross and Ross (1987) curve correspond to times of known maximum glaciation.

Ray et al. (2019) used records of Cretaceous sea-level change with duration of 3 Myr or less. By doing so, they reduced the influence of local tectonics and long-term drivers of eustasy (e.g., seafloor spreading and sedimentation) in favor of a short-term, climate-driven eustatic signal linked to orbital forcing mechanisms. Almost 800 individual estimates of sea-level rise and fall were included in the synthesis, following a rigorous selection process using the criteria previously described. A consensus view was extracted from this data in a stepwise manner. First, a preliminary statistical analysis of the entire dataset was undertaken to identify robust temporal trends in magnitude estimates and to establish intervals characterized by a particular range of magnitudes. After these intervals were established an in-depth review was performed of the geologic setting and methods, from which the magnitude estimates were derived in each interval. This geologic review identified the most robust studies, discounted anomalous data, and identified a robust maximum short-term magnitude for each of the time intervals. Finally, as a means of validating these geologically defined maximum short-term magnitude limits, a further statistical review focused on the upper magnitude limits.

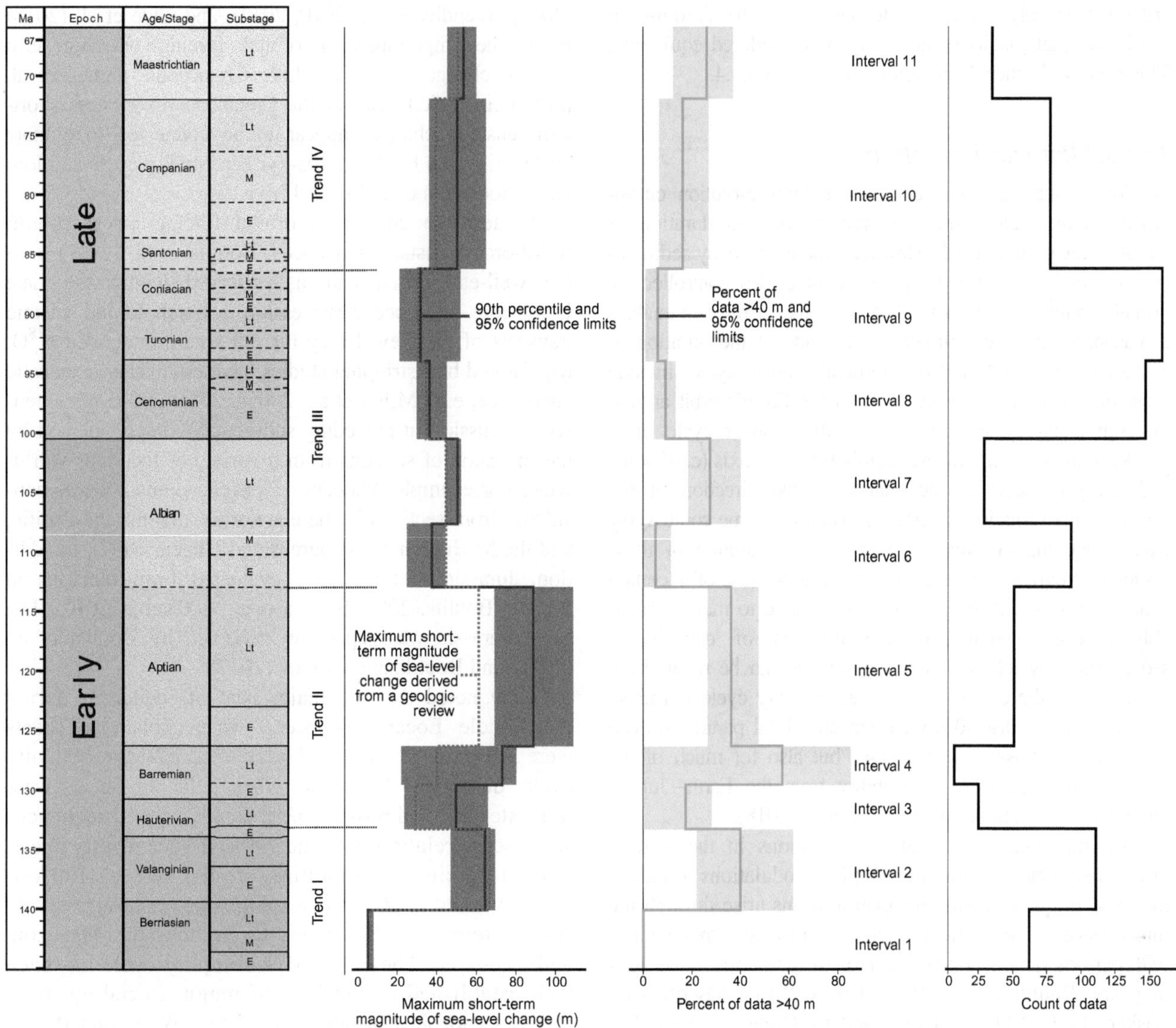

FIGURE 13.16 Maximum magnitudes of short-term Cretaceous eustasy based on a statistical analysis of a synthesis of published magnitudes. Maximum magnitude estimates based on a qualitative review of the geologic evidence (*red dotted line*) are shown for comparison. Maximum magnitude estimates are based upon the 90th percentile of the entire dataset, alongside the percentage of data of more than 40 m, and a count of the overall data for each of the 11 intervals. The maximum magnitude estimates derived from a review of the geologic record is given for comparison. The 11 intervals are derived from magnitude trends evident in the median magnitudes. After Ray et al. (2019).

The initial review of the entire Cretaceous dataset, weighing each data point equally, gave a median value for short-term eustatic change of 12 m, with the data approximating a log-normal distribution with a mean of $11.9 + 23.5/-7.9$ m (1σ); consequently, the majority of sea-level estimates are of relatively low magnitude with few examples of large magnitude. Examining *median* estimates at a stage level, following standard statistical resampling procedures, demonstrated that elevated magnitude values occurred during the Valanginian, Barremian to Aptian, and Santonian to Maastrichtian, with low magnitude values in the Berriasian, Hauterivian, and Albian to Coniacian. More specifically, *maximum* magnitude limits were derived (Fig. 13.16), which are consistent with some estimates derived from backstripping (e.g., Miller et al., 2003a,b, 2005a), but are in contrast with some of the greater magnitudes suggested by Haq (2014) (Fig. 13.11). Even though the Cretaceous eustatic estimates suggested by Ray et al. (2019) are relatively modest, 50% of the Cretaceous is associated with significant (greater than 40 m) eustatic changes that may be considered to be characteristic of glacio-eustasy (Valanginian, Aptian, Albian, and Maastrichtian). Furthermore, in the presence of significant eustatic change, the immediately older intervals of modest magnitudes (10–40 m) may be interpreted as representing the growth and demise of land-grounded icecaps. Based on these criteria, it is only within the Berriasian and the Turonian to Coniacian that glacio-eustasy may be considered equivocal. This point is further discussed in Section 13.3.3.4.

13.3.3.3 Rate and duration

Outside of the Late Neogene, where high-resolution chronometers exist, calculating the precise rate and duration of eustatic change is difficult. However, there are many sedimentary successions where the presence of cycles controlled by orbital forcing (see Hinnov, 2018 for a recent review) enables a reasonably precise estimate to be made of the duration of eustatic sea-level fall and rise. Orbitally forced cycles include those arising from the *eccentricity* of the Earth's orbit around the Sun (each cycle c. 100 kyr, with a longer cycle of c. 405 kyr); the *obliquity* of the Earth's tilt on its axis (c. 40 kyr); and the *precession* of the change in the direction of the Earth's axis of rotation (c. 20 kyr). Although some controversy exists regarding our understanding of the duration of these cycles in progressively older time periods because of uncertain changes in celestial mechanics, it is possible to make reasonably precise estimates of the duration of depositional sequences in which orbital forcing cycles can be recognized. In particular, the c. 405-kyr long eccentricity cycle is robust, not only for the last 50 Myr, when all orbital parameters can be estimated (Laskar et al., 2004), but also for much of the Phanerozoic because of its stability from the Earth–Jupiter interactions (see discussion by Kent et al., 2018).

An important feature of the variations in the Earth's orbital parameters is that they display modulations in amplitude and frequency. The modulation terms arise through the interference of individual cycles to produce "resultants," with periods ranging from hundreds of thousands to millions of years (Boulila et al., 2011). This was first described by Laskar (1990, 1999) and reviewed by Hinnov (2000). The most well-known long-period modulation cycles are those of eccentricity (c. 2.4 Myr) and obliquity (c. 1.2 Myr).

The Kimmeridge Clay succession of southern England and northern France is one such succession in which orbital forcing has been considered to have been a major driver of the deposition sequences present. Huang et al. (2010) noted that the c. 405-kyr eccentricity cycle plays a major role in controlling the transgressive/regressive cyclicity observed in the Kimmeridge Clay (see also Boulila et al., 2008a,b,c, 2010; Simmons, 2012).

Orbital forcing has enabled the estimation of the duration of significant short-term transgressions and regressions with Cenomanian successions. Voigt et al. (2006) noted that one such transgression of a rocky shoreline in Germany, with a magnitude of 22–28 m, occurred in the *geslinianum* Zone of the Late Cenomanian with a duration of 80–180 kyr. Gale et al. (2002, 2008) noted that significant transgressions in the *rhotomagense* Zone of the Middle Cenomanian had durations of c. 150 kyr. More recently, Laurin and Sageman (2007), Wendler et al. (2010, 2014), and Olde et al. (2015) noted the importance of orbital forcing on short-term eustatic change within the Late Cretaceous. Sames et al. (2016) concluded that, for the Cretaceous in general, short-term eustatic changes appear to be connected to climate cycles triggered by the c. 405-kyr eccentricity cycle and longer periodicities of c. 1.0–2.4 Myr.

To test the control of orbital forcing on short-term (third-order) eustatic sequences, Boulila et al. (2011) used the well-established patterns observed within the Late Cretaceous to Miocene succession in borehole and seismic transects of the New Jersey margin where integrated $\delta^{18}O$, Mg/Ca and backstripping studies have established a eustatic curve (see, e.g., Miller et al., 2005a, 2011, 2020; and extensive discussion in preceding subsections), supplemented by the inclusion of sections from a variety of locations worldwide. For example, Pliocene–Pleistocene eustasy was considered from sections in the equatorial Atlantic, the Pacific, and the Mediterranean (Lourens and Hilgen, 1997). In addition, Jurassic sections were evaluated from outcrops in France (Boulila, 2008; Boulila et al., 2008a,b,c, 2010). The Early Jurassic was separately reviewed by Boulila et al. (2014) and Boulila and Hinnov (2017).

They noted that the major beat of sequences during the Middle Eocene–Holocene, when polar ice sheets were extensive, correspond to the c. 1.2-Myr obliquity cycle; during the Mesozoic, when polar ice sheets were less extensive and possibly periodically absent, sequences show some relation with the 2.4 Myr eccentricity cycle. Orbital forcing periodicities of 405 kyr, c. 100 kyr, c. 40 kyr, and c. 20 kyr exert control over progressively shorter term eustatic cycles throughout the Mesozoic and Cenozoic. The c. 1.2-Myr obliquity cycle has been well established as the beat of major glacial episodes in the Cenozoic (Zachos et al., 2001; Wade and Pälike, 2004; Pälike et al., 2006). Interesting, recent work by Liu et al. (2019), examining sequences in the East China Sea, calibrated to eustatic events worldwide, has noted that the c. 1.2-Myr obliquity cycle may exert strong control over eustatic cycles in the early Paleogene, an interval not fully studied by Boulila et al. (2011). In contrast to Boulila et al. (2011), Wendler et al. (2014) suggested that it is the c. 1.2-Myr obliquity cycle that provides control on eustasy in the Cenomanian–Turonian, modulated through aquifer-eustasy, rather than glacio-eustasy (further discussed in Section 13.3.3.1).

Integrated seismic, core, and log studies of the Miocene on the New Jersey shallow shelf by IODP Expedition 313 (Mountain et al., 2010) provide insight into the sedimentary response to icehouse conditions. The cause of the SBs is generally inferred to be sea-level change attributable to waxing and waning ice sheets in Antarctica, although sediment input determines the preservational potential of sequences.

The most prominent sequences observed are those associated with ~1.2-Myr tilt cycles; however, in areas and times when high sedimentation input and attendant rates occurred, higher order (405 and quasi-100 kyr) sequences are preserved (Miller et al., 2013a,b). In these cases, the 1.2-Myr scale sequences are composites with higher order sequences embedded. In addition, changes in the dominant forcing periodicity affect preservational potential; sequences are more likely to be preserved when strong 100-kyr eccentricity dominated forcing but are more likely to be eroded away during times the 41-kyr tilt cycle dominated (Browning et al., 2013). These studies establish that continental margin sedimentation, especially during intervals of large, rapid glacioeustatic change, acts as low-pass filter, concatenating and truncating precessional, tilt, short eccentricity, and even longer eccentricity (405 kyr) cycles. It appears, though it has not been unequivocally demonstrated because of limitations in chronostratigraphic control of ~0.5 Myr, that SBs are associated with the most rapid glacioeustatic falls. These studies suggest that during icehouse worlds, there is a hierarchical order (not fractal) of sequences on the tilt (1.2 Myr) and eccentricity scales (100 and 405 kyr).

The rate of short-term eustatic sea-level change in the Paleozoic is particularly difficult to establish in the absence of accurate chronometric proxies and the uncertainties of extending orbital forcing time scales further back in geologic time. Nonetheless, the well-known eustatically driven cyclothems (Fig. 13.17) of the Late Carboniferous (e.g., Eros et al., 2012a) were estimated to span 235–400 kyr for major cycles and 40–120 kyr for minor cycles (Heckel, 1986, 1990, 2008). More recently, Davydov et al. (2010), Falcon-Lang et al. (2011), and Schmitz and Davydov (2012) have suggested that c. 405-kyr eccentricity cycles exert a major control over Carboniferous cyclothem deposition, whereas Elrick and Scott (2010) have noted the importance of long-period obliquity c. 1.2 Myr on mid-Pennsylvanian cyclothems in New Mexico. During the Early Carboniferous (late Visean), Giles (2009) reported major transgressions separated in time by c. 2.4 Myr, with smaller scale transgressive–regressive cycles paced by either the 100- or c. 405-kyr eccentricity cycles. Fang et al. (2015) suggested an orbital forcing control on Middle Permian eustatic sequences.

For parts of the early Paleozoic an increasing number of studies recognize orbital forcing periodicities in successions deemed to be eustatically controlled (Cherns et al., 2013). For example, Dabard et al. (2015) recognize 11 "third-order" sequences in the Middle to early Late Ordovician of the Armorican Massif in western France, calibrated by chitinozoan biostratigraphy. They are each typically composed of three "forth-order" sequences with a duration of c. 405 kyr (eccentricity cycles). The 1.2-Myr duration of the third-order cycles suggests they are related to long-period obliquity cycles. Brett et al. (2011) note a strong control exerted by the short- and long-term eccentricity cycles of orbital forcing (c. 100 and 405 kyr, and longer modulations) on the Middle Devonian succession and eustatic cyclicity of North America. It seems likely that the eustatic cycles interpreted for other periods in Paleozoic (e.g., the Silurian sea-level cycles documented by Calner, 2008 and Johnson, 2010) will be related to orbital forcing. Although this remains to be proven, increasing research into orbital forcing time scales for the Paleozoic (e.g., Radzevičius et al., 2017; http://www.geolsed.ulg.ac.be/IGCP_652/) may provide the answers in the near future.

13.3.3.4 Determining a model for short-term eustasy

As discussed in the preceding subsections, the magnitudes of eustasy can be detected (with uncertainties) from backstripping, $\delta^{18}O$ records, and a synthesis of mainly stratigraphic observations (or an integration of more than one of

FIGURE 13.17 Carboniferous cyclothems in the Limestone Coal Formation, Spireslack open-cast mine, southern Scotland. Photograph used with kind permission of the International Appalachian Trail, Newfoundland and Labrador.

these techniques). The rate and duration of eustasy is best determined from identification of Milankovitch cyclicities within the rock record, supported by age proxies in the form of biostratigraphy and geochemical records. Based on these interpretations of the magnitude, rate, and duration of past eustasy, arguments exist for glacio-eustasy operating throughout much of the geologic record, even during times of relatively warm (greenhouse) climates (e.g., Miller et al., 2005a,b, 2011; Simmons, 2012; Davies et al., 2020), especially considering that there is increasing evidence for greater climatic instability in the geologic past than was previously thought (e.g., Hu et al., 2012).

The Cretaceous represents an increasingly well-studied period of the Earth's history when rapid, moderately high-magnitude eustatic changes were occurring (see previous section and Immenhauser, 2005; Miller et al., 2005a,b; Voigt et al., 2006; Ray et al., 2019) at a time when the Earth's climate was generally regarded as warmer than today. Two mechanisms have been proposed to explain short-term eustatic change within the Cretaceous: (1) short glacial episodes (Stoll and Schrag, 1996, 2000; Miller et al., 2005b, 2011; Maurer et al., 2013) (glacio-eustasy) and (2) the alternating charge and discharge of aquifers (Hay and Leslie, 1990; Jacobs and Sahagian, 1993; Wendler et al., 2016; Wendler and Wendler, 2016; Föllmi, 2012; Wagreich et al., 2014; Sames et al., 2016; Laurin et al., 2019) (aquifer- or limno-eustasy).

Critical to distinguishing between these two mechanisms are the upper magnitude limits of eustatic change they enable. The upper limit of glacio-eustatic magnitudes is 200 m or more (Miller et al., 2005a,b); the upper limits of aquifer-eustasy are uncertain, but significantly less than glacio-eustasy (Fig. 13.6). Jacobs and Sahagian (1993) suggested as little as 8 m as a maximum, whereas Hay and Leslie (1990) and Wagreich et al. (2014) suggested a 50 m upper limit, based on estimates of present-day aquifer storage with isostatic adjustment. The 50 m limit requires the alternate filling and emptying of all available aquifers, so it may be considered to be unrealistic. However, estimates of significantly larger aquifers during the Cretaceous (twice the size of those today) have led some to consider 10–40 m magnitude changes as possible from aquifer-eustasy (Wendler and Wendler, 2016; Wendler et al., 2016). Davies et al. (2020) modelled aquifer-eustasy in the Cretaceous considering palaeoclimate models and aquifer availability, and concluded that aquifer-eustasy was unlikely to contribute more than 5 m of eustatic change, even under the most favorable conditions.

Ray et al. (2019) and Davies et al. (2020) reviewed the options for the drivers of short-term eustasy in the Cretaceous that could also be applied in other geologic periods. Given the maximum likely contributions that thermo-eustasy (c. 10 m), aquifer-eustasy (c. 5 m), and glacio-eustasy (c. 200 m) may make to the total short-term eustatic signal, knowledge of the magnitude of eustasy can help define possible driving mechanisms. Thus short-term magnitudes of no more than 10 m may be accounted for solely by thermo-eustasy, or any combination of drivers, whereas magnitudes in excess of 15 m appear to be unachievable without a contribution from glacio-eustasy.

As magnitudes of short-term eustasy increase toward 15 m, it is more likely that glacio-eustasy makes a contribution. This is because of the environmental extremes required to drive the other two mechanisms toward their maximum capacity. For example, a 9 m short-term thermo-eustatic change requires the temperature of the oceans to change by approximately 15°C (Sundquist, 1990), which is comparable to the difference in temperature between the oceans of the warmest Late Cretaceous and the most recent major glaciation (Grossman, 2012). Clearly, repeated short-term changes of this magnitude are inconsistent with the mass of climate proxy data for much of the geologic record (e.g., O'Brien et al., 2017 for the Cretaceous).

Similarly, the enhanced hydrological cycle that appears necessary for aquifer-eustasy would require extreme episodes of aridity and humidity to operate at its maximum capacity (Davies et al., 2020). During the Cretaceous, humid-arid cycles are inferred (Föllmi, 2012; Wendler et al., 2016), but not at the extremes required to be the sole driver of short-term eustasy (Davies et al., 2020). This led Föllmi (2012) to suggest that giant lakes may have played a role but, overall, the water capacity of lakes is negligible (Wagreich et al., 2014; Sames et al., 2016).

Ray et al. (2019) concluded that during the Cretaceous, glacio-eustasy dominates the intervals of significant short-term eustatic change (Valanginian, Aptian, Albian, and Maastrichtian) and episodes of modest eustatic fluctuation preceding and proceeding. Only during the Berriasian, Turonian, and Coniacian is the likelihood of glacio-eustatic influence equivocal. Wagreich et al. (2014) noted that, notwithstanding age calibration uncertainties, Turonian eustatic signals appear to be out of phase with lacustrine water-level changes (as determined from the Songliao Basin, China). Out-of-phase relationships between continental water storage and ocean water levels can be advanced as an argument for aquifer-eustasy, although this must be tested by the study of multiple age-calibrated lacustrine successions on separate continents. Indeed, Davies et al. (2020) recently demonstrated that the greatest aquifer charge is more likely during cooler intervals, indicating that aquifer-eustasy might work in phase with both glacio- and thermo-eustasy in contrast to the current aquifer-eustasy paradigm.

The conclusions of Ray et al. (2019) and Davies et al. (2020) support a growing view that glacio-eustasy was a dominant eustatic mechanism during much of the Cretaceous, mediated by changes in volume of relatively small polar ice sheets and episodic cold spells (Miller et al., 2003a,b, 2005b; Miller, 2009; Koch and Brenner, 2009; Maurer et al., 2013; Davies et al., 2020; Lin et al., 2020). Despite ongoing perceptions in much of the geological community that the Cretaceous was dominated by persistent warm climates (e.g., Hay, 2008; Jenkyns et al., 2012; Föllmi, 2012; Wendler and Wendler, 2016), this view is increasingly challenged by both evolving climate science (e.g., Donnadieu et al., 2011; Hu et al., 2012; Hong and Lee, 2012; Ludvigson et al., 2015; Tabor et al., 2016; Ladant and Donnadieu, 2016), the gathering of sedimentological and geochemical proxies for the presence of polar ice (e.g., Price, 1999; Alley and Frakes, 2003; Macquaker and Keller, 2005; McArthur et al., 2007; Price and Nunn, 2010; Simmons, 2012; Föllmi, 2012; Hore et al., 2015; Herrle et al., 2015; Rodríguez-López et al., 2016; Grasby et al., 2017; Rogov et al., 2017; Vickers et al, 2019; Horner et al., 2019; Alley et al., 2019), and changes in the global populations of microfossils that indicate episodes of marked cooling (e.g., Mutterlose et al., 2009; McAnena et al., 2013).

Sedimentological proxies are relatively scarce in the Late Cretaceous, but temperature proxies, such as TEX_{86}, $\delta^{18}O$, and seasonal diatom production and sediment flux, have identified a broad middle Campanian to end-Maastrichtian cooling and the presence of seasonal sea ice (Davies et al., 2009; Bowman et al., 2013; Kemp et al., 2014; O'Brien et al., 2017; Niezgodzki et al., 2019). The balance of evidence is leading to the increasing acceptance that within the Cretaceous there were at least episodes of polar glaciation (e.g., Donnadieu et al., 2011; Ladant and Donnadieu, 2016). However, this view is often in contrast with geochemical evidence (e.g., TEX_{86}, $\delta^{18}O$, Mg/Ca), which generally implies that temperatures were too warm for ice sheet growth (e.g., compare the TEX_{86} proxy data of Jenkyns et al., 2004 with the diatom productivity and sediment flux data of Davies et al., 2009). One explanation for this may be the presence of a seasonal bias in many of the proxy temperature estimates, especially at high latitudes (e.g., Davies et al., 2019a).

The relatively high magnitudes and rapid rate of sea-level change driven by glacio-eustasy can lead to the creation of spectacular incised valley systems and prominent subaerial exposure surfaces. In the Aptian, for example, such features have been documented from numerous basins around the world (van Buchem et al., 2010b; Husinec et al., 2012; Maurer et al., 2013; Peropadre et al., 2013; Millán et al., 2014; Bover-Arnal et al., 2014; Pictet et al., 2015; Horner et al., 2019). In the McMurray Formation of the Western Canadian Foreland Basin, four distinct composite channel-form bodies can be documented across an area of more than 14,000 km^2 (Horner et al., 2019). Composite channel-form bodies are up to 50 km wide and locally exceed 70 m thick. Furthermore, transgressive rock units can be correlated over a minimum of 280 km, suggesting that shorelines advanced and retreated more than 300 km, creating a distinctive stratigraphic architecture. Similar scale incised valley systems were described by Koch and Brenner (2009) from Albian/Cenomanian boundary strata (Dakota Formation) of the US Western Interior Seaway, which were attributed to have a glacio-eustatic origin.

The increased likelihood that glacio-eustasy was the dominant driver of short-term eustasy during the Cretaceous highlights the possibility that it was also an important driver in other periods previously regarded as being dominated by warm climates. Evidence for glaciation and episodic cool/cold climates is being gathered for every Phanerozoic period, even at the end of the Triassic (Schoene et al., 2010). Significant glaciation is envisaged for parts of the Cambrian (Landing and MacGabhann, 2010; Cherns et al., 2013; Babcock et al., 2015); the pre-Hirnantian Ordovician (Page et al., 2007; Cherns et al., 2013; Dabard et al., 2015; Pohl et al., 2016); the post-Llandovery Silurian (Page et al., 2007; Grahn and Caputo, 1992; Diaz-Martinez and Grahn, 2007; Caputo, 1998; Cherns et al., 2013); and the Middle Devonian to earliest Carboniferous (Caputo et al., 2008; Isaacson et al., 2008; Elrick et al., 2009; Montañez and Poulsen, 2013; Lakin et al., 2016; Elrick and Witzke, 2016).

Cold spells in the Jurassic have been suggested by, for example, Korte and Hesselbo (2011), Korte et al. (2015), Rogov and Zakharov (2010), Donnadieu et al. (2011), Dromart et al. (2003), Krencker et al. (2019), and Rogov et al. (2019) and references therein. In the pre-Oligocene Cenozoic continental ice sheets in both the southern and northern hemispheres have been envisaged by, among others, Tripati et al. (2005, 2008), and Middle to Late Eocene ice sheets appear to be incontrovertible (Peters et al., 2010; Gulick et al., 2017).

Thus a growing body of evidence exists to support the presence of volumetrically significant polar ice in what are commonly regarded as greenhouse times. What is remarkable is that short-term (third-order) eustatic sea-level change often seems to show a correlation with proxy records of paleotemperature changes (e.g., sea-level falls are associated with evidence for cooling events) (Cherns et al., 2013). Moreover, the likely (orbitally forced) pace and (at least moderate—c. 50 m or greater) magnitude of eustasy in many parts of the stratigraphic column (e.g., Brett et al., 2011; Elrick and Witzke, 2016—Middle Devonian) is at least suggestive of glacio-eustasy, even though more research is needed to firmly establish this. The increasing evidence for orbital forcing of climate, extinction events, and sedimentation patterns in, for example, the Devonian (e.g., De Vleeschouwer et al., 2017) and Ordovician (Cherns et al., 2013; Dabard et al., 2015) suggests a causal link with glacio-eustasy may soon be established.

The frequency and magnitude of eustatic events appear to be rather different for the Triassic, as compared to the rest of the geologic record (Davies and Simmons, 2018; Haq, 2018). Davies and Simmons (2018) noted eight major sequences on the Arabian Plate that they suggested may have a eustatic origin. Haq (2018) noted more eustatic events (see also Franz et al., 2014), but only six were major with amplitudes suggested to be in excess of 75 m. Major Triassic eustatic cycles thus appear to have an unusually long, uneven periodicity, although smaller scale depositional cyclicity appears to follow orbital forcing periodicities of 20, 100, and occasionally 405 kyr (e.g., Ajdanlijsky et al., 2019). That humid/arid climate shifts were particularly dramatic in the Triassic (e.g., Preto et al., 2010; Stefani et al., 2010; Trotter et al., 2015) has led some (e.g., Jacobs and Sahagian, 1993; Wagreich et al., 2014; Li et al., 2016) to invoke aquifer-eustasy as a control on Triassic short-term eustasy. The revised aquifer-eustasy paradigm of Davies et al. (2020) is supported by the observation that Triassic warming events appear to correspond to eustatic highs and cooling to eustatic lows (Davies and Simmons, 2018; Simmons and Davies, 2018; Haq, 2018), but the magnitudes of eustatic change (e.g. Haq, 2018), whilst needing further assessment, suggest aquifer-eustasy is an unlikely driver. Therefore the driving mechanism for Triassic short-term eustasy remains enigmatic, although glacio-eustasy has been cited as the cause of end-Triassic sea-level fall (Schoene et al., 2010).

13.4 Phanerozoic eustasy: a review

Although some consensus on the timing of eustatic events is emerging, there are still significant differences between workers for most geologic periods (especially for the pre-Cenozoic). Perhaps this is not surprising, given that inherent differences exist in how eustatic change has been recognized in the geologic record, be that from stratigraphic synthesis, backstripping, or geochemical approaches (e.g., use of $\delta^{18}O$), noting that interpretation strategy of sedimentary successions and biostratigraphic calibration will inevitably differ between authors. It should also be noted that different eustatic schemes should be recalibrated to a single geologic time scale, although what is important is the position of eustatic events within standard biozonation schemes.

Given these uncertainties, we would hesitate to recommend any one particular eustatic sea-level curve over another. Instead, we simply highlight the key interpretations that are available and encourage the stratigraphic community to continue to gather data, which will help the advancement of a true consensus. It is encouraging that some stratigraphic subcommissions for the various periods of the Phanerozoic are developing consensus views on eustasy for their particular interval of geologic time. The Permian Subcommission, for example, maintains a view on transgressive and regressive cycles (http://permian.stratigraphy.org/per/per.asp).

13.4.1 Major syntheses

There are several publications, some much cited, that provide an analysis of short-term eustasy over multiple geologic periods or eras, and some of which were used in previous Geologic Time Scale publications.

Haq et al. (1987, 1988)—Summarized EPR research into Mesozoic and Cenozoic eustasy, with a sea-level curve that has been widely reproduced and cited. The data behind the eustatic model was not published, which led to criticism from some quarters (see review in Miall, 2010). Numerous short-term eustatic cycles were depicted, which some have argued (Miall, 1991, 1992) go beyond the capabilities of tools of correlation and calibration to resolve. Others have found the timing of events to be plausible, although the magnitudes to be excessive (e.g., Miller et al., 2005a; also see Ray et al., 2019 and discussion in Section 13.3.3.2). Nonetheless, and despite relatively recent updates (Haq and Al-Qahtani, 2005; Haq, 2014, 2017, 2018), the model continues to be widely regarded as the de facto statement on eustasy. The update by Haq and Al-Qahtani (2005) integrating Arabian Plate stratigraphy with minor modification was adopted for the Triassic portion of the GTS2016 compilation of Ogg et al. (2016).

Hardenbol et al. (1998)—Intended as an update to the Haq et al. (1987, 1988) Mesozoic and Cenozoic synthesis based on the study of outcrops from around Europe, synthesizing the work by a large group of experts (e.g., Hesselbo and Jenkyns, 1998). This work was adopted for the Mesozoic and Cenozoic portions of the 2012 geologic time scale compilation of Gradstein et al. (2012) and for the Jurassic and Cenozoic portions of the 2016 geologic time scale compilation of Ogg et al. (2016).

Haq and Schutter (2008)—Much cited representation of Paleozoic eustasy based on the study of multiple sections originally identified at EPR from regions thought tectonically stable. One hundred and seventy-two eustatic events were listed for the Paleozoic, varying in magnitude from a few tens of meters to ~125 m. Although commonly cited, the eustatic curve within this paper has often been found to contrast with more detailed studies on a period-by-period basis, not least in the number of cycles represented and their magnitude (see, e.g., discussion in Eros et al., 2012b and Johnson, 2010). As with the syntheses by Haq et al. (1987, 1988) for the Mesozoic and Cenozoic, details of interpretation strategy and biostratigraphic calibration are lacking, which hinders comparison and evaluation. A recalibrated version of the Silurian portion was presented by Melchin et al. (2012) in the 2012 geologic time scale compilation. This work was adopted for the Paleozoic portion of the 2016 geologic time scale compilation of Ogg et al. (2016) with minor modification.

Snedden and Liu (2010)—Recalibration of the Haq et al. (1987), Hardenbol et al. (1998), and Haq and Schutter (2008) eustatic curves to the 2008 geologic time scale. No new data appears to have been applied.

Ross and Ross (1985, 1988, 1992, 1995, 1996)—Pioneering attempts to synthesize knowledge on Paleozoic eustasy, drawing on mainly North American stratigraphy. These papers continue to be widely cited, despite strong criticism from those who have performed more recent detailed studies (e.g., Eros et al., 2012a).

Sahagian and Jones (1993) and Sahagian et al. (1996)—An attempt to produce a sea-level curve for the Jurassic, Cretaceous, and Paleocene of the Russian Platform, by backstripping stratigraphic data from numerous wells. Because of the supposed stability of the Russian Platform, the sea-level curve is thought to be eustatic in origin. The presence of numerous unconformities within the stratigraphy may be a limitation on the provision of a continuous eustatic record.

Miller et al. (2005a)—Much cited review of Phanerozoic eustasy incorporating data from various previous studies, but with a focus on the significance of the backstripped Late Cretaceous–Cenozoic stratigraphic record of the New Jersey onshore that, in turn, was updated by Kominz et al. (2008, 2016).

Simmons et al. (2007)—Argued that the latest Precambrian–Phanerozoic Arabian Plate sequence stratigraphic model of Sharland et al. (2001) and updated by Davies et al. (2002) and Sharland et al. (2004) was essentially a eustatic model. Davies and Simmons (2018), Horbury (2018), and Lunn et al. (2019) have recently suggested updates to the Triassic part of the model, whereas Simmons and Davies (2018) and van Buchem et al. (2011) have updated parts of the Jurassic and Cretaceous model, respectively. Van Buchem et al. (2010b) and Maurer et al. (2013) paid particular attention to the Barremian and Aptian parts of this model, using detailed, high-resolution outcrop and subsurface studies and global comparisons to advance a case for glacio-eustasy, at least during the late Aptian.

There are also important syntheses for specific time periods (see also other chapters in this book). The following subsections describe some of the more recent and often-cited compilations and commentaries, noting that some examine long-term trends, whereas others can be focused on specific short-term events.

13.4.1.1 Cambrian

Babcock et al. (2015)—Provided a review of the state of knowledge of Cambrian sea-level history in the light of improved chronostratigraphy with an onlap curve for the upper part of the Cambrian–basal Ordovician. Abrupt transgressions that led to deposition of black shales or black limestones and the evolutionary inceptions of key agnostoid trilobites are suspected to be glacio-eustatic in origin. This paper drew upon information in the following detailed studies: Miller et al. (2003a, 2003b), Runkel et al. (2007), Nielsen and Schovsbo (2011), Peng et al. (2012), and Álvaro et al. (2014).

Nielsen and Schovsbo (2015)—A particularly comprehensive review of the Early–Middle Cambrian, with suggestions that their analysis of sea-level change in Baltoscandia may correspond with global patterns. The codification of sea-level events (e.g., Hawkes Bay Event) makes them particularly useful.

Lee et al. (2015)—Provided a discussion of the major sea-level fall immediately postdating the Cambrian Epoch 3—Furongian boundary that is recognized on both Laurentia and Gondwana and is thus considered to be eustatic in origin. This event had major effect on the composition of reef communities.

13.4.1.2 Ordovician

Nielsen (2004, 2011)—Presented a sea-level curve for Baltoscandia. Because of the tectonic quiescent nature of the region during the Ordovician and slow depositional rates, many parts of the curve were suspected as being eustatic in origin. The 2011 version was recalibrated to the time scale of Ogg et al. (2008) and included minor revisions in the Late Ordovician. The difficulty in estimating amplitudes was emphasized. Events were codified for ease of use. The 2004 version was used by Cooper and Sadler (2012) in the 2012 geologic time scale compilation. Note that interpretation of Ordovician sea-level change from the deeper water facies of Baltoscandia by Dronov et al. (2011) differs substantially from that of Nielsen (2004, 2011).

Videt et al. (2010)—Recognized 16 third-order cycles in the Ordovician stratigraphy of northern Gondwana (North Africa), calibrated by chitinozoan biostratigraphy, several of which they believed to be eustatic in origin based on a comparison with sea-level events on several other continents. Loi et al. (2010) and Dabard et al. (2015) presented related detail.

Munnecke et al. (2010)—Presented a comprehensive review of the challenges in recognizing eustatic changes in Ordovician sediments. They provided a compilation of published regional sea-level curves and, as subsequently noted by Dronov (2017), whereas there are good matches between some curves there are apparent mismatches, with western Gondwana and Avalonia especially, displaying differences from other continents, mostly as a result of local tectonics.

Creveling et al. (2018)—Provided a discussion of how sea-level histories at continental margins in both the near- and far-field of the Late Ordovician ice sheet can differ significantly from eustasy because of isostatic adjustments. Dietrich et al. (2018) and Pohl and Austermann (2018) provided further discussion of this topic.

13.4.1.3 Silurian

Johnson et al. (1998) and Johnson (2006, 2010)—Using comparisons of Silurian stratigraphy on multiple paleocontinents, often based on first-hand experience, Markes Johnson has been at the forefront of developing an understanding of Silurian eustasy in the manner of the pioneer

Grabau (1936a,b, 1940). His sea-level curves, the most recent being the 2006 version, are much cited. His 2010 paper is a comparison of the 2006 eustatic curve with the Silurian portion of the Haq and Schutter (2008) Paleozoic synthesis. Although driven by different approaches, 8 of 10 highstands of Johnson (2006) match 8 of 15 highstands suggested by Haq and Schutter (2008). A recalibrated version of the 2006 curve was presented by Melchin et al. (2012) in the 2012 geologic time scale compilation.

Loydell (1998, 2007)—Defined episodes of sea-level rise and fall in the Early Silurian, based primarily on the oxidation state of the strata under investigation and the graptolite fauna contained therein. The 2007 paper expanded this concept to include carbon isotope data. A recalibrated version of the 1998 curve was presented by Melchin et al. (2012) in the 2012 geologic time scale compilation. See also Page et al. (2007).

Munnecke et al. (2010)—This was a comprehensive review of the challenges in recognizing eustatic changes in Silurian sediments. They provided a compilation of published Silurian eustatic curves and, as subsequently noted by Simmons (2012), although there is a good deal of commonality, differences can be ascribed to differing interpretation strategies for recognizing sea level and eustasy and differences in biostratigraphic calibration. See also Calner (2008).

Davies et al. (2016)—This was another comprehensive review of Early Silurian sea-level change, comparing the pattern observed in the type Llandovery succession of mid-Wales with 62 other published datasets, including global and regional baselevel curves. The concept of a Eustasy Index as extracted from the commonality in this data was used to argue that eustatic changes can only be confidently identified for highstands associated with ice-sheet collapse.

13.4.1.4 Devonian

Johnson et al. (1985)—Using sections in relatively stable cratonic interiors and continental margins, they defined a series of 12 cycles in the Devonian portion of the Kaskaskia Megasequence of North America (Sloss, 1963) and subdivided them into two series of cycles (I and II) separated by the major Taghanic unconformity. This work, and an updated version (Johnson et al., 1996), has become entrenched as a standard for Devonian eustatic cyclicity, as noted by Brett et al. (2011).

House and Ziegler (1997)—This was a seminal description of Devonian eustasy in multiple worldwide sections, building the pioneering work of House (1983) and Johnson et al. (1985).

Ma et al. (2009)—Important comparison of sea-level changes as expressed in the Devonian stratigraphy of South China with other sections worldwide, leading to insights into eustasy.

Brett et al. (2011)—Presented a sea-level curve for the Middle Devonian of eastern North America that, because of the persistence of its pattern over a wide geographic area and its linkage to the short- and long-term eccentricity cycles of orbital forcing (100 and 405 kyr), was thought to be glacio-eustatic in origin. Eight third-order cycles were recognized within the Eifelian–Givetian.

Becker et al. (2012)—Presented a new curve for the GTS2012 compilation (Gradstein et al., 2012), based on a synthesis of past global curves, although without detailed explanation. Becker et al. (2020, Ch. 22: The Devonian Period, this book) developed a very detailed relative sea-level curve calibrated to ammonoid and conodont zones.

Wong et al. (2016)—Presented a revision of Frasnian sea-level curve based on decades of sequence stratigraphic analysis of outcrops in the Canadian Rocky Mountains and of the adjacent, hydrocarbon-bearing, subsurface. This study stands out for the detail of the biostratigraphic, sedimentological, and information about depositional geometries over a large area, that assist in the recognition of global patterns.

13.4.1.5 Carboniferous

Izart et al. (2003)—This was a near-global comparison of Late Carboniferous and Permian sequences, leading to the recognition of interregional stratigraphic patterns and the timing of eustatic changes.

Heckel (2008)—Regarded the late middle through late Pennsylvanian cyclothems of midcontinent North America as the result of large-scale eustatic fluctuations related to the large-scale, but short-term, waxing and waning of Gondwanan continental ice sheets, in turn moderated by long eccentricity cycles of orbital forcing.

Eros et al. (2012a)—Demonstrated the correlation of 252 cyclothems across a 250 km long depositional ramp profile of the Donets Basin, within a 33 my span of the Mississippian–Pennsylvanian. Their occurrence on orbital forcing time scales and correspondence to cyclicity in other basins suggests a glacio-eustatic origin for the RSL curve generated from this data. Ruban (2012) and Eros et al. (2012b) provide a discussion about a comparison of this work with the Paleozoic eustatic curve of Haq and Schutter (2008). See also van Hinsbergen et al. (2015).

Aretz et al. (2020, Ch. 23: The Carboniferous Period, this book) present a revised Early Carboniferous sequence stratigraphy history calibrated to European biostratigraphic zones.

13.4.1.6 Permian

Izart et al. (2003)—This was a near-global comparison of Late Carboniferous and Permian sequences, leading to the recognition of interregional stratigraphic patterns and the timing of eustatic changes.

Rygel et al. (2008)—Provided a comprehensive review of the magnitude of Late Paleozoic eustatic change, discussed in detail in the Section 13.3.3.2 on eustatic magnitudes. They are critical of the Ross and Ross (1985, 1987) curves because they cannot be replicated.

Jin et al. (2006)—Related the proposed GSSP for the base Lopingian to a major eustatic fall calibrated by a negative carbon isotope excursion and major faunal turnover. This paper is a good example of the way in which chronostratigraphy and eustasy can possibly be integrated.

13.4.1.7 Triassic

Embry (1988, 1997)—Provided seminal descriptions of the sequence stratigraphy of the Canadian Triassic succession with global comparisons to yield a eustatic signal that could also be linked to chronostratigraphic subdivision (i.e., stage and substage boundaries). See also Mørk (1994).

Gianolla and Jacquin (1998)—Provided a description of the Triassic stratigraphy of Western Europe with global comparisons (incorporated in eustatic model of Hardenbol et al., 1998).

Franz et al. (2014)—Documented evidence for eustasy from the Carnian succession of the epicontinental Central European Basin.

Haq (2018)—Provided a reappraisal of the Haq et al. (1988) and Hardenbol et al. (1998) synthesis incorporating subsequent published data from Europe, Arabia, India, Pakistan, China, and Australia (see https://www.geosociety.org/datarepository/2018/2018390.pdf—14 key references were cited, including previous syntheses). Twenty-two third-order sequences were recognized, with sea-level change amplitudes estimated as mostly varying between less than 25 m and c. 75 m. Six were estimated as exceeding 75 m.

13.4.1.8 Jurassic

Hallam (2001)—This was a much cited global compilation of stratigraphic data to extract a eustatic signal and challenged the notion of major, rapid sea-level falls within the Jurassic.

Zimmermann et al. (2015)—Reviewed the sequence stratigraphy of the Early and Middle Jurassic of the North German Basin, noting correspondence with the short-term (second-order) Boreal cyclicity described by De Graciansky et al. (1998) and Jacquin et al. (1998). The influence of local tectonics on deposition cyclicity in the Jurassic of northern Europe was emphasized (see also Underhill and Partington, 1993; Hesselbo and Jenkyns, 1998; Hesselbo, 2008), although high-frequency (fourth-order) sequences are suggested to have a glacio-eustatic origin because of their inferred periodicity and interregional correlation.

Haq (2017) —Provided a reappraisal of the Haq et al. (1988) and Hardenbol et al. (1998) synthesis incorporating subsequent published data from Europe, Arabia, India, and Argentina (see http://www.geosociety.org/datarepository/2017/2017387.pdf—15 key references were cited, including previous syntheses). Incorporation of data away from these regions was thought to be hindered by uncertainties in interregional biostratigraphic calibration. Fifty-six third-order sequences were recognized, with sea-level change amplitudes estimated as varying between less than 25 m and c. 150 m.

13.4.1.9 Cretaceous

Hoedemaeker (1995)—Used variations in ammonite diversity to recognize eustatic highs and lows in the Berriasian–Barremian stratigraphy of southeast Spain. Eustasy is implied because of correlation of the cyclicity to other parts of Europe and Russia. The duration of the cyclicity (c. 3.4 Myr, using the time scale of the publication) is intermediate between the "third-order" and "second-order" cyclicity of Haq et al. (1987, 1988) for the same period.

Haq (2014)—Provided a reappraisal of the Haq et al. (1988) and Hardenbol et al. (1998) syntheses incorporating subsequent published data from a global set of locations. Fifty-eight third-order sequences were recognized, with sea-level change amplitudes estimated as varying between less than 20 m and c. 100 m. See also Haq and Huber (2017). The review of Haq (2014) was adopted for the Cretaceous portion of the 2016 geologic time scale compilation of Ogg et al. (2016) with minor modification.

Wendler et al. (2014)—Recognized long-term obliquity and long- and short-term eccentricity orbitial forcing cycles as a primary control on mid-Cretaceous sea-level changes on the Levant margin of the Arabian Plate. This was interpreted as a eustatic pattern, with aquifer-eustasy invoked as a driving mechanism (see discussion in Section 13.3.3.1).

Scott et al. (2018)—Placed Cenomanian–Turonian flooding events as recognized in North America into a precise chronostratigraphic framework that permitted correlation with Tunisian sections. Commonality provided support to the eustatic model of Haq (2014) and Haq and Huber (2017). See also Gale et al. (2002, 2008), Galeotti et al. (2009), and Koch and Brenner (2009).

Dujoncquoy et al. (2018)—Provided a comprehensive study of the Early Cretaceous of Oman using outcrop, 3D seismic, and well log data to generate a RSL curve. Comparison of this with that from the Vocontian Basin of France (Gréselle and Pittet, 2010) suggested a eustatic origin. Reasonable comparison with the eustatic curve of Snedden and Liu (2010) was also demonstrated.

13.4.1.10 Cenozoic

Abreu and Anderson (1998)—Used a smoothed $\delta^{18}O$ isotope curve as a proxy for eustasy. Correspondence with other eustatic curves suggested a strong glacio-eustatic signature from the Middle Eocene onward.

Sluijs et al. (2008)—Constructed a eustatic curve for the Paleocene–Eocene transition using palynological and sedimentological data from multiple sites from around the globe.

Miller et al. (1998, 2013b)—Backstripped onshore New Jersey data to provide a testable history of sea-level change. Miocene portions were tested using offshore cores collected by IODP Expedition 313 on the New Jersey shelf, as presented in Miller et al. (2013a,b), Katz et al. (2013), Browning et al. (2013), and McCarthy et al. (2013). See also Van Sickel et al. (2004) and Gasson et al. (2012).

Kominz et al. (2016)—Backstripped RSL estimates of Middle to Late Miocene sequences from the New Jersey coastal plain and three IODP shelf sites are generally internally consistent with respect to the timing of SBs and RSL variations. Coastal plain sedimentation tends to predict RSL changes that are consistent with those observed offshore. Where onshore and offshore sedimentation corresponds, the rising and falling portions of the RSL curve can be correlated, although the magnitude of offshore and onshore estimates is offset. This result requires that the New Jersey passive margin has undergone epeirogeny and, in particular, that the offshore shelf has subsided less than the coastal plain. Thus it is consistent with relative epeirogeny attributable to subduction of the Farallon Plate (Moucha et al., 2008) and arising from glacial isostatic adjustments effects of the last deglaciation (Raymo et al., 2011).

John et al. (2011)—The timing and magnitude of Miocene eustasy was calculated for the succession on the Marion Plateau, offshore northeastern Australia, as calibrated to other successions, notably offshore New Jersey. Eight sea-level falls correspond to $\delta^{18}O$ increases that reflect increased Antarctic ice volumes. From backstripping, ranges of individual sea falls were from 26–28 to 53–81 m. Overall sea level fell between 53 and 69 m and between 16.5 and 13.9 Ma.

Cramer et al. (2011)—Reconciled onshore New Jersey backstripped sea-level estimates with a different approach, using deep-sea benthic foraminiferal $\delta^{18}O$ and Mg/Ca records to extract changes in seawater $\delta^{18}O$ proportional to ice-volume and sea-level changes. Because of limitations in the data, this approach (as illustrated in Fig. 13.13) was restricted to periods longer than 2 Myr and showed similar changes from both methods. Ongoing studies use higher resolution $\delta^{18}O$ records to compare changes on the Myr scale (Miller et al., 2020).

13.5 Summary

Many challenges still exist to isolating the eustatic signal in the rock record. The basic interpretation of water depth changes or transgressive–regressive cycles in any given succession can be fraught with difficulties (Brett et al., 2011; Simmons, 2012), and eminent workers can come to differing conclusions on the interpretation of the same outcrop or well stratigraphy. If carried through multiple sections, there will inevitably be differing conclusions on the timing and magnitude of eustasy. Even assuming a consistent approach to the interpretation of changing RSL, demonstrating that the same changes can be seen in multiple sections on different paleocontinents, and are synchronous can be challenging, given the limitations of biostratigraphy and other correlation proxies (Miall, 1991, 1992, 2010). Nonetheless, stratigraphers have a variety of techniques at their disposal to develop an understanding of eustasy ranging from backstripping, to $\delta^{18}O$ (for the Cenozoic), to synthesis techniques evaluating multiple stratigraphic sections. High-resolution biostratigraphy, carbon, and strontium isotope studies and the identification of orbital forcing can provide a robust framework in which to correlate. As a consequence, knowledge of the timing, magnitude, and duration of eustasy is evolving, especially for short-term (10^5–10^6 years) cyclicity, which clearly relates to the orbital forcing of climate change.

Given the relatively high magnitudes (tens of meters) of short-term eustatic change (although not as great as suggested, e.g., by Haq et al., 1987, 1988 and Haq, 2014) and its occurrence on astronomical forcing time scales (Boulila et al., 2011), it seems likely that glacio-eustasy is the primary driver of eustasy throughout much of the Phanerozoic, even in "greenhouse" times, such as the Cretaceous (Ray et al., 2019). Aquifer-eustasy has a growing number of advocates (e.g., Sames et al., 2016) but cannot explain the higher magnitudes of eustatic change observed and the observed relationships between eustasy and climate (Davies et al., 2020). In support of the notion of the dominance of glacio-eustasy as a control on short-term sea-level changes is the growing body of direct, proxy, and circumstantial evidence that supports glaciation for parts of all periods of the Phanerozoic with the possible exception of the Triassic.

The magnitude and timing of long-term (10^7–10^8 years) eustasy was often qualitatively estimated by stratigraphic observations on the extent of continental flooding (e.g., Hallam, 1992). Progress on geodynamic modeling has enabled more quantitative approaches to be taken (e.g., Conrad, 2013; Vérard et al., 2015). Spreading ridge volume is a key factor driving long-term eustasy and this, alongside other geodynamic features, can be modeled, to derive a long-term eustatic curve (Fig. 13.9). However, the choice of plate model is key, and different plate models can derive quite different results. These different results pose some challenges when attempting to integrate long-term sea-level trends with local observations to isolate the true magnitude of short-term sea-level events.

Long-term trends can act to amplify or suppress short-term trends.

An understanding of eustasy is a powerful means of understanding the often incomplete nature of the sedimentary record. Knowledge of eustatic cyclicity is useful in determining the selection of chronostratigraphic reference sections (GSSPs) and provides a context for the evolution of the subdivisions of the geologic time scale. With this in mind, it is worth recalling that when d'Orbigny (1842) introduced the term *étage* (stage), he did so with a catastrophists' view of the Earth's history. Stages were "the expression of the boundaries which Nature has drawn with bold strokes across the globe." Stage boundaries occurred at horizons of faunal turnover, in turn caused by dramatic paleoenvironmental change. Such changes and major sea-level falls can easily be coincident (e.g., Gaskell, 1991). Thus the early definitions of stages often related to probable time gaps in proximal depositional settings caused by sea-level falls of significant magnitude and rate. We would no longer view such locations as optimal as reference sections for the boundaries of the subdivisions of the geologic time scale, preferring to place these in sections of continuous stratigraphy. These may include the distal equivalents of SBs observed in proximal settings (Simmons, 2012).

More broadly, an understanding of eustasy provides context for the subdivision of geologic time. Increasingly, the definition of stages is related to changes in the Earth system, of which eustasy is one component (e.g., Babcock et al., 2015). The biostratigraphic events that typically act as proxies for the definition of stage boundaries can be related to changes in paleoclimate, geodynamics, ocean chemistry, and eustasy.

The developments in the understanding of eustasy are not always well known within the broader geological community, as is evidenced by the continuing reference to older papers (e.g., Haq et al., 1987; Johnson et al., 1985) that have now been superseded, not only by work by their primary authors, but also by several other independent workers. Such a situation could be regarded as "chaos" (Ruban, 2016), or, more positively, as choice. The geologist interested in understanding eustasy within a given geologic period can evaluate several options and choose that which adopted a methodology they regard as robust. Moving forward, we hope that the subcommissions for each geologic period of the International Subcommission on Stratigraphy will drive the attempts to arrive at consensus view, using consistent and well-calibrated approaches.

Acknowledgments

Many of the ideas on eustasy described herein have been discussed and debated with colleagues at Neftex Petroleum Consultants (now part of Halliburton) over the last 20 years. Peter Sharland, Roger Davies, Dave Casey, and Peter Wells are thanked for driving this research in the early years. This paper is published with the permission of Halliburton to whom the authors are grateful for technical support. We thank numerous colleagues who participated in the generation of the "New Jersey sea-level curve" (especially M. Kominz, G. Mountain, P. Sugarman, and S. Pekar), the IODP paloceanographic community for their efforts in generating the $\delta^{18}O$ and Mg/Ca records, and B. Cramer for his Mg/Ca synthesis. Douwe van der Meer is thanked for his helpful comments. The contribution by Ken Miller is supported by NSF grant OCE1657013.

Bibliography

Abreu, V.S., and Anderson, J.B., 1998, Glacial eustasy during the Cenozoic: sequence stratigraphic implications. *The American Association of Petroleum Geologists Bulletin*, **82**: 1385–1400.

Ager, D.V., 1981, *The Nature of the Stratigraphic Record*, 2nd ed. John Wiley, New York, p. 122.

Ager, D.V., 1993, *The New Catastrophism: The Importance of the Rare Event in Geological History*. Cambridge University Press, Cambridge, p. 231.

Ajdanlijsky, G., Strasser, A., and Götz, A.E., 2019, Integrated bio- and cyclostratigraphy of Middle Triassic (Anisian) ramp deposits, NW Bulgaria. *Geologica Carpathica*, **70**: 325–354.

Algeo, T.J., and Seslavinsky, K.B., 1995, Reconstructing eustatic and epeirogenic trends from Paleozoic continental flooding records. *In* Haq, B.U. (ed), *Sequence Stratigraphy and Depositional Response to Eustatic, Tectonic and Climatic Forcing*. Springer, Dordrecht, pp. 209–246.

Al-Husseini, M., 2018, Arabian orbital sequences. *In* Montenari, M. (ed), *Stratigraphy and Timescales, Volume Three: Cyclostratigraphy and Astrochronology*. Elsevier, Amsterdam, pp. 219–264.

Allen, P.A., 2017, *Sediment Routing Systems*. Cambridge University Press, Cambridge, p. 407.

Alley, N.F., and Frakes, L.A., 2003, First known Cretaceous glaciation: Livingstone Tillite Member of the Cadna-owie Formation, South Australia. *Australian Journal of Earth Sciences*, **50**: 139–144.

Alley, N.F., Hore, S.B., and Frakes, L.A., 2019, Glaciations at high-latitude Southern Australia during the Early Cretaceous. *Australian Journal of Earth Sciences*, **2019**: 1–51.

Álvaro, J.J., Benziane, F., Thomas, R., Walsh, G.J., and Yazidi, A., 2014, Neoproterozoic–Cambrian stratigraphic framework of the Anti-Atlas and Ouzellagh promontory (High Atlas), Morocco. *Journal of African Earth Sciences*, **98**: 19–33.

Aretz, M., Herbig, H.G., and Wang, X.D., 2020, Chapter 23 – The Carboniferous Period. *In* Gradstein, F.M., Ogg, J.G., Schmitz, M.D., and Ogg, G.M. (eds), *The Geologic Time Scale 2020*. **Vol. 2** (this book). Elsevier, Boston, MA.

Arkell, W.J., 1933, *The Jurassic System in Great Britain*. Clarendon Press, Oxford, p. 681.

Armentrout, J.M., 1996. High resolution sequence biostratigraphy: examples from the Gulf of Mexico Plio-Pleistocene. *In* Howell, J.A., and Aitken, J.F. (eds). *High Resolution Sequence Stratigraphy: Innovations and Applications*. Geological Society, London, Special Publications, **104**: p. 65–86.

Armentrout, J.M., 2019, Tectonic events and eustatic cycle correlation: a review of biostratigraphic issues for depositional cycle chart construction and sequence dating. *In* Denne, R.A., and Kahn, A. (eds),

Geologic Problem Solving with Microfossils IV. SEPM Special Publication, **111**.

Babcock, L.E., Peng, S.-C., Brett, C.E., Zhu, M.-Y., Ahlberg, P., Bevis, M., et al., 2015, Global climate, sea-levels, and biotic events in the Cambrian Period. *Palaeoworld*, **24**: 5–15.

Banner, F.T., and Simmons, M.D., 1994, Calcareous algae and foraminifera as water-depth indicators: an example from the Early Cretaceous carbonates of northeast Arabia. *In* Simmons, M.D. (ed), *Micropalaeontology and Hydrocarbon Exploration in the Middle East*, British Micropalaeontological Society Publications Series: pp. 243–252.

Barrell, J., 1917, Rhythms and the measurement of geologic time. *Geological Society of America Bulletin*, **28**: 745–904.

Bartek, L.R., Vail, P.R., Anderson, J.B., Emmet, P.A., and Wu, S., 1991, Effect of Cenozoic ice sheet fluctuations in Antarctica on the stratigraphic signature of the Neogene. *Journal of Geophysical Research*, **96B**: 6753–6778.

Becker, R.T., Gradstein, F.M., and Hammer, O., 2012, The Devonian period. In Gradstein, F.M., Ogg, J.G., Schmitz, M.D., and Ogg, G.M. (eds), *The Geologic Time Scale 2012*, Elsevier, **2**: 559–602.

Becker, R.T., Marshall, J.E.A., and Da Silva, A.-C., 2020, Chapter 22 – The Devonian Period. *In* Gradstein, F.M., Ogg, J.G., Schmitz, M.D., and Ogg, G.M. (eds), *The Geologic Time Scale 2020*. **Vol. 2** (this book). Elsevier, Boston, MA.

Bergen, J.A., Truax III, S., de Kaenel, E., Blair, S., Browning, E., Lundquist, J., et al., 2019, BP Gulf of Mexico Neogene Astronomically-tuned Time Scale (BP GNATTS). *Geological Society of America Bulletin*, **131**: 1871–1888.

Bergström, S.M., Chen, X., Gutierrez-Marco, J.C., and Dronov, A., 2008, The new chronostratigraphic classification of the Ordovician system and its relations to major regional series and stages and to $\delta^{13}C$ chemostratigraphy. *Lethaia*, **42**: 97–107.

Billups, K., and Schrag, D.P., 2002, Paleotemperatures and ice volume of the past 27Myr revisited with paired Mg/Ca and $^{18}O/^{16}O$ measurements on benthic foraminifera. *Paleoceanography*, **17**: 1–3.

Bishop, J.W., Montañez, I.P., Gulbranson, E.L., and Brenckle, P.L., 2009, The onset of mid-Carboniferous glacio-eustasy: sedimentologic and diagenetic constraints, Arrow Canyon, Nevada. *Palaeogeography, Palaeoclimatology, Palaeoecology*, **276**: 217–243.

Blakey, R., 2008, Pennsylvanian – Jurassic sedimentary basins of the Colorado Plateau and Southern Rocky Mountains. *In* Miall, A.D. (ed), *The Phanerozoic Sedimentary Basins of the United States and Canada. Sedimentary Basins of the World*. Elsevier, **5**: 245–296.

Bond, G.C., 1979, Evidence for some uplifts of large magnitude in continental platforms. *Tectonophysics*, **61**: 285–305.

Bond, C.E., Gibbs, A.D., Shipton, Z.K., and Jones, S., 2007, What do you think this is? "Conceptual uncertainty" in geoscience interpretation. *GSA Today*, **17**: 4–11.

Boulila, S., 2008, *Cyclostratigraphie des séries sédimentaires du Jurassique supérieur (Sud-Est de la France, Nord de la Tunisie): contrôle astroclimatique, implications géochronologiques et séquentielles*. Ph.D. thesis. Pierre et Marie Curie University, Paris, France. p. 313.

Boulila, S., and Hinnov, L.A., 2017, A review of tempo and scale of the early Jurassic Toarcian OAE: implications for carbon cycle and sea level variations. *Newsletters on Stratigraphy*, **50**: 363–389.

Boulila, S., Galbrun, B., Hinnov, L.A., and Collin, P.-Y., 2008a, Orbital calibration of the Early Kimmeridgian (southeastern France): implications for geochronology and sequence stratigraphy. *Terra Nova*, **20**: 455–462.

Boulila, S., Galbrun, B., Hinnov, L.A., and Collin, P.Y., 2008b, High-resolution cyclostratigraphic analysis from magnetic susceptibility in a Lower Kimmeridgian (Upper Jurassic) marl-limestone succession (La Méouge, Vocontian Basin, France). *Sedimentary Geology*, **203**: 54–63.

Boulila, S., Hinnov, L.A., Huret, E., Collin, P.Y., Galbrun, B., Fortwengler, D., et al., 2008c, Astronomical calibration of the Early Oxfordian (Vocontian and Paris basins, France): consequences of revising the Late Jurassic time scale. *Earth and Planetary Science Letters*, **276**: 40–51.

Boulila, S., de Rafelis, M., Hinnov, L.A., Gardin, S., Galbrun, B., and Collin, P.-Y., 2010, Orbitally forced climate and sea-level changes in the paleoceanic Tethyan domain (marl-limestone alternations, Lower Kimmeridgian, SE France). *Palaeogeography, Palaeoclimatology, Palaeoecology*, **292**: 57–70.

Boulila, S., Galbrun, B., Miller, K.G., Pekar, S.F., Browning, J.V., Laskar, J., et al., 2011, On the origin of Cenozoic and Mesozoic "third-order" eustatic sequences. *Earth-Science Reviews*, **109**: 94–112.

Boulila, S., Galbrun, B., Huret, E., Hinnov, L.A., Rouget, I., Gardin, S., et al., 2014, Astronomical calibration of the Toarcian Stage: implications for sequence stratigraphy and duration of the early Toarcian OAE. *Earth and Planetary Science Letters*, **386**: 98–111.

Boulila, S., Laskar, J., Haq, B.U., Galbrun, B., and Hara, N., 2018, Long-term cyclicities in Phanerozoic sea-level sedimentary record and their potential drivers. *Global and Planetary Chang*, **165**: 128–136.

Bover-Arnal, T., Salas, R., Guimerà, J., and Moreno-Bedmar, J.A., 2014, Deep incision in an Aptian carbonate succession indicates major sea-level fall in the Cretaceous. *Sedimentology*, **61**: 1558–1593.

Bowman, V.C., Francis, J.E., and Riding, J.B., 2013, Late Cretaceous winter sea ice in Antarctica? *Geology*, **41**: 1227–1230.

Brett, C.E., Boucot, A.J., and Jones, B., 1993, Absolute depths of Silurian benthic assemblages. *Lethaia*, **26**: 25–40.

Brett, C.E., Ferretti, A., Histon, K., and Schönlaub, H.P., 2009, Silurian sequence stratigraphy of the Carnic Alps, Austria. *Palaeogeography, Palaeoclimatology, Palaeoecology*, **279**: 1–28.

Brett, C.E., Baird, G.C., Bartholomew, A.J., DeSantis, M.K., and Ver Straeten, C.A., 2011, Sequence stratigraphy and a revised sea-level curve for the Middle Devonian of eastern North America. *Palaeogeography, Palaeoclimatology, Palaeoecology*, **304**: 21–53.

Browning, J.V., Miller, K.G., Sugarman, P.J., Barron, J., McCarthy, F.M., Kulhanek, D.K., et al., 2013, Chronology of Eocene–Miocene sequences on the New Jersey shallow shelf: implications for regional, interregional, and global correlations. *Geosphere*, **9**: 1434–1456.

Burgess, P.M., 2008, Phanerozoic evolution of the sedimentary cover of the North American craton. *In* Miall, A.D. (ed), *The Sedimentary Basins of the United States and Canada*. Elsevier, 31–63.

Burgess, P.M., and Gurnis, M., 1995, Mechanisms for the formation of cratonic stratigraphic sequences. *Earth and Planetary Science Letters*, **136**: 647–663.

Burton, R., Kendall St. C., C.G., and Lerche, I., 1987, Out of our depth: on the impossibility of fathoming eustasy from the stratigraphic record. *Earth-Science Reviews*, **24**: 237–277.

Buso, V.V., Danielski Aquino, C., Gomes Paim, P.S., Alves de Souza, P., Mori, A.L., Fallgatter, C.F., et al. 2019. Late Palaeozoic glacial cycles and subcycles in western Gondwana: correlation of surface and subsurface data of the Paraná Basin, Brazil. Palaeogeography,

Palaeoclimatology, Palaeoecology, 531. Part B, article #108435: 16 pp. https://doi.org/10.1016/j.palaeo.2017.09.004.

Calner, M., 2008, Silurian global events – at the tipping point of climate change. *In* Elewa, A.M.T. (ed), *Mass Extinction*. Springer, Berlin, 21–57.

Caputo, M.V., 1998, Ordovician-Silurian glaciations and global sea-level changes. *In* Landing, E., and Johnson, M.E. (eds), *Silurian Cycles: Linkages of Dynamic Stratigraphy With Atmospheric, Oceanic, and Tectonic Changes*. New York State Museum Bulletin, **491**: 15–25.

Caputo, M.V., de Melo, J.H.G., Streel, M., and Isbell, J.L., 2008, Late Devonian and Early Carboniferous glacial records of South America. *In* Fielding, C.R., Frank, T.D., and Isbell, J.L. (eds), *Resolving the Late Paleozoic Ice Age in Time and Space*. Geological Society of America Special Paper 441. 161–173.

Carter, R.M., Abbott, S.T., Fulthorpe, C.S., Haywick, D.W., and Henderson, R.A., 1991, Application of global sea-level and sequence-stratigraphic models in Southern Hemisphere Neogene strata from New Zealand. *In* Macdonald, D.I.M. (ed), *Sedimentation, Tectonics, Eustasy: Sea-Level Changes Active Margins*. International Association of Sedimentologists Special Publication 12. 41–65.

Catuneanu, O., 2006, *Principles of Sequence Stratigraphy*. Elsevier, Amsterdam, p. 375.

Catuneanu, O., 2017, Sequence stratigraphy: guidelines for a standard methodology. *In* Montenari, M. (ed), *Stratigraphy and Timescales, Volume Two: Advances in Sequence Stratigraphy*. Elsevier, 1–58.

Catuneanu, O., 2019a, Model-independent sequence stratigraphy. *Earth-Science Reviews*, **188**: 312–388.

Catuneanu, O., 2019b, Scale in sequence stratigraphy. *Marine and Petroleum Geology*, **106**: 128–159.

Catuneanu, O., Abreu, V., Bhattacharya, J.P., Blum, M.D., Dalrymple, R.W., Eriksson, P.G., et al., 2009, Towards the standardization of sequence stratigraphy. *Earth-Science Reviews*, **92**: 1–33.

Chamberlin, T.C., 1899, An attempt to frame a working hypothesis on the cause of glacial periods on an atmospheric basis. *The Journal of Geology*, **7**: 545–584.

Chamberlin, T.C., 1909, Diastrophism as the ultimate basis for correlation. *The Journal of Geology*, **17**: 685–693.

Chen, J., Sheng, Q., Hu, K., Yao, L., Lin, W., Montañez, I.P., et al., 2019, Late Mississippian glacio-eustasy recorded in the eastern Paleo-Tethys Ocean (South China). *Palaeogeography, Palaeoclimatology, Palaeoecology*, **531**.

Cherns, L., Wheeley, J.R., Popov, L.E., Ghobadi Pour, M., Owens, R. M., and Hemsley, A.R., 2013, Long-period orbital climate forcing in the early Palaeozoic? *Journal of the Geological Society, London*, **170**: 707–710.

Christie-Blick, N., 1990, Sequence stratigraphy and sea-level changes in Cretaceous time. *In* Ginsburg, R.N., and Beaudoin, B. (eds), *Cretaceous Resources, Events and Rhythms Background and Plans for Research*. Kluwer, Dordrecht, 1–22.

Christie-Blick, N., and Driscoll, N.W., 1995, Sequence stratigraphy. *Annual Review of Earth and Planetary Sciences*, **23**: 451–478.

Christie-Blick, N., Mountain, G.S., and Miller, K.G., 1990, Seismic stratigraphy: record of sea-level change. *In* Revelle, R. (ed), *Sea-Level Change, National Research Council, Studies in Geophysics*. National Academy Press, 116–140.

Cloetingh, S., and Haq, B.U., 2015, Inherited landscapes and sea-level change. *Science*, **347**: 1258375.

Cloetingh, S., and Kooi, H., 1990, Intraplate stresses: a new perspective on QDS and Vail's third-order cycles. *In* Cross, T.A. (ed), *Quantitative Dynamic Stratigraphy*. Prentice-Hall, Englewood Cliffs, NJ, 127–148.

Cloetingh, S., McQueen, H., and Lambeck, K., 1985, On a tectonic mechanism for regional sea-level variations. *Earth and Planetary Science Letters*, **75**: 157–166.

Cloetingh, S., Burov, E., and Francois, T., 2013, Thermo-mechanical controls on intra-plate deformation and the role of plume-folding interactions in continental topography. *Gondwana Research*, **24**: 815–837.

Cogné, J.P., and Humler, E., 2006, Trends and rhythms in global seafloor generation rate. *Geochemistry, Geophysics, Geosystems*, **7**: 1–17.

Cogné, J.-P., Humler, E., and Courtillot, V., 2006, Mean age of oceanic lithosphere drives eustatic sea-level change since Pangea breakup. *Earth and Planetary Science Letters*, **245**: 115–122.

Conrad, C.P., 2013, The solid Earth's influence on sea-level. *Geological Society of America Bulletin*, **125**: 1027–1052.

Conrad, C.P., and Husson, L., 2009, Influence of dynamic topography on sea-level and its rate of change. *Lithosphere*, **1**: 110–120.

Cooper, R.A., and Sadler, P.M., 2012, The Ordovician period. *In* Gradstein, F.M., Ogg, J.G., Schmitz, M.D., and Ogg, G.M. (eds), *The Geologic Time Scale*. Elsevier, **2**: 489–524.

Cooper, R.A., Crampton, J.S., Raine, J.I., Gradstein, F.M., Morgans, H.E., Sadler, P.M., et al., 2001, Quantitative biostratigraphy of the Taranaki Basin, New Zealand: a deterministic and probabilistic approach. *The American Association of Petroleum Geologists Bulletin*, **85**: 1469–1498.

Cramer, B.S., Brett, C.E., Melchin, M.J., Männik, P., Kleffner, M.A., McLaughlin, P.I., et al., 2010a, Revised correlation of Silurian Provincial Series of North America with global and regional chronostratigraphic units and $\delta^{13}C_{carb}$ chemostratigraphy. *Lethaia*, **44**: 185–202.

Cramer, B.D., Loydell, D.K., Samtleben, C., Munnecke, A., Kaljo, D., Männik, P., et al., 2010b, Testing the limits of Paleozoic chronostratigraphic correlation via high-resolution (<500 ky) integrated conodont, graptolite, and carbon isotope ($\delta^{13}C_{carb}$) biochemostratigraphy across the Llandovery–Wenlock (Silurian) boundary: is a unified Phanerozoic time scale achievable? *Geological Society of America Bulletin*, **122**: 1700–1716.

Cramer, B.S., Miller, K.G., Barrett, P.J., and Wright, J.D., 2011, Late Cretaceous – Neogene trends in deep ocean temperature and continental ice volume: reconciling records of benthic foraminiferal geochemistry ($\delta^{18}O$ and Mg/Ca) with sea-level history. *Journal of Geophysical Research*, **116**: C12023.

Creveling, J.R., Finnegan, S., Mitrovica, J.X., and Bergmann, K.D., 2018, Spatial variation in Late Ordovician glacioeustatic sea-level change. *Earth and Planetary Science Letters*, **496**: 1–9.

Cuvier, G., and Brongniart, A., 1811, *Essai sur la géographie minéralogique des environs de Paris: avec une carte géognostique, et des coupes de terrain*. Baudouin, Paris.

d'Orbigny, A., 1842, *Paléontologie Francaise. Terrains crétacés, Céphalopodes*. Masson, Paris, p. 662.

Dabard, M.P., Loi, A., Paris, F., Ghienne, J.F., Pistis, M., and Vidal, M., 2015, Sea-level curve for the Middle to early Late Ordovician in the Armorican Massif (western France): icehouse third-order glacio-eustatic cycles. *Palaeogeography, Palaeoclimatology, Palaeoecology*, **436**: 96–111.

Davies, R.B., and Simmons, M.D., 2018, Triassic sequence stratigraphy of the Arabian Plate. *In* Pöppelreiter, M.C. (ed), *Lower Triassic to Middle Jurassic Sequence of the Arabian Plate*. EAGE (European Assoc. Geoscientists and Engineers), 101–162.

Davies, R.B., Casey, D.M., Horbury, A.D., Sharland, P.R., and Simmons, M.D., 2002, Early to mid-Cretaceous mixed carbonate-clastic shelfal systems: examples, issues and models from the Arabian Plate. *GeoArabia*, **7**: 541–598.

Davies, A., Kemp, A.E., and Pike, J., 2009, Late Cretaceous seasonal ocean variability from the Arctic. *Nature*, **460**: 254–258.

Davies, J.R., Waters, R.A., Molyneux, S.G., Williams, M., Zalasiewicz, J.A., and Vandenbroucke, T.R., 2016, Gauging the impact of glacioeustasy on a mid-latitude early Silurian basin margin, mid Wales, UK. *Earth-Science Reviews*, **156**: 82–107.

Davies, A., Hunter, S.J., Gréselle, B., Haywood, A.M., and Robson, C., 2019a, Evidence for seasonality in early Eocene high latitude sea-surface temperatures. *Earth and Planetary Science Letters*, **519**: 274–283.

Davies, R.B., Simmons, M.D., Jewell, T.O., and Wyton, J., 2019b, Regional controls on siliciclastic input into Mesozoic depositional systems of the Arabian Plate and their petroleum significance. *In* AlAnzi, H.R., Rahmani, R.A., Steel, R.J., and Soliman, O.M. (eds), *Siliciclastic Reservoirs of the Arabian Plate*. AAPG Memoir, **116**: 103–140.

Davies, A., Gréselle, B., Hunter, S.J., Baines, G., Robson, C., Haywood, A.M., et al., 2020, Assessing the impact of aquifer-eustasy on short-term Cretaceous sea-level. *Cretaceous Research*, **112**, article #104445: 12 pp. https://doi.org/10.1016/j.cretres.2020.104445.

Davydov, V.I., Crowley, J.L., Schmitz, M.D., and Poletaev, V.I., 2010, High-precision U-Pb zircon age calibration of the global Carboniferous time scale and Milankovitch band cyclicity in the Donets Basin, eastern Ukraine. *Geochemistry, Geophysics, Geosystems*, **11**: Q0AA04.

De Graciansky, P.C., Hardenbol, J., Jacquin, T., and Vail, P.R. (eds), 1998, *Mesozoic and Cenozoic Sequence Stratigraphy of European Basins*. SEPM Special Publication, **60**: 786pp.

De Vleeschouwer, D., Da Silva, A.C., Sinnesael, M., Chen, D., Day, J.E., Whalen, M.T., et al., 2017. Timing and pacing of the Late Devonian mass extinction event regulated by eccentricity and obliquity. *Nature Communications*, **8**: article #2268. https://doi.org/10.1038/s41467-017-02407-1.

Dechamps, P., Durand, N., Bard, E., Hamelin, B., Camoin, G., Thomas, A.L., et al., 2012, Ice-sheet collapse and sea-level rise at the Bølling warming 14,600 years ago. *Nature*, **483**: 559–564.

Dewey, J.F., and Pitman, W.C., 1998, Sea-level changes: mechanisms, magnitudes and rates. *In* Pindell, J.L., and Drake, C.L. (eds), *Paleogeographic Evolution and Non-glacial Eustasy, Northern South America*. SEPM Special Publication, **58**: 1–16.

Diaz-Martinez, E., and Grahn, Y., 2007, Early Silurian glaciation along the western margin of Gondwana (Peru, Bolivia and Northern Argentina): Palaeogeographic and geodynamic setting. *Palaeogeography, Palaeoclimatology, Palaeoecology*, **245** (1), 62–81.

Dickinson, W.R., Soreghan, G.S., and Giles, K.A., 1994, Glacio-eustatic origin of Permo-Carboniferous stratigraphic cycles: evidence from the southern Cordilleran foreland region. *In* Dennison, J.M., and Ettensohn, F.R. (eds), *Tectonic and Eustatic Controls on Sedimentary Cycles, Society of Sedimentary Geology, Concepts in Sedimentology and Palaeontology*. **4**: 25–34.

Dietrich, P., Ghienne, J.-F., Lajeunesse, P., Deschamps, R., and Razin, P., 2018. Deglacial sequences and Glacio-Isostatic adjustment: Quaternary compared with Ordovician glaciations. *In* Le Heron, D.P., Hogan, K.A., Phillips, E.R., Huuse, M., Busfield, M.E., and Graham, A.G.C. (eds.). *Glaciated Margins: The Sedimentary and Geophysical Archive*. Geological Society, London, Special Publications, **475**: 149–179.

Donnadieu, Y., Dromart, G., Goddéris, Y., Pucéat, E., Brigaud, B., Dera, G., et al., 2011, A mechanism for brief glacial episodes in the Mesozoic greenhouse. *Paleoceanography*, **26**: PA3212.

Donovan, A.D., Ratcliffe, K., and Zaitlin, B.A., 2010, The sequence stratigraphy family tree: understanding the portfolio of sequence methodologies, Special Publication. *In* Ratcliff, K.T., and Zaitlin, B.A. (eds), *Application of Modern Stratigraphic Techniques: Theory and Case Histories*. SEPM, **94**: 5–33.

Dromart, G., Garcia, J.-P., Picard, S., Atrops, F., Lecuyer, C., and Sheppard, S.M.F., 2003, Ice age at the Middle-Late Jurassic transition? *Earth and Planetary Science Letters*, **213**: 205–220.

Dronov, A., 2017, Ordovician sequence stratigraphy of the Siberian and Russian platforms. *In* Montenari, M. (ed), *Stratigraphy and Timescales, Volume 2: Advances in Sequence Stratigraphy*. Elsevier, 187–241.

Dronov, A.V., Ainsaar, L., Kaljo, D., Meidla, T., Saadre, T., and Einasto, R., 2011, Ordovician of Baltoscandia: facies, sequences and sea-level changes. *In* Gutiérrez-Marco, J.C., Rábano, I., and García-Bellido, D. (eds), *Ordovician of the World, Cuadernos del Museo Geominero*. Instituto Geologico y Minero de España, Madrid, 143–150.

Drummond, C.N., and Wilkinson, B.H., 1996, Stratal thickness frequencies and the prevalence of orderdness in stratigraphic sequences. *The Journal of Geology*, **104**: 1–18.

Dujoncquoy, E., Grélaud, C., Razin, P., Imbert, P., van Buchem, F., Dupont, G., et al., 2018, Seismic stratigraphy of a Lower Cretaceous prograding carbonate platform (Oman) and implications for the eustatic sea-level curve. *The American Association of Petroleum Geologists Bulletin*, **102**: 509–543.

Edwards, L.E., 1989, Supplemented graphic correlation: a powerful tool for paleontologists and nonpaleontologists. *Palaois*, **4**: 127–143.

Ehrenberg, S.N., Pickard, N.A.H., Laursen, G.V., Monibi, S., Mossadegh, Z.K., Svånå, T.A., et al., 2007, Strontium isotope stratigraphy of the Asmari Formation (Oligocene-Lower Miocene), SW Iran. *Journal of Petroelum Geology*, **30**: 107–128.

Einsele, G., Ricken, W., and Seilacher, A., 1991, Cycles and events in stratigraphy – basic concepts and terms. *In* Einsele, G., Ricken, W., and Seilacher, A. (eds), *Cycles and Events in Stratigraphy*. Springer-Verlag, 1–19.

Elrick, M., Berkyová, S., Klapper, G., Sharp, Z., Joachimski, M., and Fryda, J., 2009, Stratigraphic and oxygen isotope evidence for My-scale glaciation driving eustasy in the Early-Middle Devonian greenhouse world. *Palaeogeography, Palaeoclimatology, Palaeoecology*, **276**: 170–181.

Elrick, M., and Scott, L.A., 2010, Carbon and oxygen isotope evidence for high-frequency (104–105 yr) and My-scale glacio-eustasy in Middle Pennsylvanian cyclic carbonates (Gray Mesa Formation), central New Mexico. *Palaeogeography, Palaeoclimatology, Palaeoecology*, **285**: 307–320.

Elrick, M., and Witzke, B., 2016, Orbital-scale glacio-eustasy in the Middle Devonian detected using oxygen isotopes of conodont apatite: implications for long-term greenhouse – icehouse climatic transitions. *Palaeogeography, Palaeoclimatology, Palaeoecology*, **445**: 50–59.

Embry, A.F., 1988, Triassic sea level changes: Evidence from the Canadian Arctic Archipelago. Sea-level changes: an integrated approach. *In* Wilgus, C.K., Hastings, B.S., Kendall St., C.G., and Posamentier, H.W. (eds), *Sea-level Changes: An Integrated Approach*. SEPM Special Publication, **42**: 249–259.

Embry, A.F., 1997, Global sequence boundaries of the Triassic and their identification in the Western Canadian Sedimentary Basin. *Bulletin of Canadian Petroleum Geology*, **45**: 415–433.

Emery, K.O., and Aubrey, D.G., 1991, Impact of sea-level/land-level change on society. *Sea-Levels, Land Levels, and Tide Gauges*. Springer, 167–174.

Emiliani, C., 1955, Pleistocene temperatures. *The Journal of Geology*, **63**: 538–578.

Eros, J.M., Montañez, I.P., Osleger, D.A., Davydov, V.I., Nemyrovska, T.I., Poletaev, V.I., et al., 2012a, Sequence stratigraphy and onlap history of the Donets Basin, Ukraine: insight into Carboniferous icehouse dynamics. *Palaeogeography, Palaeoclimatology, Palaeoecology*, **313**: 1–25.

Eros, J.M., Montañez, I.P., Davydov, V.I., Osleger, D.A., Nemyrovska, T.I., Poletaev, V.I., et al., 2012b, Reply to the comment on "Sequence stratigraphy and onlap history of the Donets Basin, Ukraine: insight into Carboniferous icehouse dynamics". *Palaeogeography, Palaeoclimatology, Palaeoecology*, **363**: 187–191.

Fairbanks, R.G., 1989, A 17,000-year glacio-eustatic sea level record: influence of glacial melting rates on the Younger Dryas event and deep-ocean circulation. *Nature*, **342**: 637.

Falcon-Lang, H.J., Heckel, P.H., Dimichele, W.A., Blake Jr., B.M., Easterday, C.R., Eble, C.F., et al., 2011, No major stratigraphic gap exists near the middle-upper Pennsylvanian (Desmoinesian-Missourian) Boundary in North America. *Palaios*, **26**: 125–139.

Fang, Q., Wu, H., Hinnov, L.A., Jing, X., Wang, X., and Jiang, Q., 2015, Geologic evidence for chaotic behaviour of the planets and its constraints on the third-order eustatic sequences at the end of the Late Paleozoic Ice Age. *Palaeogeography, Palaeoclimatology, Palaeoecology*, **440**: 848–859.

Fielding, C.R., Frank, T.D., and Isbell, J.L., 2008, The late Paleozoic ice age—a review of current understanding and synthesis of global climate patterns. *Geological Society of America Special Papers*, **441**: 343–354.

Finnegan, S., Bergmann, K., Eiler, J.M., Jones, D.S., Fike, D.A., Eisenman, I., et al., 2011, The magnitude and duration of Late Ordovician–Early Silurian glaciation. *Science*, **331**: 903–906.

Föllmi, K.B., 2012, Early Cretaceous life, climate and anoxia. *Cretaceous Research*, **35**: 230–257.

Franz, M., Nowak, K., Berner, U., Heunisch, C., Bandel, K., Röhling, H.G., et al., 2014, Eustatic control on epicontinental basins: the example of the Stuttgart Formation in the Central European Basin (Middle Keuper, Late Triassic). *Global and Planetary Chang*, **122**: 305–329.

Fretwell, P., Pritchard, H.D., Vaughan, D.G., Bamber, J.L., Barrand, N. E., Bell, R., et al., 2013, Bedmap2: improved ice bed, surface and thickness datasets for Antarctica. *Cryosphere*, **7**: 375–393.

Gale, A.S., Hardenbol, J., Hathway, B., Kennedy, W.J., Young, J.R., and Phansalkar, V., 2002, Global correlation of Cenomanian (Upper Cretaceous) sequences: evidence for Milankovitch control on sea-level. *Geology*, **30**: 291–294.

Gale, A.S., Voigt, S., Sageman, B.B., and Kennedy, W.J., 2008, Eustatic sea-level record for the Cenomanian (Late Cretaceous)—extension to the Western Interior Basin, USA. *Geology*, **36**: 859–862.

Galloway, W.E., 1989, Genetic stratigraphic sequences in basin analysis, I. Architecture and genesis of flooding-surface bounded depositional units. *American Association of Petroleum Geologists Bulletin*, **73**: 125–142.

Galeotti, S., Rusciadelli, G., Sprovieri, M., Lanci, L., Gaudio, A., and Pekar, S., 2009, Sea-level control on facies architecture in the Cenomanian–Coniacian Apulian margin (Western Tethys): a record of glacio-eustatic fluctuations during the Cretaceous greenhouse? *Palaeogeography, Palaeoclimatology, Palaeoecology*, **276**: 196–205.

Gaskell, B.A., 1991, Extinction patterns in Paleogene benthic foraminiferal faunas: relationship to climate and sea level. *Palaois*, **6**: 2–16.

Gasson, E., Siddall, M., Lunt, D.J., Rackham, O.J., Lear, C.H., and Pollard, D., 2012, Exploring uncertainties in the relationship between temperature, ice volume, and sea-level over the past 50 million years. *Reviews of Geophysics*, **50**: RG1005.

Ghienne, J.F., 2011, The Late Ordovician glacial record: state of the art. Ordovician of the World. *Cuadernos del Museo Geominero*, **14**: 13–19.

Ghienne, J.F., Desrochers, A., Vandenbroucke, T.R., Achab, A., Asselin, E., Dabard, M.P., et al., 2014, A Cenozoic-style scenario for the end-Ordovician glaciation. *Nature Communications*, **5**: 4485.

Gianolla, P., and Jacquin, T., 1998, Triassic sequence stratigraphic framework of western European basins, Special Publication. *In* de Graciansky, P.-C., Hardenbol, J., Jacquin, T., and Vail, P.R. (eds), *Mesozoic and Cenozoic Sequence Stratigraphy of European Basins*. SEPM, **60**: 719–747.

Giles, P.S., 2009, Orbital forcing and Mississippian sea-level change: time series analysis of marine flooding events in the Visean Windsor Group of eastern Canada and implications for Gondwana glaciation. *Bulletin of Canadian Petroleum Geology*, **57**: 449–471.

Golonka, J., 2007, Phanerozoic paleoenvironment and paleolithofacies maps: Mesozoic. *Geologia*, **33**: 211–264.

Gordon, R.G., and Jurdy, D.M., 1986, Cenozoic global plate motions. *Journal of Geophysical Research*, **91**: 12389–12406.

Grabau, A.W., 1936a, Revised classification of the Paleozoic System in the light of the pulsation theory. *Geological Survey of China Bulletin*, **15**: 23–51.

Grabau, A.W., 1936b, Oscillation or pulsation. *International Geological Congress*, **1**: 539–553.

Grabau, A.W., 1940, *The Rhythm of the Ages*. Henri Vetch, Peking, p. 561.

Gradstein, F.M., Ogg, J.G., Schmitz, M.D., and Ogg, G.M. (eds), 2012. *The Geologic Time Scale*. **Vols. 1 and 2**. p. 1144.

Grahn, Y., and Caputo, M.V., 1992, Early Silurian glaciations in Brazil. *Palaeogeography, Palaeoclimatology, Palaeoecology*, **99**: 9–15.

Grasby, S.E., McCune, G.E., Beauchamp, B., and Galloway, J.M., 2017, Lower Cretaceous cold snaps led to widespread glendonite occurrences in the Sverdrup Basin, Canadian High Arctic. *Geological Society of America Bulletin*, **129**: 771–787.

Gregory, J.M., Griffies, S.M., Hughes, C.W., Lowe, J.A., Church, J.A., Fukimori, I., et al., 2019, Concepts and terminology for sea level: mean, variability and change, both local and global. *Surveys in Geophysics*, **2019**: 1–39.

Gréselle, B., and Pittet, B., 2010, Sea-level reconstructions from the Peri-Vocontian Zone (South-east France) point to Valanginian glacio-eustasy. *Sedimentology*, **57**: 1640–1684.

Grossman, E.L., 2012, Oxygen isotope stratigraphy. *In* Gradstein, F.M., Ogg, J.G., Schmitz, M.D., and Ogg, G.M. (eds), *The Geologic Time Scale 2012*. Elsevier, **1**: 181–206.

Guillaume, B., Pochat, S., Monteux, J., Husson, L., and Choblet, G., 2016, Can eustatic charts go beyond first order? Insights from the Permian–Triassic. *Lithosphere*, **8**: 505–518.

Guillocheau, F., 1995, Nature, rank and origin of Phanerozoic sedimentary cycles. *Comptes rendus de l'Académie des Sciences Paris*, **320**: 1141–1157.

Gulick, S.P.S., Shevenell, A.E., Montelli, A., Fernandez, R., Smith, C., Warny, S., et al., 2017, Initiation and long-term instability of the East Antarctic Ice Sheet. *Nature*, **552**: 225–229.

Hall, R., 2002, Cenozoic geological and plate mode evolution of SE Asia and the SW Pacific: computer-based reconstructions, model and animations. *Journal of Asian Earth Sciences*, **20**: 353–434.

Hallam, A., 1963, Major epeirogenic and eustatic changes since the Cretaceous and their possible relationship to crustal structure. *American Journal of Science*, **261**: 397–423.

Hallam, A., 1992, *Phanerozoic Sea-Level Changes*. Columbia University Press, p. 224.

Hallam, A., 2001, A review of the broad pattern of Jurassic sea-level changes and their possible causes in the light of current knowledge. *Palaeogeography, Palaeoclimatology, Palaeoecology*, **167**: 23–37.

Hambrey, M.J., 1985, The Late Ordovician—Early Silurian glacial period. *Palaeogeography, Palaeoclimatology, Palaeoecology*, **51**: 273–289.

Haq, B.U., 2014, Cretaceous eustasy revisited. *Global and Planetary Chang*, **113**: 44–58.

Haq, B.U., 2017, Jurassic sea-level variations: a reappraisal. *GSA Today*, **28**: 4–10.

Haq, B.U., 2018, Triassic eustatic variations reexamined. *GSA Today*, **28**: 4–9.

Haq, B.U., and Al-Qahtani, A.M., 2005, Phanerozoic cycles of sea-level change on the Arabian Platform. *GeoArabia*, **10**: 127–160.

Haq, B.U., and Huber, B.T., 2017, Anatomy of a eustatic event during the Turonian (Late Cretaceous) hot greenhouse climate. *Science China Earth Sciences*, **60**: 20–29.

Haq, B.U., and Schutter, S.R., 2008, A chronology of Paleozoic sea-level changes. *Science*, **322**: 64–68.

Haq, B.U., Hardenbol, J., and Vail, P.R., 1987, Chronology of fluctuating sea levels since the Triassic (250 million years ago to present). *Science*, **235**: 1156–1167.

Haq, B.U., Hardenbol, J., and Vail, P.R., 1988, Mesozoic and Cenozoic chronostratigraphy and eustatic cycles, Special Publication. *In* Wilgus, C.K., Ross, C.A., and Posamentier, H. (eds), *Sea-level Changes: An Integrated Approach*. SEPM, **42**: 71–108.

Hardenbol, J., Thierry, J., Farley, M.B., Jacquin, T., de Graciansky, P.C., and Vail, P.R., 1998, Mesozoic and Cenozoic sequence chronostratigraphic framework of European basins. *In* de Graciansky, P.C., Hardenbol, J., Jacquin, T., and Vail, P.R. (eds), *Mesozoic and Cenozoic Sequence Stratigraphy of European Basins*. SEPM Special Publication 60. 3–13.

Harrison, C.G.A., 1990, Long-term eustasy and epeirogeny in continents. *In* Revelle, R. (ed), *Sea-Level Change, National Research Council, Studies in Geophysics*. National Academy Press, 141–158.

Hay, W.W., 2008, Evolving ideas about the Cretaceous climate and ocean circulation. *Cretaceous Research*, **29**: 725–753.

Hay, W.W., and Leslie, M.A., 1990, Could possible changes in global groundwater reservoir cause eustatic sea-level fluctuations? *In* Revelle, R. (ed), *Sea-Level Change, National Research Council, Studies in Geophysics*. National Academy Press, 161–170.

Hay, C.C., Morrow, E., Kopp, R.E., and Mitrovica, J.X., 2015, Probabilistic reanalysis of twentieth-century sea-level rise. *Nature*, **517**: 481.

Heckel, P.H., 1986, Sea-level curve for Pennsylvanian eustatic marine transgressive-regressive depositional cycles along midcontinent outcrop belt, North America. *Geology*, **14**: 330–334.

Heckel, P.H., 1990, Evidence for global (glacio-eustatic) control over Upper Carboniferous (Pennsylvanian) cyclothems in midcontinent North America, Special Publication. *In* Hardman, R.F.P., and Brooks, J. (eds), *Tectonic Events Responsible for Britain's Oil and Gas Reserves*. Geological Society, London, **55**: 35–47.

Heckel, P.H., 2008, Pennsylvanian cyclothems in Midcontinent North America as far-field effects of waxing and waning of Gondwana ice sheets, Special Paper. *In* Fielding, C.R., Frank, T.D., and Isbell, J.L. (eds), *Resolving the Late Paleozoic Ice Age in Time and Space*. *Geological Society of America*, **441**: 275–289.

Heller, P.L., Anderson, D.L., and Angevine, C.L., 1996, Is the middle Cretaceous pulse of rapid sea-floor spreading real or necessary? *Geology*, **24**: 491–494.

Herrle, J.O., Schröder-Adams, C.J., Davis, W., Pugh, A.T., Galloway, J.M., and Fath, J., 2015, Mid-Cretaceous High Arctic stratigraphy, climate, and oceanic anoxic events. *Geology*, **43**: 403–406.

Hesselbo, S.P., 2008, Sequence stratigraphy and inferred relative sea-level change from the onshore British Jurassic. *The Proceedings of the Geologists' Association*, **119**: 19–34.

Hesselbo, S.P., and Jenkyns, H.C., 1998, British Lower Jurassic sequence stratigraphy, Special Publication. *In* De Graciansky, P.C., Hardenbol, J., Jacquin, T., and Vail, P.R. (eds), *Mesozoic and Cenozoic Sequence Stratigraphy of European Basins*. SEPM, **60**: 561–581.

Hinnov, L.A., 2000, New perspectives on orbitally forced stratigraphy. *Annual Review of Earth and Planetary Sciences*, **28**: 419–475.

Hinnov, L.A., 2018, Cyclostratigraphy and Astrochronology in 2018. *In* Montenari, M. (ed), *Stratigraphy and Timescales, Volume Three: Cyclostratigraphy and Astrochronology*. Elsevier, 1–80.

Hoedemaeker, P.J., 1995, Ammonite evidence for long-term sea-level fluctuations between the 2nd and 3rd order in the lowest Cretaceous. *Cretaceous Research*, **16**: 231–241.

Hohenegger, J., Ćorić, S., and Wagreich, M., 2014, Timing of the middle Miocene Badenian stage of the central Paratethys. *Geologica Carpathica*, **65**: 55–66.

Holland, S.M., and Patzkowsky, M.E., 1998, Sequence stratigraphy and relative sea-level history of the Middle and Upper Ordovician of the Nashville Dome, Tennessee. *Journal of Sedimentary Research*, **68**: 684–699.

Hollis, C.J., Dunkley Jones, T., Anagnostou, E., Bijl, P.K., Cramwinckel, M. J., Cui, Y., et al., 2019, The DeepMIP contribution to PMIP4: methodologies for selection, compilation and analysis of latest Paleocene and early Eocene climate proxy data, incorporating version 0.1 of the DeepMIP database. *Geoscientific Model Development Discussions*, **2019**: 1–98.

Hong, S.K., and Lee, Y.I., 2012, Evaluation of atmospheric carbon dioxide concentrations during the Cretaceous. *Earth and Planetary Science Letters*, **327**: 23–28.

Horbury, A., 2018, Petroleum geology and its relation to stratigraphic architecture of the Triassic to Middle Jurassic (Induan to Aalenian) interval on the Arabian Plate. *In* Pöppelreiter, M.C. (ed), *Lower Triassic to Middle Jurassic Sequence of the Arabian Plate*. EAGE (European Association of Geoscientists and Engineers), 49–100.

Hore, S.B., Reid, A.J., and Hill, S.M., 2015, Definition and age of the enigmatic Sprigg Diamictite Member, northern Flinders Ranges, South Australia. *MESA Journal*, **77**: 42–54.

Horner, S.C., Hubbard, S.M., Martin, H.K., Hagstrom, C.A., and Leckie, D.A., 2019, The impact of Aptian glacio-eustasy on the stratigraphic architecture of the Athabasca Oil Sands, Alberta, Canada. *Sedimentology*, **66**: 1600–1642.

Horton, D.E., and Poulsen, C.J., 2009, Paradox of late Paleozoic glacioeustasy. *Geology*, **37**: 715–718.

House, M.R., 1983, Devonian eustatic events. *Proceedings of the Ussher Society*, **5**: 396–405.

House, M.R., and Ziegler, W., 1997, Devonian eustatic fluctuation in North Eurasia. *Courier Forschungsinstitut Senckenberg*, **199**: 13–23.

Hu, X., Wagreich, M., and Yilmaz, I.O., 2012, Marine rapid environmental/climatic change in the Cretaceous greenhouse world. *Cretaceous Research*, **38**: 1–6.

Huang, C., Hesselbo, S.P., and Hinnov, L., 2010, Astrochronology of the Late Jurassic Kimmeridge Clay (Dorset, England) and implications for Earth system processes. *Earth and Planetary Science Letters*, **289**: 242–255.

Husinec, A., Harman, C.A., Regan, S.P., Mosher, D.A., Sweeney, R.J., and Read, J.F., 2012, Sequence development influenced by intermittent cooling events in the Cretaceous Aptian greenhouse, Adriatic platform, Croatia. *The American Association of Petroleum Geologists Bulletin*, **96**: 2215–2244.

Immenhauser, A., 2005, High-rate sea-level change during the Mesozoic: new approaches to an old problem. *Sedimentary Geology*, **175**: 277–296.

Immenhauser, A., 2009, Estimating palaeo-water depth from the physical rock record. *Earth-Science Reviews*, **96**: 107–139.

Immenhauser, A., and Matthews, R.K., 2004, Albian sea-level cycles in Oman: the "Rosetta Stone" approach. *GeoArabia*, **9**: 11–46.

Isaacson, P.E., Diaz-Martinez, E., Grader, G.W., Kalvoda, J., Babek, O., and Devuyst, F.X., 2008, Late Devonian–earliest Mississippian glaciation in Gondwanaland and its biogeographic consequences. *Palaeogeography, Palaeoclimatology, Palaeoecology*, **268**: 126–142.

Isbell, J.L., Miller, M.F., Wolfe, K.L., and Lenaker, P.A., 2003, Timing of late Paleozoic glaciation in Gondwana: was glaciation responsible for the development of Northern Hemisphere cyclothems? *Geological Society of America Special Paper*, **370**: 5–24.

Izart, A., Stephenson, R., Vai, G.B., Vachard, D., Le Nindre, Y., Vaslet, D., et al., 2003, Sequence stratigraphy and correlation of late Carboniferous and Permian in the CIS, Europe, Tethyan area, North Africa, Arabia, China, Gondwanaland and the USA. *Palaeogeography, Palaeoclimatology, Palaeoecology*, **196**: 59–84.

Jacobs, D.K., and Sahagian, D.L., 1993, Climate-induced fluctuations in sea-level during non-glacial times. *Nature*, **361**: 710.

Jacquin, T., Dardeau, G., Durlet, C., de Graciansky, P.C., and Hantzpergue, P., 1998, The North Sea cycle: an overview of 2nd-order transgressive/regressive facies cycles in Western Europe, Special Publication. *In* De Graciansky, P.C., Hardenbol, J., Jacquin, T., and Vail, P.R. (eds), *Mesozoic and Cenozoic Sequence Stratigraphy of European Basins*. SEPM, **60**: 445–446.

Jarvis, I.A.N., Gale, A.S., Jenkyns, H.C., and Pearce, M.A., 2006, Secular variation in Late Cretaceous carbon isotopes: a new $\delta^{13}C$ carbonate reference curve for the Cenomanian–Campanian (99.6–70.6 Ma). *Geological Magazine*, **143**: 561–608.

Jenkyns, H.C., Forster, A., Schouten, S., and Sinninghe Damsté, J.S., 2004, High temperatures in the late Cretaceous Arctic Ocean. *Nature*, **432**: 888.

Jenkyns, H.C., Schouten-Huibers, L., Schouten, S., and Sinninghe Damsté, J.S., 2012, Warm Middle Jurassic–Early Cretaceous high-latitude sea-surface temperatures from the Southern Ocean. *Climate of the Past*, **8**: 215–226.

Jervey, M.T., 1988, Quantitative geological modelling of siliciclastic rock sequences and their seismic expression. *In* Wilgus, C.K., Hastings, B.S., Kendall, C.G. St. C., Posamentier, H.W., Ross, C.A., and Van Wagoner, J.C. (eds), *Sea level Changes – an Integrated Approach. SEPM Special Publication*, **42**: 47–69.

Jin, Y., Shen, S., Henderson, C.M., Wang, X., Wang, W., Wang, Y., et al., 2006, The Global Stratotype Section and Point (GSSP) for the boundary between the Capitanian and Wuchiapingian stage (Permian). *Episodes*, **29**: 253–262.

John, C.M., Karner, G.D., and Mutti, M., 2004, $\delta^{18}O$ and Marion Plateau backstripping: combining two approaches to constrain late middle Miocene eustatic amplitude. *Geology*, **32**: 829–832.

John, C.M., Karner, G.D., Browning, E., Leckie, R.M., Mateo, Z., Carson, B., et al., 2011, Timing and magnitude of Miocene eustasy derived from the mixed siliciclastic-carbonate stratigraphic record of the northeastern Australian margin. *Earth and Planetary Science Letters*, **304**: 455–467.

Johnson, M.E., 1992, A.W. Grabau's embryonic sequence stratigraphy and eustatic curve. *In* Dott Jr., R.H. (ed), *Eustasy: The Ups and Downs of a Major Geological Concept. Geological Society of America Memoir*, **180**: 43–54.

Johnson, M.E., 2006, Relationship of Silurian sea-level fluctuations to oceanic episodes and events. *GFF*, **128**: 115–121.

Johnson, M.E., 2010, Tracking Silurian eustasy: alignment of empirical evidence or pursuit of deductive reasoning? *Palaeogeography, Palaeoclimatology, Palaeoecology*, **296**: 276–284.

Johnson, J.G., Klapper, G., and Sandberg, C.A., 1985, Devonian eustatic fluctuations in Euramerica. *Geological Society of America Bulletin*, **96**: 567–587.

Johnson, M.E., Kaljo, D.L., and Jiayu, R., 1991, Silurian eustasy. *Special Papers in Palaeontology*, **44**: 145–163.

Johnson, J.G., Klapper, G., and Elrick, M., 1996, Devonian transgressive-regressive cycles and biostratigraphy, northern Antelope Range, Nevada: establishment of reference horizons for global cycles. *Palaois*, **11**: 3–14.

Johnson, M.E., Rong, J.Y., and Kershaw, S., 1998, Calibrating Silurian eustasy against the erosion and burial of coastal paleotopography. *In* Landing, E., and Johnson, M.E. (eds), *Silurian Cycles: Linkages of Dynamic Stratigraphy With Atmospheric, Oceanic and Tectonic Changes. New York State Museum Bulletin*, **491**: 3–13.

Karlsen, K.S., Conrad, C.P., and Magni, V., 2019, Deep water cycling and sea-level change since the breakup of Pangea. *Geochemistry, Geophysics, Geosystems*, **20**: 2919–2935.

Katz, M.E., Browning, J.V., Miller, K.G., Monteverde, D.H., Mountain, G.S., and Williams, R.H., 2013, Paleobathymetry and sequence stratigraphic interpretations from benthic foraminifera: insights on New Jersey shelf architecture *Geosphere*, **9**: 1488–1513.

Kemp, D.B., Robinson, S.A., Crame, J.A., Francis, J.E., Ineson, J., Whittle, R.J., et al., 2014, A cool temperate climate on the Antarctic Peninsula through the latest Cretaceous to early Paleogene. *Geology*, **42**: 583–586.

Kent, D.V., Olsen, P., Rasmussen, C., Lepre, C., Mundil, R., Irmis, R., et al., 2018, Empirical evidence for stability of the 405 kyr Jupiter-Venus eccentricity cycle over hundreds of millions of years. *Proceedings of the National Academy of Science*, **115** (24): 6153–6158.

Kirschner, J.P., Kominz, M.A., and Mwakanyamale, K.E., 2010, Quantifying extension of passive margins: implications for sea-level change. *Tectonics*, **29**: TC4006.

Koch, J.T., and Brenner, R.L., 2009, Evidence for glacioeustatic control of large, rapid sea-level fluctuations during the Albian-Cenomanian: Dakota formation, eastern margin of western interior seaway, USA. *Cretaceous Research*, **30**: 411–423.

Kominz, M.A., Van Sickel, W.A., Miller, K.G., and Browning, J.V., 2003. Sea-level estimates for the latest 100 million years: one-dimensional backstripping of onshore New Jersey boreholes. *In* Armentrout, J. (ed), Sequence Stratigraphic models for Exploration and Production: Evolving Methodology, Emerging Models, and Application Histories. *Proceedings of the 22nd Annual GCSSEPM Foundation Bob F. Perkins Research Conference, 2002, Houston, 303–315.*

Kominz, M.A., Browning, J.V., Miller, K.G., Sugarman, P.J., Mizintseva, S., and Scotese, C.R., 2008, Late Cretaceous to Miocene sea-level estimates from the New Jersey and Delaware coastal plain coreholes: an error analysis. *Basin Research*, **20**: 211–226.

Kominz, M.A., Miller, K.G., Browning, J.V., Katz, M.E., and Mountain, G.S., 2016, Miocene relative sea-level on the New Jersey shallow continental shelf and coastal plain derived from one-dimensional backstripping: a case for both eustasy and epeirogeny. *Geosphere*, **12**: 1437–1456.

Korte, C., and Hesselbo, S.P., 2011, Shallow-marine carbon-and oxygen-isotope and elemental records indicate icehouse-greenhouse cycles during the Early Jurassic. *Paleoceanography*, **26**: PA4219.

Korte, C., Hesselbo, S.P., Ullmann, C.V., Dietl, G., Ruhl, M., Schweigert, G., et al., 2015, Jurassic climate mode governed by ocean gateway. *Nature Communications*, **6**: 10015.

Krencker, F.-N., Lindström, S., and Bodin, S., 2019, A major sea-level drop briefly precedes the Toarcian oceanic anoxic event: implications for Early Jurassic climate and carbon cycle. *Scientific Reports*, **9**: article # 12518.

Ladant, J.-B., and Donnadieu, Y., 2016, Palaeogeographic regulation of glacial events during the Cretaceous supergreenhouse. *Nature Communications*, **7**: article # 12771.

Lakin, J.A., Marshall, J.E.A., Troth, I., and Harding, I.C., 2016. Greenhouse to icehouse: a biostratigraphic review of latest Devonian–Mississippian glaciations and their global effects. *In* Becker, R.T., Königshof, P., and Brett, C.E. (eds). *Devonian Climate, Sea Level and Evolutionary Events.* Geological Society, London, Special Publications, **423**: 439–464.

Lambeck, K., Rouby, H., Purcell, A., Sun, Y., and Sambridge, M., 2014, Sea level and global ice volumes from the Last Glacial Maximum to the Holocene. *Proceedings of the National Academy of Sciences of the United States of America*, **111**: 15296–15303.

Landing, E., and MacGabhann, B.A., 2010, First evidence for Cambrian glaciation provided by sections in Avalonian New Brunswick and Ireland: additional data for Avalon–Gondwana separation by the earliest Palaeozoic. *Palaeogeography, Palaeoclimatology, Palaeoecology*, **285**: 174–185.

Laskar, J., 1990, The chaotic motion of the solar system: a numerical estimate of the size of the chaotic zones. *Icarus*, **88**: 266–291.

Laskar, J., 1999, The limits of Earth orbital calculations for geological time-scale use. *Philosophical Transactions of the Royal Society of London. Series A*, **357**: 1735–1759.

Laskar, J., Robutel, P., Joutel, F., Gastineau, M., Correia, A.C.M., and Levrard, B., 2004, A long-term numerical solution for the insolation quantities of the Earth. *Astronomy & Astrophysics*, **428**: 261–285.

Laurin, J., and Sageman, B.B., 2007, Cenomanian–Turonian coastal record in SW Utah, USA: orbital-scale transgressive–regressive events during Oceanic Anoxic Event II. *Journal of Sedimentary Research*, **77**: 731–756.

Laurin, J., Barclay, R.S., Sageman, B.B., Dawson, R.R., Pagani, M., Schmitz, M., et al., 2019, Terrestrial and marginal-marine record of the mid-Cretaceous Oceanic Anoxic Event 2 (OAE 2): high-resolution framework, carbon isotopes, CO_2 and sea-level change. *Palaeogeography, Palaeoclimatology, Palaeoecology*, **524**: 118–136.

Lee, J.H., Chen, J., and Chough, S.K., 2015, The middle–late Cambrian reef transition and related geological events: a review and new view. *Earth-Science Reviews*, **145**: 66–84.

Li, M., Huang, C., Hinnov, L., Ogg, J., Chen, Z.Q., and Zhang, Y., 2016, Obliquity-forced climate during the Early Triassic hothouse in China. *Geology*, **44**: 623–626.

Lin, W., Bhattacharya, J.P., Jicha, B.R., Singer, B.S. and Matthews, W., 2020, Has Earth ever been ice-free? Implications for glacio-eustasy in the Cretaceous greenhouse age using high-resolution sequence stratigraphy. *Geological Society of America Bulletin*: B35582.1.

Lisiecki, L.E., and Raymo, M.E., 2005, A Pliocene-Pleistocene stack of 57 globally distributed benthic $\delta^{18}O$ records. *Paleoceanography*, **20**: 1–17.

Liu, Y., Huang, C., Ogg, J.G., Algeo, T.J., Kemp, D.B., and Shen, W., 2019, Oscillations of global sea-level elevation during the Paleogene correspond to 1.2-Myr amplitude modulation of orbital obliquity cycles. *Earth and Planetary Science Letters*, **522**: 65–78.

Loi, A., Ghienne, J.F., Dabard, M.P., Paris, F., Botquelen, A., Christ, N., et al., 2010, The Late Ordovician glacio-eustatic record from a high-latitude storm-dominated shelf succession: the Bou Ingarf section (Anti-Atlas, Southern Morocco). *Palaeogeography, Palaeoclimatology, Palaeoecology*, **296**: 332–358.

Lourens, L.J., and Hilgen, F.J., 1997, Long-periodic variations in the Earth's obliquity and their relation to third-order eustatic cycles and late Neogene glaciations. *Quaternary International*, **40**: 43–52.

Lovell, B., 2010, A pulse in the planet: regional control of high-frequency changes in relative sea-level by mantle convection. *Journal of the Geological Society*, **167**: 637–648.

Loydell, D.K., 1998, Early Silurian sea-level changes. *Geological Magazine*, **135**: 447–471.

Loydell, D.K., 2007, Early Silurian positive $\delta^{13}C$ excursions and their relationship to glaciations, sea-level changes and extinction events. *The Journal of Geology*, **42**: 531–546.

Luber, T.L., Bulot, L.G., Redfern, J., Nahim, M., Jeremiah, J., Simmons, M., et al., 2019, A revised chronostratigraphic framework for the Aptian of the Essaouira-Agadir Basin, a candidate type section for the NW African Atlantic Margin. *Cretaceous Research*, **93**: 292–317.

Ludvigson, G.A., Joeckel, R.M., Murphy, L.R., Stockli, D.F., Gonzalez, L.A., Suarez, C.A., et al., 2015, The emerging terrestrial record of Aptian-Albian global change. *Cretaceous Research*, **56**: 1–24.

Lunn, G.A., Miller, S., and Samarrai, A., 2019, Dating and correlation of the Baluti Formation, Kurdistan, Iraq: implications for the regional recognition of a Carnian "marker dolomite", a review of the Triassic to Early Jurassic sequence stratigraphy of the Arabian Plate. *Journal of Petroelum Geology*, **42**: 5–36.

Ma, X.P., Liao, W., and Wang, D., 2009. The Devonian System of China, with a discussion on sea-level change in South China. *In* Königshof, P. (ed.). *Devonian Change: Case Studies in Palaeogeography and Palaeoecology*. Geological Society, London, Special Publications, **314**: 241–262.

Macquaker, J.H., and Keller, M.A., 2005, Mudstone sedimentation at high latitudes: ice as a transport medium for mud and supplier of nutrients. *Journal of Sedimentary Research*, **75**: 696–709.

Maloney, J.M., Bentley, S.J., Xu, K., Obelcz, J., Georgiou, I.Y., and Miner, M.D., 2018, Mississippi River subaqueous delta is entering a stage of retrogradation. *Marine Geology*, **400**: 12–23.

Matthews, R.K., and Al-Husseini, M.I., 2010, Orbital-forcing glacio-eustasy: a sequence-stratigraphic time scale. *GeoArabia*, **15**: 155–167.

Maurer, F., Van Buchem, F.S., Eberli, G.P., Pierson, B.J., Raven, M. J., Larsen, P.H., et al., 2013, Late Aptian long-lived glacio-eustatic lowstand recorded on the Arabian Plate. *Terra Nova*, **25**: 87–94.

McAnena, A., Flögel, S., Hofmann, P., Herrle, J.O., Griesand, A., Pross, J., et al., 2013, Atlantic cooling associated with a marine biotic crisis during the mid-Cretaceous period. *Nature Geoscience*, **6**: 558.

McArthur, J.M., Janssen, N.M.M., Reboulet, S., Leng, M.J., Thirlwall, M.F., and Van de Schootbrugge, B., 2007, Palaeotemperatures, polar ice-volume, and isotope stratigraphy (Mg/Ca, $\delta^{18}O$, $\delta^{13}C$, $^{87}Sr/^{86}Sr$): the Early Cretaceous (Berriasian, Valanginian, Hauterivian). *Palaeogeography, Palaeoclimatology, Palaeoecology*, **248**: 391–430.

McArthur, J.M., Howarth, R.J., and Shields, G.A., 2012, Strontium isotope stratigraphy. *In* Gradstein, F.M., Ogg, J.G., Schmitz, M.D., and Ogg, G.M. (eds), *The Geologic Time Scale 2012*, Elsevier, **1**: 127–144.

McCarthy, F.M., Katz, M.E., Kotthoff, U., Browning, J.V., Miller, K.G., Zanatta, R., et al., 2013, Sea-level control of New Jersey margin architecture: palynological evidence from Integrated Ocean Drilling Program Expedition 313. *Geosphere*, **9**: 1457–1487.

McDonough, K.J., and Cross, T.A., 1991, Late Cretaceous sea level from a paleoshoreline. *Journal of Geophysical Research: Solid Earth*, **96** (B4), 6591–6607.

Melchin, M.J., Sadler, P.M., and Cramer, B.D., 2012, The Silurian period. *In* Gradstein, F.M., Ogg, J.G., Schmitz, M.D., and Ogg, G.M. (eds), *The Geologic Time Scale 2012*. Elsevier, **2**: 525–558.

Miall, A.D., 1991, Stratigraphic sequences and their chronostratigraphic correlation. *Journal of Sedimentary Petrology*, **61**: 497–505.

Miall, A.D., 1992, The Exxon global cycle chart: an event for every occasion? *Geology*, **20**: 787–790.

Miall, A.D., 2010, *The Geology of Stratigraphic Sequences*, 2nd ed. Springer-Verlag, p. 522.

Miall, A.D., 2016, *Stratigraphy. A Modern Synthesis*. Springer, p. 454.

Miall, A.D., and Miall, C.E., 2001, Sequence stratigraphy as a scientific enterprise: the evolution and persistence of conflicting paradigms. *Earth-Science Reviews*, **54**: 321–348.

Millán, M.I., Weissert, H.J., and López-Horgue, M.A., 2014, Expression of the Late Aptian cold snaps and the OAE1b in a highly subsiding carbonate platform (Aralar, northern Spain). *Palaeogeography, Palaeoclimatology, Palaeoecology*, **411**: 167–179.

Miller, K.G., 2002, The role of ODP in understanding the causes and effects of global sea level change. *JOIDES Journal*, **28** (1), 23–28.

Miller, K.G., 2009, Broken greenhouse windows. *Nature Geoscience*, **2**: 465–466.

Miller, K.G., and Mountain, G.S., 1996, Drilling and dating New Jersey Oligocene-Miocene sequences: ice volume, global sea level, and Exxon records. *Science*, **271**: 1092–1095.

Miller, K.G., Fairbanks, R.G., and Mountain, G.S., 1987, Tertiary oxygen isotope synthesis, sea level history, and continental margin erosion. *Paleoceanography*, **2**: 1–19.

Miller, K.G., Wright, J.D., and Fairbanks, R.G., 1991, Unlocking the ice house: Oligocene-Miocene oxygen isotopes, eustasy, and margin erosion. *Journal of Geophysical Research: Solid Earth*, **96** (B4), 6829–6848.

Miller, K.G., Mountain, G.S., Browning, J.V., Kominz, M., Sugarman, P.J., Christie-Blick, N., et al., 1998, Cenozoic global sea-level, sequences, and the New Jersey Transect: results from coastal plain and slope drilling. *Reviews of Geophysics*, **36**: 569–601.

Miller, J.F., Evans, K.R., Loch, J.D., Ethington, R.L., Stitt, J.H., Holmer, L., et al., 2003a, Stratigraphy of the Sauk III (Cambrian-Ordovician) in the Ibex Area, Western Millard County, Utah and Central Texas. *Brigham Young University of Geological Studies*, **47**: 23–141.

Miller, K.G., Sugarman, P.J., Browning, J.V., Kominz, M.A., Hernández, J.C., Olsson, R.K., et al., 2003b, Late Cretaceous chronology of large, rapid sea-level changes: glacioeustasy during the greenhouse world. *Geology*, **31**: 585–588.

Miller, K.G., Sugarman, P.J., Browning, J.V., Kominz, M.A., Olsson, R.K., Feigenson, M.D., et al., 2004, Upper Cretaceous sequences and sea-level history, New Jersey Coastal Plain. *Geological Society of America Bulletin*, **116**: 368–393.

Miller, K.G., Kominz, M.A., Browning, J.V., Wright, J.D., Mountain, G.S., Katz, M.E., et al., 2005a, The Phanerozoic record of global sea-level change. *Science*, **310**: 1293–1298.

Miller, K.G., Wright, J.D., and Browning, J.V., 2005b, Visions of ice sheets in a greenhouse world. *Marine Geology*, **217**: 215–231.

Miller, K.G., Mountain, G.S., Wright, J.D., and Browning, J.V., 2011, A 180-million-year record of sea-level and ice volume variations from continental margin and deep-sea isotopic records. *Oceanography*, **24**: 40–53.

Miller, K.G., Browning, J.V., Mountain, G.S., Bassetti, M.A., Monteverde, D., Katz, M.E., et al., 2013a, Sequence boundaries are impedance contrasts: core-seismic-log integration of Oligocene–Miocene sequences, New Jersey shallow shelf. *Geosphere*, **9**: 1257–1285.

Miller, K.G., Mountain, G.S., Browning, J.V., Katz, M.E., Monteverde, D., Sugarman, P.J., et al., 2013b, Testing sequence stratigraphic models by drilling Miocene foresets on the New Jersey shallow shelf. *Geosphere*, **9**: 1236–1256.

Miller, K.G., Lombardi, C.J., Browning, J.V., Schmelz, W.J., Gallegos, G., Mountain, G.S., et al., 2018, Back to basics of sequence stratigraphy: Early Miocene and mid-Cretaceous examples from the New Jersey paleoshelf. *Journal of Sedimentary Research*, **88**: 148–176.

Miller, K.G., Browning, J.V., Schmelz, W.J., Kopp, R.E., Mountain, G.S., and Wright, J.D. 2020. Cenozoic sea-level and cryospheric evolution from deep-sea $\delta^{18}O$ and continental margin records. *Science Advances*. 6 (20), article #eaaz1346: 15 pp. https://advances.sciencemag.org/content/6/20/eaaz1346.full.

Milne, G.A., Gehrels, W.R., Hughes, C.W., and Tamisiea, M.E., 2009, Identifying the causes of sea-level change. *Nature Geoscience*, **2**: 471.

Montañez, I.P., and Poulsen, C.J., 2013, The Late Paleozoic ice age: an evolving paradigm. *Annual Review of Earth and Planetary Sciences*, **41**: 629–656.

Mørk, A., 1994, Triassic transgressive – regressive cycles of Svalbard and other Arctic areas: a mirror of stage subdivision. Recent developments on Triassic stratigraphy. *Mémoires de Géologie, Lausanne*, **22**: 69–82.

Moucha, R., Forte, A.M., Mitrovica, J.X., Rowley, D.B., Quéré, S., Simmons, N.A., et al., 2008, Dynamic topography and long-term sea-level variations: there is no such thing as a stable continental platform. *Earth and Planetary Science Letters*, **271**: 101–108.

Mountain, G., Proust, J.-N., and the Expedition 313 Science Party, 2010. The New Jersey margin scientific drilling project (IODP Expedition 313): untangling the record of global and local sea-level changes. *Scientific Drilling*, **10**: 26–34. https://sd.copernicus.org/articles/10/26/2010/sd-10-26-2010.pdf.

Müller, R.D., Sdrolias, M., Gaina, C., Steinberger, B., and Heine, C., 2008, Long-term sea-level fluctuations driven by ocean basin dynamics. *Science*, **319**: 1357–1362.

Müller, R.D., Seton, M., Zahirovic, S., Williams, S.E., Matthews, K.J., Wright, N.M., et al., 2016, Ocean basin evolution and global-scale plate reorganization events since Pangea breakup. *Annual Review of Earth and Planetary Sciences*, **44**: 107–138.

Munnecke, A., Calner, M., Harper, D.A.T., and Servais, T., 2010, Ordovician and Silurian sea-water chemistry, sea-level, and climate: a synopsis. *Palaeogeography, Palaeoclimatology, Palaeoecology*, **296**: 389–413.

Mutterlose, J., Bornemann, A., and Herrle, J., 2009, The Aptian-Albian cold snap: evidence for "mid" Cretaceous icehouse interludes. *Neues Jahrbuch für Geologie und Paläontologia Abhandlungen*, **252**: 217–225.

Myers, K.J., and Milton, N.J., 1996, Concepts and principles of sequence stratigraphy. *In* Emery, D., and Myers, K.J. (eds), *Sequence Stratigraphy*. Blackwell, Oxford, 11–44.

Naish, T., Powell, R., Levy, R., Wilson, G., Scherer, R., Talarico, F., et al., 2009, Obliquity-paced Pliocene West Antarctic ice sheet oscillations. *Nature*, **458**: 322.

Nance, R.D., and Murphy, J.B., 2013, Origins of the supercontinent cycle. *Geoscience Frontiers*, **4**: 439–448.

Neal, J., and Abreu, V., 2009, Sequence stratigraphy hierarchy and the accommodation succession method. *Geology*, **37**: 779–782.

Nerem, R.S., Chambers, D., Choe, C., and Mitchum, G.T., 2010, Estimating Mean Sea Level Change from the TOPEX and Jason Altimeter Missions. *Marine Geodesy*, **33**: 435.

Newell, A.J., 2000, Fault activity and sedimentation in a marine rift basin (Upper Jurassic, Wessex Basin, UK). *Journal of the Geological Society*, **157**: 83–92.

Nielsen, A.T., 2004, Ordovician sea level changes: a Baltoscandian perspective. *In* Webby, B.D., Paris, F., Droser, M.L., and Percival, I.G. (eds), *The Great Ordovician Biodiversification Event*. Columbia University Press, New York, 84–93.

Nielsen, A.T., 2011, A re-calibrated revised sea-level curve for the Ordovician of Baltoscandia. *In* Gutiérrez-Marco, J.C., Rábano, I., and García-Bellido, D. (eds), *Ordovician of the World, Cuadernos del Museo Geominero*. Instituto Geologico y Minero de España, Madrid, 399–401.

Nielsen, A.T., and Schovsbo, N.H., 2011, The Lower Cambrian of Scandinavia: depositional environment, sequence stratigraphy and palaeogeography. *Earth-Science Reviews*, **107**: 207–310.

Nielsen, A.T., and Schovsbo, N.H., 2015, The regressive Early-Mid Cambrian 'Hawke Bay Event' in Baltoscandia: epeirogenic uplift in concert with eustasy. *Earth-Science Reviews*, **151**: 288–350.

Niezgodzki, I., Tyszka, J., Knorr, G., and Lohmann, G., 2019, Was the Arctic Ocean ice free during the latest Cretaceous? The role of CO_2 and gateway configurations. *Global and Planetary Change*, **177**: 201–212.

O'Brien, C.L., Robinson, S.A., Pancost, R.D., Damste, J.S.S., Schouten, S., Lunt, D.J., et al., 2017, Cretaceous sea-surface temperature evolution: constraints from TEX_{86} and planktonic foraminiferal oxygen isotopes. *Earth-Science Reviews*, **172**: 224–247.

Ogg, J.G., Ogg, G., and Gradstein, F.M., 2008, *The Concise Geologic Time Scale*. Cambridge University Press, Cambridge, 177 pp.

Ogg, J.G., Ogg, G., and Gradstein, F.M., 2016, *A Concise Geologic Time Scale 2016*. Elsevier, Amsterdam, 234 pp.

Olde, K., Jarvis, I., Uličný, D., Pearce, M.A., Trabucho-Alexandre, J., Čech, S., et al., 2015, Geochemical and palynological sea-level proxies in hemipelagic sediments: a critical assessment from the Upper Cretaceous of the Czech Republic. *Palaeogeography, Palaeoclimatology, Palaeoecology*, **435**: 222–243.

Oxford, M.J., Hart, M.B., and Watkinson, M.P., 2004, Foraminiferal characterisation of mid-upper Jurassic sequences in the Wessex Basin (United Kingdom). *Rivista Italiana di Paleontologia e Stratigrafia*, **110**: 209–218.

Page, A.A., Zalasiewicz, J.A., Williams, M., and Popov, L.E., 2007, Were transgressive black shales a negative feedback modulating glacioeustasy in the Early Palaeozoic Icehouse? *In* Williams, M., Haywood, A.M., Gregory, F.J., and Schmidt, D.N. (eds), *Deep-Time Perspectives on Climate Change: Marrying the Signal From Computer Models and Biological Proxies*. The Micropalaeontological Society, Special Publications. The Geological Society, London, 123–156.

Pälike, H., Norris, R.D., Herrle, J.O., Wilson, P.A., Coxall, H.K., Lear, C.H., et al., 2006, The heartbeat of the Oligocene climate system. *Science*, **314**: 1894–1898.

Pearson, P.N., 2012, Oxygen isotopes in foraminifera: overview and historical review. *The Paleontological Society Papers*, **18**: 1–38.

Pekar, S.F., Christie-Blick, N., Kominz, M.A., and Miller, K.G., 2002, Calibration between eustatic estimates from backstripping and oxygen isotopic records for the Oligocene. *Geology*, **30**: 903–906.

Peltier, W.R., and Fairbanks, R.G., 2006, Global glacial ice volume and Last Glacial Maximum duration from an extended Barbados sea level record. *Quaternary Science Reviews*, **25**: 3322–3337.

Pemberton, S.G., Bhattacharya, J.P., MacEachern, J.A., and Pemberton, E.A., 2016, Unsung Pioneers of Sequence Stratigraphy: Eliot Blackwelder, Joseph Barrell, Amadeus Grabau, John Rich and Harry Wheeler. *Stratigraphy*, **13**: 223–243.

Peng, S., Babcock, L.E., and Cooper, R.A., 2012, The Cambrian Period. *In* Gradstein, F.M., Ogg, J.G., Schmitz, M.D., and Ogg, G.M. (eds), *The Geologic Time Scale 2012*. Elsevier, **2**: 437–488.

Peropadre, C., Liesa, C.L., and Meléndez, N., 2013, High-frequency, moderate to high-amplitude sea-level oscillations during the late Early Aptian: insights into the Mid-Aptian event (Galve sub-basin, Spain). *Sedimentary Geology*, **294**: 233–250.

Peters, S.E., Carlson, A.E., Kelly, D.C., and Gringerich, P.D., 2010, Large-scale glaciation and deglaciation of Antarctica during the Late Eocene. *Geology*, **38**: 723–726.

Petersen, K.D., Nielsen, S.B., Clausen, O.R., Stephenson, R., and Gerya, T., 2010, Small-scale mantle convection produces stratigraphic sequences in sedimentary basins. *Science*, **329**: 827–830.

Pictet, A., Delanoy, G., Adatte, T., Spangenberg, J.E., Baudouin, C., Boselli, P., et al., 2015, Three successive phases of platform demise during the early Aptian and their association with the oceanic anoxic Selli episode (Ardèche, France). *Palaeogeography, Palaeoclimatology, Palaeoecology*, **418**: 101–125.

Pitman III, W.C., 1978, Relationship between eustasy and stratigraphic sequences of passive margins. *Geological Society of America Bulletin*, **89**: 1389–1403.

Pitman III, W.C., and Golovchenko, X., 1983, The effect of sea-level change on the shelf edge and slope of passive margins. *In* Stanley, D.I. (ed), The Shelfbreak: Critical Interface on Continental Margins. *Society of Economic Paleontologists and Mineralogists Special Publication*, **33**: 41–58.

Pohl, A., and Austermann, J., 2018, A sea-level fingerprint of the Late Ordovician ice-sheet collapse. *Geology*, **46**: 595–598.

Pohl, A., Donnadieu, Y., Le Hir, G., Ladant, J.B., Dumas, C., Alvarez-Solas, J., et al., 2016, Glacial onset predated Late Ordovician climate cooling. *Paleoceanography*, **31**: 800–821.

Posamentier, H.W., and Vail, P.R., 1988, Eustatic controls on clastic deposition II—sequence and systems tract models. *In* Wilgus, C.K., Ross, C.A., and Posamentier, H. (eds), *Sea-Level Changes: An Integrated Approach*. SEPM Special Publication, **42**: 125–154.

Preto, N., Kustatscher, E., and Wignall, P.B., 2010, Triassic climates—state of the art and perspectives. *Palaeogeography, Palaeoclimatology, Palaeoecology*, **290**: 1–10.

Price, G.D., 1999, The evidence and implications of polar ice during the Mesozoic. *Earth-Science Reviews*, **48**: 183–210.

Price, G.D., and Nunn, E.V., 2010, Valanginian isotope variation in glendonites and belemnites from Arctic Svalbard: transient glacial temperatures during the Cretaceous greenhouse. *Geology*, **38**: 251–254.

Radzevičius, S., Tumakovaitė, B., and Spiridonov, A., 2017, Upper Homerian (Silurian) high-resolution correlation using cyclostratigraphy: an example from western Lithuania. *Acta Geologica Polonica*, **67**: 307–322.

Ray, D.C., van Buchem, F.S.P., Baines, G., Davies, A., Gréselle, B., Simmons, M.D., et al., 2019. The magnitude and cause of short-term eustatic Cretaceous sea-level change: a synthesis. *Earth-Science Reviews*, 197, article #102901: 20 pp. https://doi.org/10.1016/j.earscirev.2019.102901.

Raymo, M.E., Mitrovica, J.X., O'Leary, M.J., DeConto, R.M., and Hearty, P.J., 2011, Departures from eustasy in Pliocene sea-level records. *Nature Geoscience*, **4**: 328–332.

Rodríguez-López, J.P., Liesa, C.L., Pardo, G., Meléndez, N., Soria, A.R., and Skilling, I., 2016, Glacial dropstones in the western Tethys during the late Aptian–early Albian cold snap: palaeoclimate and palaeogeographic implications for the mid-Cretaceous. *Palaeogeography, Palaeoclimatology, Palaeoecology*, **452**: 11–27.

Rogov, M.A., and Zakharov, V.A., 2010, Jurassic and Lower Cretaceous glendonites occurrences and their implication for Arctic paleoclimate reconstructions and stratigraphy. *Frontiers in Earth Science*, **17**: 345–347.

Rogov, M.A., Ershova, V.B., Shchepetova, E.V., Zakharov, V.A., Pokrovsky, B.G., and Khudoley, A.K., 2017, Earliest Cretaceous (late Berriasian) glendonites from Northeast Siberia revise the timing of initiation of transient Early Cretaceous cooling in the high latitudes. *Cretaceous Research*, **71**: 102–112.

Rogov, M.A., Zverkov, N.G., Zakharov, V.A., and Arkhangelsky, M.S., 2019, Marine reptiles and climates of the Jurassic and Cretaceous of Siberia. *Stratigraphy and Geological Correlation*, **27**: 398–423.

Ross, C.A., and Ross, J.R., 1985, Late Paleozoic depositional sequences are synchronous and worldwide. *Geology*, **13**: 194–197.

Ross, C.A., and Ross, J.R.P., 1987, Late Palaeozoic sea levels and depositional sequences. *Cushman Foundation Foraminiferal Research Special Publication*, **24**: 137–149.

Ross, C.A., and Ross, J.R.P., 1988, Late Paleozoic transgressive-regressive deposition. *In* Wilgus, C.K., Ross, C.A., and Posamentier, H. (eds), *Sea-Level Changes: An Integrated Approach. SEPM Special Publication*, **42**: 227–247.

Ross, J.R.P., and Ross, C.A., 1992, Ordovician sea-level fluctuations. *In* Webby, B.D., and Laurie, J.R. (eds), *Global Perspectives on Ordovician Geology*. Balkema, Rotterdam, 327–335.

Ross, C.A., and Ross, J.R.P., 1995, North American depositional sequences and correlations. *In* Cooper, J.D., Droser, M.L., and Finney, S.F. (eds), *Ordovician Odyssey: Short Papers for the Seventh International Symposium on the Ordovician System*. The Pacific Section for the Society of Sedimentary Geology, Fullerton, p. 309–314.

Ross, C.A., and Ross, J.R.P., 1996, Silurian sea-level fluctuations, Special Paper. *In* Witzke, B.J., Ludvigson, G.A., and Day, J. (eds), *Palaeozoic Sequence Stratigraphy: Views From the North American Craton*. Geological Society of America, Special Paper, **306**: 187–192.

Rovere, A., Stocchi, P., and Vacchi, M., 2016, Eustatic and relative sea-level changes. *Current Climate Change Reports*, **2**: 221–231.

Rowley, D.B., 2002, Rate of plate creation and destruction: 180Ma to present. *Geological Society of America Bulletin*, **114**: 927–933.

Rowley, D.B., 2013, Sea-level: Earth's dominant elevation – implications for duration and magnitudes of sea-level variations. *The Journal of Geology*, **121**: 445–454.

Ruban, D.A., 2012, Comment on "Sequence stratigraphy and onlap history of the Donets Basin, Ukraine: insight into Carboniferous icehouse dynamics" by Eros, J.M., Montañez, I.P., Osleger, D.A., Davydov, V.I., Nemyrovska, T.I., Poletaev, V.I., Zhykalyak, M. V., 2012. Sequence stratigraphy and onlap history of the Donets Basin, Ukraine: insight into Carboniferous icehouse dynamics. [Palaeogeography, Palaeoclimatology, Palaeoecology 313, 1-25]. *Palaeogeography, Palaeoclimatology, Palaeoecology*, **363–364**: 184–186.

Ruban, D.A., 2016, A "chaos" of Phanerozoic eustatic curves. *Journal of African Earth Sciences*, **116**: 225–232.

Ruban, D.A., Conrad, C.P., and van Loon, A.J., 2010, The challenge of reconstructing the Phanerozoic sea-level and the Pacific Basin tectonics. *Geologos*, **16**: 235–243.

Runkel, A.C., Miller, J.F., McKay, R.M., Palmer, A.R., and Taylor, J.F., 2007, High-resolution sequence stratigraphy of lower Paleozoic sheet sandstones in central North America: the role of special conditions of cratonic interiors in development of stratal architecture. *Geological Society of America Bulletin*, **119**: 860–881.

Rygel, M.C., Fielding, C.R., Frank, T.D., and Birgenheier, L.P., 2008, The magnitude of Late Paleozoic glacioeustatic fluctuations: a synthesis. *Journal of Sedimentary Research*, **78**: 500–511.

Sadler, P.M., 2004, Quantitative biostratigraphy – achieving finer resolution in global correlation. *Annual Review of Earth and Planetary Sciences*, **32**: 187–213.

Sahagian, D., and Jones, M., 1993, Quantified Middle Jurassic to Paleocene eustatic variations based on Russian Platform stratigraphy: stage level resolution. *Geological Society of America Bulletin*, **105**: 1109–1118.

Sahagian, D., Pinous, O., Olferiev, A., and Zakharov, V., 1996, Eustatic curve for the Middle Jurassic - Cretaceous based on Russian Platform and Siberian stratigraphy zonal resolution. *The American Association of Petroleum Geologists Bulletin*, **80**: 1433–1458.

Saltzman, M.R., and Thomas, E., 2012, Carbon isotope stratigraphy. *In* Gradstein, F.M., Ogg, J.G., Schmitz, M.D., and Ogg, G.M. (eds), *The Geologic Time Scale 2012*. Elsevier, **1**: 207–232.

Sames, B., Wagreich, M., Wendler, J.E., Haq, B.U., Conrad, C.P., Melinte-Dobrinescu, M.C., et al., 2016, Short-term sea-level changes in a greenhouse world—a view from the Cretaceous. *Palaeogeography, Palaeoclimatology, Palaeoecology*, **441**: 393–411.

Schlager, W., 2004, Fractal nature of stratigraphic sequences. *Geology*, **32**: 185–188.

Schlager, W., 2005, Carbonate sedimentology and sequence stratigraphy. *SEPM Concepts Sedimentology Paleontology*, **8**: 200.

Schlager, W., 2010, Ordered hierarchy versus scale invariance in sequence stratigraphy. *International Journal of Earth Sciences*, **99**: 139–151.

Schmitz, M.D., and Davydov, V.I., 2012, Quantitative radiometric and biostratigraphic calibration of the Pennsylvanian–Early Permian (Cisuralian) time scale and pan-Euramerican chronostratigraphic correlation. *Geological Society of America Bulletin*, **124**: 549–577.

Schoene, B., Guex, J., Bartolini, A., Schaltegger, U., and Blackburn, T. J., 2010, Correlating the end-Triassic mass extinction and flood basalt volcanism at the 100 ka level. *Geology*, **38**: 387–390.

Scott, R.W., Oboh-Ikuenobe, F.E., Benson Jr, D.G., Holbrook, J.M., and Alnahwi, 'A., 2018, Cenomanian-Turonian flooding cycles: US Gulf Coast and Western Interior. *Cretaceous Research*, **89**: 191–210.

Seton, M., Gaina, C., Müller, R.D., and Heine, C., 2009, Mid-Cretaceous seafloor spreading pulse: fact or fiction? *Geology*, **37**: 687–690.

Shackleton, N., 1967, Oxygen isotope analyses and Pleistocene temperatures re-assessed. *Nature*, **215**: 15.

Sharland, P.R., Archer, R., Casey, D.M., Davies, R.B., Hall, S., Heward, A., et al. 2001, Arabian Plate sequence stratigraphy. *GeoArabia Special Publication*, **2**: 387 pp.

Sharland, P.R., Casey, D.M., Davies, R.B., Simmons, M.D., and Sutcliffe, O.E., 2004, Arabian Plate sequence stratigraphy: updates to SP2. *GeoArabia*, **9**: 199–214.

Siddall, M., Rohling, E.J., Almogi-Labin, A., Hemleben, C., Meischner, D., Schmelzer, I., et al., 2003, Sea-level fluctuations during the last glacial cycle. *Nature*, **423**: 853.

Simmons, M.D., 2012, Sequence stratigraphy and sea-level change. *In* Gradstein, F.M., Ogg, J.G., Schmitz, M.D., and Ogg, G.M. (eds), *The Geologic Time Scale 2012*. Elsevier, **1**: 239–268.

Simmons, M.D., 2015, Age is an interpretation. *In* Cullum, A., and Martinius, A.W. (eds), *52 Things You Should Know About Palaeontology*, Agile Libre, Canada. 26–27.

Simmons, M.D., 2018, *Great Geologists*. Halliburton, Abingdon, p. 141.

Simmons, M.D., and Davies, R.B., 2018, Triassic to Middle Jurassic stratigraphy of the Arabian Plate: an introduction. *In* Pöppelreiter, M.C. (ed), *Lower Triassic to Middle Jurassic Sequence of the Arabian Plate*. EAGE (European Association of Geoscientists and Engineers), 9–32.

Simmons, M.D., Sharland, P.R., Casey, D.M., Davies, R.B., and Sutcliffe, O.E., 2007, Arabian Plate sequence stratigraphy: potential implications for global chronostratigraphy. *GeoArabia*, **12**: 101–130.

Sloss, L.L., 1963, Sequences in the cratonic interior of North America. *Geological Society of America Bulletin*, **74**: 93–113.

Sluijs, A., Brinkhuis, H., Crouch, E.M., John, C.M., Handley, L., Munsterman, D., et al., 2008, Eustatic variations during the Paleocene-Eocene greenhouse world. *Paleoceanography*, **23**: PA4216.

Snedden, J.W., and Liu, C., 2010, A compilation of Phanerozoic sea-level change, coastal onlaps and recommended sequence designations. *Search and Discovery Article, American Association of Petroleum Geologists*, article # 40594.

Spasojevic, S., Liu, L.J., Gurnis, M., and Müller, R.D., 2008, The case for dynamic subsidence of the U.S. east coast since the Eocene. *Geophysical Research Letters,* 35, article #, L08305: 6 pp, https://doi.org/10.1029/2008GL033511.

Spasojevic, S., and Gurnis, M., 2012, Sea-level and vertical motion of continents from dynamic earth models since the Late Cretaceous. *The American Association of Petroleum Geologists Bulletin*, **96**: 2037–2064.

Stanford, J.D., Rohling, E.J., Hunter, S.E., Roberts, A.P., Rasmussen, S. O., Bard, E., et al., 2006, Timing of meltwater pulse 1a and climate responses to meltwater injections. *Paleoceanography*, **21**: PA4103.

Stefani, M., Furin, S., and Gianolla, P., 2010, The changing climate framework and depositional dynamics of Triassic carbonate platforms from the Dolomites. *Palaeogeography, Palaeoclimatology, Palaeoecology*, **290**: 43–57.

Stoll, H.M., and Schrag, D.P., 1996, Evidence for glacial control of rapid sea level changes in the Early Cretaceous. *Science*, **272**: 1771–1774.

Stoll, H.M., and Schrag, D.P., 2000, High-resolution stable isotope records from the Upper Cretaceous rocks of Italy and Spain: glacial episodes in a greenhouse planet? *Geological Society of America Bulletin*, **112**: 308–319.

Strasser, A., Hillgärtner, H., Hug, W., and Pittet, B., 2000, Third-order depositional sequences reflecting Milankovitch cyclicity. *Terra Nova*, **12**: 303–311.

Strauss, P., Harzhauser, M., Hinsch, R., and Wagreich, M., 2006, Sequence stratigraphy in a classic pull-apart basin (Neogene, Vienna Basin). A 3D seismic based integrated approach. *Geologica Carpathica*, **57**: 185–197.

Suess, E., 1888, *Das antlitz der erde*. F. Tempsky, Vienna, 772 pp.

Suess, E., 1906, *In* Sollas, W.J. (ed), *The Face of the Earth*, translated by Sollas, W.J., Clarendon Press, Oxford: 556 pp.

Sun, S.Q., 1989, A new interpretation of the Corallian cycles of the Dorset coast. *The Journal of Geology*, **24**: 139–158.

Sundquist, E.T., 1990, Long-term aspects of future atmospheric CO_2 and sea-level changes. *In* Revelle, R. (ed), *Sea-Level Change, National*

Research Council, Studies in Geophysics. National Academy Press, Washington, DC, 193–207.

Sutcliffe, O.E., Dowdeswell, J.A., Whittington, R.J., Theron, J.N., and Craig, J., 2000, Calibrating the Late Ordovician glaciation and mass extinction by the eccentricity cycles of Earth's orbit. *Geology*, **28**: 967–970.

Tabor, C.R., Poulsen, C.J., Lunt, D.J., Rosenbloom, N.A., Otto-Bliesner, B.L., Markwick, P.J., et al., 2016, The cause of Late Cretaceous cooling: a multimodel-proxy comparison. *Geology*, **44**: 963–966.

Torsvik, T.H., Steinberger, B., Gurnis, M., and Gaina, C., 2010, Plate tectonics and net lithosphere rotation over the past 150 My. *Earth and Planetary Science Letters*, **291**: 106–112.

Tripati, A.K., Backman, J., Elderfield, H., and Ferretti, P., 2005, Eocene bipolar glaciation associated with global carbon cycle changes. *Nature*, **436**: 341–346.

Tripati, A.K., Eagle, R.A., Morton, A., Dowdeswell, J.A., Atkinson, K.L., Bahé, Y., et al., 2008, Evidence for glaciation in the Northern Hemisphere back to 44Ma from ice-rafted debris in the Greenland Sea. *Earth and Planetary Science Letters*, **265**: 112–122.

Trotter, J.A., Williams, I.S., Nicora, A., Mazza, M., and Rigo, M., 2015, Long-term cycles of Triassic climate change: a new $\delta^{18}O$ record from conodont apatite. *Earth and Planetary Science Letters*, **415**: 165–174.

Underhill, J.R., and Partington, M.A., 1993, Use of genetic sequence stratigraphy in defining and determining a regional tectonic control on the "Mid-Cimmerian unconformity" – implications for North Sea basin development and the global sea level chart. *In* Weimer, P., and Posamentier, H.W. (eds), *Siliciclastic Sequence Stratigraphy*. American Association of Petroleum Geologists Memoir, **58**: 449–484.

Vail, P.R., 1987, Seismic stratigraphy interpretation using sequence stratigraphy: Part 1: Seismic stratigraphy interpretation procedure. *In* Bally, A.W. (ed), Atlas of Seismic Stratigraphy. *AAPG Studies in Geology*, **27**: 1–10.

Vail, P.R., 1992, The evolution of seismic stratigraphy and the global. *In* Dott Jr., R.H. (ed), Eustasy: The Historical Ups and Downs of a Major Geological Concept. *Geological Society of America Memoir*, **180**: 83–92.

Vail, P.R., Mitchum Jr., R.M., Todd, R.G., Widmier, J.M., Thompson III, S., Sangree, J.B., et al., 1977, Seismic stratigraphy and global changes of sea-level. *In* Payton, C.E. (ed), Seismic Stratigraphy – Applications to Hydrocarbon Exploration. *American Association of Petroleum Geologists Memoir*, **26**: 49–212.

Vakarelov, B.K., Bhattacharya, J.P., and Nebrigic, D.D., 2006, Importance of high-frequency tectonic sequences during greenhouse times of Earth history. *Geology*, **34**: 797–800.

van Buchem, F.S.P., and Simmons, M.D., 2017, Stratigraphic sweet spots—exploration insights from a eustatic model. *In* Hart, B., Rosen, N.C., West, D., D'Agostino, A., Messina, C., Hoffman, M., and Wild, R. (eds), *Sequence Stratigraphy: The Future Defined*. GCSSEPM, 247–265.

van Buchem, F.S.P., Allan, T.L., Laursen, G.V., Lotfpour, M., Moallemi, A., Monibi, S., et al., 2010a. Regional stratigraphic architecture and reservoir types of the Oligo-Miocene deposits in the Dezful Embayment (Asmari and Pabdeh Formations) SW Iran. *In* van Buchem, F.S.P., Gerdes, K.D., and Esteban, M., (eds). *Mesozoic and Cenozoic Carbonate Systems of the Mediterranean and the Middle East: Stratigraphic and Diagenetic Reference Models*, Geological Society, London, Special Publications, **329**: 219–263.

van Buchem, F.S.P., Al-Husseini, M.I., Maurer, F., Droste, H.J., and Yose, L.A., 2010b, Sequence-stratigraphic synthesis of the Barremian–Aptian of the eastern Arabian Plate and implications for the petroleum habitat. *In* van Buchem, F.S.P., Al-Husseini, M.I., Maurer, F., and Droste, H. (eds), *Barremian-Aptian Stratigraphy and Hydrocarbon Habitat of the Eastern Arabian Plate*. GeoArabia Special Publication, **4**: 9–48.

van Buchem, F.S.P., Simmons, M.D., Droste, H.J., and Davies, R.B., 2011, Late Aptian to Turonian stratigraphy of the eastern Arabian Plate–depositional sequences and lithostratigraphic nomenclature. *Petroleum Geoscience*, **17**: 211–222.

van der Meer, D.G., van Saparoea, A.V.D.B., Van Hinsbergen, D.J.J., Van de Weg, R.M.B., Godderis, Y., Le Hir, G., et al., 2017, Reconstructing first-order changes in sea-level during the Phanerozoic and Neoproterozoic using strontium isotopes. *Gondwana Research*, **44**: 22–34.

van Hinsbergen, D.J.J., Abels, H.A., Bosch, W., Boekhout, F., Kitchka, A., Hamers, M., et al., 2015, Sedimentary geology of the middle Carboniferous of the Donbas region (Dnieper-Donets Basin, Ukraine). *Scientific Reports*, **5**: article #9099: 8 pp. https://doi.org/10.1038/srep09099.

Van Sickel, W.A., Kominz, M.A., Miller, K.G., and Browning, J.V., 2004, Late Cretaceous and Cenozoic sea-level estimates: backstripping analysis of borehole data, onshore New Jersey. *Basin Research*, **16**: 451–465.

Van Wagoner, J.C., Posamentier, H.W., Mitchum, R.M., Vail, P.R., Sarg, J.F., Loutit, T.S., et al. 1988. An overview of the fundamentals of sequence stratigraphy and key definitions. *In* Wilgus, C.K., Hastings, B.S., Kendall, C.G. St., and Posamentier, H.W. (eds). *Sea-level Changes: An Integrated Approach*. SEPM Special Publication, **42**: 39–45.

Van Wagoner, J.C., Mitchum, R.M., Campion, K.M., and Rahmanian, V.D., 1990, Siliciclastic sequence stratigraphy in well logs, cores, and outcrops: concepts for high-resolution correlation of time and facies. *American Association of Petroleum Geologists, Methods in Exploration*, **7**: 55.

Veevers, J.J., 1990, Tectonic-climatic supercycle in the billion-year plate-tectonic eon: Permian Pangean icehouse alternates with Cretaceous dispersed-continents greenhouse. *Sedimentary Geology*, **68**: 1–16.

Vérard, C., Hochard, C., Baumgartner, P.O., and Stampfli, G.M., 2015, 3D palaeogeographic reconstructions of the Phanerozoic versus sea-level and Sr-ratio variations. *Journal of Palaeogeography*, **4**: 64–84.

Vickers, M.L., Price, G.D., Jerrett, R.M., Sutton, P., Watkinson, M.P., and FitzPatrick, M., 2019, The duration and magnitude of Cretaceous cool events: evidence from the northern high latitudes. *Geological Society of America Bulletin*, **131** (11-12), 1979–1994.

Videt, B., Paris, F., Rubino, J.L., Boumendjel, K., Dabard, M.P., Loi, A., et al., 2010, Biostratigraphical calibration of third order Ordovician sequences on the northern Gondwana platform. *Palaeogeography, Palaeoclimatology, Palaeoecology*, **296**: 59–375.

Voigt, S., Gale, A.S., and Voigt, T., 2006, Sea-level change, carbon cycling and palaeoclimate during the Late Cenomanian of northwest Europe: an integrated palaeoenvironmental analysis. *Cretaceous Research*, **27**: 836–858.

Wade, B.S., and Pälike, H., 2004, Oligocene climate dynamics. *Paleoceanography*, **19**: PA4019.

Wagreich, M., Lein, R., and Sames, B., 2014, Eustasy, its controlling factors, and the limn-eustatic hypothesis – concepts inspired by Eduard Suess. *Austrian Journal of Earth Sciences*, **107**: 115–131.

Wendler, J.E., and Wendler, I., 2016, What drove sea-level fluctuations during the mid-Cretaceous greenhouse climate? *Palaeogeography, Palaeoclimatology, Palaeoecology*, **441**: 412–419.

Wendler, J.E., Lehmann, J., and Kuss, J., 2010. Orbital time scale, intra-platform basin correlation, carbon isotope stratigraphy and sea-level history of the Cenomanian–Turonian Eastern Levant platform, Jordan. *In* Homberg, C., and Bachman, M. (eds). *Evolution of the Levant Margin and Western Arabia Platform Since the Mesozoic*. Geological Society, London, Special Publications, **341**: 171–186.

Wendler, J.E., Meyers, S.R., Wendler, I., and Kuss, J., 2014, A million-year-scale astronomical control on Late Cretaceous sea-level. *Newsletters on Stratigraphy*, **47**: 1–19.

Wendler, J.E., Wendler, I., Vogt, C., and Kuss, J., 2016, Link between cyclic eustatic sea-level change and continental weathering: evidence for aquifer-eustasy in the Cretaceous. *Palaeogeography, Palaeoclimatology, Palaeoecology*, **441**: 430–437.

Wong, P.K., Weissenberger, J.A.W., and Gilhooly, M.G., 2016, Revised regional Frasnian sequence stratigraphic framework, Alberta Outcrop and subsurface. *In* Playton, T.E., Kerans, C., and Weissenberger, J.A.W. (eds), *New Advances in Devonian Carbonates: Outcrop Analogs, Reservoirs, and Chronostratigraphy*. SEPM Special Publication, **107**: 16–79.

Worsley, T.R., Nance, D., and Moody, J.B., 1986, Tectonic cycles and the history of the Earth's biogeochemical and paleoceanographic record. *Paleoceanography*, **1**: 233–263.

Wright, V.P., and Vanstone, S.D., 2001, Onset of Late Palaeozoic glacio-eustasy and the evolving climates of low latitude areas: a synthesis of current understanding. *Journal of the Geological Society*, **158**: 579–582.

Xu, X., Lithow-Bertelloni, C., and Conrad, C.P., 2006, Global reconstructions of Cenozoic seafloor ages: implications for bathymetry and sea-level. *Earth and Planetary Science Letters*, **243**: 552–564.

Zachos, J., Pagani, M., Sloan, L., Thomas, E., and Billups, K., 2001, Trends, rhythms, and aberrations in global climate 65Ma to present. *Science*, **292**: 686–693.

Zimmermann, J., Franz, M., Heunisch, C., Luppold, F.W., Mönnig, E., and Wolfgramm, M., 2015, Sequence stratigraphic framework of the Lower and Middle Jurassic in the North German Basin: epicontinental sequences controlled by Boreal cycles. *Palaeogeography, Palaeoclimatology, Palaeoecology*, **440**: 395–416.

Geomathematics

Chapter outline

Geologic Time Scale 2020. DOI: https://doi.org/10.1016/B978-0-12-824360-2.00014-0

SubChapter 14A

Geomathematical and Statistical Procedures

F.P. Agterberg, A-C. Da Silva and F.M. Gradstein

Abstract

The input for the calculation of a numerical time scale is a set of radioisotopic dates with variable uncertainty in both time (in Myr) and stratigraphic position (in biozones). These selected input dates are irregularly distributed with respect to a biostratigraphic scale derived from graphical correlation, constrained optimization, or a stack of successive biozonal units. Spline fitting with error estimation produces a linear time scale with error bars on the geologic stage boundary ages. These methods were applied to data sets developed for the Ordovician–Silurian, Devonian, and Carboniferous–Permian periods. Detailed Early and Late Cretaceous data sets were both splined and results adjusted from comparative summations and adjusting of cyclostratigraphic and M-sequence splining durations.

14A.1 History

Geologic time scales (GTS) are constructed by combining stratigraphic information with radioisotopic dates and their standard deviations. The stratigraphic record to be used includes litho-, bio-, chrono-, cyclo-, and magnetostratigraphy. For the construction of several previous time scales, ages of stage boundaries were estimated by application of the chronogram method (Harland et al., 1982, 1990), or maximum likelihood (Gradstein et al., 1994, 1995), to a worldwide database of chronostratigraphically classified dates. These methods, which can also be applied to more closely spaced zone boundaries (Pálfy et al., 2000), resulted in age estimates accompanied by approximate 95% confidence intervals. A final time scale was obtained by calibration using graphical and curve-fitting methods, including cubic smoothing splines.

Odin (1994) discussed three separate approaches to numerical time scale construction: statistical, geochronological, and graphical methods, but in the end preferred subjective reasoning to estimate ages of samples and stratigraphic boundaries. Gradstein et al. (1994, 1995) used all three approaches in a stepwise procedure involving maximum likelihood, use of stratigraphically constrained dates, and recalibration by curve fitting.

14A.1.1 The chronogram method

The chronogram method used by Harland et al. (1982, 1990) is suitable for the estimation of the age of chronostratigraphic boundaries from a radioisotopic database when most rock samples used for age determination are subject to significant relative uncertainty. Inconsistencies in the vicinity of chronostratigraphic boundaries can then be ascribed to imprecision of the age determination method.

Cox and Dalrymple (1967) originally developed an approach for estimating the age of Cenozoic chron boundaries from inconsistent K–Ar age determinations of basaltic rocks. Harland et al. (1982, 1990) adopted this method in their calculations of ages of stage boundaries for the 1982 and 1990 time scales. The basic principle of this approach is as follows: assuming a hypothetical trial age for an observed chronostratigraphic boundary, rock samples from above this boundary should be younger, and those below it should be older. An inconsistent date is either an older date for a rock sample known to be younger than the trial date or a younger date for a sample known to be older. The difference between each inconsistent date and the trial age can be standardized by dividing it by the standard deviation of the inconsistent date. Thus relatively imprecise dates receive less weight than more precise dates. The underlying assumptions are that (1) the rock samples are uniformly distributed along the time axis and (2) the error of each date satisfies a normal (Gaussian) error distribution with standard deviation equal to that of the age determination method used.

Standardized differences between inconsistent dates and trial age can be squared and the sum of squares (written as E^2) determined for all inconsistent dates corresponding to the same trial age. Chronograms constructed by Harland et al. (1982) were U-shaped plots of E^2 against different trial ages spaced at narrow time intervals. The optimum choice of age was at the trial age where E^2 was a minimum.

Agterberg (1988) made the following improvement to this method. In addition to inconsistent dates, there are generally more consistent dates for any trial age selected for a chronostratigraphic boundary. The statistical maximum likelihood method can be used to combine consistent with inconsistent dates resulting in an improved estimate of the age of the chronostratigraphic boundary considered. Each standardized difference with respect to a trial age was interpreted as the fractile of the normal distribution in standard form and transformed into its corresponding probability. Summation of the logarithmically transformed probabilities then yields the log-likelihood value of the trial date. In this type of calculation, inconsistent dates receive more weight than consistent dates. Consequently, the improvement resulting from using consistent dates, in addition to the inconsistent dates, is relatively minor. However, when there are relatively few dates, use of the consistent dates yields significantly better results. The log-likelihood function is beehive-shaped. For example, see Gradstein et al. (1995).

A general disadvantage of chronogram methods is that the relative stratigraphic position of the sample is generalized with respect to stage boundaries that are relatively far apart in time. The relative stratigraphic position of one sample with respect to another within the same stage is not considered. A better approach is to incorporate relative stratigraphic positions of fewer samples for which precise age determinations are available.

14A.1.2 The McKerrow method

McKerrow et al. (1985) described the following type of method to construct a numerical time scale for the Ordovician, Silurian, and Devonian. Use was made of an iterative construction involving a sequence of diagrams wherein the isotopic age of the sample was plotted along the x-axis and its stratigraphic age along the y-axis. They stated (p. 73),

> *Most graphs are constructed with definite numerical scales along both the x and y axes; this is not the case with fig. 1, where only the horizontal (x) axis is numerical. The vertical (y) axis is a stratigraphic time scale, showing periods, series, stages and zones; the precise duration of each of these time divisions is unknown. In fact, the whole object of this documentation is to determine, as far as possible with the evidence available, what estimates can be given on the duration of these stratigraphic divisions. Thus, in the course of preparing this figure, we have constructed a series of graphs, each with slightly differing vertical scales, until we obtained a scale which allowed a straight line to pass through almost all the rectangles representing the analytical errors (2σ) and the stratigraphic uncertainties in the data we use.*

In a later paper on the Ordovician time scale, Cooper (1999) used 14 analytically reliable and stratigraphically controlled high-resolution TIMS U–Pb zircon dates and a single Sm–Nd date. Adopting a modified version of the McKerrow method, Cooper plotted these Ordovician dates along a relative time scale that was then reproportioned as necessary to achieve a good fit with a straight line obtained by linear regression. This method of relative shortening and lengthening of parts of the Ordovician time scale was based mainly on a comparison of sediment accumulation rates in widely different regions and, to some extent, on empirical reproportioning. Agterberg (2002) subjected Cooper's (1999) data to spline fitting and found that the optimum smoothing factor (SF) corresponds to a straight-line fit. He then used Ripley's MLFR (Maximum Likelihood for Functional Relationship, Ripley and Thompson, 1987) method to fit a straight line in which stratigraphic uncertainty was considered as well.

14A.2 Spline fitting in GTS2004

The approach adopted by GTS2004 placed more emphasis on the relative stratigraphic position of the few samples for which precise age dates were available. It was based on methods of straight-line construction applied to more or less homogeneous data sets previously developed for Paleozoic periods. The starting point for construction of numerical time scales is a data set of radioisotopic ages, measured in millions of years, with 2-sigma error bars, for samples positioned along a relative stratigraphic scale of which the unit is approximately proportional to time (also measured in millions of years). In GTS2004, spline-curve fitting was used to relate the observed ages to their stratigraphic position. GTS2012 used the same method except for a new approach to the estimation of error bars on zonal boundaries.

The first stage consists of fitting a cubic smoothing spline curve according to the method previously described in detail for the Mesozoic time scale in Gradstein et al. (1994, 1995) and Agterberg (1988, 1994). As shown in the example in Fig. 14A.1 age determinations are plotted in the vertical direction (along the y-axis) against relative stratigraphic position (x-axis). Relative stratigraphic position is according to a continuous scale that is the same for all age determinations used. To some extent, the scale initially used for relative stratigraphic position determines the shape of the final spline curve. A relative stratigraphic scale should be used that is as close as possible to the numerical GTS (in millions of years) except for a linear transformation. Less satisfactory relative stratigraphic scales used in the past included scales based on sediment accumulation corrected for differences in rates of sedimentation, the hypothesis of equal duration of stages (Harland et al., 1982), and the hypothesis of equal duration of biozones (Kent and Gradstein, 1986; Harland et al., 1990; Gradstein et al., 1995).

14A.2.1 Incorporation of stratigraphic uncertainty

Each age determination is weighted according to the inverse of its variance corresponding to the published 2-sigma (or 1-sigma) error bar. If stratigraphic uncertainty is incorporated, this variance becomes $s_t^2(y) = s^2(x) + s^2(y)$ instead of $s^2(y)$. The rationale behind this relatively simple transformation is that the x-axis also represents a time scale. Uncertainty in relative stratigraphic position should also be reflected in uncertainty of the location of a date in the $x-y$ plot. In Paleozoic applications the stratigraphic error bars can be relatively large. Stratigraphic uncertainty then adds to the uncertainty expressed by the 2-sigma error bars of the age determinations. A rectangular frequency distribution model represents stratigraphic uncertainty better than the Gaussian frequency distribution model employed for the measurement errors of the dates. The underlying assumption is that a sample reported to occur within a particular zone, or within two or more consecutive

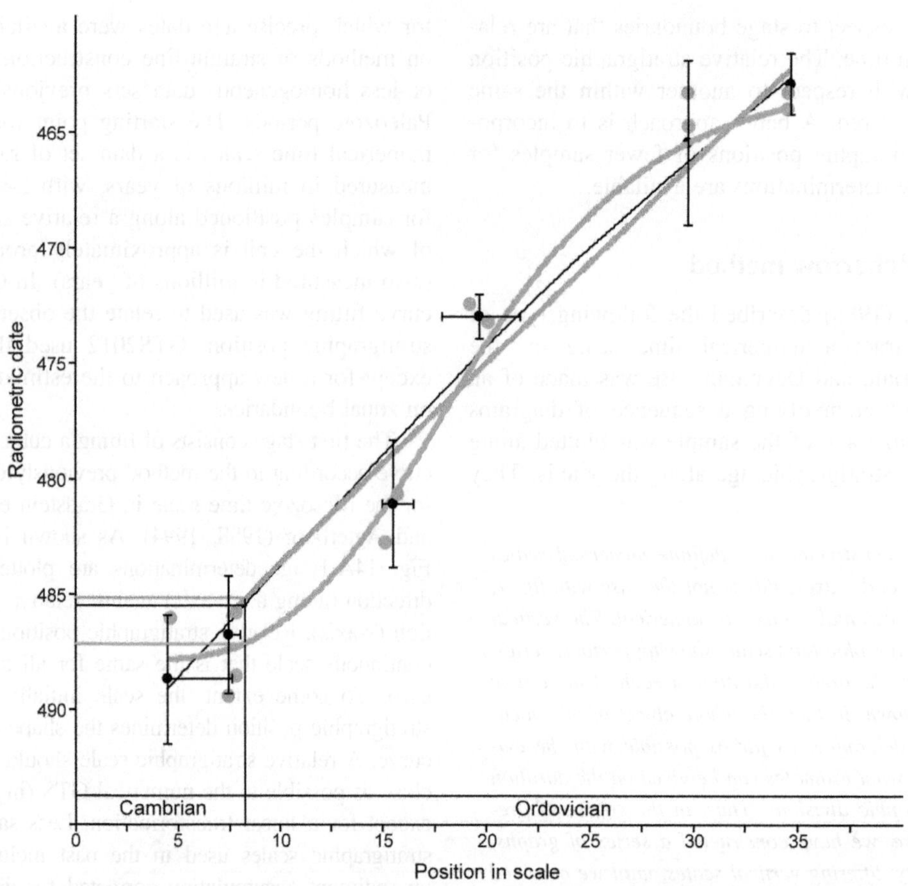

FIGURE 14A.1 Illustration of the splining procedure with a small set of data points around the Cambrian–Ordovician boundary (from GTS2012, this figure). Black dots: given data with stratigraphic and radioisotopic dating error bars (total range and 2-sigma). Black curve: spline of the given data, cross-validated SF = 1.075. Blue dots: random replicate of the input data generated according to the given points and their error bars, SF = 2.125. Blue curve: spline of the random replicate. Green dots and curve: another random replicate and its spline, SF = 0.85. The Cambrian–Ordovician boundary age from the spline of the given data is 485.39 Ma. The ages computed from the random replicates are 485.17 and 487.06 Ma. *SF*, Smoothing factor.

zones, could occur anywhere within this chronostratigraphic interval with equal probability for all places where it truly occurs. If the length of a stratigraphic error bar is written as q, the variance of a rectangular frequency density distribution (with base q) is $q^2/12$ instead of $q^2/16$ for the Gaussian distribution. This translates into a standard deviation $s(x) = 1.15q/4$ (cf. Agterberg, 2002). The stratigraphic error bars used for analysis in GTS2004 and GTS2020 were treated in this manner.

Ideally, when stratigraphic standard deviations $s(x_i)$ are to be combined with $s(y_i)$ values, x_i and y_i as well as $s(x_i)$ and $s(y_i)$ are expressed in millions of years and the line of best fit would have the simple equation $y = x$. This strategy followed for GTS2004 applications is comparable to that discussed by Press et al. (1992) for straight-line fitting with both variables subject to uncertainty. The procedure goes back to a simple method for dealing with this problem originally devised in 1984 by Lybanon (1984). In our applications the final spline curves are usually not very different from straight lines and variances along both axes become comparable when Ma is used for both scales. For $s(x_i)$ values a good approximation is obtained by setting the interval between oldest and youngest observed ages along the relative scale equal to the difference between these two ages in millions of years. However, with the increases of both quantity and quality of age determinations, deviations between best fitting spline curves and straight lines have become better established than in the past.

14A.2.2 Smoothing splines

A cubic smoothing spline $f(x)$ is fully determined by n pairs of values (x_i, y_i), the standard deviations of the dates $s(y_i)$, and an SF representing the square root of the average value of the squares of scaled residuals $r_i = (y_i - f(x_i))/s(y_i)$. In general, if all $s(y_i)$ values are unbiased, SF ≈ 1, or SF is equal to a value slightly less than 1 (cf. Agterberg, 1994). If SF significantly exceeds 1, this suggests that some or all of the variances used are too small (underreported). Thus the spline-fitting method may provide an independent method of assessing mutual consistency and average precision of published 2-sigma error bars.

The method of "leaving-one-out" cross-validation (CV) can be used to determine the optimum SF. In this method, all observed dates y_i, between the oldest and youngest one, are successively left out from spline fitting with preselected trial values of SF. The result is $(n-2)$ spline curves for each SF tried. The CV value for any SF is the sum of squares of deviations between y_i and estimated values on the $(n-2)$ spline curves with the same x_i values as y_i. The best SF has the smallest CV value.

It is noted that even if the CV pattern shows a well-developed minimum at a value not close to 1, adoption of the optimum SF value instead of SF = 1 generally constitutes only a minor improvement of the spline curve. In Paleozoic applications (see Section 8.2, Chapter 8 in Gradstein et al., 2004), the optimum SF is generally smaller than 1. Setting SF = 1 would result in slightly more smooth-spline curves.

Unless its unit is consistently proportional to geologic time measured in millions of years, the numerical time scale resulting from spline fitting is not linearly related to the initial relative time scale. It is, however, linearly related to geologic time in millions of years. This allows for gradual changes over time in the original hypothetical process on the basis of which the initial relative time scale is constructed. For example, deviations from a straight line on a fitted spline curve may represent corrections of changes in sedimentation rate or rate of evolutionary change.

In GTS2004, distances between successive points along the x-axis in $x-y$ plots were not zero or close to zero. In the spline fitting, separate cubic polynomials are fitted between pairs of points taking care that the resulting spline curve is continuous not only in age but also in its first derivative (changes in age). If distances between successive points are either zero or negligibly small, cubic polynomials cannot be fitted. Situations of this type arise when successive ash layers, which are close to one another, are dated separately. This can result in problems in the spline fitting, especially when the leaving-one-out method is used for CV. Such problems can be avoided by calculating the weighted average of dates with approximately the same values along the stratigraphic scale, as will be discussed in Section 14A.5.1.

14A.2.3 Treatment of outliers

It often happened that a few points ended up far away from the smoothing spline curve. These outliers are handled by assuming that their standard deviations must have been underestimated. The procedure contains a step where outliers are identified and their standard deviations adjusted. The spline can then be recomputed.

Individual scaled residuals are either positive or negative and should be approximately distributed as z-values (from the "standard normal" Gaussian frequency distribution). Their squares are then chi-square distributed with one degree of freedom and can be converted into probabilities to test the hypothesis that they are not greater than can be expected on the basis of the $s(y)$ values used for scaling the residuals. The sum of squares of several scaled residuals is also approximately distributed as chi-square but with a larger number of degrees of freedom. A statistical test can therefore be used for identifying the relatively few outliers exhibiting error bars that are much narrower than expected on the basis of most ages in the same data set.

The $s(y)$ values can be revised by replacing probabilities that are too small ($P<.05$) by 0.5. Setting the probability equal to 50% is equivalent to replacing the chi-square value by 0.4549. This is the same as adopting a new z-value of 0.674, because chi-square with a single degree of freedom is z^2. The new $s(y)$ value is then computed by dividing the old z-value (scaled residual) by 0.674, and multiplying the result with the original $s(y)$.

14A.2.4 Ages of zonal boundaries

Ages of zonal boundaries, and durations of zones, are estimated by interpolating the spline curve. In GTS2004, error bars on zonal boundaries were estimated through a sequence of steps. First, the spline curve was "rectified" by plotting the original dates y_i on the x-axis and the spline values $f(x_i)$ on the y-axis. This data set was subjected to a linear regression (MLFR), giving error bars on slope and intercept. These were again used to estimate standard deviations of residuals. Finally, the latter deviations formed the basis of errors on zonal boundaries using adjustment and smoothing (ramping). This procedure assumed that the spline fitting had provided an exact adjustment for variation in slope of the chronostratigraphy versus age curve.

14A.3 Modifications in GTS2012

New stratigraphic information, including new age dates, had become available after GTS2004. This information was incorporated for GTS2012, which was an update of GTS2004. Statistical methods were not changed significantly except for a new method for the estimation of error bars on stage boundary ages. The new age estimates result mainly from the fact that new spline curves were fitted relating updated age data sets to earlier time scales. These earlier time scales were either GTS2004 or other GTS.

In GTS2004, error bars were estimated using an MLFR regression of the rectified spline. GTS2012 uses a more direct approach, but also a somewhat different definition of errors. Given our spline-fitting procedure and the inaccuracy of the estimates of radioisotopic dates and stratigraphic positions, we may ask how much an interpolated zonal boundary date would have varied if we carried out the datings, spline fitting, and interpolation repeatedly.

14A.3.1 Bootstrap splines

This is simulated by a Monte Carlo procedure, picking random stratigraphic positions and dates with distributions as given (normal or rectangular) and then running the spline fitting anew with CV (Fig. 14A.1). This is repeated say 10,000 times, producing a histogram of interpolated values from which a 95% confidence interval can be derived. The procedure is computer intensive; for each of the 10,000 Monte Carlo replicates, a number of splines must be computed in the CV procedure. Analytical approaches for the computation of confidence intervals on smoothing splines with error bars on both axes are not available.

The analogy to actual repeated measurement is only approximate, because the replicate distributions are not centered on the actual precise radioisotopic dates, nominally corresponding to the population means of repeated measurement, but on *estimated* radioisotopic dates. It was not investigated to what extent this may influence the error bars.

14A.3.2 Monotonicity

Some replicates may have combinations of extreme random data values that produce serious wiggles in the spline curve resulting from the bootstrap method. To reduce the possibly large effects of this phenomenon on interpolated values, the SF was automatically increased from the optimum value until the curve in monotonically increasing (no time reversal).

The splining procedure rests on the assumption that absolute time is a smooth function of stratigraphic position. This is a pragmatic, parsimonious assumption, but it is easy to imagine situations where it is not true (e.g., a global hiatus). Possible violations of the smoothness assumption may increase error bars by an unknown amount.

In addition, it should be noted that the Monte Carlo procedure for generating error bars assumes that the errors in radioisotopic dates are independent. In reality, these errors are partitioned into "internal" and "external" errors. Only the internal errors are truly independent, while the external errors are highly correlated across samples. Our treatment of all errors as completely independent is expected to lead to some underestimation of the errors on interpolated boundary ages. For the estimation of error bars on *durations*, we use only the internal errors for the Monte Carlo procedure, because external errors will influence the age of the lower and upper boundaries of a stage or period by approximately the same amount and therefore will not contribute significantly to duration error. The iterative procedure involving random sampling of rectangular uncertainty boxes used in GTS2012 worked well except for the Devonian where part of the final spline curve was replaced by a straight-line segment connecting the age determinations for samples D7 in the Eifelian and D9 in the Frasnian. These two dates had relatively small 2-sigma values and no significant stratigraphic uncertainty.

Obvious problems with the GTS2012 Devonian spline are that several of the 18 original age determinations (D4, D5, D6, D9, and D15) used have 2-sigma error bars that do not intersect with the age-stratigraphic position curve in Fig. 22.14 of GTS2012. Only approximately 5% of these error bars (i.e., probably a single error bar for the Devonian) should intersect with the curve. It indicates that the method of constructing the Devonian GTS2012 spline curve was not fully satisfactory. Problems encountered when the bootstrap spline was fitted to the Devonian were already described in GTS2012 (p. 587) as follows: In the first run of the smoothing spline procedure the CV suggested an optimum SF of 1.85. With such a high SF, six of the data points did not pass the chi-square test (D4, $\chi^2 = 8.12$, $P = .004$; D5, $\chi^2 = 21.7$, $P = .000$; D6, $\chi^2 = 0.005$, $P = .020$; D8, $\chi^2 = 7.85$, $P = .005$; D9, $\chi^2 = 4.86$, $P = .032$; and D15, $\chi^2 = 4.43$, $P = .035$). For each of these points the combined stratigraphic and radioisotopic error $s_t(y)$ was therefore increased to enforce a P value of .5. The adjusted errors were used for a second computation of the spline. In this new run the optimum SF was 0.45. The resulting final spline was shown in GTS2012 Fig. 22.14A. As pointed out before, it deviates significantly from six observed dates and probably needed the straight-line segment correction for top and base of the Givetian.

14A.3.3 Multipeaked BChron confidence intervals

The GTS2012 Devonian time scale was critically evaluated by De Vleeschouwer and Parnell (2014). These authors applied the BChron *R* software package (Haslett and Parnell, 2008) to the Devonian time scale using GTS2012 dates as input (also see later in this chapter). BChron is based on a continuous Markov monotone stochastic process model originally used for combining chronological information arising from ^{14}C dates with depth data in sedimentary sections. The sedimentary process is simulated using compound Poisson-gamma density functions. The gamma function used by Haslett and Parnell (2008) has two parameters and resembles a Gaussian curve that is bounded at both ends so that the principle of monotonicity is not violated. In addition, the Poisson distribution has a single parameter.

In their application to the Devonian, De Vleeschouwer and Parnell (2014) point out that their estimates of the stage boundary ages do not differ significantly from those in GTS2012. However, the uncertainty limits of their estimates are significantly different because they depend strongly on density of age determinations along the geologic time line. Clustering of age determinations will be discussed in more detail in the next section. Here it is noted that the BChron software used by De Vleeschouwer and Parnell (2014) requires that the input dates satisfy the principle of monotonicity in that younger dates should not be preceded by older dates in the direction of time along the stratigraphic scale. Nonoverlapping error bars are manually shifted in order to satisfy this input requirement.

When there are obvious inconsistencies of this type like the one involving D4 and D5 in Fig. 14A.2, it is not clear what should be done. Shifting one or both data points along the time axis is equivalent to assuming one or two inaccuracies. The approach taken in GTS2004 and GTS2012 was that, when inconsistencies of this type arise, precision of one or both dates was probably overestimated and error bars along the y-axis were made longer by using the chi-square test. In the approach that resulted in Fig. 14A.2 uncertainties were enlarged to some extent by incorporating the stratigraphic uncertainty before the spline curve was fitted.

In general, BChron results show a 95% confidence belt with relatively many points of narrowing and widening (also see Ovtcharova et al., 2015). These points tend to coincide with the locations of one or more relatively precise age determinations. De Vleeschouwer and Parnell (2014) argue that a confidence belt of this type is to be preferred to the type of confidence belt resulting from least-squares curve fitting, which tends to be narrow near the middle and widens toward the points at the beginning and end of the series of x-values used. The reason for these widenings of the 95% confidence belt is simply that there are no data points before and after the beginning and end of the time series. If locally there is high density of points along the x-axis, these points will contribute more than average to the coefficients that are being estimated by the method of least squares. It is noted that best fitting spline curves also satisfy the principle of least squares.

14A.3.4 Silver spikes

The relatively high confidence points in the BChron curve could be regarded as "silver spikes" in analogy with the golden spikes at stage boundaries where quality and quantity of information are above average. It is likely that in the immediate vicinities of the sample locations selected for age determination, quality of geological information is

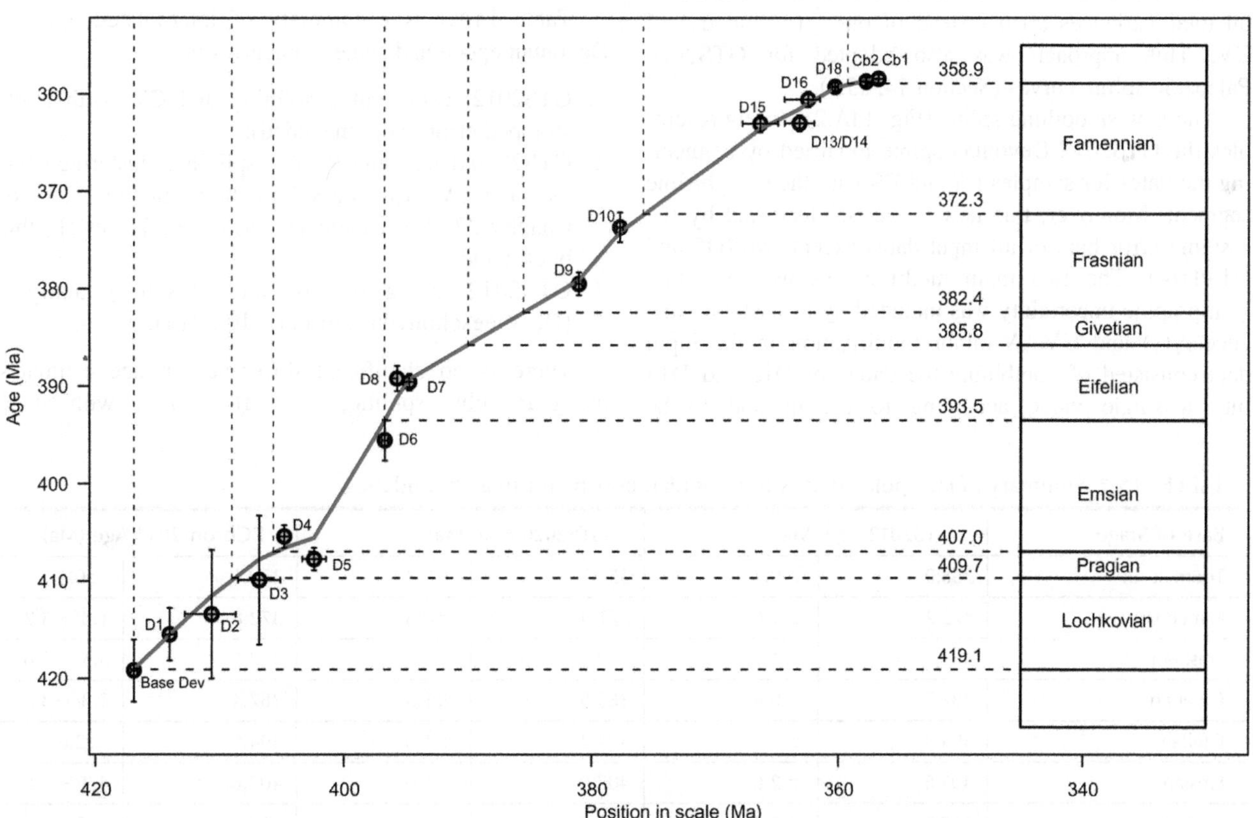

FIGURE 14A.2 Devonian time scale based on smoothing spline fitted to composite interval age determinations and stratigraphic uncertainties in GTS2012.

above average but not as good as at the golden spikes. Depending on how the silver spikes in Figures 1 and 2 of De Vleeschouwer and Parnell (2014) are counted, there would be about 10 silver spikes in the Devonian. On the other hand, statistically (see Section 14A.4), there is no conclusive evidence of significant clustering for so many silver spikes along the stratigraphic scale. In the next section the problem of clustering of ash layers with age determinations will be considered in more detail and later (Section 14A.5.5) an approximate 95% confidence belt will be constructed on the basis of the GST2020 age determinations for the Devonian.

It is noted that a technique such as LOWESS or its later version LOESS (see, e.g., Howarth and McArthur, 1997) also can produce 95% confidence belts with local maxima and minima in thickness. However, when there are relatively few data points as for the Devonian dates, no meaningful LOESS confidence belts can be computed.

14A.3.5 Revised Devonian Spline

The smoothing spline shown in Fig. 14A.2 does not show any of these drawbacks mentioned previously. It was derived using the publicly available *R*-program *smooth-spline* as implemented by B.D. Ripley and M. Maechler in *R*.Stats Package version 3.6.0, with uncertainties based on total variances $s_t^2(y)$ instead of on s^2 (y) and use of CV. This approach was also adopted for GTS2020 Paleozoic spline curves (Section 14A.5.5).

The new smoothing spline (Fig. 14A.2) closely resembles the GTS2012 Devonian spline modified by connecting the dates for samples D7 and D9 with the straight-line segment. Moreover, this new curve is intersected by the 2-sigma error bars of all input dates except two (D5 and D13/D14). The two main modifications used are that stratigraphic uncertainty was included by using total variance $s_t^2(y)$ and CV. A minor modification in the input data consisted of combining the dates for D13 and D14 into a single value according to the method to be described in Section 14A.5.1, because they have the same position in stratigraphic scale. Their weighted average has narrower 2-sigma error bar.

In comparison with other Paleozoic periods, relatively few age determinations continue to be available for the Devonian. For GTS2012 a bootstrap method was used obtaining an average spline curve based on 10,000 individual splines each based on random sampling of random variables for all dates with normal (Gaussian) distributions in the *y*-direction and rectangular distributions in the *x*-direction. As mentioned before, the Devonian also has been the subject of a study by De Vleeschouwer and Parnell (2014) who applied a different method (Bchron) for deriving the curve relating the age determinations to the stratigraphic scale. In this section special attention is paid to the Devonian, which has a notable lack of data for the Givetian and parts of its adjoining stages. It suggests that worldwide there exist gaps in the density distribution of age determinations along the stratigraphic scale. This may present a third source of uncertainty in time scale estimation that is independent of age determination errors and stratigraphic uncertainty. The original GST2012 data for the Devonian, which were also used by De Vleeschouwer and Parnell (2014), will be used in the next section to investigate the possibility of spatial clustering of Devonian ash beds used for the age determinations.

Table 14A.1 is a summary of interpolated ages of Devonian epoch and stage boundaries in:

1. GTS2012, using cubic splining and CV, with bootstrapped error bars (one-sided);
2. GTS2020 data, using *R* cubic splining, clustering analysis and CV, with the spline shown in Fig. 22.14 of Chapter 22, The Devonian Period (Becker et al., this book); and
3. GTS2012, using BChron and clustering analysis (De Vleeschouwer and Parnell, 2014).

There is no significant difference in age estimates using *R* cubic splining + or BChron +, with stage

TABLE 14A.1 Summary of interpolated ages of Devonian epoch and stage boundaries.

Base of Stage	GTS2012 Age (Ma)		GTS2020 Age (Ma)		BChron-2014 Age (Ma)	
Tournaisian	358.9	± 0.4	359.3	± 0.3	359.1	± 0.4
Famennian	372.2	± 1.6	371.4	± 0.6	372.8	1.8/ − 3.2
Frasnian	382.7	± 1.0	379	± 0.9	382.5	3.5/ − 2.6
Givetian	387.7	± 0.8	385.9	± 1.5	387.4	1.8/ − 3.3
Eifelian	393.3	± 1.2	394.2	± 1.6	394.9	± 2.6
Emsian	407.6	± 2.6	407.9	± 1.0	407.6	4.3/ − 2.5
Pragian	410.8	± 2.8	414.4	± 1.1	411	± 3.5
Lochkovian	419.2	± 3.2	420	± 0.9	418.8	± 2.7

durations also being comparable. The main difference in results obtained by these two different methods is that the BChron 95% error bar width shows rapid fluctuations in its width. It contains about 10 local maxima in places of minimal density of occurrences of samples that were dated. Differences in error bar values are difficult to assess, but BChron assigns relatively large uncertainty where there is a lack of age dates around or on one side of the interpolated age of a stage boundary. In the latter case BChron appears to squeeze zones too much, in excess of their (thickness) duration uncertainty. The *R* cubic splining methods honor zonal stratigraphic uncertainty better, limiting how far a stage can expand in time. The mention of thickness in parenthesis just before the previous sentence is a reference to the fact that the Devonian position scale axis for the splines is derived from a subjective estimate of the duration of the Devonian zones and their link to the stage boundaries using relative thickness estimates. More information is provided by Becker et al. (Chapter 22: The Devonian Period, this book). The other Paleozoic periods, with the exception of the Cambrian that has no scaling of zones and stages, use different quantitative or semiquantitative methods for stratigraphic compositing to calculate a linear scale along the stratigraphic axis of events, zones, and stages. Hence, such a linear stratigraphic scale can be compared to the scale with radioisotopic ages in a two-way plot, using the splines, under discussion here.

14A.4 Statistical distribution of age determinations along the geologic time scale

How much weight should be given to the specific location of an age determination along the stratigraphic time scale? This is a philosophical question that suddenly has become important in GTS construction because of the conceptual modeling on which the BChron algorithm is based.

Conceptually, we believe that differences of expected frequency of age determinations per unit of geologic time probably exist. For example, the 29 $^{40}Ar/^{39}Ar$ bentonite dates of Obradovich (1993) for the Late Cretaceous do not seem to be uniformly distributed. Within the 65–100 Ma time interval, only 7 dates occur within the 65–82.5 Ma time interval versus 22 within the 82.5–100 Ma interval. If the bentonites that were dated would be randomly distributed over the entire 35 Myr time interval, the probability of it occurring in the younger time interval is 0.5. The probability that only 7 (of the 29) would occur within this interval becomes 0.0029 and the probability of 7 or fewer than 7 is 0.0041. Both these probabilities are less than 0.05 or 0.01. This suggests that there are probably fewer dates in the 65–82.5 Ma interval (and more in the 85.5–100 Ma interval) than expected for a random Poisson-type distribution. The probability of occurrence of a bentonite in the Late Cretaceous probably therefore depends on its age but how could we describe its time-dependent probability function?

In BChron the estimated probability of a predicted age being correct is relatively large at the place of occurrence of a dated rock sample and even somewhat larger if nearby there are other dated rock samples, but why? The Devonian time scale of Fig. 14A.2 is based on 18 irregularly distributed dates only. Any discrete statistical model to test for systematic changes in the number of dates per unit of time would not indicate significant clustering in time because sample size is too small. We could, however, look at differences between dates along the Devonian time scale. The following purely hypothetical example illustrates why this may provide a more promising approach. Suppose that in a large study area the same ash layer is sampled twice at locations that are relatively far removed from one another. The age determinations for these two ash samples will be different but they would have exactly the same position along the relative GTS. The probability that two age determinations would exactly coincide along the time scale is infinitesimally small. A definite result of this type could not be obtained from the original data when a Poisson-type model is used because the sample is too small. This is the reason that it will be good to look at first-order differences between locations of age determinations instead of at the locations themselves.

14A.4.1 Power-law models

Simple power-law models are often used for the construction of contour maps for noisy geochemical data irregularly distributed across a study area. The most popular model along these lines is quadratic with $\hat{y}_k = (1/n) \cdot \sum_{i=1}^{n} c_k \cdot y_{ik} \cdot d_{ik}^{-2}$ where the n values y_{ik} represent all observations located within a circular area with predefined radius around point k with estimated contour value $\hat{y}_k$ at its center, and d_{ik} is the distance between the points of occurrence of $\hat{y}_k$.and y_{ik}. In our application this isotropic squared deviation model can be used as follows. Every age determination y_k occurs at distance d_{ik} from other age determinations y_{ik} in its neighborhood. For example, the age determination y_k with value x_k along the geologic distance scale is distance d_{ik} removed from its closest neighbors with locations $x_{ik} = c_{ik} \cdot (x_k - x_{ik})^{-2}$. Use is made of the fact that x_{ik} already represents an estimate of y_{ik}. For convenience a simplified linear scale was used instead of original position along the stratigraphic scale. There is a linear relation between the stratigraphic scale of Fig. 14A.2 and the horizontal scale in Figs. 14A.3 and 14A.4 in which $x_k = 17$ represents sample D1 and $x_k = 136$ represents Cb1. The central point in Fig. 14A.3 with horizontal coordinate equal to 0 represents the point with $x_k = 17$. The six other points in

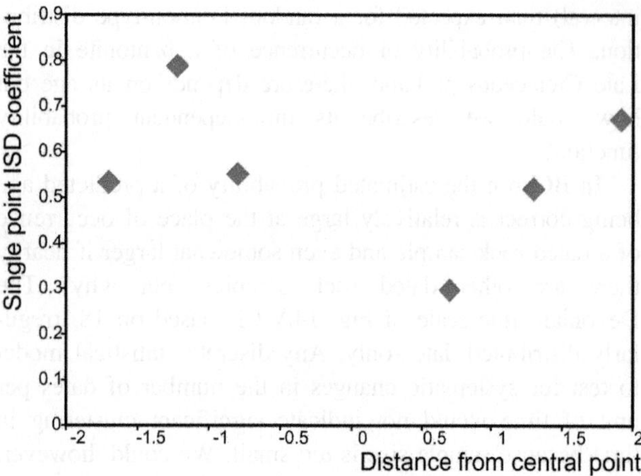

FIGURE 14A.3 Example of coefficients derived for quadratic power-law model connecting age determination with $x = 17$ to its three neighbors along the relative stratigraphic scale on each side (older and younger). Average coefficient of these six values is shown at point with Dev1 in Fig. 14A.2.

Fig. 14A.3 represent the three closest neighbors at either side of x_k. In order to reduce edge effects the series of 18 age determinations was enlarged at both the base and top of the Devonian using the end point reflection technique often used in time series analysis. If there would be no clustering of x_k values, all values c_{ik} would be realizations of the same random variable and independent of choice of x_k value with its neighbor's x_{ik}.

Averages of c_k values within selected neighborhoods would also be the same if the points would occur randomly. The average of the six c_{ik} values shown in Fig. 14A.3 is $c_k = 0.657$. Fig. 14A.4 shows similar average c_k values for all 18 x_k values. Standard deviations for all 18 6-point samples of relative ages were computed and multiplied by ± 1.96 to estimate 95% confidence limits for these average

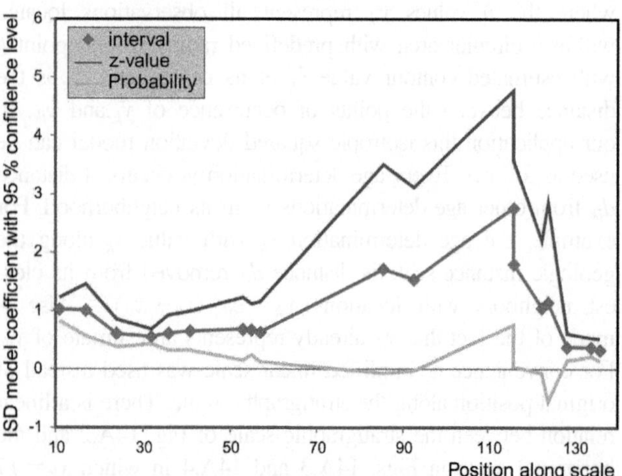

FIGURE 14A.4 Estimated coefficients for separate applications of quadratic power-law model at every sampling point along the relative geologic time scale with 95% confidence interval.

c_k values, which are also shown in Fig. 14A.4. Clearly there are significant differences between these values. It is noted that the version of the inverse square distance model used here is only applicable within relatively narrow neighborhoods. For x_k values within clusters of sampling points, wider neighborhoods could have been used; on the other hand, the choice of three neighbors on each side can be too wide for more isolated data points as illustrated by some points with unrealistic negative lower 95% confidence interval values shown in Fig. 14A.4. It can be concluded from the preceding exercise that the assumption of existing significant clustering in time of Devonian ages is reasonable. This tentative conclusion was confirmed to some extent in the following one-dimensional (1D) application of hot spot analysis.

14A.4.2 Hot spot analysis

Hot spot analysis (see, e.g., Getis and Ord, 1992) is widely applied by geographers to enhance two-dimensional (2D) patterns of random variables that exhibit spatial clustering. Typical examples are counts (x_{ij}) of occurrences (e.g., cases of a specific disease or accidents) for small areas (e.g., counties). Originally, the technique was based on Moran's I statistic for spatial correlation. It led to the Getis $G_i(d)$ statistic that satisfies:

$$G_i(d) = \frac{\sum_{j=1}^{n} w_{ij}(d)x_j}{\sum_{j=1}^{n} x_j}, \quad j \text{ not equal to } i,$$

where $\{w_{ij}\}$ is an asymmetric one/zero spatial weight matrix with ones for all links defined as being within distance d of a given i, all other links being zero (cf. Getis and Ord, 1992). Setting $W_i = \sum_{j=1}^{n} w_{ij}(d)$ it can be shown that the expected value of $G_i(d)$ and its variance satisfies:

$$E[G_i(d)] = \frac{W_i}{n-1}; \quad \sigma^2[G_i(d)] = \frac{W_i(n-1-W_i)Y_{i2}}{(n-1)^2(n-2)Y_{i1}^2}$$

where E denotes mathematical expectation, σ^2 is variance,

$$Y_{i1} = \frac{\sum_{j=1}^{n} x_j}{n-1}; \quad \text{and } Y_{i2} = \frac{\sum_{j=1}^{n} x_j^2}{n-1} - Y_{i1}^2.$$

Although this technique was developed for 2D applications, it can be used in 1D as well. We simply have to think of a rectangular area in 2D that is being compressed onto a 1D line segment. It implies that all distances between points become positive. Assuming that $G_i(d)$ is approximately normally distributed, the standard normal random variable becomes:

$$Z_i = \left\{ G_i(d) - \frac{E[G_i(d)]}{\sigma[G_i(d)]} \right\}$$

In the application to the relative age locations along the x-axis of Fig. 14A.2, weights for all distances less than 6.0 were set equal to 1, and all other weights were

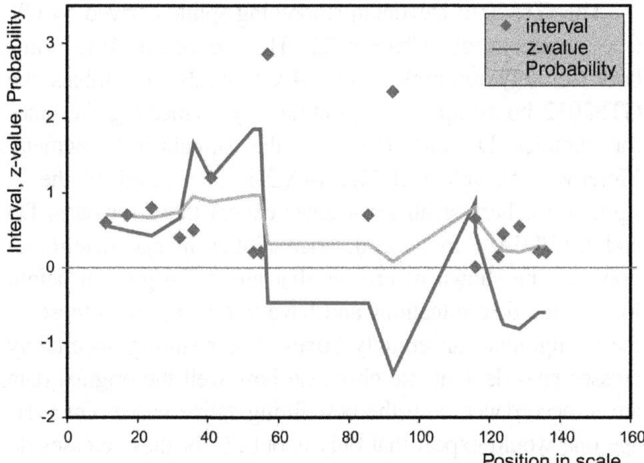

FIGURE 14A.5 Results of 1D hot spot analysis. Local neighborhoods of the age determination locations were used to estimate *z*-values, which are shown together with their standard normal probabilities. *1D*, One-dimensional.

set equal to zero. Application of the preceding equations then results in the *z*-values graphically shown in Fig. 14A.5. Locally these *z*-values almost reach the 95% confidence limit. It is noted that in Fig. 14A.5 the same vertical scale is used for different quantities. As in the previous exercise that resulted in Fig. 14A.4, the possibility of clustering of ages along the horizontal scale is indicated. It is noted that anticlustering locally is statistically significant at the 0.05 level of significance in the vicinity of the Givetian where density of age determinations is at its lowest. Later (see Section 14A.5.1) this fact will be used to modify the width of the 95% confidence belt on the best fitting smoothing spline. It is also noted that the *z*-values and probabilities in Fig. 14A.5 show downward trends at the beginning and the end. These are end point effects that could have been reduced to some extent by application of the 1D end point reflection technique used to construct Fig. 14A.4.

14A.4.3 Clustering of ash beds

It seems worthwhile to recognize age clustering as a third source of uncertainty (in addition to the radioisotopic 2-sigma error and stratigraphic uncertainty) and to incorporate it in the time scale construction procedure. Of course, this is already done automatically when BChron is used. This procedure would involve relatively increasing the weights for age determinations occurring within clusters as will be done in Section 14A.5.5.

It seems that the local maximal precision estimates coinciding with single dates or clusters of observed dates in the BChron solution would suggest that the positions of the samples that were taken are somehow special. It is better to consider the positions of the samples within the periods not as special but as purely random although these positions are probably subject to some clustering in time.

14A.5 Modifications in GTS2020

Essentially, statistical treatment of GTS2020 age data for Paleozoic periods or two successive periods is similar to the methodology described in Sections 14A.2.2 for treatment of Paleozoic age determinations in GTS2004 and in Section 14A.3.5 for treatment of the GTS2012 Devonian age data. A major difference between the Ordovician–Silurian and Carboniferous–Permian age databases contrary to the Devonian database is that there are many more age determinations that are more or less equally spaced and without significant (listed) stratigraphic uncertainty. This improvement of the radioisotopic database is noticeable at the boundaries between periods at which different methods were employed to construct the stratigraphic scales. Incorporation of some dates from neighboring older or younger periods can help to overcome problems of this type provided that stratigraphic scales at both sides of a period boundary are constructed by means of the same method. In GTS2004 such discrepancies at stage boundaries were eliminated by the rather imprecise method of "ramping." Estimation of the ages of the Paleozoic stage boundaries will be based on smoothing splines obtained by means of the *R smooth-spline* technique with CV. Successive spline curves fitted to different data sets may result in two slightly different ages for the same period boundary. Two age estimates then can be combined with one another by computing their weighted average as discussed in the next section.

14A.5.1 Combining dates at the same stratigraphic level

Suppose that y_i and y_{i+1} are two successive values with the same x-value. Their approximate 95% confidence interval can be written as $2 \cdot \sigma(y_i)$ and $2 \cdot \sigma(y_{i+1})$. From these two values the weights of the two observations can be computed as $w_i = 1/\sigma^2(y_i)$ and $w_{i+1} = 1/\sigma^2(y_{i+1})$. The sum of these two weights can be written as $w(x) = w_i + w_{i+1}$ where x represents location of both y_i and y_{i+1} along the x-axis. The same procedure can be followed when more than two dates have the same value of x. If there are two dates only, their weighted average is:

$$y_x = \frac{w_i y_1 + w_{i+1} y_{1+1}}{w(x)}.$$

Again, the same procedure can be followed if there are more than two dates with the same value of x. Application of this procedure to the GTS2020 age determinations for the Devonian reduces the total number of dates from 31 to 19.

The preceding statistical procedure also can be used for combining two different estimates at a series boundary. For example, the spline curves for the Devonian and the Carboniferous–Permian produced slightly different estimates for base Tournaisian (358.8 ± 0.7 and 359.9 ± 0.4 Ma, respectively). The weighted average of these two estimates (359.3 ± 0.3 Ma) is probably the best estimate of the age of the base of the Carboniferous. It is somewhat closer to 359.9 Ma with less uncertainty than 358.8 Ma.

14A.5.2 Smoothing splines

In our GTS2020 applications use was made of the *R*-program *smooth-spline* as implemented by B.D. Ripley and M. Maechler in *R*.Stats Package version 3.6.0, with uncertainties based on total variances $s_t^2(y)$ instead of on $s^2\ (y)$ gave the result shown in Fig. 14A.2. This program is freely available on the Internet and widely used. Originally, the technique used now was based on code in the GAMBIT FORTRAN program by Hastie and Tibshirani (1990) using a smooth-spline function similar to the one described in Chambers and Hastie (1992).

The default application in *R smooth-spline* is application of a technique called generalized CV (GCV). This technique was originally introduced by Wahba (1985) as a possible refinement of leaving-one-out CV. Differences between CV and GCV are discussed by Wang (2011). Usually the two methods give approximately the same results. However, in several of our applications to Paleozoic data sets, CV provided better results than GCV. This is because it is more robust in situations that relatively many points along the *x*-axis are close together or coinciding, even after application of the weighted average method described in the previous section. In such situations, CV produces a smooth curve, whereas the GCV result may reduce to a set of straight-line segments connecting neighboring points. Best fitting smooth curves were obtained by CV in all Paleozoic applications. Because of scarcity of dates for the Devonian, the spline curve for this period has more uncertainty associated with it than the spline curves for the other periods.

It is noted that in some of our *smooth-spline* applications the initial output contained a warning that results (automatic *smooth-spline* estimation of CV) were not necessarily accurate because locally one or more successive *x*-values were equal or nearly equal to one another. In such situations, we have combined successive values (with the same position along the stratigraphic axis) with one another so that the *smooth-spline* warning sign would disappear. The method used to combine successive values was explained in the previous subsection.

The GTS2020 Devonian smoothing spline derived by CV (see Becker et al., Chapter 22: The Devonian Period, this book) closely resembles Fig. 14A.2. It also resembles the GTS2012 bootstrap spline modified by connecting the dates for samples D7 and D9 with the straight-line segment. Moreover, the spline of Fig. 14A.2 is intersected by the 2-sigma error bars of all input dates except those for dates D5 and D13/D14A. In general, uncertainties in age determinations can be shown as crosses that are ± 2-sigma in height for the age determinations and have widths equal to those of the stratigraphic uncertainty boxes. The resulting uncertainty crosses provide a simple check on how well the original data are in accordance with the best fitting spline curve. On average one would expect that only about 5% of these crosses do not intersect the curve. This simple approximate goodness-of-fit test will be passed by all GTS2020 Paleozoic period spline curves fitted by us but not for the Early Cretaceous spline as will be discussed later in this chapter.

Curve fitting for the other Paleozoic periods is rather straightforward in that various techniques (smoothing spline, polynomial regression, or LOESS) yield more or less the same solution. Moreover, 2-sigma values for successive age determinations are similar and it is possible to interpolate between these values to obtain reasonably good estimates of the 95% confidence intervals for the estimated stage boundary ages.

14A.5.3 Application to the Ordovician–Silurian

As previously for GTS2012 constrained optimization (CONOP) values for graptolites in the Ordovician and Silurian periods were obtained by Peter Sadler for GTS2020 (cf. Section 14A.2) as a basis for time scale estimation on a scale from 1 to 100 composite units. CONOP scale duration of the two periods is about 85 composite units. Similar data are available for Ordovician conodonts. The combined duration of these two periods is about 68 Myr. Thus one composite unit is equivalent to about 0.8 Myr. As for GTS2012, smoothing splines were obtained by relating the dates for both periods combined with one another to the CONOP values. Numbers of dates used were 51 for the Ordovician and Silurian graptolites and 24 for the Ordovician conodonts. For both Ordovician–Silurian graptolites and Ordovician conodonts, the number of dates for which CONOP values are available exceeds the number of dates in Table 14A.2.

The best fitting spline curves for graptolites and conodonts are shown in Figs. 14A.6 and 14A.9, respectively. Spline-curve estimates of the Ordovician and Silurian stage boundaries are shown in Table 14A.2. In the period chapters the same spline curves are shown along with the error bars for the age determinations (Fig. 20.15C in Goldman et al., Chapter 20: The Ordovician Period, this book). Results for the Ordovician and Silurian graptolites were

TABLE 14A.2 Estimates of Ordovician–Silurian stage boundary ages.

	Graptolites		Conodonts	
Base of Stage	Spline	2-sigma	Spline	2-sigma
Lochkovian	419.00	1.77		
Pridolian	422.73	1.62		
Ludfordian	425.01	1.53		
Gorstian	426.74	1.47		
Homerian	430.62	1.32		
Sheinwoodian	432.93	1.24		
Telychian	438.59	1.05		
Aeronian	440.49	0.99		
Rhuddanian	443.07	0.91		
Hirnantian	445.21	0.86	446.16	1.63
Katian	452.75	0.73	452.98	1.45
Sandbian	458.18	0.73	458.76	0.79
Darriwilian	469.42	0.93	470.40	0.71
Dapingian	471.26	0.98	473.93	0.90
Floian	477.08	1.17	478.72	1.21
Tremadocian	486.45	1.53	487.20	1.83

accepted for GTS2020. The results for conodonts shown in Fig. 14A.9 were not used for GTS2020. Two-sigma values for the stage boundaries (also shown in Table 14A.2) were estimated in two steps. First, approximate 95% half-confidence limits were estimated for the spline curve for graptolites according to the method to be explained in Section 14A.5.5 for the Devonian where the approach will be taken a step further to account for probable lack of ash layers in the Givetian. It is noted that in the spline-curve fitting every age determination was weighted according to the inverse of its variance, which is the square of its sigma value. These weights are shown in Fig. 14A.7. The 95% half-confidence interval for the Ordovician and Silurian graptolites is shown in Fig. 14A.8.

CONOP values for graptolites and conodonts in the Ordovician–Silurian are not directly comparable with one another, because time scales based on them are significantly different as can be seen from Figs. 14A.6 and 14A.9 in which the spline curves have different shapes. However, both spline-curve values for CONOP values of graptolites and conodonts provide stage boundary age estimates for the same single event and, therefore, could be averaged by combining the two separate uncertainty estimates with one another in a second step. A method for this type of averaging can be based on elementary statistical theory. It differs from the weighted average calculation procedure presented in Section 14A.5.1. The overall mean value for stage boundary estimates satisfies:

$$\overline{y} = \frac{n_g \cdot \overline{y_g} + n_o \cdot \overline{y_o}}{n_g + n_o}$$

where n_g and n_o are numbers of dates for graptolites and conodonts representing weights for the two age estimates ($\overline{y_g}$ and $\overline{y_o}$) for any stage boundary. The corresponding 2-sigma values then can be derived from the sample variances for graptolites and conodonts that can be written as s_g^2 and s_o^2, respectively. The 2-sigma value of the overall mean value follows from the pooled variance that satisfies:

$$s^2 = \frac{(n_g - 1)\cdot s_g^2 + (n_o - 1)\cdot s_o^2}{n_g + n_o - 2}.$$

Table 14A.2 shows separate estimates of Ordovician stage boundaries only. It could be assumed that averaging the stage boundary estimates obtained by two different methods for the Ordovician provides better estimates than those obtained by using time scales based on graptolites and conodonts separately. However, conodont uncertainties are significantly larger than graptolite uncertainties and it was decided to base the GTS2020 Ordovician–Silurian time scale on graptolites only as was done for GTS2012.

14A.5.4 Application to the Devonian

At several locations GTS2020 age data for the Devonian have two or more age determinations with the same values (and their uncertainties) along the stratigraphic scale (x-axis). The reason for this is that at these locations more than one a single ash layer was sampled. More than one y-value with the same x-value can present a problem for some techniques of curve fitting. For example, in BChron output, strong and rapid fluctuations that are not realistic may arise near such locations. In spline-curve fitting with CV, which is our preferred method for time scale construction, successive points along the x-axis are connected by cubic polynomials that each have four coefficients. Obviously, a cubic polynomial cannot be estimated when two successive ages have the same x-value. The R smooth-spline program attempts to take care of situations of this type but issues a warning that the final smoothing spline is not necessarily correct. In order to avoid possible problems of this type, we have computed weighted averages for Devonian age determinations with the same x-value (Fig. 14A.10) according to the method given in Section 14A.5.1. The resulting spline curve for Devonian is in Fig. 22.14 of Chapter 22, The Devonian Period (this book).

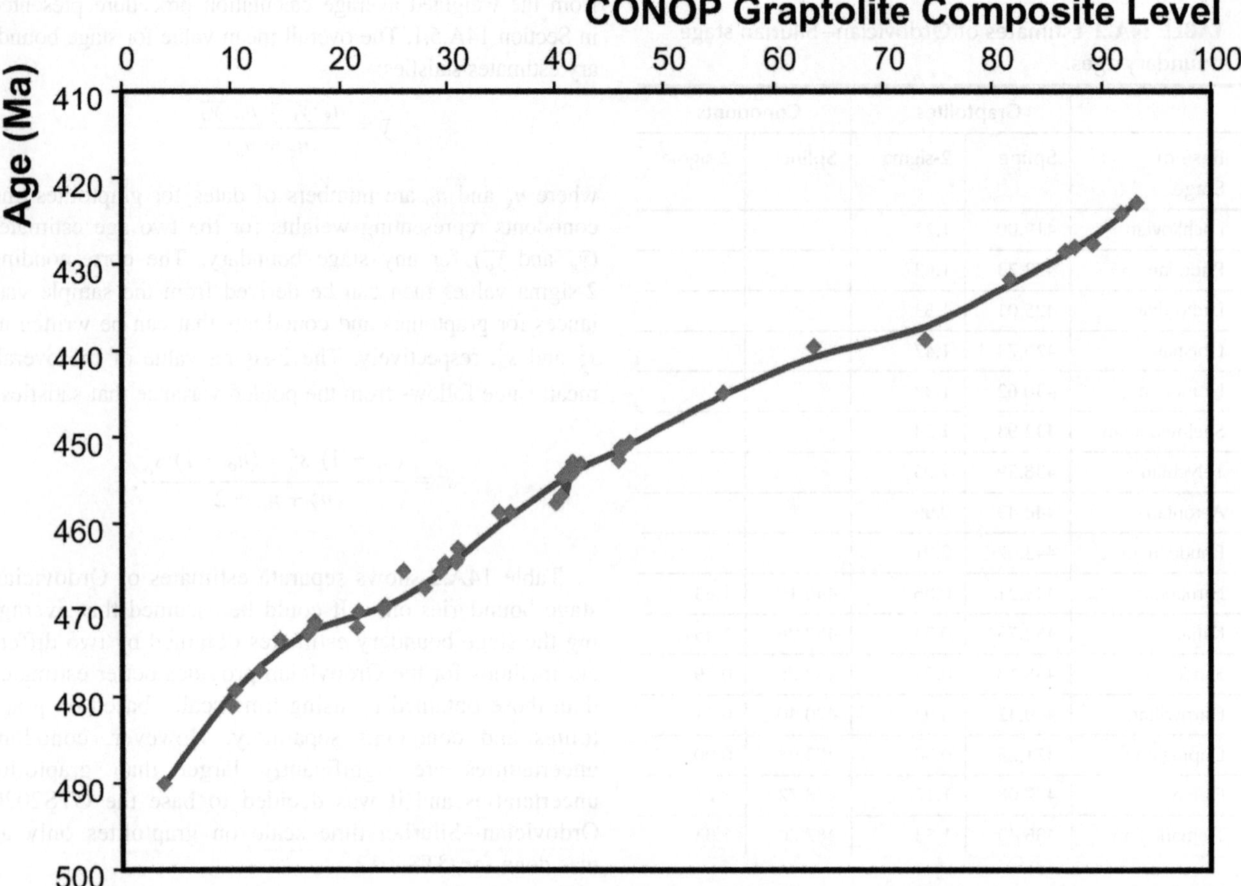

FIGURE 14A.6 Best fitting spline curve for the composite of the Ordovician–Silurian graptolite ranges and events.

It is noted that the Devonian spline curve that was fitted to the input data gave estimated ages of 358.7 and 420.6 Ma for top and base of the Devonian, respectively. However, these two estimates deviate slightly from estimates obtained by means of spline fitting for the Carboniferous–Permian (cf. Fig. 14A.12) and Ordovician–Silurian (cf. Table 14A.2).

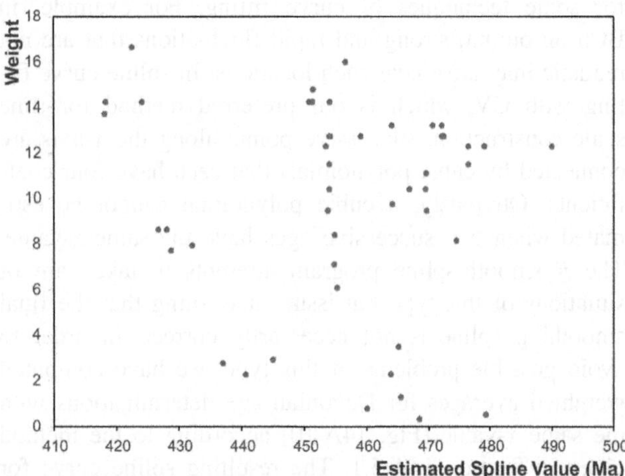

FIGURE 14A.7 Weights of Ordovician-Silurian graptolite age dates as a function of estimated spline values.

By using the method of averaging two different estimates for the same stratigraphic event, the estimated age for top of the Devonian was revised to 359.3 Ma. The final GTS2020 age and error for Silurian–Devonian boundary value (419.0 ± 1.8 Ma) is taken from the Ordovician–Silurian data and spline fit, using a more updated data set for Ludfordian–Pridoli stage intervals than used in the slightly earlier "crunched" Devonian ages (Brad Cramer, pers. comm. to F. Gradstein, August 2019).

As shown in Section 14A.4, some clustering of GTS2012 Devonian dates along the x-axis (or y-axis) probably exists. For example, the lack of bentonite layers between upper Eifelian and lower Frasnian is probably real. For this reason an approximate method can be used to obtain 95% confidence intervals for the estimated stage boundary ages shown in Fig. 14A.11. Although the Devonian spline curve is not a straight line, the deviations from this curve at the sampling point locations may be assumed to maintain equal variance along the line. Fig. 14A.10 shows the 19 Devonian weights plotted against the estimated smoothing spline value. The best fitting straight line in this diagram is almost horizontal indicating that the weights are approximately constant during the entire Devonian period.

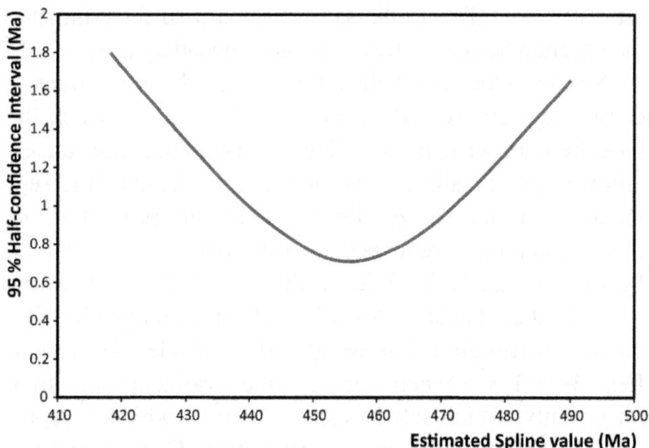

FIGURE 14A.8 Two-sigma values for estimated spline-curve for Ordovician-Silurian graptolites shown in Figure 14A.6.

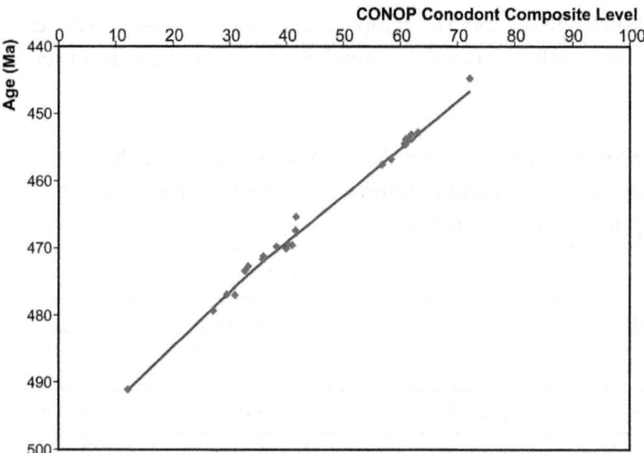

FIGURE 14A.9 Best-fitting spline-curve for the composite of Ordovician-Silurian conodont events and ranges.

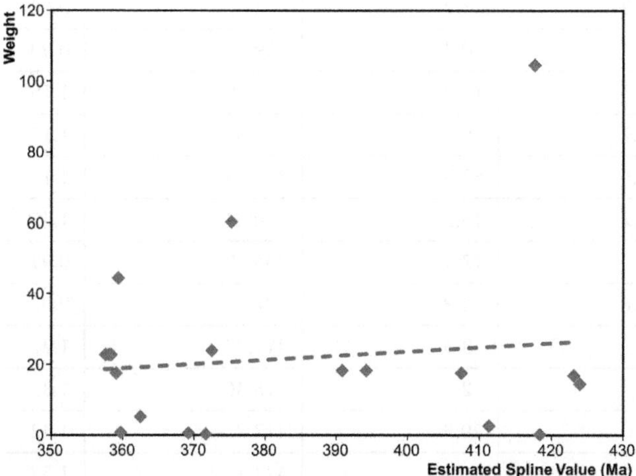

FIGURE 14A.10 Weights of Devonian dates as a function of estimated spline values.

14A.5.5 New approximate Devonian 95% confidence interval

As mentioned before, the procedure of Paleozoic time scale construction followed in GTS2004 was based on the idea that a plot of the observed age determinations against the estimated spline ages is approximately according to a straight line with the simple equation $y = x$. This procedure is equivalent to the method originally used by McKerrow et al. (1985) and Cooper (1999). The 95% confidence belt for this line at any point (x_k, y_k) satisfies:

$$y_k \pm t(n-2) \cdot s_e \sqrt{1 - R_k}$$

where

$$R_k = (1/n) + \left(\left\{x_k - \left(\sum x_k/n\right)\right\}^2 / \sum\left(\left(x_k - \left(\sum x_k/n\right)\right)^2\right)\right)$$

(cf. Agterberg, 1974, Equation 8.31).

The total number of observations $n = 19$ and Student's t (17) = 2.11. There are two ways in which the standard deviation s_e can be calculated: weighted or unweighted. In the weighted method, which is to be preferred, every age determination is weighted according to the inverse of its variance. In the unweighted method, all age determinations are given equal weights. In the current application the weighted method was used. Fig. 14A.11 shows the 95% half-confidence belt for the Devonian as a solid line. The same procedure was used for the Ordovician–Silurian graptolite graph shown in Fig. 14A.6. For the Devonian the approach is taken one step further to account for the probable variations in density of sampling points in this period.

Suppose that m_k for point k is the number of other observations within a time interval of 10 Myr. The maximum number of other observations within a time interval of 10 Myr is $\max(m_k) = 7$. Density of observations for point k can be set equal to $d_k = m_k/\max(m_k)$. The reciprocal of is measure of

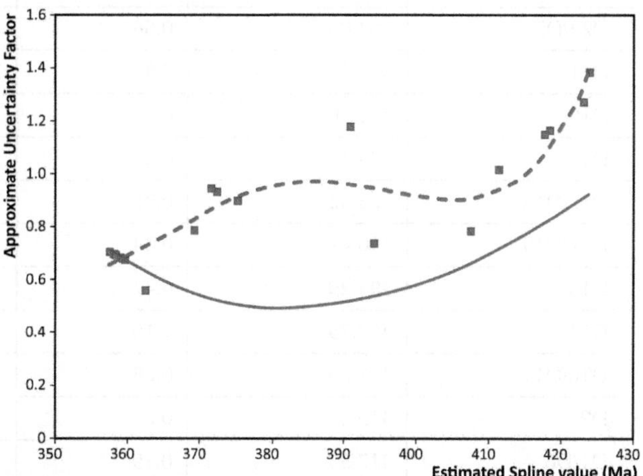

FIGURE 14A.11 Approximate uncertainty factor used to widen 95% confidence belt incorporating changes of density of dates along the Devonian time scale.

density provides a measure of sparseness of observations at any data point. Dividing the values of the 95% half-confidence interval results in the values shown in Fig. 14A.11 as solid squares. These values fall approximately on the broken line also shown in this figure. This broken line provides approximate 95% confidence intervals for the estimated ages of the GTS2020 Devonian stage boundaries shown in Table 14A.1. In addition to the increases in uncertainty toward top and base of the Devonian, Fig. 14A.11 also shows more uncertainty at top and bottom of the Givetian where there is a relative lack of age determinations. The preceding procedure for the Devonian remains approximate and speculative because of lack of information.

Table 14A.3 shows a comparison of the GTS2020 Devonian age determinations with their estimated spline values. The weights (*W*) in this table were determined by both the original 2-sigma values of the age determinations and the stratigraphic uncertainties as explained previously. Age determinations with the same position along the stratigraphic scale were averaged, which involved relative weight increases. The uncertainties ($2\sigma'$) of the spline values were estimated according to the same method used for estimating the uncertainties of the Devonian stage boundary ages.

Stratigraphic uncertainty for the age determinations is commonly represented as a rectangular box of which the base here is written as q. For the Devonian this uncertainty is graphically represented as a horizontal line segment with length q. From statistical properties of the rectangular frequency distribution summarized in Section 14A.2.1, it follows that $q = 3.48 \cdot s_q(x)$ where $s_q(x)$ is the standard deviation of this rectangular frequency distribution. The weight (*W*) in Table 14A.3 satisfies $W = 1/s_t^2$ where s_t^2 is the variance of total uncertainty, which satisfies $s_t^2 = s^2 + s_q^2$ in which s^2 represents variance of the age determination. Consequently, q can be derived from $s_q^2 = W^{-1} - s^2$. Stratigraphic uncertainty will also be considered in this way for the Early Cretaceous (Table 14A.4). It is noted that in Table 14A.3 and similar tables, in which original age determinations or averages of age determinations with the successive data points along the stratigraphic axis are compared with estimated spline values, the weights *W* are significantly different

TABLE 14A.3 Columns 1–3 list the latest Silurian through earliest Carboniferous radioisotopic age dates with their 2-sigma uncertainties for calculation of the Devonian geologic time scale, and columns 4–7 list the corresponding estimated spline values and ages; $2\sigma'$ represents estimated spline value uncertainty.

Sample number and Radioisotopic Age			Spline used for GTS2020			
No.	Age (Ma)	2σ	x-Axis	weight	Age (Ma)	$2\sigma'$
CB3	357.26	0.42	356.9	15.4	357.57	0.87
CB2	358.43	0.42	357.9	17.4	358.07	0.85
CB1	358.71	0.42	358.5	21.1	358.35	0.85
D27	358.89	0.48	360.1	15.4	359.05	0.84
D25/D26	359.11	0.3	360.7	38	359.34	0.84
D24	361.3	2.4	361.3	0.5	359.68	0.83
D22/D23	363.06	0.88	365.2	3.2	362.42	0.68
D21	367.7	2.8	374	0.4	369.23	0.98
D19	372.36	0.41	377.6	13.9	372.49	1.15
D20	374.2	4.2	376.7	0.2	371.64	1.16
D17/D18	375.32	0.26	380.5	52.3	375.25	1.1
D14/D15	390.47	0.34	395.2	18.2	390.84	1.45
D13	394.29	0.47	397	17.1	394.19	0.91
D12	407.75	1.16	403.8	2.9	407.52	0.97
D10/D11	411.64	0.88	408	3.3	411.38	1.27
D9	415.6	0.8	412	2	418.36	1.37
D1/D8	417.53	0.19	415	29.5	417.7	1.42
S8	422.91	0.49	421.8	9.4	423.1	1.57
S7	424.08	0.53	423.3	11	423.93	1.72

from one another. However, unless the spacing between successive points along the stratigraphic axis is markedly uneven as for the Devonian, estimated spline values are relatively insensitive to differences in *W*. The estimated spline values then are not significantly different from those obtained after setting are weights *W* equal to one.

14A.5.6 Application to the Carboniferous–Permian

The input data for the Carboniferous and Permian differ from those of the earlier Paleozoic periods in that uncertainties are much smaller. Fig. 14A.12 (also shown in Fig. 23.8 of Chapter 23: The Carboniferous Period, this book) shows that the best fitting spline curve almost exactly follows the input data. For this reason the original 2-sigma values where accepted to express the 95% confidence limits of the estimated ages on the spline curve as well.

Table 14A.4 shows a comparison of the GTS2020 Carboniferous–Permian age determinations with their estimated spline values. The weights (*W*) in this table were determined by both the original 2-sigma values of the age determinations. In comparison with other periods there is relatively little difference between the age determinations and the spline values. Uncertainties of Carboniferous–Permian stage boundary age estimates in GTS2020 were determined by the original 2-sigma values of the age determinations.

14A.5.7 Application to the Early Cretaceous

Spline fitting as applied to Paleozoic periods in GTS2020 was also used to help obtain the GTS2020 Cretaceous time scale. The critical factor for the Early Cretaceous scale in GTS2020 is that a rather high-resolution U–Pb radioisotopic and cyclostratigraphic data set is now available for the Tithonian through Barremian, which is quite different than the values used during the construction of GTS2012 (see discussions in Chapter 5: Geomagnetic Polarity Time Scale, and in Chapter 27: The Cretaceous Period, this book).

Fig. 14A.13 is a plot of radioisotopic dates against mid-km M-sequence magnetic anomaly distances that span ca. 1200 km in total (see Table 5.4 in Chapter 5: Geomagnetic Polarity Time Scale, this volume). In order to incorporate stratigraphic uncertainty, $s(x)$ was estimated for each distance value (x) by multiplying its sigma value

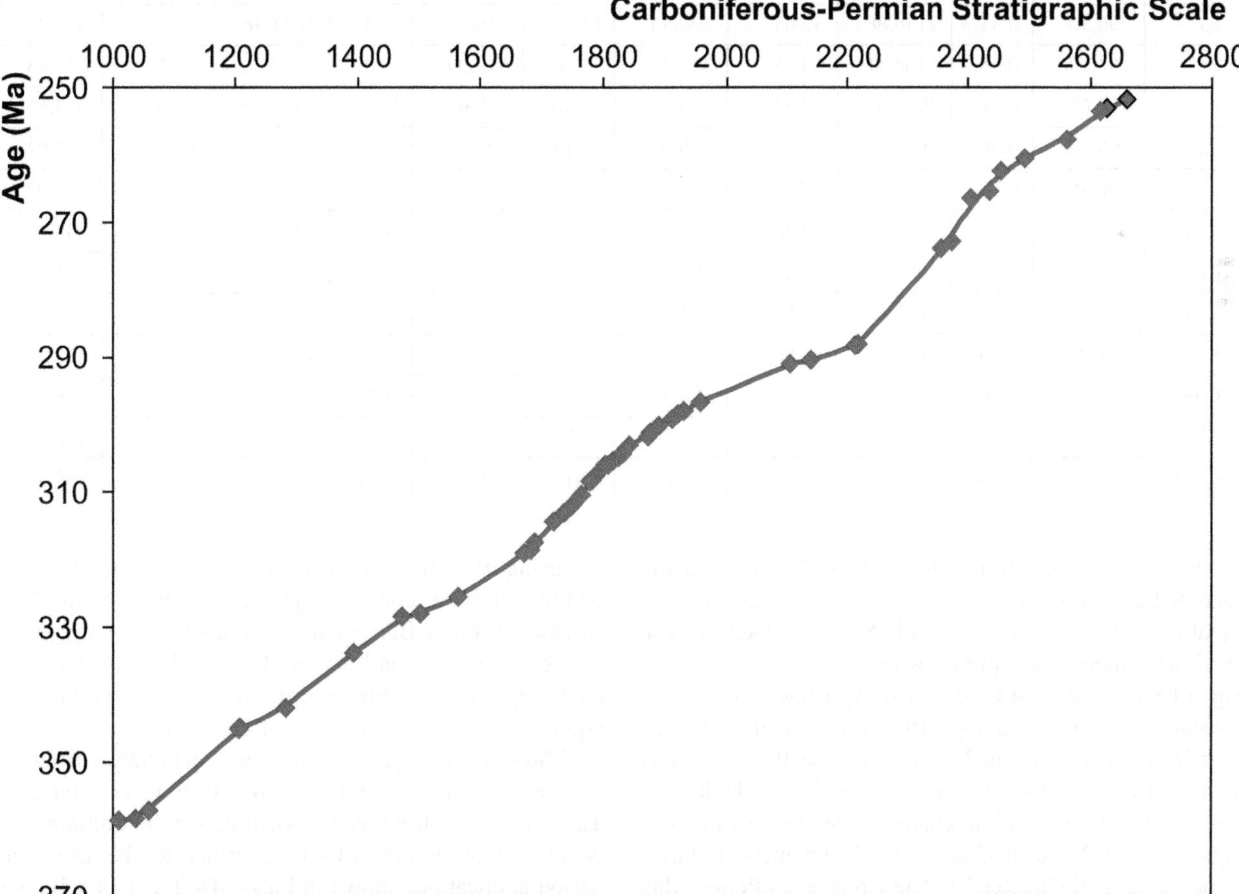

FIGURE 14A.12 Best-fitting spline-curve for the Carboniferous-Permian.

TABLE 14A.4 Comparison of composite standard age determinations for the Carboniferous–Permian with estimated spline values.

Radioisotopic age			Spline			Radioisotopic age			Spline		
No.	Age (Ma)	2σ	x-axis	Weight	Age (Ma)	No.	Age (Ma)	2σ	x-axis	Weight	Age (Ma)
P37	251.94	0.28	2658.97	51.02	251.81	CB40	304.83	0.36	1823.94	30.86	304.72
P24	253.24	0.45	2627.25	19.75	253.31	CB38	305.51	0.39	1815.63	26.22	305.36
P23	253.60	0.29	2616.07	47.56	253.92	CB37	305.95	0.37	1808.17	29.22	305.96
P22	257.79	0.31	2561.00	41.62	257.38	CB36	305.96	0.36	1803.58	30.86	306.35
P17	260.57	0.31	2493.70	41.62	260.59	CB35	307.66	0.37	1787.42	29.22	307.84
P16	262.45	0.37	2455.10	29.22	262.98	CB33	308.36	0.38	1781.19	27.70	308.47
P14	265.46	0.39	2435.07	26.30	264.68	CB32	308.50	0.36	1778.65	30.86	308.73
P13	266.50	0.37	2405.00	29.22	267.80	CB30	310.55	0.38	1764.26	27.70	310.24
P11	272.90	0.34	2374.00	34.60	271.84	CB29	312.01	0.37	1749.94	29.22	311.74
P9	274.00	0.34	2354.18	34.60	274.37	CB28	312.23	0.37	1746.73	29.22	312.07
P8	288.21	0.34	2218.44	34.60	288.04	CB27	313.16	0.37	1736.65	29.22	313.08
P7	288.36	0.35	2213.92	32.65	288.29	CB24	314.40	0.37	1719.12	29.22	314.77
P6	290.81	0.35	2133.26	32.65	290.66	CB23	317.54	0.38	1688.24	27.70	317.65
P5	290.50	0.35	2138.88	32.65	290.56	CB21	318.63	0.40	1681.38	25.00	318.23
P4	291.10	0.36	2104.31	30.86	291.22	CB20	319.09	0.38	1670.76	27.70	319.13
P3	296.69	0.37	1956.62	29.22	296.69	CB18	325.64	0.40	1563.00	25.00	325.58
P2	298.05	0.56	1931.16	12.76	298.04	CB14	328.14	0.40	1501.14	25.00	327.87
P1	298.49	0.37	1921.55	29.22	298.57	CB12	328.48	0.41	1472.00	23.80	328.97
CB47	299.22	0.37	1912.24	29.22	299.10	CB10	333.87	0.39	1392.63	26.30	333.87
CB46	300.22	0.35	1889.68	32.65	300.43	CB6	342.01	0.41	1281.96	23.80	341.58
CB45	301.29	0.36	1876.25	30.86	301.25	CB5	345.00	0.40	1208.19	25.00	345.27
CB44	301.82	0.36	1873.47	30.86	301.42	CB4	345.17	0.41	1206.37	23.80	345.39
CB43	303.10	0.36	1842.09	30.86	303.41	CB3	357.26	0.42	1059.84	22.68	356.94
CB42	303.54	0.39	1837.87	26.30	303.70	CB2	358.43	0.42	1037.63	22.68	358.10
CB41	304.49	0.36	1830.75	30.86	304.21	CB1	358.71	0.42	1010.44	22.68	359.16

by the ratio of total time interval (=47.8 Myr) and the span of 1200 km in order to make use of the total variance equation: $s_t^2(y) = s^2(x) + s^2(y)$ (cf. Section 14A.2.1). The resulting smoothing spline, which is also shown in Fig. 14A.13, is almost exactly a straight line representing constant seafloor spreading. The corresponding weights $w_t = 1/s_t^2(y)$ are given in Fig. 14A.14 and the deviations themselves are shown in Fig. 14A.15. These deviations are very small. The spline curve in Fig. 14A.13 (also in Figs. 5.4 and 27.10 of Chapter 5: Geomagnetic Polarity Time Scale, and Chapter 27: The Cretaceous Period, this book) is approximately a straight line with the equation $y = 0.0372x + 122.77$, a result that can also be obtained by using the method of ordinary least squares. This would imply a constant spreading rate for the Late Jurassic through Barremian portion of the M-sequence. Degree of fit for this line could not be improved significantly by including higher order terms in the polynomial equation fitted by the method of least squares.

Mid-km M-sequence magnetic anomaly distances assigned to stage boundaries are given in column 2 of Table 14A.5 with the corresponding ages in column 3. It is noted that in Fig. 14A.13 contrary to the Devonian period applications shown in Figs. 14A.2 and 14A.10, and similar figures for the other Paleozoic period applications, relatively many uncertainty crosses do not intercept the

TABLE 14A.5 Callovian–Cenomanian spline-curve age estimates adjusted for Milanković-based stage duration estimates. Final age estimates, 2-sigma values and revised stage durations are provided in last three columns.

		M-Sequence Spline			Cycles Spline			Final Age		
Base of Stage	M-Sequence Distance (km)	Spline Age	2-Sigma	Duration	Milankowić cycle duration (Myr)	duration-2	Age-2	Revised Age	2-Sigma	Revised duration
Cenomanian		~100.5	0.14				100.5	100.5	0.1	
Albian		~113.1	0.3	12.6	12.45	12.84	113.34	113.2	0.3	12.7
Aptian	0	122.77	0.9	9.67	8.1	8.35	121.69	121.4	0.9	8.2
Barremian	120	127.23	0.78	4.46	5	5.16	126.85	126.5	0.8	5.1
Hauterivian	198	130.13	0.72	2.9	5.93	6.12	132.96	132.6	0.7	6.1
Valanginian	347	135.67	0.63	5.54	5.06	5.22	138.18	137.7	0.6	5.1
Berriasian	523	142.21	0.62	6.54	5.27	5.43	143.62	143.1	0.6	5.4
Tithonian	701	148.82	0.71	6.61	5.67	5.85	149.46	148.9	0.7	5.8
Kimmeridgian	845.2	154.18	0.84	5.36	5.2	5.36	154.83	154.8	0.8	5.9
Oxfordian	1013.69	160.44	1.03	6.26	5.8	5.98	160.81	160.8	1	6
Callovian	1082.58	163	1.11	2.56	3	3.09	163.9	163.9	1.1	3.1

After final stratigraphic evaluation selected uncertainties were slightly decreased. See text in Chapter 27, for further explanation.

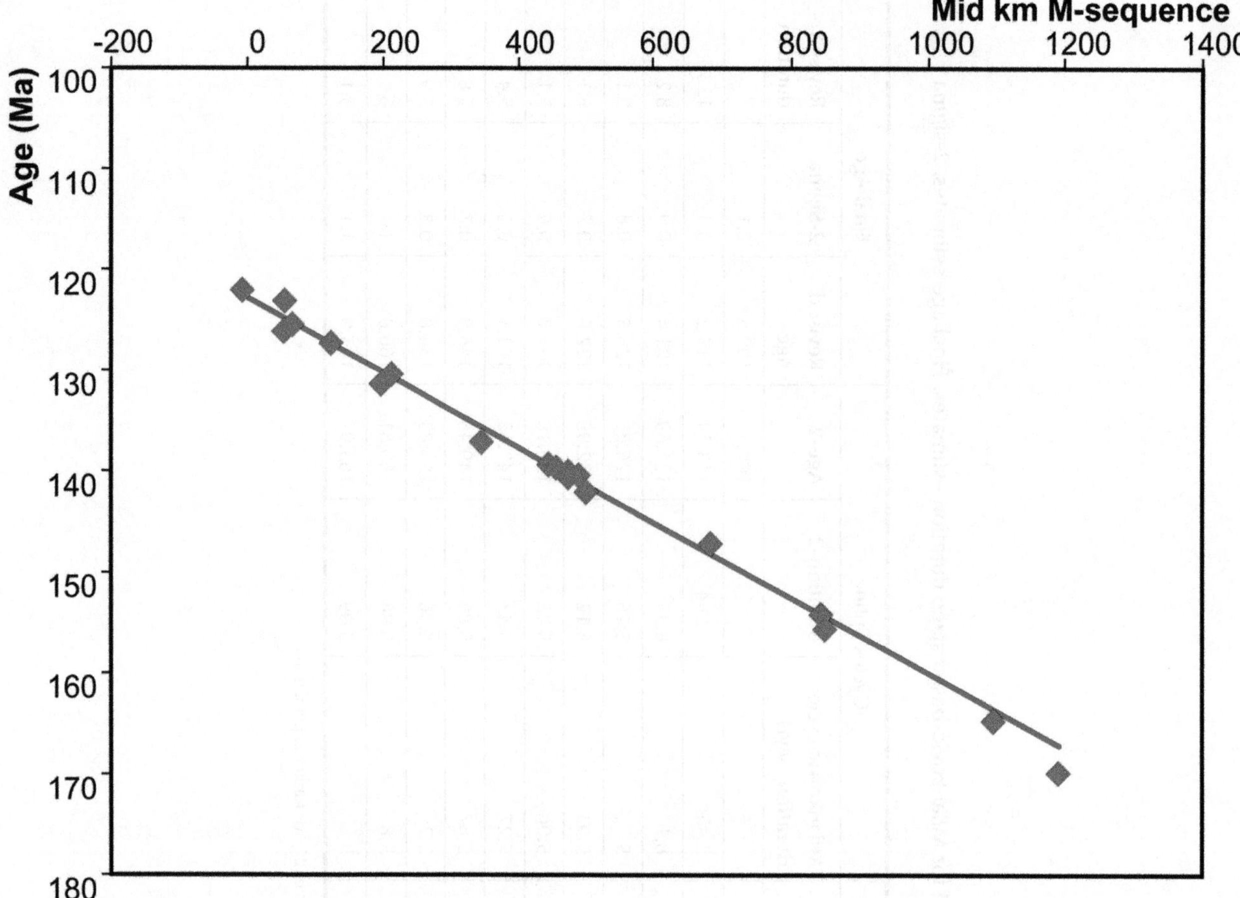

FIGURE 14A.13 Best fitting spline curve for the Early Cretaceous.

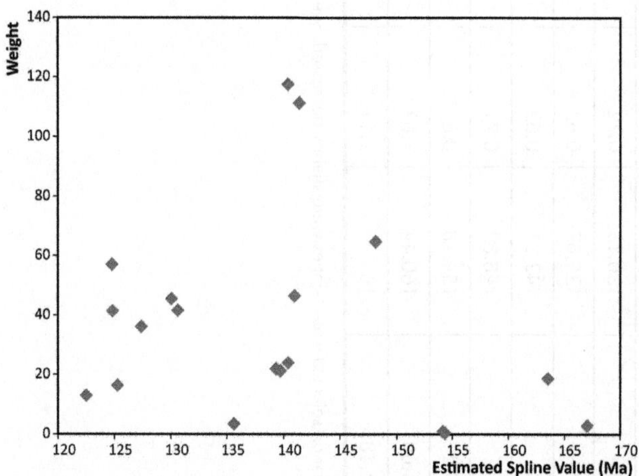

FIGURE 14A.14 Weights of Early Cretaceous dates as a function of estimated spline values.

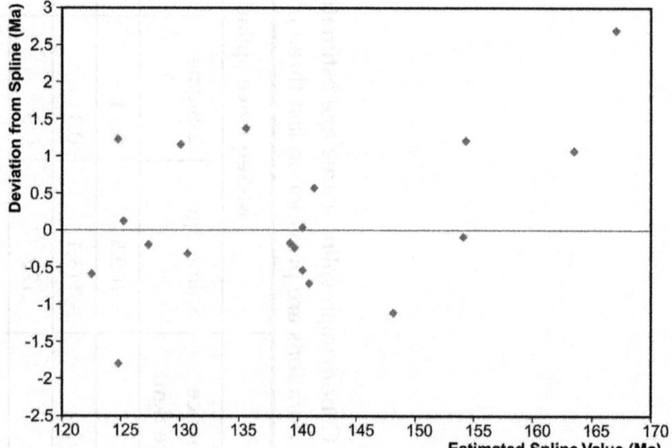

FIGURE 14A.15 Deviations of input ages from spline curve of Fig. 14A.13.

best fitting cubic spline curve. A probable explanation of this fact is that the reported 2-sigma values of the age determinations are systematically too low. Nearly all uncertainties in the mid-km M-sequence magnetic anomaly values are negligibly small. In GTS2004 Appendix 3 (Agterberg, 2004) it was pointed out that, if all standard deviations of the dependent variable all too small by a factor *c*, the estimates of the two coefficients of the best fitting straight line remain unbiased. It is only that their standard deviations, and their covariance, are underestimated by the factor *c*. The doubly hyperbolic 95%

TABLE 14A.6 Comparison of marine magnetic anomaly M-sequence age determinations with estimated spline values; $2\sigma'$ represents estimated spline value uncertainty.

M-sequence			Spline		
M-sequence (km)	Age (Ma)	2σ	Weight	Age (Ma)	$2\sigma'$
−4.9	122.01	0.52	12.96	122.60	0.52
57	123.10	0.30	41.51	124.90	0.51
68.5	125.45	0.43	16.39	125.33	0.51
55.8	126.07	0.25	56.98	124.86	0.51
125.5	127.24	0.25	36.16	127.45	0.51
198	131.29	0.25	45.48	130.15	0.51
213.5	130.39	0.25	41.59	130.72	0.51
347	137.05	1.00	3.54	135.69	0.53
447.8	139.24	0.16	22.03	139.44	0.56
457.7	139.55	0.18	21.24	139.81	0.56
476.9	139.96	0.17	24.02	140.53	0.57
491.8	140.34	0.18	46.55	141.08	0.58
476.3	140.51	0.16	117.59	140.50	0.57
500	146.48	1.63	1.48	141.50	0.58
503	142.04	0.17	111.37	141.39	0.58
684.7	147.11	0.18	64.71	148.26	0.68
845.2	154.10	2.10	0.90	154.23	0.80
851	155.60	0.89	0.49	154.45	0.80
1097.9	164.64	0.27	18.74	163.63	1.05
1193.3	169.80	1.15	3.01	167.18	1.17

confidence interval on the best fitting straight line also would be biased (by the factor *c*). In order to avoid this problem and to obtain 2-sigma values of the stage base estimates, we have followed the simple alternative method described previously (see section on estimation of approximate 95% Devonian confidence interval) by assigning equal weights to all data points plotted in Fig. 14A.13.

Already Kent and Gradstein (1985) in their Cretaceous and Jurassic geochronology study for the Decade of North America Geology publications arrived at constant and linear spreading of the M-sequence as a reasonable template to interpolate the Oxfordian through Barremian time scale. Despite use of few tie points for the age versus M-sequence km plot, the Jurassic–Cretaceous boundary was interpolated by Kent and Gradstein (1985, 1986) at 144 Ma, although they used a different working definition for that period boundary. This is only slightly older than current proposed placement of that boundary relative to the M-sequence, which would project to an age of 142.3 Ma from the direct spline fit of radiometric dates to magnetic anomalies and final 143.1 ± 0.6 Ma after adjusting for astronomical tuning of stage durations used in GTS2020.

Although the patterns of 2D distribution of points in Figs. 14A.14 and 14A.15 are similar to patterns obtained for Paleozoic periods, including the Devonian, the slightly different procedure (using the unweighted deviations from the spline curve shown in Fig. 14A.15) was used for estimating the 95% confidence limits of the estimated Early Cretaceous stage boundary ages. As pointed out before, unweighted deviations from the spline were used instead of weighted deviations because the 2-sigma values for the dates are probably underestimated. Table 14A.5 contains estimated spline ages for Aptian to Callovian stage bases for which mid-km M-sequence values were available along with their estimated 2-sigma values and the corresponding durations.

In the next three columns of Table 14A.5 durations according to the spline curve are compared with Milanković-based duration estimates. Although the spline ages are probably unbiased estimates of the true ages, the Milanković durations are probably better estimates of stage durations. Much

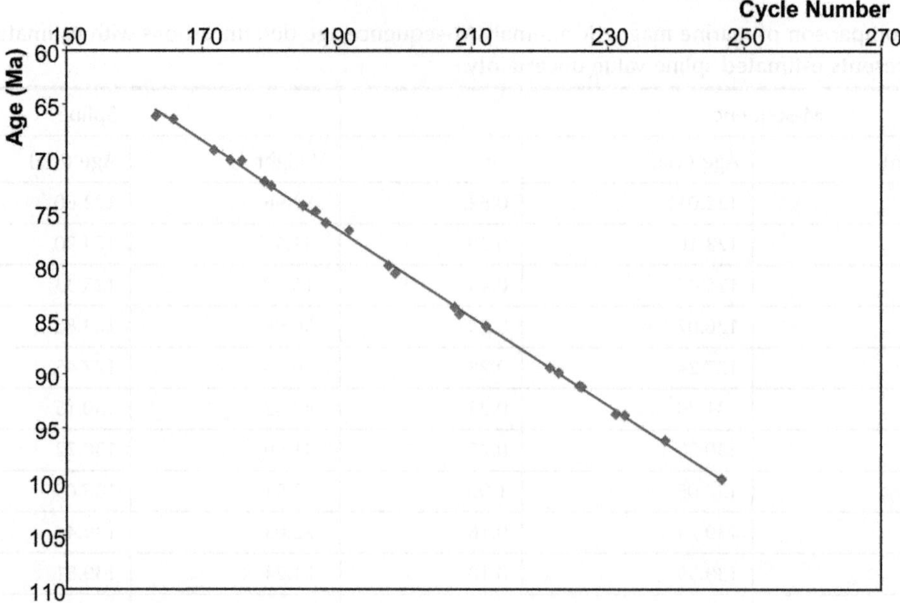

FIGURE 14A.16 Best fitting spline curve for the Late Cretaceous.

of the astronomical tuning of Aptian–Albian time has been based on the Piobbico core drilled into pelagic and hemipelagic strata in the Umbria–Marche Apennines, central Italy. Although the Albian duration using cycles of 12.45 ± 0.5 Myr has been verified by radioisotopic dating, the same is not the case for the Aptian. In GTS2012 the published duration of 13.3 Myr (Huang et al., 2010) is now being contested and a shorter duration of 8.1 ± 0.5 Myr is considered more likely and is adhered to in GTS2020 (see discussions in Ogg, Chapter 5: Geomagnetic Polarity Time Scale, and in Gale et al., Chapter 27: The Cretaceous Period, this book).

Sums of durations from the Albian to the Callovian in Table 14A.5 are 63.4 Myr (spline durations) and 61.5 Myr (M-durations), respectively. The difference between these two sums of durations is 1.9 Myr. Assuming that the Albian and Callovian spline-based age estimates are unbiased, the M-durations can be corrected so that their sum also becomes 63.4 Myr. The resulting ages are shown in the Age-2 column of Table 14A.5. However, when the summation is carried out from the Albian to the Oxfordian (instead of from the Albian to the Callovian), the spline age interval becomes 48.3 Myr and the difference between sums of duration is reduced to 0.84 Myr. Assuming that this estimate is unbiased, the M-durations can be adjusted so that their sum becomes 48.3 Myr as well. The corrected Milanković cycle-durations then can be used to estimate stage base age estimates between the Albian and the Oxfordian. These adjusted estimates together with the previously obtained estimates for the Kimmeridgian, Oxfordian, and Callovian are shown as final age estimates

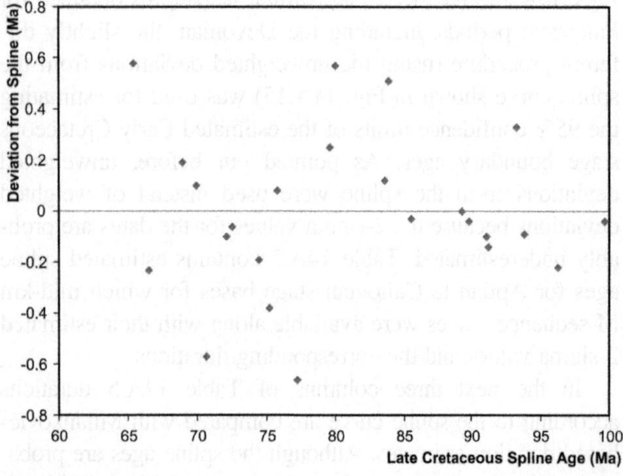

FIGURE 14A.17 Deviations of Late Cretaceous dates (Table 14A.7) as a function of estimated spline values.

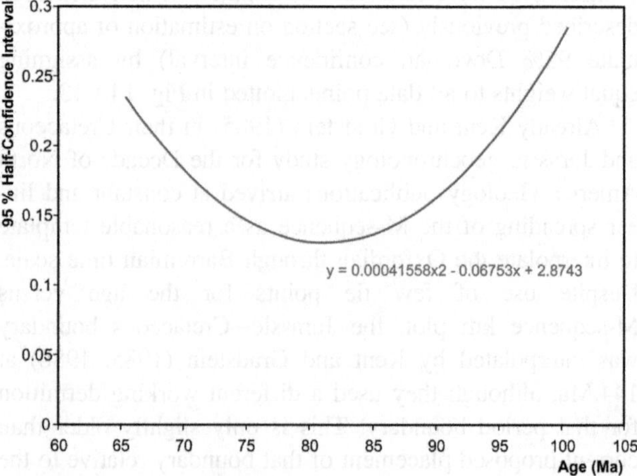

FIGURE 14A.18 Two-sigma values for estimated spline curve of the Late Cretaceous shown in Fig. 14A.6.

TABLE 14A.7 Comparison of Late Cretaceous cycle age determinations with estimated spline age values; $2\sigma'$ represents estimated spline value uncertainty.

Cycles			Spline	
Cycle Value	Age (Ma)	2σ	Age (Ma)	$2\sigma'$
163.18	66.04	0.05	65.46	0.25
165.8	66.31		66.54	0.23
171.8	69.19		69	0.2
174.2	70.08		69.98	0.19
176	70.15		70.72	0.18
180.5	72.5		72.56	0.16
179.5	72.05		72.15	0.17
187	74.85	0.43	75.23	0.14
185.2	74.3		74.49	0.15
188.5	75.92		75.84	0.14
192	76.62		77.28	0.13
197.8	79.9		79.65	0.13
198.8	80.63		80.06	0.13
207.5	83.75		83.63	0.13
208.2	84.43	0.15	83.92	0.13
212.2	85.53	0.35	85.56	0.14
221.5	89.37	0.37	89.37	0.16
222.8	89.86	0.26	89.9	0.16
225.9	91.07	0.28	91.17	0.17
226.2	91.15	0.26	91.29	0.18
231.2	93.67	0.31	93.34	0.2
232.5	93.79	0.26	93.88	0.2
238.5	96.12	0.31	96.34	0.24
246.8	99.7	0.3	99.74	0.29

After final stratigraphic evaluation selected spline uncertainties were slightly revised. See text in Chapter 27, The Cretaceous Period, for further explanation.

in Table 14A.5 along with the original spline-based 2-sigma values and the corresponding revised durations.

Table 14A.6 shows a comparison of the GTS2020 Early Cretaceous age determinations with their estimated spline values. The weights (*W*) in this table were determined by both the original 2-sigma values of the age determinations and the uncertainties of the mid-km M-sequence magnetic anomaly values. Spline values for the ages of the stage boundaries were modified by accounting for the Milanković cycle-durations. However, this revision that incorporated astronomical-tuned durations for the Berriasian through Barremian stages required another application of the spline-fit procedure to smooth the spreading rates for the M-sequence magnetic anomaly suite (Fig. 5.5 in Chapter 5: Geomagnetic Polarity Time Scale, this volume); and that revised M-sequence age model (Table 5.4 in that chapter) was used for the Middle Jurassic through Early Cretaceous in this book.

TABLE 14A.8 Estimates of the ages of the Late Cretaceous stage boundaries along with their uncertainties, using the spline data in Table 14A.7.

Base of Stage	Age	2-sigma
Danian	66.04	0.05
Maastrichtian	72.15	0.17
Campanian	83.63	0.13
Santonian	85.68	0.14
Coniacian	89.37	0.16
Turonian	93.88	0.2
Cenomanian	100.5	0.14

14A.5.8 Application to the Late Cretaceous

Age determinations for the Late Cretaceous could be correlated with Milanković cycles as shown in Fig. 14A.16 (see Fig. 27.11 in Chapter 27: The Cretaceous Period, this book). A number of dates for which C-sequence and cycle input was available did not have reported 2-sigma values (Table 14A.7) and all dates plotted in Fig. 14A.16 were given equal weights for the spline fitting. The best fitting spline curve is approximately a straight line. Fig. 14A.17 shows the deviations from this spline, which are small. The quadratic 95% half-confidence interval based on these differences is given in Fig. 14A.18 along with its mathematical equation. Spline-curve estimates of the ages of the stage boundaries are listed in Table 14A.8 along with their uncertainties.

The ages and 2-sigma values of base Danian (66.04 ± 0.05 Ma) and base Cenomanian (100.50 ± 0.14 Ma) in Table 14A.7 are not based on the spline curve, because they were determined by other methods as explained in (Chapter 27, The Cretaceous Period, this book). These estimates differ from the spline-curve estimates for the two boundaries, which are 65.43 ± 0.23 and 100.50 ± 0.29 Ma, respectively. The age of base Cenomanian falls slightly outside the range of the Milanković cycle values used for the spline in Fig. 14A.16. However, the quadratic equation of the curve in Fig. 14A.18 was used to derive a spline-based 2-sigma estimate ($=0.29$ Myr) comparable with the 2-sigma values for the other Late Cretaceous stage boundaries of which the ages are also shown in Fig. 27.11 of Chapter 27, The Cretaceous Period (this book).

It is noted that, like in the previous subsection for the Early Cretaceous, the procedure used to estimate the 95%

half-confidence interval is based on the deviations between the input dates and the spline curve, rather than on weights based on the published 2-sigma values of the input dates. The reason for this is that for several of the input dates, the error bars do not intersect the spline curve indicating that, as in the previous subsection, precision of the age determinations was probably overestimated. As discussed in Section 14A.3.2 a similar problem was encountered previously for Paleozoic dates used for GTS2004 and GTS2008. However, for GTS2020 the 2-sigma values of the Paleozoic dates all conform with the 95% half-confidence intervals.

Table 14A.7 shows a comparison of the GTS2020 Late Cretaceous cycle age determinations with their estimated spline values. Weights for the spline fitting were set equal to 1 in this application. Spline values for the ages of the stage boundaries were modified by accounting for the Milanković-durations. Finalized stage boundary ages, combining cycle, radiometric, and C-sequence data are in Table 14A.8.

Bibliography

Agterberg, F.P., 1974, *Geomathematics*. Amsterdam: Elsevier, p. 596.

Agterberg, F.P., 1988, Quality of time scales – a statistical appraisal. *In* Merriam, D.F. (ed), *Current Trends in Geomathematics*. New York: Plenum, 57–103.

Agterberg, F.P., 1994, Estimation of the Mesozoic geological time scale. *Mathematical Geology*, **26**: 857–876.

Agterberg, F.P., 2002, Construction of numerical geological time scales. *Terra Nostra*, **04/2002**: 227–232.

Agterberg, F.P., 2004, Appendix 3: Geomathematics. *In* Gradstein, F.M., Ogg, J.G., and Smith, A.,G. (eds), *A Geologic Time Scale 2004*. Cambridge University Press, 485–486.

Cantrell, C.A., 2008, Technical note: review of methods for linear least-squares fitting of data and application to atmospheric chemistry problems. *Atmospheric Chemistry and Physics*, **8**: 5477–5487.

Chambers, J.M., and Hastie, T.J., 1992, *Statistical Models in S*. London: Wadsworth and Brooks/Cole, p. 608.

Cooper, R.A., 1999, The Ordovician Time Scale – calibration of graptolite and conodont zones. *Acta Universitatis Carolinae Geologica*, **43** (1/2), 1–4.

Cox, A.V., and Dalrymple, G.B., 1967, Statistical analysis of geomagnetic reversal data and the precision of potassium-argon dating. *Journal of Geophysical Research*, **72** (10), 2603–2614A.

De Vleeschouwer, D., and Parnell, A.C., 2014, Reducing th0me-scale uncertainty for the Devonian by integrating astrochronology and Bayesian statistics. *Geology*, **42** (6), 491–494.

Getis, A., and Ord, J.K., 1992, The analysis of spatial association by use of distance statistics. *Geographical Analysis*, **24** (3), 189–206.

Gradstein, F.M., Agterberg, F.P., Ogg, J.G., Hardenbol, J., van Veen, P., Thierry, T., et al., 1994, A Mesozoic time scale. *Journal of Geophysical Research*, **99** (B12), 24051–24074.

Gradstein, F.M., Agterberg, F.P., Ogg, J.G., Hardenbol, J., van Veen, P., Thierry, T., et al., 1995, A Triassic, Jurassic and Cretaceous time scale. *In* Berggren, W.A., Kent, D.V., Aubry, M.-P., and Hardenbol, J. (eds), Geochronology, Time Scales and Global Stratigraphic Correlations: A Unified Temporal Framework for a Historical Geology. *Society for Sedimentary Geology Special Publication*, **54**: 95–128.

Gradstein, F.M., Ogg, J.G., and Smith, A.G. (eds), 2004. A Geologic Time Scale 2004. Cambridge University Press. Cambridge.

Gradstein, F.M., Ogg, J.G., Schmitz, M.D., and Ogg, G.M. (eds), 2012. The Geologic Time Scale 2012. Elsevier. Amsterdam.

Haslett, J., and Parnell, A., 2008, A simple monotone process with application to radiocarbon-dated depth chronologies. *Applied Statistics*, **57** (4), 399–418.

Hastie, T.J., and Tibshirani, R.J., 1990, *Generalized Adaptive Models*. London: Chapman and Hall, p. 328.

Harland, W.B., Cox, A.V., Llewellyn, P.G., Pickton, C.A.G., Smith, A. G., and Walters, R., 1982, *A Geologic Time Scale*. Cambridge: Cambridge University Press, p. 131.

Harland, W.B., Armstrong, R.L., Cox, A.V., Craig, L.A., Smith, A.G., and Smith, D.G., 1990, *A Geologic Time Scale 1989*. Cambridge: Cambridge University Press, p. 263.

Howarth, R.J., and McArthur, J.M., 1997, Statistics for Strontium isotope stratigraphy: a robust LOWESS fit to the marine Sr-isotope curve for0 t0 206 Ma, with look-up table for derivation of numeric age. *Journal of Geology*, **105**: 441–456.

Huang, C., Hinnov, L., Fischer, A.G., Grippo, A., and Herbert, T., 2010, Astronomical tuning of the Aptian Stage from Italian reference sections. *Geology*, **38**: 899–902.

Kent, D.V., and Gradstein, F.M., 1985, A Cretaceous and Jurassic geochronology. *Geological Society of America Bulletin*, **96**: 1419–1427.

Kent, D.V., and Gradstein, F.M., 1986, A Jurassic to Recent geochronology. *In* Vogt, P.R., and Tucholke, B.E. (eds), *The Geology of North America. Vol. M, The Western North Atlantic Region*. Boulder, CO: Geological Society of America, 45–50.

Lybanon, M., 1984, A better least-squares method when both variables have uncertainties. *American Journal of Physics*, **52**: 22–26.

McKerrow, W.S., Lambert, R.S.J., and Cocks, L.R.M., 1985, The Ordovician, Silurian and Devonian Periods. *In* Snelling, N.J. (ed), The Chronology of the Geological Record. *Geological Society of London, Memoir,* **10**: 73–80.

Obradovich, J.D., 1993. A Cretaceous time scale. *In* Caldwell, W.G.E., and Kaufman, E.G., (eds), Evolution of the Western Interior Basin. *Geological Association of Canada Special Paper*, **39**: 379–396.

Odin, G.S., 1994, Geologic Time Scale 1994. *Comptes rendus de l'Académie des Science de Paris, série II*, **318**: 59–71.

Ovtcharova, M., Goudemand, N., Hammer, Ø., Guodun, K., Cordey, F., Galfetti, T., et al., 2015, Developing a strategy for accurate definition of a geological boundary through radio-isotopic and Biochronological dating: the Early-Middle Triassic boundary (South China). *Earth-Science Reviews*, **146**: 65–76.

Pálfy, J., Smith, P.L., and Mortensen, J.K., 2000, A U-Pb and $^{40}Ar/^{39}Ar$ time scale for the Jurassic. *Canadian Journal of Earth Sciences*, **37**: 923–944.

Press, W.H., Teukolsky, S.A., Vettering, W.T., and Flannery, B.R., 1992, *Numerical Recipes in FORTRAN*. Cambridge: Cambridge University Press, p. 963.

Ripley, B.D., and Thompson, M., 1987, Regression techniques for the detection of analytical bias. *Analyst*, **112**: 377–383.

Wahba, G., 1985, A comparison of GCV and GNL for choosing the smoothing parameters in the generalized spline smoothing problem. *Annals of Statistics*, **4**: 1378–1402.

Wang, Y., 2011, *121. Smoothing Splines. Methods and Applications, Monographs on Statistics and Applied Probability*. Boca Raton, FL: CRC Press, p. 370.

SubChapter 14B

Global Composite Sections and Constrained Optimization

P. Sadler

Abstract

Stratigraphic information from a wide array of locations must be combined to mitigate incompleteness in local stratigraphic records, to capture the geographic distribution and diachronism of index taxon ranges, to amalgamate provincial biotic successions in different environments, and to encompass enough reliably dated events. Constrained optimization seeks a single succession of events to which all local sequences can be fit with minimum net adjustment of locally observed event horizons. This optimized composite sequence is constrained to honor any immutable superpositional relationships between event pairs established at local sections, such as taxon cooccurrences. The optimization proceeds by iterative improvement to find the best fit order of events. An objective function is chosen according to the desired properties of the emergent composite. It sums misfits between feasible composites and all the real local sections. Two nested optimizations are performed. The outer optimization finds the fittest global sequence of events, an ordinal composite sequence with no differentiation of interevent spacing. The inner optimization finds the most parsimonious adjustment of local event horizons to match the global sequence. The optimal spacing of events across all adjusted local sequences guides conversion of the ordinal composite to a scaled composite section on which age is then interpolated between dated events by curve-fitting techniques. The smoothing factor in LOWESS regression, for example, highlights the question of how closely the regression should track individual dated events or run more smoothly through the ensemble. This is the last in a series of assumptions and uncertainties that accumulate with each step in the time scale building process. Ideally, weaker assumptions enter at later stages. In particular, event spacing requires more questionable assumptions than event ordering.

14B.1 The geologic time scale challenge

One of the necessary first steps toward a geologic time scale (GTS) places a suite of fossil events in global order of occurrence, as determined from numerous local stratigraphic sections. Taxon originations and extinctions in the global succession of fossil organisms account for the majority these events (Fig. 14B.1). There order must be inferred from local appearances and extirpations. Other events to be placed in the time line include geomagnetic field reversals, rapid stable isotopic changes, and radioisotopic-dated ashfalls. The numerous biotic events cluster unevenly, recording rare intervals of mass extinction or rapid innovation. Historically, these clusters were used to divide the biotic succession into a series of named stratigraphic units. This step established a relative time scale and a vocabulary of named units for coarse global correlation (Berry, 1968). The final steps interpolate ages from the relatively few dated events in the succession to the conventional unit boundaries and key events in geologic history. Thus rate estimates become possible for past changes in the Earth's environment, landscape, and life. We shall explore several factors that render these steps particularly challenging: the huge volume of information, its geographic variability, its local incompleteness, and the relative paucity of dated events.

14B.1.1 Scope of the task

The volume of stratigraphic data relevant to the GTS can overwhelm even expert individuals. Consider the Ordovician and Silurian Periods. Successions of rich graptolite and conodont faunas allow local recognition of finely resolved biozones in basin and shelf environments. The continual compilation of local range charts for the early Paleozoic record of these two clades, since GTS2004 (Gradstein et al., 2004; Sadler et al., 2009, 2011), has now accrued records for 2651 graptolite taxa from 836 locations and 2196 conodont taxa from 1056 locations. The number of locally recorded taxon range ends and associated environmental change events is now 33,531 and 40,959, respectively, for these two databases (Fig. 14B.2)—a superb evidence base for reconstructing global biotic succession, but one requiring sophisticated numerical methods and computer assistance.

Dell et al. (1992) recognized that stratigraphic sequencing and correlation is a strongly "NP-hard" problem. This class of optimization task includes the classic traveling salesman problem. Computation time increases exponentially, or faster (Kemple et al., 1995), with the number of sections and taxa. It is not feasible to undertake an exhaustive examination of all possible sequences of events and yet the remedy is not to reduce the size of the database. Fortunately, several efficient search algorithms have been developed for this class of problem. To take advantage of one of these methods, simulated annealing, we map the GTS problem into the traveling salesman problem (Kemple et al., 1995). Cities on the salesman's route become events, geologic events; the number of them determines the scope of the problem. Distances between cities become local range-end adjustments; the sum to be minimized. The shortest route that visits every city once and only once emerges as the optimal geologic time line.

14B.1.2 Incomplete parochial records

It is generally not feasible to build a global GTS upon a few key stratigraphic sections. Most sections yield an incomplete sedimentary record (Sadler, 1981) and a less complete record of the ranges of fossil species (Marshall, 2010).

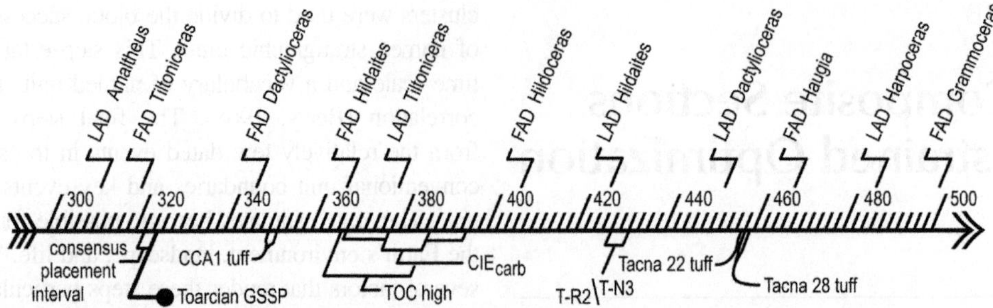

FIGURE 14B.1 Example components from a 200-event segment of an early Jurassic ammonite time line fitted to 10,033 local event records for 490 genera in 354 sections, worldwide. Events are uniformly spaced; taxon range-end events shown here above the line, with a few examples labeled. Other example events (labeled below the line): traceable ashfall tuffs (some dated); a stage-boundary GSSP; a consensus interval that represents the overlap of locally inferred stage boundary uncertainties; a magnetostratigraphic polarity reversal (T-R2\T-N3) interval; a peak in TOC; and a CIE consensus interval, with the onset and decline separated. *CIE*, Carbon isotopic excursion; *TOC*, total organic carbon.

Sediment accumulation is intermittent; organisms are patchy distributed; their preservation is uncertain and fossil collecting is imperfect. As a consequence, the sequence of recorded taxon appearances and extirpations varies from section to section, even within a single province. A suite of sections is desirable to compensate for many sources of incompleteness. Some sections enjoy rich preservation and closely spaced sampling but are inevitably restricted to a tiny part of a dynamic environmental mosaic. They are not globally representative. Many regions must be interrogated to capture the geographic scope and diachronism of taxon range limits. This inclusive approach is typically necessary to incorporate those few and disparate local sections that include dated events. Such sections must be incorporated whether or not they yield a rich fossil record.

There is a strong statistical argument in favor of composite sequences (Strauss and Sadler, 1989; Glazner and Sadler, 2016). For a uniform random distribution of n local samples within a local taxon range, the expected full taxon range $\overline{R}$ becomes increasingly larger than the observed range R_{obs} as n decreases (Fig. 14B.3).

$$\overline{R} = R_{\text{obs}}\left(\frac{n+1}{n-1}\right) \tag{14B.1}$$

Note that the denominator $(n-1)$ is the number of gaps between the finds that establish the observed range. The numerator $(n+1)$ adds two more gaps, one between the true appearance and the oldest find and the second between the youngest find and the true extirpation.

Eq. (14B.1) has discouraging implications for the correlation of range-end events. Because the collection success (n) varies between sections and taxa, it is unlikely that the sequence of reported range ends will match even between nearby sections. Truly coincident range ends are likely to be separated in the preserved record. False range-end coincidences will be created at richly fossiliferous levels and at

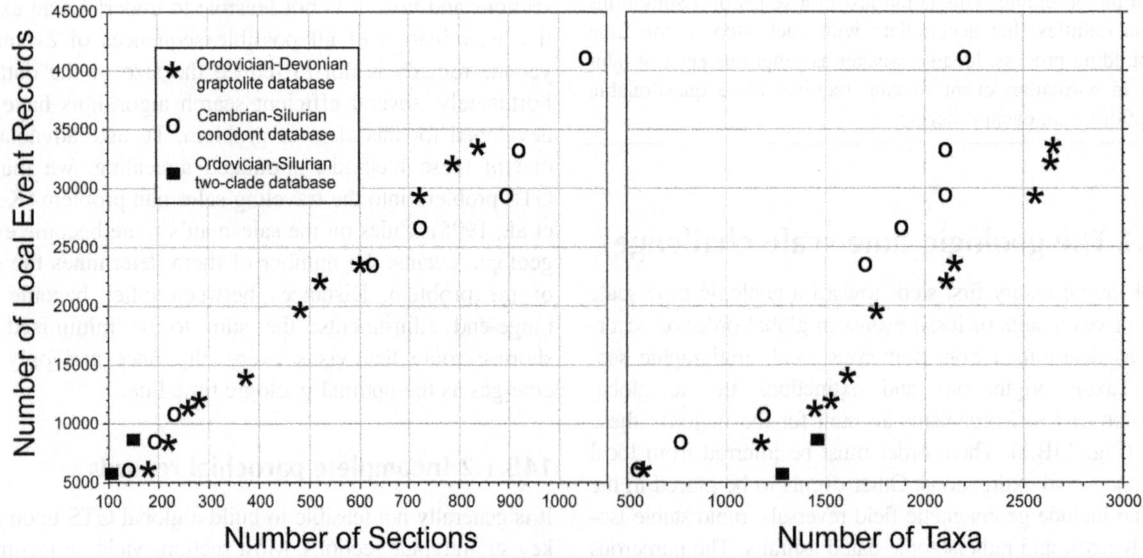

FIGURE 14B.2 Growth of graptolite and conodont databases compiled in support of the Ordovician and Silurian composite sections. The two-clade database is limited to sections from which taxa of both clades have been identified.

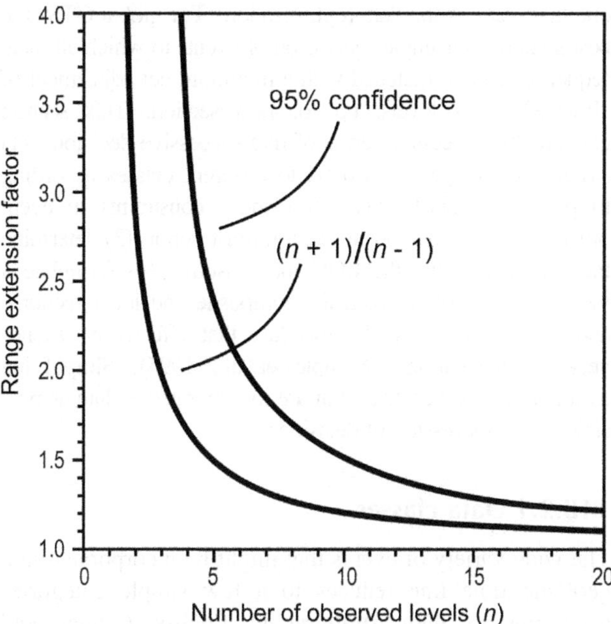

FIGURE 14B.3 Extension factors to correct observed ranges drawn through n random samples from the true range. Lower curve: the mean duration of true taxon ranges, expressed as a multiple of the observed range, that could be expected to yield the observed span of n occurrence levels. Upper curve: greater extension corrections needed to capture 95% of true ranges that could have yielded the n random finds.

hiatuses. The shortfall of the observed range duration may be greater than Eq. (14B.1) suggests, because fossils are not expected to be found uniformly with the taxon range. The abundance of a taxon is likely low near its first appearance and likely falls again near extirpation.

For a local taxon range based upon only a single sample, the expected range is unconstrained—the denominator in Eq. (14B.1) goes to zero. How do we instinctively determine whether a single local find indicates an abundant short-ranged taxon or a rare long-ranged taxon? We compare many localities. A composite section achieves this rigorously. In compensation for some uncertainties in correlation, the composite sequence increases n and with it our confidence in the sequence of range ends. With local information about the order and overlap of taxon ranges, various numerical methods are available to identify most likely sequences of range-end events (Tipper, 1988; Guex, 1991; Sadler, 2004; for summaries). Radioisotopic dates, paleomagnetic records, and stable isotope time series help narrow further the likely true sequences (Sadler, 2006, 2010).

14B.1.3 Optimized global composite sections

Early biostratigraphy and GTSs progressed (Berry, 1968) by combining information from multiple locations to improve resolving power and fidelity. A stack of successive biozones, derived from observations of the biotic succession in several stratigraphic sections, provides a composite ordinal scale into which dated events can be inserted subjectively. Interpolation on an ordinal scale is necessarily coarse, however, and the process becomes less satisfactory as the number and geographic scope of dated events increases, accelerated by the GSSP (Global Boundary Stratotype Section and Point) convention. It is preferable to build a composite section of taxon ranges and other events without the a priori inclusion of zone boundaries. Instead, zone boundaries can be identified subsequently in the emergent composite as they would be located in a local, but less complete, section.

One of the first numerically approaches to composite stratigraphic information at the taxon range-end scale was Shaw's (1964) graphic correlation (Mann and Lane, 1995; Shaw, 1995). Using a line of correlation (LOC) in a manner comparable to linear regression on two-axis graphs, Shaw built a scaled composite section by projecting new information, one section at a time, into the thickness scale of the best of the real local sections. The underlying assumption was that locally preserved and collected taxon ranges tend to be shorter than true regional or global ranges. Shaw's method has been widely adopted to compile regional and global composite sequences for graptolite ranges (e.g., Cooper and Lindholm, 1990; Grubb and Finney, 1995) and conodont ranges (e.g., Sweet, 1984, 1995, 2005; Kaufmann, 2006; Kleffner and Barrick, 2011). This iterative, two-dimensional approach quickly becomes unwieldy when dealing with dozens of sections, but some efficiency has been regained with computer-assisted versions (Hood, 1986; Fan and Zhang, 2000).

Several programs have been developed that build composite sections from larger data sets than is feasible by graphic correlation (Sadler et al., 2014). They treat information from all sections at once and differ according to the data they select and the question answered. Graphic correlation uses the local sequence and spacing of events and seeks, for each taxon, the earliest of the local first appearances and latest of the last appearances. Edwards's (1978) "no-space graphs" and the RASC (Ranking and Scaling) program (Agterberg and Nel, 1982; Agterberg and Gradstein, 1999) seek the sequence before attempting spacing, because that eliminates the complication of locally variable accumulation rates. Like graphic correlation, the no-space graphs seek the succession of extreme range end events—the biologic history. RASC uses locally observed pairwise sequencing of events and builds a composite succession from the most frequently observed of the two possible pairwise orders. In effect, it asks what the next real section will most likely yield. Other programs prefer to trust only those local observations that cannot be artifacts of underrepresented local ranges. The methods of unitary association (Guex, 1977, 1991; Savary and Guex, 1991; Monnet et al., 2011) and conjunction (Alroy, 1992) use observed coexistences. Appearance event ordination (Alroy, 1994) uses taxon pairs for which the first appearance of one precedes the last appearance of the other.

The core of the CONOP (constrained optimization) program (Kemple et al., 1989, 1995; Sadler et al., 2003) is a search algorithm. Its parameters may be set to mimic the logic and preferences of the programs mentioned previously. CONOP extends graphic correlation from two to as many dimensions as there are local sections (Kemple et al., 1995), thus, eliminating worries about the order in which sections are added. The preferred CONOP settings for time scale calibration effectively measure stratigraphic distance in the manner of no-space graphs and use the logic of unitary association and appearance event ordination to add constraints. The program has been successfully applied to biostratigraphic data from the Neoproterozoic (Riedman and Sadler, 2018) and Paleozoic (e.g., Hints et al., 2011; Rubel et al., 2006; Sadler and Sabado, 2009; Sadler et al., 2011; Shen et al., 2011; Webster et al., 2003), to the Cenozoic Era (e.g., Cooper et al., 2001; Cody et al., 2008; Daneshian et al., 2017). CONOP uses only taxon range ends.

14B.1.4 Two nested optimizations

If the fitness of a composite sequence is judged solely by how few taxon coexistences it implies, beyond those known from the local fossil records, only a single optimization is needed to minimize the excess implied coexistences. If fitness is judged by comparison with all local orderings of events, whether or not these could be an artifact of underrepresented ranges, optimization must be performed on two nested levels (Kemple et al., 1995). An outer optimization examines the relative fitness of numerous possible global sequences of events. The inner optimization returns the most parsimonious adjustment of observed event levels that brings each local section into alignment with the composite sequence. The outer (global) optimization is concerned only with the order of events, not their spacing. The inner (local) optimization arranges the record of these events on each local thickness or sampling scale and lays the foundation for subsequently scaling the intervals between events in a global composite section. Only the inner optimization needs to consider the complication that two or more events seem to occur at the same time; that is, they are placed at the same local stratigraphic level and any interval separating them is locally irresolvable (zero spacing).

14B.2 Constrained optimization of a composite section

CONOP solves problems by discarding illegitimate solutions (constraint), while exploring the remaining solution space for one that best fits the data (optimization). For global GTSs the best solution is a single succession of events to which all local sequences can be matched with a minimum net adjustment of observed event levels, up- or downsection. This section explains the process in terms of five successive decisions: (1) assign the stratigraphic events to different classes according to permitted adjustments; (2) identify constraints in event ordering that the composite section must honor; (3) determine the complexity that the LOC may assume; (4) formulate a measure of misfit between the composite and local sections; and (5) choose a search procedure that effectively reaches very good solutions (Kemple et al., 1995). Simplifying assumptions are necessary but are incorporated as late as possible in the succession of decisions.

14B.2.1 Data classes

The wide variety of events that might be incorporated in a geologic time line reduces to a few simple categories according to their stratigraphic fidelity (Sadler and Cervato, 2011); that is, the associated uncertainty in local position that determines their reasonable adjustment when fitting the local sequence to a global composite succession. The three most useful classes share some properties with jacks, clamps, and nails (Fig. 14B.4). By using these workshop names for the data classes, we can more readily appreciate how a locally observed sequence limits our degrees of freedom in the search for the best fit global sequence of events. The optimal sequence becomes the one that avoids pulling any nails and requires the least effort in adjusting all the jacks and clamps.

Taxon ranges dominate the available information. They are intervals between local first and last occurrences. The local ranges might approximate the duration of the true global range but are more likely shorter. They belong to the stretch-to-fit data class. The composite taxon range spans the interval where the taxon is known *anywhere*. Imagine the base (oldest find) and top (youngest find) of the local range as separated by a *jack*. At the cost of some effort the ends of the range may be jacked farther apart, increasing the local duration. The optimal global sequence minimizes the physical effort represented by all the jacks as they stretch local ranges to fit the global succession of range ends. Local first appearances may only adjust downsection and last appearances upsection. This is the operating principle of graphic correlation. Jacks may stretch a range end to the limit of the local section. No greater effort is then required to fit placements far beyond the age of the local section limit. In effect, range ends that coincide with the limits of a section do not limit the extent of the global composite range.

In the physical analogy, another class of data would be represented by a *clamp*. This class shrinks to fit. It includes uncertainty intervals that overestimate true

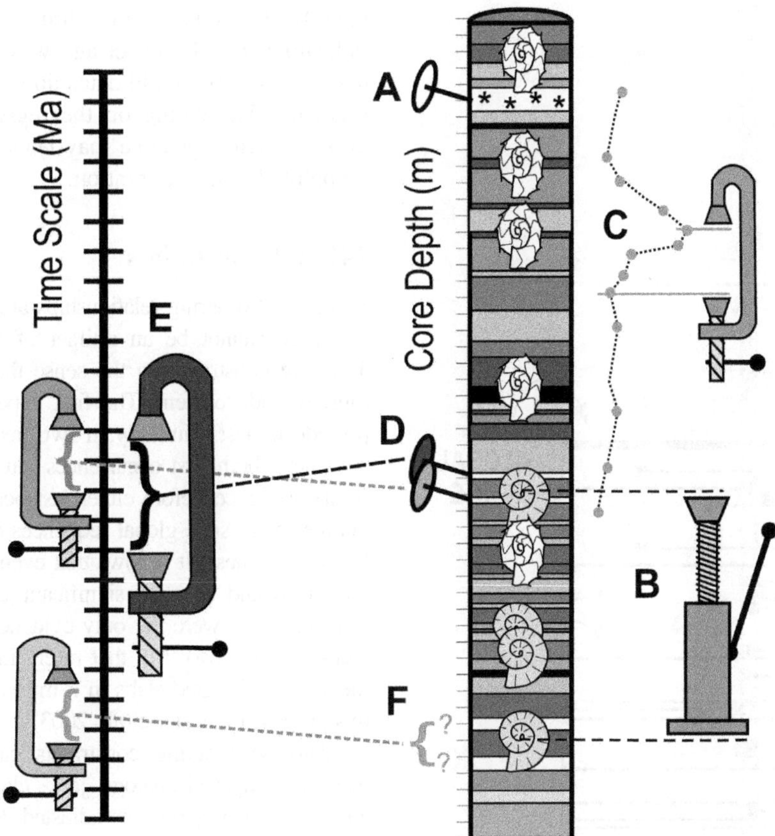

FIGURE 14B.4 Examples for three classes of uncertainty in stratigraphic information—"nails, jacks, and clamps." (A) Uniquely fingerprinted marker bed: a "nail" point that may not be adjusted. (B) Observed local taxon range that likely underrepresents the global range; a "jack" interval that may stretch to fit the composite sequence of events. (C) A conservative uncertainty interval on the position of steepest change in a stable isotope anomaly; a "clamp" interval that may shrink to fit. (D) The local "nailed" position of two samples for radioisotopic dating. (E) The analytical uncertainty of the ages of the same samples now "clamped" onto an age scale shared with other dated events. (F) "Clamp" expresses ambiguity in the location of a dated sample. For (D) and (E) the sampled positions indicate that the analytical mean ages are out of order; the corresponding clamp intervals overlap and will shrink to fit the superpositional evidence of order. The local ranges of the two fossil taxa overlap; the composite sequence must be constrained to include this relationship.

duration and, at the cost of some effort, may be clamped down. For example, the rock intervals between adjacent samples that record normal and reversed remanent magnetization are such intervals for geomagnetic chron boundaries. We use the same class for carbon isotope anomalies (Sadler, 2012), entering their maximum reasonable extent in local sections. All the local uncertainties are assumed to overlap in time and the composite placement of the anomaly lies within these uncertainty limits *everywhere*. In contrast to jacks that may stretch beyond the local section, the shrinkage of a clamp is limited to closure. Where uncertainty vanishes the clamp becomes a nail—the event class that may not be adjusted up- or downsection. Each local occurrence of a chemically fingerprinted ashfall behaves a *nail*. If the local placement is in conflict with better constrained events, the identification is in question and the nail must be removed.

A dated ash bed usually has the property of a nail in the section where it was sampled, but a clamp when recorded in an age-scaled "section" with other dated events. The 2-sigma analytical uncertainty, which is used to scale the width of the clamp, may shrink in response to superpositional relationships with other events and dates. If the reported location of the sampled ash bed is ambiguous, it too may be treated as a "shrink-to-fit" clamp. In earlier GTS volumes, dated Ordovician and Silurian K-bentonites were identified by their mean ages and treated as nails. With increasing numbers of dated events, some of the 2-sigma intervals overlap. To recognize that mean ages might not record the true order of such events, it has become safer to assign these dated events to the clamp category (Fig. 14B.5).

Many local taxon ranges stretch to fit their final composite extent as guided by multiple interactions with other range-end events. Only a few of the 2-sigma uncertainty intervals on radioisotopic dates shrink to fit the composite sequence. This data class is not numerous, and opportunity for shrinkage is limited to the age-scaled section.

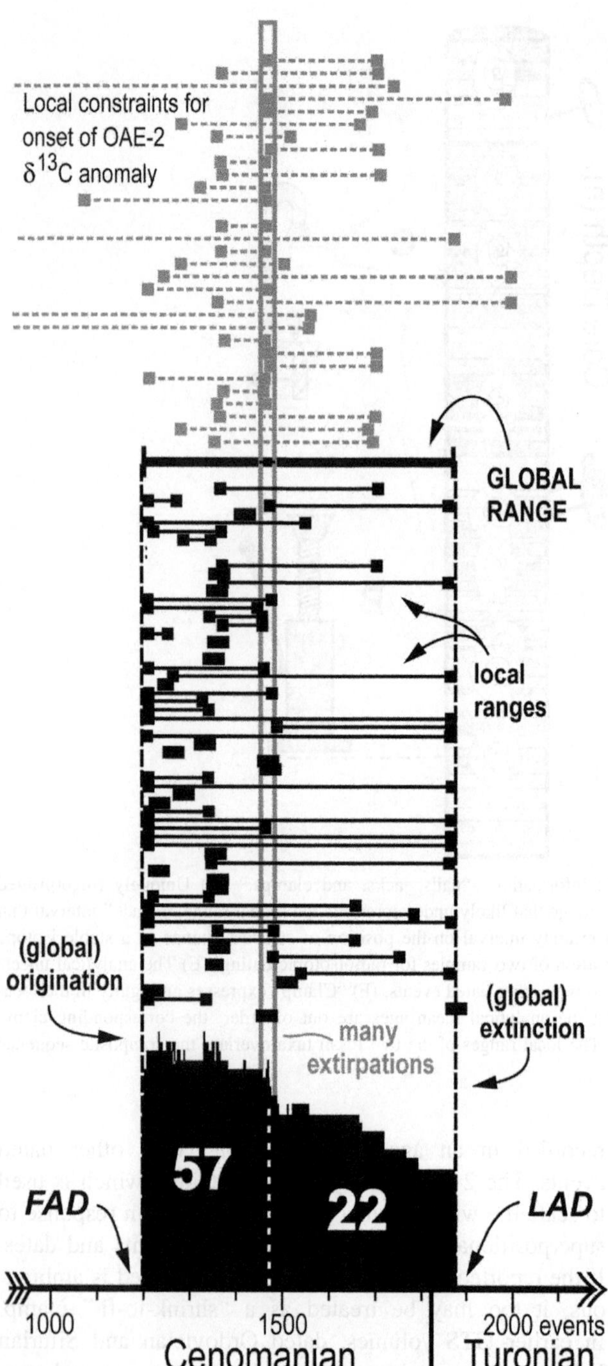

FIGURE 14B.5 Part of a best fit ordinal time line of 3275 mid-Cretaceous events from 489 localities. Gray rectangle: global consensus interval is the overlap of local uncertainty intervals (shrink-to-fit "clamps") for the onset of a carbon isotope anomaly. Black bars: global composite range encompasses all local ranges for *Rotalipora cushmani* (stretch-to-fit "jacks"). Black histogram sums the number of local ranges that support global composite range.

Imprecise dates from earlier GTS projects tend to shrink significantly within their large published uncertainties, without distorting the calibration regressions. This shrinkage is often very asymmetric. The published mean age may be left outside the shrunken uncertainty interval, indicating that the mean age was misleading. As shrink-to-fit clamps, these old dates do no harm to the composite sequence. Depending on the regression technique, however, the safest practice may leave them out of the set of tie points for age calibration.

14B.2.2 Constraints

Some local ordering relationships are immutable in the sense that they cannot be an artifact of incomplete preservation. They are constraints in the sense that the composite section must reproduce them. The first appearance of a taxon must precede its last. Similarly, if two taxa are proven to coexist, anywhere, both first occurrences must be placed in the composite sequence before either last occurrence. This limits the number of feasible global sequences of events that need to be tested for fitness. It follows that even a very taxon-poor local section would place a significant constraint on the global sequence, if it were the only evidence for a coexisting taxon pair—perhaps two taxa that rarely inhabit the same environment. Even isolated slabs in a museum collection may serve this purpose (Webster et al., 2003).

Pairwise ordering constraints can best be summarized using the physical analogs, jack, clamp, and nail. Wherever an event that may only be adjusted downsection, if at all, has been reported below an event that adjusts upsection only (younger limit of a jack, or older limit of a clamp), or not at all (the nail category), that pairwise ordering is a constraint that cannot be an artifact of incomplete preservation. The same is true for an event that may only be adjusted upsection and has been observed anywhere above one that adjusts downsection only (older limit of a jack interval, or younger limit of a clamp) or one that may not adjust (a nail). Note that this logic assumes that reworked fossils have been culled from the input data. If not, locally reported ranges must be allowed to shrink from the top, but with a much smaller probability than stretching to fit (Cody et al., 2008).

We also assume that taxa have been identified correctly. Such mistakes do occur, or course. Some are first identified by gaps and outliers in the emergent composite ranges. Thus the compositing process serves as one source of quality control (Sadler, 2010).

14B.2.3 Line of correlation

The LOC by which local information is projected from a local section into the composite sequence during graphic correlation must have a positive slope; age does not reverse. Shaw (1964) initially favored linear regression. Here (Fig. 14B.6), we adopt the opposite end-member in permissible complexity, a piecewise linear regression with no limit on the degree of segmentation and permissive of segments that parallel the axes and imply hiatuses in the local sections

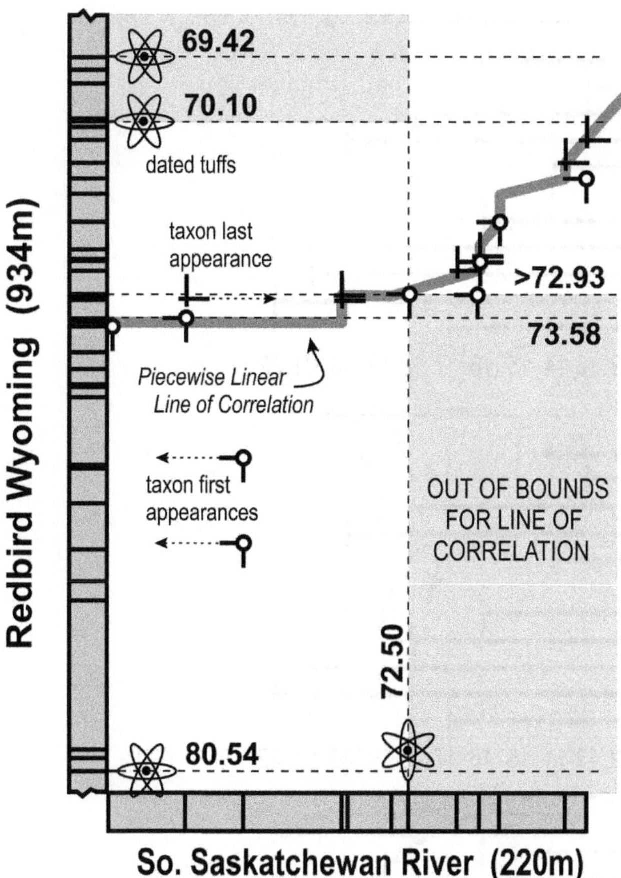

FIGURE 14B.6 Graphic line of correlation (LOC) between two Cretaceous ammonite-bearing sections with radioisotopic dates and a dated paleomagnetic interval. Dated events divide graphic plot into rectangles; piecewise linear LOC must cross rectangle boundaries in order of ages, leaving some rectangles (*pale gray fill*) impossible for LOC to enter. Best fit LOC (*thick gray line*) is projected into this 2-section plane from a global, 561-section, constrained optimization of 1213 ammonite taxon ranges, and 162 other events. Circle and cross symbols are coordinates of first- and last-appearance levels, respectively, for shared ammonite taxa; the attached bars indicate permitted directions of range extension to fit LOC. Most parsimonious range extensions (*dashed arrows*) all impact the less richly fossiliferous South Saskatchewan River section.

(MacLeod and Sadler, 1995). In graphic correlation the LOC is manipulated by the stratigrapher on a series of two-dimensional graphs. In CONOP the LOC exists in $j+1$ dimensions—the number of local sections (j) plus the composite sequence—and is managed by the objective function (Eq. 14B.2). Full piecewise complexity is facilitated by omitting any smoothing term in the objective function (Kemple et al., 1995). Without a smoothing term the objective function effectively optimizes only the global order of events, not their spacing. It develops a composite *sequence*. The differential spacing of events necessary for a composite *section* or proxy time scale is determined with additional assumptions, *after* an optimal sequence is determined without them (Sadler et al., 2009). Simplifying assumptions about local rate and age need not compromise optimization of the order of events.

14B.2.4 Objective function

The optimal composite sequence minimizes the objective function (Eq. 14B.2), which sums the misfit of trial composite sequences relative to all the real local sections. Symbols $\boldsymbol{a}$ and $\boldsymbol{b}$ are the locally observed downsection and upsection limits of an interval. They have been adjusted to α and β, respectively, by stretching or shrinking depending on data class. The absolute sizes of the adjustments are considered ($|\boldsymbol{a}-\alpha|$) and ($|\beta-\boldsymbol{b}|$); stretch-to-fit and shrink-to-fit adjustments do not compensate for one another.

$$F=\left(\sum_i\sum_j\left[w_{1ij}\left(|\boldsymbol{a}_{ij}-\alpha_{ij}|\right)+w_{2ij}\left(|\beta_{ij}-\boldsymbol{b}_{ij}|\right)\right]\right)+K\left(N^c_{\text{comp}}-N^c_{\text{obs}}\right) \tag{14B.2}$$

Subscripts i and j indicate events and sections, respectively. Weights w_{1ij} and w_{2ij} allow differential emphasis on every locally observed event but are all usually set to 1.00 by default when a composite sequence is first optimized. The summation terms mean that more commonly occurring events inherently carry more weight than rare events.

The dual summation in the first term ceases to grow when the end of a stretch-to-fit interval is "jacked" beyond the limits of a local section. A stretched range is likely to overlap with increasing numbers of other taxon ranges, however, and if any of these coexistences are not observed elsewhere, the difference term without ij subscripts ($N^c_{\text{comp}}-N^c_{\text{obs}}$) discourages further stretching. This second term in the objective function subtracts from the number of coexisting taxon pairs implied by the composite sequence N^c_{comp} only those confirmed by overlapping ranges in at least one local section N^c_{obs}. The impact of this term on the total misfit is adjusted by the weight K, usually between 0.1 and 0.001.

Although the numerous possible weights w_{1ij} and w_{2ij} are typically all set to 1.00 for time scale purposes, the measurement scale for ($|\boldsymbol{a}-\alpha|$) and ($|\beta-\boldsymbol{b}|$) does determine which sections most influence the outcome. Traditional graphic correlation uses rock thickness (penalty = "interval" in CONOP configuration file) and, thus, favors sequences seen in thicker sections. To favor richer and more finely sampled sections, we measure the size of adjustments by their span of event levels (penalty = "level").

14B.2.5 Simulated annealing

Of the various search algorithms developed for NP-hard problems, CONOP adopts the simulated annealing heuristic (Kirkpatrick et al., 1983). It manages a trial-and-error process analogous to tracking the free energy changes in an attempt to grow a perfect crystal by slow cooling from a molten state. The search begins with a sequence of events π that merely satisfies the coexistence constraints (Fig. 14B.7A): first occurrences are placed in random order at the start of the sequence

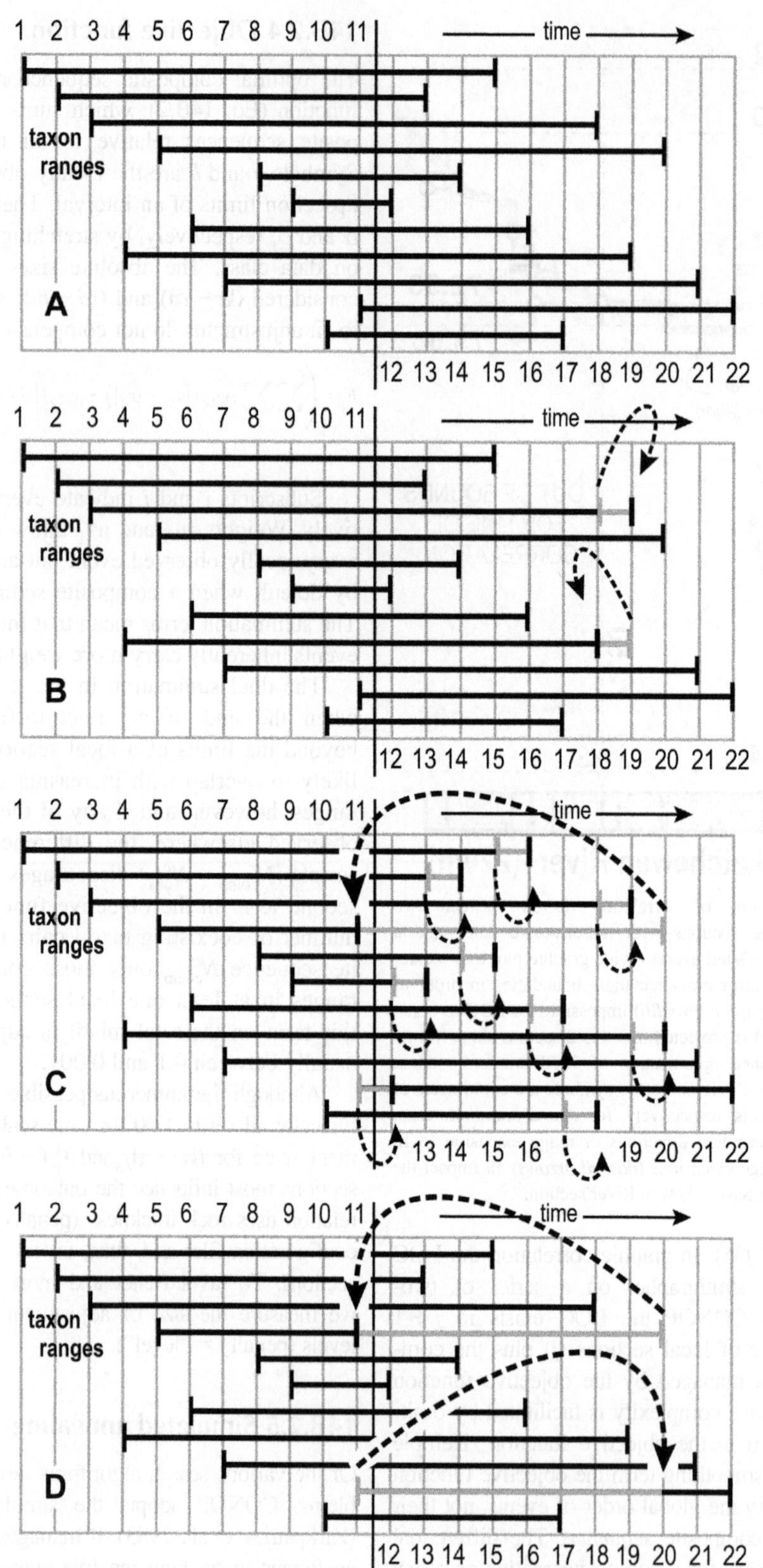

FIGURE 14B.7 Sequence permutation by CONOP: (A) initial configuration; all taxa coexist; all coexistence constraints satisfied; (B) random neighboring events swap positions; small changes, best near end of search; (C) random event moves to new random position; all intervening events shift one position; efficient throughout search; and (D) random event pair swaps positions; large changes, best near beginning of search. *CONOP*, Constrained optimization.

and last occurrences at random at the end. Events of other classes are initially placed in the mid-section and internally ordered according to pairwise constraints. Each trial then moves a randomly chosen event to a new random position (Fig. 14B.7C). Moves that violate any constraint are immediately rejected. Moves that reduce or do not alter the misfit are always retained. Moves that increase the objective function ($\delta F > 0$), making the developing solution temporarily less fit, are evaluated by a Boltzmann-like term (Eq. 14B.3), which yields the probability P_T of accepting the new sequence (π) in spite of some loss of fitness.

$$P_T(\pi) = \begin{cases} 1, & \delta F \leq 0 \\ e^{-(\delta F/T)}, & \delta F > 0 \end{cases} \tag{14B.3}$$

The temperature term T in the exponent prevents the optimization from becoming trapped in a local minimum. T is reduced stepwise by a factor 0.95 during the search and with it the likelihood of accepting a move that worsens the fit of the composite sequence to the local sections (Eq. 14B.2). Initially, T is set large enough that at least half of all moves would be accepted. As T decreases, acceptance becomes more dependent on δF until, at the end of the search, T is close enough to zero that only improvements in fit are accepted.

The cooling rate determines the number of trial moves attempted at each cooling step. For small data sets, this number may be fixed at a few thousand (Kemple et al., 1995). For the huge data sets used in the time scale challenge, an adaptive simulated annealing algorithm determines its own cooling rate by tracking diminished returns. At each cooling step, modifications of the sequence are attempted in batches of 20,000. T is not reduced until a whole batch fails to find a better fit sequence. Cooling steps continue until 50 successive steps fail to generate a better fit. These two stopping values might need to be increased for larger data sets or those with more regional differences in sequence than we have encountered for Ordovician and Silurian graptolites.

The progress of an optimization may be watched via a screen graphic (Fig. 14B.8) that updates a misfit time series and animates a range chart or taxon richness curve with every trial. Thus CONOP enables users to recognize cooling schedules that are too fast (rapid initial fall in misfit comes to an abrupt halt) or too slow (falling misfit is continually interrupted by long batches of trials with no improvement in fitness). With a good cooling schedule the misfit curve approaches its minimum value smoothly and asymptotically. Rapid initial improvements in fitness give way to diminishing returns as the composite sequence is more finely tuned near the end of the search. On a good personal computer, data sets of the size described here may take almost a week to optimize.

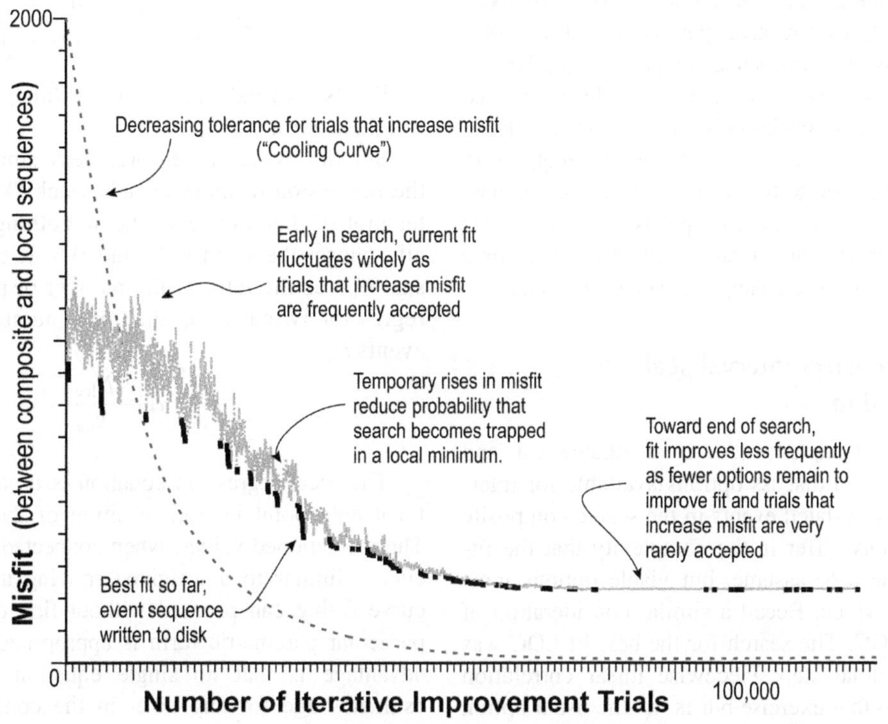

FIGURE 14B.8 Trajectory of generally improving fit (*black dots*) and diminishing returns during a simulated annealing search for the composite sequence that best fits a small problem set. The gray dots track accepted changes to the developing composite sequence; that is, all trials that reduce misfit and some that increase it. The acceptability of worsening fit decreases with the size of the deterioration and with time since the start of the search (*dashed line*).

14B.3 Projecting the composite sequence onto a time scale

The move from a composite sequence to a time scale proceeds in two steps. First, the spacing of events on the local thickness scales is used to generate a scaled composite section from the optimal global sequence. Second, a regression is chosen to interpolate an age scale between the dated events in the scaled composite section.

14B.3.1 From an ordinal to an interval composite sequence scale

Adjacent pairs of events in the optimized global sequence also have placements in the adjusted local sections (the inner optimization). These separations on local thickness scales may be combined in various ways to scale the separation of the events in the composite sequence (Sadler et al., 2009). Those pairs that are not placed at separate levels in any section, but always fall together, are now considered tied (zero spacing); they may contribute to evidence of mass extinction or bursts of origination. For the separable pairs a variety of averaging options is possible, but the "right" choice requires too much insight about variable rates of sediment accumulation and biotic turnover. Lacking adequate theoretical guidance, the practical choice is the one that simplifies the regression of the dated events. The consistently simplest option averages all the local spacing intervals for each pair of successive events, including zero values, after all sections have first been rescaled according to their relative span on the ordinal global sequence of events. The implicit assumption would be that biotic turnover tends to be more stable in the long term and large scale, while relative thickness is a better guide to relative duration in the short term and local scales (Sadler et al, 2009). There is no strong reason to believe that a smoother or more nearly linear disposition of dated tie points along the scaled composite sequence indicates more nearly true proxy time scale. It is preferred because it simplifies age interpolation.

14B.3.2 From a proxy interval scale to a time-scaled section

Agterberg et al. (Chapter 14A: Geomathematical and Statistical Procedures) discuss options available for interpolating age between dated events in the scaled composite section. The options differ in the complexity that the fitted curve is allowed to assume, but viable options must have nonnegative slope. Recall a similar consideration of options for the LOC. The search for the best fit LOC was an essentially ordinal step. Piecewise linear correlation was well suited to that exercise but is not the usual option of choice for timescaling. The preceding step that built the proxy time scale was already guided by a preference for smoothness in the distribution of dated events. By fitting the dated points in ensemble fashion, the global regression line does not necessarily pass through all dated calibration points. This may run counter to local expectations, where a very precise local age determination has been obtained from a bed very close to a stratigraphic unit boundary. The mismatch between regression and dated event may reach millions of years.

To explore this dilemma it is useful to examine locally weighted regression (LOWESS or its derivative LOESS), which can fit a curve with more or less complexity and approach something similar to piecewise linear correlation. Although LOWESS is often illustrated for broader and richer scatterplots, it is applicable to sparse and irregularly distributed data points such as arise during time scale calibration (Fig. 14B.9).

The spline technique, described in Chapter 14A, Geomathematical and Statistical Procedures, performs polynomial regressions between chosen data points or "knots." LOWESS (Cleveland, 1979, 1981; Cleveland and Devlin, 1988) performs a series of low-order (often linear) regressions within a sliding window that is focused (centered) on each calibration point in turn. The window captures a fixed number of points, the weights ω of which decrease with distance from the focal point. The weighting function is typically tricubic, with distance measured as a fraction of the maximum distance from the focal point. For points inside the sliding window, (dist/max dist ≤ 1),

$$\omega = \left(1 - \left(\frac{\text{dist}}{\text{max dist}}\right)^3\right)^3 \tag{14B.4}$$

Points beyond the window (dist/max dist > 1) are weighted zero.

Smaller windows enforce less smoothing, allowing the regression to more closely track "kinks" in the scatter plot of dated events. The smoothing factor α is usually chosen between 0.25 and 0.5. It expresses window size N_{loc} as the ratio of the number of points in the local regression window to the total number of calibration events N_{tot}.

$$\alpha = \frac{N_{\text{loc}}}{N_{\text{tot}}} \tag{14B.5}$$

The local regression equation is used to reposition the focal data point in each position of the sliding window. The repositioned values, when connected, form the LOESS curve. Similar to a weighted moving average, LOWESS curve fitting can proceed without first determining that a particular parametric form is appropriate. A corollary disadvantage is that no single equation is generated that estimates age for any level in the composite section. In effect, the regression slope is estimated at every point. Interpolations must be made by the LOWESS programs, which are available in R, for Excel and for other platforms.

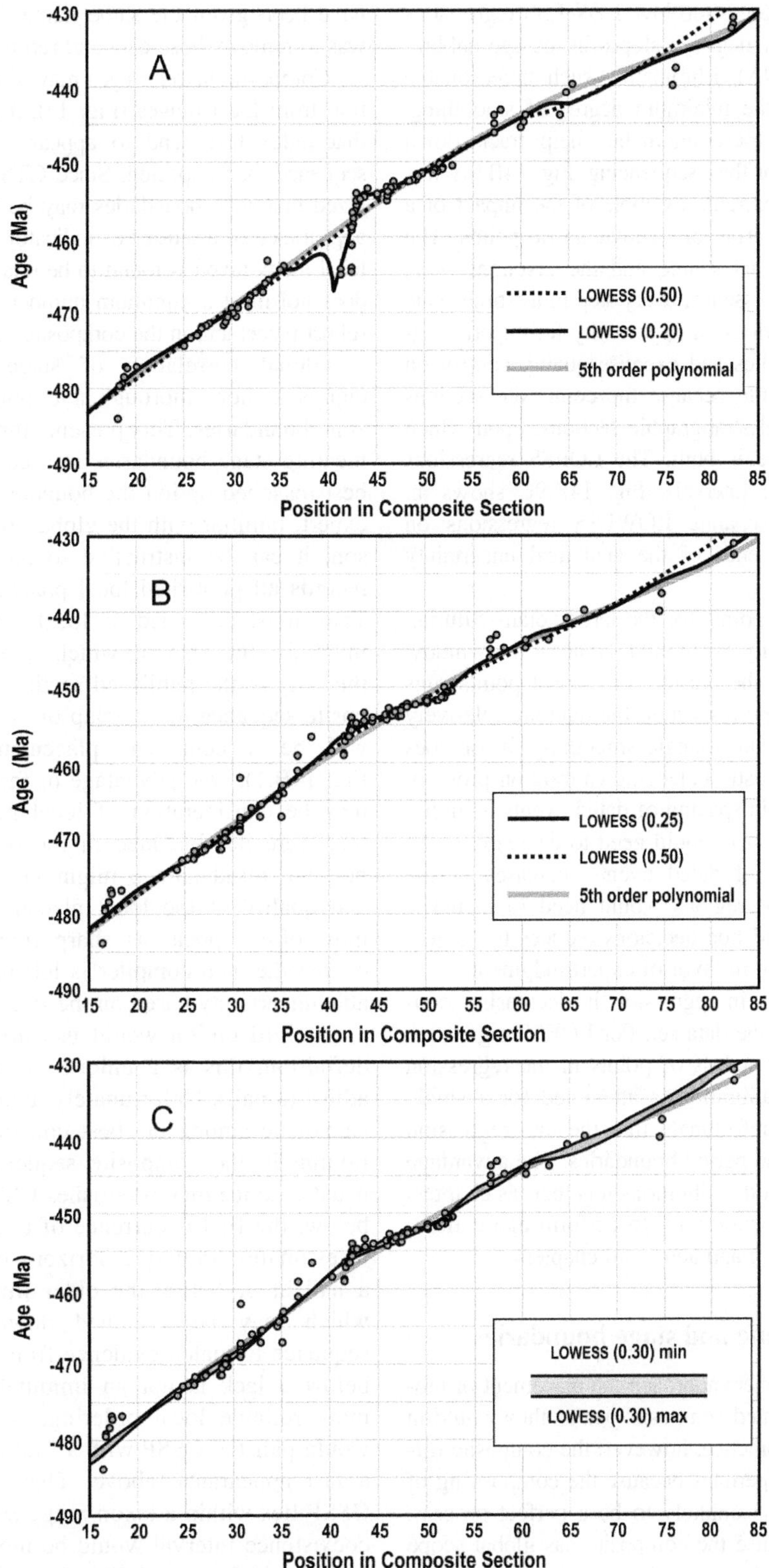

FIGURE 14B.9 Illustrative experiments with LOWESS regression of dated events entered as limits of uncertainty intervals (two circles per date): (A) regression (*black lines*) with limited smoothing (*solid line*) that overfits an anomaly in the distribution of dated events, which was caused by taxonomic error, and includes unacceptable negative slopes in portions of the regression; (B) improved fit with more smoothing, after taxonomic correction repositioned tie points in the global composite section; and (C) separate regressions for older and younger limits of uncertainty interval.

If the smoothing factor is too low, LOWESS regressions fit the data using locally negative slopes in the age calibration curves (Fig. 14B.9A). Eliminating such unreasonable slopes may determine the minimum degree of smoothing. More often, however, these anomalies help track down errors in the input data or their sequencing. Fig. 14B.9A was chosen to illustrate an extreme example of the impact of a taxonomic error on the array of Ordovician tie points. The anomaly was traced to its source and the taxonomy corrected (Fig. 14B.9B). In essence, every step in the time scale calibration exercise provides an opportunity for expert judgment to identify anomalies and exercise quality control on the input. This is possible because the composite sections bear resemblance to real stratigraphic sections, upon which biostratigraphic expertise is built. The LOESS regressions can develop confidence intervals. Fig. 14B.9C shows an experiment that used separate LOWESS regressions on the older and younger ends of the analytical uncertainty intervals.

The age calibration points for the Ordovician–Silurian time interval are unevenly distributed. None of the window sizes that are suited to the clusters of control points runs close to all calibration points where the data are relatively sparse. That is to say that a single smoothing factor does not fit all parts of a realistic Paleozoic calibration problem in which the stratigraphic spacing of dated events is highly uneven. Either window size would need to decrease as the stratigraphic separation of dated events increases or the weighting of the sparse regions would need to increase. Introducing too many ad hoc decisions reduces the objectivity of the interpolation in favor of expert judgment.

A common problem in regression is decreasing constraint near the ends of the data set. For LOESS regression this is clearly linked to a loss of points in the regression window. When time calibration is attempted for a single geologic period, it is unfortunate that the age regression weakens approaching the period boundaries. The advantage of placing geologic period calibrations together, as chapters in one volume, is the opportunity to perform age calibration exercises both within and across all chapters.

14B.3.3 Locating zone and stage boundaries

Ideally, expert stratigraphers approach the placement of biozone boundaries in a scaled composite just as they would in a real local section. In practice, however, the composite differs from real sections, perhaps because the compositing of so many local records is unlikely to be a perfect process, but more certainly because the composite has global scope that combines different local provinces and complex geographic ranges. Some anomalies in the composite section may be traced back to problems with the input data. Ordovician and Silurian composite sections revealed cases in which different stable isotope excursions appeared to have been given the same name. The immediate solution was to remove those data and rerun the optimization.

Composite taxon ranges may differ significantly in duration from local ranges (Fig. 14B.5). Experience has shown that index taxa tend to appear earlier in the composite sequence than expected. Since GTS2004 it has been recognized that zone boundaries may be better placed at the first appearance of a cluster of indicator taxa. Less commonly, a local index taxon is found to be relatively rare, globally, and does not meet a minimum number of local occurrences for robust placement in the composite sequence.

Global correlation of stage boundaries typically enjoys a more thorough and published effort than for zone boundaries. This presents three possible options for locating stage boundaries in a composite section. In the best reasoned option the boundary level is picked by an expert, familiar with the global discussion. For comparison, it can be instructive to include among the input records all published local placements of the boundary. They must be coded as local, shrink-to-fit uncertainty intervals, the size of which depends on the sampling intensity in the published section. In the emergent composite sequence the overlap of all the local uncertainties will be a consensus placement (e.g., Toarcian in Fig. 14B.1). One advantage of the published placements may be consideration of local ranges for fossil clades that were not included in the optimization process. A possible disadvantage might be the variety in vintage and quality of the local placements. Stage boundaries most often appear as sharp lines on published range charts; the data compiler is left to reconstruct a reasonable uncertainty based on the spacing of range ends.

A third option would use the definitive GSSP. By definition, this is a unique local event that does not adjust (a nail). Unfortunately, a unique local occurrence cannot be among the best constrained events for positioning in the composite sequence. Consider also the usual practice that establishes GSSPs at, or immediately below, the first occurrence of a taxon that is then used to estimate correlative horizons elsewhere. This places a nail at or below the older limit of a jack interval, which may be stretched downward in the global sequence to match evidence from other sections. A nail below a jack is not an immutable pairwise order. A more reliable local ordering, for correlation purpose, would pair the GSSP with a first appearance below it or a last appearance above. That is, recognizing that a GSSP lies within a taxon range zone or, better, within a coexistence interval would be more reliable and practical criteria for correlation. It might appear less precise but does represent a realistic uncertainly interval for time correlation. Finer resolving power could be achieved by increasing the number of concurrent taxon ranges that span the GSSP.

Stage and zone boundaries may be picked as uncertainty intervals. These uncertainties must be expected to expand when projected into the time scale across the confidence interval for the regression of dated calibration events.

14B.4 Slotting composite sections

Not only do expert zonal schemes differ by biotic province, they may also use different fossil clades. Ordovician and Silurian zones have been established for both graptolites and conodonts. Some dated events are best constrained by graptolite ranges, others by conodonts. Why not optimize data from both clades? Although nearly 2000 sections have been compiled that contain either conodonts or graptolites in this time interval, less than 150 of them record both clades in useful detail. If combined into one CONOP, events in the resulting composite sequence are unnaturally clustered by clade, because there is too little evidence of cross-clade coexistences.

Sadler and Cooper (2008) suggest how two separately optimized composite sequences might instead be slotted together, using constraints from those sections that yield taxa from both clades. Slotting algorithms (Clark, 1985; Gordon and Reyment, 1979; Thompson and Clark, 1993; and the more sophisticated dynamic programming variation, Lisiecki and Lisiecki, 2002) compare two sections, the samples of which form the rows and columns of a matrix. All pairs of samples are compared and a path of highest correlation is drawn, sample by sample across the matrix. With conodont and graptolite composite sequences as the rows and columns (Fig. 14B.10), Sadler and Cooper imagined identifying two off-diagonal areas of the matrix that the pathway could not enter without violating partial-ordering constraints derived from observations that a graptolite taxon FAD preceded a conodont LAD or a conodont FAD preceded a graptolite LAD in at least one of the local sections. The remaining cells would define a crudely diagonal channel for all feasible correlation pathways. Channel width would indicate the uncertainty of correlation. For the current graptolite and conodont composites, we find parts of the matrix where the pathway is occluded by overlap of the two out-of-bound regions (Fig. 14B.10). In other words the separate optimal composites for graptolites and conodonts are locally incompatible with sections that yield both clades. Assuming there are no taxonomic errors in the sections reporting both clades, one or both composites need adjustment.

One measure of the success of these time scale books is the extent to which they encourage researchers the most powerful new data. Clearly, progress for the older parts of the GTS problem places a premium on range charts from outcrops that yield two or more fossil clades, ideally with other events.

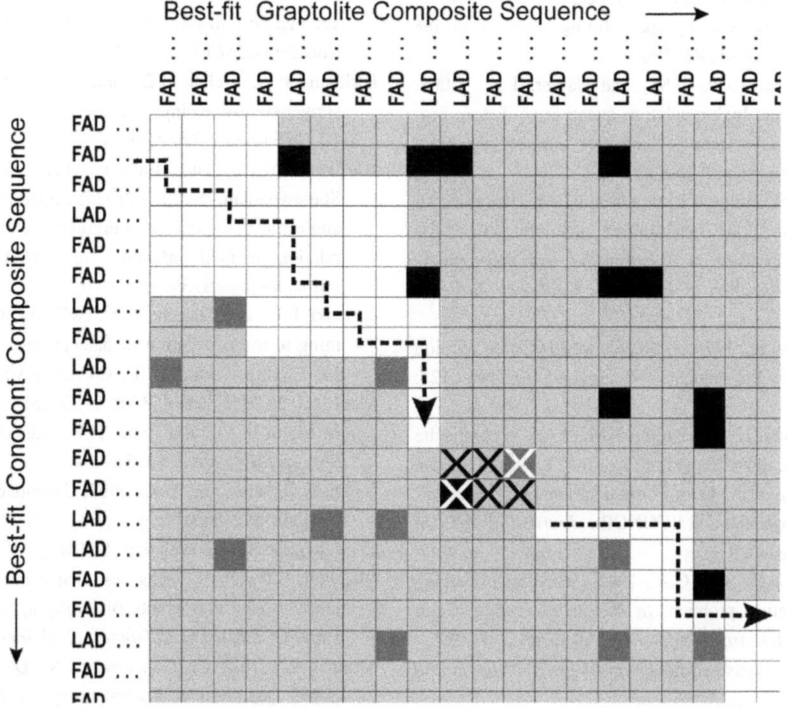

FIGURE 14B.10 Characteristics of slotting matrices that combine two composite sequences. Black cells: conodont FAD (First Appearance Datum) preserved below graptolite LAD (Last Appearance Datum). Dark gray cells: graptolite FAD preserved below conodont LAD. White cells: permissible pathways for line of correlation (LOC *dashed arrow*). Light gray cells: areas out of bounds to LOC. Crossed cells: occlusion of LOC pathway, indicating ordering error(s) in composite sequences. *LOC*, Line of correlation.

14B.5 Technical information

Technical information on the CONOP method and applications is in the website: https://drive.google.com/drive/folders/1xj5uZATaANSvhfauB-Je_YXsjSM468OH.

Bibliography

Agterberg, F.P., and Gradstein, F.M., 1999, The RASC method for ranking and scaling of biostratigraphic events. *Earth Science Reviews*, **46**: 1–25.

Agterberg, F.P., and Nel, L.D., 1982, Algorithms for the ranking of stratigraphic events. *Computers and Geoscience*, **8**: 69–90.

Alroy, J., 1992, Conjunction among taxonomic distributions and the Miocene mammalian biochronology of the Great Plains. *Paleobiology*, **18**: 326–343.

Alroy, J., 1994, Appearance event ordination: a new biochronologic method. *Paleobiology*, **20**: 191–207.

Berry, W.B.N., 1968, *Growth of a Prehistoric Time Scale Based on Organic Evolution*. San Francisco, CA: W. H. Freeman, p. 158.

Clark, R.M., 1985, A FORTRAN program for constrained sequence-slotting based on minimum combined path length. *Computers and Geoscience*, **11**: 605–617.

Cleveland, W.S., 1979, Robust locally weighted regression and smoothing scatterplots. *Journal of the American Statistical Association*, **74**: 829–836.

Cleveland, W.S., 1981, LOWESS: a program for smoothing scatter plots by robust locally weighted regression. *The American Statistician*, **35**: 54, https://doi.org/10.2307/268359.

Cleveland, W.S., and Devlin, S.J., 1988, Locally weighted regression: an approach to regression analysis by local fitting. *Journal of the American Statistical Association*, **83**: 596–610.

Cody, R.D., Levy, R.H., Harwood, D.M., and Sadler, P.M., 2008, Thinking outside the zone: high-resolution quantitative diatom biochronology for the Antarctic Neogene. *Palaeogeography, Paleoclimatology, Palaeoecology*, **260**: 92–121.

Cooper, R.A., Crampton, J.S., Raine, J.I., Gradstein, F.M., Morgans, H. E.G., Sadler, P.M., et al., 2001, Quantitative biostratigraphy of the Taranaki Basin, New Zealand: a deterministic and probabilistic approach. *American Association of Petroleum Geologists Bulletin*, **85**: 1469–1498.

Cooper, R.A., and Lindholm, K., 1990, A precise worldwide correlation of early Ordovician graptolite sequences. *Geological Magazine*, **127**: 497–525.

Daneshian, J., Ramezani Dana, L., and Sadler, P.M., 2017, A composite foraminiferal biostratigraphic sequence for the Lower Miocene deposits in the type area of the Qom Formation, central Iran, developed by constrained optimization (CONOP). *Journal of African Earth Sciences*, **125**: 214–229.

Dell, R.F., Kemple, W.G., and Tovey, C.A., 1992, Heuristically solving the stratigraphic correlation problem. *In Proceedings of the First Industrial Engineering Research Conference*, Vol. 1, pp. 293–297.

Edwards, L.E., 1978, Range charts and no-space graphs. *Computers and Geoscience*, **4**: 247–255.

Fan, J., and Zhang, Y.D., 2000, Sinocor 1.0, a biostratigraphic program for graphic correlation. *Acta Palaeontologica Sinica*, **39**: 573–583.

Glazner, A.F., and Sadler, P.M., 2016, Estimating the duration of geologic intervals from a small number of age determinations: a challenge common to petrology and paleobiology. *Geochemistry, Geophysics, Geosystems*, **17**: 4892–4898, https://doi.org/10.1002/2016GC006542.

Gordon, A.D., and Reyment, R.A., 1979, Slotting of borehole sequences. *Mathematical Geology*, **11**: 309–327.

Gradstein, F., Ogg, J.G., and Smith, A.G., 2004, *A Geological Time Scale*. Cambridge University Press, p. 589.

Grubb, B.J., and Finney, S.C., 1995, Graphic correlation of Middle Ordovician graptolite-rich shales, southern Appalachians: successful application of a technique to inadequate stratigraphic sections. *In* Mann, K.O., and Lane, H.R. (eds), Graphic Correlation. *SEPM Special Publication,* **53**: 151–158.

Guex, J., 1977, Une nouvelle méthode d'analyse biochronologique. *Bulletin Laboratoire Géologique Lausanne*, **224**: 309–322.

Guex, J., 1991, *Biochronological Correlations*. Berlin: Springer Verlag, p. 250.

Hints, O., Nõlvak, J., Paluveer, L., and Tammekänd, M., 2011, Conventional and CONOP9 approaches to biodiversity of Baltic Ordovician chitinozoans. *Cuadernos del Museo Geominero del Instituto Geológico y Minero de España*, **14**: 243–249.

Hood, K.C., 1986, *Graphcor – Interactive Graphic Correlation*, version 2.2: copyright K. C, Hood.

Kaufmann, B., 2006, Calibrating the Devonian time scale: a synthesis of U-Pb-TIMS ages and conodont stratigraphy. *Earth Science Reviews*, **76**: 175–190, https://doi.org/10.1016/j.earscirev.2006.01.001.

Kemple, W.G., Sadler, P.M., and Strauss, D.J., 1989, A prototype constrained optimisation solution to the time correlation problem. *In* Agterberg, F.P., and Bonham-Carter, G.F. (eds), *Statistical Applications in the Earth Sciences*. Ottawa, ON: Geological Survey of Canada Paper, 417–425.

Kemple, W.G., Sadler, P.M., and Strauss, D.J., 1995, Extending graphic correlation to many dimensions: stratigraphic correlation as constrained optimization. *In* Mann, K.O., and Lane, H.R. (eds), Graphic Correlation. *SEPM Special Publication,* **53**: 65–82.

Kirkpatrick, S., Gelatt, C.D., and Vecchi, M.P., 1983, Optimization by simulated annealing. *Science*, **220**: 671–680, https://doi.org/10.1126/science.220.4598.671.

Kleffner, M.A., and Barrick, J.E., 2011, Telychian – early Sheinwoodian (Early Silurian) conodont-, graptolite-, chitinozoan- and event-based chronostratigraphy developed using the graphic correlation method. *Memoirs of the Association of Australasian Palaeontologists*, **39**: 191–210.

Lisiecki, L.E., and Lisiecki, P.A., 2002, Application if dynamic programming to the correlation of paleoclimate records. *Paleoceanography*, **17**: 12, https://doi.org/10.1029/2001PA000733.

MacLeod, N., and Sadler, P.M., 1995, Estimating the line of correlation. *In* Mann, K.O., and Lane, H.R. (eds), Graphic Correlation. *SEPM Special Publication,* **53**: 51–64.

Mann, K.O., and Lane, H.R., 1995, Graphic correlation: a powerful stratigraphic technique comes of age. *In* Mann, K.O., and Lane, H.R. (eds), Graphic Correlation. *SEPM Special Publication,* **53**: 3–13.

Marshall, C.R., 2010, Using confidence intervals to quantify the uncertainty in the end points of stratigraphic ranges. *In* Alroy, J., and Hunt, G. (eds), *The Paleontological Society Papers* **16**: 291–316.

Monnet, C., Klug, C., Goudemand, N., De Baets, K., and Bucher, H., 2011, Quantitative biochronology of Devonian ammonoids from Morocco and proposals for a refined unitary association method. *Lethaia*, **44**: 469–489.

Riedman, L.A., and Sadler, P.M., 2018, Global species richness and biostratigraphic potential of early to middle Neoproterozoic eukaryote fossils. *Precambrian Research*, **319**: 6–18, https://doi.org/10.1016/j.precamres.2017.10.008.

Rubel, M., Nestor, V., Harris, M.T., Sheehan, P.M., Ainsaar, L., Männik, P., et al., 2006, A new high-resolution chitinozoan composite standard for the East Baltic Lower Silurian succession based on numerical analysis. *Geological Quarterly*, **50**: 323–332.

Sadler, P.M., 1981, Sediment accumulation rates and the completeness of stratigraphic sections. *Journal of Geology*, **89**: 569–584.

Sadler, P.M., 2004, Quantitative biostratigraphy – achieving finer resolution in Global Correlation. *Annual Reviews of Earth and Planetary Sciences*, **32**: 187–213.

Sadler, P.M., 2006, Composite time lines: a means to leverage resolving power from radioisotopic dates and biostratigraphy. *In* Olszewski, T. (ed), Geochronology: Emerging Opportunities. *Paleontological Society Papers,* **12**: 145–170.

Sadler, P.M., 2010, Brute-force biochronology: sequencing paleobiologic first- and last-appearance events by trial and error. *In* Alroy, J., and Hunt, G. (eds), Quantitative Methods in Paleobiology. *Paleontological Society Papers,* **16**: 271–289.

Sadler, P.M., 2012, Integrating carbon isotope excursions into automated stratigraphic correlations: an example from the Silurian of Baltica. *Bulletin of Geosciences*, **84**: 681–694, https://doi.org/10.3140/bull.geosci.1307.

Sadler, P.M., and Cervato, C., 2011, Data and tools for geologic timelines and timescales. *In* Keller, G.R., and Baru, C. (eds), *Geoinformatics*. Cambridge University Press, 145–165.

Sadler, P.M., and Cooper, R.A., 2008, Improved resolution and quantified stratigraphic uncertainty – time scales of the future. *Newsletters on Stratigraphy*, **43**: 49–53, https://doi.org/10.1127/0078-0421/2008/0043-0049.

Sadler, P.M., Kemple, W.G., and Kooser, M.A., 2003, CONOP9 programs for solving the stratigraphic correlation and seriation problems as constrained optimization. *In* Harries, P.J. (ed), High-Resolution Approaches in Stratigraphic Paleontology. Topics in Geobiology. *Dordrecht: Kluwer Academic Publishers,* **21**: 461–465.

Sadler, P.M., Cooper, R.A., and Melchin, M.J., 2009, High-resolution, early Paleozoic (Ordovician-Silurian) time scales. *Geological Society of America Bulletin*, **121**: 887–906.

Sadler, P.M., Cooper, R.A., and Melchin, M.J., 2011, Sequencing the graptoloid clade: building a global diversity curve from local range charts, regional composites and global time-lines. *Proceedings of the Yorkshire Geological Society*, **58**: 329–343.

Sadler, P.M., Cooper, R.A., and Crampton, J.S., 2014, High-resolution geobiologic time lines: progress and potential, fifty years after the advent of graphic correlation. *The Sedimentary Record*, **12**: 4–9, https://doi.org/10.2110/sedred.2014.3.

Sadler, P.M., and Sabado, J.A., 2009, Automated correlation, seriation, and the treatment of biotic dissimilarity. *Museum of Northern Arizona Bulletin*, **65**: 21–35.

Savary, J., and Guex, J., 1991, Biograph: un nouveau programme de contsruction des correlations biochronologique basées sur les associations unitaires. *Bulletin Laboratoire Géologique Lausanne*, **313**: 317–340.

Shaw, A.B., 1964, *Time in Stratigraphy*. New York: McGraw-Hill, p. 365.

Shaw, A.B., 1995, Early history of graphic correlation. *In* Mann, K.O., and Lane, H.R. (eds), Graphic Correlation. *SEPM Special Publication,* **53**: 15–19.

Shen, S.Z., Crowley, J.L., Wang, Y., Bowring, S.A., Erwin, D.H., Sadler, P.M., et al., 2011, Calibrating the End-Permian mass extinction. *Science*, **334**: 1367–1372.

Strauss, D.J., and Sadler, P.M., 1989, Classical confidence intervals and the Bayesian probability estimates for ends of local taxon ranges. *Mathematical Geology*, **21**: 411–427.

Sweet, W.C., 1984, Graphic correlation of upper Middle and Upper Ordovician rocks, North American Midcontinental Province, USA. *In* Bruton, D.L. (ed), Aspects of the Ordovician System. *Paleontological Contributions of the University of Oslo,* **295**: 23–25.

Sweet, W.C., 1995, Graphic assembly of a conodont-based composite standard for the Ordovician system of North America. *In* Mann, K. O., and Lane, H.R. (eds), Graphic Correlation. *SEPM Special Publication,* **53**: 139–150.

Sweet, W.C., 2005, Graphical refinement of the conodont database: examples and a plea. *Palaeontology*, **73**: 135–141.

Thompson, R., and Clark, R.M., 1993, Quantitative marine sediment core matching using a modified sequence-slotting algorithm. *In* Hailwood, E.A., and Kidd, R.B. (eds), *High Resolution Stratigraphy*. London: Geological Society of London, 39–49.

Tipper, J.C., 1988, Techniques for quantitative stratigraphic correlations: a review and annotated bibliography. *Geological Magazine*, **125**: 475–494.

Webster, M., Sadler, P.M., Kooser, M.A., and Fowler, E., 2003, Combining stratigraphic sections and museum collections to increase biostratigraphic resolution. *In* Harries, P.J. (ed), *High Resolution Approaches in Stratigraphic Paleontology*. Dordrecht: Kluwer Academic Publishers, 95–128.

Part III

Geologic Periods: Planetary and Precambrian

Chapter 15

H. Hiesinger and K. Tanaka

The Planetary Time Scale

Chapter outline

Abstract

Understanding the geologic and thermal history and evolution of planets, moons, and planetary bodies requires detailed knowledge of the timing of events. On Earth, this information can be readily obtained by detailed fieldwork, something impossible for planetary objects to which we have no direct access. Nevertheless, we have a good, although not perfect, understanding of the relative and absolute timing of geologic processes throughout the solar system from remote sensing data. Complementary information from a variety of sources and techniques can be combined to decipher the geologic history of remote object. This not only allows us to better understand the evolutionary path of each object but also to compare its history with those of other objects. As a result, we now have a broad understanding of the importance of specific geologic processes during different phases of solar system evolution. We will discuss these aspects and the stratigraphic systems of several planetary bodies, including the Moon, Mars, Mercury, Venus, outer solar system moons, asteroids, and comets.

15.1 Introduction and methodologies

From decades of comparative planetology studies, it has become obvious that the terrestrial planets share to some extent a common geologic record, albeit there are also fundamental differences among these planetary objects. For example, all terrestrial bodies show evidence for bombardment of their surfaces with projectiles mostly from the asteroid belt and comets. They also show abundant evidence for volcanism and tectonism, although the styles can be quite different. Stratigraphic studies are the key to deciphering the geologic record of each body and to estimate the relative importance of geologic processes throughout time. Impacts occurred particularly frequently during earlier solar system evolution, leaving a record of preserved impact basins and craters on the surfaces of the terrestrial planets. However, while the Moon, Mercury and Mars record a substantial history of incoming projectiles, other planets like Earth and Venus have retained only a small number of impact craters on their surfaces. For Earth, plate tectonics and erosion accounts for its resurfacing, whereas the Venusian crust appears to have been renewed by convective overturn.

With the onset of modern spacecraft missions that enable close-up observations with the aid of high-resolution cameras and spectrometers, our understanding of planetary surfaces has increased dramatically. For example, we now have images at pixel resolutions of 25 cm for selected regions on Mars, 50 cm for the Moon, 3 m for the asteroid Ceres, 6-m pixel for Jupiter's moon Europa, 15-m pixel for the Saturnian moon Enceladus, 23 m for the asteroid Vesta, and radar imaging data for Venus at a pixel scale of 100 m. Thus we now have data that allow geological mapping of planetary surfaces at scales unimaginable only a few decades ago. However, formal planetary geologic mapping is a lengthy process involving development of high-quality spatial reference systems, innovation and application of specialized image processing techniques, and comprehensive scientific analysis. Because of this, not all planetary bodies have been completely mapped using the latest and highest-resolution data sets. For example, we still rely on lunar geologic mapping dating from the 1960s to 1970s. Thus while concerted geologic mapping efforts in recent years have greatly improved and expanded our understanding of the geologic histories of solid bodies in our solar

Geologic Time Scale 2020. DOI: https://doi.org/10.1016/B978-0-12-824360-2.00015-2

system, more work remains. Chronostratigraphy for objects such as Vesta and Ceres, for example, only now is in the process of definition.

Stratigraphic systems on Earth are defined by boundary stratotype sections, occurrence or disappearance of index fossils, radiogenic ages dates, cycle-magneto, and chemostratigraphy that correlate globally within a short period of time. In other words, it is the abrupt change in fauna/flora and physical properties that merit definition of a chronostratigraphic system. However, because these criteria are either impossible or difficult to apply on planetary bodies, other ways of subdividing geologic time are required. Large impact basins and craters that deposit ejecta material globally or at least across large parts of a planetary surface occur more or less instantaneously. Thus similar to the emergence/extinction of species on Earth, the ejecta blankets of basins are excellent chronostratigraphic markers that can be used to infer a relative stratigraphy of events at local, regional, and global scales.

Methods such as measuring crater density (Fig. 15.1); describing the degradation state of impact craters; and interpreting onlap, embayment, and cross-cutting relationships among geologic materials and features have been applied to investigate the stratigraphic sequence of geologic units and their ages (Hartmann, 1965; Soderblom and Lebofsky, 1972; Boyce and Dial, 1975; Neukum et al., 1975; Wilhelms, 1980; Hiesinger et al., 2012). Whereas the first two methods can be calibrated with radioisotopic and exposure ages of the samples to derive absolute model ages (AMAs), the latter, stratigraphic relationships only provide relative ages of adjacent geologic units. Once the planetary community accepted that most craters on planets and moons were formed by impacts, this opened the possibility to date these surfaces. In principle, the older a surface is, the longer it has been exposed to the bombardment of incoming projectiles. Hence, an older surface will exhibit a larger number of craters than a younger surface. Also, given that smaller projectiles are relatively greater in abundance, smaller diameter craters also make up a greater proportion of the crater population. Thus by counting the number of craters and measuring their sizes, it is possible to derive relative ages of

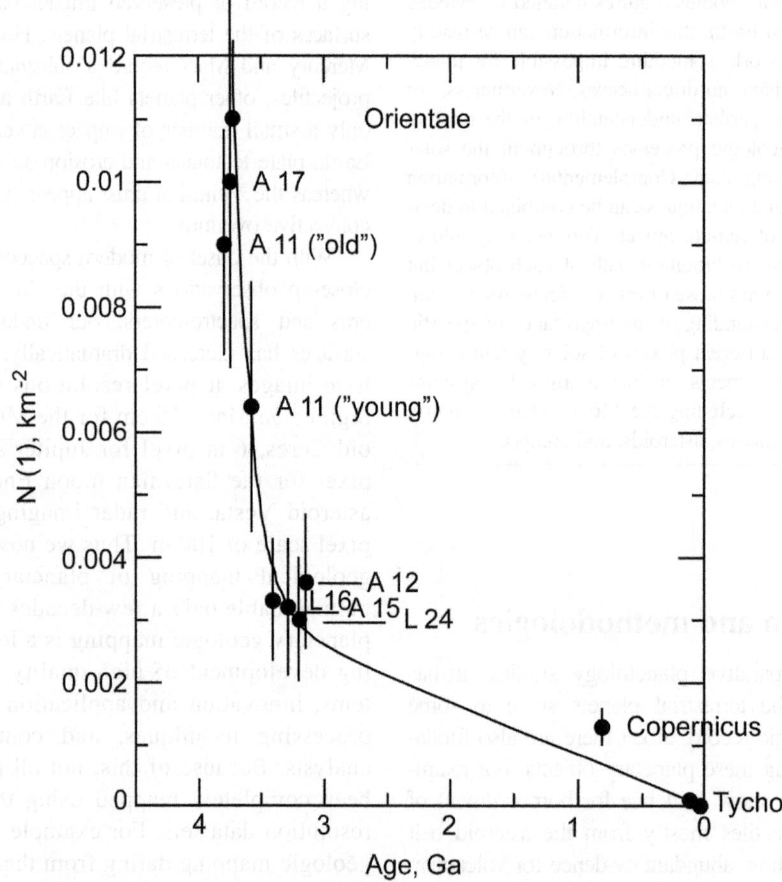

FIGURE 15.1 The lunar chronology, showing the crater density of lunar landing sites with their corresponding radiometric and exposure ages (see text for discussion). The plot shows the crater density in cumulative form. N(1) represents the number of craters of $D > 1$ km, per square km. From the figure it becomes evident that the crater production rate was much higher prior to about 3.6 Ga compared to more recent times. The extrapolation of this trend indicates that surfaces older than ~4.1–4.2 Ga should be saturated with craters, so that survival of older rock units appears unlikely. Adapted from Neukum et al. (2001).

geologic units. Commonly, the crater size-frequency distribution (CSFD) is displayed in log–log plots that show the crater diameter on the x-axis and the crater frequency, that is, the number of craters per unit area, on the y-axis. The Cratering Analysis Techniques Working Group (1979) recommended the graphing and reporting of CSFDs in three different ways: (1) cumulative densities of craters from largest to smallest diameters, (2) incremental densities with diameter bin sizes that increase by a factor of $\sqrt{2}$, and (3) relative crater densities that are normalized to a power-law function with a -3 slope.

CSFDs have proven to be generally accurate and reliable in determining relative ages for planetary surfaces that have statistically disparate crater populations. In combination with stratigraphic information obtained from geologic mapping, CSFD measurements allow us to decipher key stages and events in the chronostratigraphic record of a planet. This approach to stratigraphic analysis has been very successful for the Moon, Mercury, Mars (Fig. 15.2), Vesta, Ceres, and some icy moons. These bodies possess surfaces of diverse relative ages amenable to geologic mapping and crater-dating techniques with available imaging data. However, these techniques are not applicable for all observed bodies. On Earth, Venus, and Jupiter's inner moon, Io, the small total number of recognizable impacts ($\sim$190 on Earth, $\sim$1000 on Venus, 0 on Io) is insufficient to derive meaningful information about relative-age relationships among geologic units. [However, in the case of Earth, we suspect that fossil extinctions and other observations at some major stratigraphic boundaries were caused by large impact events (e.g., Archibald, 2014; Jones, 2014).] In the case of Jupiter's heavily cratered outer moon Callisto, neither CSFDs nor geologic mapping has thus far revealed surfaces of distinguishable relative age; therefore this body has largely developed uniformly in its recorded surface geology. Another complexity is that craters on bodies with significant icy components undergo topographic relaxation. Hence, they might show significantly fewer craters than a nonicy body for surfaces of the same age. Thus geologic mapping and cratering statistics provide the underpinnings for establishing planetary stratigraphic boundaries. However, it must be kept in mind that their accuracy can vary substantially due to the quality and nature of the observations and how they are interpreted.

CSFDs combined with radioisotopic age dates provide the basis for methods of estimating absolute ages of planetary surfaces and materials and thus planetary stratigraphic boundaries. The CSFD methodology enabled Hartmann (1965) to correctly estimate the age of lunar mare basalts. Comparing

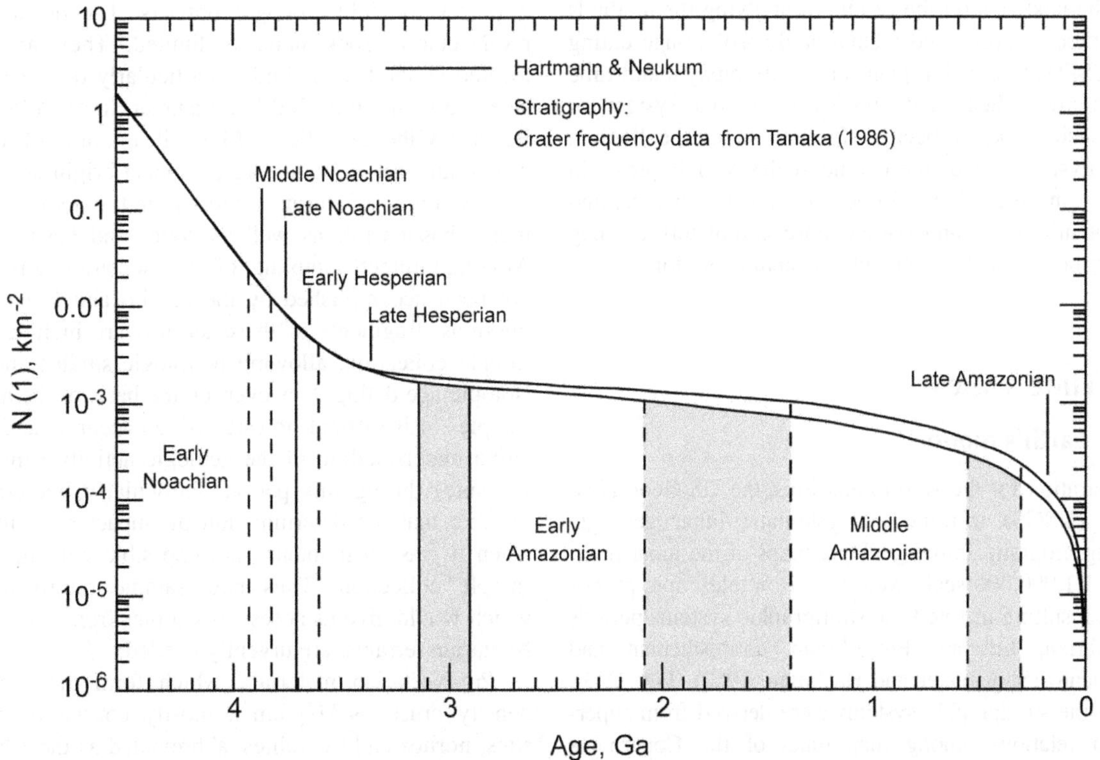

FIGURE 15.2 Log-linear plot of the Martian chronology. The plot shows the crater density, expressed as N(1), that is, the number of craters of D >1 km, per square km, and the corresponding age. The two curves represent the chronologies by Hartmann and Neukum. On the basis of CSFD measurements, the Martian eras were defined by Tanaka. Vertical lines and shaded bands are best estimates for the divisions between the eras, taking into account the uncertainties in the Hartmann/Neukum curves, which are mainly related to uncertainties in the Martian crater production rate. Adapted from Hartmann and Neukum (2001).

the record of terrestrial craters and their ages to lunar CSFDs, Hartmann (1965) proposed that lunar mare regions formed at about 3.6 Ga, a finding that was later confirmed by radioisotopic dating of the returned Apollo samples.

Since the return of the lunar samples in the late 1960s and early 1970s, a large number of absolute radioisotopic ages have been derived by laboratory analyses using a variety of radio isotopic-decay systems, including $^{40}Ar-^{39}Ar$, $^{147}Sm-^{143}Nd$, and $^{207}Pb-^{204}Pb$. Correlating the CSFDs of the surroundings of the Apollo and Luna landing sites with their radioisotopic and exposure ages yielded the lunar chronology function (LCF), which allows for the determination of AMAs for the entire lunar surface (e.g., Hartmann, 1970, 1972; Ryder et al., 1991; Wilhelms, 1987; Neukum and Ivanov, 1994; Stöffler and Ryder, 2001; Neukum et al., 2001).

In addition, making certain assumptions (e.g., a common source of projectiles for all planetary bodies, impact velocities, impact flux at any given object, possible spikes in impact flux), the LCF has been extrapolated to other planetary bodies, including Mars, Mercury, Venus, asteroids, and icy moons of Jupiter and Saturn (e.g., Neukum et al., 2001; Wagner et al., 2006; Werner et al., 2011; Hiesinger et al., 2016). However, extrapolation of the LCF to determine AMAs for bodies in the outer solar system may be problematic (e.g., Bierhaus et al., 2005, 2018).

In the next section the results of applying the methods of geologic mapping and relative and absolute-age dating using CSFDs to develop planetary stratigraphy's and time scales are described for the bodies in our solar system for which such work has been performed. As data collection and analysis proceed, these time scales will improve in accuracy and precision, will develop for new bodies, and will potentially be understood more completely as they relate to both planetary and solar system evolution.

15.2 Time scales

15.2.1 Earth's moon

In preparation for the Apollo missions, the US Geological Survey (USGS) instituted a systematic lunar geologic mapping program. Initial geologic maps of the lunar nearside at 1:1,000,000-scale were based on telescopic photographs, resulting in five time-stratigraphic systems/periods (pre-Imbrian, Imbrian, Procellarian, Eratosthenian and Copernican) (Shoemaker and Hackman, 1962) (Fig. 15.3). Those time-stratigraphic systems were derived from superposition relations among map units of the Copernicus region, where the Copernicus and Eratosthenes craters as well as the basin and mare-fill materials of the Imbrium impact dominate (Fig. 15.4). In the late 1960s and early 1970s, those maps were augmented and improved by about 10 times higher resolution (70–150 m) images from the Lunar Orbiter missions. As a result, in 1971, Wilhelms and McCauley published the seminal map of the nearside of the Moon at 1:5,000,000-scale, applying the same stratigraphic principles as Shoemaker and Hackman (1962) but extending them to the entire lunar nearside.

Further mapping resulted in modifications to the planetary stratigraphy, including division of the pre-Imbrian into the pre-Nectarian and Nectarian introduced by Stuart-Alexander and Wilhelms (1975) and the Imbrian into the Lower and Upper Imbrian Series by Wilhelms (1987). As a consequence of this new understanding, the former Procellarian Period has been eliminated. Yet another major improvement of these maps consists in the assignment of AMAs derived from CSFD measurements to the boundaries of the stratigraphic systems (e.g., Basaltic Volcanism Study Project, 1981; Wilhelms, 1987) (Fig. 15.5 and Table 15.1).

15.2.1.1 Pre-Nectarian Period

Introduced by Stuart-Alexander and Wilhelms (1975), the pre-Nectarian Period represents the time between the formation of the Moon and the Nectaris Basin impact. Thus the pre-Nectarian is the oldest lunar period and consists of ancient, yet still visible terrains and structures that have survived obliteration and burial by subsequent processes. However, pre-Nectarian materials have certainly been reworked by younger impacts. The occurrence of pre-Nectarian rock units is limited. They are mostly located at southern latitudes, particularly on the lunar far side and within the 2300-km-diameter South Pole–Aitken Basin (Wilhelms, 1987). Most, if not all, of the pre-Nectarian geologic units are of impact origin and consist, for example, of basin interiors and exteriors, impact melts, basin rims, as well as crater and basin deposits. Although direct sampling of pre-Nectarian terrains has not been accomplished by the Apollo and Luna landing missions, fragments of these terrains are included in the sample collection, allowing petrologic studies and radioisotopic age dating. However, on the basis of the available samples, it is difficult to establish an accurate and quantitative understanding of the geologic activity (impact and volcanic) during this period. Particularly bothersome is the fact that the determination of impact rates for times when it was most intense is impossible with the current sample collection. Thus new sample return missions, which would give us access to samples from such old pre-Nectarian terrains, are urgently needed.

Pre-Nectarian materials, which form the early low-density crust ($\sim$3.0 g/cm^2), mostly consist of anorthosites, norites and troctolites, abbreviated as the ANT suite (Taylor, 1975; Prinz and Keil, 1977), as well as highly differentiated KREEP rocks that contain relatively large abundances of potassium (K), rare-earth elements (REE), phosphorus (P), and other trace elements (e.g., Hubbard et al., 1971). On the basis of detailed analyses of the

Apollo and Luna samples, the concept of a several hundred-of-kilometers-deep global magma ocean has been developed, and the crust and upper mantle were interpreted as differentiation products of this magma ocean. In this scenario, the lower density ANT suite would buoyantly rise to the surface, while denser ultramafic rocks would sink to the bottom (e.g., Walker et al., 1975). Containing many elements that are incompatible with the crystal structures of rock-forming minerals, KREEP rocks would accumulate as residues at the base of the crust. Unaltered pre-Nectarian rocks have not been unambiguously identified. In fact, the petrographic textures and meteoritic trace-element contamination of pre-Nectarian rocks have been interpreted to indicate impact melting and mixing of multiple lithologies, explaining the wide variability in their textures and compositions (e.g., McKay et al., 1979). Radioisotopic ages of pre-Nectarian rocks derived from several methods (^{40}Ar$-^{39}$Ar, ^{87}Rb$-^{87}$Sr, ^{147}Sm$-^{143}$Nd, ^{235}U$-^{207}$Pb, ^{207}Pb$-^{204}$Pb) range from 3.93 to 4.52 Ga (e.g., Wilhelms, 1987; Stöffler and Ryder, 2001). From the sample collection, it is clear that the solidification of the crust between 4.1 and 4.4 Ga must have been a complex process, including intrusions and bombardment. During the pre-Nectarian Period about 33 (11 are provisional) impact basins >300 km in diameter were formed, including the 2300-km-diameter South Pole–Aitken Basin and the highly debated, 3200-km-diameter Procellarum Basin. Applying superposition criteria, Wilhelms (1987) subdivided these 33 basins into 9 age groups.

15.2.1.2 Nectarian Period

Stuart-Alexander and Wilhelms (1975) defined the Nectarian Period to begin with the impact of the 860-km-diameter Nectaris Basin and to end with the formation of the Imbrian Basin. Wilhelms (1987) proposed that Nectarian materials might have originally covered as much as 75% of the lunar surface. Today, Nectarian units compose parts of the lunar highlands and were emplaced by Nectaris and other basins as well as numerous impact craters. Among the 10–12 Nectarian basins with diameters in excess of 300 km, the 1060-km-diameter Crisium Basin is the largest. Nectarian rocks were sampled by the Apollo 16, 17, and Luna 20 missions and were thought to be related to the Nectarian-age basins of Nectaris, Serenitatis and Crisium, although the exact assignment of samples to a specific basin remains elusive and highly debated. In addition, Nectarian plains might have formed by volcanism, although the importance of volcanic processes during the Nectarian Period remains unclear. If it were the consequence of primordial impact heating, it might have been widespread and abundant. Alternatively, if Nectarian volcanism resulted from heating from radioactive decay, it might have been relatively minor. However, there is evidence for widespread volcanism in the form of cryptomaria, that is, volcanic deposits that were subsequently buried by ejecta but are still recognizable by dark halo craters that penetrated the ejecta to excavate dark volcanic material (e.g., Schultz and Spudis, 1979; Antonenko et al., 1995; Hawke and Bell, 1981).

Assigning an absolute age to the Nectaris Basin has proven to be very difficult, because it remains unclear which sample best dates the impact event. Consequently, on the basis of radioisotopic dating, Nectaris was proposed to be 3.85 ± 0.05 (Stöffler et al., 1985) or 3.92 ± 0.03 Ga (Deutsch and Stöffler, 1987), whereas CSFD measurements of Neukum and Ivanov (1994) indicate an AMA of 4.1 ± 0.1 Ga. Because the dated samples show a spread in ages, this raises the question of which age actually is representative of the basin-formation. Some groups argue that the youngest radioisotopic age for molten inclusions best dates the impact (e.g., Jessberger et al., 1974; Basaltic Volcanism Study Project, 1981; Wilhelms, 1987), whereas other groups prefer the most abundant age (e.g., Neukum, 1983; Neukum and Ivanov, 1994). In the latter view the youngest age only reflects postbasin-forming events. In addition, Hartmann (2003) proposed that impact melts older than 4 Ga were so heavily comminuted by subsequent impacts that they were rarely collected and radioisotopically dated. Accurate knowledge of the formation ages of Nectarian basins is crucially important to lunar chronostratigraphy, because it has implications for the understanding of the temporal fluctuations of the impact rate. For example, if the basin-forming period was short (e.g., 20–200 Myr), this would result in a spike in impact rate, known as the "lunar cataclysm" or the "late heavy bombardment" (e.g., Turner et al., 1973; Stöffler and Ryder, 2001; Strom et al., 2005). To explain such a spike in impact rate, dynamical models have been developed that predict the migration of Jupiter and Saturn (e.g., Gomes et al., 2005; Tsiganis et al., 2005) or the formation and migration of outer planets (e.g., Liou and Malhotra, 1997; Levison et al., 2001). However, the initial observation that many Apollo samples show radioisotopic dates of 3.9–4.0 Ga, that is, the "classical" cataclysm (Tera et al., 1973), might simply reflect the fact that most samples were retrieved from the ejecta blanket of the Imbrium impact. If true, the peak in ages would only date the Imbrium Basin rather than allowing measurement of the Nectarian impact rate. Consequently, most researchers favor a longer period of basin-forming events and declining cratering (e.g., Hartmann, 2003; Hiesinger et al., 2012), although spikes related to asteroid collisions remain plausible.

15.2.1.3 Early Imbrian Epoch

On the lunar nearside, the 1160-km-diameter Imbrium Basin is the most dominant impact structure. The basin defines the base of the Imbrian Period. It deposited ejecta, characterized by radial grooves known as "Imbrium sculpture," across

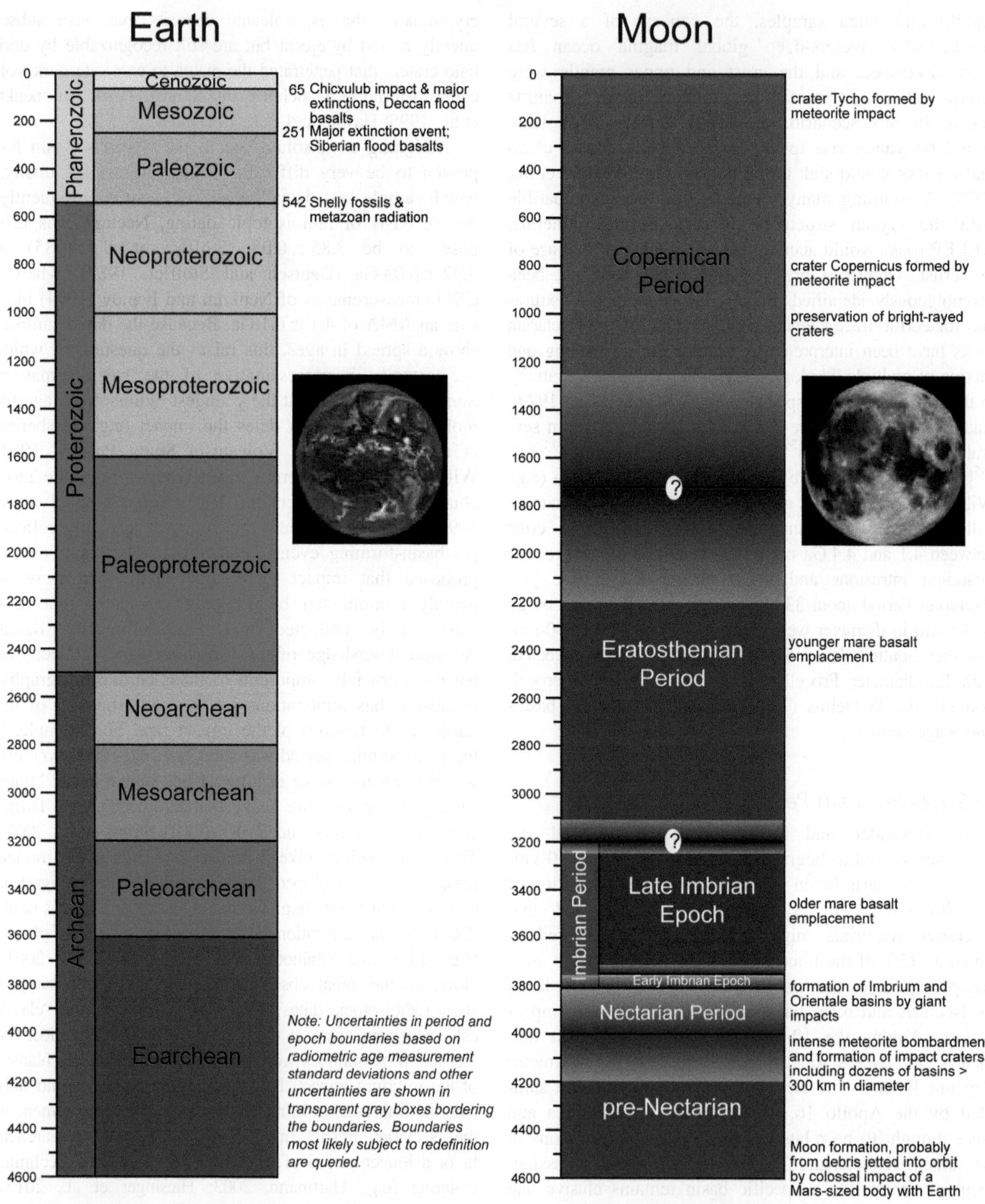

FIGURE 15.3 Planetary time scales of the Earth, Moon, Mars and Venus. The thick dashed line separates the Venus and Mercury time scales.

large parts of the Moon. The basin exhibits a prominent ring composed of uplifted material and thick ejecta deposits known as the Fra Mauro Formation that extends hundreds of kilometers away from the basin. The interior of the basin has been flooded by mare basalts of various ages. Partly superposed on the Imbrium ejecta is ejecta of the 930-km-diameter Orientale Basin, which is the youngest and best-preserved lunar impact basin. Like the Imbrium Basin, the

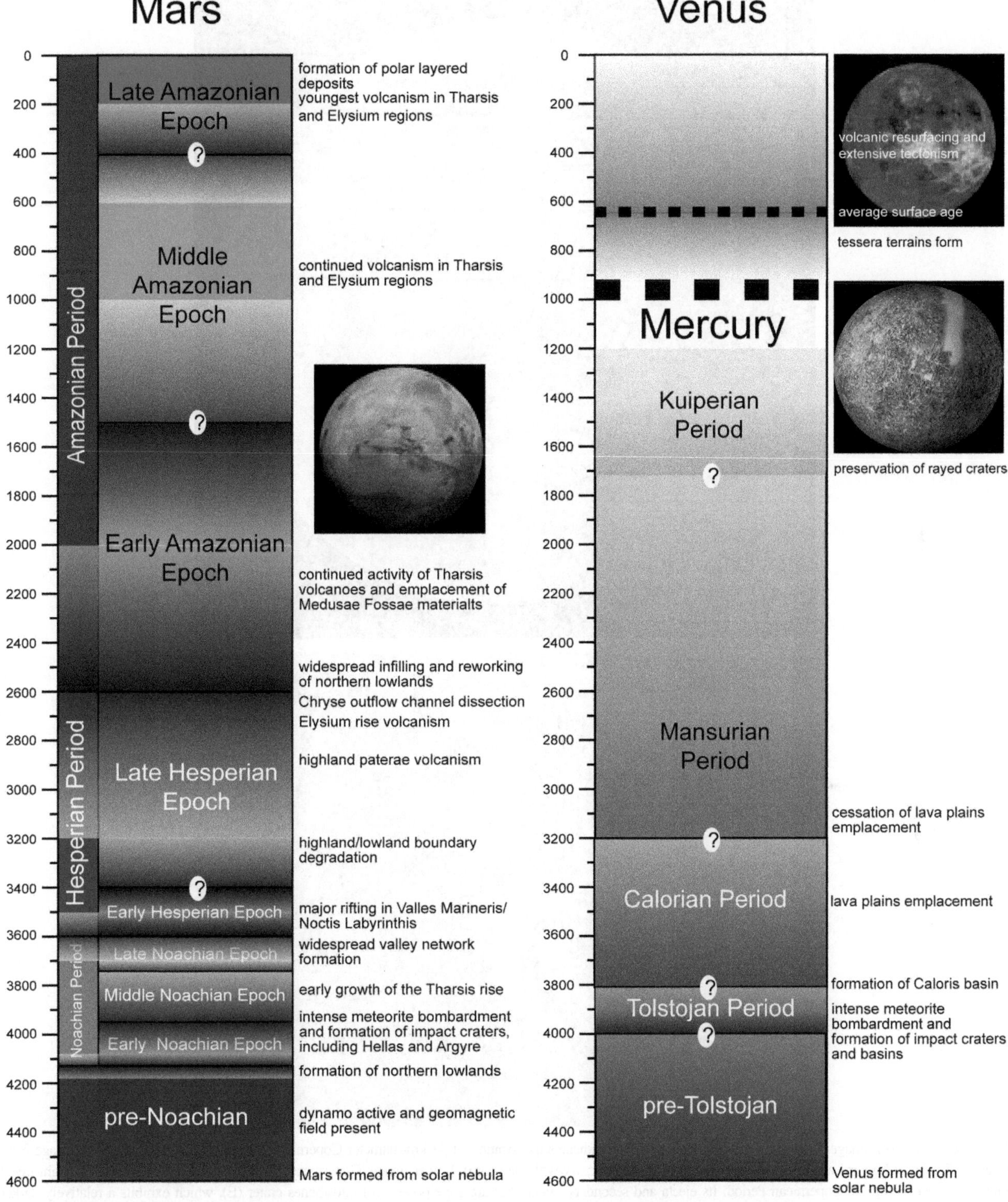

FIGURE 15.3 (Continued).

Orientale Basin was also formed during the Early Imbrian Epoch. On the basis of his mapping, Wilhelms (1987) proposed that some mare basalts were superposed by Orientale ejecta. In addition, some of the oldest exposed mare basalts in Oceanus Procellarum and Mare Nubium likely were erupted during this epoch (Hiesinger et al., 2003). By the end of the epoch, Early Imbrian materials covered ~20% of the planet (Wilhelms, 1987).

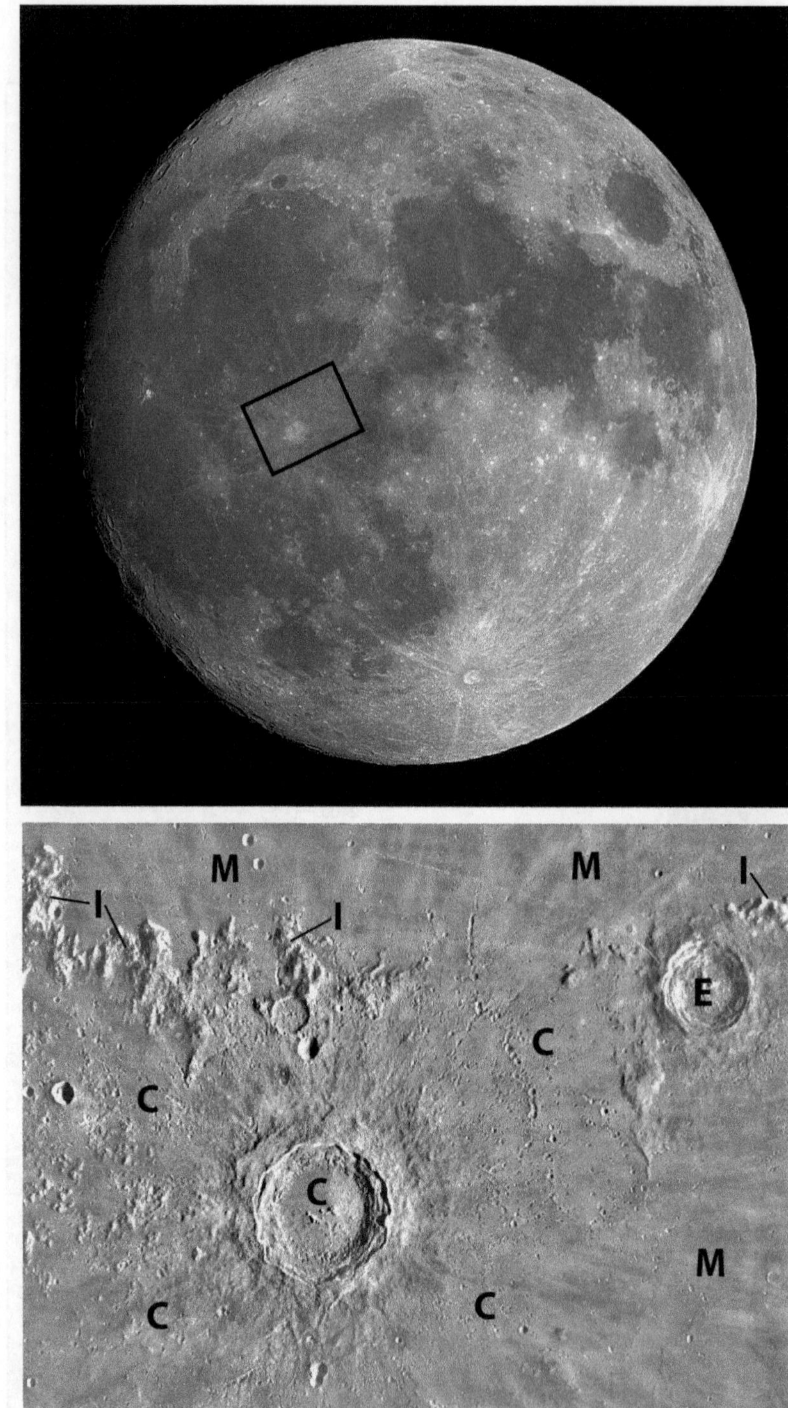

FIGURE 15.4 Top image: The lunar nearside. The black box indicates the location of 93-km-diameter Copernicus crater at 9.7°N, long 20.1°W (Image from Gregory Terrance; Finger Lakes Instrumentation, Lima, New York; www.fli-cam.com). Lower image: Copernicus crater (C) is the type locality for bright-rayed craters formed during the Copernican Period. Its ejecta and secondary craters (C) are superposed on Eratosthenes crater (E), which exhibits a relatively darker albedo and no visible rays, thus representing the Eratosthenian Period. The Eratosthenes crater impacted relatively smooth mare materials (M) of the Late Imbrian Epoch, hence being younger. The rugged rim of the Imbrium Basin (I), which defines the base of the Early Imbrian Epoch, is the oldest geologic unit in the area (Lunar Orbiter IV image mosaic; north at top; illumination from right; courtesy of USGS Astrogeology Team).

The absolute age of Imbrium Basin remains unclear. On the basis of radioisotopic ages of impact melt rocks and KREEP-rich breccias from the Apollo 14, 15, and 16 landing sites, it has been argued that the Imbrium impact occurred either at 3.77 ± 0.02 (Stöffler and Ryder, 2001) or at 3.85 ± 0.02 Ga (Wilhelms, 1987; Stöffler and Ryder, 2001),

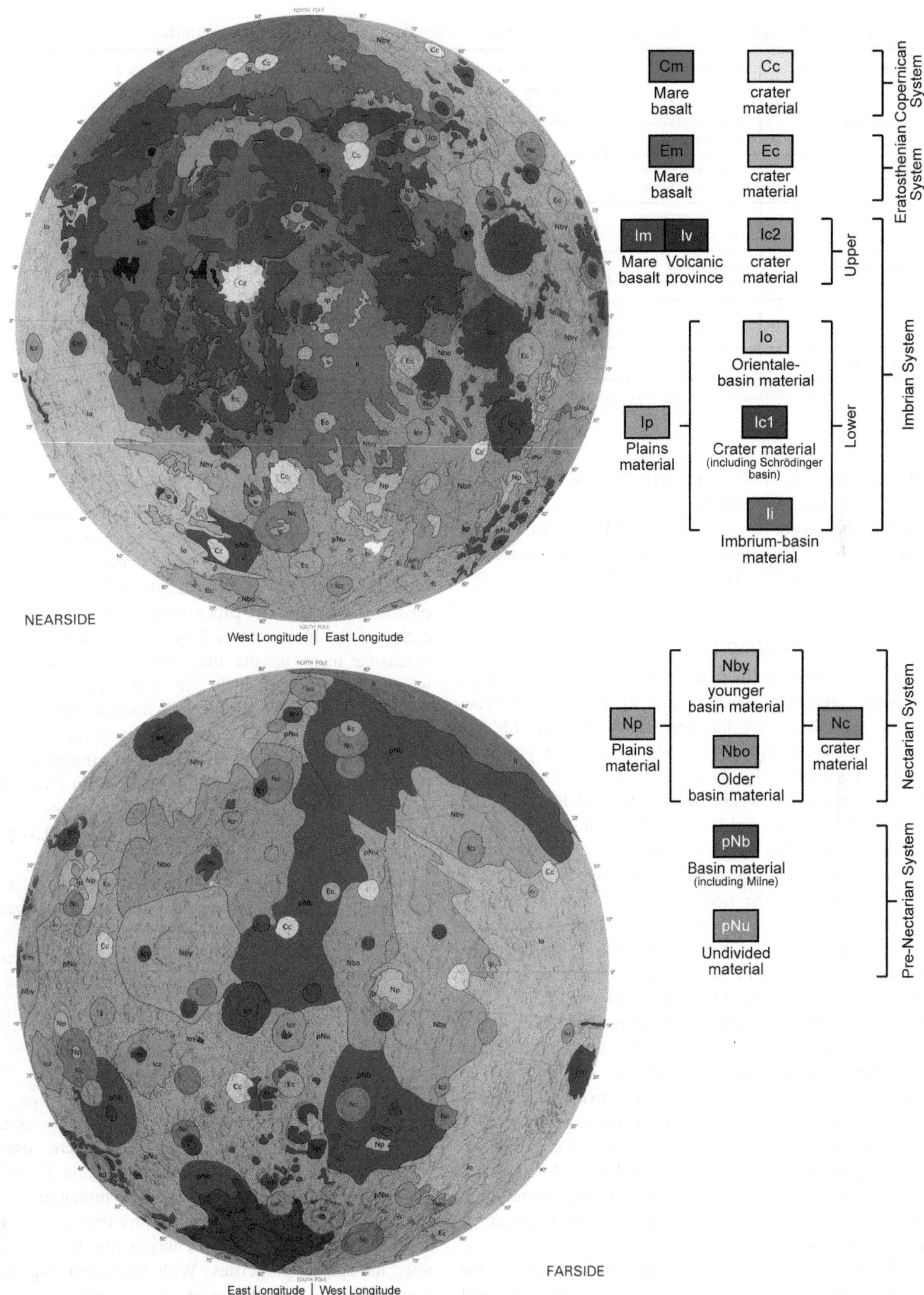

FIGURE 15.5 Generalized geologic map of the lunar surface.

TABLE 15.1 Stratigraphic, radiometric-age, and crater-density data for lunar chronologic units.

Chronologic unit	Referent unit	Lower radiometric-age boundary (Ga)	No. craters ≥1 km per 10^6 km^2	No. craters ≥20 km per 10^6 km^2
Copernican Period	Bright-rayed craters (e.g., Copernicus)	2.2–1.25	<750 (mare) <1000 (crater)	n/a
Eratosthenes Period	Low-albedo craters (e.g., Eratosthenes)	3.24–3.11	750 to ~2500 (mare)	n/a
Late Imbrian Epoch	Post–Orientale mare basalts	3.80–3.72	~2500 (mare) to ~22,000	28
Early Imbrian Epoch	Imbrian Basin materials	3.87–3.75	~22,000–48,000 (basin)	18–33
Nectarian Period	Nectaris Basin materials	4.20–3.80	n/a	23–88
Pre-Nectarian Period	n/a	~4.5	n/a	>70

See text for discussion of referent units and radiometric-age boundaries. Crater-density ranges from Wilhelms (1987; Table 7.3).

whereas Neukum (1983) favored an age of 3.92 Ga. Although Orientale Basin material has not been sampled directly, the superposition of its ejecta by an Ap17 basalt dated to be 3.72 Ga suggests that it formed sometime between 3.85 and 3.72 Ga (Wilhelms, 1987).

15.2.1.4 Late Imbrian Epoch

Wilhelms (1987) defined the top of the Early Imbrian Orientale materials as the base of the Late Imbrian Epoch. This boundary has been dated at 3.80–3.85 Ga (see summary in Hiesinger et al., 2011) or as young as 3.72 Ga (Wilhelms, 1987), given the ages of the Imbrium Basin (see also discussion in Stöffler and Ryder, 2001) and the oldest measured Late Imbrian mare basalts at the Apollo 17 site. The major characteristic of this epoch is the occurrence of widespread and voluminous mare basalt eruptions on both the nearside as well as the far side. These basalts make up two-thirds of nearside, plains-forming mare or approximately one-sixth of the lunar surface. Samples from these basalts were returned by the Apollo 11, 15, 16, and 17 missions, as well as the Luna 24 mission. These samples, in concert with multispectral remote sensing observations, show that lunar mare basalts are heterogeneous in composition, age, and texture. The discovery of sinuous rilles, domes, and pyroclastic deposits suggests a diversity of eruption and ascent styles of lunar volcanics of this age. Due to extended periods of impact gardening, actual outcrops of Late Imbrian volcanic and other intact rocks are mostly missing on the lunar surface, because they are most likely buried beneath a few-meters-thick regolith.

By the beginning of the Late Imbrian Epoch, the impact rate had declined drastically, and no additional large basins formed since then.

15.2.1.5 Eratosthenian Period

This period was introduced by Shoemaker and Hackman (1962) to describe a period that is characterized by formation of low- to intermediate-albedo craters superposed on Imbrian-age units. The type locality is Eratosthenes crater on the lunar nearside. Since then, detailed mapping and dating of the lunar surface have revealed the existence of extensive mare basalts that are of Eratosthenian age, which cover approximately 5% of the lunar surface (e.g., Wilhelms and McCauley, 1971; Wilhelms, 1987; Hiesinger et al., 2003). However, the exact timing of the beginning of the Eratosthenian Period, as well as its stratigraphic merit remains a matter of debate. Stöffler and Ryder (2001) linked the base of the Eratosthenian Period to the ages of Apollo 12 mare materials, which are at least 3.15 ± 0.04 Ga but younger than 3.30 ± 0.02 Ga, and Luna 24 mare samples, which exhibit an age of 3.22 ± 0.02 Ga. Its significance has been challenged, because no large impact basins formed during this time. However, volcanism showed a pronounced transition from high flux rates during the Imbrian Period to significantly lower fluxes during the Eratosthenian Period (Hiesinger et al., 2003).

15.2.1.6 Copernican Period

On the lunar nearside, Copernicus crater can be seen with the naked eye and is easily recognized by its extensive bright-ray pattern. Such bright rays were used by Shoemaker and Hackman (1962) to define the Copernican Period. The bright rays are formed by immature soil that has been freshly exposed/deposited by the impact, yet not exposed long enough to space weathering to significantly alter its optical properties. With continued exposure to micrometeorite bombardment, solar wind implantation, and cosmic ray exposure, bright rays become darker until they blend with the surrounding terrain. Materials of the Copernican Period only cover a few percentage of the lunar surface, because volcanism and impact cratering had decreased drastically. Copernicus material was supposedly collected at the Apollo 12 landing site, which is situated on top of one of its bright rays. Radioisotopic dating of these samples revealed an age of $\sim 800 \pm 15$ Ma for Copernicus (Bogard et al., 1994), although older ages have also been proposed (Stöffler and Ryder, 2001). Copernicus crater itself does not date the beginning of the Copernican Period, because it is younger than many other bright-ray craters. Recent studies also indicate that some bright rays might have a compositional origin and thus not provide any time information as do maturity rays. While the exact beginning of the Copernican Period remains fuzzy, Wilhelms (1987) proposed a sample from the Apollo 15 landing site, possibly from either Aristillus or Autolycus craters, might represent the oldest Copernican sample. If true, this would place the beginning of the Copernican Period at about 1.29 ± 0.04 Ga (Bernatowicz et al., 1978). Alternatively, Ryder et al. (1991) argued that the $\sim 2.1 \pm 0.1$ Ga age for a shock-melted KREEP basalt sample, also collected at the Apollo 15 site, may be Autolycus ejecta. Because Autolycus is a relatively degraded bright-ray crater, it might define the base of the Copernican Period (Wilhelms, 1987; Stöffler and Ryder, 2001). During the Copernican Period, impact cratering and volcanic activity further declined and only a few Copernican basalts are known (Hiesinger et al., 2003). However, a study by Bottke et al. (2007) proposed a spike in cratering at about 160 Ma and a study by Mazrouei et al. (2019) even argued for an increase in cratering by a factor of 2.6 at about 290 Ma. Recently, irregular mare patches have been suggested to be less than 100 Ma, although such young ages have been challenged (Braden et al., 2014; Qiao et al., 2017). Thus the end of lunar volcanism remains uncertain.

15.2.2 Mars

Over the past few decades, spacecraft missions have resulted in Mars becoming the most geologically investigated and mapped extraterrestrial body. Although early Earth-based telescopes enabled viewing of the waxing and waning of the Martian polar caps, smaller geologic features were not resolved. Thus detailed geologic mapping and the derivation of a chronostratigraphy had to wait for higher resolution images returned by spacecraft missions, beginning with the Mariner missions of the early 1960s. On the basis of Mariner 9 mission data, the USGS initiated the first global mapping program, which subdivided the planet's surface into 30 quadrangles. These data had a spatial pixel scale of 1–2 km and resulted in geologic maps at 1:5,000,000-scale. Scott and Carr (1978) produced a geologic map at 1:25,000,000-scale and defined the Noachian, Hesperian and Amazonian periods based on specific terrains of selected type locations. Early CSFD measurements provided the first ages of Martian surfaces (e.g., Hartmann, 1973). Image resolution improved drastically with the two Viking spacecraft, which provided images with 100–300-m pixel scales. With the improvement in image resolution came new geologic maps at 1:15,000,000-scale (Scott and Tanaka, 1986; Greeley and Guest, 1987) and a new subdivision of the chronostratigraphic periods into eight epochs, that is, the Early, Middle and Late Noachian, the Early and Late Hesperian, and the Early, Middle and Late Amazonian (Tanaka, 1986) (Figs. 15.2, 15.3, and 15.6). The earlier Martian epochs may be roughly equivalent to the early lunar periods and epochs, because they shared similar high impact rates and CSFDs (e.g., Neukum and Wise, 1976; Tanaka, 1986; Hartmann and Neukum, 2001; Strom et al., 2005).

Much improved topographic data from the Mars Global Surveyor (MGS) mission, as well as planet-wide thermal and visual imaging and other datasets from the Mars Odyssey, Mars Express and Mars Reconnaissance Orbiter missions, enabled more detailed geologic mapping and CSFD studies, as well as reassessments of the global stratigraphy (Fig. 15.7). As a result, Werner and Tanaka (2011) fitted the boundaries of each Martian epoch (Table 15.2), beginning with the end of the Early Noachian, to idealized size-frequency distributions at single crater diameters and derived ages based on the crater production models of Ivanov (2001) and Hartmann (2005). In addition, the concept of a pre-Noachian Period emerged, based on preservation of buried and subtle basin landforms and development of crustal signatures of remanent magnetization, thought to end with the formation of the northern lowlands (e.g., Nimmo and Tanaka, 2005; Frey, 2006).

These efforts led to updated global mapping and relative-age dating based on 48 detailed, targeted crater counts of 23 key stratigraphic units (Platz et al., 2012; Tanaka et al., 2014b). In addition, a global database of craters ≥ 1 km in diameter (Robbins and Hynek, 2012) enabled dating of individual outcrops, although with lower precision. These investigations enabled global assignments of relative ages to all map outcrops, including surface units that have broadly time-transgressive formational histories (Tanaka et al., 2014a).

Today, we have a reasonably good understanding of the cratering rate on Mars, which comes from observations of Mars-crossing asteroids and comets and their calibration/scaling to the lunar cratering rate (e.g., Basaltic Volcanism Study Project, 1981; Neukum and Ivanov, 1994; Hartmann and Neukum, 2001; Ivanov, 2001; Neukum et al., 2001). This knowledge will grow as we acquire higher resolution imaging data (e.g., HiRISE images at 25 cm/pixel; MOC images at ~ 2 m/pixel) that will allow us to study craters down to meter scale (e.g., Malin et al., 2006). Thus AMAs of the Martian surface and its chronostratigraphic markers can be derived from CSFD measurements. However, like

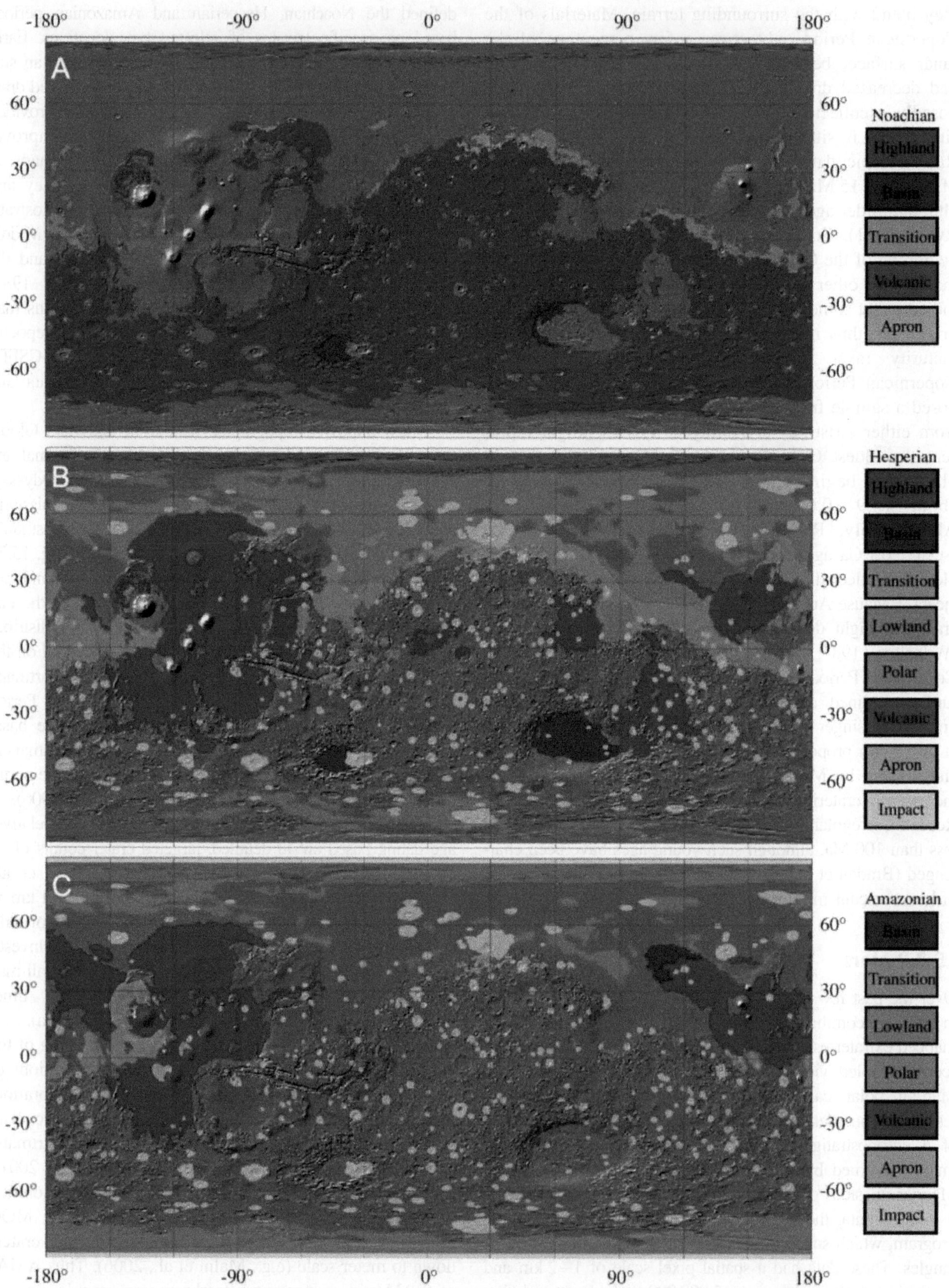

FIGURE 15.6 Simplified geologic maps of Mars, which show the distribution of major material types and their ages: (A) Noachian, (B) Hesperian, (C) Amazonian. Some units span two periods. Basemap is a MOLA shaded-relief digital elevation model (128 pixel/degree) superposed by a global THEMIS daytime infrared mosaic (100 m/pixel). Equirectangular projection, 30 degree grid (Tanaka et al., 2014a). *MOLA*, Mars Orbiter Laser Altimeter.

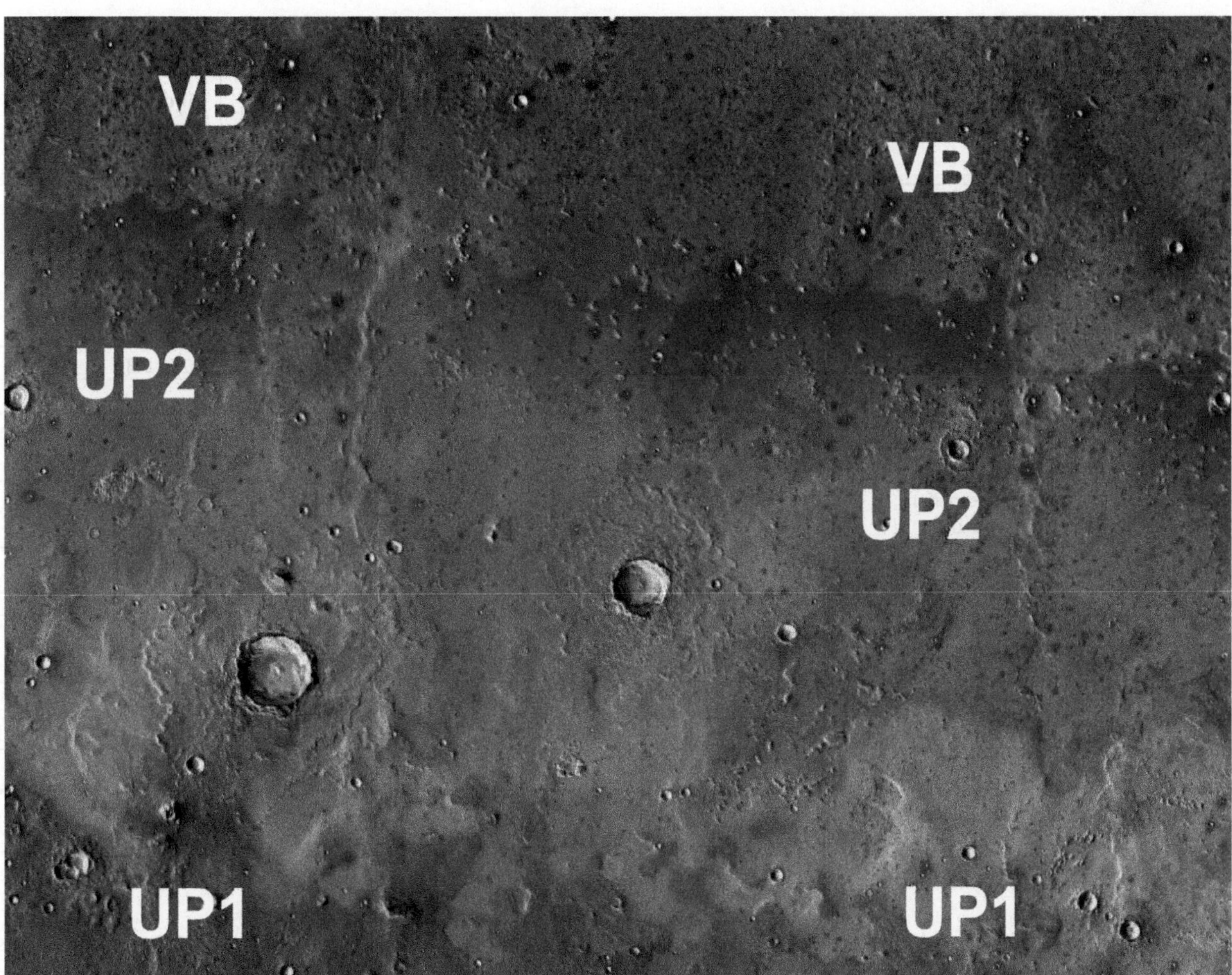

FIGURE 15.7 Type locality of geologic units of Tanaka et al. (2005) in south-central Utopia Planitia in the northern lowlands of Mars. The Vastitas Borealis units (VB), which define the base of the Amazonian Period, are characterized by a relatively bright (i.e., warmer), finely ridged, and hummocky surface. They show a lobate margin with superposed smooth, locally knobby and ridged Late Hesperian Utopia Planitia 2 unit (UP2). The UP2 embays the Early Hesperian Utopia Planitia 1 unit (UP1), which shows depressions and scarps resulting in a rolling and hollowed surface. Center of the 412-km wide figure is near 19°N, 113°E. The figure combines a Thermal Emission Imaging System daytime infrared image mosaic (~230 m/pixel) in which brightness indicates surface temperature and a color shaded-relief digital elevation model from Mars Orbiter Laser Altimeter data (brown is high, purple is low; ~460 m/pixel).

on the Moon, dating small surfaces with small impact craters are challenging and require careful interpretation. In particular, small craters are more difficult to identify and measure, are more prone to resurfacing, and are more heavily affected by secondary cratering and the effects of the Martian atmosphere than larger craters (e.g., Chapman et al.,1969; Hartmann, 1971; Chapman, 1974; Soderblom et al., 1974; Basaltic Volcanism Study Project, 1981; Tanaka, 1986; Hiesinger et al., 2011). Again, the new higher resolution images will allow us to improve our understanding of these factors on the CSFD measurements. McEwen et al. (2005), for example, proposed that more than 50% of all craters smaller than ~600 m in Hesperian areas are secondary craters and that the age determinations are wrong by factors of several hundreds or a thousand. However, the formation rate of new decameter craters on Mars (e.g., Malin et al., 2006) is much higher than predicted by McEwen et al. (2005) and is within a factor of 3 of the rates used in the Hartmann and Neukum (2001) isochrons. Not only AMAs can be obtained from CSFD measurements. As the size frequency-distribution of craters on Mars (i.e., the production function) has been measured independently by several groups (e.g., Neukum et al., 2001; Hartmann, 2005; Werner, 2006; Hartmann et al., 2007), we can use CSFDs also to determine the thickness of the resurfacing younger deposit or the thickness of the eroded layer (e.g., Hiesinger et al., 2002). This is possible because the CSFD of such a unit will deviate from the production function and the depth/diameter ratios of craters for which this deviation occurs can be used to calculate the deposited/eroded layer

TABLE 15.2 Referent units and crater-density data and model absolute ages for bases of Martian chronologic units.

Chronologic Unit	Referent Unit	No. Craters ≥1 km per 10^6 km^2	No. Craters ≥5 km per 10^6 km^2	No. Craters ≥16 km per 10^6 km^2	Model Age of Lower Boundary (Ga)
Late Amazonian	Amazonian polar undivided unit	<160	n/a	n/a	0.27–0.33
Middle Amazonian	Middle Amazonian layered unit	160–600	<25	n/a	1.03–1.23
Early Amazonian	Early Amazonian Basin unit	600–2100	25–67	n/a	3.24–3.37
Late Hesperian	Late Hesperian lowland unit	2100–3000	67–125	n/a	3.39–3.61
Early Hesperian	Early Hesperian volcanic unit	3000–4800	125–200	<25	3.56–3.71
Late Noachian	Late Noachian highland unit	n/a	200–400	25–100	3.83–3.85
Middle Noachian	Middle Noachian highland unit	n/a	>400	100–200	3.94–3.96
Early Noachian	Early Noachian highland unit	n/a	n/a	>200	4.18–4.08
Pre-Noachian	n/a	n/a	n/a	n/a	~4.5

Chronologic and referent units and crater densities from Tanaka (1986), Werner and Tanaka (2011), and Tanaka et al. (2014b). Model-age boundaries from Michael (2013).

thickness. For example, should a given area exhibit a deficiency of craters smaller than 100 m, this would imply that a layer thickness equivalent to the rim height/diameter ratio has been eroded/deposited.

Additional relevant information on the surface of Mars can be obtained from Martian meteorites. CSFD measurements suggest that the majority of lava plains on Mars were erupted in the Noachian to early Hesperian, with infrequent eruptions continuing into the Late Hesperian and Amazonian (Platz et al., 2015). In the Martian meteorite collection, we find mostly igneous rocks that were ejected from less than 10 source regions on Mars (Nyquist et al., 2001). The radioisotopic ages determined for these meteorites match the CSFD age range with the exception of meteorite ALH84001, which is much older and appears to be an igneous cumulate of the ancient Martian crust. In terms of composition, Shergotty–Nakhla–Chassigny (SNC) meteorites indicate that the surface of Mars is composed of basalt, lherzolite, clinopyroxenite and dunite (e.g., Nyquist et al., 2001, and references therein). Using spectral mapping techniques, the bedrock was found to generally have pyroxene-rich basaltic to andesitic compositions, although local areas also are enriched in hematite, phyllosilicate minerals, and hydrated sulfates (e.g., Christensen et al., 2000a, 2000b; Bibring et al., 2005). Unfortunately, this remote sensing compositional information is limited to a few regions where ubiquitously occurring ferric-oxide rich dust does not obscure the bedrock compositions.

15.2.2.1 Pre-Noachian Period

Although not a formal period, the pre-Noachian is commonly considered to cover the time between crustal formation and the formation of the northern lowlands of Mars (e.g., Frey, 2005, 2006; Nimmo and Tanaka, 2005). The early crust likely formed from a solidifying magma ocean, similar to the lunar magma ocean about ~4.5 Ga, having a basaltic andesite or andesite composition (Nimmo and Tanaka, 2005). Because subsequent impact bombardment destroyed most of the evidence, not much is known about the geologic activity during the pre-Noachian period. Thus the period is mainly manifested in the occurrence of "quasi-circular depressions" (QCDs), presumably old impact craters that have been identified by Frey et al. (2002) in topography data. There are no exposed pre-Noachian outcrops known from the surface, although the lower walls of uplifted and eroded Valles Marineris might be good candidates. The only meteorite that might represent pre-Noachian materials is the orthopyroxenite ALH84001, which exhibits radioisotopic dates of ~3.89–4.56 Ga. On the basis of Sm–Nd isotopic abundances, Nyquist et al. (2001) argued for an age of 4.51 ± 0.11 Ga. In their interpretation, the younger age derived from $^{39}Ar-^{40}Ar$ and Rb−Sr measurements is related to later heating, plausibly by impacts.

Another characteristic of the pre-Noachian Period is a significant crustal remanent magnetization of highland rocks that have been detected by the MGS magnetometer (Connerney et al., 2001). These data revealed that the magnetization associated with the two large southern hemisphere impact basins, Hellas and Argyre, as well as the Tharsis rise is much weaker than elsewhere on Mars. It has been speculated that large impacts and magmatic activity can obliterate the magnetization of these terrains, although the timing of the end of the magnetization remains speculative. On the basis of his study of QCDs superposed on the Utopia and other basins, Frey (2006) proposed that the northern lowlands might have formed at around ~4.13 ± 0.05 Ga. However, this age has been derived from the −2 power-law extrapolation of 16−200 km diameter craters of the crater density versus age relationship of Tanaka (1986). Thus because lunar CSFDs do not follow simple power laws but rather a complex function (e.g., Neukum et al., 2001), this age should be used with caution.

15.2.2.2 Early Noachian Epoch

The exact timing of the onset of the Noachian Period is unclear, but Frey (2006) proposed that the beginning of the Noachian Period occurred after the formation of the northern lowlands. Heavily cratered highland materials making up the rim of Hellas Basin (~2400 km diameter) and other rugged terrains in the middle and southern latitudes are the primary materials formed during and defining the Early Noachian Epoch (Tanaka et al., 2014b). Early Noachian heavily cratered isolated massifs around the southern outskirts of Daedalia Planum show evidence for both crustal contraction and extension that demonstrate strong tectonism during the Noachian Period (e.g., Scott and Tanaka, 1986; Tanaka, 1986; Greeley and Guest, 1987; Dohm et al., 2001; Frey, 2006; Hauber et al., 2010). Tanaka et al. (2014a) reported that at present about 12% of the Martian surface is covered by Early Noachian materials. Presumably, the entire planet was once covered by Early Noachian and remnant pre-Noachian terrains, but since then has been largely buried, eroded, or obliterated by impacts and other geological processes. In particular, Hellas Basin scarred a large proportion of the highland surface at about 3.99 Ga (Werner, 2008), and at least 65 basins greater than 150 km in diameter formed during this epoch based on CSFD measurements and stratigraphic relationships (Werner, 2008; Irwin et al., 2013; Robbins and Hynek, 2012; Robbins et al., 2013; Tanaka et al., 2014b). Depending on the absolute age model applied, the end of the Early Noachian Epoch was around 3.94−3.96 Ga (Michael, 2013).

15.2.2.3 Middle Noachian Epoch

Although relatively short, this epoch is important because Middle Noachian materials cover about 24% of the Martian surface, consisting of rugged cratered terrains of impact ejecta and melt, as well as of volcanic and sedimentary origin (e.g., Werner, 2006; Irwin et al., 2013). Tanaka et al. (1988) proposed that Middle Noachian terrains originally might have covered as much as two-thirds of the planet. Fifteen or more basins greater than 150 km in diameter are formed during this epoch, including Isidis (~2100 km diameter) and Argyre (~1500 km diameter) basins (Tanaka et al., 2014b). Today, Middle Noachian terrains are located mostly in equatorial and southern highlands but also farther north (~40°N) in Arabia Terra. In the Tharsis volcanic province, few Middle Noachian materials have been identified (e.g., Dohm et al., 2001). However, Phillips et al. (2001) suggested that in the Middle Noachian, emerging Tharsis might have altered the gravity field of Mars and the drainage pattern. Additional evidence for a volatile-rich environment also stems from the OMEGA near-infrared spectrometer, which identified phyllosilicates in Middle Noachian terrains (e.g., Bibring et al., 2005). Commonly, Middle Noachian crater rims and scarps exhibit layering, presumably of volcanic or sedimentary origin, much of which may be related to the early formation of the Tharsis rise (e.g., Witbeck et al., 1991; McEwen et al., 1999; Malin and Edgett, 2000, 2001). In particular, the Thaumasia plateau, which makes up much of the southeastern quadrant of the Tharsis rise, uplifted during this epoch and included formation of narrow grabens and rift features (Dohm et al., 2001; Hauber et al., 2010). Later resurfacing makes the identification and dating of Middle Noachian terrains challenging. Thus the base of the Middle Noachian Epoch is not very well established stratigraphically. Tanaka (1986) compared CSFDs of the lunar Nectarian Period (Wilhelms et al., 1978) with those of the Middle Noachian Epoch and proposed that the Middle Noachian might have started for materials having densities of craters larger than 16 km diameter of 200 per 10^6 km^2. Based on this value, Werner and Tanaka (2011) calculated AMAs for the boundary of 3.96−3.97 Ga.

15.2.2.4 Late Noachian Epoch

The Late Noachian Epoch is generally characterized by a pervasive degradation of the Martian surface by impact processes such as impact gardening, erosion due to a thicker atmosphere, and volcanism and geothermal heating (e.g., Tanaka et al., 1998, 2014a, 2014b; Craddock and Howard, 2002; Irwin et al., 2005; Fassett and Head, 2008a, 2008b). Three impact basins greater than 150 km in diameter are assigned this age (Tanaka et al., 2014b). During the Late Noachian Epoch, intercrater plains formed, embaying Early and Middle Noachian units. Subsequent impact cratering affected most of the units and makes interpretation of the origin of Late Noachian outcrops challenging. However, numerous fluvial channels point toward a fluvial or lacustrine origin of many Late Noachian materials (e.g., Fassett and Head, 2008a, 2008b; Irwin et al., 2002, 2013; Malin and Edgett, 2003). In addition, degradation and erosion along the highland–lowland boundary resulted in fields of mesa and knobs surrounded by debris aprons and plains materials (Tanaka et al., 2014b). Wilhelms and Baldwin (1989) interpreted the formation of small knobs and mesas in some highland lows as evidence for water release from materials intruded by igneous sills. During the Late Noachian, the Tharsis volcanic complex of lava flow fields and shields continued to grow. Further evidence for volcanic deposits includes low edifices, broad depressions, and furrowed plains in the vicinity of the Hellas rim, the Tyrrhenus and Apollinaris Montes composite volcanoes, as well as severely degraded massifs south of Tharsis (e.g., Scott and Tanaka, 1981; Tanaka, 1986; Crown et al., 1992; Leonard and Tanaka, 2001). Today, about 9% of the Martian surface is covered by Late Noachian units (Tanaka et al., 2014a). On the basis of the CSFD of Late Noachian units combined with Early Hesperian units, which is similar to that of the Imbrian Period on the Moon, Tanaka (1986) proposed that the Late Noachian might have begun at 3.72–3.80 Ga (Table 15.1). Hartmann and Neukum (2001) argued for a beginning at ~3.80 Ga and according to Hartmann (2005), the Late Noachian Epoch began at ~3.6–3.9 Ga. Finally, based on updated Martian cratering-rate models, Werner and Tanaka (2011) and Michael (2013) proposed AMAs of 3.85–3.86 Ga or 3.83–3.85 Ga, respectively, for the beginning of the Late Noachian.

15.2.2.5 Early Hesperian Epoch

Compared to Noachian surfaces, Hesperian and younger surfaces are much better preserved, maintaining many primary textures such as lava flow fronts, small vents and impact craters, and layering. This preservation is related to the general decline in impact rate and resurfacing, for example, by erosion caused by precipitation. At least three impact basins greater than 150 km in diameter are assigned this age; a fourth is either Early or Late Hesperian in age (Tanaka et al., 2014b) Thus because fluvial erosion became less efficient in modifying the Martian surface, most Early Hesperian and younger materials of the highlands and within Valles Marineris might plausibly be lava flows, volcanic air-fall, and aeolian deposits (Scott and Tanaka, 1986; Greeley and Guest, 1987; Chapman, 2002; Chapman and Tanaka, 2002; Irwin et al., 2002; Hynek et al., 2003). The Hellas Basin floor is also covered in large parts with Early Hesperian sedimentary deposits of aeolian and fluvial/lacustrine origin (Tanaka and Leonard, 1995; Moore and Wilhelms, 2001; Bernhardt et al., 2015, 2016a).

According to Tanaka et al. (2014b), some of the plains and rugged terrains along the highland/lowland boundaries, thought to have formed from mass wasting of older terrains, also have an Early Hesperian age. In summary, Early Hesperian terrains cover about 10% of the surface. Original type locality of the Hesperian Period is Hesperia Planum, which was considered to define the base of this period (Scott and Carr, 1978). However, later it was recognized that Hesperia Planum is not a good stratigraphic marker horizon that could be applied globally, thus resulting in a poorly defined beginning of the Hesperian Period. Performing crater-density measurements, Tanaka (1986) and Tanaka et al. (2014b) dated many Early Hesperian units, including Hesperia Planum. The ranges of these crater densities at several specific crater diameters are given in Table 15.2. Based on this range, the beginning of the Hesperian was most recently assigned to 3.56 or 3.71 Ga, depending on chronology system (Michael, 2013).

15.2.2.6 Late Hesperian Epoch

The stratigraphic definition of the Late Hesperian remains challenging even with modern imaging data. For example, using Viking images (Scott and Tanaka, 1986; Greeley and Guest, 1987; Tanaka, 1986) originally proposed that the deposition of the Vastitas Borealis Formation in the northern lowlands as a result of outflow channel erosion marks the beginning of the Late Hesperian Epoch. Those materials were temporarily reassigned to form the base of the Amazonian Period (Tanaka et al., 2005). However, these materials were assigned in the most recent global mapping to the Late Hesperian lowland unit, the current referent for this epoch—although most applicable for defining the end of the epoch (Tanaka et al., 2014b). Given its geologic character and relationship to the outflow channels, the unit is considered to be a marine/lacustrine sedimentary deposit (Parker et al., 1989), and its boundaries have lobate forms attributed to impact-generated tsunami deposition (Rodriguez et al., 2016). Together with the deposits in the Isidis Basin, the Late Hesperian lowland unit exhibits a relatively uniform distribution of craters > 5 km. This has been interpreted to indicate the deposition of an extensive unit (1/8 of the surface) within a short period of time. Thus at this time, Late Hesperian units cover approximately 20% of the surface of Mars. Based on CSFD measurements, Hartmann and Neukum (2001), Hartmann (2005), Werner and Tanaka (2011), and Michael (2013) propose AMAs for the beginning of the Late Hesperian of 3.2–3.65 Ga. Late

Hesperian materials are not limited to the northern lowlands but also occur as lava flows, large shield volcanoes, and fields of small shields and vents on the Tharsis and Elysium volcanic complexes. These lava flows are more distinct in morphology than those of the Early Hesperian Epoch. It has been argued that they may be characterized by a more viscous rheology and less impact gardening (Tanaka and Hartman, 2012). However, rheologic studies of numerous lava flows of several Martian volcanoes did not reveal systematic changes of rheologic properties with time (Hiesinger et al., 2007; Pasckert et al., 2012). Other Late Hesperian units (some forming continuously since the Early Hesperian) are found in ice-rich south polar plains, in higher elevation plains in the northern lowlands, and forming broad edifices and depressions in the north polar Scandia region (e.g., Scott and Tanaka, 1986; Witbeck et al., 1991; Head and Pratt, 2001; Tanaka and Kolb, 2001; Tanaka et al., 2005, 2011, 2014b). Less clear is the possibility that the lower part of the north polar, water-ice plateau could be Late Hesperian in age (Tanaka et al., 2008). As radar data indicate the existence of ice-rich Hesperian polar deposits, this implies that such ices have been stable for more than 3 Ga (e.g., Plaut et al., 2007).

15.2.2.7 Early Amazonian Epoch

The youngest stratigraphic period of Mars is subdivided into the Early, Middle and Late Amazonian Epochs. Originally defined in early Mariner 9 images, the Amazonian System type locality was southwestern Amazonis Planitia (e.g., Scott and Carr, 1978). Later, Tanaka et al. (2005) used the base of the Vastitas Borealis Formation for the definition of the Early Amazonian. The referent unit for the Early Amazonian Epoch has been redefined on the basis of geologic mapping using more recent higher resolution images (from the Thermal Emission Imaging Spectrometer and the Context Camera) as the Early Amazonian Basin unit, which covers part of the floor of Utopia Basin and overlies the Late Hesperian lowland unit (Tanaka et al., 2014b). Additional Early Amazonian units consist of vast lava and sedimentary deposits in the Tharsis and Elysium regions, as well as sequences of layered, friable materials of the Medusae Fossae region west of the Tharsis rise (Scott and Tanaka, 1982; Chapman, 2002; Hynek et al., 2003), now mapped as Amazonian and Hesperian transition units (Tanaka et al., 2014b). Much of the exposed flows surrounding the Tharsis Montes shields are Early Amazonian; however, rather than forming largely discrete aprons of flows becoming gradually younger toward the center of Tharsis as mapped by Scott and Tanaka (1986), more recent, detailed crater-dating of large lava flows show a mixture of ages over much of the Tharsis Montes region, as well as for the similar, but smaller Elysium rise (Platz and Michael, 2011); thus the flow field is now mapped largely as Amazonian and Hesperian, undivided (Tanaka et al., 2014b). Although impact bombardment rates waned during the Amazonian, Lyot and Galle craters, each forming 220-km-diameter double-ringed basins, formed during the Early Amazonian (Tanaka et al., 2014b). Applying the current definition of the Early Amazonian Epoch implies that about 11% of Mars is covered by rocks of this age. Early Amazonian or younger craters >1 km in diameter can be easily distinguished from rimless depressions, that is, buried craters, as their morphology is well preserved. In studying surfaces formed at the Hesperian/Amazonian boundary, Werner et al. (2011) found cumulative N(1) crater densities of ~ 1200. Depending on the used production function, this results in widely variable AMAs for the beginning of the Early Amazonian of 2.9–3.3 (Hartmann and Neukum, 2001), 2.0–3.2 (Hartmann, 2005), 3.00–3.46 (Werner and Tanaka, 2011), and 3.24–3.37 Ga (Michael, 2013). Taking into account the modified definition of the Early Amazonian would lead to slightly older AMAs by $\sim 0.1–0.2$ Gyr for the 2001 and 2005 studies. Several researchers have observed a steeper CSFD distribution of craters >5 km than for many other Martian and lunar surface units (e.g., Werner et al., 2011). On the basis of this observation, Tanaka et al. (2006) cautioned that if this steep distribution reflects the pristine CSFD, all other CSFD measurements would be affected by stronger obliteration of smaller craters and/or contamination by larger, partly buried craters.

15.2.2.8 Middle Amazonian Epoch

Context Camera images (6 m/pixel) revealed a broadly occurring but largely degraded Middle Amazonian lowland unit, considered to be a loess-like deposit, with consistent crater ages that constitute the referent for the Middle Amazonian Epoch. The unit is about 1 Ga (Skinner et al., 2012; Tanaka et al., 2014b) and appears to explain a resurfacing age detected in other crater counts for northern lowland surfaces by Werner et al. (2011). The lobate aureoles surrounding Olympus Mons and apron-forming materials in Valles Marineris and perhaps in other locations where long-term slope retreat has occurred are also largely of Middle Amazonian age (Tanaka et al., 2005, 2014b). Altogether, Middle Amazonian rocks constitute approximately 6%–8% of the Martian surface, although the exact definition of the base of the Middle Amazonian Epoch remains debatable. Assigning AMAs for the beginning of the Middle Amazonian based on the crater-density boundary defined by Tanaka (1986) resulted in ages of 1.4–2.1 (Hartmann and Neukum, 2001), $\sim 1.0–2.0$ (Hartmann, 2005), 0.88–1.45 (Werner and Tanaka, 2011), and 1.03–1.23 Ga (Michael, 2013). If correct, some of the Martian SNC meteorites might originate from Middle Amazonian terrains. For example, Chassigny, a dunitic rock, and Nakhlites, which are clinopyroxenites, exhibit ages of ~1.35 and ~1.30 Ga, respectively,

15.2.2.9 Late Amazonian Epoch

This epoch was originally defined on the basis of Viking Orbiter images of lavas in southern Elysium Planitia (Tanaka, 1986), but later was redefined by the layered sequences of ices forming the polar plateaus, Planum Boreum (north) and Planum Australe (south) (Tanaka et al., 2014b). The surfaces of these units are partly buried by meters-thick caps of water ice at the North Pole and water and carbon dioxide ices at the South Pole. Radar sounding and geologic mapping also indicate a largely buried volume of carbon dioxide ice in Planum Australe, which if sublimated would substantially increase atmospheric pressure (Phillips et al., 2011) Newer imaging data with better spatial resolution allowed for better identification, mapping, and dating of Late Amazonian lava flows. At Viking resolution, these plains appear smooth and show evidence for small-scale volcanic shield and fluvial channels. On the basis of modern high-resolution images these plains are characterized by multiple episodes of volcanic eruptions and fluvial activity history (e.g., Keszthelyi et al., 2000; Burr et al., 2002; Plescia, 2003; Tanaka et al., 2005). The most extensive flows can be traced from Cerberus Rupes and nearby fields of small shields and fissure vents and cover much of Elysium Planitia and the flat Amazonis Planitia; the latter also source from fissures in southeastern Amazonis Planitia (Vaucher et al., 2009; Tanaka et al., 2014b). On the basis of CSFD measurements, the plains appear to extend in age from ~200 to ~2 Ma (Berman and Hartmann, 2002; Vaucher et al., 2009). In addition, several other terrains are considered to be of Late Amazonian age, including the youngest volcanic flows and vent fields of Tharsis Montes and Olympus Mons, dune fields primarily surrounding the north polar plateau, and ridged apron deposits on the northwest flanks of the Tharsis Montes and Olympus Mons that maybe remnant deposits of cold-based glaciers emplaced during a former mid-latitude colder climate (Head et al., 2003; Tanaka et al., 2014b). Together, these materials cover approximately 6%–7% of the Martian surface (Tanaka et al., 2014a). Although detailed CSFD measurements for the Cerberus Fossae 2 unit are still lacking, various CSFD measurements indicate that the Late Amazonian began 300–550 (Hartmann and Neukum, 2001), 200–600 (Hartmann, 2005), 235–387 (Werner and Tanaka, 2011), or 274–328 Ma (Michael, 2013). Work by Malin et al. (2006) and Hartmann (2007) shows that the rate of current bombardment of Mars in the 2–125 m diameter range is consistent within a factor of ~3 with the predictions of Hartmann (2005). Basaltic and ultramafic lherzolitic Shergottite meteorites from Mars exhibit crystallization ages of ~150–500 Ma (Nyquist et al., 2001) and might have formed during the Late Amazonian Epoch, although Bouvier et al. (2005) reported older ages. Using cosmic ray exposure ages indicates that the Martian SNC meteorites were launched off Mars within the last 0.7–20 Myr (Nyquist et al., 2001, and references therein).

15.2.3 Mercury

Of all planets, Mercury is the closest to the Sun, has one of the highest bulk densities, exhibits the largest temperature variations, receives the strongest solar radiation, is deformed by strong tidal forces, and is characterized by a heavily altered geochemistry compared to its primordial composition (e.g., Chapman, 1988). Thus Mercury truly is an "end-member" planet. With Earth-based telescopes, Mercury is difficult to observe due to its vicinity to the Sun, the long distance, and its low albedo. Thus for detailed geologic mapping, spacecraft data are crucial. Unfortunately, only two spacecraft missions visited Mercury. In 1974–75 Mariner 10 had three flybys at Mercury, covering about 45% of the surface with images of 100–1500 m/pixel resolutions. The MESSENGER (Mercury Surface, Space Environment, Geochemistry, and Ranging) mission observed Mercury from three flybys in 2008–09 and from orbit between 2011 and 2015. On board were several scientific instruments, including the Mercury Dual Imaging System (MDIS), several spectrometers operating in a range of wavelengths (MASCS, EPPS, XRS), a laser altimeter (MLA), a magnetometer (MAG), and a radio science experiment (RS). The wide-angle camera of MDIS provided us with a global monochromatic image mosaic at about 250-m pixel scale and color images of about 40% of the surface of Mercury. The narrow-angle camera of MDIS has a pixel resolution as high as 5.2 m.

On the basis of Mariner 10 images, 9 geologic quadrangle maps at 1:5,000,000-scale were produced and a stratigraphy (Table 15.3) developed (e.g., Schaber and McCauley, 1980; McCauley et al., 1981). Originally limited to the Caloris Basin, the stratigraphy was later applied to the entire imaged surface (e.g., Spudis, 1985; Spudis and Guest, 1988). It was found that Mercury's major geologic events are generally similar to those of the Moon (Table 15.3). For example, Mercury's stratigraphy exhibits the same uncertainty, that is, the poor definition of the two youngest stratigraphic periods. The equivalent to the lunar pre-Nectarian Period is the informal pre-Tolstojan Period, which ends with the impact of the Tolstoj Basin. During this period, many multiring basins formed. Most of them exhibit one particularly prominent ring structure that is considered as the main crater rim. Besides the formation of multiring basins, the formation of extensive intercrater plains falls into this period. These intercrater plains either have a volcanic or impact origin and frequently erased smaller (<500-km diameter) basins (Strom, 1977). The base of the Tolstojan Period is characterized by the emplacement of lineated terrain surrounding the Tolstoj impact, that is, the Goya Formation. There are also numerous craters of Tolstojan age and smooth plains deposits.

TABLE 15.3 Referent units, lunar counterparts, and carter-density data and model absolute ages for bases of Mercurian chronologic units.

Chronologic Unit	Referent Unit	Lunar Counterpart	No. Craters ≥ 20 km per 10^6 km^2	Lower Lunar Model-Age Boundary (Ga)
Kuiperian	Bright-rayed craters (e.g., Kuiper)	Copernican	n/a	2.2−1.25
Mansurian	Slightly degraded craters (e.g., Mansur)	Eratosthenian	$<24 \pm 7$	3.24−3.11
Calorian	Caloris Group	Imbrian	58 ± 13	3.87−3.75
Tolstojan	Goya Formation	Nectarian	85 ± 14	4.20−3.80
Pre-Tolstojan	n/a	Pre-Nectarian	$\sim > 85$	~4.5

Most data from Spudis and Guest (1988). Model-age boundaries are assumed to be roughly equivalent to those of their lunar counterparts (Table 15.1). The crater-density boundary for the Mansurian is a maximum, based on the lowest crater-density measured for smooth plains material (Spudis and Guest, 1988; Table 3).

Caloris, the largest basin on Mercury, defines the onset of the Calorian Period. The Caloris impact drastically and extensively resurfaced the surface of Mercury and, thus, is an excellent marker horizon (e.g., Schaber and McCauley, 1980; McCauley et al., 1981; Guest and Greeley, 1983). The Caloris group materials comprise melt and rim deposits as well as some lineated ejecta. The interior of the basin is flooded with lava plains that have been tectonically deformed, as evidenced by wrinkle ridges and grabens (Spudis and Guest, 1988). Antipodal to the Caloris Basin, extremely rough, furrowed, and hilly units have been identified and interpreted as results of seismic wave focusing (e.g., Schultz and Gault, 1975). Extensive smooth volcanic plains can be observed outside the basin, and these plains are superposed by craters and basins that formed during the remainder of the Calorian Period. The Mansurian Period follows the Calorian Period and starts with the impact of Mansur crater. Mansurian units comprise somewhat degraded craters without bright rays and some smooth crater fills. Finally, the youngest stratigraphic period on Mercury is the Kuiperian Period, which includes the formation of bright-rayed craters such as Kuiper, although its base is not well defined.

The shapes of CSFDs of the Moon and Mercury are similar (Strom and Neukum, 1988; Strom et al., 2005). Strom and Neukum (1988) derived relative cratering rates between these two bodies and proposed a formation of the Caloris Basin at the end of the heavy bombardment, that is, at ~3.85 Ga. Strom and Neukum (1988) used this as a reference point to determine the ages of Tolstoj (4.06 Ga) and 4.02−4.22 Ga for the intercrater plains. Table 15.3 provides a comparison between the stratigraphies of the Moon and Mercury and also gives crater densities and AMAs for the stratigraphic periods on Mercury.

15.2.4 Venus

The surface of Venus is shrouded in thick clouds, making it impossible to observe it without radar techniques capable of penetrating them. For planetary investigations, radar instruments have only recently become available. Thus despite centuries of Venus observations, detailed studies of its surface geology only became feasible within the last few decades, both from Earth (e.g., Arecibo and Goldstone observatories) and spacecraft (Venera 15 and 16 and Magellan). Because radar is an active remote sensing technique, it is possible to extract information on the topography, morphology, surface roughness, emissivity, and other physical characteristics of the Venusian surface. The Soviets had an incredibly successful program to explore Venus, which culminated in several landings and in situ investigations, serving as important calibration points for information derived from orbit. From those landers it is known that most of the surface of Venus is basaltic in nature and, thus, volcanic in origin. Orbital information, particularly the radar data of Magellan, revealed that the surface is indeed characterized by extensive volcanism and in some specific terrains by extensive tectonic deformation. Compared to the Moon, Mars and Mercury, Venus exhibits only approximately 1000 impact craters, interpreted to be the result of global resurfacing and atmospheric effects. These impact craters are more or less randomly distributed across the surface. Together with their low number, this implies a global and very young surface age. In particular, Strom et al. (1994) proposed a surface model age of 288 $+311/-98$ Ma (or range of 599−190 Ma), while Neukum and Ivanov (1994) argued for a model age of 630 ± 100 Ma. On the basis of their own estimates ($\sim 750 \pm 0$ Ma) and those of earlier studies, McKinnon et al. (1997) concluded that the surface might be 300−1000 Ma old. These young ages indicate a rapid, mantle plume−driven rate of resurfacing that was considerably higher than those on the Moon, Mars and Mercury, all of which are characterized by decreasing volcanic activity. However, the spread in model ages indicates that the resurfacing was not brief and catastrophic as proposed, for example, by Hauck et al. (1998). Intense volcanism or the impact of a comet could have introduced substantial amounts of water and sulfur dioxide in a relatively short amount of time. This in turn might have led to intense greenhouse

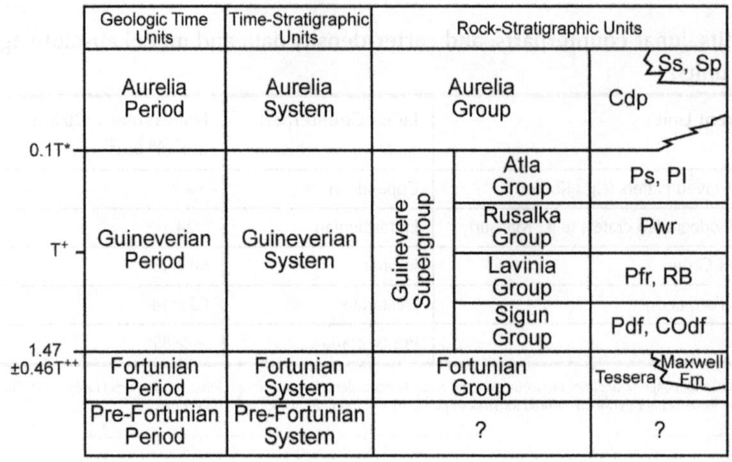

	Geologic Time Units	Time-Stratigraphic Units	Rock-Stratigraphic Units		
	Aurelia Period	Aurelia System	Aurelia Group		Ss, Sp; Cdp
0.1T*					
	Guineverian Period	Guineverian System	Guinevere Supergroup	Atla Group	Ps, Pl
				Rusalka Group	Pwr
T⁺				Lavinia Group	Pfr, RB
				Sigun Group	Pdf, COdf
1.47 ±0.46T⁺⁺	Fortunian Period	Fortunian System	Fortunian Group		Tessera; Maxwell Fm
	Pre-Fortunian Period	Pre-Fortunian System	?		?

FIGURE 15.8 Proposed (but not widely accepted; see text) Venus regional and global rock-stratigraphic, time-stratigraphic, and geologic time units of Basilevsky and Head (1995). *Basilevsky (1993), Strom (1993); ⁺*T* is crater retention age of the surface. $T = 0.5-1.0$ (Basilevsky et al., 1985), ~1 (Basilevsky et al., 1987; Kryuchov, 1987), 0.1–0.5 (Schaber et al., 1987), 0.3–0.9 (Ivanov and Basilevsky, 1987), 0.2–0.7 or ~0.5 (Schaber et al., 1992), 0.19–0.6 or ~0.3 Ga (Strom et al., 1994); ⁺⁺Ivanov and Basilevsky (1993).

heating of the entire planet, which has effects on the global volcanic and tectonic evolution by modifying the mechanical characteristics and thermal stress state of the lithosphere (e.g., Solomon et al., 1999; Bullock and Grinspoon, 2001). Basilevsky and Head (1995) presented four geologic time units—the pre-Fortunian Period, the Fortunian Period, the Guineverian Period and the Aurelian Period (Fig. 15.8). According to this publication, the transition between the Fortunian and Guineverian periods occurs at 1.47 ± 0.46 T, with T defined as 0.5–1.0 (Basilevsky et al., 1985), ~1 (Basilevsky et al., 1987; Kryuchov, 1987), 0.1–0.5 (Schaber et al., 1987), 0.3–0.9 (Ivanov and Basilevsky, 1987), 0.2–0.7 (Schaber et al., 1992), or 0.19–0.6 Ga (Strom et al., 1994). The transition between the Guineverian and the Aurelian periods occurs at 0.1 T (Basilevsky and Head, 1995). Possibly the oldest terrain of Venus is the Fortunian Period tesserae terrain, which shows evidence for intense compressional and extensional tectonic deformation. However, it is still debated whether local stratigraphic relationships can be used to derive a global stratigraphy. While some workers have suggested a global surface evolution in support of a system of discrete chronologic units (e.g., Namiki and Solomon, 1994; Price and Suppe, 1995; Price et al., 1996; Basilevsky and Head, 1995; Basilevsky et al., 1997), alternative interpretations have been presented. For example, Guest and Stofan (1999) and Hansen (2000) proposed a complex evolution of the surface, with overlapping formation ages of volcanic and tectonic features. Thus several researchers have cautioned the use of crater-densities for large groupings of features and outcrops at regional/global scales (e.g., Hamilton and Stofan, 1996; Chapman and Zimbelman, 1998; Guest and Stofan, 1999; Hansen, 2000). Consequently, up to now, a formal stratigraphic system has not yet been established for Venus.

15.2.5 Other cratered bodies

The cratered surfaces of several asteroids and moons of Jupiter and Saturn have been observed by spacecraft. Although none of these bodies have formal stratigraphies, at least some of them exhibit complex resurfacing histories as indicated by detailed geologic mapping and CSFD measurements. CSFD measurements have shown that asteroids (e.g., Gaspra, Ida, Vesta, Ceres), as well as the Martian moons Phobos and Deimos have distributions similar to that of the Moon (e.g., Neukum and Ivanov, 1994; Chapman et al., 1996; Veverka et al., 1997). Earth-based telescopic investigations (e.g., Jedicke and Metcalfe, 1998; Yoshida and Nakamura, 2004) confirm that asteroids are the main source of the observed CSFD in the inner solar system (Neukum et al., 2001). A special case is asteroid Itokawa, a rubble-pile asteroid that shows no impact craters. A likely scenario for its formation is reagglomeration and sporadic impact-shaking of the fragmented parent asteroid (Fujiwara et al., 2006; Whiteley et al., 2002). Knowing the size-frequency distributions and orbits of asteroids and comets that are responsible for the current impactor population is important to understand and model current and past impact rates and CSFDs (e.g., Zahnle et al., 1998, 2003; Schenk et al., 2004; Strom et al., 2005). Impact rates might show some variations because of collisional breakups of asteroids that produce meteor showers. Schmitz et al. (1997), for example, proposed that the up to two orders of magnitude increased delivery of L-chondrites to Earth at ~500–450 Ma and the increase of large terrestrial impacts during the last 100 Myr (e.g., Bottke et al., 2007) might be related to such spikes in impact rate.

The planets and moons of the outer solar system were first inspected in the 1970s by the Voyager 1 and 2 spacecraft flybys. In addition, between 1995 and 2003, the Galileo mission provided high-resolution images of the Galilean satellites Io, Europa, Ganymede and Callisto. Similarly, from 2004 to 2017 the Cassini spacecraft investigated the Saturnian system at high resolution with multiple instruments and even landed the Huygens probe on Titan. Although these missions allowed us to study impact craters on icy objects, the relaxation of impact craters on these bodies is still complicated to understand, because each body has its own unique composition, thermal evolution and resurfacing history (e.g., McKinnon et al., 1991; Schenk et al., 2004). Thus CSFDs of Ganymede, Callisto and Europa are different from that of the Moon for reasons that are still debated. For example, there is an ongoing debate regarding the source of the impactor population that has dominated the cratering record in the outer solar system. One hypothesis argues that ecliptic comets from the Kuiper belt in the outer solar system are the primary source (e.g., Shoemaker and Wolfe, 1982; Duncan and Levison, 1997; Zahnle et al., 1998), whereas Neukum et al. (1998, 1999) favor a single impactor population for the entire solar system, that is, the asteroid belt. As a consequence, estimates of cratering rates in the outer solar system and age determinations with CSFDs are subject to larger uncertainties compared to the inner solar system (e.g., McKinnon et al., 1991). If we assume a single impactor population (e.g., Neukum et al., 1998, 1999), this would result in low impact rates and older surface ages. In this scenario, large impact basins on Ganymede and Callisto were formed during the heavy bombardment. The sparsely cratered surfaces of Europa and Enceladus have generally been interpreted as being very young, because there is evidence for volatile eruptions that resurfaced the object, including gas/debris plumes emanating from the south polar region of Enceladus (Porco et al., 2006). Other factors that affect CSFD measurements might be the synchronous rotation of some moons that would presumably result in higher cratering rates for the leading hemispheres compared to their trailing sides. Ganymede and Calisto, however, do not show such asymmetries in crater densities, implying that they once rotated nonsynchronously (Schenk et al., 2004).

15.2.5.1 Jupiter's moons

Jupiter has almost 80 moons, and a large number of them have provisional names, because their orbits have not yet been determined with the required accuracy. By far the largest moons are the Galilean moons with diameters in excess of 3000 km, whereas all other moons are smaller than 200 km. The smaller moons have not yet been geologically mapped, nor have chronostratigraphies been developed for them. Thus we focus on the four Galilean satellites, Io, Europa, Ganymede and Callisto.

15.2.5.1.1 Io

In 2011 Williams et al. produced the first global 1:15,000,000 geologic map of Io (Fig. 15.9). On the basis of Voyager and Galileo image mosaics, they identified 19 geologic units that differ in albedo, color, and surface morphology. By far the most extensive are plains units, which cover about 65.8% of the surface: there also exist lava flow units (28.5%), mountain units (3.2%), and patera floor units (2.5%). Diffuse deposits cover about 18% of Io's surface and can be subdivided into red (8.6%), white (6.9%), yellow (2.1%), black (0.6%), and green deposits (0.01%). Io is tidally heated and the volcanically most active object in the solar system (Smith et al., 1979a, 1979b; McEwen et al., 1998a, 1998b; Porco et al., 2003; Spencer et al., 2007; Williams et al., 2011). In fact, the volcanic resurfacing rate on Io is so high that the surface does not show any impact crater. Thus the surface is extremely young and CSFD measurements cannot be utilized to derive AMAs. Williams et al. (2011) estimated that all geologic units were formed within "millions of years." A formal chronostratigraphy has not yet been established for Io (Table 15.4).

15.2.5.1.2 Europa

Like Io, the second Galilean moon, Europa, shows evidence for resurfacing, resulting in a surface age as young as 60 Ma (e.g., Lucchitta and Soderblom, 1982; Papparlado et al., 1999; Bierhaus et al., 2001; Figueredo and Greeley, 2004; Doggett et al., 2009). The small number of impact craters, that is, less than 50 confirmed craters, makes it difficult to determine AMAs for geologic units (Fig. 15.10). Thus we currently only have relative ages of mapped geologic units, which are based on superposition and embayment relationships. Senske et al. (2018) pointed out that even this determination of relative ages is challenging due to the complexity of the surface and the image quality. Despite these difficulties, Senske et al. (2018) proposed an informal chronostratigraphy that consists of three unnamed periods, which, however, are not well defined and strongly overlapping. The oldest period is characterized by ridged plains and undifferentiated linea, indicating that this period was dominated by compressive tectonic forces that led to the formation of ridges. During the second period, Band and High-Albedo Band formation prevailed. Cycloids—rilles made up of linked, cuspate sections—were also formed during this period. The most recent, third period includes the formation of chaotic terrain, which is only superposed by a small number of impacts but otherwise does not show any cross-cutting units (Senske et al., 2018).

15.2.5.1.3 Ganymede

The Galileo spacecraft had six close flybys at Ganymede. On the basis of these high-resolution (<200 m/pixel) images, Patterson et al. (2010) produced a global 1:15,000,000 geologic map of Ganymede (Fig. 15.11). This mapping effort resulted in a better understanding of the processes operating on

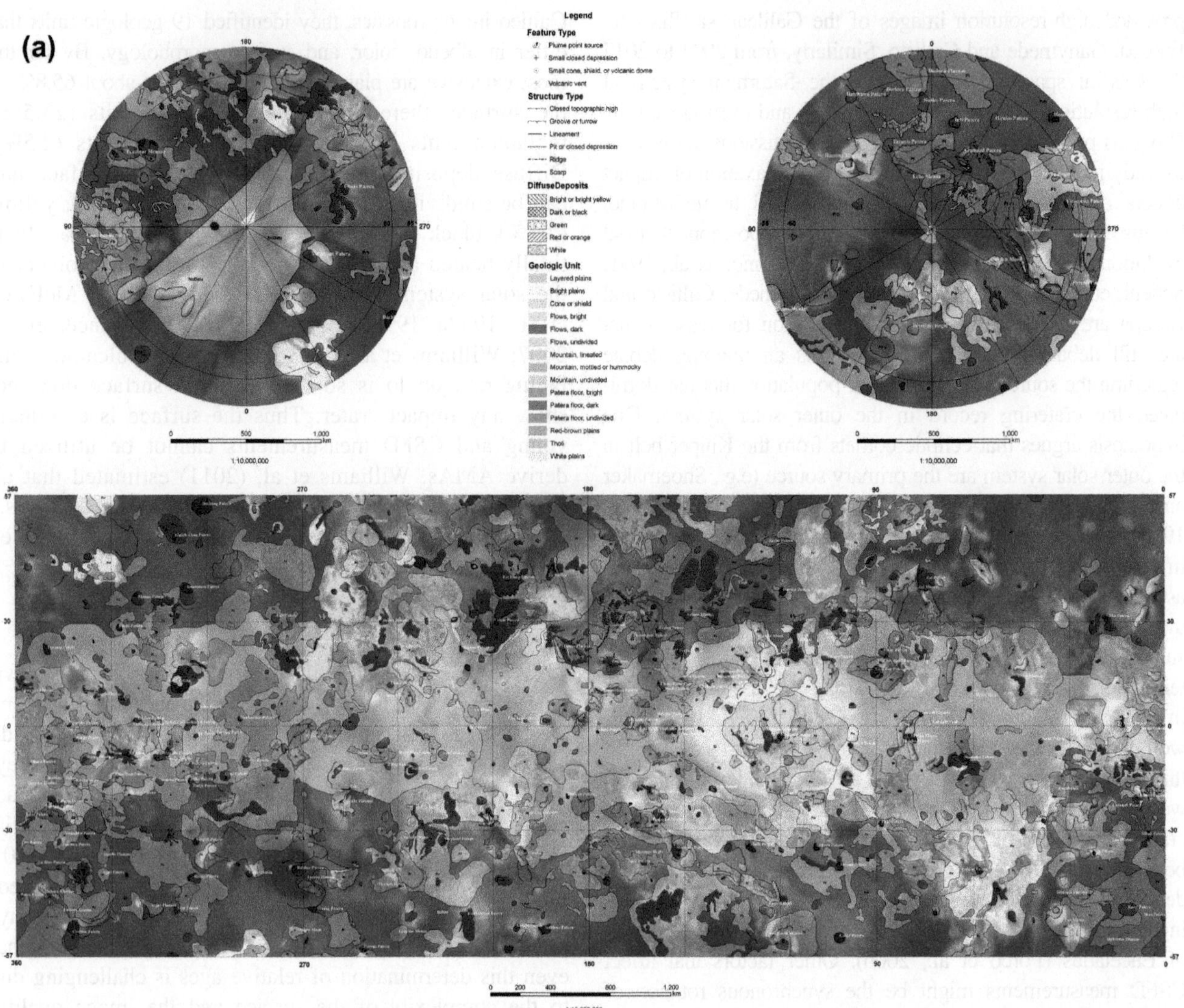

FIGURE 15.9 The geologic map of Io. North and south poles (top images) are in polar stereographic projection; the equatorial region (lower image) is in Mercator projection centered on the antijovian point (0°, 180°W). Reproduced from figure 2a in Williams et al. (2011); detailed version at https://pubs.usgs.gov/sim/3168/.

TABLE 15.4 Suggested surface ages for the Galilean satellites of Jupiter.

Satellite	Suggested surface age (Ma)	References
Io	2.3 to <0.3	Schenk et al. (2004), Zahnle et al. (2003)
Europa	10	Zahnle et al. (1998)
Europa	60	Zahnle et al. (2003)
Europa	3000–1000	Neukum et al. (1999)
Ganymede	700 (Gilgamesh) 2000 (bright terrains)	Zahnle et al. (2003)
Ganymede	3600 (bright terrains) 3800 (Gilgamesh) 4200 (dark terrains)	Neukum et al. (1998)
Callisto	2000 (Lofn and Valhalla impacts)	Zahnle et al. (2003)
Callisto	4300–3900 (various terrains and impacts)	Neukum et al. (1998), Wagner et al. (1999)

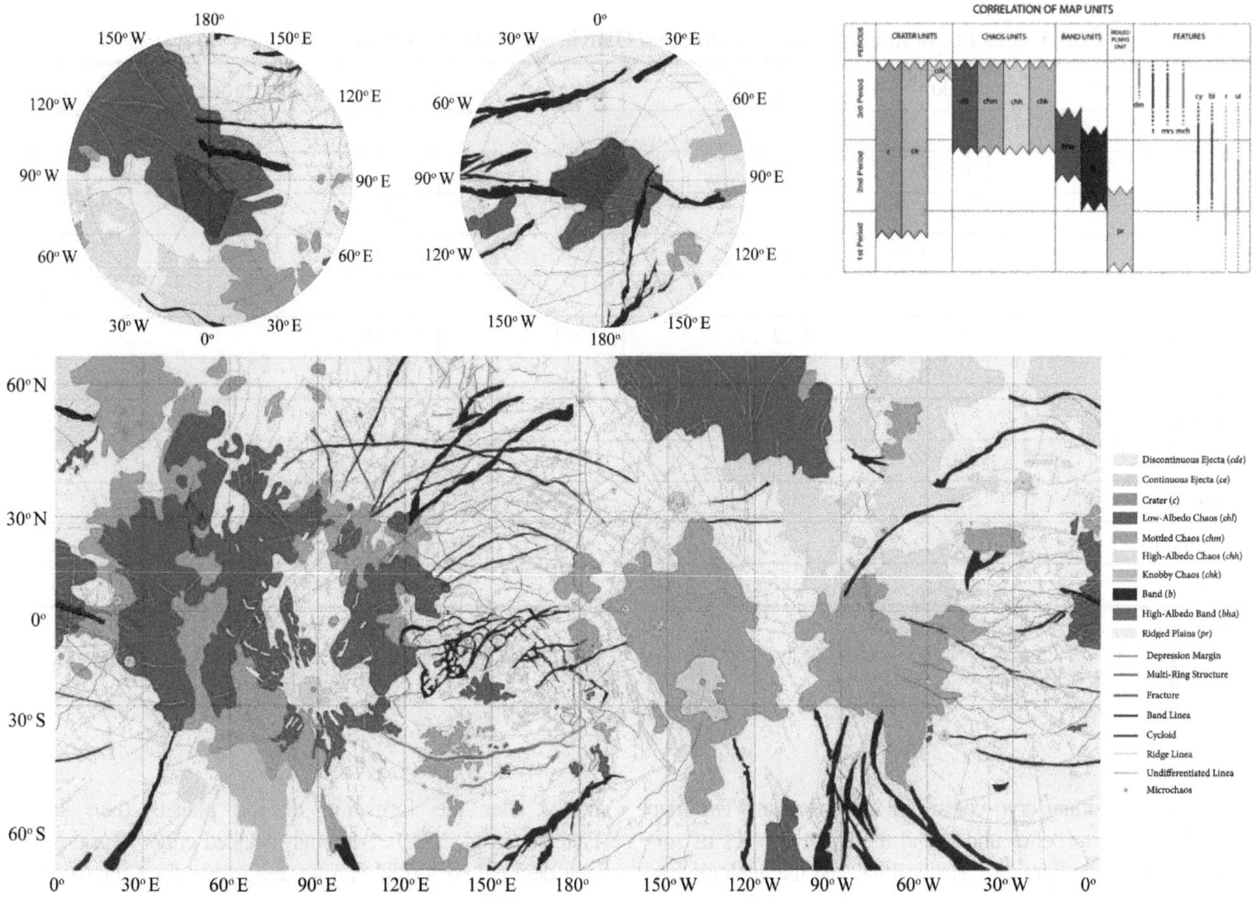

FIGURE 15.10 The geologic map of Europa (Senske et al., 2018).

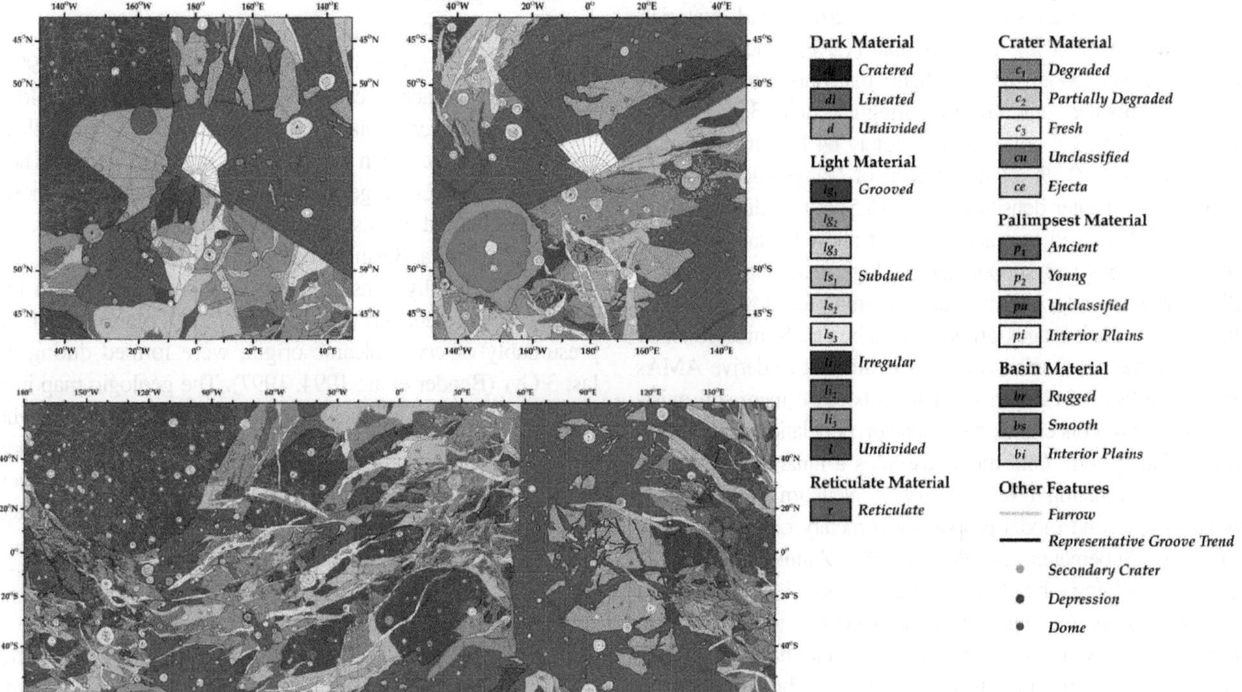

FIGURE 15.11 The geologic map of Ganymede (Patterson et al., 2010).

TABLE 15.5 Crater densities of mapped geologic units on Ganymede (Patterson et al., 2010).

Material type[a]	10 km[b]	20 km[b]	30 km[b]	Area of zone used for counting (10^6 km^2)
Light				
Grooved	39 ± 2	14 ± 1	18 ± 1	9.29 (5.71)
Irregular	30 ± 4	13 ± 3	6 ± 2	1.94 (0.99)
Subdued	42 ± 2	18 ± 1	9 ± 1	8.24 (4.90)
Dark				
Cratered	85 ± 2	32 ± 1	15 ± 1	21.9 (16.3)
Lineated	67 ± 8	19 ± 4	8 ± 3	1.06 (1.01)
Reticulate				
Reticulate	39 ± 12	18 ± 8	4 ± 4	0.28 (0.28)
Impact				
Palimpsest	61 ± 7	23 ± 4		1.37
Basin	19 ± 5	11 ± 4		0.80

[a] *Undivided units are not included.*
[b] *Number of craters ≥ the quoted diameter. Normalized to a counting area of 10^6 km^2. The numbers in parentheses indicate values calculated from image data at resolutions <1.5 km/pixel.*

Ganymede, including cryo-volcanism and tectonism. The map also allowed us to better understand the characteristics of surface units, their stratigraphic relationships, and the geologic history of Ganymede. For example, on the basis of the detailed mapping it appears that dark lineated and reticulate materials represent intermediate stages between dark cratered material and light material units (Patterson et al., 2010). Dark materials [cratered unit (25.8%); lineated unit (1.9%); undivided unit (7.7%)] cover about 35.4%, light materials [grooved unit (14.1%); subdued unit (18.0%); irregular unit (3.7%); undivided unit (28.3%)] cover approximately 64.1%, and reticulate material covers 0.5% of the surface of Ganymede (Patterson et al., 2010). Crater densities (Table 15.5) at two diameters (10 and 20 km) derived for each map unit allow for an estimation of relative ages and support the geologic mapping. However, differences in crater densities are too small to allow for a distinction of relative ages among the subunits. Similar to other bodies in the outer solar system, it is difficult to derive AMAs for the surface of Ganymede. This is because there still exists a controversy concerning the impactor population and flux in the Jovian system. One model assumes a lunar-like asteroidal production function (Neukum, 1997; Neukum et al., 1998), whereas a second model proposes a cometary origin of impactors (e.g., Shoemaker and Wolfe, 1982; Zahnle et al., 1998, 2003). Applying the first model would yield AMAs of 3.6–4.2 Ga for the light and dark materials, respectively. In the second model, the light material would have an age of about 2 Ga. Despite this uncertainty, there is broad consensus that the dark material is ancient and most likely formed shortly after the formation of the planets (i.e., 4.5 Ga) (Patterson et al., 2010). Although detailed crater densities have been derived, no formal chronostratigraphy for Ganymede has been established.

15.2.5.1.4 Callisto

The 1:15,000,000 geologic map of Callisto (Fig. 15.12) is characterized by a surprising simplicity (Bender et al., 1997). Most of the surface is covered by a rather uniform geologic unit, that is, cratered plains. Light plains and smooth plains also occur but are much more limited in spatial extent. There are only 128 craters larger than 60 km in diameter superposed onto the cratered plains, as well as two larger basins, the 1100-km Valhalla Basin and the 700-km Asgard Basin. The surface is generally considered to be ancient and only a few bright-rayed craters and possibly the smooth plains, which are presumably of cryo-volcanic origin, were formed during the last 3 Gyr (Bender et al., 1994, 1997). The geologic map indicates that the units of the Valhalla Formation are somewhat younger than those of the Asgard Formation, although there is considerable overlap. Although 10 geologic units were mapped and their stratigraphic relationships were investigated, no formal chronostratigraphy has been proposed.

15.2.5.2 Saturn's moons

Saturn has more than 60 moons, 13 of which have diameters larger than 50 km. The large moons can be subdivided into inner large moons, that is, moons that orbit

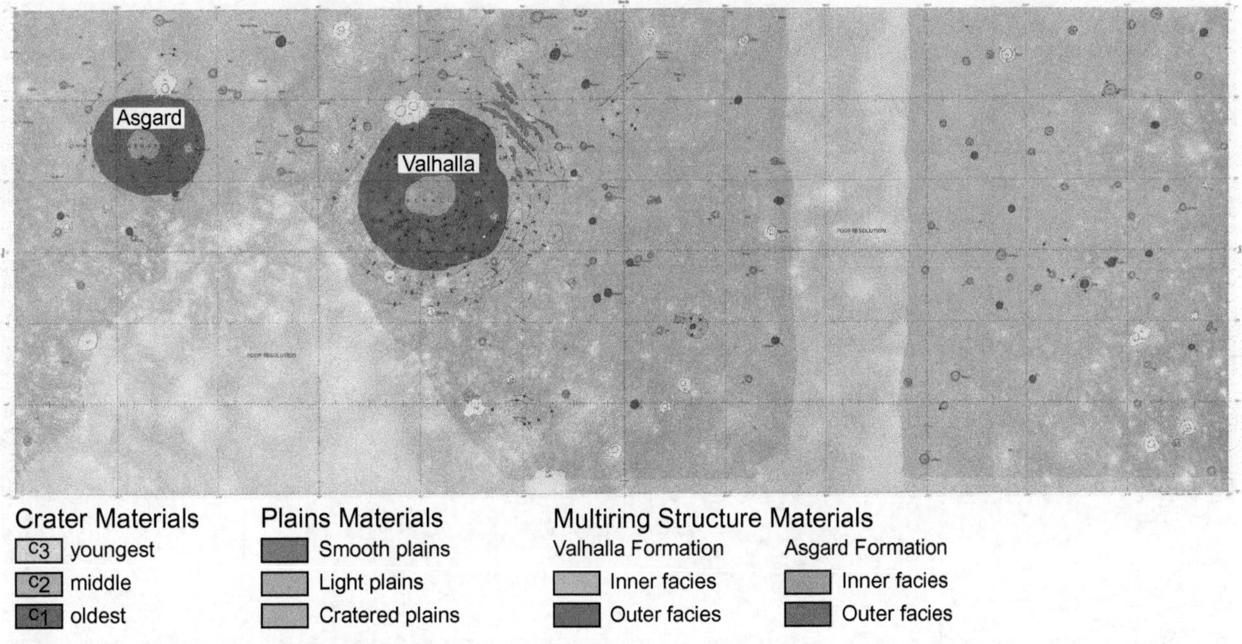

FIGURE 15.12 The geologic map of Callisto. After Bender et al. (1997).

TABLE 15.6 Crater frequencies for geologic units on Dione (Plescia, 1983).

Geologic unit	Crater diameter					Counting area
	10	20	30	40	50	
Heavily cratered	780 ± 86	275 ± 51	100 ± 31	70 ± 26	50 ± 22	105,443
Cratered plains	500 ± 87	75 ± 34	33 ± 22	14 ± 15	8 ± 11	66,292
Cratered plains	600 ± 75	72 ± 26	21 ± 14	8 ± 9	(5 ± 7)	106,930
Lightly cratered	280 ± 67	16 ± 16	(4 ± 8)	(2 ± 5)	<1	62,503
Lobate deposits	100 ± 50	(7 ± 14)	(2 ± 7)	<1	<1	34,331

Crater numbers $\geq D/10^6$ km^2.

Saturn inside the E-ring (Mimas, Enceladus, Tethys, Dione) and outer large moons with orbits beyond the E-ring (Rhea, Titan, Hyperion, Iapetus).

15.2.5.2.1 Dione

With a diameter of 1123 km, Dione is the largest of the inner moons. An early map of Plescia (1983) distinguishes between heavily cratered terrain, cratered plains, lightly cratered plains, lobate deposits, crater rim deposits, and bright whispy material, in order of decreasing age. Dione is currently tidally locked but does not show a leading/trailing hemisphere asymmetry in crater frequencies as predicted by Shoemaker and Wolfe (1982) nor does any other Saturnian satellite (Plescia, 1983). This could imply that Dione was not locked when most craters were formed during the heavy bombardment (Plescia, 1983) (Table 15.6).

The Cassini spacecraft had one flyby at Dione and this resulted in an updated global mosaic with up to 154-m pixel scale. Stephan et al. (2010) produced a geologic map (Fig. 15.13) and proposed that the densely cratered terrain is the oldest geologic unit on Dione. This unit is widespread, has a high albedo and

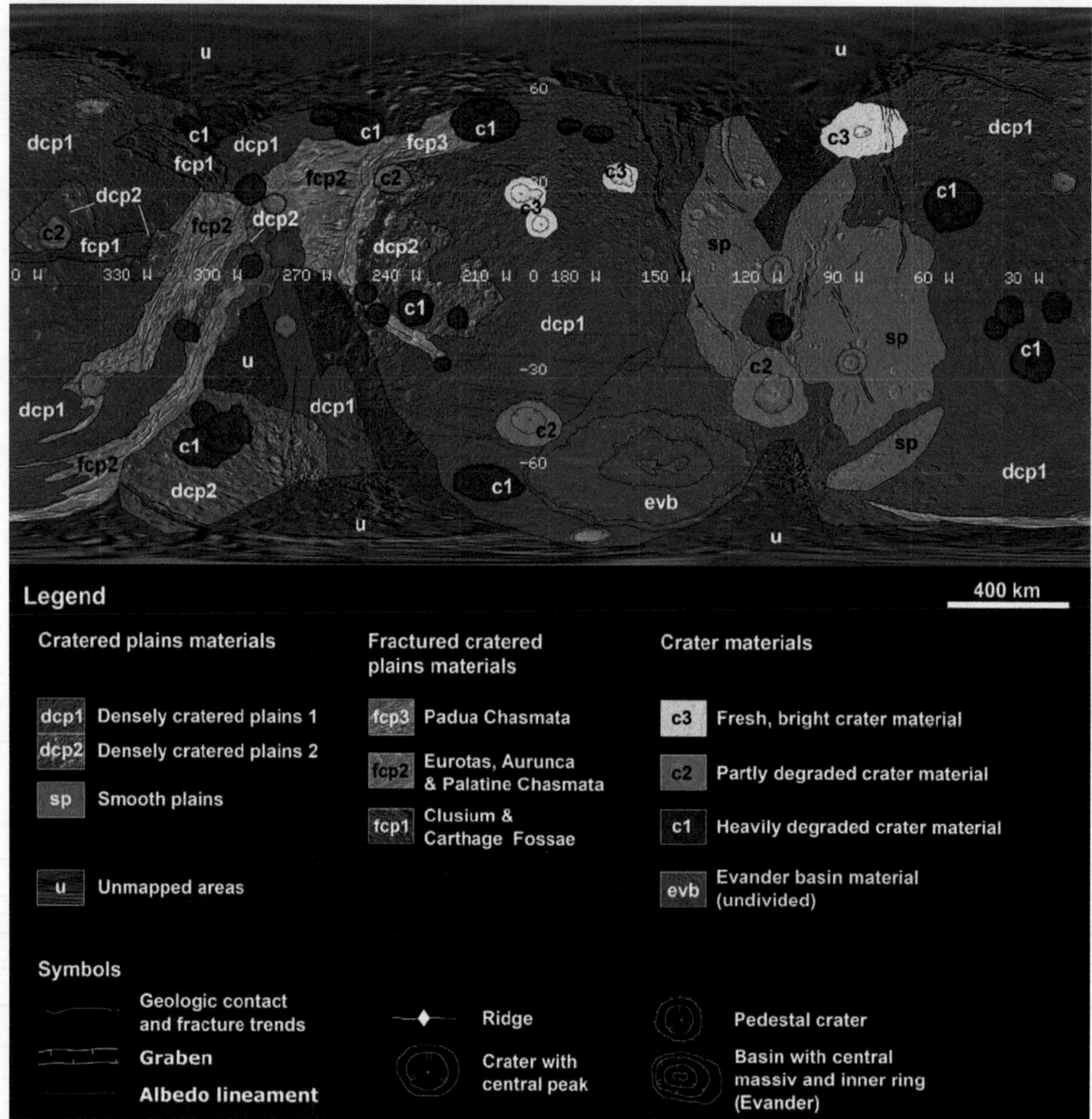

FIGURE 15.13 The geologic map of Dione (Stephan et al., 2010).

rough morphology, and shows impact craters of all sizes and degradation states. CSFDs show that this unit has a crater distribution close to equilibrium, thus, being about 4 Ga old (e.g., Neukum et al., 2006). Smooth plains, that is, the cratered and lightly cratered plains of Plescia (1983), have a significantly lower number of impact craters and must therefore be younger than the densely cratered plains. The fractured cratered plains represent the youngest geologic unit. CSFD measurements indicate a model age of ~3.7 Ga (lunar-like flux model; Neukum et al., 2006) or as young as 1 Ga (constant flux model, Zahnle et al., 2003). Despite these CSFD measurements and the geologic mapping, no formal chronostratigraphy has been established yet (Table 15.7).

15.2.5.2.2 Tethys

Cassini spacecraft imaging resulted in a global image mosaic of Tethys (1060 km diameter) with 293 m per pixel at the equator. Tethys exhibits smooth plains at the trailing hemisphere and a large 450-km impact, the Odysseus Basin, on its leading hemisphere. The cratered

TABLE 15.7 Relative terrain ages for $D \geq 5$ km (Kirchoff and Schenk, 2010).

Terrain	Cumulative crater density	Scaled density[a]	Relative age to Odysseus[b]	Relative age to Dione–sp[b]	Relative age to Mimas[b]
Mimas	4497 ± 136	844 ± 59	4.2–7.3	1.0–1.3	–
Tethys—cp	2978 ± 272	910 ± 188	3.8–8.9	≤ 1.6	≤ 1.4
Tethys—Odysseus	717 ± 71	156 ± 33	–	–	–
Dione—cp	2723 ± 1467	1089 ± 823	1.4–15.5	≤ 2.8	≤ 2.4
Dione—sp	2327 ± 112	743 ± 63	3.6–6.6	–	–
Rhea—cp	2759 ± 480	1422 ± 531	4.7–15.9	1.1–2.9	1.0–2.5
Iapetus—dark	2687 ± 1501	2687 ± 1501	6.3–34.0	1.5–6.2	1.3–5.3
Iapetus—bright	1846 ± 112	1846 ± 112	9.2–15.9	2.2–2.9	1.9–2.5
Phoebe	2233 ± 1117	1117 ± 790	1.7–15.5	≤ 2.8	≤ 2.4

cp, Cratered plains; *sp*, smooth plains.
[a]*Cumulative crater density for D ≥ 5 km scaled to Iapetus.*
[b]*Values are the ratio of the scaled density of the terrain specified in the row to the terrain specified in the column header.*

terrain might be ancient, whereas the youngest unit is located within the Odysseus Basin, showing a model age of 1.06–3.76 Ga, depending on the chronology used (Dones et al., 2009). Wagner et al. (2013) subdivided the geologic units of Tethys into cratered plains, large impact basins, and impact craters, each of which consists of several subunits. CSFD measurements indicate that Ithaca Chasma is older than the Odysseus Basin and thus cannot have been formed by the stress created by this impact (Wagner et al., 2013). A formal chronostratigraphy for Tethys is still lacking.

15.2.5.2.3 Enceladus

The surface of Enceladus is diverse and symmetric with respect to the rotation axis as well as the direction to Saturn (Crow-Willard and Pappalardo, 2010; Spencer and Nimmo, 2013). The south polar terrain is intensely tectonically deformed and geologically active. The geologic map (Fig. 15.14) of Crow-Willard and Pappalardo (2010) shows 11 units—heavily cratered terrain, moderately cratered terrain, finely striated ridge and trough terrain, curvilinear terrain, ridged terrain, wide shallow trough terrain, central leading hemisphere terrain, smooth terrain, leading edge curvilinear terrain, southern curvilinear terrain, and south polar terrain. Because a correlation chart was not produced, the relative timing of unit formation is generally unclear. Spencer and Nimmo (2013) proposed that the cratered terrain is the oldest unit on Enceladus with surface ages ranging from 1 to 4 Ga (Kirchoff and Schenk, 2009). Centered on the leading and trailing hemispheres are younger units with model ages between 2 and 10 Ma (Spencer and Nimmo, 2013). As for the other Saturnian moons, there is no formal chronostratigraphy established.

15.2.5.2.4 Titan

Like Venus, the surface of Titan is shrouded in clouds that hinder the unobstructed view of geologic features. For example, Pioneer 11 and Voyager 1 had difficulties to see the surface but confirmed the existence of a methane atmosphere. This atmosphere is transparent at radar wavelengths, which allows us to observe the geology. However, these 300 m/pixel data are limited to a few passes taken during the flybys of the Cassini–Huygens spacecraft. Cassini VIMS can image the surface of Titan through specific windows in which the atmosphere is almost transparent and delivers spectra with about 1 km/pixel, on average. In addition, the descent yielded images with tens to hundreds of meters pixel resolutions. Resolution increased to centimeters at the landing site of the Huygens lander. Cassini–Huygens found that Titan, like Earth, has aeolian, pluvial, fluvial, lacustrine, tectonic, impact, and possibly cryo-volcanic processes operating on its surface. Making use of the diverse data sets, Lopes et al. (2010) mapped several geologic/geomorphic units (Fig. 15.15), including hummocky and mountainous terrain, impact crater, dunes, a fluvial valleys, a cryo-volcanic candidates, a labyrinthic terrains, an undifferentiated plans, and a mottled plain.

The hummocky and mountainous terrains unit that also includes Xanadu covers about 14% of Titan's surface and appears to be the oldest terrain (Lopes et al., 2010). On Titan, the few impact craters that have been observed show

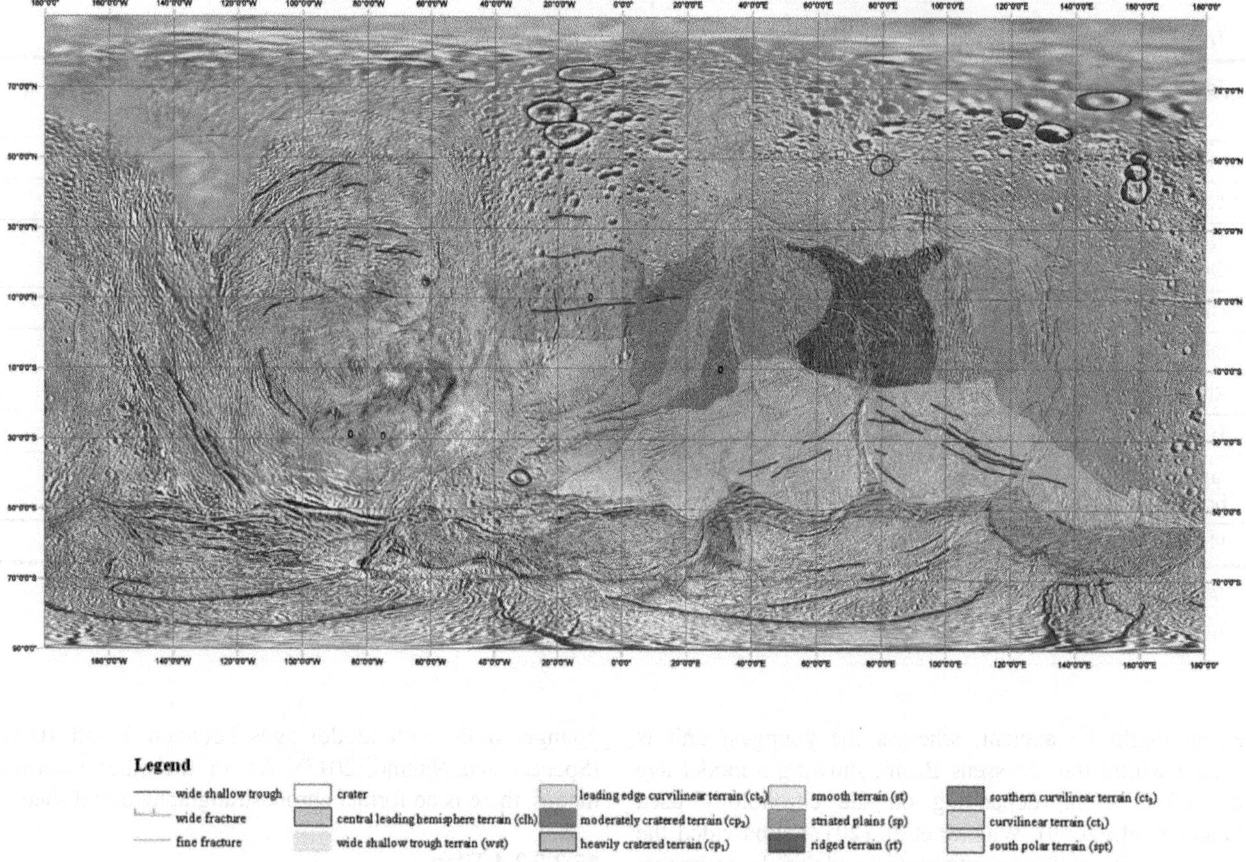

FIGURE 15.14 The geologic map of Enceladus (Crow-Willard and Pappalardo, 2010).

a wide range in morphologies and preservation. Craters and crater-form structures cover 1% and 0.2% of the known surface, respectively. In contrast, dunes are widespread and cover about 18% of the known surface. They occur mostly at low latitudes and indicate a substantial supply of sand-sized particles that can be easily mobilized and transported by Titan's atmosphere. Fluvial features are also widely distributed. Although some fluvial valleys might be too small to be seen in the radar data, they form networks and terminate in lakes at high latitudes. There have been several types of lakes distinguished on Titan and altogether they cover approximately 1.5% of its imaged surface. Lobate, flow-like features have been interpreted as candidates for cryo-volcanic activity. However, a cryogenic origin is still debated and Moore and Pappalardo (2011) argued that there might not be any cryo-volcanic features on Titan. The cryo-volcanic candidates unit covers about 0.6% of the studied surface and occurs preferentially between 30°W and 120°W. The labyrinthic terrains unit occurs at high latitudes, covers 0.19% of Titan, and might represent a continuation of channel and valley networks. Particularly at high latitudes, an extensive featureless plains unit with gradational boundaries formed by fluvial, lacustrine, or cryo-volcanic processes. The unit extends over 14% of the imaged surface and occurs preferentially at mid-latitudes. Finally, a mottled plains unit might be erosional in origin and might consist of several other units (Aharonson et al., 2014, and references therein). However, the mottled plains have not yet been mapped on a global scale because of difficulties to determine whether different exposures on different terrains have the same characteristics and the same origin (Aharonson et al., 2014).

15.2.5.3 Asteroids

Vesta and Ceres, the two largest and most massive asteroids in the main belt, are considered to be protoplanets that provide important information for our understanding of planet-forming processes. The Dawn spacecraft visited the two asteroids in 2001–12 (Vesta) and 2015–18 (Ceres). Utilizing the data from the Framing Camera (FC) and the infrared spectrometer (VIR), Dawn scientists compiled a global, 1:1,000,000-scale and 15-regional, 1:500,000-scale geologic quadrangle (see Greeley and Batson, 1990) maps of both bodies (e.g., Yingst et al., 2014; Williams et al., 2014). Thus these are the only two objects for which global geologic maps became available during the lifetime of a mission.

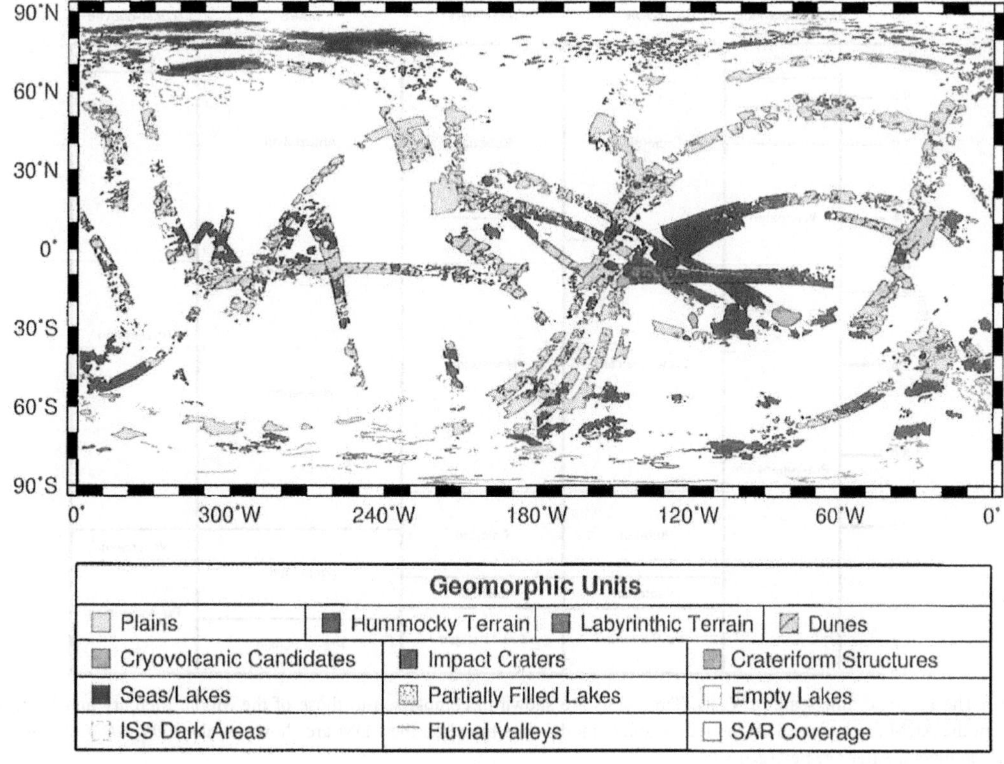

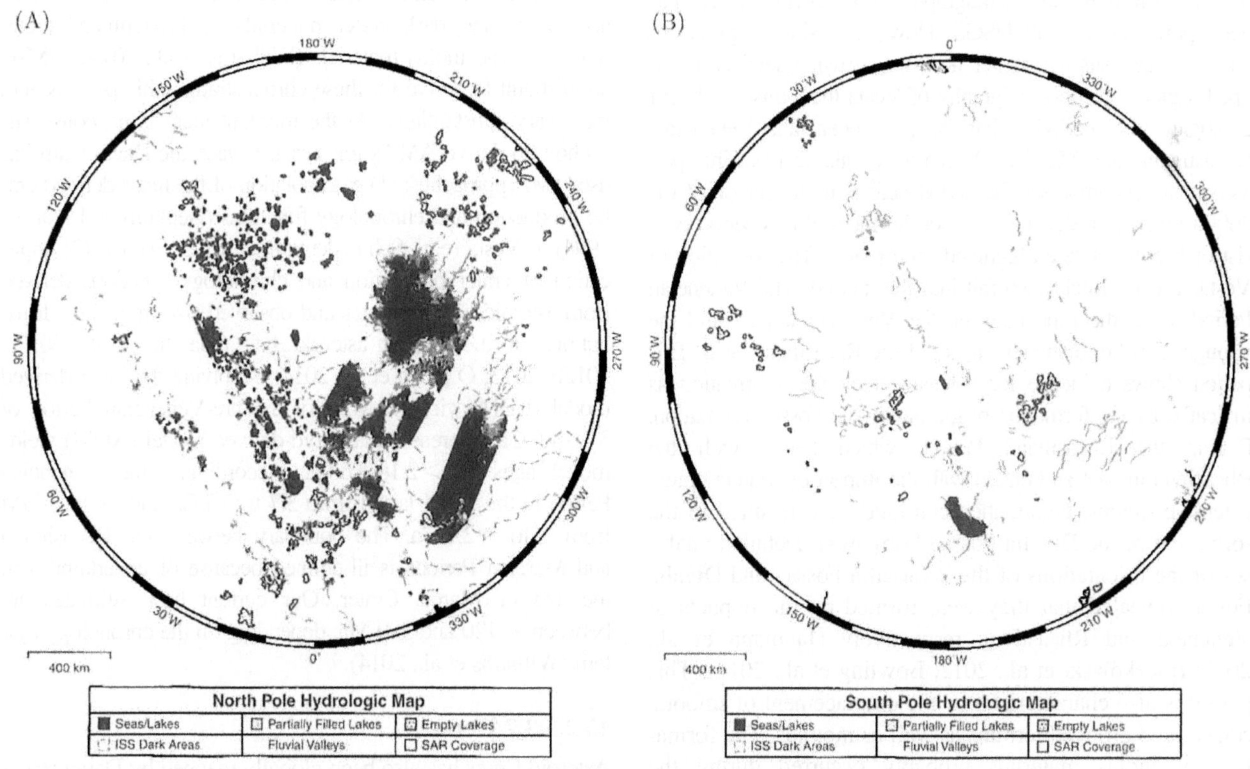

FIGURE 15.15 The geomorphic map of Titan (Aharonson et al., 2014). Based on Lopes et al. (2010).

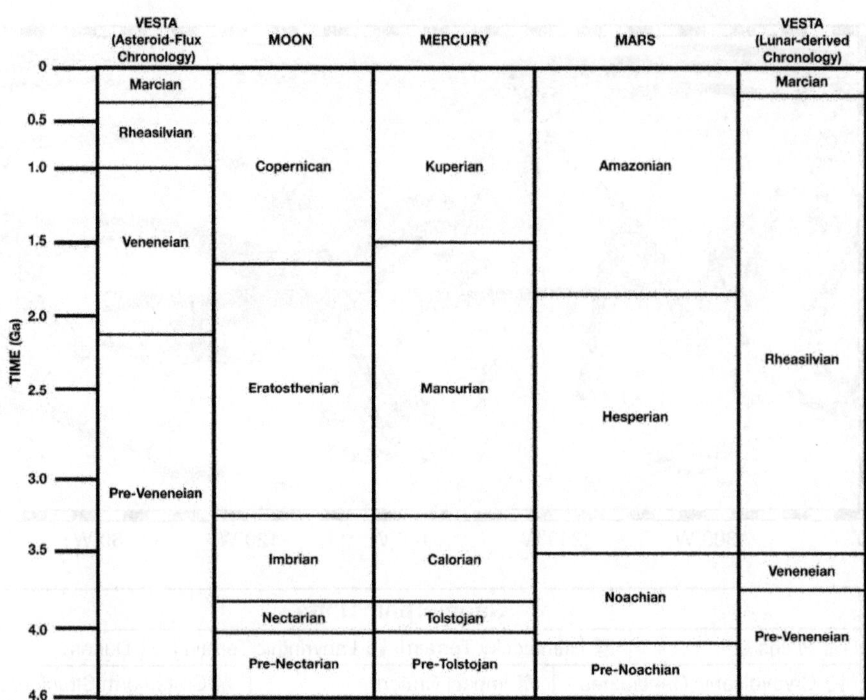

FIGURE 15.16 The geologic time scale of Vesta. Time units are shown in comparison to those of the Moon, Mercury and Mars. Absolute model ages derived from the ADM are indicated on the left; absolute model ages based on the LDM are shown on the right. *ADM*, Asteroid-derived model; *LDM*, lunar-derived model. After Greeley (2013).

15.2.5.3.1 Vesta

So far, no formal chronostratigraphy of Vesta (Fig. 15.16) has been published by the USGS. However, using large basins and their deposits as marker horizons, Dawn scientists developed a global chronostratigraphy of Vesta that consists of four geologic time periods, that is, pre-Veneneian, Veneneian, Rheasilvian and Marcian (Williams et al., 2014). The pre-Veneneian encompasses the period before the formation of the 400-km diameter Veneneia impact. Surfaces of this period consist of heavily cratered highlands and plains. The formation of Vestalia Terra might also fall into this period. The Veneneian Period spans the time between the Veneneia impact and the younger 500-km diameter impact of the Rheasilvia Basin. This period shows evidence for extensive tectonic deformation as indicated by the formation of the Saturnalia Fossae Formation. During the Rheasilvian Period, which began with the Rheasilvia impact and ended with the impact of Marcia crater, extensive tectonic deformation continued and resulted in the formation of the Divalia Fossae Formation. Detailed analyses of the orientations of the Saturnalia Fossae and Divalia Fossae revealed that they were formed by the impacts of Veneneia and Rheasilvia, respectively (Jaumann et al., 2012; Buczkowski et al., 2012; Bowling et al., 2014). This period is also characterized by the emplacement of smooth, ridged, and grooved terrains as well as mounds. The formation of tholus materials probably occurred during the Rheasilvian and impact cratering continued. The youngest period, the Marcian Period began with the formation of Marcia Crater and continues until today. The young Marcian surfaces comprise crater wall and ejecta materials, mass wasting materials, bright and dark crater materials, undifferentiated crater materials, and tholus materials (Williams et al., 2014). AMAs are difficult to derive for these chronostratigraphic periods and, thus, vary substantially. At the moment there is no consensus on how to derive AMAs for Vesta. In fact, the Dawn team has used two approaches: (1) extrapolation of the lunar-derived crater production and chronology functions (Neukum and Ivanov, 1994) to Vesta (e.g., Schmedemann et al., 2014) and (2) application of crater production and chronology functions derived from asteroid belt dynamics and observed size-frequency distributions of the current asteroid belt (Marchi et al., 2012a, 2012b, 2013; O'Brien et al., 2014). Applying the lunar-derived model (LDM) yields AMAs of the pre-Veneneian Period of 3.7–4.6 Ga whereas the asteroid-derived model (ADM) yields model ages of >2.1–4.6 Ga. Accordingly, the Veneneian Period in the LDM lasted from 3.7 to 3.5 Ga and in the ADM from 1 to >2.1 Ga. The boundary between the Rheasilvian and Marcian Periods is ill-defined because of uncertainties in the age of Marcia Crater. Our current best estimates are between ~120 and 390 Ma, depending on the chronology system (Williams et al., 2014).

15.2.5.3.2 Ceres

Asteroid Ceres has also been globally mapped by Dawn scientists, following the same successful approach applied at Vesta. For Ceres there is no formal chronostratigraphy defined yet, and there is considerable discussion within the Dawn team as to how to best subdivide its chronostratigraphic periods (Mest et al., 2018). In addition, obtaining AMAs for surface units on Ceres faces the same uncertainties as on Vesta (e.g., Hiesinger et al., 2016). This results in two models of age determinations, the LDM and the ADM. Currently, the Dawn team is working on a publication on the chronostratigraphy of Ceres. One proposal for the definition of the time stratigraphy discussed within the Dawn team suggests that key units should be the ejecta deposits of Yalode and Urvara craters, as CSFDs at the investigated diameter range accumulated on their ejecta blankets seem to be linked to their formation events. Applying the LDM, these CSFD measurements show that the age of Yalode is ~940 Ma and Urvara is ~170 Ma. The pre-Yalodian Period would contain the formation of heavily cratered terrain, which covers large parts of the surface of Ceres. According to the LDM, the cratered terrain averaged globally would be about 2.3 Ga. Also, during the pre-Yalodian Period, smooth terrain was deposited at approximately 1.1 Ga. Although the smooth terrain is spatially associated with Kerwan Crater, it is unclear whether it formed with the impact or much later. Thus neither the AMA for the smooth terrain, nor the AMA for the cratered terrain can be used as the starting point for the postulated Kerwanan Period, as suggested by the third and fourth proposal discussed in the Dawn team (Fig. 15.17). In addition, the cratered terrain exhibits a complex geologic history and varies in age depending on location and, thus, most likely does not represent a well-defined single geologic unit. Hence, using the cratered terrain as a potential stratigraphic marker horizon of the chronostratigraphy would violate the principle that such a unit should have been emplaced within a narrow time frame. CSFD measurements of almost 23,000 craters with diameters from a few hundred meters to 11 km in diameter showed that Urvara exhibits many secondary craters, thus, further complicating the age determinations. However, if we exclude all obvious secondary craters, an AMA of ~170 Ma can be derived for the formation of Urvara Crater. Other proposals suggest using Azacca Crater to define the base of the youngest time period. However, because this crater has been modified severely by secondary craters, it is impossible to derive a precise age for its formation and, thus, makes it less valuable for chronostratigraphic purposes. In summary, the definition of a chronostratigraphy for Ceres is complicated at multiple levels and requires significantly more research. Hence, at this time the chronostratigraphy for Ceres should be treated as preliminary.

15.2.5.4 Comets

The Rosetta mission entered orbit around the ~4.3 × 4.1-km sized comet 67P/Churyumov–Gerasimenko (67P) in 2014 and observed its surface (Fig. 15.18) from as low as 10 to 30 km. In addition, the mission carried the Philae lander, which successfully touched down to perform in situ measurements.

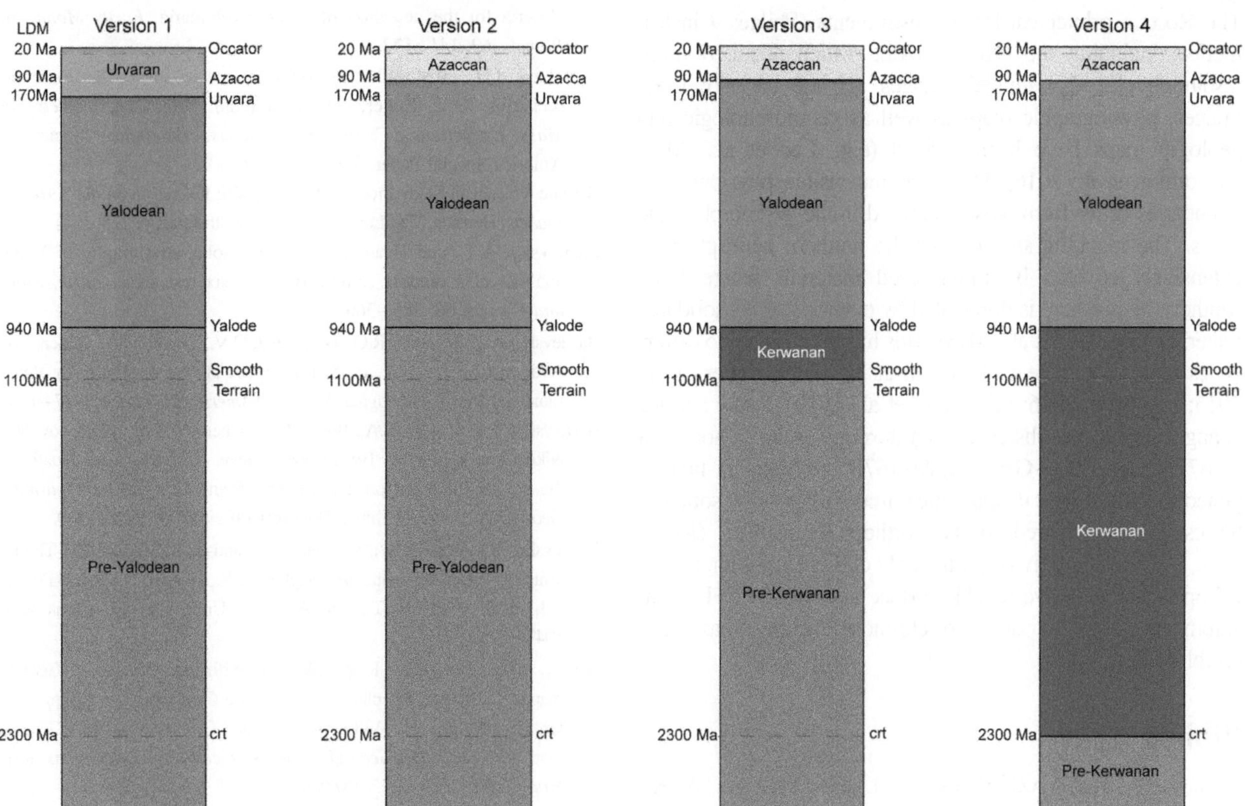

FIGURE 15.17 Four possible geologic time scales of Ceres. See text for details.

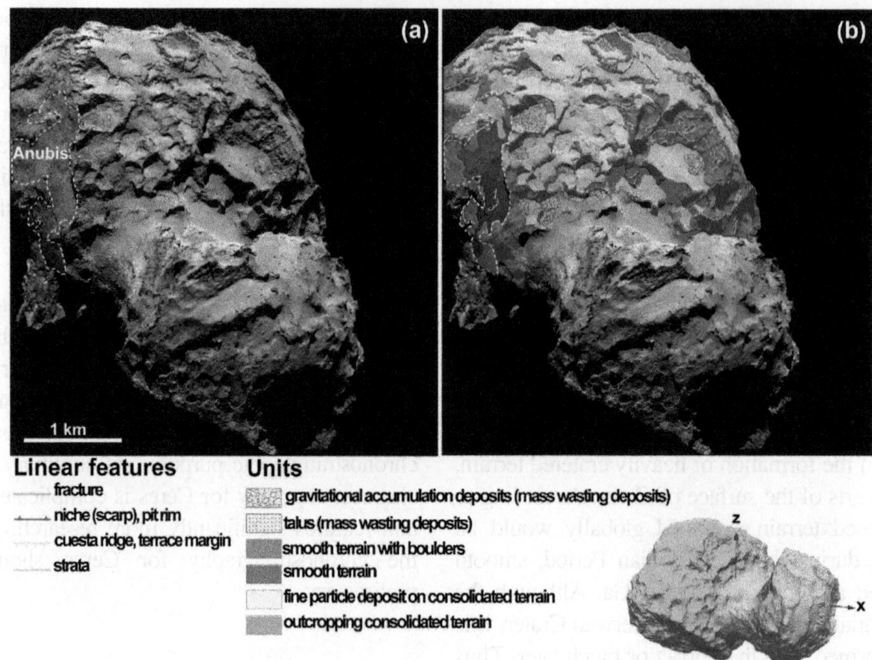

FIGURE 15.18 Geologic map of parts of comet 67P/Churyumov-Gerasimenko. (a) View of the upper side of the body. (b) Corresponding geologic mapping result. The depressed region III (Anubis) has been outlined with dashed white line. Fig. 7 in (Giacomini et al., 2016).

One of the major findings of Rosetta was that its D/H ratio is significantly different from that of Earth, implying that this type of comet is not responsible for delivering water to Earth. The Rosetta orbiter carried 12 instruments (Philae: 9 instruments), including the Osiris camera, which acquired high-resolution (1.2–2.4 m/pixel) images. On the basis of these images, physiographic maps as well as geomorphologic and geologic maps have been derived (e.g., Lee et al., 2016; Giacomini et al., 2016). However, the visible physiographic boundaries differ from those identified in the geomorphologic maps. The mapping showed that the northern hemisphere is extensively covered by fine-grained materials whereas the southern hemisphere is dominated by outcrops of consolidated materials (e.g., Lee et al., 2016). This has been linked to differences in insolation (e.g., Groussin et al., 2015; Keller et al., 2015; Lee et al, 2016; Giacomini et al., 2016). Many surface changes have been observed even during Rosetta's short visit of 67P/Churyumov–Gerasimenko (67P), resulting in heterogeneous erosion rates that are three times larger in the southern hemispheres compared to the northern hemisphere (Keller et al., 2015). This activity, particularly during perihelion makes it impossible to derive reliable surface ages from CSFD measurements. Thus to date no chronostratigraphy has been established.

Bibliography

Aharonson, O., Hayes, A.G., Hayne, P.O., Lopes, R.M., Lucas, A., and Perron, J.T., 2014, Titan's surface geology. *In* Müller-Wodarg, I., Griffith, C.A., Lellouch, E., and Cravens, T.E. (eds), *Titan – Interior, Surface, Atmosphere, and Space Environment*. New York: Cambridge University Press, 63–101.

Antonenko, I., Head III, J.W., Mustard, J.F., and Hawke, B.R., 1995, Criteria for the detection of lunar cryptomaria. *Earth, Moon, and Planets*, **69**: 141–172.

Archibald, J.D., 2014. What the dinosaur record says about extinction scenarios. *In* G. Keller, A.C. Kerr (eds). *Volcanism, Impacts, and Mass Extinctions: Causes and Effects*. Geological Society of America Special Paper, **505**, 213–224.

Basaltic Volcanism Study Project, 1981, *Basaltic Volcanism on the Terrestrial Planets*. Houston, TX: Lunar and Planetary Institute, p. 1286.

Basilevsky, A.T., and Head, J.W., 1995, Global stratigraphy of Venus: analysis of a random sample of thirty-six test areas. *Earth, Moon, and Planets*, **66**: 285–366.

Basilevsky, A.T., Kuzmin, R.O., Nikolaeva, O.V., Pronin, A.A., Ronca, L.B., Avduevsky, V.S., et al., 1985, The surface of Venus revealed by Venera Landings: Part II. *Geological Society of America Bulletin*, **96**: 137–144.

Basilevsky, A.T., Ivanov, B.A., Burba, G.A., Chernaya, I.M., Kryuchov, V.P., Nikolaeva, O.V., et al., 1987, Impact craters on Venus: a continuation of the analysis of data from the Venera 15 and 16 spacecraft. *Journal of Geophysical Research*, https://doi.org/10.1029/JB092iB12p12869.

Basilevsky, A.T., Head, J.W., Schaber, G.G., and Strom, R.G., 1997, The resurfacing history of Venus. *In* Bougher, S.W., Hunten, D.M., and Phillips, R.J. (eds), *Venus II*. Tucson, AZ: The University of Arizona Press, 1047–1084.

Bender, K.C., Greeley, R., Rice, J.W., and Wilhelms, D.E., 1994, Geologic map of Callisto, Lunar planet. *25th Science Conference*, 91–92 pp.

Bender, K.C., Rice, J.W., Wilhelms, D.E., and Greeley, R., 1997, Geologic map of Callisto. *US Geological Survey Geologic Investigations Series Map I-2581, Scale, 1:15,000,000.*

Berman, D.C., and Hartmann, W.K., 2002, Recent fluvial, volcanic, and tectonic activity on the Cerberus plains on Mars. *Icarus*, **159**: 1–17.

Bernatowicz, T.J., Hohenberg, C.M., Hudson, B., Kennedy, B.M., and Podosek, F.A., 1978, Argon ages for lunar breccias 14064 and 15405. *Proceedings of the Lunar Science Conference*, **9**: 905–919.

Bernhardt, H., Hiesinger, H., Ivanov, M., Erkeling, G., Ruesch, O., Reiss, D., 2015. Geomorphological analysis of the Hellas Basin floor, Mars: New implications for its geologic history. 46th Lunar and Planetary Science Conference, abstract #1336, https://www.hou.usra.edu/meetings/lpsc2015/pdf/1336.pdf.

Bernhardt, H., Hiesinger, H., Ivanov, M.A., Ruesch, O., Erkeling, G., and Reiss, D., 2016a, Photogeologic mapping and geologic history of the Hellas Basin floor. *Mars. Icarus*, **264**: 407–442, https://doi.org/10.1016/j.icarus.2015.09.031.

Bernhardt, H., Reiss, D., Hiesinger, H., and Ivanov, M.A., 2016b, The honeycomb terrain on the Hellas Basin floor, Mars: a case for salt or ice diapirism. *Journal of Geophysical Research*, **121**: 714–738, https://doi.org/10.1002/2016JE005007.

Bibring, J.-P., Langevin, Y., Gendrin, A., Gondet, B., Poulet, F., Berthé, M., et al., 2005, Mars surface diversity as revealed by the OMEGA/Mars Express observations. *Science*, **307**: 1576–1581.

Bierhaus, E.B., Chapman, C.R., Merline, W.J., Brooks, S.M., and Asphaug, E., 2001, Pwyll secondaries and other small craters on Europa. *Icarus*, **153**: 264–276.

Bierhaus, E.B., Chapman, C.R., and Merline, W.J., 2005, Secondary craters on Europa and implications for cratered surfaces. *Nature*, **437**: 1125–1127.

Bierhaus, E.B., McEwen, A.S., Robbins, S.J., Singer, K.N., Dones, L., Kirchoff, M.R., et al., 2018, Secondary craters and ejecta across the solar system: populations and effects on impact-crater-based chronologies. *Meteoritics & Planetary Science*, **53** (4), 638–671, https://doi.org/10.1111/maps.13057.

Bogard, D.D., Garrison, D.H., Shih, C.-Y., and Nyquist, L.E., 1994, 40Ar-39Ar dating of two lunar granites: the age of Copernicus. *Geochimica et Cosmochimica Acta*, **58**: 3093–3100.

Bottke, W.F., Vokrouhlicky, D., and Nesvorny, D., 2007, An asteroid breakup 160 Myr ago as the probable source of the K/T impactor. *Nature*, **449**: 48–53.

Bouvier, A., Blichert-Toft, J., Vervoort, J.D., and Albarède, F., 2005, The age of SNC meteorites and the antiquity of the Martian surface. *Earth and Planetary Science Letters*, **240**: 221–233.

Bowling, T.J., Johnson, B.C., and Melosh, H.J., 2014, Formation of equatorial graben following the Rheasilvia impact on asteroid 4 Vesta. *Vesta in the Light of Dawn: First Exploration of a Protoplanet in the Asteroid Belt*, 2018 p.

Boyce, J.M., and Dial Jr., A.L., 1975, Relative ages of flow units in Mare Imbrium and Sinus Iridum. *Proceedings of the Lunar Science Conference*, **6**: 2585–2595.

Braden, S.E., Stopar, J.D., Robinson, M.S., Lawrence, S.J., van der Bogert, C.H., and Hiesinger, H., 2014, Evidence for basaltic volcanism on the moon within the past 100 million years. *Nature Geoscience*, https://doi.org/10.1038/NGEO2252.

Buczkowski, D.L., Wyrick, D.Y., Iyer, K.A., Kahn, E.G., Scully, J.E.C., Nathues, A., et al., 2012, Large-scale troughs on Vesta: a signature of planetary tectonics. *Geophysical Research Letters*, https://doi.org/10.1029/2012GL052959.

Bullock, M.A., and Grinspoon, D.H., 2001, The recent evolution of climate on Venus. *Icarus*, **150**: 19–37.

Burr, D.M., Grier, J.A., McEwen, A.S., and Keszthelyi, L.P., 2002, Repeated aqueous flooding from the Cerberus Fossae: evidence for very recently extant, deep groundwater on Mars. *Icarus*, **159**: 53–73.

Chapman, C.R., 1974, Cratering on Mars. I. Cratering and obliteration history. *Icarus*, **22**: 272–291.

Chapman, C.R., 1988, Mercury: introduction to an end-member planet. *In* Vilas, F., Chapman, C.R., and Matthews, M.S. (eds), *Mercury*. Tucson, AZ: The University of Arizona Press, 1–23.

Chapman, M.G., 2002. Layered, massive, and thin sediments on Mars: possible Late Noachian to Late Amazonian tephra? *In* Smellie, J.L., Chapman, M.G. (eds), *Volcano-Ice Interactions on Earth and Mars*. Geological Society of London Special Publications, **202**, 273–293.

Chapman, M.G., and Tanaka, K.L., 2002, Related magma-ice interactions: possible origin for chasmata, chaos, and surface materials in Xanthe, Margaritifer, and Meridiani Terrae, Mars. *Icarus*, **155**: 2324–2339.

Chapman, M.G., and Zimbelman, J.R., 1998, Coronae associations and their implications for Venus. *Icarus*, **132**: 344–361.

Chapman, C.R., Pollack, J., and Sagan, C., 1969, An analysis of the Mariner 4 photography of Mars. *Astronomical Journal*, **74**: 1039–1051.

Chapman, C.R., Ryan, E.V., Merline, W.J., Neukum, G., Wagner, R., Thomas, P.C., et al., 1996, Cratering on Ida. *Icarus*, **120**: 77–86.

Christensen, P.R., Bandfield, J.L., Clark, R.N., Edgett, K.S., Hamilton, V.E., Hoefen, T., et al., 2000a, Detection of crystalline hematite mineralization on Mars by the Thermal Emission Spectrometer data. *Journal of Geophysical Research*, **105**: 9623–9642.

Christensen, P.R., Bandfield, J.L., Smith, M.D., Hamilton, V.E., and Clark, R.N., 2000b, Identification of a basaltic component on the Martian surface from Thermal Emission Spectrometer data. *Journal of Geophysical Research*, **105**: 9609–9621.

Connerney, J.E.P., Acuna, M.H., Wasilewski, P.J., Kletetschka, G., Ness, N.F., Re'me, H., et al., 2001, *The global magnetic field of Mars and implications for crustal evolution, Geophysical Research Letters*, 28. pp. 4015–4018.

Craddock, R.A., and Howard, A.D., 2002, The case for rainfall on a warm, wet early Mars. *Journal of Geophysical Research*, **107** (E11), 5111, https://doi.org/10.1029/2001JE001505.

Crater Analysis Techniques Working Group, 1979, *Standard techniques for presentation and analysis of crater size-frequency data, Icarus*, **vol. 37**. 467–474.

Crown, D.A., Price, K.H., and Greeley, R., 1992, Geologic evolution of the east rim of the Hellas Basin, Mars. *Icarus*, **100**: 1–25.

Crow-Willard, E.N., and Pappalardo, R.T., 2010, Global geological mapping of Enceladus. *41st Lunar and Planetary Science Conference*, 2715 p.

Deutsch, A., and Stöffler, D., 1987, Rb-Sr analyses of Apollo 16 melt rocks and a new age estimate for the Imbrium basin: lunar basin chronology and the early heavy bombardment of the Moon. *Geochimica et Cosmochimica Acta*, **51**: 1951–1964.

Doggett, T., Greeley, R., Figueredo, P., and Tanaka, K., 2009, *Geologic Stratigraphy and Evolution of Europa's Surface*. Europa, University of Arizona Press, pp. 137–159.

Dohm, J.M., Tanaka, K.L., and Hare, T.M., 2001, Geologic, paleotectonic, and paleoerosional maps of the Thaumasia region, Mars. *US Geological Survey Geologic Investigations Series Map I-2650, Scale, 1:5,000,000.*

Dones, L., Chapman, C.R., McKinnon, W.B., Melosh, H.J., and Kirchoff, M.R., 2009, Icy satellites of Saturn: impact cratering and age determination. *In* Doughert, M.K., Esposito, L.W., and Krimigis, S.M. (eds), *Saturn From Cassini-Huygens*. Dordrecht: Springer, 613–635.

Duncan, M.J., and Levison, H.F., 1997, A scattered comet disk and the origin of Jupiter family comets. *Science*, **276**: 1670–1672.

Fassett, C.I., and Head III, J.W., 2008a, The timing of Martian valley network activity: constraints from buffered crater counting. *Icarus*, **195**: 61–89.

Fassett, C.I., and Head III, J.W., 2008b, Valley network-fed, open-basin lakes on Mars: distribution and implications for Noachian surface and subsurface hydrology. *Icarus*, **198**: 37–56.

Figueredo, P.H., and Greeley, R., 2004, Resurfacing history of Europa from pole-to-pole geological mapping. *Journal of Geophysical Research*, **105** (22), 629–646.

Frey, H.V., 2005, Impact constraints on the age and origin of the lowlands on Mars. *Geophysical Research Letters*, **33**: L08S02, https://doi.org/10.1029/2005GL024484.

Frey, H.V., 2006, Impact constraints on, and a chronology for, major events in early Mars history. *Journal of Geophysical Research*, **111**: E08S91, https://doi.org/10.1029/2005JE002449.

Frey, H.V., Roark, J.H., Shockey, K.M., Frey, E.L., and Sakimoto, S.E.H., 2002, Ancient lowlands on Mars. *Geophysical Research Letters*, **29**: 1384, https://doi.org/10.1029/2001GL013832.

Fujiwara, A., Kawaguchi, J., Yeomans, K., Abe, M., Mukai, T., Okada, T., et al., 2006, The rubble-pile asteroid Itokawa as observed by Hayabusa. *Science*, **312**: 1330–1334.

Giacomini, L., Massironi, M., El-Maarry, M.R., Penasa, L., Pajola, M., Thomas, N., et al., 2016, Geologic mapping of the Comet 67P/Churyumov-Gerasimenko's Northern hemisphere. *Monthly Notices of the Royal Astronomical Society*, **462** (Suppl. 1): S352–S367.

Gomes, R., Levison, H.F., Tsiganis, K., and Morbidelli, A., 2005, Origin of the cataclysmic Late Heavy Bombardment period of the terrestrial planets. *Nature*, **435**: 466–469.

Greeley, R., 2013, *Introduction to Planetary Geomorphology*. Cambridge University Press.

Greeley, R., and Batson, R.M., 1990, *Planetary Mapping*. Cambridge University Press 296 pp.

Greeley, R., and Guest, J.E., 1987, Geologic map of the eastern equatorial region of Mars. *US Geological Survey Miscellaneous Investigations Series Maps I-1802-B, Scale 1:15,000,000*.

Groussin, O., Sierks, H., Barbieri, C., Lamy, P., Rodrigo, R., Koschny, D., et al., 2015, Temporal morphological changes in the Imhotep region of comet 67P/Churyumov-Gerasimenko. *Astronomy & Astrophysics*, **583**, https://doi.org/10.1051/0004-6361/201527020.

Guest, J.E., and Greeley, R., 1983, Geologic map of the Shakespeare quadrangle of Mercury. *US Geological Survey Miscellaneous Investigations Series Map I-1408, Scale 1:5,000,000*.

Guest, J.E., and Stofan, E.R., 1999, A new view of the stratigraphic history of Venus. *Icarus*, **139**: 55–66.

Hamilton, V.E., and Stofan, E.R., 1996, The geomorphology and evolution of Hecate Chasma, Venus. *Icarus*, **121**: 171–194.

Hansen, V.L., 2000, Geologic mapping of tectonic planets. *Earth and Planetary Science Letters*, **176**: 527–542.

Hartmann, W.K., 1965, Terrestrial and lunar flux of large meteorites in the last two billion years. *Icarus*, **4**: 157–165.

Hartmann, W.K., 1970, Lunar cratering chronology. *Icarus*, **13**: 209e301.

Hartmann, W.K., 1971, Martian cratering III: Theory of crater obliteration. *Icarus*, **15**: 410–428.

Hartmann, W.K., 1972, Paleocratering of the Moon: review of post-Apollo data. *Astrophysics and Space Science*, **12**: 48–61.

Hartmann, W.K., 1973, Martian cratering, 4, Mariner 9 initial analysis of cratering chronology. *Journal of Geophysical Research*, **78**: 4096–4116.

Hartmann, W.K., 2003, Megaregolith evolution and cratering cataclysm models—lunar cataclysm as a misconception (28 years later). *Meteoritics & Planetary Science*, **38**: 579–593.

Hartmann, W.K., 2005, Martian cratering 8: isochron refinement and the chronology of Mars. *Icarus*, **174**: 294–320.

Hartmann, W.K., 2007, Martian chronology: toward resolution of the 2005 "controversy" and evidence for obliquity-driven resurfacing processes. *Seventh International Conference on Mars*, Lunar and Planetary Institute, Houston, TX. Abstract on CD-ROM, #3318.

Hartmann, W.K., and Neukum, G., 2001, Cratering chronology and the evolution of Mars. *Space Science Reviews*, **96**: 165–194.

Hartmann, W.K., Neukum, G., and Werner, S., 2007, Confirmation and utilization of size-frequency distributions of impact craters produced on Mars. *Geophysical Research Letters*, **35**: L02205, https://doi.org/10.1029/2007GL031557.

Hauber, E., Grott, M., and Kronberg, P., 2010, Martian rifts—structural geology and geophysics. *Earth and Planetary Science Letters*, **294**: 393–410, https://doi.org/10.1016/j.epsl.2009.11.005.

Hauck II, S.A., Phillips, R.J., and Price, M.H., 1998, Venus: crater distribution and plains resurfacing models. *Journal of Geophysical Research*, **103**: 13635–13642.

Hawke, B.R., and Bell, J.F., 1981, Remote sensing studies of lunar dark-halo impact craters: preliminary results and implications of early volcanism. *Proceedings of the Lunar and Planetary Science Conference*, **12B**: 665–678.

Head III, J.W., and Pratt, S., 2001, Extensive Hesperian-aged south polar ice sheet on Mars—evidence for massive melting and retreat, and lateral flow and ponding of melt-water. *Journal of Geophysical Research*, **106** (E6), 12,275–12,299.

Head, J.W., Mustard, J.F., Kreslavsky, M.A., Milliken, R.E., and Marchant, D.R., 2003, Recent ice ages on Mars. *Nature*, **426**: 797–802.

Hiesinger, H., Head, J.W., Wolf, U., Jaumann, R., and Neukum, G., 2002, Lunar mare basalt flow units: thicknesses determined from crater size-frequency distributions. *Geophysical Research Letters*, **29** (8), https://doi.org/10.1029/2002GL014847.

Hiesinger, H., Head III, J.W., Wolf, U., Jaumann, R., and Neukum, G., 2003, Ages and stratigraphy of mare basalts in Oceanus Precellarum, Mare Nubium, Mare Cognitum, and Mare Insularum. *Journal of Geophysical Research*, **108**, https://doi.org/10.1029/2002JE001985.

Hiesinger, H., Head, J.W., and Neukum, G., 2007, Young lava flows on the eastern flank of Ascraeus Mons: rheological properties derived from High Resolution Stereo Camera (HRSC) images and Mars Orbiter Laser Altimeter (MOLA) data. *Journal of Geophysical Research*, **112**: E05011, https://doi.org/10.1029/2006JE002717.

Hiesinger, H., Head, J.W., Wolf, U., Jaumann, R., and Neukum, G., 2011, Ages and stratigraphy of lunar mare basalts: a synthesis. *In* Ambrose, W.A., and Williams, D.A. (eds), *Recent Advances and Current Research Issues in Lunar Stratigraphy*. Geological Society of America Special Paper, **477**: 1–51. https://doi.org/10.1130/2011.2477(01).

Hiesinger, H., van der Bogert, C.H., Pasckert, J.H., Funcke, L., Giacomini, L., Ostrach, L.R., et al., 2012, How old are young lunar craters? *Journal of Geophysical Research*, **117**, https://doi.org/10.1029/2011JE003935.

Hiesinger, H., Marchi, S., Schmedemann, N., Schenk, P., Pasckert, J.H., Neesemann, A., et al., 2016, Cratering on Ceres: implications for its crust and evolution. *Science*, **353**, https://doi.org/10.1126/science.aaf4759.

Hubbard, N.J., Meyer Jr., C., Gast, P.W., and Wiesmann, H., 1971, The composition and derivation of Apollo 12 soils. *Earth and Planetary Science Letters*, **10**: 341–350.

Hynek, B.M., Phillips, R.J., and Arvidson, R.E., 2003, Explosive volcanism in the Tharsis region: global evidence in the Martian geologic record. *Journal of Geophysical Research*, **108**: 5111, https://doi.org/10.1029/2003JE002062.

Irwin III, R.P., Maxwell, T.A., Howard, A.D., Craddock, R.A., and Leverington, D.W., 2002, A large paleolake basin at the head of Ma'adim Vallis, Mars. *Science*, **296**: 2209–2212.

Irwin III, R.P., Howard, A.D., Craddock, R.A., and Moore, J.M., 2005, An intense terminal epoch of widespread fluvial activity on early Mars: 2. Increased runoff and paleolake development. *Journal of Geophysical Research*, **110**: E12S15, https://doi.org/10.1029/2005JE002460.

Irwin III, R.P., Tanaka, K.L., and Robbins, S.J., 2013, Distribution of Early, Middle, and Late Noachian cratered surfaces in the Martian highlands—implications for resurfacing events and processes. *Journal of Geophysical Research*, **118**: 1–14, https://doi.org/10.1002/jgre.20053.

Ivanov, B.A., 2001, Mars/Moon cratering rate ratio estimates. *Space Science Reviews*, **96**: 87–104.

Ivanov, B.A., and Basilevsky, A.T., 1987, Comparison of crater retention age of Earth and Venus. *Astronomicheskij Vestnik*, **21**: 136–143.

Ivanov, M.A., and Basilevsky, A.T., 1993, Density and morphology of impact craters on Tessera Terrain, Venus. *Geophysical Research Letters*, **20**: 2579–2582.

Jaumann, R., Williams, D.A., Buczkowski, D.L., Yingst, R.A., Preusker, F., Hiesinger, H., et al., 2012, Vesta's shape and morphology. *Science*, **336**: 687–690.

Jedicke, R., and Metcalfe, T.S., 1998, The orbital and absolute magnitude distributions of main belt asteroids. *Icarus*, **131**: 245–260.

Jessberger, E.K., Huneke, J.C., Podosek, F.A., and Wasserburg, G.G., 1974, High resolution argon analysis of neutron irradiated Apollo rocks and separate minerals. *Proceedings of the Lunar and Planetary Science Conference*, **5**: 1419–1449.

Jones, A.P., 2014, Impact volcanism and mass extinction. *In* Keller, G., and Kerr, A.C. (eds), *Volcanism, Impacts, and Mass Extinctions: Causes and Effects*. Geological Society of America Special Paper, **505**: 369–382.

Keller, H.U., Mottola, S., Davidson, B., Schröder, S.E., Skorov, Y., Kührt, E., et al., 2015, Insolation, erosion, and morphology of comet 67P/Churyumov-Gerasimenko. *Astronomy & Astrophysics*, **583**, https://doi.org/10.1051/0004-6361/201525964.

Keszthelyi, L., McEwen, A.S., and Thordarson, T., 2000, Terrestrial analogs and thermal models for Martian flood lavas. *Journal of Geophysical Research*, **105**: 15027–15050.

Kirchoff, M.R., and Schenk, P., 2009, Crater modification and geologic activity in Enceladus' heavily cratered plains: evidence from the impact crater distribution. *Icarus*, **202**: 656–668.

Kirchoff, M.R., and Schenk, P., 2010, Impact cratering records of mid-sized, icy Saturnian satellites. *Icarus*, **206**: 485–497.

Kryuchov, V.P., 1987, Analysis of population of Venusian impact craters. *Izvestiya Akademii Nauk Sssr, Seriya Geologicheskaya*, **6**: 75–83.

Lee, J.-C., Massironi, M., Ip, W.-H., Giaccomini, L., Ferrari, S., Penasa, L., et al., 2016, Geomorphological mapping of comet 67P/Churyumov-Gerasimenko's southern hemisphere. *Monthly Notices of the Royal Astronomical Society*, **462**: 573–592.

Leonard, G.J., and Tanaka, K.L., 2001, Geologic map of the Hellas region of Mars. *US Geological Survey Geologic Investigations Series Maps I-2694, Scale 1:5,000,000.*

Levison, H.F., Dones, L., Chapman, C.R., Stern, S.A., Duncan, M.J., and Zahnle, K., 2001, Could the lunar "Late Heavy Bombardment" have been triggered by the formation of Uranus and Neptune? *Icarus*, **151**: 286–306.

Liou, J.-C., and Malhotra, R., 1997, Depletion of the outer asteroid belt. *Science*, **275**: 375–377.

Lopes, R.M., Stofan, E.R., Peckyno, R., Radebaugh, J., Mitchell, K.L., Mitri, G., et al., 2010, Distribution and interplay of geologic processes on Titan from Cassini radar data. *Icarus*, **205**: 540–558.

Lucchitta, B.K., and Soderblom, L.A., 1982, *The geology of Europa. Satellites of Jupiter*. University of Arizona Press, pp. 521–555.

Malin, M.C., and Edgett, K.S., 2000, Sedimentary rocks of early Mars. *Science*, **290**: 1927–1937.

Malin, M.C., and Edgett, K.S., 2001, Mars Global Surveyor Mars Orbiter Camera—interplanetary cruise through primary mission. *Journal of Geophysical Research*, **106**: 23429–24570.

Malin, M.C., and Edgett, K.S., 2003, Evidence for persistent flow and aqueous sedimentation on early Mars. *Science*, **302**: 1931–1934.

Malin, M.C., Edgett, K.S., Posiolova, L.V., McColley, S.M., and Noe Dobrea, E.Z., 2006, Present-day impact cratering rate and contemporary gully activity on Mars. *Science*, **314**: 1573–1577.

Marchi, S., McSween, H.Y., O'Brien, D.P., Schenk, P., DeSanctis, M.C., Gaskell, R., et al., 2012a, The violent collisional history of asteroid 4 Vesta. *Science*, **336**: 690–694.

Marchi, S., et al., 2012b, The cratering history of Asteroid (21) Lutetia. *Planetary and Space Science*, **66**: 87–95.

Marchi, S., et al., 2013, High-velocity collisions from the lunar cataclysm recorded in asteroidal meteorites. *Nature Geoscience*, **6**: 303–307.

Mazrouei, S., Ghent, R.R., Bottke, W.F., Parker, A.H., and Gernon, T.M., 2019, Earth and Moon impact flux increased at the end of the Paleozoic. *Science*, **363**: 253–257.

McCauley, J.F., Guest, J.E., Schaber, G.G., Trask, N.J., and Greeley, R., 1981, Stratigraphy of the Caloris basin, Mercury. *Icarus*, **47**: 184–202.

McEwen, A.S., Keszthelyi, L., Geissler, P., Simonelli, D.P., Carr, M.H., Johnson, T.V., et al., 1998a, Active volcanism on Io as seen by Galileo SSI. *Icarus*, **135**: 181–219.

McEwen, A.S., Kesthelyi, L., Spencer, J.R., Schubert, G., Matson, D.L., Lopes-Gautier, R., et al., 1998b, High-temperature silicate volcanism on Jupiter's moon Io. *Science*, **281**: 87–90.

McEwen, A.S., Malin, M.C., Carr, M.H., and Hartmann, W.K., 1999, Voluminous volcanism on early Mars revealed in Valles Marineris. *Nature*, **397**: 584–586.

McEwen, A.S., Preblich, B.S., Turtle, E.P., Artemieva, N.A., Golombek, M.P., Hurst, M., et al., 2005, The rayed crater Zunil and interpretations of small impact craters on Mars. *Icarus*, **176**: 351–381.

McKay, G.A., Wiesmann, H., Bansal, J.L., and Shih, C.-Y., 1979, Petrology, chemistry, and chronology of Apollo 14 KREEP basalts. *Proceedings of the Lunar and Planetary Science Conference*, **10**: 181–205.

McKinnon, W.B., Chapman, C.R., and Housen, K.R., 1991, Cratering of the Uranian satellites. *In* Bergstralh, J.T., Miner, E.D., and Matthews, M.S. (eds), *Uranus*. Tucson, AZ: The University of Arizona Press, 629–692.

McKinnon, W.B., Zahnle, K.J., Ivanov, B.A., and Melosh, H.J., 1997, Cratering on Venus: models and observations. *In* Bougher, S.W., Hunten, D.M., and Phillips, R.J. (eds), *Venus II*. Tucson, AZ: The University of Arizona Press, 1047–1084.

Mest, S.C., Crown, D.A., Yingst, A.R., Berman, D.C., Williams, D.A., Buczkowski, D.L., et al., 2018, The HAMO-based global geologic map and chronostratigraphy of Ceres. *Lunar and Planetary Science Conference*, **49**: 2730.

Michael, G.G., 2013, Planetary surface dating from crater size-frequency distribution measurements—multiple resurfacing episodes and differential isochron fitting. *Icarus*, **226**: 885−890, https://doi.org/10.1016/j.icarus.2013.07.004.

Moore, J.M., and Pappalardo, R.T., 2011, Titan: an exogenic world? *Icarus*, **212**: 790−806.

Moore, J.M., and Wilhelms, D.E., 2001, Hellas as a possible site of ancient ice-covered lakes on Mars. *Icarus*, **154**: 258−276.

Namiki, N., and Solomon, S.C., 1994, Impact crater densities on volcanoes and coronae on Venus: implications for volcanic resurfacing. *Science*, **265**: 929−933.

Neukum, G., 1983, Meteoritenbombardement und Datierung planetarer Oberflächen. *Habilitation thesis*. University of München, Munich.

Neukum, G., 1997, Bombardment history of the Jovian system. *In* Barbieri, C., Rahe, J., Johnson, T.V., and Sohus, A.M. (eds), *The Three Galileos: The Man, the Spacecraft, The Telescope*. Springer, 201−212.

Neukum, G., and Ivanov, B.A., 1994, Crater size distributions and impact probabilities on Earth from lunar, terrestrial-planet, and asteroid cratering data. *In* Gehrels, T. (ed), *Hazards Due to Comets & Asteroids*. Tucson, AZ: The University of Arizona Press, 359−416.

Neukum, G., and Wise, D.U., 1976, Mars: a standard crater curve and possible new time scale. *Science*, **194**: 1381−1387.

Neukum, G., König, B., and Arkani-Hamed, J., 1975, A study of lunar impact crater size-distribution. *Moon*, **12**: 201−229.

Neukum, G., Wagner, R., Wolf, U., Ivanov, B.A., Head III, J.W., Pappalardo, R.T., et al., 1998. Cratering chronology in the Jovian system and derivation of absolute ages. *29th Annual Lunar and Planetary Science Conference, Houston, TX, March 16–20, 1998, Abstract on CD-ROM, 1742*.

Neukum, G., Wagner, R., Wolf, U., and the Galileo SSI Team, 1999, Cratering record of Europa and implications for time scale and crustal development. *29th Annual Lunar and Planetary Science Conference, Houston, TX, March 16–20, 1999, Abstract on CD-ROM, 1992*.

Neukum, G., Ivanov, B.A., and Hartmann, W.K., 2001, Cratering records in the inner solar system in relation to the lunar reference system. *Space Science Reviews*, **96**: 55−86.

Neukum, G., Wagner, R.J., Wolf, U., Denk, T., 2006, The cratering record and cratering chronologies of the Saturnian satellites and the origin of impactors: results from Cassini ISS Data. *First Europlanet Conference, EPSC2006-A-00610, Berlin*.

Nimmo, F., and Tanaka, K., 2005, Early crustal evolution of Mars. *Annual Review of Earth and Planetary Sciences*, **33**: 133−161.

Nyquist, L.E., Bogard, D.D., Shish, C.-Y., Greshake, A., Stöffler, D., and Eugster, O., 2001, Ages and geologic histories of Martian meteorites. *Space Science Reviews*, **96**: 105−164.

O'Brien, D.P., Marchi, S., Morbidelli, A., et al., 2014, Constraining the cratering chronology of Vesta. *Planetary and Space Science*, https://doi.org/10.1016/j.pss.2014.05.013.

Pappalardo, R.T., Belton, M.J.S., Breneman, H.H., Carr, M.H., Chapman, C.R., Collins, G.C., et al., 1999, Does Europa have a subsurface ocean? Evaluation of the geological evidence. *Journal of Geophysical Research*, **104**: 24015−24055.

Parker, T.J., Saunders, R.S., and Schneeberger, D.M., 1989, Transitional morphology in west Deuteronilus Mensae, Mars: implications for modification of the lowland/upland boundary. *Icarus*, **82**: 111−145.

Pasckert, J.H., Hiesinger, H., and Reiss, D., 2012, Rheologies and ages of lava flows on Elysium Mons, Mars. *Icarus*, **219**: 443−457, https://doi.org/10.1016/j.icarus.2012.03.014.

Patterson, W.G., Collins, G.C., Head, J.W., Pappalardo, R.T., Prockter, L.M., Lucchitta, B.K., et al., 2010, Global geological mapping of Ganymede. *Icarus*, **207**: 845−867.

Phillips, R.J., Zuber, M.T., Solomon, S.C., Golombek, M.P., Jakosky, B.M., Banerdt, W.B., et al., 2001, Ancient geodynamics and global-scale hydrology on Mars. *Science*, **291**: 2587−2591.

Phillips, R.J., Davis, B.J., Tanaka, K.L., Byrne, S., Mellon, M.T., Putzig, N.E., et al., 2011, *Science*, **332**: 838−841, https://doi.org/10.1126/science.1203091.

Platz, T., and Michael, G.G., 2011, Eruption history of the Elysium Volcanic Province, Mars. *Earth and Planetary Science Letters*, **312**: 140−151, https://doi.org/10.1016/j.epsl.2011.10.001.

Platz, T., Byrne, P.K., Massironi, M., and Hiesinger, H., 2015, Volcanism and tectonism across the inner solar system: an overview. *In* Platz, T., Massironi, M., Byrne, P.K., and Hiesinger, H. (eds), *Volcanism and Tectonism Across the Inner Solar System*. Geological Society, London, Special Publications, **401**: 1−56.

Platz, T., Michael, G., Tanaka, K.L., Skinner Jr., J.A., and Fortezzo, C.M., 2012, Crater-based dating of geological units on Mars: methods and application for the new geological map. *Icarus*, **225**: 806−827, https://doi.org/10.1016/j.icarus.2013.04.021.

Plaut, J.J., Picardi, G., Safaeiniti, A., Ivanov, A.B., Milkovich, S.M., Cicchetti, A., et al., 2007, Subsurface radar sounding of the south polar layered deposits of Mars. *Science*, **316**: 92−95.

Plescia, J.B., 1983, The geology of Dione. *Icarus*, **56**: 255−277.

Plescia, J.B., 2003, Cerberus Fossae, Elysium, Mars: a source for lava and water. *Icarus*, **164**: 79−95.

Porco, C.C., West, R.A., McEwen, A., Del Genio, A.D., Ingersoll, A.P., Thomas, P., et al., 2003, Cassini imaging of Jupiter's atmosphere, satellites, and rings. *Science*, **299**: 1541−1547.

Porco, C.C., Helfenstein, P., Thomas, P.C., Ingersoll, A.P., Wisdom, J., West, R., et al., 2006, Cassini observes the active south pole of Enceladus. *Science*, **311**: 1393−1401.

Price, M., and Suppe, J., 1995, Constraints on the resurfacing history of Venus from the hypsometry and distribution of volcanism, tectonism, and impact craters. *Earth, Moon, and Planets*, **71**: 99−145.

Price, M.H., Watson, G., Suppe, J., and Brankman, C., 1996, Dating volcanism and rifting on Venus using impact crater densities. *Journal of Geophysical Research*, **101**: 4657−4671.

Prinz, M., and Keil, K., 1977, Mineralogy, petrology and chemistry of ANT-suite rocks from the lunar highlands. *Physics and Chemistry of the Earth*, **10**: 215−237.

Qiao, L., Head, J., Wilson, L., Xiao, L., Kreslavsky, M., and Dufek, J., 2017, Ina pit crater on the Moon: extrusion of waning-stage lava lake magmatic foam results in extremely young crater retention ages. *Geology*, **45**: 455−458.

Robbins, S.J., and Hynek, B.M., 2012, A new global database of Mars impact craters ≥1 km—1. Database creation, properties, parameters. *Journal of Geophysical Research*, **117**: E05004, https://doi.org/10.1029/2011JE003966.

Robbins, S.J., Hynek, B.M., Lillis, R.J., and Bottke, W.F., 2013, Large impact crater histories of Mars—the effect of different model crater age techniques. *Icarus*, **225**: 173−184, https://doi.org/10.1016/j.icarus.2013.03.019.

Rodriguez, J.A.P., Fairén, A.G., Tanaka, K.L., Zarroca, M., Linares, R., Platz, T., et al., 2016, Tsunami waves extensively resurfaced the shorelines of an early Martian ocean. *Nature Scientific Reports*, **6**: 25106, https://doi.org/10.1038/srep25106.

Ryder, G., Bogard, D.D., and Garrison, D., 1991, Probable age of Autolycus and calibration of lunar stratigraphy. *Geology*, **19**: 143–146.

Schaber, G.G., and McCauley, J.F., 1980, Geological map of the Tolstoj quadrangle of Mercury (H-8). *US Geological Survey Miscellaneous Investigations Series Map I-1199, Scale 1:5,000,000*.

Schaber, G.G., Shoemaker, E.M., and Kozak, R.C., 1987, The surface age of Venus. *Solar System Research*, **21**: 89–94.

Schaber, G.G., Strom, R.G., Moore, H.J., Soderblom, L.A., Kirk, R.L., Chadwick, D.J., et al., 1992, Geology and distribution of impact craters on Venus: what are they telling us? *Journal of Geophysical Research*, **97**: 13,256–13,301.

Schenk, P.M., Chapman, C.R., Zahnle, K., and Moore, J.M., 2004, Ages and interiors: the cratering record of the Galilean satellites. *In* Bagenal, F., Dowling, T.E., and McKinnon, W.B. (eds), *Jupiter: The Planet, Satellites and Magnetosphere*. Cambridge: Cambridge University Press, 427–456.

Schmedemann, N., Kneissl, T., Ivanov, B.A., Michael, G.G., Wagner, R.J., Neukum, G., et al., 2014, The cratering record, chronology, and surface ages of (4) Vesta in comparison to smaller asteroids and the ages of HED meteorites. *Planetary and Space Science*, **103**: 104–130.

Schmitz, B., Peucker-Ehrenbrink, B., Lindström, M., and Tassinari, M., 1997, Accretion rates of meteorites and cosmic dust in the Early Ordovician. *Science*, **278**: 88–90.

Schultz, P.H., and Gault, D.E., 1975, Seismic effects from major basin formation on the Moon and Mercury. *Moon*, **12**: 159–177.

Schultz, P.H., and Spudis, P.D., 1979, Evidence for ancient mare volcanism. *Proceedings of the Lunar and Planetary Science Conference*, **10**: 2899–2918.

Scott, D.H., and Carr, M.H., 1978, Geologic map of Mars. *US Geological Survey Miscellaneous Investigations Series Map I-1083, Scale 1:25,000,000*.

Scott, D.H., and Tanaka, K.L., 1981, Mars: paleostratigraphic restoration of buried surfaces in Tharsis Montes. *Icarus*, **45**: 304–319.

Scott, D.H., and Tanaka, K.L., 1982, Ignimbrites of Amazonis Planitia region of Mars. *Journal of Geophysical Research*, **87**: 1179–1190.

Scott, D.H., and Tanaka, K.L., 1986, Geologic map of the western equatorial region of Mars. *US Geological Survey Miscellaneous Investigations Series Maps I-1802-A, Scale 1:15,000,000*.

Senske, D.A., Leonard, E.J., Patthoff, D.A., and Collins, G.C., 2018, The Europa global geologic map. *Proceedings of the Lunar and Planetary Science Conference*, **49**: 1340.

Shoemaker, E.M., and Hackman, R.J., 1962, Stratigraphic basis for a lunar time scale. *In* Kopal, Z., and Mikhailov, Z.K. (eds), *The Moon*. London: Academic Press, 289–300.

Shoemaker, E.M., and Wolfe, R.F., 1982, Cratering time scales for the Galilean satellites. *In* Morrison, D. (ed), *Satellites of Jupiter*. Tucson, AZ: The University of Arizona Press, 277–339.

Skinner Jr., J.A., Tanaka, K.L., and Platz, T., 2012, Widespread, loess-like deposit in the Martian northern lowlands identifies Middle Amazonian climate change. *Icarus*, **186**: 41–59, https://doi.org/10.1016/j.icarus.2006.08.013.

Smith, B.A., Soderblom, L.A., Johnson, T.V., Ingersoll, A.P., Collins, S.A., Shoemaker, E.M., et al., 1979a, The Jupiter system through the eyes of Voyager 1. *Science*, **204**: 951–972.

Smith, B.A., Soderblom, L.A., Beebe, R., Boyce, J., Briggs, G., Carr, M., et al., 1979b, The Galilean satellites and Jupiter: Voyager 2 imaging science results. *Science*, **206**: 927–950.

Soderblom, L.A., and Lebofsky, L.A., 1972, Technique for rapid determination of relative ages of lunar areas from orbital photography. *Journal of Geophysical Research*, **77**: 279–296.

Soderblom, L.A., Condit, C.D., West, R.A., Herman, B.M., and Kriedler, T.J., 1974, Martian planetwide crater distributions: implications for geologic history and surface processes. *Icarus*, **22**: 239–263.

Solomon, S.C., Bullock, M.A., and Grinspoon, D.H., 1999, Climate change as a regulator of tectonics on Venus. *Science*, **286**: 87–90.

Spencer, J.R., and Nimmo, F., 2013, Enceladus: an active ice world in the Saturn system. *Annual Review of Earth and Planetary Sciences*, **41**: 693–717.

Spencer, J.R., Stern, S.A., Cheng, A.F., Weaver, H.A., Reuter, D.C., Retherford, K., et al., 2007, Io volcanism seen by New Horizons: a major eruption of the Tvashtar volcano. *Science*, https://doi.org/10.1126/science.1147621.

Spudis, P.D., 1985, A Mercurian chronostratigraphic classification. Reports of the Planetary Geology and Geophysics Program, NASA. *Technical Memorandum*, **87563**: 595–597.

Spudis, P.D., and Guest, J.E., 1988, Stratigraphy and geologic history of Mercury. *In* Vilas, F., Chapman, C.R., and Matthews, M.S. (eds), *Mercury*. Tucson, AZ: The University of Arizona Press, 118–164.

Stephan, K., Jaumann, R., Wagner, R., Clark, R., Cruikshank, D., Hibbitts, C., et al., 2010, Dione's spectral and geological properties. *Icarus*, **206**: 631–652, https://doi.org/10.1016/j.icarus.2009.07.036.

Stöffler, D., and Ryder, G., 2001, Stratigraphy and isotope ages of lunar geologic units: chronological standard for the inner solar system. *Space Science Reviews*, **96**: 9–54.

Stöffler, D., Bischoff, A., Borchardt, R., Burghele, A., Deutsch, A., Jessberger, E.K., et al., 1985, Composition and evolution of the lunar crust in the Descartes highlands, Apollo 16. *Journal of Geophysical Research*, **89**: 449–506.

Strom, R.G., 1977, Origin and relative age of lunar and Mercurian intercrater plains. *Physics of the Earth and Planetary Interiors*, **15**: 156–172.

Strom, R.G., 1993, Parabolic features and the erosion rate on venus. *Lunar and Planetary Science Conference*, **24**: 1371–1372.

Strom, R.G., and Neukum, G., 1988, The cratering record on Mercury and the origin of impacting objects. *In* Vilas, F., Chapman, C.R., and Matthews, M.S. (eds), *Mercury*. Tucson, AZ: The University of Arizona Press, 336–373.

Strom, R.G., Schaber, G.G., and Dawson, D.D., 1994, The global resurfacing of Venus. *Journal of Geophysical Research*, **99**: 10899–10926.

Strom, R.G., Malhotra, R., Ito, T., Yoshida, F., and Kring, D.A., 2005, The origin of planetary impactors in the inner solar system. *Science*, **309**: 1847–1850.

Stuart-Alexander, D.E., and Wilhelms, D.E., 1975, The Nectarian System, a new lunar time-stratigraphic unit. *US Geological Survey Journal of Research*, **3**: 53–58.

Tanaka, K.L., 1986, The stratigraphy of Mars. Proceedings of the lunar and planetary science conference 17, part 1. *Journal of Geophysical Research*, **91**: E139–E158.

Tanaka, K.L., and Hartman, W., 2012. The Planetary Time Scale. *In* Gradstein, F.M., Ogg, J.G., Schmitz, M., Ogg, G. (eds), *The Geologic Time Scale 2012*. Elsevier. 1176 pp.

Tanaka, K.L., and Kolb, E.J., 2001, Geologic history of the polar regions of Mars based on Mars Global Surveyor Data: I. Noachian and Hesperian Periods. *Icarus*, **154**: 3–21.

Tanaka, K.L., and Leonard, G.J., 1995, Geology and landscape evolution of the Hellas region of Mars. *Journal of Geophysical Research*, **100**: 5407–5432.

Tanaka, K.L., Isbell, N.K., Scott, D.H., Greeley, R., and Guest, J.E., 1988, The resurfacing history of Mars: a synthesis of digitized, Viking-based geology. *Proceedings of the Lunar and Planetary Science Conference*, **18**: 665–678.

Tanaka, K.L., Dohm, J.M., Lias, J.H., and Hare, T.M., 1998, Erosional valleys in the Thaumasia region of Mars—hydrothermal and seismic origins. *Journal of Geophysical Research*, **103**: 31407–31419.

Tanaka, K.L., Skinner J.A., Jr., and Hare, T.M., 2005, Geologic map of the northern plains of Mars. *US Geological Survey Scientific Investigations Map SIM-2888, Scale 1:15,000,000.*

Tanaka, K.L., Skinner J.A., Jr., and Barlow, N.G., 2006, How geology affects crater size-frequency distributions and determinations of the crater production function for craters >5 km in diameter on Mars. *Workshop on Surface Ages and Histories: Issues in Planetary Chronology, Houston, TX, May 21–23, 2006, Abstract on CD-ROM, #6014.*

Tanaka, K.L., Rodriguez, J.A.P., Skinner Jr., J.A., Bourke, M.C., Fortezzo, C.M., Herkenhoff, K.E., et al., 2008, North polar region of Mars—advances in stratigraphy, structure, and erosional modification. *Icarus*, **196**: 318–358.

Tanaka, K.L., Fortezzo, C.M., Hayward, R.K., Rodriguez, J.A.P., and Skinner, J.A., 2011, History of plains resurfacing in the Scandia region of Mars. *Planetary and Space Science*, **59**: 1128–1142, https://doi.org/10.1016/j.pss.2010.11.004.

Tanaka, K.L., Robbins, S.J., Fortezzo, C.M., Skinner Jr., J.A., and Hare, T.M., 2014a, The digital global geologic map of Mars—chronostratigraphic ages, topographic and morphologic characteristics, and updated resurfacing history. *Planetary and Space Science*, **95**: 11–24, https://doi.org/10.1016/j.pss.2013.03.006.

Tanaka, K.L., Skinner, J.A. Jr., Dohm, J.M., Irwin, R.P., III, Kolb, E.J., Fortezzo, C.M., et al., 2014b, Geologic map of Mars. *US Geological Survey Scientific Investigations Map SIM-3292, Scale 1:20,000,000.*

Taylor, S.R., 1975, *Lunar Science: A Post-Apollo View*. New York: Pergamon, p. 372.

Tera, F., Papanastassiou, D.A., and Wasserburg, G.J., 1973, A lunar cataclysm at ~3.95 AE and the structure of the lunar crust. *Lunar and Planetary Science Conference*, **4**: 723–724.

Tsiganis, K., Gomes, R., Morbidelli, A., and Levison, H.F., 2005, Origin of the orbital architecture of the giant planets of the solar system. *Nature*, **435**: 459–461.

Turner, G., Cadogan, P.H., and Yonge, C.J., 1973, Argon selenochronology. *Proceedings of the Lunar Science Conference*, **4**: 1889–1914.

Vaucher, J., Baratoux, D., Mangold, N., Pinet, P., Kurita, K., and Grégoire, 2009, The volcanic history of central Elysium Planitia: implications for martian magmatism. *Icarus*, **204**: 418–442, https://doi.org/10.1016/j.icarus.2009.06.032.

Veverka, J., Thomas, P., Harch, A., Clark, B., Bell, J.F., Carcich, B., et al., 1997, NEAR's flyby of 253 Mathilde: images of a C asteroid. *Science*, **278**: 2109–2114.

Wagner, R., Wolf, U., Neukum, G., and the Galileo SSI Team, 1999, Ages of individual craters on the Galilean satellites Ganymede and Callisto. *30th Lunar and Planetary Science Conference Houston, TX, March 15–19, 1999, Abstract on CD-ROM, #1818.*

Wagner, R., Neukum, G., Giese, B., Roatsch, T., Wolf, U., Denk, T., et al., 2006, Geology, ages and topography of Saturn's satellite Dione observed by the Cassini ISS camera. *LPSC XXXVII, 1805.*

Wagner, R.J., Stephan, K., Schmedemann, N., Roatsch, T., Kersten, E., Neukum, G., et al., 2013, Geology and stratigraphy of Saturn's moon Tethys. *European Planetary Science Congress*, **8**: EPSC2013-713.

Walker, D., Longhi, J., and Hays, J.F., 1975, Differentiation of a very thick magma body and implications for the source regions of mare basalts. *Proceedings of the Lunar Science Conference*, **6**: 1103–1120.

Werner, S.C., 2006, *Major Aspects of the Chronostratigraphy and Geologic Evolutionary History of Mars*. Göttingen: Cuvillier Verlag, p. 160 [reprinted *PhD thesis*. Freien Universität, Berlin, 2005].

Werner, S.C., 2008, The early Martian evolution—constraints from basin formation ages. *Icarus*, **195**: 45–60.

Werner, S.C., and Tanaka, K.L., 2011, Redefinition of the crater-density and absolute-age boundaries for the chronostratigraphic system of Mars. *Icarus*, **215** (2), 603–607.

Werner, S.C., Tanaka, K.L., and Skinner Jr., J.A., 2011, Mars: the evolutionary history of the northern lowlands based on crater counting and geologic mapping. *Planetary and Space Science*, **59**: 1143–1165.

Whiteley, R.J., Tholen, D.J., and Hergenrother, C.W., 2002, Light curve analysis of four new monolithic fast-rotating asteroids. *Icarus*, **157**: 139–154.

Wilhelms, D.E., 1980, Stratigraphy of part of the lunar nearside. *US Geological Survey Professional Paper 1046-A, A1-A71.*

Wilhelms, D.E., 1987, The geologic history of the Moon. *US Geological Survey Professional Paper 1348, 302.*

Wilhelms, D.E., and Baldwin, R.J., 1989, The role of igneous sills in shaping the Martian uplands. *Proceedings of the Lunar and Planetary Science Conference*, **19**: 355–365.

Wilhelms, D.E., and McCauley, J.F., 1971, Geologic map of the nearside of the Moon. *US Geological Survey Map I-703, Scale 1:5,000,000.*

Wilhelms, D.E., Oberbeck, V.R., and Aggarwal, H.R., 1978, Size-frequency distributions of primary and secondary lunar impact craters. *Proceedings of the Lunar and Planetary Science Conference*, **9**: 3735–3762.

Williams, D.A., Keszthelyi, L.P., Crown, D.A., Yff, J.A., Jaeger, W.L., Schenk, P.M., et al., 2011, Volcanism on Io: new insights from global mapping. *Icarus*, **214**: 91–112.

Williams, D.A., Yingst, R.A., and Garry, W.B., 2014, Introduction: the geologic mapping of Vesta. *Icarus*, http://dx.doi.org/10.1016/j.icarus.2014.03.001.

Witbeck, N.E., Tanaka, K.L., Scott, D.H., 1991, Geologic map of the Valles Marineris region, Mars. *US Geological Survey Miscellaneous Investigations Series Map I-2010, Scale 1:2,000,000.*

Yingst, R.A., Mest, S.C., Berman, D.C., Garry, W.B., Williams, D.A., Buczkowski, D., et al., 2014, Geologic mapping of Vesta. *Planetary and Space Science*, https://doi.org/10.1016/j.pss.2013.12.014.

Yoshida, F., and Nakamura, T., 2004, Basic nature of sub-km main-belt asteroids: their size and spatial distributions. *Advances in Space Research*, **33**: 1543–1547.

Zahnle, K., Dones, L., and Levison, H.F., 1998, Cratering rates on the Galilean satellites. *Icarus*, **153**: 111–129.

Zahnle, K., Schenk, P., Levison, H., and Dones, L., 2003, Cratering rates in the outer solar system. *Icarus*, **163**: 263–289.

R. Strachan, J.B. Murphy, J. Darling, C. Storey and G. Shields Chapter 16

Precambrian (4.56–1 Ga)

Chapter outline

Abstract

Knowledge of the Precambrian history of the Earth between the birth of the Solar System (c. 4.567 Ga) and the end of the Mesoproterozoic (1.0 Ga) has improved dramatically as a result of the acquisition of a range of isotopic and geochemical data and new fossil discoveries. None the less, subdivision of the Precambrian in a comparable manner to that achieved for the Phanerozoic continues to be extremely challenging. Global Standard Stratigraphic Ages (GSSAs) have long been used to subdivide the Precambrian into eons, eras, and periods. It accepted that there are shortcomings in this approach and a move toward a revised time scale based as closely as possible around geobiological events would be desirable. However, development of such a "naturalistic" time scale is still a "work in progress" as shown by the state of flux in the understanding of particular biogeochemical events and the extent to which they are globally synchronous given the fragmentary state of the preserved rock record. Until these issues are resolved (if at all possible) the GSSA approach continues to serve geoscientists well in broadly delimiting major parts of the Earth's history that are characterized by particular tectonic and biogeochemical regimes.

16.1 International subdivisions

This chapter deals with the Precambrian history of the Earth between the birth of the Solar System (c. 4.567 Ga) and the end of the Mesoproterozoic (1.0 Ga). The following two chapters deal with the post-1 Ga parts of the Precambrian. The term "Precambrian" is not formal, it simply refers to the time interval and the rocks that formed before the beginning of the Cambrian Period at c. 538 Ma, and thus the Precambrian spans over 4 billion years. However, subdivision of the Precambrian in a comparable manner to that achieved for younger rocks has proved to be extremely challenging. This is principally because of the fragmentary nature of the Precambrian rock record, much of which is strongly deformed and metamorphosed, and a lack of fossils. For this reason, Global Standard Stratigraphic Ages (GSSAs) have long been used to subdivide the Precambrian (Plumb and James, 1986; Plumb, 1991). The principal divisions of the Precambrian consist of the Hadean, Archean, and Proterozoic eons (Fig. 16.1A). The Hadean Eon refers to the interval with no preserved rock record from the time of the formation of the Earth at 4.567 to c. 4 Ga. The Hadean is followed at 4 Ga by the Archean and at 2.5 Ga by the Proterozoic. The Hadean Eon is not formally subdivided. The Archean Eon is subdivided into 4 eras (rounded to 100 Myr boundaries), and the Proterozoic into 3 eras and 10 periods (the first 8 rounded to 50 Myr boundaries). The dates for the boundaries (and the names chosen for the periods) were thought delimit major cycles of sedimentation, orogeny, and magmatism (Plumb 1991; Fig. 16.1A).

Our knowledge of the Precambrian has improved dramatically over the past 20–30 years as a result of (1) the revolution in precise U–Pb zircon dating, (2) the utilization of various isotopic and geochemical proxies for understanding the evolution of the solid Earth as well as the atmosphere and biosphere, and (3) new fossil discoveries. It is clear that geological processes cannot be pigeonholed into slices of time of equal length and thus it could be argued that the current GSSA approach is outdated and requires revision to a more "naturalistic" framework (e.g., Bleeker 2004; Van Kranendonk et al., 2012 and references therein).

Geologic Time Scale 2020. DOI: https://doi.org/10.1016/B978-0-12-824360-2.00016-4

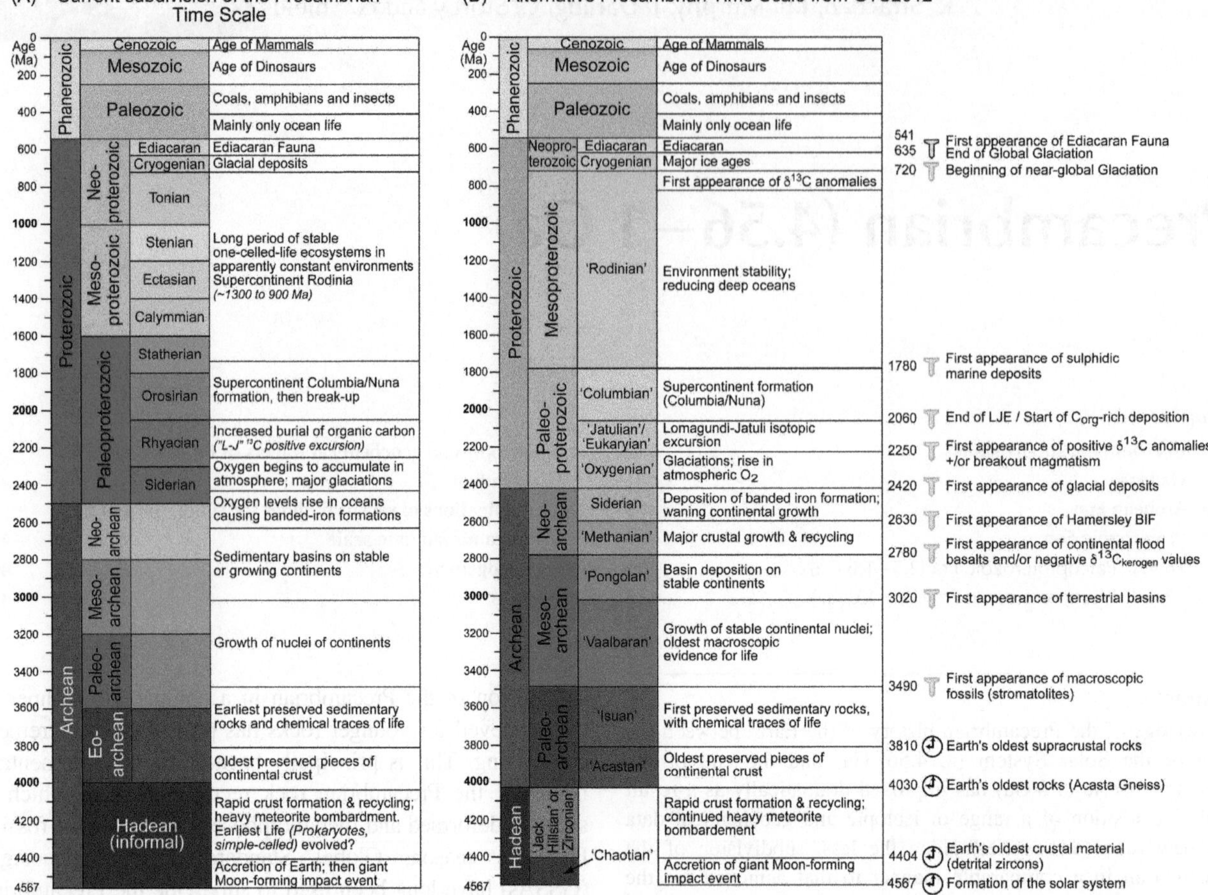

FIGURE 16.1 (A) The current Precambrian time scale from the International Commission on Stratigraphy, based on Plumb and James (1986) and Plumb (1991) (and including the 2014/15 revision of the base of the Cryogenian Period to c. 720 Ma); (B) a proposed revised Precambrian time scale using geologic events (Van Kranendonk et al., 2012).

Identified shortcomings with the GSSA approach are (1) a lack of ties to the actual rock record; (2) the diachronous nature of the global tectonic events on which the current scheme is based; and (3) the lack of any major sedimentological, geochemical, and biological events or criteria that can be used to correlate subdivision boundaries. An alternative stratigraphic scheme for the Precambrian was therefore developed for discussion based on potential Global Boundary Stratotype Sections and Points (Fig. 16.1B) (Van Kranendonk et al., 2012). Following the rationale of Cloud (1972), the approach taken was to base a revised Precambrian time scale as closely as possible around geobiological events such as changes to oceans, atmosphere, climate, or the carbon cycle that would be near instantaneous compared to changes in geotectonic processes. Currently, such naturalistic or "rock-based" definitions exist for the uppermost Proterozoic Cryogenian and Ediacaran systems (periods) only.

The following summary discusses recent thinking on the origins, timings, and nature of Precambrian events that occurred between the formation of the Earth and 1.0 Ga and the implications for the subdivision of over 3.5 billion years of geologic time.

16.2 Hadean

Spanning the interval between the formation of the solar system (c. 4.567 Ga) and the first evidence for the crust on the Earth (c. 4.0 Ga), the Hadean Eon was a time of planetary accretion, differentiation, and major change. Defining an absolute time scale for the eon is challenging due to the criterion on which it is typically defined: a lack of a preserved rock record on the Earth. Nevertheless, our understanding of the geological processes that shaped our planet during the Hadean continues to improve, and a wide range of new and refined timing constraints have been established since publication of "The Geologic Time Scale 2012" (Van Kranendonk et al., 2012).

The beginning of the Hadean is taken from the absolute age of the first solids known to have formed in the solar system: calcium–aluminum-rich inclusions (CAIs) that occur within chondritic meteorites (MacPherson, 2014 and references therein). These can be dated using the U–Pb isotope system, although there has been significant debate over the resulting ages with the recognition that $^{238}U/^{235}U$ in planetary materials is not invariant (Brennecka et al., 2010; Tissot et al., 2016). Analysis of U-isotope-corrected Pb–Pb ages by Connelly et al. (2017) has led to a revised age for CAIs of 4567.30 ± 0.16 Ma (4.567 Ga; data from Connelly et al., 2012, and Amelin et al., 2010). This date is taken to represent the current best estimate of the age of the solar system and, hence, start of the Hadean Eon.

The age of the Earth–Moon system should be fundamental to the geologic time scale, but absolute ages for its formation are debated. Whereas planetesimal differentiation occurred within a few million years of the start of the solar system (Kleine and Wadhwa, 2017 and references therein), and there is evidence of crust formation on Mars by 4.547 Ga (Bouvier et al., 2018), differentiation of the Earth and Moon is thought to have occurred significantly later. Recently proposed ages for Moon formation range from 4.510 to 4.417 Ga. These include evidence from (1) Hf–W isotopes that the Moon differentiated at least 70 million years after CAI growth (Kruijer and Kleine, 2017), (2) Lu–Hf isotope data from lunar zircons that are interpreted as evidence of differentiation by 4.510 Ga (Barboni et al., 2017), and (3) a change in the bulk U/Pb ratio of the Earth's mantle between 4.426 and 4.417 Ga that may be a result of a Moon-forming impact (Connelly and Bizzarro, 2016). The age of the oldest lunar zircon at 4.417 ± 0.006 Ga (Nemchin et al., 2009) provides a minimum age constraint on formation of the Moon.

The oldest known fragments of the Earth are also zircons, with grains from the Jack Hills metasedimentary rocks of Western Australia having ages as old as c. 4.4 Ga. These grains have provided a wealth of information about conditions on the early Earth (Cavosie et al., 2019 and references therein). Such is the importance of this first appearance of crustal material in the rock record that Van Kranendonk et al. (2012) propose subdivision of the Hadean into a "Chaotian" Era (pre–oldest zircon; 4.404 Ga, Wilde et al., 2001) and a "Jack Hillsian" or "Zirconian" Era (post–oldest zircon) (Fig. 16.1B). This subdivision is not included on the formal international chronostratigraphic chart or any subsequent updates (Cohen et al., 2013; updated), and these terms have not been widely used in the literature, despite the global significance of the first appearance of a crustal fragment. One challenge to the use of the Jack Hills zircons in this way is the fact that the U–Pb isotope systematics of these grains are complex at the nanoscale, due to the mobility of Pb during postdeposition metamorphic events. Some of the oldest concordant U–Pb ages measured by ion microprobe (> 4.42 Ga) are erroneous due to the incorporation of unsupported radiogenic Pb during analysis (Ge et al., 2018), and the oldest grain for which U–Pb systematics have been demonstrated to be robust at the length scales of ion microprobe analysis is the 4.374 ± 0.006 Ga grain studied by Valley et al. (2014).

The end of the Hadean is not yet formally defined by the International Commission on Stratigraphy and is taken as 4.0 Ga (Fig. 16.1A). However, several studies suggest that the Hadean–Archean boundary be taken as the age of the oldest preserved crustal rock (Van Kranendonk et al., 2012; Ogg et al., 2016). The oldest unambiguously dated rocks are 4.031 ± 0.003 Ga orthogneisses from the Acasta Gneiss of the Slave Craton, Canada (Bowring and Williams, 1999), and Van Kranendonk et al. (2012) propose that the boundary should be placed at c. 4.03 Ga (Fig. 16.1B). Controversially, older ages of up to ~4.4 Ga have been inferred for mafic gneisses in the Nuvvuagittuq Supracrustal Belt in the Superior Province, Canada (O'Neil et al., 2008, 2012), based on contested interpretations of the short-lived $^{146}Sm–^{142}Nd$ systematics in these highly metamorphosed rocks. Zircon U–Pb ages from felsic orthogneisses in the Nuvvuagittuq Belt suggest a formation age of >3.8 Ga (e.g., Darling et al., 2014), and coupled Lu–Hf and Sm–Nd model ages of ~3.9 Ga for the mafic gneisses have been taken as evidence for an Archean, rather than Hadean origin (e.g., Guitreau et al., 2013). However, O'Neil et al. (2012) report a $^{147}Sm–^{143}Nd$ isochron from intrusive gabbros in the belt of 4.115 ± 0.1 Ga. Taken together, these studies highlight the difficulty in unambiguously dating highly deformed and metamorphosed ancient crustal rocks, and the potential for significant changes to the timing of the Hadean–Archean boundary if it is defined on the basis of the oldest preserved crustal rocks.

16.3 Archean Eon

The Archean has traditionally been divided into four Eras: Eoarchean (4.0–3.6 Ga), Paleoarchean (3.6–3.2 Ga), Mesoarchean (3.2–2.8 Ga), and Neoarchean (2.8–2.5 Ga) (Fig. 16.1A) (Plumb and James, 1986; Plumb, 1991). An alternative subdivision was proposed by Van Kranendonk et al. (2012), which simplified these to three: the Paleoarchean (4.03–3.49 Ga), Mesoarchean (3.49–2.78 Ga), and Neoarchean (2.78–2.42 Ga), each composed of a number of periods (Fig. 16.1B). The base of the Paleoarchean in the 2012 proposal was defined by the age of the oldest extant rocks, the Acasta Gneiss, Canada, and the top by the oldest putative signs of life in sedimentary rocks, stromatolites of the North Pole Dome, Australia, representing the oldest potential "golden spike" (Fig. 16.1B). The Paleoarchean contained an "Acastan Period," the lower limit of which was defined by the oldest preserved rocks (Acasta Gneiss, Canada) and an "Isuan Period," the lower limit of which was defined at 3810 Ma (the age of the Earth's oldest supracrustal rocks, the Isua Supracrustal Belt in Greenland) and the upper limit at 3490 Ma (the North Pole Dome stromatolites). As discussed previously in relation to the Hadean, an admitted problem with this approach is that using the oldest occurrence of a particular rock type to define a stratigraphic boundary may simply identify preservation rather than any fundamental change in geological processes. As a further illustration of the difficulties in defining golden spikes in the deep Precambrian, a recent study suggests that the oldest stromatolites in fact occur in the 3.7 Ga Isua Supracrustal Belt, Greenland (Nutman et al., 2016, 2019; see however Allwood et al., 2018). The potentially localized evolution (and preservation) of life at different times also renders the questionable value of using the oldest identified fossils as the basis for subdivision. However, it is potentially easier to subdivide the later stages of the Archean as more well-preserved sedimentary sequences are found and studied. Van Kranendonk et al. (2012) thus proposed changing the end of the Archean to 2.42 Ga, based on the first appearance of glacial deposits in the rock record and the approximately contemporaneous change to an oxygenated atmosphere (Great Oxygenation Event or GOE). This approach is reasonable based on the rock record (Gumsley et al., 2017), but these events are difficult to define and date radiometrically.

The GOE can be defined as the time when atmospheric oxygen had accumulated sufficiently to prevent the formation and/or preservation of mass-independent S isotope fractionation (MIF-S) in sedimentary rocks (Farquhar et al., 2000). However, it is currently unclear whether this was a globally synchronous event with estimates for MIF-S disappearance varying from 2.45 to 2.31 Ga due to uncertainties over memory effects caused by oxidative weathering (Philippot et al., 2018). Signal reworking should not affect other geochemical or isotopic markers of surface ocean oxygenation, for example, redox-sensitive elemental and isotopic enrichments, but some of these first appear earlier during the Neoarchean due to regional or short-lived pulses of oxygen, the so-called whiffs of oxygen (Anbar et al., 2007; Kendall et al., 2015).

The most striking records of change in the Archean are arguably better provided by geochemical and isotopic studies of magmatic rocks, which appear to indicate major secular changes in tectonic processes. On this basis, Griffin et al. (2014) argued that the Archean is best divided into three eras, the Paleoarchean (4.0−3.6 Ga), the Mesoarchean (3.6−3.0 Ga), and the Neoarchean (3.0−2.4 Ga). In this interpretation, during the Paleoarchean the Earth's crust was dominantly stagnant and mafic in composition. The Mesoarchean was dominated by major episodes of mantle overturn and plume activity leading to development of the subcontinental lithospheric mantle. The Neoarchean was characterized by frequent plume activity, the beginning of some form of plate tectonics, and the development of significant volumes of continental crust. Clear evidence for the transport of surface crustal material to the deep mantle is found in diamonds within kimberlites. Their stable isotope compositions, geochronology, and mineral inclusions imply deep transport to the lower mantle of eclogitized basaltic protoliths that had interacted with seawater as long ago as 3 Ga (Shirey and Richardson, 2011; Schulze et al, 2013). Johnson et al. (2019) identified 3.5 Ga as defining the time at which tonalite–trondhjemite–granodiorite (TTG) rocks occur widely, followed by a second magmatic peak at 3.2 Ga, the first occurrence of passive margin sediments post-3.0 Ga, and the emergence of continents above sea-level. Recent efforts to assess these changes and relate them to changes in geodynamics have suggested that the interval 3.2−2.5 Ga records a major transition, culminating in cratonization and a globally stable "supercraton" regime (Fig. 16.2) (Cawood et al., 2018). This configuration set up the lithospheric conditions, due to secular cooling of the mantle, for a switch to a full mode of plate tectonics, which arguably began with rift and drift of these Archean cratons and amalgamation of the first supercontinent, Columbia (Nuna), by 1.8 Ga.

16.4 Proterozoic Eon

The Archean and Proterozoic eons represent fundamentally different Earth systems and the boundary between the two is traditionally placed at 2.5 Ga. This boundary approximates to the change from an early Earth that had gradually developed many aspects of a modern-style plate tectonic regime and was characterized by a reducing atmosphere and oceans, and primitive microbial life, to one that was characterized by stabilized continental cratons and a supercontinent cycle, an oxidized atmosphere and surface ocean, anoxic deep ocean with sulfidic margins, and the development of eukaryotic life.

16.4.1 Paleoproterozoic Era (2.5−1.6 Ga)

The Paleoproterozoic Era was a time of major geological change, incorporating the transition from an Archean tectonic regime of scattered, small supercratons (Bleeker, 2003) to the formation of the Earth's first supercontinent, Columbia (Nuna) (Hoffman, 1989; Rogers and Santosh, 2002; Zhao et al., 2002). A distinctive feature of the Paleoproterozoic is a tectono-magmatic lull between c. 2.3 and 2.2 Ga (Spencer et al., 2018), during which continental magmatism and orogenic activity decreased, passive margin sedimentation was lacking, and relative plate motions were reduced, presumably as a result of cooling of the mantle. Subduction-related magmatism could still have been ongoing, albeit at reduced rates, but if so, it was probably focused on oceanic arcs that have low potential for preservation and for generating zircons that would have been preserved as detritus. This period of tectono-magmatic quiescence ended at c. 2.2 Ga when there was a major flare-up of juvenile magmatism, thought to have been caused by the release of thermal energy that had built up in the mantle over time (Condie et al., 2009; Spencer et al., 2018).

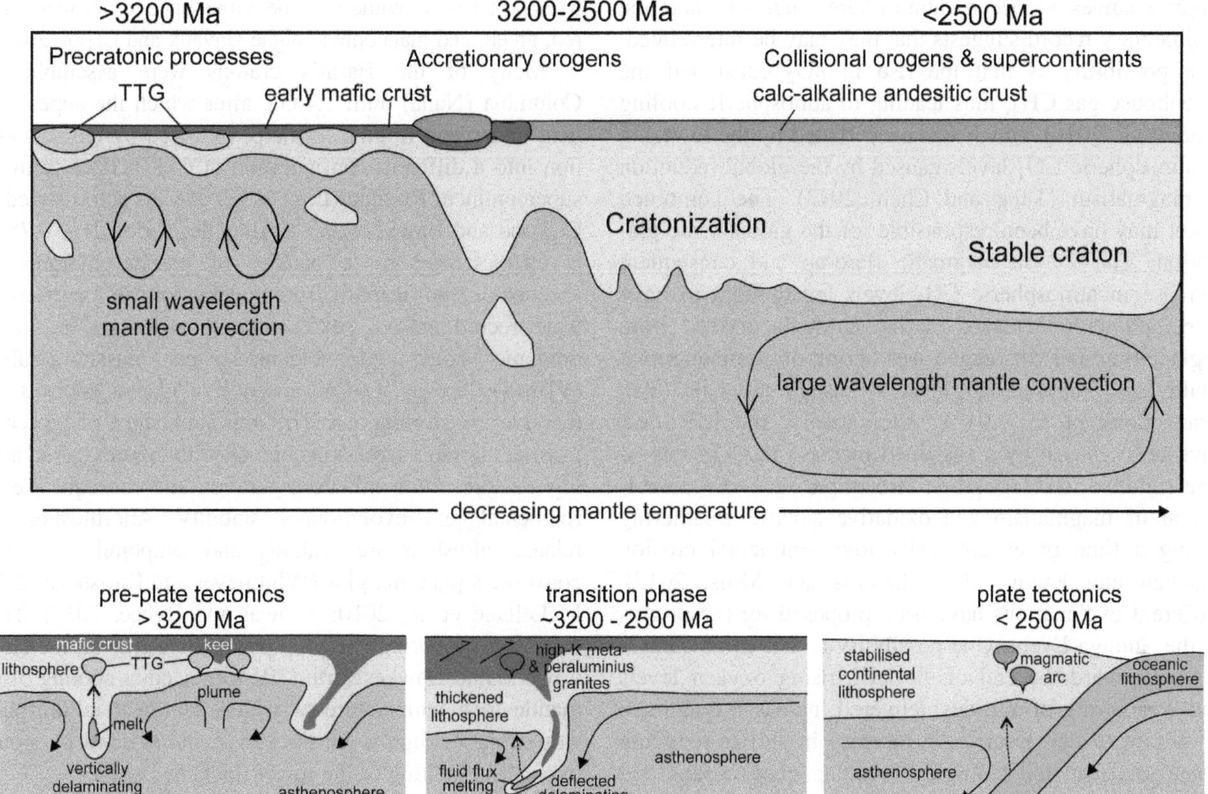

FIGURE 16.2 Schematic temporal evolution of the lithosphere associated with decreasing mantle temperature from >3200 to <2500 Ma. *TTG*, Tonalite–trondhjemite–granodiorite. From Cawood et al. (2018).

The Paleoproterozoic sedimentary record provides clues to significant events, some of which are likely to have been of global-scale and can be related to the large-scale tectonic processes outlined previously. Accumulation of banded iron formations (BIFs) peaked at the Archean–Proterozoic boundary. Although BIF deposition is widely reported to have continued until c. 1.8 Ga (Klein, 2005), only reappearing during the Cryogenian Period (see Chapter 17, The Tonian and Cryogenian Periods), economic-grade sedimentary iron deposits and BIFs were deposited at other times during the Proterozoic, (e.g., Canfield et al., 2018). The decline in BIF accumulation is generally attributed to the titration of ferrous iron from the oceans as pyrite, following the onset of oxidative weathering after the GOE (Canfield, 1998). The disappearance of redox-sensitive detrital minerals such as pyrite, uraninite, siderite, and Fe-rich paleosols has long been attributed to an abrupt pO_2 increase that corresponds to the Great Oxygenation Event (GOE) (Holland, 1984, 2006; Van Kranendonk et al., 2012). The cause remains uncertain, some attributing it to cyanobacterial evolution (Kirschvink and Kopp, 2008), whereas others suggest that it resulted from changes in the redox balance of the Earth's surface (Catling et al., 2001; Kump et al., 2001; Holland, 2009). Temporal constraints on the duration of the GOE are imprecise. The GOE was thought to have started between c. 2.4 and 2.3 Ga and to have ended between 2.1 and 2.0 Ga (Bekker, 2014). However, data from the Transvaal Supergroup, South Africa, suggest that it took place over a relatively short duration of 1–10 million years starting at 2.33 Ga (Luo et al., 2016) and was therefore nearly synchronous with what some workers have interpreted as the Earth's first global-scale glaciation, the Huronian Glaciation Event at 2.29–2.25 Ga (Tang and Chen, 2013, see, however, Young, 2019). Glaciation was followed by the Earth's largest known positive excursion of $\delta^{13}C$, the Lomagundi–Jatuli Event (LJE) with a minimum duration of 128 ± 9 Myr between c. 2.221 and 2.106 Ma (Martin et al., 2013) and then by the c. 2.0 Ga Shunga Event, which is defined by a major accumulation of C_{org}-rich sedimentary rocks and the generation of giant petroleum deposits (Melezhik et al., 2004) as well as the formation of the earliest significant phosphorite (Bekker et al., 2003; Papineau, 2010) and evaporite (Blättler et al., 2018) deposits. The very first large organic-walled fossils, *Grypania spiralis*, appear within Paleoproterozoic strata, by c. 1.87 Ga (Javaux and Lepot, 2018).

The coincidence in timing between the tectono-magmatic lull (Spencer et al., 2018) and some of these major changes in ocean–atmosphere chemistry and the sedimentary record suggests that they may be interrelated. One possibility is that the rise in pO_2 consumed the greenhouse gas CH_4, thus leading to atmospheric cooling (Luo et al., 2016), which was exacerbated by the lowering of atmospheric CO_2 levels caused by the global reduction in magmatism (Tang and Chen, 2013). The combined effect may have been responsible for the global-scale glaciation. The 2.2 Ga magmatic flare-up and consequent increase in atmospheric CO_2 levels are thought to have coincided with increased marine nutrients derived from deglaciation and rift-related weathering of continents that could have supplied nutrients to sustain the LJE (Van Kranendonk et al., 2012). Alternatively, the LJE may have been caused by a sustained increase in CO_2 outgassing (relative to total carbon throughput) due to a combination of magmatism and oxidative siderite weathering during a time of exceptionally low continental erosion (Bachan and Kump, 2015; Shields and Mills, 2017). Different explanations have been proposed for the origins of the Shunga Event. One possibility is that as volcanism slowed toward the end of the LJE, rising oxygen levels and weathering of sulfides delivered increased quantities of sulfate to the oceans. An increase in sulfate-reducing organisms then led to highly reducing deep oceans and the deposition of shungite (a mineraloid consisting of >98% carbon), which ceased when a new balance in the carbon cycle was established (Van Kranendonk et al., 2012). Alternatively, the Shunga Event has been interpreted by Young (2013) as a major organic extinction event that resulted from the Vredefort meteorite impact in South Africa at 2023 ± 4 Ma (Moser et al., 2011).

A period of major crustal growth from c. 2.06 to 1.78 Ga (Condie, 1998) culminated in the formation of the Earth's first supercontinent, Columbia (Nuna) (Rogers and Santosh, 2002; Zhao et al., 2002). Although this is commonly thought to have assembled by 1.8 Ga and to mark a key event toward the end of the Paleoproterozoic, maximum packing of continental masses may not have occurred until 1.5–1.4 Ga (Meert and Santosh, 2017), well within the Mesoproterozoic Era as traditionally defined.

16.4.2 Mesoproterozoic Era (1.6–1.0 Ga)

The Mesoproterozoic Era represents a period of seeming overall stability in the Earth's history, during which there was long thought to be few changes in the sedimentary record, biogeochemical cycles, and the evolution of life. Increasingly convincing discoveries of fossil eukaryotes, in the form of large, multicellular organic-walled fossil fronds and ornamented acritarchs (Zhu et al., 2016), in rocks that span the 1.6 Ga Paleoproterozoic–Mesoproterozoic boundary, indicate that we still know very little about the Proterozoic fossil record. Current fossil and molecular evidence both indicate that the Mesoproterozoic witnessed the emergence of crown group red, green, and glaucophyte algae (Javaux and Lepot, 2018).

Many of the Earth's cratons were assembled as Columbia (Nuna) until 1.4 Ga, after which the supercontinent underwent limited breakup, followed by reamalgamation into a different configuration at c. 1.0 Ga to form the supercontinent Rodinia (Li et al., 2008). As summarized by Cawood and Hawkesworth (2014), the period 1.7–0.75 Ga is characterized by a paucity of passive margins, an absence of significant Sr isotope deviations in the paleoseawater record and $\varepsilon_{Hf(t)}$ excursions in detrital zircon, limited orogenic gold and volcanic-hosted massive sulfide (VHMS) deposits, and an absence of glacial deposits and massive iron formations. The low abundance of preserved passive margin successions has been interpreted as indicating a stable continental configuration and consequent environmental and evolutionary stability. Anorthosites and related intrusions are spatially and temporally linked to convergent plate margins (Whitmeyer and Karlstrom, 2007; McLelland et al., 2010; Ashwal and Bybee, 2017). Their development during the Mesoproterozoic was attributed by Cawood and Hawkesworth (2014) to secular cooling of the mantle to a temperature at which continental lithosphere was strong enough to be thickened, but still warm enough to result in melting of the lower thickened crust.

The lack of any stratigraphically useful new life forms, major climatic changes, and Sr or C isotope excursions throughout the Mesoproterozoic makes it particularly difficult to subdivide the eon in a "naturalistic" way. However, the lack of C isotope fluctuations might derive in part from the lack of high-resolution data (Zhang, et al., 2018a). Regional-scale magmatic events such as the McKenzie dyke swarm in Canada (c. 1.27 Ga) and the Midcontinent Rift System (c. 1.12–1.09 Ga) do not appear to be linked to any global-scale isotopic excursions that could be used for correlation, although the coincidence of large igneous provinces (LIPs) and black shales has been proposed as a potential marker for Mesoproterozoic subdivision, for example, at the Calymmian–Ectasian boundary (Zhang et al., 2018b).

16.5 Isotopic and geochemical tracers of Precambrian evolution

Much recent research has focused on understanding episodicity and major secular trends in the Precambrian geological record, recognizing that the supercontinent cycle and mantle dynamics exert a fundamental control on the evolution of not only the Earth's lithosphere, but also the atmosphere and biosphere via a series of complex, and incompletely understood, feedback systems (e.g., Worsley et al., 1985; Cawood et al., 2013; Young, 2013; O'Neill et al., 2015; Hawkesworth et al., 2016; Van Kranendonk and Kirkland, 2016; Nance and Murphy, 2019).

Various workers have proposed that the Precambrian can be divided into a number of major stages based on the dominant tectonic process at any one time. Hawkesworth et al. (2016) suggested five stages: (1) initial accretion, core/mantle differentiation, development of magma ocean, and an undifferentiated mafic crust; (2) plume-dominated tectonics presubduction at c. 4.5–3.0 Ga; (3) stabilization of cratons and onset of "hot subduction" at c. 3.0–1.7 Ga; (4) the "boring billion" at 1.7–0.75 Ga; and (5) Rodinia breakup and development of "cold subduction" from 0.75 Ga onward. Similarly, Van Kranendonk and Kirkland (2016) suggested five stages, each of which starts with a pulse of mafic–ultramafic magmatism, includes the formation of a supercontinent, and ends with an often-protracted period of relative quiescence as the previously formed supercontinent drifts and breaks apart. Following c. 4.03–3.20 Ga—the period from the start of the preserved rock record to the onset of modern-style plate tectonics—these stages are (1) 3.20–2.82 Ga—the onset of modern-style plate tectonics and the oldest recognized Wilson cycle; (2) 2.82–2.25 Ga—commencing with major crustal growth, emergence of the continents and formation of superior-type BIFs, and closing with magmatic slowdown and stagnant-lid behavior; (3) 2.25–1.60 Ga—global mafic/ultramafic magmatism followed by global terrane accretion and the formation of Columbia (Nuna); (4) 1.60–0.75 Ga—the "Boring Billion" but involves breakup of the core of Columbia and the subsequent formation of Rodinia during the Grenville Orogeny; and (5) 0.75 Ga to present—breakup of Rodinia, the Pangean supercontinent cycle, and present transition to Amasia (Safanova and Maruyama, 2014).

Worsley et al. (1985) and Nance et al. (1986) pointed out that processes associated with the supercontinent cycle can be tracked over time by several isotopic proxies that vary in response to stages in the cycle. For example, the distribution of U–Pb zircon ages for the past 4.0 Ga (Fig. 16.3) in orogenic granitoids and detrital sedimentary rocks records similar peaks at 2.7, 1.87, 1.0, 0.6, and 0.3 Ga, which correspond to the times of global-scale collisional orogenesis and magmatism associated with the amalgamations (respectively) of Kenorland, Nuna (Columbia), Rodinia, Pannotia, and Pangea. Similarly, variations in the mean initial ε_{Hf} and $\delta^{18}O$ values from detrital zircons in recent sediments show negative troughs and positive peaks (respectively) that correspond with times of supercontinent assembly (Fig. 16.4). Both proxies are consistent with extensive crustal reworking at the time of assembly with more juvenile contributions representing times of supercontinent breakup and dispersal.

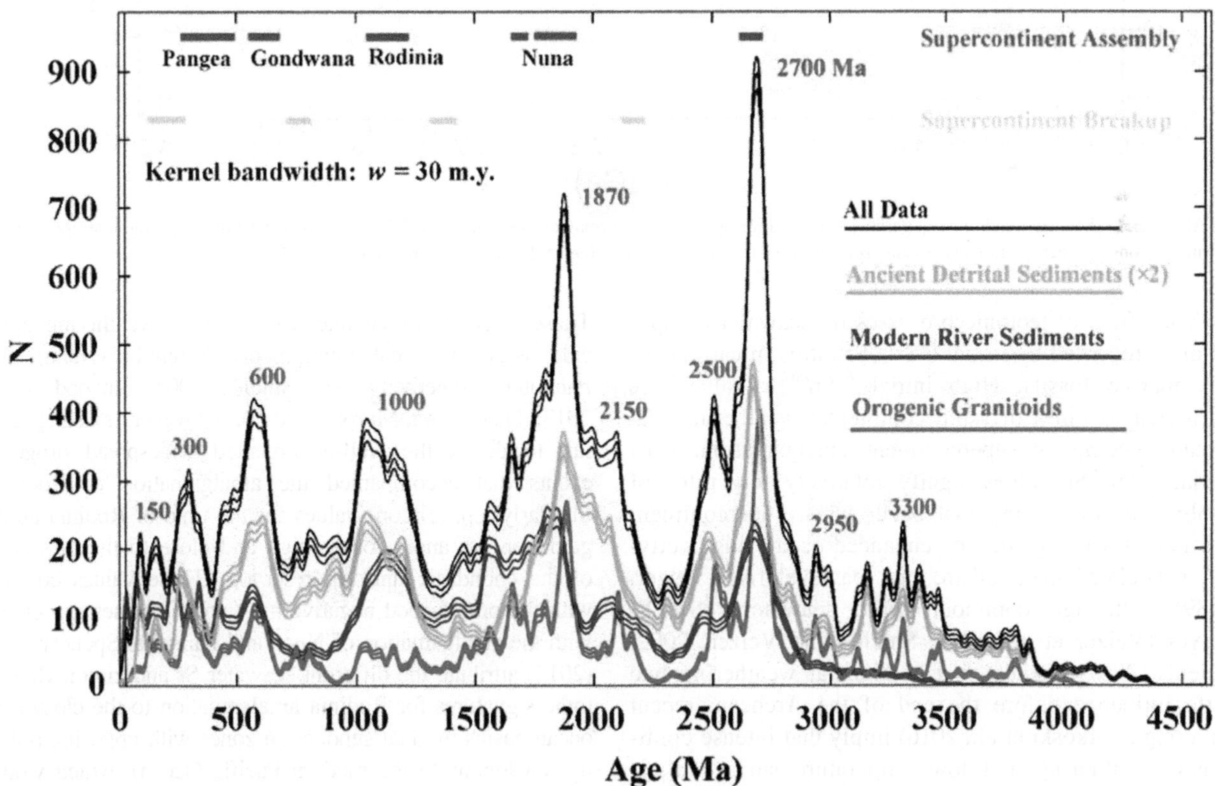

FIGURE 16.3 Peaks in the distribution (1σ error) of U–Pb zircon ages for orogenic granitoids and detrital zircons match intervals of supercontinent assembly, whereas troughs correspond to intervals of breakup. Black: total ages ($n = 37,830$); green: detrital ancient sedimentary rocks ($n = 21,849$); blue: detrital modern sediments ($n = 7053$; 2 ×); red: orogenic granitoids ($n = 8928$). N (vertical axis) is the number of zircon ages as a function of time for a Gaussian kernel bandwidth of three standard deviations (30 m.y.).

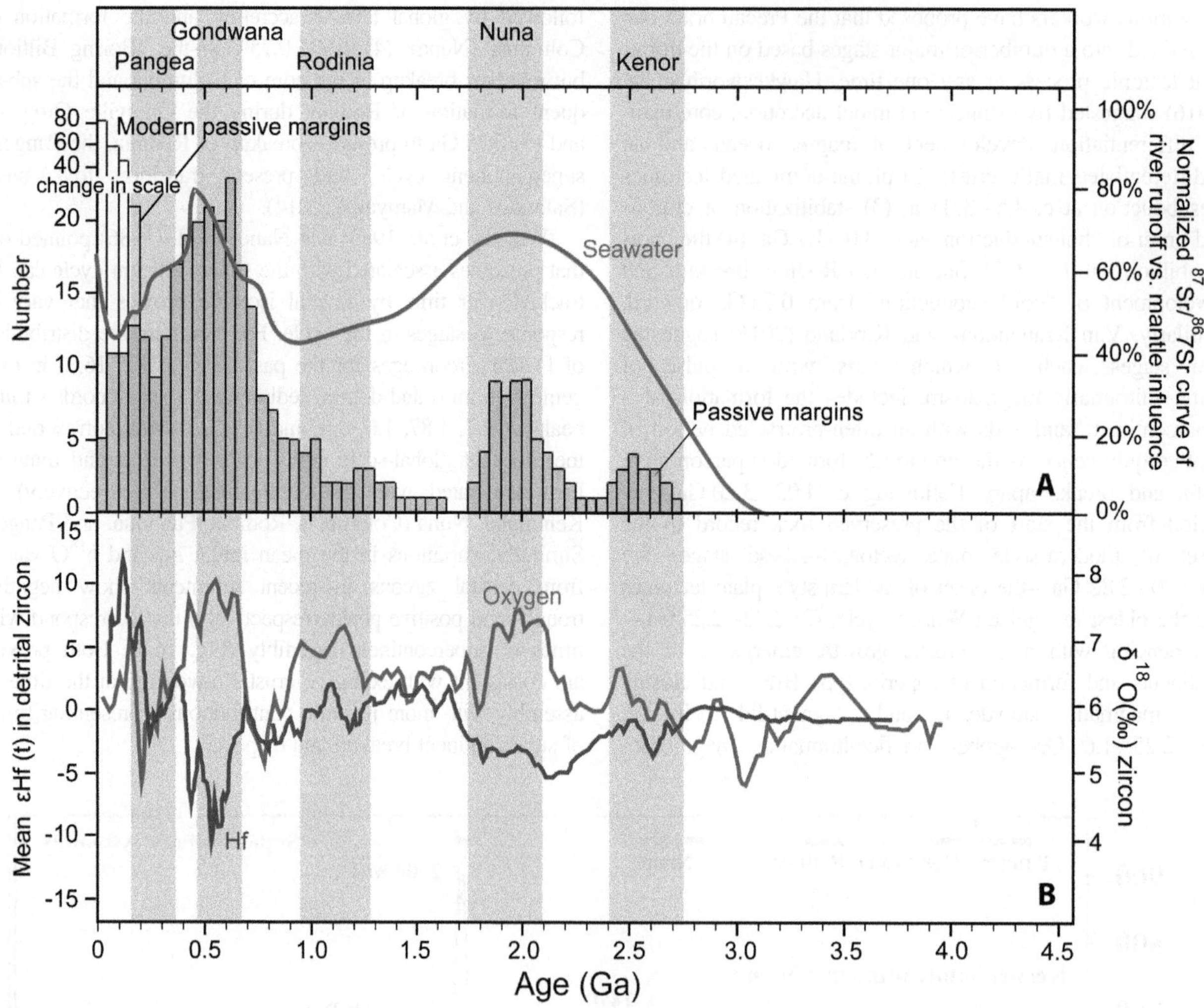

FIGURE 16.4 Secular trends in (A) passive margin development and normalized seawater $^{87}Sr/^{86}Sr$ and (B) mean initial ε_{Hf} and average $\delta^{18}O$ of detrital zircons in recent sediments. Shaded regions show tenure of supercontinents. From Hawkesworth et al. (2016).

The effect of tectonic processes on seawater composition is recorded by initial $^{87}Sr/^{86}Sr$ ratios in carbonates and marine fossils. High initial $^{87}Sr/^{86}Sr$ values are attributed to times of rapid continental weathering that would accompany supercontinent amalgamation. Low initial $^{87}Sr/^{86}Sr$ values signify relatively low rates of continental weathering that occur when supercontinent breakup is accompanied by enhanced ocean ridge activity, rift-related magmatism, and sea level rise (Veizer, 1989). Although commonly used seawater $^{87}Sr/^{86}Sr$ curves (Veizer et al., 1999; Shields and Veizer, 2002; Shields, 2007) suggest that continental weathering had little influence before the end of the Archean, recent data (e.g., Satkoski et al., 2016) imply that intense continental weathering and low-temperature surface alteration may have been more important than previously suspected during the Archean. Two prolonged peaks correspond with the Paleoproterozoic–Mesoproterozoic and Neoproterozoic–Phanerozoic transitions (Fig. 16.4). These intervals of enhanced continental weathering coincide with the amalgamation of Columbia (Nuna) and Pannotia, respectively (e.g., Shields, 2007; Cawood et al., 2013; Nance and Murphy, 2019). However, existing data fail to detect the well-documented widespread orogenic events that accompanied the amalgamation of Rodinia. Similarly, ε_{Hf} (zircon) values for the time of Rodinia amalgamation are anomalously high and close to the ε_{Hf} value of the chondritic uniform reservoir. These values contrast with the pronounced negative ε_{Hf} (zircon) values associated with the amalgamation of Nuna and Pannotia. Spencer et al. (2013) attribute the different seawater Sr and zircon Hf isotopic signatures for Rodinia amalgamation to the closure of ocean basins by dual subduction zones with opposing polarity (analogous to the modern Pacific Ocean), which would have preferentially reworked juvenile continental and oceanic arcs.

Elevated weathering rates during supercontinent amalgamation should increase nutrient availability (including

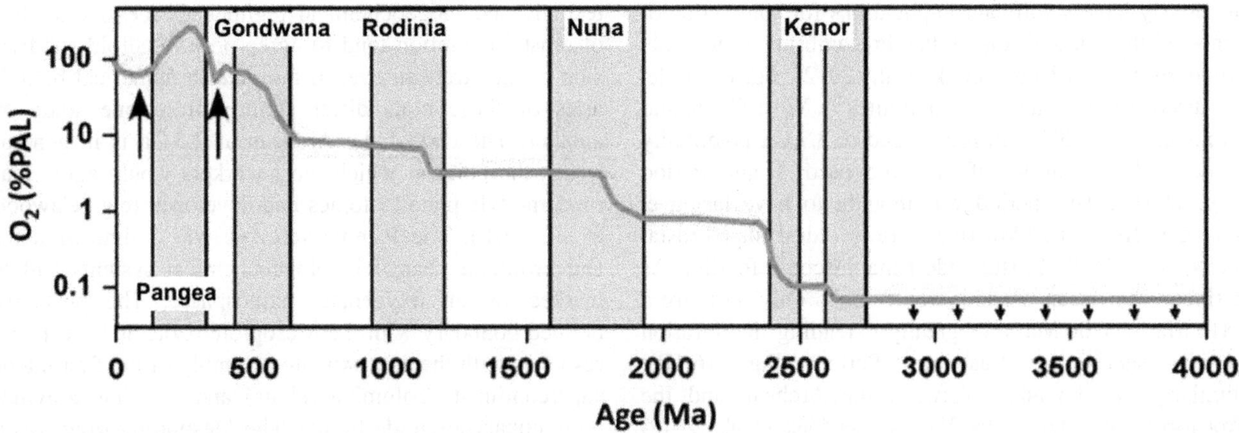

FIGURE 16.5 Step-increases in atmospheric oxygen levels relative to present atmospheric levels (PAL) compared to time intervals (shaded) of supercontinent amalgamation. From Campbell and Allen (2008).

important biolimiting nutrients such as iron and phosphorus, e.g., Tyrell, 1999) and organic production (Lyons et al., 2014), although how this translates into oxygenation is still debated (Shields and Mills, 2017). Campbell and Allen (2008) propose that oxygenation of the atmosphere occurred in six or seven step increases (2.65, 2.45, 1.8, 0.6, 0.3, and 0.04 and possibly 1.2 Ga), each step corresponding with the amalgamation of a supercontinent (Fig. 16.5). In their model, elevated weathering rates led to "an explosion of algae and cyanobacteria," an increase in photosynthetic production of O_2, and the burial of organic carbon and pyrite (thus preventing their reaction with free oxygen). The combination of these processes would have led to a stepwise increase in atmospheric oxygen. Lee et al. (2016) draw particular attention to two time intervals, the c. 2.5–2.0 Ga interval (Great Oxygenation Event, GOE) and a c. 0.8–0.5 Ga (Neoproterozoic) oxygenation event (NOE). They attribute the rise of oxygen during the GOE to the origin of plate tectonics, which changed the composition of the Earth's crust from mafic to felsic, causing a decrease in the oxidative efficiency of the Earth's surface, thereby allowing atmospheric O_2 increase. As the continental reservoir of carbon increased during the Proterozoic, metamorphic and magmatic reactions caused a gradual increase in the input of CO_2 to the ocean–atmosphere system triggering a second rise in O_2 during the Neoproterozoic Era, a time of significant carbon and pyrite burial.

Most models maintain that in the Proterozoic Eon surface oceans were oxygen-rich due to mixing with the oxygenated atmosphere, but the deep ocean tended toward anoxia with sulfidic conditions at productive ocean margins, reflecting the activity of sulfate-reducing bacteria (Holland, 2006; Canfield, 1998; Shen et al., 2002; Arnold et al., 2004; Poulton et al., 2004; Farquhar et al., 2010; Blättler et al., 2018). How these characteristics were modulated by the supercontinent cycle remains uncertain. Enhanced weathering that accompanies supercontinent amalgamation might be expected to result in the sequestering of ^{12}C relative to ^{13}C in sedimentary organic matter and of ^{32}S relative to ^{34}S in pyrite, resulting in positive excursions in $\delta^{13}C$ and more negative $\delta^{34}S$ in the reciprocal marine platform reservoir (Worsley et al., 1985; Nance et al., 1986). However, erosional forcing of organic burial may be outweighed by that of carbonate burial (Shields and Mills, 2017), resulting in the commonly observed inverse covariation between $\delta^{13}C$ and $\delta^{34}S$ (Nance et al., 1986). Moreover, supercontinent breakup may lead to the release of nutrient phosphorus from the weathering of eruptive basalts (Horton, 2015) despite relatively low overall weathering rates due to supercontinent peneplanation.

There is a clear consensus that the Earth evolved in a series of events that were controlled ultimately by the supercontinent cycle. But there are significant gaps in understanding, particularly with regard to the feedback systems between the lithosphere, atmosphere, and biosphere. Nevertheless, understanding of these and the various isotopic and geochemical proxies that track the supercontinent cycle offers prospects for a more "naturalistic" Precambrian time scale.

16.6 Implications of recent findings for subdivision of the Precambrian time scale

Development of a "naturalistic" Precambrian time scale is still a "work in progress" as shown by the state of flux in the understanding of timing of particular biogeochemical events and the degree to which they are globally synchronous given the fragmentary nature of the preserved rock record. Many of the new discoveries summarized previously have significant implications for some components of the subdivision of the Precambrian time scale proposed by Van Kranendonk et al. (2012). For example, the discovery of putative stromatolites in West Greenland (Nutman et al., 2016) in rocks aged c. 3.7 Ga potentially reduces the duration of the proposed Isuan Period (Fig. 16.1B). This period was thought to have lasted c. 320 Myr, from 3810 Ma (the Earth's oldest supracrustal rocks) to c. 3490 Ma (the oldest macroscopic fossils). As defined, the Isuan Period would now only last from 3810 Ma to 3700 Ma, thus greatly extending the duration of the succeeding Vaalbaran Period (Fig. 16.1B). Similarly, the boundary between the Archean and the Proterozoic was moved by Van Kranendonk et al. (2012) from 2500 Ga as defined previously (Fig. 16.1A) to 2420 Ma (Fig. 16.1B), this being the age of the Duitschland glacial diamictites in South Africa, thought to be the oldest deposits associated with the Huronian glaciation. However, Tang and Chen (2013) argue that these deposits are a local anomaly, not connected to what they interpret as a global Huronian event, which started at c. 2.29 Ga. If correct, and if the appearance of the oldest Huronian deposits is still viewed as a viable criterion for defining the Archean–Proterozoic boundary, the latter could be moved to 2.29 Ga, but see Gumsley et al (2017) for reiteration of the view that the first of the Paleoproterozoic global glaciations coincided with the onset of the GOE between 2.46 and 2.42 Ga.

Recent findings have similar implications for parts of the revised Proterozoic time scale proposed by Van Kranendonk et al. (2012). The oldest period proposed in the revised scheme is the Oxygenian, which was thought to have a duration of 170 Myr from 2420 (the base of the Proterozoic, see earlier) to 2250 Ma (Fig. 16.1B). This proposition was based in part on the inferred length of the GOE, but if this event occurred over only 1–10 myr (Luo et al., 2016), its duration would be much shorter than the Oxygenian Period. The succeeding "Jatulian"/Eukaryian Period was tied to the duration of the Lomagundi–Jatuli isotopic excursion between 2250 and 2060 Ma (Van Kranendonk et al., 2012). However, the concept of this as a single global event, and hence the viability of using it as the basis for dividing the time scale, has been questioned by Martin et al. (2013) who instead identify a series of temporally discrete carbon burial depositional events that differ in age from craton to craton between c. 2.1 and 1.85 Ga.

Although there is continuing uncertainty as to how the Precambrian time scale might be modified in a "naturalistic" way (and if indeed this is achievable), we should not lose sight of the merits of the established scheme that has arguably served geologists well over the last 30 years. The established boundaries for the Hadean, Archean, and Proterozoic Eons do help to broadly delimit major parts of the Earth's history that are characterized by particular tectonic and biogeochemical regimes. Successive studies of crustal evolution tend to agree on a threefold subdivision of the Archean even if the precise numerical boundaries of those eons differ slightly from one study to another. The end of the Archean at 2.5 Ga is in general terms, the point at which most workers would agree that modern-style plate tectonics had developed (e.g., Cawood et al., 2018). The Paleoproterozoic was a time of rapid and profound change in biogeochemical systems and is marked by an oxygenated atmosphere. The presently defined boundary with the Mesoproterozoic at 1.6 Ga corresponds with the approximate assembly of the first major supercontinent, Columbia (Nuna) and the first convincingly eukaryote-grade fossils. The Mesoproterozoic was a time of relative crustal and environmental stability, the end of which was broadly marked by assembly of the Rodinia supercontinent. The ensuing Neoproterozoic Era saw the breakup of Rodinia, Cryogenian glaciations, and the emergence of multicellular metazoan life. Subdivision of these broadly definable eras into periods is more problematic and the current names are less suitable than envisaged originally as our understanding of Precambrian geology has advanced. Therefore, the establishment of a revised "naturalistic" time scale may be some way off.

Acknowledgement

The manuscript was completed while RAS was in receipt of the Dr. W.F. James Chair of Studies in the Pure and Applied Sciences at St Francis Xavier University, May–September 2018. The authors thank Peter Cawood (who provided an editable version of Fig. 16.4), Damian Nance, and Tony Prave for insightful comments that helped to improve the manuscript.

References

Allwood, A.C., Rosing, M.T., Flannery, D.T., Hurowitz, J.A., and Heirwegh, C.M., 2018, Reassessing evidence of life in 3,700-million-year-old rocks of Greenland. *Nature*, **563**: 241–244.

Amelin, Y., Kaltenbach, A., Iizuka, T., Stirling, C.H., Ireland, T.R., Petaev, M., et al., 2010, U–Pb chronology of the Solar System's oldest solids with variable 238U/235U. *Earth and Planetary Science Letters*, **300**: 343–350.

Anbar, A.D., Duan, Y., Lyons, T.W., Arnold, G.L., Kendall, B., Creaser, R.A., et al., 2007, A whiff of oxygen before the Great Oxidation Event. *Science*, **317**: 1903–1906.

Arnold, G.L., Anbar, A.D., Barling, J., and Lyons, T.W., 2004, Molybdenum isotope evidence for widespread anoxia in mid-Proterozoic oceans. *Science*, **304**: 87–90.

Ashwal, L.D., and Bybee, G.M., 2017, Crustal Evolution and the temporality of anorthosites. *Earth-Science Reviews*, **173**: 307–330.

Bachan, A., and Kump, L.R., 2015, The rise of oxygen and siderite oxidation during the Lomagundi Event. *Proceedings of the National Academy of Sciences of the United States of America*, **112**: 6552–6567.

Barboni, M., Boehnke, P., Keller, B., Kohl, I.E., Schoene, B., Young, E.D., et al., 2017, Early formation of the Moon 4.51 billion years ago. *Science Advances*, **3**: 1–9.

Bekker, A., 2014, Great oxygenation event. *Encyclopedia of Astrobiology*Springer-Verlag, Berlin, Heidelberg, https://doi.org/10.1007/978-3-642-27833-4_1752-4.

Bekker, A., Karhu, J.A., Eriksson, K.A., and Kaufman, A.J., 2003, Chemostratigraphy of Paleoproterozoic carbonate successions of the Wyoming Craton: tectonic forcing of biogeochemical change? *Precambrian Research*, **120**: 279–325.

Blättler, C.L., Claire, M.W., Prave, A.R., Kirsimäe, K., Higgins, J.A., and Medvedev, P.V., 2018, Two-billion-year-old evaporites capture Earth's great oxidation. *Science*, **360**: 320–323.

Bleeker, W., 2003, The late Archean record: a puzzle in ca. 35 pieces. *Lithos*, **71**: 99–134.

Bleeker, W., 2004, Towards a "natural" Precambrian Time Scale. *In* Gradstein, F.M., Ogg, J.G., and Smith, A.G. (eds), *A Geologic Time Scale*. Cambridge University Press, Cambridge, pp. 141–146.

Bouvier, L.C., Costa, M.M., Connelly, J.N., Jensen, N.K., Wielandt, D., Storey, M., et al., 2018, Evidence for extremely rapid magma crystallization and crust formation on Mars. *Nature*, **558**: 586–589.

Bowring, S.A., and Williams, I.S., 1999, Prisocan (4.00–4.03 Ga) orthogneisses from northwestern, Canada. *Contributions Mineralogy Petrology*, **134**: 3–16.

Brennecka, G.A., Weyer, S., Wadhwa, M., Janney, P.E., Zipfel, J., and Anbar, A.D., 2010, $^{238}U/^{235}U$ variations in meteorites: extant ^{247}Cm and implications for Pb–Pb dating. *Science*, **327**: 449–451.

Campbell, I.H., and Allen, C.M., 2008, Formation of supercontinents linked to increases in atmospheric oxygen. *Nature Geoscience*, **1**: 554–558.

Canfield, D.E., 1998, A new model for Proterozoic ocean chemistry. *Nature*, **396**: 450–453.

Canfield, D.E., Zhang, S., Wang, H., Wang, X., Zhao, W., Su, J., et al., 2018, A Mesoproterozoic iron formation. *Proceedings of the National Academy of Sciences of the United States of America*, **115**: E3895–E3904. https://doi.org/10.1073/pnas.1720529115.

Catling, D.C., Zahnle, K.J., and MacKay, C.P., 2001, Biogenic methane, hydrogen escape, and the irreversible oxidation of early Earth. *Science*, **293**: 245–257.

Cavosie, A.J., Valley, J.W., and Wilde, S.A., 2019, Chapter 12 – The oldest terrestrial mineral record: thirty years of research on hadean zircon from Jack Hills, Western Australia. *In* Van Kranendonk, M.J., Bennett, V.C., and Hoffmann, J.E. (eds), *Earth's Oldest Rocks*, 2nd ed. *Elsevier*, pp. 255–278.

Cawood, P.A., and Hawkesworth, C.J., 2014, Earth's middle age. *Geology*, **42**: 503–506.

Cawood, P.A., Hawkesworth, C.J., and Dhuime, B., 2013, The continental record and the generation of continental crust. *Geological Society of America Bulletin*, **125**: 14–32.

Cawood, P.A., Hawkesworth, C.J., Pisarevsky, S.A., Dhuime, B., Capitanio, F., and Nebel, O., 2018, Geological archive of the onset of plate tectonics. *Philosophical Transactions of the Royal Society A*, **376**: 20170405. http://dx.doi.org/10.1098/rsta.2017.0405.

Cloud, P., 1972, A working model of the primitive Earth. *American Journal of Science*, **272**: 537–548.

Cohen, K.M., Finney, S.C., Gibbard, P.L., and Fan, J.-X., 2013, The ICS International Chronostratigraphic Chart. *Episodes*, **36**: 199–204.

Condie, K.C., 1998, Episodic continental growth and supercontinents: a mantle avalanche connection? *Earth and Planetary Science Letters*, **163**: 97–108.

Condie, K.C., 2014, Growth of continental crust: a balance between preservation and recycling. *Mineralogical Magazine*, **78**: 623–637.

Condie, K.C., and Aster, R.C., 2010, Episodic zircon age spectra of orogenic granitoids: the supercontinent connection and continental growth. *Precambrian Research*, **180**: 227–236.

Condie, K.C., O'Neill, C., and Aster, R.C., 2009, Evidence and implications for a widespread magmatic shutdown for 250 Myr on Earth. *Earth and Planetary Science Letters*, **282**: 294–298.

Connelly, J.N., and Bizzarro, M., 2016, Lead isotope evidence for a young formation age of the Earth–Moon system. *Earth and Planetary Science Letters*, **452**: 36–43.

Connelly, J.N., Bizzarro, M., Krot, A.N., Nordlund, A., Wielandt, D., and Ivanova, M.A., 2012, The absolute chronology and thermal processing of solids in the solar protoplanetary disk. *Science*, **338**: 651–655.

Connelly, J.N., Bollard, J., and Bizzarro, M., 2017, Pb–Pb chronometry and the early Solar System. *Geochimica et Cosmochimica Acta*, **201**: 345–363.

Darling, J.R., Moser, D.E., Heaman, L.M., Davis, W.J., O'Neil, J., and Carlson, R., 2014, Eoarchean to neoarchean evolution of the Nuvvuagittuq Supracrustal belt: new insights from U-Pb zircon geochronology. *American Journal of Science*, **313**: 844–876.

Farquhar, J., Bao, H., and Thiemens, M., 2000, Atmospheric influence of Earth's earliest sulphur cycle. *Science*, **289**: 756–758.

Farquhar, J., Nanping, W., Canfield, D.E., and Oduro, H., 2010, Connections between sulfur cycle evolution, sulfur isotopes, sediments, and base metal sulfide deposits. *Economic geology*, **105**: 509–533.

Ge, R., Wilde, S.A., Nemchin, A.A., Whitehouse, M.J., Bellucci, J.J., Erickson, T.M., et al., 2018, A 4463 Ma apparent zircon age from the Jack Hills (Western Australia) resulting from ancient Pb mobilization. *Geology*, **46**: 303–306.

Griffin, W.L., Belousova, E.A., O'Neill, C., O'Reilly, S.Y., Malkovets, V., Pearson, N.J., et al., 2014, The world turns over: Hadean-Archean crust-mantle evolution. *Lithos*, **189**: 2–15.

Guitreau, M., Blichert-Toft, J., Mojzsis, S.J., Roth, A.S.G., and Bourdon, B., 2013, A legacy of Hadean silicate differentiation inferred from Hf isotopes in Eoarchean rocks of the Nuvvuagittuq supracrustal belt (Québec, Canada). *Earth and Planetary Science Letters*, **362**: 171–181.

Gumsley, A.P., Chamberlain, K.R., Bleeker, W., Söderlund, U., de Kock, M.O., Larsson, E.R., et al., 2017, Timing and tempo of the Great Oxidation Event. *Proceedings of the National Academy of Sciences of the United States of America*, **114**: 1811–1816.

Hawkesworth, C.J., Cawood, P.A., and Dhuime, B., 2016, Tectonics and crustal evolution. *GSA Today*, **26**: 4–11.

Hoffman, P.F., 1989, Speculations on Laurentia's first gigayear (2.0 to 1.0 Ga). *Geology*, **17**: 135–138.

Holland, H.D., 1984, *The Chemical Evolution of the Atmosphere and Oceans*. Princeton University Press, Princeton, NJ, pp. 582.

Holland, H.D., 2006, The oxygenation of the atmosphere and oceans. *Philosophical Transactions of the Royal Society B*, **361**: 903–915.

Holland, H.D., 2009, Why the atmosphere became oxygenated: a proposal. *Geochimica et Cosmochima Acta*, **73**: 5241–5255.

Horton, F., 2015, Did phosphorus derived from the weathering of large igneous provinces fertilize the Neoproterozoic ocean? *Geochemistry, Geophysics, Geosystems*, **16**: 1723–1738.

Javaux, E.J., and Lepot, K., 2018, The Paleoproterozoic fossil record: implications for the evolution of the biosphere during Earth's middle-age. *Earth-Science Reviews*, **176**: 68–86.

Johnson, T.E., Kirkland, C.L., Gardiner, N.J., Brown, M., Smithies, R.H., and Santosh, M., 2019, Secular change in TTG compositions: implications for the evolution of Archaean geodynamics. *Earth and Planetary Science Letters*, **505**: 66–75.

Kendall, B., Creaser, R.A., Reinhard, C.Y., Lyons, T.W., and Anbar, A.D., 2015, Transient episodes of mild environmental oxygenation and oxidative weathering during the late Archean. *Science Advances*, **1** (10): e1500777. https://doi.org/10.1126/sciadv.1500777.

Kirschvink, J.L., and Kopp, R.E., 2008, Palaeoproterozoic ice-houses and the evolution of oxygen-mediating enzymes: the case for a late origin of photosystem II. *Philosophical Transactions of the Royal Society B*, **363**: 2755–2765.

Klein, C., 2005, Some Precambrian banded iron-formations (BIFs) from around the world: their age, geologic setting, mineralogy, metamorphism, geochemistry, and origin. *American Mineralogist*, **90**: 1473–1499.

Kleine, T., and Wadhwa, M., 2017, Chronology of planetesimal differentiation. *In* Elkins-Tanton, L., and Weiss, B. (eds), *Planetesimals: Early Differentiation and Consequences for Planets*. Cambridge: Cambridge University Press, pp. 224–245.

Kruijer, T.S., and Kleine, T., 2017, Tungsten isotopes and the origin of the Moon. *Earth and Planetary Science Letters*, **475**: 15–24.

Kump, L.R., Kasting, J.F., and Barley, M.E., 2001, Rise of atmospheric oxygen and the "upside-down" Archaean mantle. *Geochemistry, Geophysics, Geosystems*, **2**: 2000GC000114.

Lee, C.T.A., Yeung, L.Y., McKenzie, N.R., Yokoyama, Y., Ozaki, K., and Lenardic, A., 2016, Two-step rise of atmospheric oxygen linked to the growth of continents. *Nature Geoscience*, **9**: 417–424.

Li, Z.X., Bogdanova, S.V., Collins, A.S., Davidson, A., DeWaele, B., Ernst, R.E., et al., 2008, Assembly, configuration and break-up history of Rodinia: a synthesis. *Precambrian Research*, **160**: 179–210.

Luo, G., Ono, S., Beukes, N.J., Wang, D.T., Xie, S., and Summons, R.E., 2016, Rapid oxygenation of Earth's atmosphere 2.33 billion years ago. *Science Advances*, **2**: e1600134.

Lyons, T.W., Reinhard, C.T., and Planavsky, N.J., 2014, The rise of oxygen in Earth's early ocean and atmosphere. *Nature*, **506**: 307–315.

MacPherson, G.J., 2014, Calcium–aluminum-rich inclusions in chondritic meteorites. *In* Turekian, K., and Holland, H. (eds), Treatise on Geochemistry. (2nd ed.). *Meteorites and Cosmochemical Processes*, **Vol. 1**: pp. 139–179.

Martin, A.P., Condon, D.J., Prave, A.R., and Lepland, A., 2013, A review of temporal constraints for the Palaeoproterozoic large, positive carbonate carbon isotope excursion (the Lomagundi-Jatuli Event. *Earth-Science Reviews*, **127**: 242–261.

McLelland, J.M., Selleck, B.W., Hamilton, M.A., and Bickford, M.E., 2010, Late- to post-tectonic setting of some major Proterozoic anorthosite-mangerite-charnokite-granite (AMCG) suites. *The Canadian Mineralogist*, **48**: 729–750.

Meert, J.G., and Santosh, M., 2017, The Columbia supercontinent revisited. *Gondwana Research*, **50**: 67–83.

Melezhik, V.A., Filippov, M.M., and Romaskin, A.E., 2004, A giant Palaeoproterozoic deposit of shungite in NW Russia: genesis and practical applications. *Ore Geology Reviews*, **24**: 135–154.

Moser, D.E., Cupelli, C.L., Barker, I.R., Flowers, R.M., Bowman, J.R., Wooden, J., et al., 2011, New zircon shock phenomena and their use for dating and reconstruction of large impact structures revealed by electron nanobeam (EBDS, CL, EDS) and isotopic U-Pb and (U-Th)/He analysis of the Vredefort dome. *Canadian Journal of Earth Sciences*, **48**: 117–139.

Nance, R.D., and Murphy, J.B., 2019, Supercontinents and the case for Pannotia. *In* Wilson, R.W., Houseman, G.A., McCaffrey, K.J.W., Doré, A.G., and Buiter, S.J.H. (eds), *Fifty Years of the Wilson Cycle Concept in Plate Tectonics*. Geological Society, London, Special Publications, **470**: 1–17.

Nance, R.D., Worsley, T.R., and Moody, J.B., 1986, Post-Archean biogeochemical cycles and long-term episodicity in tectonic processes. *Geology*, **14**: 514–518.

Nemchin, A., Timms, N., Pidgeon, R., Geisler, T., Reddy, S., and Meyer, C., 2009, Timing of crystallization of the lunar magma ocean constrained by the oldest zircon. *Nature Geoscience*, **2** (2), 133–136.

Nutman, A.P., Bennett, V.C., Friend, C.R.L., Van Kranendonk, M.J., and Chivas, A.R., 2016, Rapid emergence of life shown by discovery of 3,700-million-year-old microbial structures. *Nature*, **537**: 535–538.

Nutman, A.P., Bennett, V.C., Friend, C.R.L., Kranendonk, M.J.V., Rothacker, L., and Chivas, A.R., 2019, Cross-examining Earth's oldest stromatolites: seeing through the effects of heterogeneous deformation, metamorphism and metasomatism affecting Isua (Greenland) ~3700 Ma sedimentary rocks. *Precambrian Research*, **331**, article nr. 105347: 17 pp. https://doi.org/10.1016/j.precamres.2019.105347.

O'Neil, J., Carlson, R.W., Francis, D., and Stevenson, R.K., 2008, Neodymium-142 evidence for Hadean mafic crust. *Science*, **321**: 1828–1832.

O'Neil, J., Carlson, R.W., Paquette, J.L., and Francis, D., 2012, Formation age and metamorphic history of the Nuvvuagittuq Greenstone Belt. *Precambrian Research*, **220–221**: 23–44.

O'Neill, C., Lenardic, A., and Condie, K.C., 2015, Earth's punctuated tectonic evolution: cause and effect. *In* Roberts, N.M.W., Ven Kranendonk, M.J., Parman, S., Shirey, S., and Clift, P.D. (eds), *Continental Formation Through Time*. Geological Society, London, Special Publications, **389**: pp. 17–40

Ogg, J.G., Ogg, J.M., and Gradstein, F.M., 2016, *A Concise Geological Time Scale*. Elesvier Publications.

Papineau, D., 2010, Global biogeochemical change at both ends of the Proterozoic: insights from phosphorites. *Astrobiology*, **10**: 165–181.

Philippot, P., Avila, J.N., Killingsworth, B.A., Tessalina, S., Baton, F., Caquineau, T., et al., 2018, *Nature Communications*. https://doi.org/10.1038/s41467-018-04621.

Plumb, K.A., 1991, New Precambrian Time Scale. *Episodes*, **14**: 139–140.

Plumb, K.A., and James, H.L., 1986, Subdivision of Precambrian time: recommendations and suggestions by the Subcommission on Precambrian Stratigraphy. *Precambrian Research*, **32**: 65–92.

Poulton, S.W., Fralick, P.W., and Canfield, D.E., 2004, The transition to a sulphidic ocean approximately 1.84 billion years ago. *Nature*, **431**: 173–177.

Rogers, J.J.W., and Santosh, M., 2002, Configuration of Columbia: a Mesoproterozoic supercontinent. *Gondwana Research*, **5**: 5–22.

Safanova, L., and Maruyama, S., 2014, Asia: a frontier for a future supercontinent Amasia. *International Geology Reviews*, **56**: 1051–1071.

Satkoski, A.M., Lowe, D.R., Beard, B.L., Coleman, M.L., and Johnson, C.M., 2016, A high continental weathering flux into Paleoarchean seawater revealed by strontium isotope analysis of 3.26 Ga barite. *Earth and Planetary Science Letters*, **454**: 28–35.

Schulze, D.J., Harte, B., Edinburgh Ion Microprobe Facility Staff, Page, Z., Valley, J.W., Channer, D.M., et al., 2013, Anticorrelation between low □^{13}C of eclogitic diamonds and high □^{18}C of their coesite and garnet inclusions requires a subduction origin. *Geology*, **41**: 455–458.

Shen, Y., Canfield, D.E., and Knoll, A.H., 2002, Middle Proterozoic ocean chemistry: evidence from the McArthur Basin, northern Australia. *American Journal of Science*, **302**: 81–109.

Shields, G.A., 2007, A normalised seawater strontium isotope curve: possible implications for Neoproterozoic-Cambrian weathering rates and the further oxygenation of the Earth. *eEarth*, **2**: 35–42.

Shields, G.A., and Mills, B.J.W., 2017, Tectonic controls on the long-term carbon isotope mass balance. *Proceedings of the National Academy of Sciences of the United States of America*. https://doi.org/10.1073/pnas.1614506114.

Shields, G., and Veizer, J., 2002, Precambrian marine carbonate isotope database: Version 1.1. *Geochemistry Geophysics Geosystems*, **3** (6): p. 1–12. https://doi.org/10.1029/2001GC000266.

Shirey, S.B., and Richardson, S.H., 2011, Start of the Wilson cycles at 3 Ga shown by diamonds from subcontinental mantle. *Science*, **333**: 434–458.

Spencer, C.J., Hawkesworth, C., Cawood, P.A., and Dhuime, B., 2013, Not all supercontinents are created equal: Gondwana-Rodinia case study. *Geology*, **41**: 795–798.

Spencer, C.J., Murphy, J.B., Kirkland, C.L., Liu, Y., and Mitchell, R.M., 2018, A Palaeoproterozoic tecton-magmatic lull as a potential trigger for the supercontinent cycle. *Nature Geoscience*, **11**: 97–101.

Tang, H., and Chen, Y., 2013, Global glaciations and atmospheric change at ca. 2.3 Ga. *Geoscience Frontiers*, **4**: 583–596.

Tissot, F.L.H., Dauphas, N., and Grossman, L., 2016, Origin of uranium isotope variations in early solar nebula condensates. *Science Advances*, **2**: e1501400.

Tyrell, T., 1999, The relative influences of nitrogen and phosphorus on oceanic primary production. *Nature*, **400**: 525–531.

Valley, J.W., Cavosie, A.J., Ushikubo, T., Reinhard, D.A., Lawrence, D. F., Larson, D.J., et al., 2014, Hadean age for a post-magma-ocean zircon confirmed by atom-probe tomography. *Nature Geoscience*, **7** (3): 219–223.

Van Kranendonk, M.J., Altermann, W., Beard, B.L., Hoffman, P.E., Johnson, C.J., Kasting, J.F., et al., 2012, A chronostratigraphic division of the Precambrian: possibilities and challenges. *In* Gradstein, F.M., Ogg, J.G., Schmitz, M., and Ogg, G. (eds), *The Geologic Time Scale 2012*. Elsevier Publications, pp. 299–392.

Van Kranendonk, M.J., and Kirkland, C.L., 2016, Conditioned duality of the Earth system: geochemical tracing of the supercontinent cycle through Earth history. *Earth-Science Reviews*, **160**: 171–187.

Veizer, J., 1989, Strontium isotopes in seawater through time. *Annual Review of Earth and Planetary Sciences*, **17**: 141–167.

Veizer, J., Ala, D., et al., 1999, $^{87}Sr/^{86}Sr$, $\delta^{13}C$ and $\delta^{18}O$ evolution of Phanerozoic seawater. *Chemical Geology*, **161**: 59–88.

Whitmeyer, S.J., and Karlstrom, K.E., 2007, Tectonic model for the Proterozoic growth of North America. *Geosphere*, **3**: 220–259.

Wilde, S.A., Valley, J.W., Peck, W.H., and Graham, C.M., 2001, Evidence from detrital zircons for the existence of continental crust and oceans on the Earth 4.4 Gyr ago. *Nature*, **409**: 175–178.

Worsley, T.R., Nance, R.D., and Moody, J.B., 1985, Proterozoic to recent tectonic tuning of biogeochemical cycles. *In* Sunquist. E.T., and Broecker, W.S. (eds), *The Carbon Cycle and Atmospheric CO_2: Natural Variations Archean to Present*. American Geophysical Union, Geophysical Monographs, **32**: 561–572.

Young, G.M., 2013, Precambrian supercontinents, glaciations, atmospheric oxygenation, metazoan evolution and an impact that may have changed the second half of Earth history. *Geoscience Frontiers*, **4**: 247–261.

Young, G.M., 2019, Aspects of the Archean-Proterozoic transition: how the great Huronian Glacial Event was initiated by rift-related uplift and terminated at the rift-drift transition during break-up of Lauroscandia. *Earth-Science Reviews*, **190**: 171–189.

Zhang, S., Ernst, R.E., Pei, J., Zhao, Y., Zhou, M., and Hu, G., 2018a, A temporal and causal link between ca. 1380 Ma large igneous provinces and black shale: implications for the Mesoproterozoic Time Scale and paleoenvironment. *Geology*, **46**: 963–966.

Zhang, K., Zhu, X., Wood, R., Shi, Y., Gao, Z., and Poulton, S.W., 2018b, Oxygenation of the Mesoproterozoic ocean and the evolution of complex eukaryotes. *Nature Geoscience*, **11**: 345–350.

Zhao, G., Cawood, P.A., Wilde, S.A., and Sun, M., 2002, Review of global 2.1-1.8 Gaorogens: implications for a pre-Rodinia supercontinent. *Earth-Science Reviews*, **59**: 125–162.

Zhu, S., Zhu, M., Knoll, A.H., Yin, Z., Zhao, F., Sun, S., et al., 2016, Decimetre-scale multicellular eukaryotes from the 1.56-billion-year-old Gaoyuzhuang Formation in North China. *Nature Communications*. https://doi.org/10.1038/ncomms11500.

G. Halverson, S. Porter and G. Shields

Chapter 17

The Tonian and Cryogenian Periods

Chapter outline

Abstract

The Tonian and Cryogenian periods together span from 1000 to c. 635.5 Ma and are currently chronometrically divided at 720 Ma. The early Tonian followed the amalgamation of the Rodinia supercontinent and is a time for which the stratigraphic, chemostratigraphic, and fossil record is relatively sparse and poorly dated. The initiation of intracratonic basins on many cratons c. 850 Ma, while Rodinia was still intact, is responsible for a much richer late Tonian record. This record preserves evidence for eukaryotic diversification and the first documented pronounced negative carbon isotope anomaly in the Neoproterozoic—the Bitter Springs Anomaly. Much of the second half of the Tonian Period is characterized by high carbon isotope values ($\delta^{13}C$ of carbonate >5‰), but recent studies indicate that at least one and probably two deep negative $\delta^{13}C$ excursions occurred after c. 740 Ma, the latter immediately preceding the onset of Cryogenian glaciation. This glaciation appears to have initiated globally at c. 717 Ma, based on consistent, high-precision U–Pb zircon ages from multiple sedimentary successions. These ages will support formal definition of the Global Stratotype Section and Point for the base of the Cryogenian System. This first Cryogenian glaciation, commonly referred to as the Sturtian glaciation, was long-lived, ending c. 660 Ma. Because the second and briefer late Cryogenian (i.e., Marinoan) glaciation is known to have initiated prior to 639 Ma and ended c. 635.5 Ma, the Cryogenian nonglacial interval must have been relatively short-lived (c. 20 Myr). Nevertheless, this interval is well represented on many cratons, due in part to the formation of widespread rift basins and passive margins as Rodinia began to break up. Although molecular clock and biomarker data suggest that the earliest animals had appeared by this time, no unambiguous metazoan fossils have been recovered from Cryogenian strata, which show low overall fossil diversity.

17.1 Introduction

The Neoproterozoic Era (1000–c. 538 Ma) is currently subdivided into the Tonian, Cryogenian, and Ediacaran periods (Knoll et al., 2006). The start of the Tonian Period is assigned a Global Standard Stratigraphic Age (GSSA) placed at precisely 1000 Ma (Plumb, 1991). The Tonian–Cryogenian boundary, previously assigned a GSSA of 850 Ma, has been revised to a rock-based boundary placed provisionally at 720 Ma (Shields-Zhou et al., 2016), pending ratification of a Global Boundary Stratotype Section and Point (GSSP) by the International Commission on Stratigraphy (Shields et al., 2018). The c. 635.5 Ma boundary

Geologic Time Scale 2020. DOI: https://doi.org/10.1016/B978-0-12-824360-2.00017-6

between the Cryogenian and Ediacaran periods is established by a GSSP placed at the base of the Nuccaleena Formation in South Australia, a *cap dolostone* that occurs globally and records the abrupt end of end Cryogenian glaciation (Hoffman and Schrag, 2002; Knoll et al., 2006). Although work has not yet begun to further subdivide the Tonian and Cryogenian periods into epochs, both intervals of time lend themselves to natural subdivisions based on carbon isotope stratigraphy and glacial stratigraphy, respectively. It is anticipated that the base of the Tonian System will ultimately be redefined with a much younger, rock-based GSSP, with microfossil and Sr isotope stratigraphy likely to provide additional constraints on where these boundaries are placed.

17.2 Historical background

The subdivision of Neoproterozoic time has largely been driven by the occurrence of widespread late Precambrian glacial strata (Kulling, 1934; Lee, 1936; Mawson, 1949) and fossils of metazoan affinity that predate the Cambrian (Glaessner, 1962). Harland (1964) first proposed the term "infra-Cambrian" or "Varangian" for the late Precambrian System encompassing these glacial strata (Fig. 17.1). He recognized two discrete episodes of glaciation and proposed that the start of this new period should correspond to the base of the lower of two glacial horizons in northeastern Norway (i.e., the Varanger Peninsula) where Precambrian glacial deposits were first recognized (Reusch, 1891). Dunn et al. (1971) subsequently introduced the terms "Sturtian" and "Marinoan" (named after Sturt Gorge and the Marino Rocks near Adelaide) for the two glacial epochs recorded in the late Proterozoic strata of the Adelaide Geosyncline of South Australia, emphasizing their utility as chronostratigraphic markers. Cloud and Glaessner (1982) proposed the term "Ediacarian" for the interval spanning from the upper limit of the last late Precambrian glacial deposits to the base of the Cambrian (Fig. 17.1). This term also originates from South Australia (the Ediacaran Hills) where Ediacaran fossils were first recognized (Sprigg, 1947). Plumb (1991) penned the name

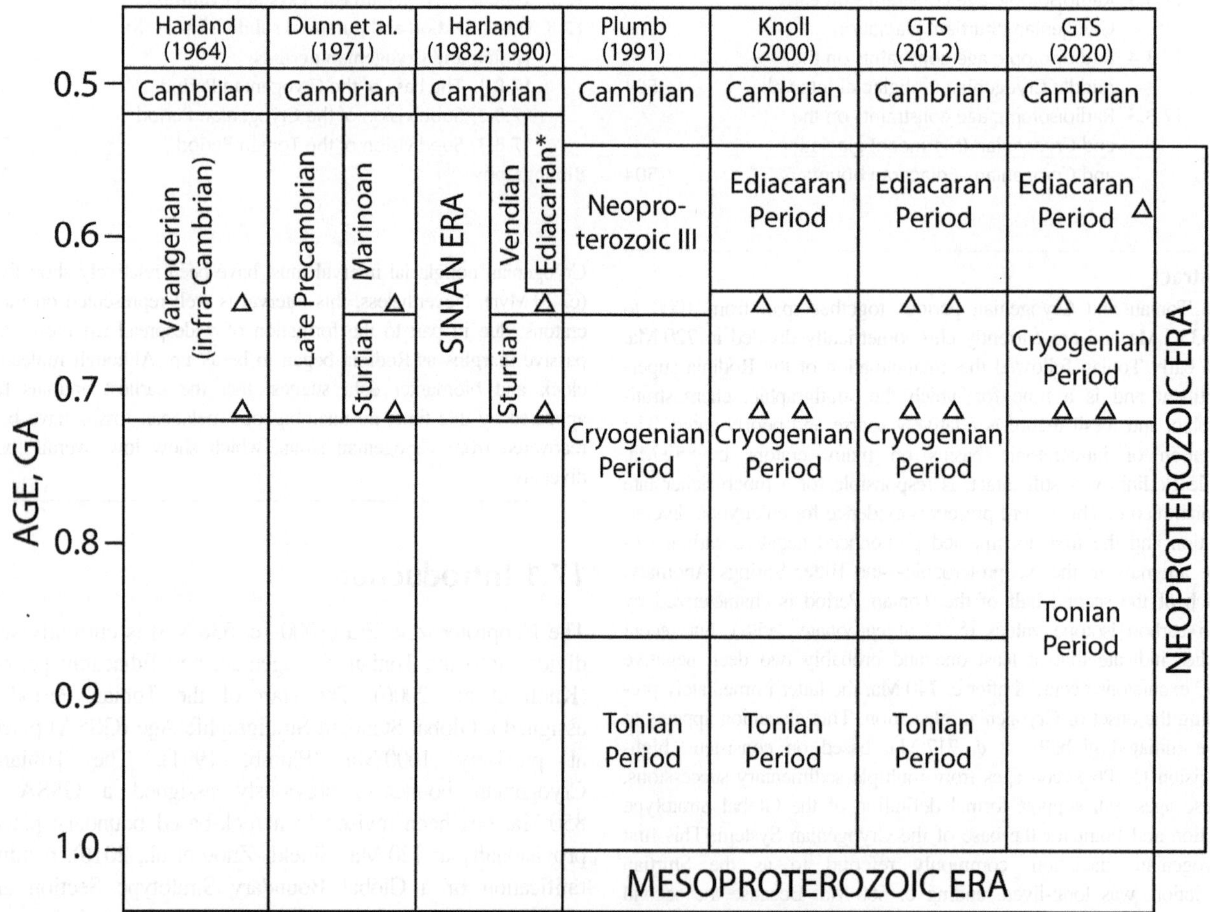

FIGURE 17.1 Evolution of stratigraphic terminology for the Neoproterozoic Era. Note that age ranges for earlier subdivisions are based on current estimates for ages of the rocks record and not necessarily the authors' original age estimates. Triangle symbol (Δ) denotes the approximate levels of glaciations relevant to the time scale subdivisions. * Denotes the term "Ediacarian" introduced by Cloud and Glaessner (1982).

"Cryogenian" for the interval of time spanning the late Neoproterozoic ice ages and the term "Tonian" (meaning stretching in Greek and in reference to the onset of rifting leading to the breakup of Rodinia) for the preceding period, setting the chronological boundary between them at precisely 850 Ma. These terms and GSSA boundaries were revised from previously suggested period rank subdivisions on the geologic time scale by the Subcommission on Precambrian Stratigraphy (Plumb and James, 1986).

Despite the early recognition of the chronostratigraphic utility of glacial deposits of global extent, the subdivision of Neoproterozoic time and correlation of strata long remained fraught with ambiguity, confusion, and controversy. The confusion has been abetted by the use of diverse terms, some of them applied inconsistently. For example, the term "Vendian" (originating in Russia) is similar to the "Ediacarian" but includes the immediately underlying glacial deposits as well as lowermost Cambrian strata containing sub-Tommotian small shelly fossils. Similarly, the "Sinian" (China) was originally broadly equivalent to the Varangian (Fig. 17.1), but it has since been redefined to be equivalent to the international Ediacaran Period. The "Late Riphean," also originating in Russia, has been used to refer to that part of the Neoproterozoic Era preceding the Vendian.

The number, duration, and intensity of the glaciations were long uncertain and widely debated (e.g., Kaufman et al., 1997; Kennedy et al., 1998; Halverson et al., 2005), often acrimoniously in the context of the Snowball Earth hypothesis (Hoffman et al., 1998; Fairchild and Kennedy, 2007; Etienne et al., 2007). Notwithstanding these debates, the base of the Ediacaran System (Period) was formally ratified in 2004 at the same stratigraphic level in the Adelaide Geosyncline (Knoll et al., 2004, 2006) as originally proposed by Cloud and Glaessner (1982) for their "Ediacarian" Period. The terms "Cryogenian" and "Tonian" are now widely accepted for the two preceding periods (Shields-Zhou et al., 2012, 2016) and should supersede other nomenclature to mitigate confusion.

As elaborated upon in the following section, a proliferation of radioisotopic ages spanning Neoproterozoic glacial deposits globally has largely resolved the question of the number and timing of late Precambrian glacial intervals. It is now well established that two discrete glaciations of global extent occurred during the Cryogenian Period (i.e., between 720 and 635.5 Ma). Despite some objections, the international community now conventionally uses the terms *Sturtian* and *Marinoan* to refer to these two glacial events ("cryochrons," cf. Hoffman et al., 2017) during the Cryogenian glaciation. This subdivision, though still informal, appears justifiable in light of the geochronological evidence that (1) the Sturtian glaciation is now thought to have begun (c. 717 Ma; Macdonald et al., 2010, 2018; MacLennan et al., 2018) and ended (c. 660 Ma; Rooney et al., 2015; Cox et al., 2018; Wang et al., 2019) synchronously worldwide (within the uncertainty of available ages) and that (2) the Marinoan glaciation, though shorter lived and of uncertain duration (between c. 4.1 and 24.5 Myr; Hoffmann et al., 2004; Condon et al., 2005; Prave et al., 2016), also ended synchronously at c. 635.5 Ma (Crockford et al., 2018). These geochronological data necessitate another as yet informal subdivision between the Sturtian and Marinoan glaciations encompassing the nonglacial interval of the Cryogenian Period, hereafter referred to for convenience as the *Cryogenian nonglacial interval.*

Whereas it had previously been suggested that some of the Neoproterozoic glacial deposits date to c. 750–745 Ma (e.g., Frimmel et al., 1996; Key et al., 2001), a combination of improved correlations (Macdonald et al., 2010) and new radioisotopic ages (Table 17.1) has effectively demonstrated that all unambiguous Neoproterozoic glacial deposits are Cryogenian

TABLE 17.1 U–Pb and Re–Os radioisotopic age constraints on the Tonian and Cryogenian periods.

Selected age constraints on the Tonian Period

No	Sample	Locality	Unit	Age (mya)	Type	Author	Comments
DT110C5	Black shale	N Canada (Victoria Island)	Boot Inlet Fm.	892 ± 13	Re–Os	van Acken et al. (2013)	Oldest Neoproterozoic age from the Tonian of northwestern Canada
DT125A	Black shale	N Canada (Victoria Island)	Wynniatt Fm.	849 ± 48	Re–Os	van Acken et al. (2013)	Maximum age on onset of Bitter Springs Anomaly in Shaler Supergroup
TS22	Felsic tuff	Ethiopia	Tambien Gp.	815.29 ± 0.32	U–Pb zircon CA-TIMS	Swanson-Hysell et al. (2015)	Maximum age for onset of Bitter Springs Anomaly in Tambien Group
F834_147.5	Felsic tuff	NW Canada (Yukon)	Fifteenmile Gp.	811.51 ± 0.25	U–Pb zircon CA-TIMS	Macdonald et al. (2010)	Maximum age for onset of Bitter Springs Anomaly in Fifteenmile Group

(Continued)

TABLE 17.1 (Continued)

MS1406	Black shale	NW Canada (Yukon)	Fifteenmile Gp.	810.7 ± 6.3	Re–Os	Cohen et al. (2017)	Maximum age for earliest scale microfossils
U1213	Rhyolite flow	SW Mongolia	Zavkhan Fm.	802.11 ± 1.0	U–Pb zircon CA-TIMS	Bold et al. (2016)	Age on Tonian volcanism in Mongolia
U1213	Rhyolite flow	SW Mongolia	Zavkhan Fm.	797.2 ± 1.1	U–Pb zircon CA-TIMS	Bold et al. (2016)	Age on Tonian volcanism in Mongolia
T2	Felsic tuff	Ethiopia	Tambien Gp.	788.72 ± 0.24	U–Pb zircon CA-TIMS	Swanson-Hysell et al. (2015)	Minimum age for end of Bitter Springs Anomaly in Tambien Group
T1-1202	Felsic tuff	Ethiopia	Tambien Gp.	787.39 ± 0.14	U–Pb zircon CA-TIMS	Swanson-Hysell et al. (2015)	Minimum age for end of Bitter Springs Anomaly in Tambien Group
M0132	Basalt	NW Canada	Little Dal Basalt	775.10 ± 0.54	U–Pb zircon CA-TIMS	Milton et al. (2017)	Minimum age for end of Bitter Springs Anomaly in Little Dal Group
PH.16A.93	Felsic tuff	NW Namibia	Devede Fm.	760.0 ± 0.9	U–Pb zircon ID-TIMS	Halverson et al. (2005)	Age on the Ombombo Group
A1407	Gray dolomite	Arizona, United States	Carbon Canyon Mb.	757.0 ± 6.8	Re–Os	Rooney et al. (2018)	Age on middle Chuar Group
J1301-62.5	Black shale	NW Canada (Yukon)	Callison Lake Fm.	752.7 ± 5.5	Re–Os	Rooney et al. (2015)	Maximum age for onset of the "Russøya" Anomaly
	Marcasite nodules	Arizona, United States	Awatubi Mb.	751.0 ± 7.6	Re–Os	Rooney et al. (2018)	Age on upper Chuar Group
PH.12.93	Ash-flow tuff	NW Namibia	Naauwpoort Fm.	746 ± 2.0	U–Pb zircon ID-TIMS	Hoffman et al. (1996)	Maximum age on Chuos glaciation in NW Namibia
J1204	Black shale	NW Canada (Yukon)	Callison Lake Fm.	739.9 ± 6.1	Re–Os	Strauss et al. (2014)	Maximum age for peak of the "Russøya" Anomaly
T46-102_2Z	Felsic tuff	Ethiopia	Matheos Fm.	735.25 ± 0.88	U–Pb zircon CA-TIMS	MacLennan et al. (2018)	Minimum age for peak of the "Russøya" Anomaly
6YR119-130	Organic-rich carbonate	NW Canada (Yukon)	Coppercap Fm.	732.2 ± 3.9	Re–Os	Rooney et al. (2014)	Minimum age for peak of the "Russøya" Anomaly
EGC1	Felsic tuff	Arizona, United States	Walcott Mb.	729.0 ± 0.9	U–Pb zircon CA-TIMS	Rooney et al. (2018)	Age on upper Chuar Group
Selected age constraints on the Tonian–Cryogenian boundary							
No	Sample	Locality	Unit	Age (mya)	Type	Author	Comments
F1203-272.1	Sandstone (detrital)	Altaids, Mongolia	Maikhan-Uul Fm.	729.8 ± 1.4	U–Pb zircon CA-TIMS	Bold et al. (2016)	Maximum age for glacial Maikhan-Uul Fm.
MJ	Black shale	Zambia (Copperbelt)	Mwashya Fm.	727.3 ± 4.9	Re–Os	Rooney et al. (2015)	Maximum age for glacial Grand Conglomerate
0509	Tiffaceous siltstone	South China	Liantuo Fm.	725 ± 10	U–Pb zircon SHRIMP	Zhang et al. (2008a)	Maximum age for glacial Nantuo Fm.
SAM-ET-04	Felsic tuff	Ethiopia	Mariam Bohkahko Fm.	719.68 ± 0.46	U–Pb zircon CA-TIMS	MacLennan et al. (2018)	Maximum age for glacial Negash Fm.

(Continued)

TABLE 17.1 (Continued)

SAM-ET-03	Felsic tuff	Ethiopia	Mariam Bohkahko Fm.	719.58 ± 0.56	U–Pb zircon CA-TIMS	MacLennan et al. (2018)	Maximum age for glacial Negash Fm.
F624b	Volcaniclastic diamictite	North Slope, Alaska	Kikiktak Volcs.	719.47 ± 0.29	U–Pb zircon CA-TIMS	Cox et al. (2015)	Maximum age for glacial Hula Hula Fm.
15PM06	Felsic tuff	NW Canada (Yukon)	Mt. Harper Volcs.	718.1 ± 0.3	U–Pb zircon CA-TIMS	Macdonald et al. (2018)	Maximum age for glacial Eagle Creek Fm.
15PM08	Felsic tuff	NW Canada (Yukon)	Mt. Harper Volcs.	718.1 ± 0.2	U–Pb zircon CA-TIMS	Macdonald et al. (2018)	Maximum age for glacial Eagle Creek Fm.
F837A	Rhyolite flow	NW Canada (Yukon)	Mt. Harper Volcs.	717.8 ± 0.2	U–Pb zircon CA-TIMS	Macdonald et al. (2018)	Maximum age for glacial Eagle Creek Fm.
F837C	Rhyolite flow	NW Canada (Yukon)	Mt. Harper Volcs.	717.7 ± 0.3	U–Pb zircon CA-TIMS	Macdonald et al. (2018)	Maximum age for glacial Eagle Creek Fm.
F837B	Rhyolite flow	NW Canada (Yukon)	Mt. Harper Volcs	717.4 ± 0.2	U–Pb zircon CA-TIMS	Macdonald et al. (2010)	Maximum age for glacial Eagle Creek Fm.
148PL02	Rhyolite clast	Idaho, United States	Pocatello Fm.	717.0 ± 4.0	U–Pb zircon SHRIMP	Fanning and Link (2004)	Maximum age on glacial Scout Mountain Mb.
F917-1	Felsic tuff	NW Canada (Yukon)	Eagle Creek Fm.	716.9 ± 0.4	U–Pb zircon CA-TIMS	Macdonald et al. (2018)	Minimum age for onset glacial Eagle Creek Fm.
F840A	Felsic tuff	NW Canada (Yukon)	Eagle Creek Fm.	716.5 ± 0.2	U–Pb zircon CA-TIMS	Macdonald et al. (2010)	Minimum age for onset glacial Eagle Creek Fm.
2013SC05	Tuffaceous siltstone	South China	Gongdong Fm.	716.1 ± 3.4	U–Pb zircon SIMS	Lan et al. (2014)	Maximum age on glacial Changdan Fm.
2013SC06	Tuffaceous siltstone	South China	Gongdong Fm.	715.9 ± 2.8	U–Pb zircon SIMS	Lan et al. (2014)	Maximum age on glacial Changdan Fm.
WQX-13-2	Sandstone (detrital)	South China	Wuqiangxi Fm.	714.6 ± 5.2	U–Pb zircon (detrital)	Song et al. (2017)	Maximum age for glacial Nantuo Fm.
13YCB	Crystal tuff	South China	Liantuo Fm.	714.0 ± 8.0	U–Pb zircon SIMS	Lan et al. (2015b)	Maximum age for glacial Nantuo Fm.
TI11-010	Basalt	NW Canada (Yukon)	Pleasant Creek V.	713.7 ± 0.9	U–Pb baddeleyite CA-TIMS	Cox et al. (2018)	Minimum age for basal Cryogenian glacial unconformity
WM54	Volcaniclastic tuff	Oman	Ghubrah Fm.	711.52 ± 0.2	U–Pb zircon ID-TIMS	Bowring et al. (2007)	Minimum age for onset of glacial Ghubrah Fm.
Selected age constraints on early Cryogenian glaciation							
No	Sample	Locality	Unit	Age (mya)	Type	Author	Comments
10-E781-2	Sandstone	NW Canada	Rapitan Gp.	711.3 ± 0.3	U–Pb zircon CA-TIMS	Baldwin et al. (2016)	Age on glacial Rapitan Fm.
06PL00	Plagioclase-phyric tuff breccia	Idaho, United States	Pocatello Fm.	708 ± 5	U–Pb zircon SHRIMP	Fanning and Link (2004)	Age on glacial Scout Mountain Member
A1418-161.8	Plagioclase-phyric andesite	N British Columbia	Gataga Volcanics	696.28 ± 0.30	U–Pb zircon CA-ID-TIMS	Eyster et al. (2018)	Age on syn-glacial volcanism
A1416-8.6	Rhyolite flow	N British Columbia	Gataga Volcanics	696.24 ± 0.22	U–Pb zircon CA-ID-TIMS	Eyster et al. (2018)	Age on syn-glacial volcanism

(*Continued*)

TABLE 17.1 (Continued)

A1418-207.5	Rhyolite flow	N British Columbia	Gataga Volcanics	695.81 ± 0.23	U–Pb zircon CA-ID-TIMS	Eyster et al. (2018)	Age on syn-glacial volcanism
YC27	Tuffaceous siltstone	South China	Xieshuihe Fm.	691 ± 12	U–Pb zircon SIMS	Lan et al. (2015a)	Syn-glacial age on Xieshuihe Formation
A1418-326.1	Volcaniclastic tuff	N British Columbia	Gataga Volcanics	690.77 ± 0.21	U–Pb zircon CA-ID-TIMS	Eyster et al. (2018)	Age on syn-glacial volcanism
A1418-343.2	Volcaniclastic tuff	N British Columbia	Gataga Volcanics	690.08 ± 0.19	U–Pb zircon CA-ID-TIMS	Eyster et al. (2018)	Age on syn-glacial volcanism
00KL040	Rhyodacite	Central Idaho	Edwardsburg Fm.	687 ± 10	U–Pb zircon SHRIMP	Lund et al. (2003)	Age on syn-glacial Wind River Meadows Member
97KE074	Rhyolite	Central Idaho	Edwardsburg Fm.	682 ± 6	U–Pb zircon SHRIMP	Lund et al. (2003)	Age on syn-glacial Hogback Rhyolite Member
145PL02	Reworked tuff	Central Idaho	Pocatello Fm.	667 ± 5	U–Pb zircon SHRIMP	Fanning and Link (2004)	Age on glacial Scout Mountain Member
P1634	Felsic tuff	South Australia	Wilyerpa Fm.	663.03 ± 0.11	U–Pb zircon CA-ID-TIMS	Cox et al. (2018)	Age on syn-glacial Wilyerpa Fm.
ZLG-5	Felsic tuff	South China	Datangpo Fm.	662.9 ± 4.3	U–Pb zircon SHRIMP	Zhou et al. (2004)	Minimum age for end of glacial Tiesi'ao Fm.
JJS-T	Tuff	South China	Datangpo Fm.	662.7 ± 6.2	U–Pb zircon LA-ICMPS	Yu et al. (2017)	Minimum age for end of glacial Tiesi'ao Fm.
TW1	OR-limestone	NW Canada	Twitya Fm.	662.4 ± 4.6	Re–Os	Rooney et al. (2014)	Minimum age for glacial Rapitan Group
A1309	OR-limestone	Mongolia	Taishir Fm.	659 ± 4.5	Re–Os	Rooney et al. (2015)	Minimum age for glacial Maikhan-Uul Fm.
TS1	Felsic tuff	South China	Tiesi'ao Fm.	659 ± 2.4	U–Pb zircon SHRIMP	Wang et al. (2019)	Age on end of the glacial Tiesi'ao Fm.
17LSJ-17	Dolomitic tuff	South China	Datangpo Fm.	658.8 ± 0.50	U–Pb zircon CA-ID-TIMS	Zhou et al. (2019)	Minimum age for end of glacial Tiesi'ao Fm.
BY2	Felsic tuff	South China	Datangpo Fm.	657.3 ± 3.2	U–Pb zircon SHRIMP	Wang et al. (2019)	Minimum age for end of glacial Tiesi'ao Fm.
Wallara-1	Black shale	Central Australia	Aralka Fm.	657.2 ± 6.9[1]	Re–Os	Kendall et al. (2006)	Minimum age for glacial Areyonga Fm.
Selected age constraints on the end Cryogenian (Marinoan) glaciation							
No	Sample	Locality	Unit	Age (mya)	Type	Author	Comments
05-NT-2	Tuff	South China	Datangpo Fm.	654.5 ± 3.8	U–Pb zircon SHRIMP	Zhang et al. (2008b)	Maximum age on glacial Nantuo Fm.
Blinman-2	Black shale	South Australia	Tindelpina Shale Mb.	645.1 ± 4.8	Re–Os	Kendall et al. (2006)	Age on interglacial Tapley Hill Fm.
Forest-1	OR-limestone	Tasmania	Black River Dolomite	640.7 ± 5.7[1]	Re–Os	Kendall et al. (2009)	Age on interglacial (?)
DW-1	Tuff	NW Namibia	Ghaub Fm.	639.29 ± 0.26	U–Pb zircon CA-ID-TIMS	Prave et al. (2016)	Minimum age for onset of glacial Ghuab Fm.
R008187	Volcanilithic wacke	Tasmania	Cottons Breccia	636.41 ± 0.48	U–Pb zircon CA-ID-TIMS	Calver et al. (2013)	Maximum age for end of glacial Cottons Breccia

(Continued)

TABLE 17.1 (Continued)

05-NT-1	Tuffaceous bed	South China	Nantuo Fm.	636.3 ± 4.9	U–Pb zircon SHRIMP	Zhang et al. (2008b)	Age on glacial Nantuo Fm.
YG-04-15	Tuff	South China	Doushantuo Fm.	635.5 ± 1.1[2]	U–Pb zircon ID-TIMS	Condon et al. (2005)	Minimum age for end of glacial Nantuo Fm.
NAV.00.2B	Felsic tuff	NW Namibia	Ghaub Fm.	635.21 ± 0.59[3]	U–Pb zircon CA-ID-TIMS	Prave et al. (2016)	Maximum age for end of glacial Ghaub Fm.
ES-1	Tuffaceous mudstone	South China	Nantuo Fm.	634.57 ± 0.88	U–Pb zircon CA-ID-TIMS	Zhou et al. (2019)	Maximum age for end of glacial Nantuo Fm.
SpB-6	Black shale	NW Canada	Sheepbed Fm.	632.3 ± 5.9	Re–Os	Rooney et al. (2015)	Minimum age for end of glacial Ice Brook Fm.

Note that this is not an exhaustive list of available radioisotopic dates from this time interval, but rather a compilation of dates that are useful for correlating Tonian–Cryogenian strata and/or constraining the ages of key boundaries or events, such as the onset and end of the Cryogenian glaciations and carbon isotope excursions. Recalculated by (1) Rooney et al. (2015), (2) Schmitz (2012), and (3) originally dated by Hoffmann et al. (2004).

or younger. Glaciation did recur during the Ediacaran Period. However, although Ediacaran-aged glacial deposits are widespread (Hoffman and Li, 2009), they are not global in extent. In the only location where Ediacaran glacial deposits have been precisely dated, they are short-lived (<0.4 Myr), confirming that they do not correspond to a "snowball-type" glaciation (Pu et al., 2016). Therefore, while glacial epochs may contribute to further subdivision of Ediacaran time (see Chapter 18: The Ediacaran Period), they will not likely figure in the refinement of the Tonian time scale.

17.3 Geochronological constraints on the Tonian and Cryogenian Periods

Great progress has been made in dating the Tonian and Cryogenian geologic record since the publication of GTS 2012. The refinement of the U–Pb zircon method (e.g., Mattinson 2005, 2010), combined with systematic efforts to date volcanic tuffs in Neoproterozoic strata, has resulted in a proliferation of important new ages. Improvements in the application of the Re–Os geochronometer to organic-rich sediments (Rooney et al., 2014, 2015) have also resulted in many new important ages, even if the level of precision is much lower (typically several millions of years, as compared to 100s of thousands of years for U–Pb zircon techniques). The result is that certain intervals of the Neoproterozoic time scale have been relatively well calibrated, most notably the onset of the first Cryogenian glaciation and the end of the second (i.e., the Cryogenian–Ediacaran boundary). However, for most of the Tonian and Cryogenian periods, ages are sparse and what ages have been generated are not necessarily easily applied to calibrating the time scale.

17.3.1 Radioisotopic age constraints on the Tonian Period

The Tonian Period as currently defined spans from 1000 to c. 720 Ma (Shields-Zhou et al., 2016). Few useful direct and precise stratigraphic age constraints exist for the first half of the Tonian Period (i.e., until c. 850 Ma). (Table 17.1). This virtual absence of precise U–Pb or Re–Os dates is due in part to the limited stratigraphic record of this interval, which preceded the onset of continental rifting related to the eventual breakup of Rodinia (Li et al., 2008), and the scarcity of dateable material in successions known to be of this age, for example, in northwestern Canada (Macdonald et al., 2012), Siberia (Bartley et al., 2001), the Urals (Kuznetsov et al., 2017), northeastern China (Xiao et al., 2014), and India (e.g., Ray 2006; Collins et al., 2014). However, increased attention to this interval in geologic time, in particular with regards to early eukaryotic evolution (Loron et al., 2019a,b), provides hope that new radioisotopic dates will emerge soon.

More dates are available for the second half of the Tonian Period, that is, c. 850–720 Ma (Fig. 17.2), although these are strongly biased toward northwestern North America and Ethiopia (Table 17.1). These ages provide reasonable calibration of the c. 810–802 Ma Bitter Springs negative carbon isotope anomaly and a c. 740 Ma late Tonian negative carbon isotope excursion (Halverson et al., 2018b; see also Section 17.5.1), but the number and range of chronostratigraphically useful ages remain limited. Several thick and complete stratigraphic successions that span the entirety or most of the upper Tonian, notably the Veteranen and Akademikerbreen groups in northeastern Svalbard (Halverson et al., 2018b) and Eleonore Bay Group in East Greenland (Tirsgaard and Sonderholm, 1997), have yet to be directly dated. Late Tonian successions

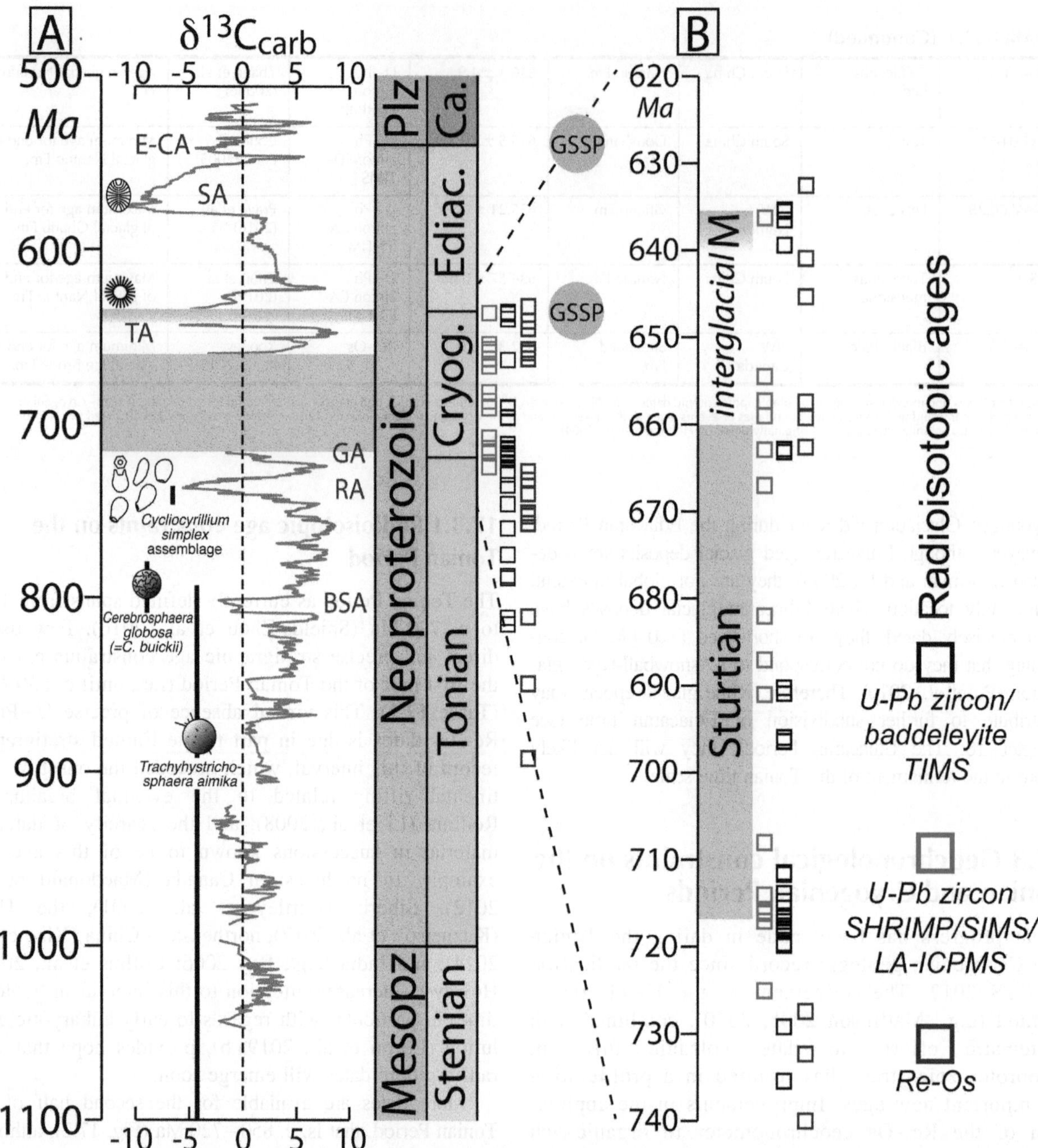

FIGURE 17.2 The geologic time scale spanning the Neoproterozoic Era. (A) The geologic time scale is modified from Gradstein et al. (2012). Compilation of the carbonate Neoproterozoic $\delta^{13}C_{carb}$ record is modified from Halverson et al. (2018b). Negative carbon isotope anomalies particularly useful for chemostratigraphic correlations are noted. Minimum biostratigraphic ranges are shown for *Trachyhystrichosphaera aimika*, *Cerebrosphaera globosa* (=*C. buickii*), and the *Cycliocyrillium simplex* assemblages. Constraints on *T. aimika* are based on its occurrence in the Draken Formation of Svalbard, above the Bitter Springs Anomaly in Svalbard (Knoll et al., 1991; Halverson et al., 2005) and in the >1100 Ma El Mreiti/Atar Gps of Mauritania (Rooney et al., 2010; Beghin et al., 2017). Constraints on *C. globosa* are based on its occurrence in the <782 Ma Chuar Group (Porter and Riedman, 2016; Dehler et al., 2017) and in the Svanbergfjellet Formation of Svalbard, associated with the uppermost part of the Bitter Springs Anomaly (Butterfield et al., 1994; Halverson et al., 2005). The *C. simplex* assemblage occurs in strata that postdate the Russøya Anomaly as well as rocks constrained to be older than 733.4 Ma (Strauss et al., 2014; Cohen et al., 2017; Riedman et al., 2018). Radioisotopic age constraints for the Tonian and Cryogenian periods (along with ages from the early Ediacaran Period that provide minima on the Cryogenian–Ediacaran boundary) are shown (in open squares) by type of age determination. (B) Highlight of the age constraints that establish the synchronous onset and end of the Cryogenian glaciations. See Table 17.1 for tabulated radioisotopic dates and references. *BSA*, Bitter Springs Anomaly; *E–CA*, Ediacaran–Cambrian Boundary Anomaly; *RA*, Russøya Anomaly; *SA*, Shuram Anomaly; *TA*, Trezona Anomaly.

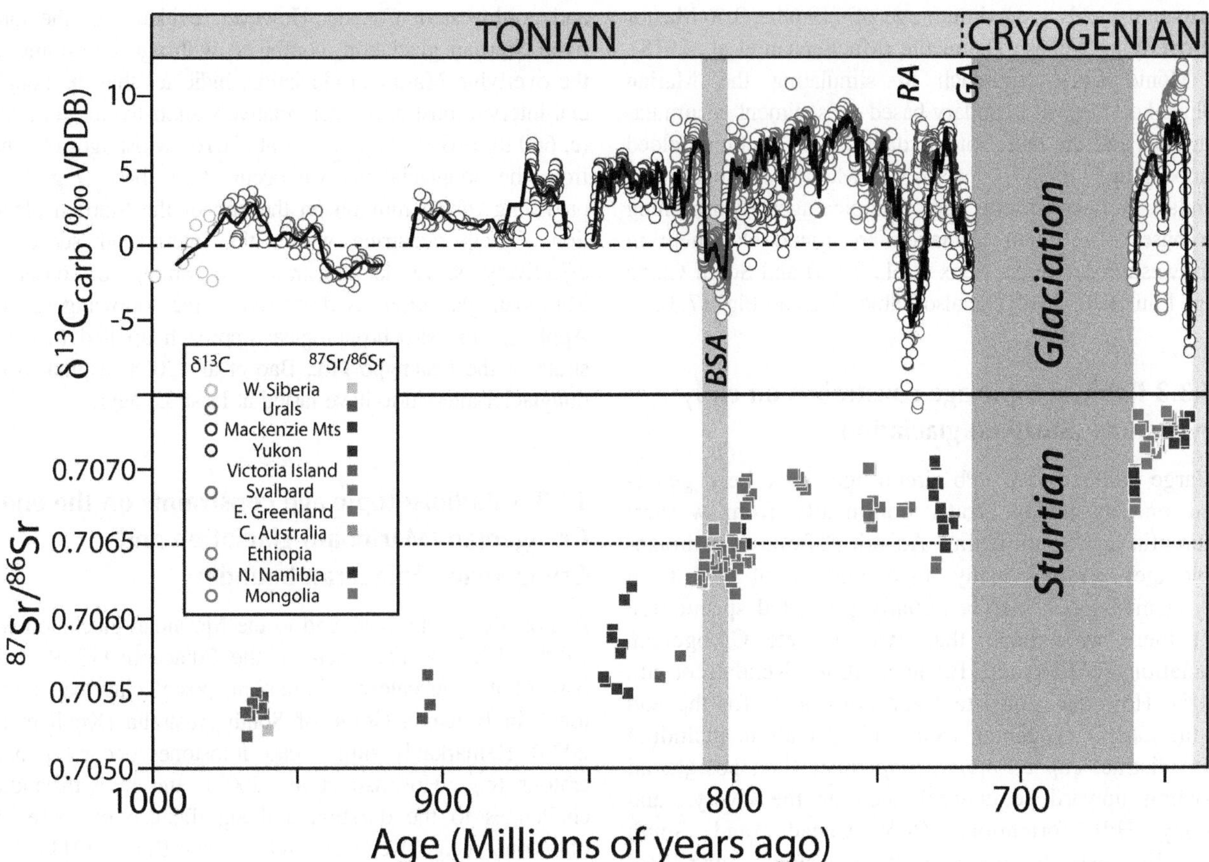

FIGURE 17.3 Composite carbon and strontium isotope curves for the Tonian and Cryogenian periods, color coded to show the successions from which data are derived and coherence of isotopic trends for overlapping sections. The solid black lines is local area regression fit to the time series data based on age models presented in Cox et al. (2016) and Halverson et al. (2018b), which minor modifications here to accommodate new age constraints (e.g., from MacLennan et al., 2018). Sources of data: W. Siberia data are from Knoll et al. (1995) and Cox et al. (2016); Urals data are from Kuznetsov et al. (2006). Mackenzie Mountains data are from Halverson (2006), Halverson et al. (2007), and Cox et al. (2016); Yukon data are from Cox et al. (2016); Victoria Island data are from Asmerom et al. (1991); Svalbard data are from Cox et al. (2016) and Halverson et al. (2007); E. Greenland data are from Cox et al. (2016); Central Australia data are from Swanson-Hysell et al. (2010) and Cox et al. (2016); Ethiopia data are from Swanson-Hysell et al. (2015); N. Namibia data are from Lamothe et al. (2019) and Halverson et al. (2007); Mongolia data are from Bold et al. (2016). *BSA*, Bitter Springs Anomaly; *GA*, Garvellach Anomaly; *RA*, Russøya Anomaly.

along the Cordilleran margin of North America have yielded a number of consistent Re–Os ages (Table 17.1; Fig. 17.3), which underpin broad sequence stratigraphic correlations and provide some calibration of the temporal distribution of vase-shaped microfossils (VSMs) (Strauss et al., 2014; Strauss et al., 2015; see Section 17.4.1).

17.3.2 Radioisotopic age constraints on the Tonian–Cryogenian boundary

Developing criteria for selecting a GSSP for the base of the Cryogenian System is a challenging task due to a combination of common erosional removal of preglacial strata, lack of diagnostic fossils, and ongoing uncertainty and debate over the structure and reliability of chemostratigraphic profiles. In light of these challenges, and until criteria for defining the basal Cryogenian GSSP are chosen, the start of the Cryogenian Period has been revised to 720 Ma (Shields-Zhou et al., 2016). This stratigraphically calibrated age was based on recognition of radioisotopic ages from northwestern Canada that constrained the onset of early Cryogenian (Sturtian) glaciation in Yukon at c. 717 Ma (Macdonald et al., 2010). A series of new ages, including additional dates from Yukon and other successions, notably the Tambien Group in Ethiopia, appears to confirm this age (MacLennan et al., 2018). In Yukon the youngest age in preglacial strata is a 717.4 ± 0.2 Ma U–Pb zircon CA-TIMS date on a rhyolite flow in the uppermost Mount Harper Volcanics and the oldest age in syn-glacial strata is a 716.9 ± 0.4 Ma age on a felsic tuff in the lower Eagle Creek Formation (Macdonald et al., 2018). In Ethiopia (southwestern Arabian-Nubian Shield), the youngest of a pair of closely spaced tuffs in the upper Marian Bohkahko

Formation yields a maximum age of 719.68 ± 0.46 Ma for the overlying Negash Diamictite (MacLennan et al., 2018). A Monte Carlo approach to simulating the Marian Bohkahko–Negash boundary based on sediment accumulation rates and the radioisotopic dates in this section yielded a model age of 717.1 + 0.7/ − 0.9 Ma for the boundary. Similar and consistent radioisotopic ages constraining the onset of Sturtian glaciation are found elsewhere in northwestern Laurentia (Cox et al., 2015) and South China (e.g., Lan et al., 2014; see also Table 17.1 and Fig. 17.3).

17.3.3 Radioisotopic age constraints on early Cryogenian (Sturtian) glaciation

A large number of U–Pb zircon ages have been generated on syn-glacial strata, dominantly from western Laurentia and South China. An initial flood of radioisotopic ages spanning many 10s of millions of years from Cryogenian glacial strata initially prompted speculation that there were more than two discrete Cryogenian glaciations (Allen and Etienne, 2008; Kendall et al., 2006). However, consistent age constraints for the end of the early Cryogenian (Sturtian) glaciation, including from distinct *cap carbonate sequences* (i.e., postglacial shoaling upward sequences) such as the Twitya and Tapley Hill formations (NW Canada and South Australia, respectively), now favor a single, long-lived glacial epoch (Rooney et al., 2014, 2015). The combination of a 663.03 ± 0.11 Ma age from the upper syn-Sturtian Wilyerpa Formation in the Flinders Ranges of South Australia (Cox et al., 2018), a tuff in the uppermost glacial Tiesi'ao Formation in South China dated at 659 ± 2.4 Ma (U–Pb zircon SHRIMP; Wang et al., 2019) and another in the overlying Datangpo Formation dated at 658.80 ± 0.88 Ma (CA-ID-TIMS; Zhou et al., 2019), and less precise Re–Os and U–Pb zircon SHRIMP and LA-ICPMS ages between 657 and 663 Ma on immediately postglacial strata from multiple regions (see Table 17.1) indicates an age of c. 659 Ma for the end of the Sturtian glaciation. In combination with ages constraining the onset of Cryogenian glaciation at 717 Ma, these remarkably consistent ages imply the Sturtian glaciation lasted c. 58 Myr.

17.3.4 Radioisotopic age constraints on the middle Cryogenian (nonglacial interval)

The Cryogenian nonglacial interval, here informally defined to begin at the end of the Sturtian glaciation and end at the onset of the subsequent (Marinoan) end-Cryogenian glaciation, is well represented by thick carbonate and mixed carbonate–siliciclastic successions in many regions, notably South Australia, northern Namibia, southwestern Mongolia, and northwestern Canada. However, evidence of the long-lived Sturtian glaciation, combined with age constraints on the overlying Marinoan glaciation, indicates that the nonglacial interval must have been relatively short-lived: ≤ 21 Myr (c. 660 to ≤ 639 Ma; Prave et al., 2016). Most ages obtained from the nonglacial interval occur at the base (Fig. 17.2), providing robust minima on the end of the Sturtian glaciation. Others occurring within the interglacial succession effectively serve to constrain the timing of onset of Marinoan glaciation, as discussed in the following section. Applying an astrochronological approach applied to cyclic strata of the Datangpo Fm., Bao et al. (2018) estimated the nonglacial interval to have lasted at least 9.8 Myr.

17.3.5 Radioisotopic age constraints on the end Cryogenian (Marinoan) glaciation and Cryogenian–Ediacaran boundary

A globally synchronous end to the Marinoan glaciation was validated by the placement of the Ediacaran GSSP at the base of the Nuccaleena Formation, postglacial "cap dolostone" in Brachina Gorge of South Australia (Knoll et al., 2006). Remarkably similar cap dolostones occur on many cratons (e.g., Hoffman et al., 2007), and notwithstanding challenges to the duration and significance of these cap dolostones (e.g., Kennedy and Christie-Blick, 2011), it is widely agreed that they were deposited synchronously globally and mark the end of Marinoan glaciation. This inference is supported by the global occurrence of a unique negative $\Delta^{17}O$ anomaly preserved in barite- and carbonate-associated sulfate in and on top of the cap dolostone (Crockford et al., 2018).

The end of the Marinoan glaciation is well constrained by tightly clustering U–Pb zircon dates spanning the Cryogenian–Ediacaran boundary: a 635.21 ± 0.59 Ma tuff in the glacial Ghaub Formation on the Congo craton of Namibia (Prave et al., 2016); a 636.41 ± 0.48 Ma date on the youngest zircon population in a volcanolithic tuff in the uppermost Cottons Breccia of King Island, Tasmania (Calver et al., 2013); and a 635.4 ± 1.3 Ma tuff in immediately postglacial strata of the basal Doushantuo (Member A) in South China (Condon et al., 2015). Collectively, these radioisotopic dates imply an age of c. 635.5 Ma for the boundary and are consistent with other available but less precise U–Pb and Re–Os ages spanning this boundary (see Table 17.1).

The onset of Marinoan glaciation is less well constrained. A second tuff in the Ghaub Formation dated at 639.29 ± 0.26 Ma (Prave et al., 2016) indicates that the glaciation lasted at least 4 million years. Otherwise, a 654.5 ± 3.8 Ma tuff in the preglacial Datangpo in South China provides the youngest unambiguous maximum age constraint from zircons. A younger Re–Os age of

640.7 ± 4.7 Ma from the upper Black River Dolomite in northwestern Tasmania has been interpreted as a maximum age for Marinoan glaciation, but the correlation of Cryogenian glacial deposits in this region is not straightforward (Kendall et al., 2009; Rooney et al., 2014).

17.4 Biostratigraphy

Pre-Phanerozoic biostratigraphy faces a number of challenges. Precambrian paleontology is a relatively young field, with the first convincing body fossils reported only a little over 60 years ago (Tyler and Barghoorn, 1954). Thus, although tremendous advances have been made, the discipline is still in its early stages with respect to fossil discovery and systematic description. It is not unusual, for example, for a new discovery to extend the stratigraphic range of a species by hundreds of millions of years. Macroscopic forms are too rare to be of much stratigraphic use, and while organic-walled microfossils are common in both fine-grained siliciclastics and black cherts, assemblages are typically dominated by simple, smooth-walled vesicles known as *Leiosphaeridia*, a biologically meaningless taxon. Nonetheless, with a growing number of taxonomic studies linked to new paleoenvironmental, chemostratigraphic and geochronologic constraints (e.g., Tang et al., 2013, 2015; Baludikay et al., 2016; Porter and Riedman 2016; Riedman and Porter, 2016; Beghin et al., 2017a,b; Loron and Moczydłowska, 2018; Loron et al., 2019a,b; Cohen et al., 2017a; Javaux and Knoll, 2017; Miao et al., 2019), the Proterozoic biostratigraphic record is taking shape.

17.4.1 Biostratigraphy of the Tonian Period

Molecular clock analyses place the origin of crown-group eukaryotes sometime in the Mesoproterozoic or late Paleoproterozoic (e.g., Berney and Pawlowski, 2006; Parfrey et al., 2011; Eme et al., 2014; Betts et al., 2018), and the Tonian is generally viewed as a time of crown-group eukaryote diversification (e.g., Knoll et al., 2006; Cohen and Macdonald, 2015; Butterfield, 2015). Late Mesoproterozoic and Tonian rocks are the first to preserve fossils with clear similarities to particular modern eukaryotic clades, including red and green algae, fungi, amoebozoans, and stramenopiles (Butterfield et al., 1994; Butterfield, 2004; Porter et al., 2003; Loron et al., 2019a,b), though the affinities of most Tonian fossils remain enigmatic. A number of eukaryotic innovations also appear in the record during this time, including scales, tests, biomineralization, and eukaryovory (Porter and Knoll, 2000; Cohen and Knoll, 2012; Cohen et al., 2017; Porter, 2016). In addition, eukaryote-derived sterane biomarkers appear for the first time c. 900–800 Ma (Brocks, 2018).

Given these evolutionary changes, it is not surprising that late Mesoproterozoic/Tonian fossil assemblages are largely distinct from those of early Mesoproterozoic age (Sergeev et al., 2017), and several organic-walled microfossils have been proposed as index fossils for this interval. These include *Trachyhystrichosphaera aimika*, spheroidal vesicles with sparse, irregularly distributed, hollow processes, which are found in more than 20 sections worldwide in rocks c. 1100–740 Ma (Butterfield et al., 1994; Tang et al., 2013; Riedman and Sadler, 2018) and *Cerebrosphaera globosa* (= *C. buickii*), robust spheroidal vesicles with distinctive wrinkles, common in units c. 800–740 Ma (Hill et al., 2000; Grey et al., 2011; Riedman and Sadler, 2018). Several other distinctive fossils from rocks c. 780–740 Ma have potential in subdividing the Tonian, but there are too few occurrences known at present to have confidence in their ranges (Riedman and Sadler, 2018). Vorob'eva et al. (2009) noted that many long-ranging Tonian and Mesoproterozoic taxa may be biostratigraphically useful with respect to their last appearances, and in this regard it is worth noting that Riedman and Sadler (2018) found that the disappearance of many ornamented taxa in the later Tonian occurred just before or around the time that the distinctive vase-shaped microfossils (VSMs) appear. This transition could be useful in subdividing Tonian time, although it is not clear the extent to which it may be controlled by taphonomic factors. The VSMs, constrained to be 790–730 Ma but likely shorter ranging (760–730 Ma according to models by Riedman and Sadler, 2018; Riedman et al., 2018), provide the most promising marker of latest Tonian time and may be useful in defining the Cryogenian GSSP (see next).

17.4.2 Biostratigraphy of the Cryogenian Period

In contrast to the Tonian, the Cryogenian nonglacial interval appears to be characterized by depressed eukaryotic diversity (Knoll et al., 2006; Cohen and Macdonald, 2015; also see Huntley et al., 2006). Organic-walled microfossil assemblages, which form the backbone of Tonian biostratigraphy, consist almost entirely of leiosphaerids and simple filaments, with almost none of the taxa characteristic of Tonian assemblages found in Cryogenian or younger rocks (Vidal and Knoll, 1982; Riedman et al., 2014). There is evidence, however, that the biosphere may have been more diverse than previously thought. Carbonate rocks, often overlooked in sampling (Cohen and Macdonald, 2015), have yielded a number of unusual forms, including organic 'warty' sheets that may represent red algae (Cohen et al., 2015; see also Cohen et al. 2020) and structures interpreted as possible foraminifera and agglutinating testate amoebae (Bosak et al., 2011, 2012). In addition, morphologically distinctive and convincingly biogenic chambered structures have been found in Australia and Namibia in reefs that formed during the Cryogenian nonglacial interval

(Wallace et al., 2014). Other reports of macrofossils from interglacial rocks (e.g., Hofmann et al., 1990; Maloof et al., 2010; Brain et al., 2012) are of more questionable biological origin (Antcliffe et al., 2014; Menon et al., 2016).

Although the Cryogenian fossil record is sparse, there are good candidates among latest Tonian fossils for defining the Cryogenian GSSP. Particularly promising are the VSMs, the last distinctive fossils to occur below Sturtian glacial deposits (Riedman et al., 2018). VSMs occur in high abundance in carbonates, cherts, and shales in 14 successions worldwide and are taphonomically robust (Morais et al., 2017; Cohen et al., 2017; Riedman et al., 2018). Of the 18 validly described species (see Morais et al., 2019 for the latest count), 5 in particular are easily identified in thin-section and dominate assemblages and could form the basis for a biozone (the "*Cycliocyrillium simplex* assemblage"; Riedman et al., 2018). Both the *C. simplex* assemblage and VSMs as a group are relatively short-ranging, with first appearances that overlie the Bitter Springs Anomaly (BSA) (c. 811 to >789 Ma; Macdonald et al., 2010; Swanson-Hysell et al., 2015) and predate the onset of the globally recorded carbon isotope anomaly dated at c. 740 Ma in the Callison Lake Formation, Canada (Strauss et al., 2014). Last appearances are constrained to have occurred after the onset of this anomaly. If, as has been suggested, they are earliest representatives of the extant arcellinid testate amoebae (Porter and Knoll, 2000; Porter et al., 2003; Porter and Riedman, 2019), then similar forms—though perhaps not these same Tonian species—must have persisted through the Cryogenian. However, other than the rather different-looking agglutinated forms found in Sturtian Cap Carbonates (Bosak et al., 2011), no VSMs have been found.

17.5 Chemostratigraphy

In lieu of a robust biostratigraphy and global chronostratigraphic markers, chemostratigraphy is currently the most practical means of correlating between widely spaced Tonian–Cryogenian stratigraphic sections. Carbon and strontium isotope stratigraphy (mainly on marine carbonates) are the most widely applied chemostratigraphic tools in the Neoproterozoic (Fig. 17.3), and notwithstanding challenges to their general robustness to diagenetic alteration (e.g., Knauth and Kennedy, 2009; Derry, 2010) and reliability as global seawater proxies (Ahm et al., 2019), they consistently reveal similar secular trends at both basinal and global scales.

Carbon-isotopic ($\delta^{13}C$) records for the Neoproterozoic are based primarily on carbonates deposited in platformal settings. Whereas organic carbon $\delta^{13}C$ records have been generated and in some cases closely conform in structure to accompanying $\delta^{13}C_{carb}$ profiles (e.g., Swanson-Hysell et al., 2010), they are regarded as less reliable than carbonate records due to low organic carbon content in most Tonian–Cryogenian sedimentary rocks (Johnston et al., 2012) and discordance between organic and carbonate carbon records during certain key intervals, such as the Trezona and Shuram–Wonoka negative carbon isotope anomalies (e.g., Fike et al., 2006; Swanson-Hysell et al., 2010). Therefore $\delta^{13}C$ records from well-preserved carbonate successions are preferred for correlation purposes. The Neoproterozoic $\delta^{13}C_{carb}$ record is generally distinguished by its high average values (≥5‰), which are punctuated by a series of deep negative carbon isotope anomalies or excursions, many of which appear to closely associated with glaciation (Fig. 17.3).

The broad contours of the secular trend in the strontium isotope ratio of Tonian–Cryogenian seawater are well established, dominated by a long-term rise in $^{87}Sr/^{86}Sr$ (from ~0.7052 to ~0.7073; Fig. 17.3). However, strontium isotope chemostratigraphy in the Neoproterozoic is severely limited by the low number of stratigraphic intervals containing limestones that are sufficiently well preserved (i.e., with high Sr/Ca and low Mn/Sr) to record reliably the $^{87}Sr/^{86}Sr$ of the seawater from which they were deposited. Therefore the record is constructed typically from small numbers of data points from discrete intervals in different successions. When combined with limited radioisotopic age control on most samples, the result is an irregular record with a large number of temporal gaps and limited verification of trends among coeval successions. Nevertheless, due to the prominent rise in $^{87}Sr/^{86}Sr$ through the Neoproterozoic, the record is sufficient to distinguish among the early Tonian (i.e., 1000–810 Ma), late Tonian (810–720 Ma), and Cryogenian nonglacial interval (c. 660–640 Ma) (Fig. 17.3). Due to the near absence of syn-glacial carbonate strata, no proxy data for seawater exist for the Cryogenian glacial intervals (i.e., c. 717–660 and ≥640–635.5 Ma).

17.5.1 Chemostratigraphy of the Tonian Period

The Tonian carbon isotope record is identified by its sustained intervals of high $\delta^{13}C_{carb} \geq +5‰$ (Fig. 17.3; Kaufman et al., 1997; Halverson et al., 2005). The shift toward the high $\delta^{13}C_{carb}$ values appears to be transitional, with moderate fluctuations (≤4‰) in $\delta^{13}C_{carb}$ beginning in the late Mesoproterozoic (Knoll et al, 1995; Bartley et al., 2001; Kah et al., 2012) and continuing into the early Neoproterozoic (Kuznetsov et al., 2006). However, due to a paucity of earliest Tonian carbonate successions globally and poor age control on those successions that do exist, the $\delta^{13}C_{carb}$ record for the interval c. 1000–850 Ma is poorly established. Available data indicate that $\delta^{13}C_{carb}$ remained ≤5‰ for all of this interval, while $^{87}Sr/^{86}Sr$ was 0.7052–0.7063 (Cox et al., 2016; Kuznetsov et al., 2017) (Fig. 17.3).

The shift toward higher sustained $\delta^{13}C_{carb}$ (≥5‰) occurs c. 850 Ma (though is not directly dated), as recorded in the Little Dal Group and equivalent strata of northwestern Canada (Fig. 17.4; Halverson, 2006;

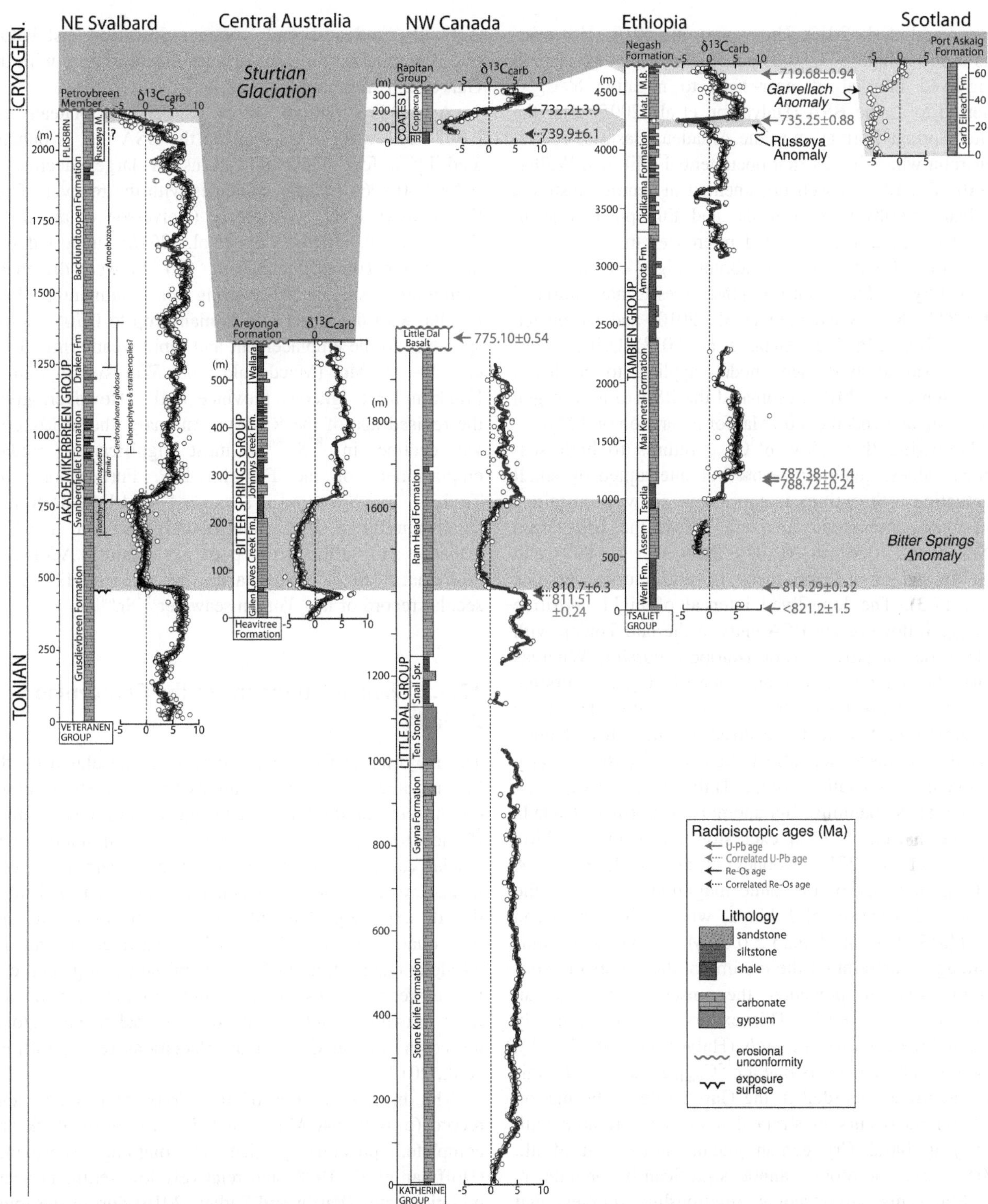

FIGURE 17.4 Stratigraphy, carbon isotope chemostratigraphy, and geochronology of key, carbonate-rich Tonian successions, showing inferred correlations of three negative $\delta^{13}C_{carb}$ anomalies. The NE Svalbard log is a composite section, with $\delta^{13}C_{carb}$ data from Halverson et al. (2018b). Key fossil ranges are shown (modified from Halverson et al., 2018b). The Central Australia (Amadeus Basin) composite section and carbon isotope data are scaled to the Wallara-1 drill hole (from Swanson-Hysell et al., 2010). NW Canada data are from the Mackenzie Mountains; Little Dal section and data from Halverson (2006) and Rooney et al. (2014). Ethiopia composite stratigraphic log and $\delta^{13}C_{carb}$ data are from Swanson-Hysell et al. (2015). Scotland (Dalradian) section of the Garb Eileach Fm., which is argued to be conformable with the glacial Port Askaig Formation on the Garvellach Islands, shows the Garvellach Anomaly (from Ali et al., 2018). A more complete Tonian composite $\delta^{13}C_{carb}$ record for Scotland is provided in Prave et al. (2009). Correlated radioisotopic ages for NW Canada are from correlative successions in Yukon. Solid gray lines over carbon isotope data (circles) represent local area regression fits to the available data at 2–5 m spacing. See Table 17.1 for sources of radioisotopic ages. *COATES L.*, Coates Lake Group; *M.B.*, Marian Bohkahko Formation; *Mat.*, Matheos Formation; *PLRSBRN*, Polarisbreen Group; *RR*, Redstone River Formation.

Macdonald et al., 2012; Thomson et al., 2015). However, this trend of high $\delta^{13}C_{carb}$ is punctuated by a discrete and long-lived interval of near zero to negative $\delta^{13}C_{carb}$, referred to as the BSA (Halverson et al., 2005) after the Bitter Springs Formation in the Amadeus Basin of central Australia where it was first documented (Hill and Walter, 2000). The BSA is well documented in central Australia, Svalbard, northwestern Canada, and Ethiopia (Swanson-Hysell et al., 2012, 2015 and references therein), where both its onset and demise are abrupt (Fig. 17.4). It is constrained by U–Pb zircon CA-TIMS ages to have initiated after 811.5 Ma (Macdonald et al., 2010) and terminated prior to 788.7 Ma (MacLennan et al., 2018). Using a thermal subsidence-type age model applied to Svalbard, Halverson et al. (2018a) estimated the BSA to have begun c. 810 Ma and ended c. 802 Ma, for a duration of 8 Myr.

Following that BSA, $\delta^{13}C_{carb}$ returns to high sustained values, generally $\geq 6‰$ but interrupted by small fluctuations. Strontium isotope data show a sustained and nearly monotonic increase across the BSA from $^{87}Sr/^{86}Sr = 0.7063$ to 0.7070 between c. 800 and 750 Ma, which is reproduced in multiple successions (Fig. 17.3). The long-lived interval of highly positive $\delta^{13}C_{carb}$ following the BSA ends in the late Tonian with at least one negative carbon isotope excursion. Whereas it had been thought that one, deep $\delta^{13}C_{carb}$ excursion, originally dubbed the *Islay Anomaly* after the Islay Formation in Scotland, occurred in the latest Tonian Period and was genetically linked to the onset of early Cryogenian glaciation (e.g., Halverson, 2006), new Re–Os ages spanning this anomaly in northern Canada indicate that this $\delta^{13}C_{carb}$ excursion is instead c. 740 Ma (Strauss et al., 2014; Rooney et al., 2014, 2015). A $\delta^{13}C_{carb}$ anomaly of the same magnitude occurs in the Matheos Formation of Ethiopa, where a U–Pb zircon CA-TIMS date of 735.25 ± 0.88 Ma provides a minimum age constraint on the minima of the excursion, confirming that it preceded the onset of Cryogenian glaciation by >18 Ma. This excursion was tentatively renamed the *Russøya Anomaly* (Halverson et al., 2018b), based on the hypothesis that a $\delta^{13}C_{carb}$ excursion of similar magnitude recorded in the Garbh Eileach Formation in Scotland occurs in strata that are conformable with overlying basal Cryogenian glacial strata (Ali et al., 2018), and therefore cannot significantly predate c. 717 Ma. This stratigraphic relationship implies that this anomaly, informally referred to as the *Garvellach Anomaly*, is close in age to the onset of early Cryogenian glaciation and much younger than the Russøya Anomaly. The Tambien Group of Namibia (MacLennan et al., 2018) and the Ugab Subgroup (Otavi Group) of north-central Namibia (Lamothe et al., 2019) record negative excursions that are consistent within available age constraints with correlation to the Russøya Anomaly, and a second, younger downturn just below overlying glacial erosion surfaces may correlate with the Garvellach Anomaly (Fig. 17.4).

Available strontium isotope data show a plateau near 0.7070 following recovery from the BSA that is punctuated by a few minor downturns. A larger decline to 0.7064–0.7065 broadly coincides with the recovery from the Russøya $\delta^{13}C_{carb}$ Anomaly (Halverson et al., 2010; Rooney et al., 2014). Cox et al. (2016) suggested that these latter Tonian declines in $^{87}Sr/^{86}Sr$ were driven by preferential silicate weathering of continental flood basalts, with the larger late Tonian drop to 0.7064 corresponding to the emplacement and rapid weathering of the c. 720–718 Ma (Macdonald and Wordsworth, 2017) Franklin large igneous province (LIP). However, given the revised age of the Russøya Anomaly, the nearly coeval decline in $^{87}Sr/^{86}Sr$ must significantly predate emplacement of the Franklin LIP. Furthermore, the Tonian $^{87}Sr/^{86}Sr$ record is strongly biased by data from a small handful of successions (mainly Svalbard and NW Canada) and suffers from poor age control. Additional high-quality Sr isotope data are necessary to fill in the secular record of late Tonian seawater $^{87}Sr/^{86}Sr$.

17.5.2 Chemostratigraphy of the Cryogenian Period

The majority of Cryogenian time is encapsulated by the Sturtian and Marinoan glaciations (c. 61 of 85 Ma based on the current definitions and age calibrations). Unlike Phanerozoic glaciations, where semicontinuous syn-glacial carbonate records exist, primary carbonate sediments are rare from Cryogenian glacial strata, and those that do exist (e.g., Fairchild et al., 2016) are patchy and inadequate proxies for glacial seawater chemistry, let alone chemostratigraphy. This missing syn-glacial carbonate record owes predominantly to the extreme sea level drawdown and severity (e.g., global to near global ice cover) of the Cryogenian glaciations (e.g., Hoffman et al., 2017).

The inverse is true of the Cryogenian interglacial record (c. 660–640 Ma), which is fortuitously thick and complete, presumably due to ongoing subsidence (Hoffman et al., 1998) and relatively low sediment accumulation rates (Partin and Sadler, 2016) during the long-lived Sturtian glaciation, leaving ample accommodation space after recovery of postglacial sea level. Nearly continuous interglacial carbonate successions occur in the Otavi Group (Abenab Subgroup) of northern Namibia (Hoffmann and Prave, 1996) and the Tsagaan-Olom Group of southwestern Mongolian (Macdonald et al., 2009). Consequently, these two successions provide the most complete chemostratigraphic records for the

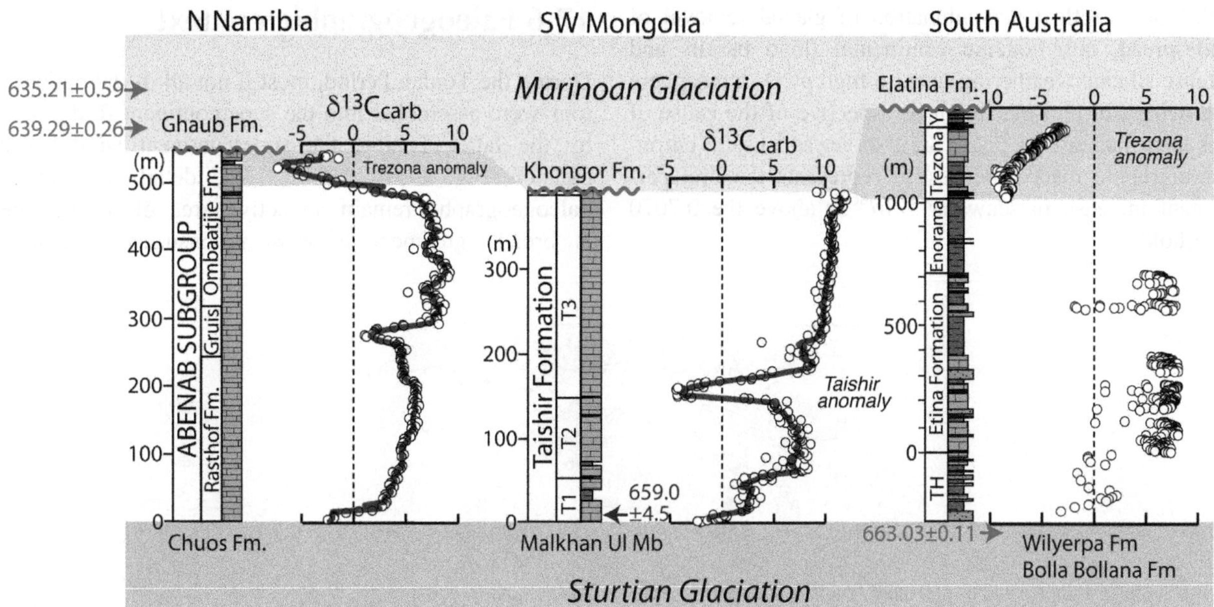

FIGURE 17.5 Key Cryogenian nonglacial interval successions with $\delta^{13}C_{carb}$ data, demonstrating the generally high ($>5‰$) values during this interval, along with inferred correlation of the Trezona Anomaly. Namibia stratigraphy and $\delta^{13}C_{carb}$ data are from a single section at Ogongo (modified from Swanson-Hysell et al., 2010). Stratigraphy and $\delta^{13}C_{carb}$ data from southwest Mongolia are adapted from the Uliastai Gorge section in Bold et al. (2016). Section of the thick Cryogenian nonglacial interval in the Flinders Ranges and $\delta^{13}C_{carb}$ data from in Rose et al. (2012). Etina Fm. through Yaltipina Fm. (Y) from Emu Gap; Tapley Hill Fm. (TH) is from Nannipinna Bore and is not to scale. Solid gray lines over carbon isotope data for the Namibian and Mongolian sections represent local area regression fits to the available data (circles) at 2–5 m spacing. See Fig. 17.4 for legend and Table 17.1 for sources of radioisotopic ages.

Cryogenian nonglacial interval (Fig. 17.5; Brasier et al., 1996; Hoffman et al., 1998; Halverson et al., 2005; Bold et al., 2016). Both northwestern Canada (Hay Creek Group; Macdonald et al., 2018) and the Flinders Ranges of South Australia (Umberatana Group; McKirdy et al., 2001; Rose et al., 2012) have mixed carbonate–siliciclastic lithologies that provide complementary chemostratigraphic records.

The Cryogenian nonglacial interval begins with a distinct but short-lived negative $\delta^{13}C_{carb}$ excursion at the base of the postglacial cap carbonate sequence (lower Rasthof Fm. in Namibia and basal member of the Taishir Fm. in Mongolia), with negative $\delta^{13}C_{carb}$ values ($<-4‰$) recovering sharply to the highly ^{13}C-enriched values ($\delta^{13}C_{carb}>6‰$) that are typical much of the nonglacial interval (Fig. 17.5). A deep negative excursion within the middle of the Taishir Formation in Mongolia (the Taishir Anomaly; Macdonald et al., 2009) may correlate with a downturn to low positive $\delta^{13}C_{carb}$ values in the middle Abenab Subgroup in Namibia, as well as a negative carbon isotope anomaly documented in multiple sections of the upper Ringwood Member in the Cryogenian nonglacial interval in the Amadeus Basin of central Australia (Verdel and Campbell, 2017).

A subsequent deep negative $\delta^{13}C_{carb}$ excursion occurs near the end of the nonglacial interval and has been named the Trezona Anomaly (Halverson et al., 2002) after the Trezona Formation in the Flinders Ranges of South Australia where the anomaly was first fully documented (McKirdy et al., 2001). In the Ombaatjie Formation of northern Namibia, the anomaly occurs as a gradual drop from $\delta^{13}C_{carb}=>\pm 6‰$ to values as low as $-5‰$, followed by a slight recovery toward slightly negative values (Fig. 17.5). In Mongolia, only the onset of the anomaly is preserved, and this only in isolated sections; its common absence is presumably attributable to erosional removal beneath the Khongor (Marinoan) glacial surface (Bold et al., 2016). In Australia the transition from highly positive values ($\delta^{13}C_{carb}>5‰$) in the Etina Formation to highly negative values ($>-10‰$) in the Trezona Formation is concealed by the intervening Enorama Shale. A trend toward less negative $\delta^{13}C_{carb}$ within the Trezona Formation appears to be synchronous with early glaciation (Rose et al., 2012). The Trezona Anomaly is also recorded in the Keele Formation of NW Canada (Hoffman and Schrag, 2002; Macdonald et al., 2018) and the middle Easdale Subgroup in the Dalradian of Scotland and Ireland (Prave et al., 2009).

Strontium isotope data show a sharp increase from $^{87}Sr/^{86}Sr=0.7066$ to 0.7072 (Shields et al., 1997) in the lowermost Cryogenian nonglacial interval, followed by a plateau of 0.7072–0.7073 throughout the remainder of the nonglacial interval (Fig. 17.3). Rooney et al. (2014) and Cox et al. (2016) attributed this salient increase in

$^{87}Sr/^{86}Sr$ to reflect a combination of glacial removal of widespread, unradiogenic continental flood basalts and intense silicate weathering under a high pCO_2 atmosphere following Sturtian glaciation. Irrespective of the cause of this large increase in $^{87}Sr/^{86}Sr$, it serves as a useful chronostratigraphic marker because it represents the first permanent increase in seawater $^{87}Sr/^{86}Sr$ above the 0.7070 threshold.

17.6 Paleogeographic context

During the Tonian Period, most if not all of the major cratons were assembled into the supercontinent Rodinia, and by the latter Tonian, the supercontinent straddled the equator (Fig. 17.6). Although the details of Rodinian paleogeography remain an active area of debate, there is broad agreement in most reconstructions that the

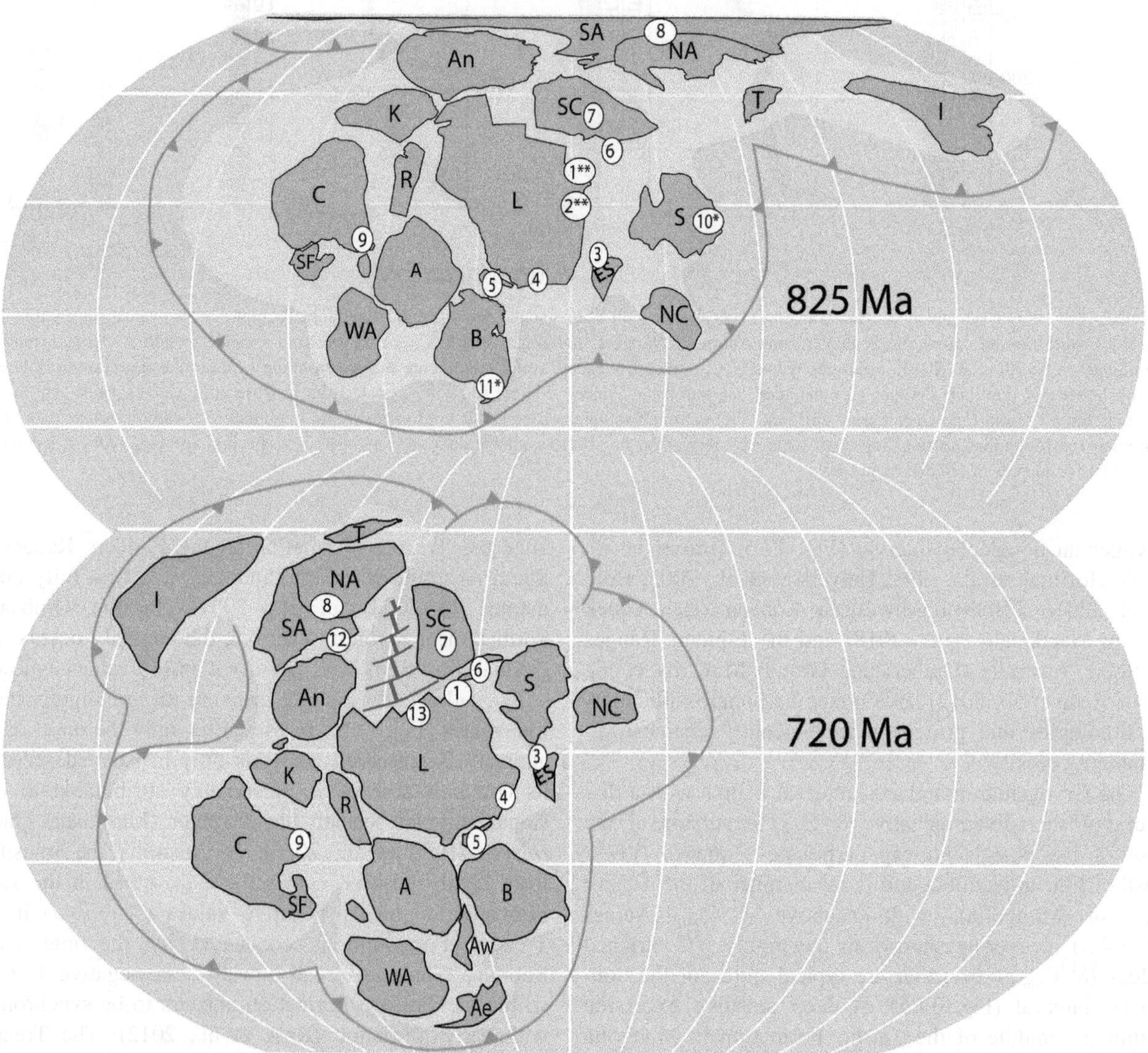

FIGURE 17.6 Global paleogeographic reconstructions for 825 and 720 Ma, modified from Li et al. (2013). Paleogeographic locations of key Tonian (top) and Cryogenian (bottom) sections for calibrating the Tonian–Cryogenian time scale or otherwise discussed in the text are shown (though note that this not an exhaustive list of succession with Tonian and Cryogenian strata). Regions with important early Tonian (> 825 Ma) sections only are denoted by *, whereas those with both early and late Tonian sections are denoted by ** and those with only late Tonian sections have no asterisk. 1 = northwestern Canada (Yukon and Mackenzie Mountains); 2 = northern Canada (Amundsen Basin); 3 = East Svalbard; 4 = East Greenland; 5 = Dalradian (Scotland and Ireland); 6 = southwestern Mongolia (Altaids); 7 = South China; 8 = Centralian Superbasin (e.g., Amadeus and Officer basins); 9 = northern Damara (Otavi Group); 10 = Yenesei Ridge/Turukhansk; 11 = southern Urals; 12 = Flinders Ranges (South Australia); 13 = Idaho/Utah. See Li et al. (2013) for more details about the methods for generating the reconstructions and a complete list of Tonian and Cryogenian successions. Cratons as follows: *A*, Amazonia; *Ae*, eastern Avalonia; *Aw*, western Avalonia; *B*, Baltica; *C*, Congo; *EA*, East Antarctica; *ES*, East Svalbard; *G*, Greenland; *I*, India; *K*, Kalahari; *L*, Laurentia; *M*, Mongolia; *NA*, northern Australia; *NC*, North China; *NS*, North Slope; *R*, Rio Plata; *SA*, southern Australia; *SC*, South China; *Sf*, Sao Francisco; *Si*, Siberia; *T*, Tarim; *WA*, West Africa.

supercontinent was centered on Laurentia, which was in turn bordered by Siberia, Baltica, Amazonia, and likely the Kalahari and Antarctic cratons (Hoffman, 1991; Li et al., 2008; Johansson, 2014; Merdith et al., 2017). And although most reconstructions also place the northern and southern cratons of Australia somewhere adjacent to the Cordilleran margin of Laurentia, it has been proposed that South China may have intervened between Laurentia and Australia (Fig. 17.6; Li et al., 1995). This arrangement remains controversial, and a strongly contrasting model places South China on the external periphery of Rodinia (e.g., Cawood et al., 2013). Less controversial but equally problematic is the location of India, which may have not been part of Rodinia at all (Merdith et al., 2017), despite evidence that the core of the Indian continent formed in the latest Mesoproterozoic (Stenian) to earliest Tonian (Bhowmik et al., 2012). Cawood et al. (2013) suggested that India and South China were amalgamated in the late Mesoproterozoic and remained connected throughout the Neoproterozoic, and Merdith et al. (2017) have followed this convention but excluded both from the supercontinent altogether in the absence of firm evidence that they amalgamated before the Ediacaran Period.

A proliferation of sedimentary basins in Rodinia between c. 850 and 800 Ma (e.g., the Centralian Superbasin of Australia; the East-Svalbard–East Greenland Basin, and the Mackenzie Mountains–Amundsen and associated basins of northern–northwestern Canada, the Nanhua rift basin of South China, and the Central African Copperbelt (Lindsay and Korsch, 1989; Hoffman et al., 2012; Rainbird et al., 1996; Wang et al., 2011; Bull et al., 2011; Li et al., 2013) has been interpreted to record an initial phase of breakup of Rodinia (Li et al., 1999; Macdonald et al., 2012), perhaps related to insolation of the underlying mantle (Lindsay, 2002) and/or the influence of a series of similarly aged mantle plumes that impinged on Rodinia at this time (Li et al., 1999; Li et al., 2003). However, evidence for extension leading to continental separation in the Tonian is lacking and true breakup probably began in earnest in the early Cryogenian (e.g., Merdith et al., 2017), followed by a peak in passive margin abundance c. 600 Ma (Bradley, 2008). Therefore, in spite of its name, Rodinia's tenure as a supercontinent almost perfectly coincided with the Tonian Period, whereas breakup occurred predominantly during the Cryogenian and early Ediacaran.

Another significant uncertainty in Tonian paleogeography relates to Rodinia's position during the middle Neoproterozoic. Whereas many reconstructions place parts of Rodinia, including Australia, in the high latitudes c. 825 Ma (Fig. 17.6), others advocate a supercontinent spanning from high to low latitudes (e.g., Johansson, 2014) or even dominantly positioned in the tropics (Pisarevsky et al., 2003). The middle Tonian basins themselves place important constraints on these paleogeographies, for abundant c. 850–800 Ma evaporites occur on multiple cratons, including in the Centralian superbasin of Australia (Lindsay, 1987), in northwestern Canada (Turner and Bekker, 2016), and in the Central African Copperbelt of the Congo craton (Bull et al., 2011). The ambiguity and diversity of paleogeographies for this time interval (Merdith et al., 2017), in addition to available paleomagnetic data, allow for the possibility of large-scale true polar wander (TPW) in the middle Tonian (e.g., Li et al., 2004), and Maloof et al. (2006) linked the BSA to a pair of hypothesized TPW events. Whereas paleomagnetic support for these TPW events remains tepid (Swanson-Hysell et al., 2012), it is evident that Rodinia did move from an overall higher latitude position sometime in the earlier Tonian to the tropics by the end of the Tonian (Fig. 17.6). Combined with the widespread LIPs emplaced in Rodinia in the middle to late Tonian (e.g., the c. 830 Ma Guibei and Willouran LIPs in China and Australia, the c. 800 Ma LIP in South China, the c. 780–775 Kanding and Gunbarrel LIPS in South China and western North America, and the c. 720 Ma Franklin LIP in North America; Ernst et al., 2008), a shift toward a tropical arrangement of the continents would have had a profound effect on continental silicate weathering, and by extension, on late Tonian climate (Goddéris et al., 2007) and seawater chemistry (Cox et al., 2016).

17.7 Tonian–Cryogenian Earth system evolution

Although the Tonian Period is named for the rifting of the supercontinent Rodinia (Plumb, 1991), it is generally agreed that breakup did not begin until the end of the Tonian (Li et al., 2008). The beginning of the Tonian Period, c. 1.0 Ga, is associated with the final stages of the amalgamation of Rodinia, and a peak in the abundance of zircons in orogenic granites and detrital sedimentary rocks (e.g., Condie, 1998; Campbell and Allen, 2008).

Just as Gondwanan assembly in the late Neoproterozoic is linked to a peak in the $^{87}Sr/^{86}Sr$ of seawater, this Grenvillean peak corresponds to a maximum of $^{87}Sr/^{86}Sr = 0.7060$ at c. 1.0 Ga (Gibson et al., 2019). Unlike the late Neoproterozioc Era, the Stenian–Tonian boundary is not associated with any as yet recognized global scale reorganization of biogeochemical cycles or the biosphere. Rather, the earliest Tonian Period, to the minimal extent that it has been documented, appears to represent a continuation of the late Stenian Earth system, characterized by $\delta^{13}C_{carb}$ moderately fluctuating about an average of 0‰ and a low-diversity biosphere in which eukaryotes, though present, did not yet leave a strong imprint in the sedimentary biogeochemical record (Brocks et al., 2017).

The interval c. 850–800 Ma in the middle Tonian witnessed fundamental changes to the Neoproterozoic Earth system. $\delta^{13}C_{carb}$ first rose to the values of >5‰ that characterize much of the remainder of the Tonian and Cryogenian periods at c. 850 Ma, but this trend was interrupted by the long-lived, c. 810–802 Ma BSA, with values dropping back to negative to near zero values akin to the middle Proterozoic (Fig. 17.3). An increase in chromium isotope fractionation recorded in iron formation and shales at about this time is interpreted to record the onset of oxidative weathering of chromium, implying an increase in atmospheric pO_2 to concentrations >0.1% present atmospheric levels (Planavsky et al., 2014; Cole et al., 2016). An increase in the marine sulfate inventory, heralded by the deposition of massive sulfate deposits around this time (Turner and Bekker, 2016), is also consistent with an increase in atmospheric oxygen levels. It has been proposed that the middle Tonian also experienced a marked diversification in eukaryotic diversity based on increase in the number of complex taxa (Knoll et al., 2006; Cohen and Macdonald, 2015), which include the oldest biomineralizers (the apatitic scale microfossils; Cohen et al., 2017), and the oldest putative chlorophytes and Amoebozoa (Halverson et al., 2018a). However, evidence for predation in earlier Neoproterozoic strata (Loron and Moczydłowska, 2018) and the first appearance of fungi in the fossil record c. 900 Ma (Loron et al., 2019b), plus consideration of the relative scarcity of early Neoproterozoic strata in the first place, suggest that this diversification could have been more drawn out. In either case the link between Neoproterozoic oxygenation and eukaryotic diversification remains a controversial topic (Lenton et al., 2014; Planavsky et al., 2014).

In the later Tonian, the sustained rise in $^{87}Sr/^{86}Sr$ of seawater from ratios of ~0.7052 to 0.7070 was interrupted and strontium compositions eventually dropped back to ~0.7064 by the onset of Cryogenian glaciation (Fig. 17.3). Cox et al. (2016) proposed that this plateau and decline in seawater $^{87}Sr/^{86}Sr$ was the result of the weathering of widespread continental flood basalts in tropical Rodinia, emplaced between c. 850 and 719 Ma, which itself may have increased phosphorus delivery to the oceans (Horton, 2015) and have been linked to abrupt global cooling that initiated Cryogenian glaciation. A reprise in increasing $^{87}Sr/^{86}Sr$ during the Cryogenian can, in turn, be interpreted in terms of a combination of erosional removal of much of that basalt from the continents during the long-lived Sturtian glaciation and high rates of continental silicate weathering afterward. Notably, the depauperate fossil record that characterizes the Cryogenian nonglacial interval is a continuation of an interval of low taxonomic diversity that began in the late Tonian (Riedman et al., 2014). Nevertheless, biomarker evidence indicates a wholesale shift toward eukaryotes as the dominant primary producers during the brief Cryogenian nonglacial interval (Brocks et al., 2017) and the appearance of sponges prior to the Marinoan glaciation (Love et al., 2009). This second global glaciation is preceded by the deep Trezona negative carbon isotope anomaly (Fig. 17.5), but if and how this anomaly is mechanistically linked to the rise of eukaryotes or the initiation of Marinoan glaciation is uncertain.

17.8 Formalization and potential subdivision of the Tonian and Cryogenian Periods

17.8.1 The base of the Cryogenian Period

The chronostratigraphic base of the Cryogenian Period has not yet been formally defined but has chronometrically been redefined from 850 Ma to a provisional age of 720 Ma (Shields-Zhou et al., 2016). This provisional age is based on recognition that the onset of Cryogenian glaciation occurred c. 717 Ma (Table 17.1) and the emphasis that the boundary "should be placed within an outcrop section at a precisely defined stratigraphic level (GSSP) beneath the oldest clearly glacigenic deposits in a Neoproterozoic succession" (Shields-Zhou et al., 2012). The reasoning behind this proposed stratigraphic position for the GSSP as opposed to the base of the glacial deposits themselves is that in most sections, this surface is an erosional unconformity. Whereas this unconformity would unambiguously delineate Cryogenian strata above from Tonian strata below, it would not be able to have a precise age ascribed to it. The challenge in choosing a viable boundary below the glacial unconformity is that in the absence of obvious sedimentological or paleontological criteria, a chemostratigraphic approach—namely carbon and/or strontium isotopes—is the most logical. However, as discussed earlier in this chapter, the chemostratigraphic record of Tonian–Cryogenian transition remains poorly established and few successions globally preserve a very complete record of unaltered marine carbonates at this level.

17.8.2 Subdivision of the Cryogenian Period

The Cryogenian Period itself lends itself to a logical subdivision into the glacial epochs, that is, the early Cryogenian Sturtian and late Cryogenian Marionan glaciations (or "Cryochrons"; Hoffman et al., 2017) and the Cryogenian nonglacial interval (or the late Cryogenian warm interval; Shields-Zhou et al., 2012). The onset of the older, Sturtian glaciation is now well constrained temporally, with consistent ages globally to within less than 1 million years (MacLennan et al., 2018). The end of the Sturtian glaciation, like the end of the younger Marinoan glaciation, appears to correspond to a global transgression. Whereas the distinct cap dolostone and transgressive systems tract characteristic of the post-Marinoan stratigraphic record (Hoffman et al., 2007) is typically absent above Sturtian glacial deposits, the end Sturtian boundary should be straightforward to identify in the stratigraphic record as a flooding surface coupled to an abrupt change from glacial to nonglacial strata.

The Cryogenian nonglacial interval now appears to have been no more than 19 Myr in duration (i.e., c. 659 to ≥ 640 Ma). Nevertheless, this record is unusually complete and thick in many successions, such as in Namibia, Mongolia, and South Australia (Fig. 17.5). At least informally the intervals encompassed by negative carbon isotope excursions, most notably the so-called Trezona Anomaly (Halverson et al., 2002), are useful for subdividing time during the nonglacial interval. The end of the nonglacial interval and onset of the Marinoan glaciation remain poorly pinned in time and selection of this boundary would ultimately be hampered by the same challenge of common erosion on the subglacial surface that plagues the selection of the basal Cryogenian boundary. However, the very thick nonglacial record in the Flinders Ranges of South Australia coupled to possible evidence for the onset of glaciation during initial recovery from the Trezona Anomaly (Rose et al., 2012) provides the possibility of identifying a future boundary that is not intrinsically an unconformity.

17.8.3 Subdivision of the Tonian period

The Tonian Period is currently chronometrically defined to last from 1000 to 720 Ma, having been lengthened by 130 Myr due to the revision to the Cryogenian Period (Shields-Zhou et al, 2016). The potential stratigraphic record for a lower boundary of the (current) Tonian Period c. 1000 Ma is limited, and with few exceptions, known latest Stenian and early Tonian strata are very poorly age calibrated. Therefore revision from a chronometric to a chronostratigraphic Stenian–Tonian boundary is perhaps immature.

Notwithstanding a relatively sparse early Tonian stratigraphic record, this long period can be usefully divided. A logical starting point for division would take advantage of the c. 810–802 Ma BSA. The BSA broadly separates an early Tonian, with a limited stratigraphic and biostratigraphic record, from a late Tonian, with a more extensive stratigraphic record and diverse fossils. In fact, the BSA also corresponds broadly in time with a proposed rise in atmospheric oxygen levels (Cole et al., 2016) and eukaryotic diversification (e.g., Cohen et al., 2017b; Riedman and Sadler, 2018). In Svalbard the BSA recovery also corresponds to a prominent transgression and the first appearance of the fossil *C. globosa* (Fig. 17.4), an acritarch with a finite stratigraphic range and potential biostratigraphic utility in the middle–late Tonian (Butterfield et al., 1994). The end of the BSA is also distinguished by first a decrease in $^{87}Sr/^{86}Sr$ from 0.7065 to 0.7063, then a sharp rise to 0.7070 (Fig. 17.3).

Bibliography

Ahm, A.-S.C., Maloof, A.C., Macdonald, F.A., Hoffman, P.F., Bjerrum, C.J., Bold, U., et al., 2019, An early diagenetic deglacial origin for basal Ediacaran "cap dolostones". *Earth and Planetary Science Letters*, **506**: 292–307.

Ali, D.O., Spencer, A.M., Fairchild, I.J., Chew, K.J., Anderton, R., Levell, B.K., et al., 2018, Indicators of relative completeness of the glacial record of the Port Askaig T Formation, Garvellach Islands, Scotland. *Precambrian Research*, **319**: 65–78.

Allen, P.A., and Etienne, J.L., 2008, Sedimentary challenge to Snowball Earth. *Nature Geoscience*, **1**: 817–825.

Antcliffe, J.B., Callow, R.H., and Brasier, M.D., 2014, Giving the early fossil record of sponges a squeeze. *Biological Reviews*, **89**: 972–1004.

Asmerom, Y., Jacobsen, S., Knoll, A.H., Butterfield, N.J., and Swett, K., 1991, Strontium isotopic variations of Neoproterozoic seawater: implications for crustal evolution. *Geochimica et Cosmochimica Acta*, **55**: 1883–1894.

Baludikay, B.K., Storme, J.Y., François, C., Baudet, D., and Javaux, E.J., 2016, A diverse and exquisitely preserved organic-walled microfossil assemblage from the Meso–Neoproterozoic Mbuji-Mayi Supergroup (Democratic Republic of Congo) and implications for Proterozoic biostratigraphy. *Precambrian Research*, **281**: 166–184.

Baldwin, G.J., Turner, E.C., and Kamber, B.S., 2016, Tectonic controls on distribution and stratigraphy of the Cryogenian Rapitan iron formation, northwestern Canada. *Precambrian Research*, **278**: 303–322.

Bao, X., Zhang, S., Jiang, G., Wu, H., Li, H., Wang, X., et al., 2018, Cyclostratigraphic constraints on the duration of the Datangpo Formation and the onset age of the Nantuo (Marinoan) glaciation in South China. *Earth and Planetary Science Letters*, **483**: 52–63.

Bartley, J.K., Semikhatov, M.A., Kaufman, A.J., Knoll, A.H., Pope, M.C., and Jacobsen, S.B., 2001, Global events across the Mesoproterozoic–Neoproterozoic boundary: C and Sr isotopic evidence from Siberia. *Precambrian Research*, **111**: 165–202.

Beghin, J., Guilbaud, R., Poulton, S.W., Gueneli, N., Brocks, J.J., Storme, J.-Y., et al., 2017a, A palaeoecological model for the late Mesoproterozoic – early Neoproterozoic Atar/El Mreïti Group, Taoudeni Basin, Mauritania, northwestern Africa. *Precambrian Research*, **299**: 1–14.

Beghin, J., Storme, J.-Y., Blanpied, C., Gueneli, N., Brocks, J.J., Poulton, S.W., et al., 2017b, Microfossils from the late Mesoproterozoic – early Neoproterozoic Atar/El Mreïti Group, Taoudeni Basin, Mauritania, northwestern Africa. *Precambrian Research*, **291**: 63–82.

Berney, C., and Pawlowski, J., 2006, A molecular time-scale for eukaryote evolution recalibrated with the continuous microfossil record. *Proceedings of the Royal Society B: Biological Sciences*, **273**: 1867–1872.

Betts, H.C., Puttick, M.N., Clark, J.W., Williams, T.A., Donoghue, P.C.J., and Pisani, D., 2018, Integrated genomic and fossil evidence illuminates life's early evolution and eukaryote origin. *Nature Ecology and Evolution*, **2**: 1556–1562.

Bhowmik, S.K., Wilde, S.A., Bhandari, A., Pal, T., and Pant, N.C., 2012, Growth of the Greater Indian Landmass and its assembly in Rodinia: Geochronological evidence from the Central Indian Tectonic Zone. *Gondwana Research*, **22**: 54–72.

Bold, U., Smith, E.F., Rooney, A.D., Bowring, S.A., Buchwaldt, R., Dudas, F.O., et al., 2016, Neoproterozoic stratigraphy of the Zavhkan terrane of Mongolia: the backbone for Cryogenian and early Ediacaran chemostratigraphic records. *American Journal of Science*, **316**: 1–63.

Bosak, T., Lahr, D.J.G., Pruss, S.B., Macdonald, F.A., Dalton, L., and Matys, E., 2011, Agglutinated tests in post-Sturtian cap carbonates of Namibia and Mongolia. *Earth and Planetary Science Letters*, **308**: 29–40.

Bosak, T., Lahr, D.J.G., Pruss, S.B., Macdonald, F.A., Gooday, A.J., Dalton, L., and Matys, E.D., 2012, Possible early foraminiferas in post-Sturtian (716–635 Ma) cap carbonates. *Geology*, **40**: 67–70.

Bowring, S.A., Grotzinger, J.P., Condon, D.J., Ramezani, J., Newall, M.J., and Allen, P.A., 2007, Geochronological constraints on the chronostratigraphic framework of the Neoproterozoic Huqf Superroup, Sultanate of Oman. *American Journal of Science*, **307**: 1097–1145.

Bradley, D.C., 2008, Passive margins through earth history. *Earth-Science Reviews*, **91**: 1–26.

Brain, C., Prave, A.R., Hoffmann, K.-H., Fallick, A.E., Botha, A., Herd, D.A., et al., 2012, The first animals: ca. 760-million-year-old sponge-like fossils from Namibia. *South African Journal of Science*, **108**, https://doi.org/10.4102/sajs.v108i1/2.658.

Brasier, M., Shields, G., Kuleshov, V., and Zhegallo, E., 1996, Integrated chemo- and biostratigraphic calibration of early animal evolution: Neoproterozoic-early Cambrian of southwest Mongolia. *Geological Magazine*, **133**: 445–485.

Brocks, J.J., 2018, The transition from a cyanobacterial to algal world and the emergence of animals. *Emerging Topics in Life Sciences*, **2**: 181–190.

Brocks, J.J., Jarrett, A.J.M., Sirantoine, E., Hallmann, C., Hoshino, Y., and Liyanage, T., 2017, The rise of algae in Cryogenian oceans and the emergence of animals. *Nature*, **548**: 578–581.

Bull, S., Selley, D., Broughton, D., Hitzman, M., Cailteux, J., Large, R., et al., 2011, Sequence and carbon isotopic stratigraphy of the Neoproterozoic Roan Group strata of the Zambian copperbelt. *Precambrian Research*, **190**: 70–89.

Butterfield, N.J., 2004, A vaucheriacean alga from the middle Neoproterozoic of Spitsbergen: implications for the evolution of Proterozoic eukaryotes and the Cambrian explosion. *Paleobiology*, **30**: 231–252.

Butterfield, N.J., 2015, Early evolution of the Eukaryota. *Palaeontology*, **58**: 5–17.

Butterfield, N.J., Knoll, A.H., and Swett, K., 1994, Paleobiology of the Neoproterozoic Svanbergfjellet Formation, Spitsbergen. *Fossils and Strata*, **34**: 1–84.

Calver, C.R., Crowley, J.L., Wingate, M.T.D., Evans, D.A.D., Raub, T.D., and Schmitz, M.D., 2013, Globally synchronous Marinoan deglaciation indicated by U-Pb geochronology of the Cottons Breccia, Tasmania, Australia. *Geology*, **41**: 1127–1130.

Campbell, I.H., and Allen, C.M., 2008, Formation of supercontinents linked to increases in atmospheric oxygen. *Nature Geoscience*, **1**: 554–558.

Cawood, P.A., Wang, Y., Xu, Y., and Zhao, G., 2013, Locating South China in Rodinia and Gondwana: a fragment of greater India lithosphere? *Geology*, **41**: 93–96.

Cloud, P., and Glaessner, M.F., 1982, The Ediacarian Period and System: Metazoa inherit the Earth. *Science*, **217**: 783–792.

Cohen, P.A., Strauss, J.V., Rooney, A.D., Sharma, M., and Tosca, N., 2017a, Controlled hydroxyapatite biomineralization in an 810 million-year-old unicellular eukaryote. *Science Advances*, **3**: e1700095.

Cohen, P.A., Irvine, S.W., and Strauss, J.V., 2017b, Vase-shaped microfossils from the Tonian Callison Lake Formation of Yukon, Canada: taxonomy, taphonomy and stratigraphic palaeobiology. *Palaeontology*, **60**: 683–701.

Cohen, P.A., and Knoll, A.H., 2012, Scale Microfossils from the Mid-Neoproterozoic Fifteenmile Group, Yukon Territory. *Journal of Paleontology*, **86**: 775–800.

Cohen, P.A., and Macdonald, F.A., 2015, The Proterozoic record of eukaryotes. *Paleobiology*, **41**: 610–632.

Cohen, P.A., Macdonald, F.A., Pruss, S., Matys, E., and Bosak, T., 2015, Fossils of putative marine algae from the Cryogenian glacial interlude of Mongolia. *Palaios*, **30**: 238–247.

Cohen, P.A., Vizcaino, M., and Anderson, R.P., 2020. Oldest fossil ciliates from the Cryogenian glacial interlude reinterpreted as possible red algal spores. Palaontology, in press: online: https://doi.org/10.1111/pala.12497.

Cole, D.B., Reinhard, C.T., Wang, X., Gueguen, B., Halverson, G.P., Gibson, T.M., et al., 2016, A shale-hosted Cr isotope record of low atmospheric oxygen during the Proterozoic. *Geology*, **44**: 555–558.

Collins, A.S., Patranabis-Deb, S., Alexander, E., Bertram, C.N., Falster, G.M., Gore, R.J., et al., 2014, Detrital mineral age, radiogenic isotopic stratigraphy and tectonic significance of the Cuddapah Basin, India. *Gondwana Research*, **28**: 1294–1309.

Condie, K.C., 1998, Episodic continental growth and supercontinents: a mantle avalanche connection? *Earth and Planetary Science Letters*, **163**: 97–108.

Condon, D., Zhu, M., Bowring, S., Jin, Y., Wang, W., and Yang, A., 2005, From the Marinoan glaciation to the oldest bilaterians: U-Pb ages from the Doushantuo Formation, China. *Science*, **308**: 95–98.

Condon, D.J., Schoene, B., McLean, N.M., Bowring, S.A., and Parrish, R.R., 2015, Metrology and traceability of the U-Pb isotope dilution geochronology (EARTHTIME Tracer Calibration Part I). *Geochimica et Cosmochimica Acta*, **164**: 464–480.

Cox, G.M., Halverson, G.P., Minarik, W.G., Le Heron, D.P., Macdonald, F.A., Bellefroid, E.J., et al., 2013, Neoproterozoic iron formation: an evaluation of its temporal, environmental and tectonic significance. *Chemical Geology*, **362**: 232–249.

Cox, G.M., Strauss, J.V., Halverson, G.P., Schmitz, M.D., McClelland, W.C., Stevenson, R.S., et al., 2015, Kikiktat volcanics of Arctic Alaska—melting of harzburgitic mantle associated with the Franklin large igneous province. *Lithosphere*, **7**: 275–295.

Cox, G.M., Halverson, G.P., Stevenson, R.K., Vokaty, M., Poirier, A., Kunzmann, M., et al., 2016, Continental flood basalt weathering as a trigger for Neoproterozoic Snowball Earth. *Earth and Planetary Science Letters*, **446**: 89–99.

Cox, G.M., Isakson, V., Hoffman, P.F., Gernon, T.M., Schmitz, M.D., Shahin, S., et al., 2018, South Australian U-Pb zircon (CA-ID-TIMS) age supports globally synchronous Sturtian deglaciation. *Precambrian Research*, **315**: 257–263.

Crockford, P.W., Hodgskiss, M.S.W., Uhlein, G.J., Caxito, F., Hayles, J.A., and Halverson, G.P., 2018, Linking paleocontinents through $\Delta^{17}O$ anomalies. *Geology*, **46**: 179–182.

Dehler, C., Gehrels, G., Porter, S., Heizler, M., Karlstrom, K., Cox, G., et al., 2017, Synthesis of the 780-740 Ma Chuar, Uinta Mountain, and Pahrump (ChUMP) groups, western USA: implications for Laurentia-wide cratonic marine basin. *Geological Society of America Bulletin*, **129**: 607–624.

Derry, L.A., 2010, A burial diagenesis origin for the Ediacaran Shuram-Wonoka carbon isotope anomaly. *Earth and Planetary Science Letters*, **292**: 152–172.

Dunn, P., Thomson, B., and Rankama, K., 1971, Late Pre-Cambrian glaciation in Australia as a stratigraphic boundary. *Nature*, **231**: 498–502.

Eme, L., Sharpe, S.C., Brown, M.W., and Roger, A.J., 2014, On the age of eukaryotes: evaluating evidence from fossils and molecular clocks. *Cold Spring Harbor Perspectives in Biology*, **6**: a016139.

Ernst, R.E., Wingate, M.T.D., Buchan, K.L., and Li, Z.-X., 2008, Global record of 1600–700 Ma large igneous provinces (LIPs): implications for the reconstruction of the proposed Nuna (Columbia) and Rodinia supercontinents. *Precambrian Research*, **160**: 159–178.

Etienne, J.L., Allen, P.A., Rieu, R., and Le Guerroué, E., 2007, Neoproterozoic glaciated basins: a critical review of the Snowball Earth hypothesis by comparison with Phanerozoic basins. *In* Hambrey, M.J., Christoffersen, P., Glasser, N.F., and Hubbard, B. (eds), *Glacial Sedimentary Processes and Products*. International Association of Sedimentologists Special Publication, **Volume 39**: 343–399.

Eyster, A., Ferri, F., Schmitz, M.D., and Macdonald, F.A., 2018, One diamictite and two rifts: stratigraphy and geochronology of the Gataga Mountain of northern British Columbia. *American Journal of Science*, **318**: 167–207.

Fairchild, I.J., Fleming, E.J., Bao, H., Benn, D.I., Boomer, I., Dublansky, Y.V., et al., 2016, Continental carbonate facies of a Neoproterozoic panglaciation, north-east Svalbard. *Sedimentology*, **63**: 443–497.

Fairchild, I.J., and Kennedy, M.J., 2007, Neoproterozoic glaciation in the Earth system. *Journal of the Geological Society*, **164**: 895–921.

Fanning, C., and Link, P., 2004, U-Pb SHRIMP ages of Neoproterozoic (Sturtian) glaciogenic Pocatello Formation, southeastern Idaho. *Geology*, **32**: 881–884.

Fike, D.A., Grotzinger, J.P., Pratt, L.M., and Summons, R.E., 2006, Oxidation of the Ediacaran Ocean. *Nature*, **160**: 744–747.

Frimmel, H.W., Klötzi, U.S., and Siegfried, P.R., 1996, New Pb-Pb single zircon age constraints on the timing of Neoproterozoic glaciation and continental break-up in Namibia. *The Journal of Geology*, **104**: 459–469.

Gibson, T.M., Wörndle, S., Crockford, P.W., Bui, T.H., Creaser, R.A., and Halverson, G.P., 2019, Radiogenic isotope chemostratigraphy reveals marine and nonmarine depositional environments in the late Mesoproterozoic Borden Basin, Arctic Canada. *Geological Society of America Bulletin*, https://doi.org/10.1130/B35060.1.

Glaessner, M.F., 1962, Pre-Cambrian fossils. *Biological Reviews*, **37**: 467–494.

Goddéris, Y., Donnadieu, Y., Dessert, C., Dupré, B., Fluteau, F., Francois, L., et al., 2007, Coupled modeling of global carbon cycle and climate in the Neoproterozoic: links between Rodinia breakup and major glaciation. *Comptes Rendus Geoscience*, **339**: 212–222.

Gradstein, F.M., Ogg, J.G., Schmitz, M.D., and Ogg, G.M. (eds), 2012. *The Geological Time Scale 2012*. Elsevier, Amsterdam, p. 1040.

Grey, K., Hill, A.C., and Calver, C., 2011, Biostratigraphy and stratigraphic subdivision of Cryogenian successions of Australia in a global context,Memoirs. In Arnaud, E., Halverson, G.P., and Shields-Zhou, G. (eds), *The Geological Record of Neoproterozoic Glaciations*. Geological Society, London, **36**: 113–134.

Halverson, G.P., 2006, A Neoproterozoic chronology. *In* Xiao, S., and Kaufman, A. (eds), *Neoproterozoic Geobiology and Paleobiology of Topics in Geobiology*. Springer, Dordrecht, **27**: 231–271.

Halverson, G.P., Hoffman, P.F., Schrag, D.P., and Kaufman, A.J., 2002, A major perturbation of the carbon cycle before the Ghaub glaciation (Neoproterozoic) in Namibia: prelude to snowball Earth? *Geochemistry, Geophysics, Geosystems*, **3**, https://doi.org/10.1029/2001GC000244.

Halverson, G.P., Hoffman, P.F., Schrag, D.P., Maloof, A.C., and Rice, A.H., 2005, Towards a Neoproterozoic composite carbon isotope record. *Geological Society of America Bulletin*, **117**: 1181–1207.

Halverson, G.P., Dudas, F.Ö., Maloof, A.C., and Bowring, S.A., 2007, Evolution of the $^{87}Sr/^{86}Sr$ composition of Neoproterozoic seawater. *Palaeogeography, Palaeoclimatology, Palaeoecology*, **256**: 103–129.

Halverson, G.P., Wade, B.P., Hurtgen, M.T., and Barovich, K., 2010, Neoproterozoic chemostratigraphy. *Precambrian Research*, **182**: 337–350.

Halverson, G.P., Kunzmann, M., Strauss, J.V., and Maloof, A.C., 2018a, The Tonian-Cryogenian transition in Svalbard. *Precambrian Research*, **319**: 79–95.

Halverson, G.P., Porter, S.M., and Gibson, T.M., 2018b, Dating the late Proterozoic stratigraphic record. *Emerging Topics in Life Sciences*, **2**: 137–147.

Harland, W., 1964, Critical evidence for a great infra-Cambrian glaciation. *Geologische Rundschau*, **54**: 45–61.

Hill, A.C., and Walter, M.R., 2000, Mid-Neoproterozoic (~830-750 Ma) isotope stratigraphy of Australia and global correlation. *Precambrian Research*, **100**: 181–211.

Hill, A.C., Cotter, K.L., and Grey, K., 2000, Mid-Neoproterozoic biostratigraphy and isotope stratigraphy in Australia. *Precambrian Research*, **100**: 28–298.

Hoffman, P.F., 1991, Did the breakout of Laurentia turn Gondwanaland inside-out? *Science*, **252**: 1409–1412.

Hoffman, P.F., and Li, Z.X., 2009, A palaeogeographic context for Neoproterozoic glaciation. *Palaeogeography, Palaeoclimatology, Palaeoecology*, **277**: 158–172.

Hoffmann, K., and Prave, A., 1996, A preliminary note on a revised subdivision and regional correlation of the Otavi Group based on glaciogenic diamictites and associated cap dolostones. *Communications of the Geological Survey of Namibia*, **11**: 81–86.

Hoffman, P.F., and Schrag, D.P., 2002, The snowball Earth hypothesis: testing the limits of global change. *Terra Nova*, **14**: 129–155.

Hofmann, H., Narbonne, G., and Aitken, J., 1990, Ediacaran remains from intertillite beds in northwestern Canada. *Geology*, **18**: 1199–1202.

Hoffman, P., Hawkins, D., Isachsen, C., and Bowring, S., 1996, Precise U-Pb zircon ages for early Damaran magmatism in the Summas Mountains and Welwitschia Inlier, northern Damara belt, Namibia. *Communications of the Geological Survey of Namibia*, **11**: 47–52.

Hoffman, P., Kaufman, A., and Halverson, G., 1998, Comings and goings of global glaciations on a Neoproterozoic tropical platform in Namibia. *GSA Today*, **8**: 1–9.

Hoffmann, K.H., Condon, D.J., Bowring, S.A., and Crowley, J.L., 2004, A U-Pb zircon date from the Neoproterozoic Ghaub Formation, Namibia: constraints on Marinoan glaciation. *Geology*, **32**: 817–820.

Hoffman, P.F., Halverson, G.P., Domack, E.W., Husson, J.M., Higgins, J.A., and Schrag, D.P., 2007, Are basal Ediacaran (635 Ma) post-glacial "cap dolostones" diachronous? *Earth and Planetary Science Letters*, **258**: 114–131.

Hoffman, P.F., Halverson, G.P., Domack, E.W., Maloof, A.C., Swanson-Hysell, N.L., and Cox, G.M., 2012, Cryogenian glaciations on the southern tropical paleomargin of Laurentia (NE Svalbard and East Greenland), and a primary origin for the upper Russøya (Islay) carbon isotope excursion. *Precambrian Research*, **206–207**: 137–158.

Hoffman, P.F., Abbott, D.S., Ashkenay, Y., Benn, D.I., Brocks, J.J., Cohen, P.A., et al., 2017, Snowball Earth climate dynamics and Cryogenian geology and geobiology. *Science Advances*, **3**: e1600983.

Horton, F., 2015, Did phosphorus derived from the weathering of large igneous provinces fertilize the Neoproterozoic ocean? *Geochemistry, Geophysics, Geosystems*, **16**: 1723–1738.

Huntley, J.W., Xiao, S., and Kowalewski, M., 2006, 1.3 Billion years of acritarch history: an empirical morphospace approach. *Precambrian Research*, **144**: 52–68.

Javaux, E.J., and Knoll, A.H., 2017, Micropaleontology of the lower Mesoproterozoic Roper Group, Australia, and implications for early eukaryotic evolution. *Journal of Paleontology*, **91**: 199–229.

Johansson, Å., 2014, From Rodinia to Gondwana with the 'SAMBA' model—a distant view from Baltica towards Amazonia and beyond. *Precambrian Research*, **244**: 226–235.

Johnston, D.T., Macdonald, F.A., Gill, B.C., Hoffman, P.F., and Schrag, D.P., 2012, Uncovering the Neoproterozoic carbon cycle. *Nature*, **483**: 320–323.

Kah, L.C., Bartley, J.K., and Teal, D.A., 2012, Chemostratigraphy of the Late Mesoproterozoic Atar Group, Taoudeni Basin, Mauritania: muted isotopic variability, facies correlation, and global isotopic trends. *Precambrian Research*, **200–203**: 82–103.

Kaufman, A.J., Knoll, A.H., and Narbonne, G.M., 1997, Isotopes, ice ages, and terminal Proterozoic Earth history. *Proceedings of the National Academy of Sciences*, **95**: 6600–6605.

Kendall, B., Creaser, R.A., Calver, C.R., Raub, T.D., and Evans, D.A.D., 2009, Correlation of Sturtian diamictite successions in southern Australia and northwestern Tasmania by Re-Os black shale geochronology and the ambiguity of "Sturtian"-type diamictite-cap carbonate pairs as chronostratigraphic marker horizons. *Precambrian Research*, **172**: 301–310.

Kendall, B., Creaser, R.A., and Selby, D., 2006, Re-Os geochronology of postglacial black shales in Australia: consequences for timing of the Sturtian glaciation. *Geology*, **34**: 729–732.

Kennedy, M.J., and Christie-Blick, N.J., 2011, Condensation origin for Neoproterozoic cap carbonates during deglaciation. *Geology*, **39**: 319–322.

Kennedy, M.J., Runnegar, B., Prave, A.R., Hoffmann, K.H., and Arthur, M., 1998, Two or four Neoproterozoic glaciations? *Geology*, **26**: 1059–1063.

Key, R.M., Liyungu, A.K., Njamu, F.M., Somwe, V., Banda, J., Mmosley, P.N., et al., 2001, The western arm of the Lufilian Arc in NW Zambia and its potential for copper mineralization. *Journal of African Earth Sciences*, **33**: 503–528.

Knauth, P., and Kennedy, M.J., 2009, The late Precambrian greening of the Earth. *Nature*, **460**: 728–732.

Knoll, A.H., Swett, K., and Mark, J., 1991, Paleobiology of a Neoproterozoic tidal flat/lagoonal complex: the Draken Conglomerate Formation, Spitsbergen. *Journal of Paleontology*, **65**: 531–570.

Knoll, A., Kaufman, A., and Semikhatov, M., 1995, The carbon-isotopic composition of Proterozoic carbonates: Riphean successions from northwestern Siberia (Anabar Massif, Turukhansk Uplift). *American Journal of Science*, **295**: 823–850.

Knoll, A., Walter, M., and Christie-Blick, N., 2004, A new period for the geological time scale. *Science*, **305**: 621–622.

Knoll, A.H., Javaux, E.J., Hewitt, D., and Cohen, P., 2006, Eukaryotic organisms in Proterozoic oceans. *Philosophical Transactions of the Royal Society B*, **361**: 1023–1038.

Knoll, A.H., Walter, M.R., Narbonne, G.M., and Christie-Blick, N., 2006, The Ediacaran Period: a new addition to the geologic time scale. *Lethaia*, **39**: 13–30.

Kulling, O., 1934, The Hecla Hoek Formation round Hinlopenstredet. *Geografiska Annaler*, **14**: 161–253.

Kuznetsov, A.B., Semikhatov, M.A., Maslov, A.V., Gorokhov, I.M., Prasolov, E.M., Krupenin, M.T., et al., 2006, New data on Sr- and C-isotopic chemostratigraphy of the Upper Riphean type section (southern Urals). *Stratigraphy and Geological Correlation*, **14**: 602–628.

Kuznetsov, A.B., Bekker, A., Ovchinnikova, G.V., Gorokhov, I.M., and Vasilyeva, I.M., 2017, Unradiogenic strontium and moderate-amplitude carbon isotope variations in early Tonian seawater after the assembly of Rodinia and before the Bitter Springs Excursion. *Precambrian Research*, **298**: 157–173.

Lamothe, K.G., Hoffman, P.F., Greenman, J.W., and Halverson, G.P., 2019, Stratigraphy and isotope geochemistry of the pre-Sturian Ugab Subgroup, Otavi/Swakop Group, northwestern Namibia. *Precambrian Research*, **332**: 105387.

Lan, Z., Li, X., Zhu, M., Chen, Z.-Q., Zhang, Q., Li, Q., et al., 2014, A rapid and synchronous initiation of the wide spread Cryogenian glaciations. *Precambrian Research*, **255**: 401–411.

Lan, Z., Li, X.-H., Zhang, Q., and Li, Q.-L., 2015a, Global synchronous initiation of the 2nd episode of Sturtian glaciation: SIMS zircon U–Pb and O isotope evidence from the Jiangkou Group, South China. *Precambrian Research*, **267**: 28–38.

Lan, Z., Li, X.-H., Zhu, M., Zhang, Q., and Li, Q.-L., 2015b, Revisiting the Liantuo Formation in Yangtze Block, South China: SIMS U–Pb zircon age constraints and regional and global significance. *Precambrian Research*, **263**: 123–141.

Lee, Y.Y., 1936, The Sinian glaciation in the lower Yangtze Valley. *Bulletin of the Geological Society of China*, **15**: 131–134.

Lenton, T.M., Boyle, R.A., Poulton, S.W., Shields-Zhou, G.A., and Butterfield, N.J., 2014, Co-evolution eukaryotes and ocean oxygenation in the Neoproterozoic era. *Nature Geoscience*, **7**: 257–265.

Li, Z.-X., et al., 2008, Assembly, configuration and break-up history of Rodinia: a synthesis. *Precambrian Research*, **160**: 179–210.

Li, Z.X., Zhang, C.M., and Powell, C.M., 1995, South China in Rodinia: part of the missing link between Australia–East Antarctica and Laurentia? *Geology*, **23**: 407–410.

Li, Z.X., Li, X.H., Kinny, P.D., and Wang, J., 1999, The breakup of Rodinia: did it start with a mantle plume beneath South China? *Earth and Planetary Science Letters*, **173**: 171–181.

Li, Z.X., Li, X.H., Kinny, P.D., Wang, J., Zhang, S., and Zhou, H., 2003, Geochronology of Neoproterozoic syn-rift magmatism in the Yangtze-Craton, South China and correlations with other continents: evidence for a mantle superplume that broke up Rodinia. *Precambrian Research*, **122**: 85–109.

Li, Z.X., Evans, D.A.D., and Zhang, S., 2004, A 90° spin on Rodinia: possible causal links between the Neoproterozoic supercontinent, superplume, true polar wander and low-latitude glaciation. *Earth and Planetary Science Letters*, **220**: 409–421.

Li, Z.-X., Evans, D.A.D., and Halverson, G.P., 2013, Neoproterozoic glaciations in a revised global palaeogeography from the breakup of Rodinia to the assembly of Gondwanaland. *Sedimentary Geology*, **294**: 219–232.

Lindsay, J.F., 1987, Upper Proterozoic evaporites in the Amadeus basin, central Australia, and their role in basin tectonics. *Geological Society of America Bulletin*, **99**: 852–865.

Lindsay, J.F., 2002, Supersequences, superbasins, supercontinents–evidence from the Neoproterozoic—early Palaeozoic basins of central Australia. *Basin Research*, **14**: 207–223.

Lindsay, J.F., and Korsch, R.J., 1989, Interplay of tectonics and sea-level changes in basin evolution: an example from the intracratonic Amadeus Basin, central Australia. *Basin Research*, **2**: 3–25.

Loron, C., and Moczydłowska, M., 2018, Tonian (Neoproterozoic) eukaryotic and prokaryotic organic-walled microfossils from the upper Visingsö Group, Sweden. *Palynology*, **42**: 220–254.

Loron, C.C., Rainbird, R.H., Turner, E.C., Greenman, J.W., and Javaux, E.J., 2018, Implications of selective predation on the macroevolution of eukaryotes: evidence from Arctic Canada. *Emerging Topics in Life Sciences*, **2**: 247–255.

Loron, C.C., François, C., Rainbird, R.H., Turner, E.C., Borensztajn, S., and Javaux, E.J., 2019a, Early fungi from the Proterozoic era in Arctic Canada. *Nature*, **270**: 232–235.

Loron, C.C., Rainbird, R.H., Turner, E.C., Greenman, J.W., and Javaux, E.J., 2019b, Organic-walled microfossils from the late Mesoproterozoic to early Neoproterozoic lower Shaler Supergroup (Arctic Canada): diversity and biostratigraphic significance. *Precambrian Research*, **321**: 349–374.

Love, G.D., Grosjean, E., Stalvies, C., Fike, D.A., Grotzinger, J.P., Bradley, A.S., et al., 2009, Fossil steroids record the appearance of Demosponges during the Cryogenian period. *Nature*, **457**: 718–721.

Lund, K., Aleinikoff, J., Evans, K., and Fanning, C., 2003, SHRIMP U-Pb geochronology of Neoproterozoic Windermere Supergroup, central Idaho: implications for rifting of western Laurentia and synchroneity of Sturtian glacial deposits. *Geological Society of America Bulletin*, **115**: 349–372.

Macdonald, F.A., and Wordsworth, R., 2017, Initiation of Snowball Earth with volcanic sulfur aerosol emissions. *Geophysical Research Letters*, **44**: 1938–1946.

Macdonald, F.A., Jones, D.S., and Schrag, D.P., 2009, Stratigraphic and tectonic implications of a newly discovered glacial diamictite-cap carbonate couplet in southwestern Mongolia. *Geology*, **37**: 123–126.

Macdonald, F.A., Schmitz, M.D., Crowley, J.L., Roots, C.F., Jones, D.S., Maloof, A.C., et al., 2010, Calibrating the Cryogenian. *Science*, **327**: 1241–1243.

Macdonald, F.A., Strauss, J.V., Rose, C.V., Dudás, F.Ö., and Schrag, D.P., 2010, Stratigraphy of the Port Nolloth Group of Namibia and South Africa and implications for the age of the Neoproterozoic iron formations. *American Journal of Science*, **310**: 862–888.

Macdonald, F.A., Halverson, G.P., Strauss, J.V., Smith, E.F., Cox, C.M., Sperling, E., et al., 2012, Early Neoproterozoic basin formation in the Yukon: Implications for the make-up and break-up of Rodinia. *Geoscience Canada*, **39**: 77–97.

Macdonald, F.A., Schmitz, M.D., Strauss, J.V., Halverson, G.P., Gibson, T.M., Eyster, A., et al., 2018, Cryogenian of Yukon. *Precambrian Research*, **319**: 114–143.

MacLennan, S., Park, Y., Swanson-Hysell, N., Maloof, A., Schoene, B., Gebreslassie, M., et al., 2018, The arc of the Snowball: U-Pb dates constrain the Islay anomaly and the initiation of the Sturtian glaciation. *Geology*, **46**: 539–542.

Maloof, A.C., Halverson, G.P., Kirschvink, J.L., Schrag, D.P., Weiss, B., and Hoffman, P.F., 2006, Combined paleomagnetic, isotopic and stratigraphic evidence for true polar wander from the Neoproterozoic Akademikerbreen Group, Svalbard. *Geological Society of America Bulletin*, **118**: 1099–1124.

Maloof, A.C., Rose, C.V., Beach, R., Samuels, B.M., Calmet, C.C., Erwin, D.H., et al., 2010, Possible animal-body fossils in pre-Marinoan limestones from South Australia. *Nature Geoscience*, **3**: 653–659.

Mattinson, J.M., 2005, Zircon U-Pb chemical abrasion ("CA-TIMS") method: Combined annealing and multi-step partial dissolution analysis for improved precision and accuracy of zircon ages. *Chemical Geology*, **220**: 47–66.

Mattinson, J.M., 2010, Analysis of the relative decay constants of ^{235}U and ^{238}U by multi-step CA-TIMS measurements of closed-system natural zircon samples. *Chemical Geology*, **275**: 186–198.

Mawson, D., 1949, The Late Precambrian ice age and glacial record of the Bibliando dome. *Journal and Proceedings of the Royal Society of New South Wales*, **82**: 150–174.

McKirdy, D.M., Burgess, J.M., Lemon, N.M., Yu, X., Cooper, A.M., Gostin, V.A., et al., 2001, A chemostratigraphic overview of the late Cryogenian interglacial sequence in the Adelaide Fold-Thrust Belt, South Australia. *Precambrian Research*, **106**: 149–186.

Menon, L.R., McIlroy, D., Liu, A.G., and Brasier, M.D., 2016, The dynamic influence of microbial mats on sediments: fluid escape and pseudofossil formation in the Ediacaran Longmyndian Supergroup, UK. *Journal of the Geological Society*, **173**: 177–185.

Merdith, A.S., Collins, A.S., Williams, S.E., Pisarevsky, S., Foden, J.D., Archibald, D.B., et al., 2017, A full-plate global reconstruction of the Neoproterozoic. *Gondwana Research*, **50**: 84–134.

Miao, L., Moczydłowska, M., Zhu, S., and Zhu, M., 2019, New record of organic-walled, morphologically distinct microfossils from the late Paleoproterozoic Changcheng Group in the Yanshan Range, North China. *Precambrian Research*, **321**: 172–198.

Milton, J.E., Hickey, K.A., Gleeson, S.A., and Friedman, R.M., 2017, New U-Pb constraints on the age of the Little Dal Basalts and Gunbarrel-related volcanism in Rodinia. *Precambrian Research*, **296**: 168–180.

Morais, L., Fairchild, T.R., Lahr, D.J., Rudnitzki, I.D., Schopf, J.W., Garcia, A.K., et al., 2017, Carbonaceous and siliceous Neoproterozoic vase-shaped microfossils (Urucum Formation, Brazil) and the question of early protistan biomineralization. *Journal of Paleontology*, **91**: 393–406.

Morais, L., Lahr, D., Rudnitzki, I., Freitas, B., Romero, G., Porter, S., et al., 2019, Insights into vase-shaped microfossil diversity and Neoproterozoic biostratigraphy in light of recent Brazilian discoveries. *Journal of Paleontology*, **93**: 612–627.

Normington, V.J., Donnellan, N., Edgoose, C., Kositcin, N., 2015. Neoproterozoic evolution of the Amadeus Basin: evidence from sediment provenance and mafic magmatism. In: Annual Geoscience Exploration Seminar (AGES) 2015 Proceedings. Northern Territory Geological Survey, Record 2015-002. pp. 73–78.

Parfrey, L.W., Lahr, D.J.G., Knoll, A.H., and Katz, L.A., 2011, Estimating the timing of early eukaryotic diversification with multigene molecular clocks. *Proceedings of the National Academy of Sciences of the United States of America*, **108**: 13624–13629.

Partin, C.A., and Sadler, P.M., 2016, Slow net sediment accumulation sets snowball Earth apart from all younger glacial episodes. *Geology*, **44**: 1019–1022.

Pisarevsky, S.A., Wingate, M.T.D., Powell, C.M., Johnson, S., and Evans, D.A.D., 2003, Models of Rodinia assembly and fragmentation. *In* Yoshida, M., Windley, B.F., and Dasgupta, S. (eds), *Proterozoic East Gondwana: Supercontinent Assembly and Breakup.* 206 of Special Publications. 35–55.

Planavsky, N.J., Reinhard, C.T., Wang, X., Thomson, D., McGoldrick, P., Rainbird, R.H., et al., 2014, Low Mid-Proterozoic atmospheric oxygen levels and the delayed rise of animals. *Science*, **346**: 635–638.

Plumb, K.A., 1991, New Precambrian time scale. *Episodes*, **14**: 139–140.

Plumb, K.A., and James, H.L., 1986, Subdivision of Precambrian time: recommendations and suggestions by Subcommission on Precambrian stratigraphy. *Precambrian Research*, **32**: 65–92.

Porter, S.M., 2016, Tiny vampires in ancient seas: evidence for predation via perforation in fossils from the 780–740 million-year-old Chuar Group, Grand Canyon, USA. *Proceedings of the Royal Society B: Biological Sciences*, **283**: 20160221.

Porter, S.M., and Knoll, A.H., 2000, Testate amoebae in the Neoproterozoic Era: evidence from vase-shaped microfossils in the Chuar Group, Grand Canyon. *Paleobiology*, **26**: 360–385.

Porter, S.M., and Riedman, L.A., 2016, Systematics of organic-walled microfossils from the ca. 780–740 Ma Chuar Group, Grand Canyon, Arizona. *Journal of Paleontology*, **90**: 815–853.

Porter, S.M., and Riedman, L.A., 2019, Evolution: ancient fossilized amoebae find their home in the tree. *Current Biology*, **29**: R212–R215.

Porter, S.M., Meisterfeld, R., and Knoll, A.H., 2003, Vase-shaped microfossils from the Neoproterozoic Chuar Group, Grand Canyon: a classification guided by modern testate amoebae. *Journal of Paleontology*, **77**: 409–429.

Prave, A.R., Fallick, A.E., Thomas, C.W., and Graham, C.M., 2009, A composite C-isotope profile for the Neoproterozoic of Scotland and Ireland. *Journal of the Geological Society*, **166**: 845–857.

Prave, A.R., Condon, D.J., Hoffmann, K.H., Tapster, S., and Fallick, A.E., 2016, Duration and nature of the end-Cryogenian (Marinoan) glaciation. *Geology*, **44**: 631–634.

Pu, J.P., Bowring, S.A., Jahandar, R., Myrow, P., Raub, T.D., Landing, E., et al., 2016, Dodging snowballs: geochronology of the Gaskiers glaciation and the first appearance of the Ediacaran biota. *Geology*, **44**: 955–958.

Rainbird, R.H., Jefferson, C.W., and Young, G.M., 1996, The early Neoproterozoic sedimentary Succession B of northwestern Laurentia: correlations and paleo-geographic significance. *Geological Society of America Bulletin*, **108**: 454–470.

Ray, J.S., 2006, Age of the Vindhyan Supergroup: a review of recent findings. *Journal of Earth System Science*, **115**: 149–160.

Reusch, H., 1891, Skuringmaerker og moraengus eftervist i Finnmarken fra en periode meget aeldre end 'istiden' (Glacial striae and boulder-clay in Norwegian Lapponie from a period much older than the last ice age). *Norges Geologiske Undersøkelse*, **1** (78–85), 97–100.

Riedman, L.A., and Porter, S., 2016, Organic-walled microfossils of the mid-Neoproterozoic Alinya Formation, Officer Basin, Australia. *Journal of Paleontology*, **90**: 854–887.

Riedman, L.A., and Sadler, P.M., 2018, Global species richness record and biostratigraphic potential of early to middle Neoproterozoic eukaryote fossils. *Precambrian Research*, **319**: 6–18.

Riedman, L.A., Porter, S.M., and Calver, C.R., 2018, Vase-shaped microfossil biostratigraphy with new data from Tasmania, Svalbard, Greenland, Sweden and the Yukon. *Precambrian Research*, **319**: 19–36.

Riedman, L.A., Porter, S.M., Halverson, G.P., Hurtgen, M.T., and Junium, C.K., 2014, Organic-walled microfossil assemblages from glacial and interglacial Neoproterozoic units of Australia and Svalbard. *Geology*, **42**: 1011–1014.

Rooney, A.D., Selby, D., Houzay, J.-P., and Renne, P.R., 2010, Re–Os geochronology of a Mesoproterozoic sedimentary succession, Taoudeni basin, Mauritania: implications for basin-wide correlations and Re–Os organic-rich sediments systematics. *Earth and Planetary Science Letters*, **289**: 486–496.

Rooney, A.D., Macdonald, F.A., Strauss, J.V., Dudás, F.Ö., Hallmann, C., and Selby, D., 2014, Re-Os geochronology and coupled Os-Sr isotope constraints on the Sturtian snowball Earth. *Proceedings of the National Academy of Sciences*, **111**: 51–56.

Rooney, A.D., Strauss, J.V., Brandon, A.D., and Macdonald, F.A., 2015, A Cryogenian chronology: two long-lasting synchronous Neoproterozoic glaciations. *Geology*, **43**: 459–462.

Rooney, A.D., Austermann, J., Smith, R.F., Li, Y., Selby, D., Dehler, C.M., et al., 2018, Coupled Re-Os and U-Pb geochronology of the Tonian Chuar Group, Grand Canyon. *Geological Society of America Bulletin*, **130**: 1085–1098.

Rose, C.V., Swanson-Hysell, N.L., Husson, J.M., Poppic, L.N., Cottle, J.M., Schoene, B., et al., 2012, Constraints on the origin and relative timing of the Trezona d13C anomaly below the end-Cryogenian glaciation. *Earth and Planetary Science Letters*, **319–320**: 241–250.

Schmitz, M.D., 2012, Radiogenic isotope geochronology. *In* Gradstein, F.M., Ogg, J.O., Schmitz, M.D., and Ogg, G.M. (eds), *The Geological Time Scale 2012*. Elsevier, Amsterdam, **vol.1**: 114–126.

Sergeev, V.N., Vorob'eva, N.G., and Petrov, P.Y., 2017, The biostratigraphic conundrum of Siberia: do true Tonian–Cryogenian microfossils occur in Mesoproterozoic rocks? *Precambrian Research*, **299**: 282–302.

Shields, G.A., Stille, P., Brasier, M.D., and Atudorei, N.V., 1997, Stratified oceans and oxygenation of the late Precambrian environment: a postglacial geochemical record from the Neoproterozoic of W Mongolia. *Terra Nova*, **9**: 218–222.

Shields-Zhou, G.A., Hill, A.C., and Macbabhann, B.A., 2012, The Cryogenian Period. Chapter 17. *In* Gradstein, F.M., Ogg, J.G., Schmitz, M.D., and Ogg, G.M. (eds), *The Geological Time Scale 2012*. Elsevier, **vol 1**: 393–411.

Shields-Zhou, G., Porter, S.A., and Halverson, G.P., 2016, A new rock-based definition for the Cryogenian Period (circa 720–635 Ma). *Episodes*, **39**: 3–9.

Shields, G.A., Halverson, G.P., and Porter, S.M., 2018, Descent into the Cryogenian. *Precambrian Research*, **319**: 1–5.

Song, G., Wang, X., Shi, X., and Jiang, G., 2017, New U-Pb age constraints on the upper Banxi Group and synchrony of the Sturtian glaciation in South China. *Geoscience Frontiers*, **8**: 1161–1173.

Sprigg, R.C., 1947, Early Cambrian jellyfishes from the Flinders Ranges, South Australia. *Transactions of the Royal Society of South Australia*, **71**: 212–224.

Strauss, J.V., Rooney, A.D., Macdonald, F.A., Brandon, A.D., and Knoll, A.H., 2014, 740 Ma vase-shaped microfossils from Yukon, Canada: implications for Neoproterozoic chronology and biostratigraphy. *Geology*, **42**: 659–662.

Strauss, J.V., Macdonald, F.A., Halverson, G.P., Tosca, N.J., Schrag, D.P., and Knoll, A.H., 2015, Stratigraphic evolution of the Neoproterozoic Callison Lake Formation: Linking the break-up of Rodinia to the Islay carbon isotope excursion. *American Journal of Science*, **315**: 881–944.

Swanson-Hysell, N.L., Rose, C.V., Calmet, C.C., Halverson, G.P., Hurtgen, M.T., and Maloof, A.C., 2010, Cryogenian glaciation and the onset of carbon-isotope decoupling. *Science*, **328**: 608–611.

Swanson-Hysell, N.L., Maloof, A.C., Kirschvink, J.L., Evans, D.A.D., Halverson, G.P., and Hurtgen, M.T., 2012, Constraints on Neoproterozoic paleogeography and Paleozoic orogenesis from paleomagnetic records of the Bitter Springs Formation, central Australia. *American Journal of Science*, **312**: 817–884.

Swanson-Hysell, N.L., Maloof, A.C., Condon, D.J., Jenkin, G.R.T., Alene, M., Tremblay, M.M., et al., 2015, Stratigraphy and geochronology of the Tambien Group, Ethiopia: evidence for globally synchronous carbon isotope change in the Neoproterozoic. *Geology*, **43**: 323–326.

Tang, Q., Pang, K., Xiao, S., Yuan, X., Ou, Z., and Wan, B., 2013, Organic-walled microfossils from the early Neoproterozoic Liulaobei Formation in the Huainan region of North China and their biostratigraphic significance. *Precambrian Research*, **236**: 157–181.

Tang, Q., Pang, K., Yuan, X., Wan, B., and Xiao, S., 2015, Organic-walled microfossils from the Tonian Gouhou Formation, Huaibei region, North China Craton, and their biostratigraphic implications. *Precambrian Research*, **266**: 296–318.

Tirsgaard, H., and Sønderholm, M., 1997, Lithostratigraphy, sedimentary evolution and sequence stratigraphy of the Upper Proterozoic Lyell Land Group (Eleonore Bay Super-group) of East and North-East Greenland. *Geology Greenland Survey Bulletin*, **178**: 60.

Thomson, D., Rainbird, R.H., Planavsky, N., and Lyons, T.W., 2015, Chemostratigraphy of the Shaler Supergroup, Victoria Island, NW Canada: A record of ocean composition prior to the Cryogenian glaciations. *Precambrian Research*, **263**: 232–245.

Tollo, R.P., and Aleinikoff, J.N., 1996, Petrology and U-PB geochronology of the Robertson River Igneous Suite, Blue Ridge province, Virginia—evidence for multistage magmatism associated with an early episode of Laurentian rifting. *American Journal of Science*, **296**: 1045–1090.

Turner, E.C., and Bekker, A., 2016, Thick sulfate evaporite accumulations marking a mid-Neoproterozoic oxygenation event (Ten Stone Formation, Northwest Territories, Canada). *Geological Society of America Bulletin*, **128**: 203–222.

Tyler, S.A., and Barghoorn, E.S., 1954, Occurrence of structurally preserved plants in Pre-Cambrian rocks of the Canadian Shield. *Science*, **119**: 606–608.

van Acken, D., Thomson, D., Rainbird, R.H., and Creaser, R.A., 2013, Constraining the depositional history of the Neoproterozoic Shaler Supergroup, Amundsen Basin, NW Canada: rhenium-osmium dating of black shales from the Wynniatt and Boot Inlet Formations. *Precambrian Research*, **236**: 124–131.

Verdel, C., and Campbell, M., 2017, Neoproterozoic carbon isotope stratigraphy of the Amadeus Basin, central Australia. *Geological Society of America Bulletin*, **129**: 1280–1299.

Vidal, G., and Knoll, A.H., 1982, Radiations and extinctions of plankton in the late Proterozoic and early Cambrian. *Nature*, **297**: 57–60.

Vorob'eva, N.G., Sergeev, V.N., and Knoll, A.H., 2009, Neoproterozoic microfossils from the northeastern margin of the East European platform. *Journal of Paleontology*, **83**: 161–196.

Wallace, M.W., Hood, A.S., Woon, E.M., Hoffmann, K.-H., and Reed, C.P., 2014, Enigmatic chambered structures in Cryogenian reefs: the oldest sponge-grade organisms? *Precambrian Research*, **255**: 109–123.

Wang, X.C., Li, Z.X., Li, X.H., Li, Q.L., and Zhang, Q.-R., 2011, Geochemical and Hf-Nd isotope data of Nanhua rift sedimentary and volcaniclastic rocks indicate a Neoproterozoic continental flood basalt provenance. *Lithos*, **127**: 427–440.

Wang, D., Zhu, X.-K., Zhao, N., Yan, B., Li, X.-H., Shi, F., et al., 2019, Timing of the termination of Sturtian glaciation: SIMS U-Pb zircon dating from South China. *Journal of Asian Earth Sciences*, **177**: 287–294.

Xiao, S., Shen, B., Tang, Q., Kaufman, A.J., Yuan, X., Li, J., et al., 2014, Biostratigraphic and chemostratigraphic constraints on the age of early Neoproterozoic carbonate successions in North China. *Precambrian Research*, **246**: 208–225.

Yu, W., Algeo, T.J., Du, Y., Zhou, Q., Wang, P., Xu, Y., et al., 2017, Newly discovered Sturtian cap carbonate in the Nanhua Basin, South China. *Precambrian Research*, **293**: 112–130.

Zhang, Q.-R., Li, X.-H., Feng, L.-J., Huang, J., and Song, B., 2008a, A new age constraint on the onset of Neoproterozoic glaciations in the Yangze Platform, South China. *The Journal of Geology*, **116**: 423–429.

Zhang, S., Jiang, G., and Han, Y., 2008b, The age of the Nantuo Formation and Nantuo glaciation in South China. *Terra Nova*, **20**: 289–294.

Zhou, C., Tucker, R., Xiao, S., Peng, Z., Yuan, X., and Chen, Z., 2004, New constraints on the ages of Neoproterozoic glaciations in south China. *Geology*, **32**: 437–440.

Zhou, C., Huyskens, M.H., Lang, X., Xiao, S., and Yin, Q.-Z., 2019, Calibrating the terminations of Cryogenian global glaciations. *Geology*, **251**: 251–254.

S.H. Xiao and G.M. Narbonne

The Ediacaran Period

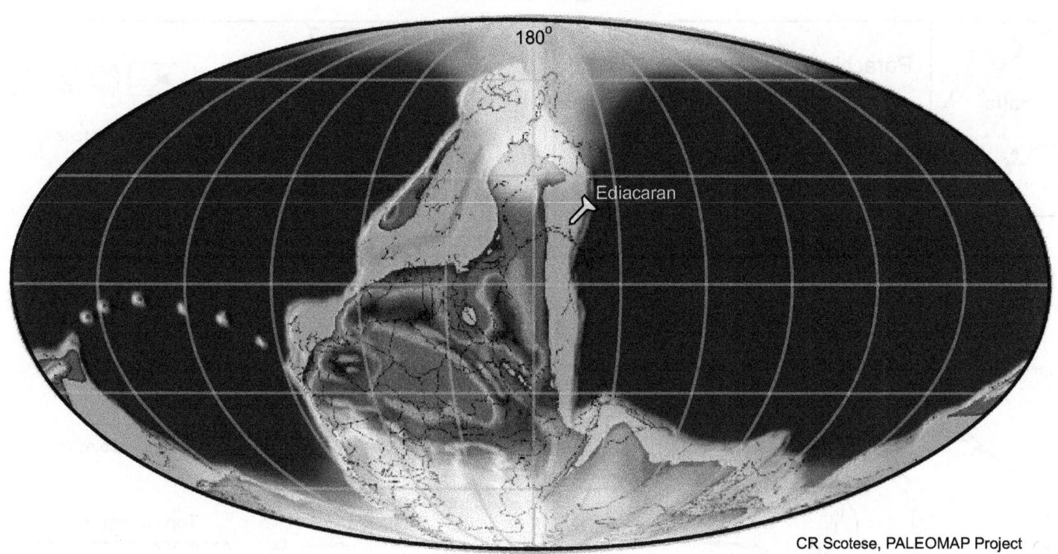

Chapter outline

Abstract

The Ediacaran Period (635–538 Ma) has the longest duration among all stratigraphically defined geological periods. The basal boundary of the Ediacaran System is defined by a horizon near the base of the Nuccaleena Formation overlying the Cryogenian diamictite of the Elatina Formation at the Enorama Creek section in South Australia. Most Ediacaran fossils represent soft-bodied organisms and their preservation is affected by taphonomic biases. Thus the Phanerozoic approach of defining stratigraphic boundaries using the first appearance datum of widely distributed, rapidly evolving, easily recognizable, and readily preservable species would have limited success in the Ediacaran System. The subdivision and correlation of the Ediacaran System must therefore be founded on a holistic approach integrating biostratigraphic, chemostratigraphic, paleoclimatic and geochronometric data, particularly carbon and strontium isotopes, glacial diamictites, acanthomorphic acritarchs, Ediacara-type megafossils, and certain tubular fossils. Our preferred scheme is to divide the Ediacaran System into two series separated by the 580 Ma Gaskiers glaciation. Stage-level subdivisions at the bottom and top of the Ediacaran System, including the definition of the second Ediacaran stage (SES) and the terminal Ediacaran stage (TES), are feasible in the near future. Additional Ediacaran stages between the SES and TES can be envisioned, but formal definition of these stages are not possible until various stratigraphic markers are thoroughly tested and calibrated at both regional and global scales.

Geologic Time Scale 2020. DOI: https://doi.org/10.1016/B978-0-12-824360-2.00018-8

18.1 Historical background

The basal boundary of the Ediacaran System was ratified in 2004 (Knoll et al., 2004, 2006), with its GSSP (Global Boundary Stratotype Section and Point) defined by a horizon near the base of the Nuccaleena Formation overlying the Cryogenian diamictite of the Elatina Formation at the Enorama Creek section in South Australia (Fig. 18.1).

The designation of the Ediacaran Period reflected the gradual solution of a problem that had vexed even Darwin (1859) in his writing of "The Origin of Species," the apparently abrupt appearance of diverse groups of shelly fossils at the base of the Cambrian System without any obvious Precambrian ancestors. Darwin attributed this absence to massive record failure, a view formalized by Walcott (1914) in his designation of the "Lipalian

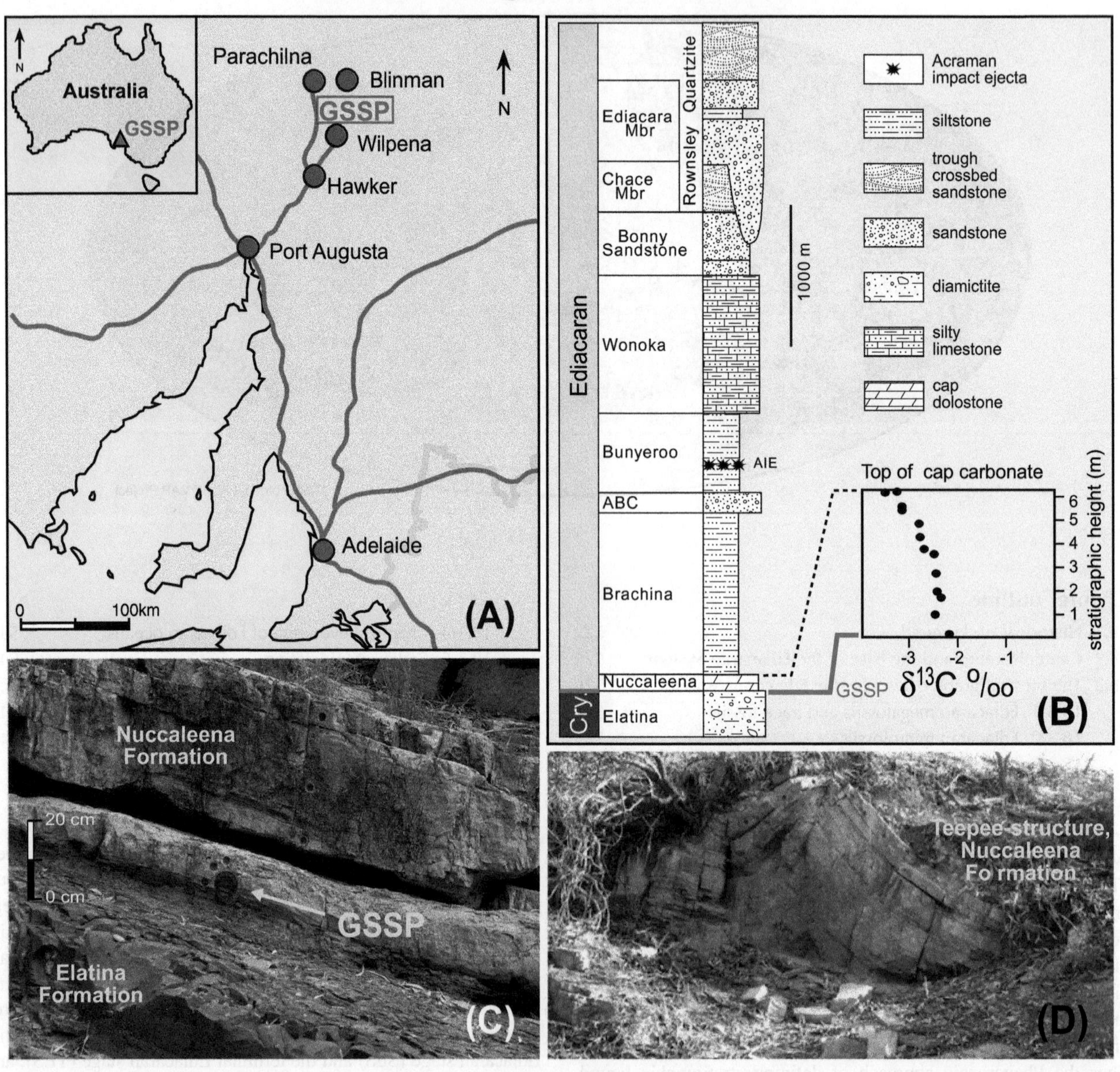

FIGURE 18.1 GSSP for base of the Ediacaran at Enorama Creek section, central Flinders Ranges, Adelaide Rift Complex, South Australia. (A) Map showing location of the GSSP. (B) Generalized stratigraphic column showing the GSSP level, which is defined as the sharp base of the cap carbonate (Nuccaleena Formation) overlying the Marinoan glacial and glaciomarine diamictite deposits (Elatina Formation). Carbonate carbon isotope values in the cap carbonate are negative and decrease upsection in the cap dolostone. (C) Field photograph showing the exact location of the GSSP. (D) Enigmatic teepee-like structures, up to 1 m in amplitude, in the Nuccaleena cap dolostone. *GSSP*, Global Boundary Stratotype Section and Point. *(A) Modified from Ogg et al. (2016); (B) Modified from Knoll et al. (2006) and Xiao et al. (2013). (C) Photograph by S. Xiao. (D) Photo courtesy Gabi Ogg.*

Interval" of erosion beneath the base of the Cambrian. The concept of a global period of erosion prior to the Cambrian was soon contradicted by discovery of thick successions of largely unmetamorphosed strata concordantly beneath the base of the Cambrian in numerous localities worldwide, most notably the "Sinian" in China (Grabau, 1922; Lee, 1924), the "Marinoan" in Australia (Mawson and Sprigg, 1950), and the "Vendian" in Russia (Sokolov, 1952). These names were originally proposed as regional lithostratigraphic units that later assumed a chronostratigraphic significance, but scarcity of reliable radioisotopic dates and a lack of consistent criteria for correlation frustrated early attempts to extend these divisions globally.

Subsequent paleontological research confirmed Darwin's view that there was abundant life before the beginning or the Cambrian but showed that most Precambrian organisms were soft-bodied and many were also microscopic. Perhaps most distinctive among these organisms were Ediacara-type megafossils, best seen in the Ediacara Hills of South Australia, which gives its name to the Ediacaran Period. These are centimeter- to meter-scale impressions of soft-bodied organisms that typically were preserved as impressions at the bases of event beds of sand or volcanic ash (Narbonne, 2005; Fedonkin et al., 2007). They were first described in the late 19th century (Billings, 1872) but few paleontologists at that time were willing to accept the widespread occurrence of megascopic Precambrian life, and even the complex Ediacaran fossils reported from Namibia and Australia in the 1930s and 1940s were tentatively regarded as "Cambrian" by their discoverers (Gürich, 1930, 1933; Sprigg, 1947). Ford's (1958) description of the frond *Charnia* from unequivocally Precambrian strata in central England led Glaessner (1959) to propose a global "Ediacara Fauna" of large, soft-bodied animal-like fossils that immediately preceded the Cambrian, a concept that exists to the present day and has proven instrumental in subsequent recognition of a terminal Proterozoic System. The discovery of abundant and diverse microfossils, particularly acanthomorphic acritarchs, has also significantly enhanced the prospects for Ediacaran biostratigraphy. This area of research was first pioneered by Russian and later Chinese micropaleontologists (Timofeev, 1966; Yin and Li, 1978; Jankauskas et al., 1989), and some of Ediacaran acanthomorphs have been shown to have restricted time ranges and a global distribution (Zang and Walter, 1992; Moczydłowska et al., 1993; Zhang et al., 1998; Grey, 2005; Vorob'eva et al., 2009b; Moczydłowska and Nagovitsin, 2012; Liu et al., 2014f; Xiao et al., 2014b).

A year after Glaessner's recognition of a global Ediacaran macrofossil assemblage below the Cambrian, Termier and Termier (1960) proposed the "Ediacarien" as Precambrian chronostratigraphic interval characterized by this distinctive fossil assemblage. Since then, the concept of an Ediacarian/Ediacaran System as the terminal Neoproterozoic chronostratigraphic interval has evolved, although Ediacara-type megafossils as a key symbol of this interval have remained the same. What has evolved is the basal boundary age and the duration of the Ediacaran System (Fig. 18.2). Jenkins (1981) formally proposed the Ediacaran System and placed its basal boundary at the base of the Wonoka Formation at Bunyeroo Gorge in South Australia. The basal boundary of Jenkins' (1981) Ediacaran System is thus stratigraphically higher than the GSSP of the Ediacaran System as currently defined (Fig. 18.1) and corresponds to the sequence boundary underlying the oldest unequivocal Ediacara-type fossils in Australia. Lacking any robust geochronological data, Jenkins (1981) estimated that his Ediacaran System began at ~640 Ma. Independent of Jenkins (1981), Cloud and Glaessner (1982) formalized the Ediacarian System, with

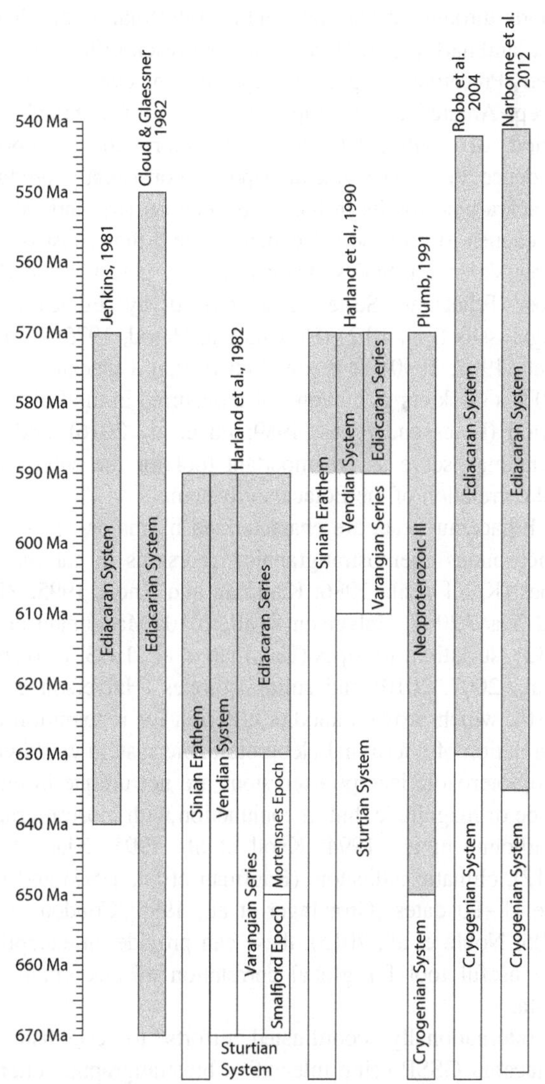

FIGURE 18.2 **Evolution of the concept of Ediacaran/Ediacarian System or Series.**

its lower boundary defined at the base of the Nuccaleena Formation in the Bunyeroo Gorge in South Australia, and estimated that the Ediacarian System began at 670 Ma. Building upon the work of Jenkins (1981), Harland et al. (1982) introduced the Ediacaran Series, placed it in the Vendian System of the Sinian Erathem, and estimated its age to be 630–590 Ma, although they later revised its age to be 590–570 Ma (Harland et al., 1990). After Ediacaran System was ratified (Knoll et al., 2004, 2006) and precise radioisotopic ages were published to constrain the Cryogenian–Ediacaran boundary (Hoffmann et al., 2004; Condon et al., 2005), the base of the Ediacaran System was fixed at 635 Ma (Robb et al., 2004; Narbonne et al., 2012a).

Climatic indicators also provide critical information for Neoproterozoic subdivision. Late Precambrian glacial deposits were first recognized in the late 1800s (Thomson, 1871; Reusch, 1891) with a steadily increasing number of reports throughout the 20th century (Hoffman et al., 2017). In a landmark paper, Harland and Rudwick (1964) summarized Precambrian glacial deposits on every continent except Antarctica and proposed the "Infra-Cambrian" as a period of continental glaciation before the Cambrian. Evidence that these glacial deposits consistently predated Ediacara-type fossils in the same sections led Harland and colleagues to propose a Vendian System that consists of a lower Varangian Series characterized by glaciations and an upper Ediacaran Series characterized by Ediacara-type megafossils (Fig. 18.2) (Harland and Herod, 1975; Harland et al., 1982, 1990). It is now known that a glaciation—the 580 Ma Gaskiers glaciation—also occurred in the Ediacaran Period (Eyles and Eyles, 1989; Pu et al., 2016), and this event may serve as an important tool for the subdivision and correlation of the Ediacaran System.

Ediacaran strata are characterized by major, apparently synchronous chemostratigraphic excursions in carbon isotopes (Knoll et al., 1986; Kaufman and Knoll, 1995; Zhou and Xiao, 2007; Halverson et al., 2010; Macdonald et al., 2013), strontium isotopes (Kaufman et al., 1993; Halverson et al., 2007, 2010) and sulfur isotopes (Halverson et al., 2010), which provide another criterion for recognition and correlation of a terminal Neoproterozoic system worldwide. Neoproterozoic isotope excursions are not unique in either shape or magnitude, but in conjunction with biostratigraphy (Narbonne et al., 1994; Knoll et al., 1995; Xiao et al., 2012), climatic indicators (Kaufman et al., 1997) and precise U–Pb dates (Grotzinger et al., 1995; Condon et al., 2005; Noble et al., 2015), these can provide an exceptionally useful tool for global correlation of Neoproterozoic strata.

Internationally coordinated efforts to establish the Ediacaran GSSP using integrative biostratigraphic, chemostratigraphic and paleoclimatic data started in 1989 when the International Commission on Stratigraphy launched a Working Group (later Subcommission) on the Terminal Proterozoic Period at the IGC in Washington, DC. Over the succeeding decade and a half, the Working Group/Subcommission formally visited terminal Neoproterozoic sections on five continents and held a series of international symposia to discuss the features that could be used to define and correlate a terminal Neoproterozoic system. These scientific discussions corresponded with rapid discoveries of new scientific techniques in geochronology, isotopic chemostratigraphy, sequence stratigraphy and paleontology that significantly elucidated the characteristics and history of the Neoproterozoic Earth. After 10 years of investigation a series of ballots increasingly focused the decision on the position of the GSSP and name for this new period (see Knoll et al., 2006 for details of the ballots and opinions). The first ballot (December 2000) asked whether the stratigraphic level of the GSSP should be placed at (1) the base of the Varanger/Marinoan glacial deposits (Harland et al., 1982; Sokolov and Fedonkin, 1982); (2) the cap carbonate atop these deposits (Cloud and Glaessner, 1982); (3) a biostratigraphic level corresponding to the first appearance of Ediacaran macrofossils in a local section (Jenkins, 1981); or (4) some other level. Most of the voting members believed that a boundary at the top rather than the base of the Varanger/Marinoan glacial deposits would be more significant in the Earth evolution since most Neoproterozoic glacial deposits would be regarded as Cryogenian, whereas all known assemblages of diverse Ediacara-type fossils would fall into the succeeding period, and that the end of a glacial interval marked by a distinctive cap carbonate would probably be more easily correlated than the base of glacial deposits, which would likely be highly diachronous both regionally and globally. There was little support for placing the system-level boundary at the first appearance of megafossils but it was considered that this level might prove useful in later subdivision into series or stages. The second ballot (March 2003) received a strong mandate (63% of votes cast) for placing a GSSP defined using these agreed characteristics at the "Enorama Creek Section, Flinders Ranges, South Australia." The final ballot (September 2003) received overwhelming approval (89% of votes cast) to establish the GSSP for the Terminal Proterozoic Period "at the base of the Nuccaleena Formation cap carbonate, immediately above the Elatina diamictite in the Enorama Creek section, Flinders Ranges, South Australia" and a clear mandate (79% of votes cast) that the new period and system be named the "Ediacaran." These decisions were ratified by the ICS on February 20, 2004. A full-length description of the GSSP and the selection process was subsequently published in *Lethaia* (Knoll et al., 2006).

Shortly after the ratification in 2004, the Subcommission on Ediacaran Stratigraphy (later renamed the Subcommission on Neoproterozoic Stratigraphy) was established to facilitate the correlation and subdivision of the Cryogenian and Ediacaran periods. The Subcommission on Neoproterozoic Stratigraphy conducted a survey in 2009 to gauge the community's opinion on how to proceed with the subdivision and correlation of the Ediacaran System. The survey results suggested that the Ediacaran System should be first divided into two series, with the lower series characterized by acanthomorphic acritarchs and the upper series by Ediacara-type macrofossils (Xiao et al., 2016). It further suggested that, ideally, the base of the upper Ediacaran series should be placed within an outcrop section that has good radioisotopic age constraints and has the potential for carbon isotope chemostratigraphic and acanthomorphic acritarch biostratigraphic correlation. At that time, it was felt that (1) the subdivision of the Ediacaran System should start with the establishment of two series before the definition of stages; (2) the most useful correlation tools included chemostratigraphy such as $\delta^{13}C$ and $^{87}Sr/^{86}Sr$ excursions, acanthomorphic acritarchs and Ediacara-type macrofossils; and (3) good GSSPs should be fossiliferous, geochronometrically dated, and have mixed lithologies and the potential for chemostratigraphic and biostratigraphic correlations.

In 2012 the Subcommission on Neoproterozoic Stratigraphy was split into the Subcommission on Cryogenian Stratigraphy and the Subcommission on Ediacaran Stratigraphy. The stated goal of the Subcommission on Ediacaran Stratigraphy is to facilitate international communication and scientific cooperation in Ediacaran stratigraphy, with the ultimate goal to define, by means of GSSPs, a hierarchy of chronostratigraphic units that provide the framework for global correlation. In the past decade the Subcommission on Ediacaran Stratigraphy and its predecessor organized and sponsored several field workshops to examine potential criteria for Ediacaran subdivision and correlation (Moczydłowska-Vidal et al., 2008; Kumar and Sharma, 2010; Xiao et al., 2011, 2014a; Gehling and Droser, 2012; Gehling et al., 2012; Kumar and Sharma, 2012; Narbonne et al., 2012b; Kaufman et al., 2014; Pandey and Dimri, 2014; Singh and Ansari, 2014; Xiao and Sharma, 2014; Liu et al., 2018a). As part of the efforts toward the establishment of intra-Ediacaran GSSPs, the Subcommission has encouraged—at various scientific meetings and workshops, notably the 2014 Ediacaran Workshop in Wuhan, China, and the STRATI 2015 meeting in Graz, Austria—community-wide discussions about the subdivision and correlation of Ediacaran strata. In 2015 the Subcommission on Ediacaran Stratigraphy established the Second Ediacaran Stage Working Group and the Terminal Ediacaran Stage Working Group to focus on these stages. This was followed by several focused field workshops to examine critical terminal Ediacaran Stage (TES) sections in Namibia (2016) (Xiao et al., 2017b), Brazil (2017) (Xiao et al., 2018), Oman (2018), western United States (2018), South China (2018), Spain (2019) and South America (planned in 2020). In 2018 the Subcommission launched a working group to focus on the series-level subdivision of the Ediacaran System.

18.2 Cap dolostones and the base of the Ediacaran System

The GSSP for the Ediacaran System in Enorama Creek, Australia was fixed at the base of the Nuccaleena Dolomite, a 6-m-thick, distinctive dolostone that caps the Marinoan glaciomarine diamictites of the Elatina Formation (Fig. 18.1A–C). The Nuccaleena cap dolostone is composed of buff-weathering, creamy pink microcrystalline dolomite organized in centimeter-scale event beds. Meter-scale teepee-like structures (Fig. 18.1D) and horizontal sheet cracks filled with synsedimentary calcite cement are common. Carbonate carbon isotopes become increasingly negative from about −2‰ to −3.5‰ upward through the Nuccaleena cap dolostone (Fig. 18.1B) (see Knoll et al., 2006 and references therein).

Strikingly similar "cap dolostones" occur worldwide on the top of terminal Cryogenian Marinoan-age glacial deposits (Fig. 18.3D) or an unconformity surface corresponding to this glaciation (Hoffman, 2011) and serve as a superb global lithostratigraphic and chemostratigraphic marker for the base of the Ediacaran. These cap dolostones are typically less than 10 m thick, and like the cap at the GSSP are buff-weathering dolostones with horizontal sheet cracks and meter-scale teepee-like structures (Fig. 18.1D). Other features typifying the basal Ediacaran cap dolostone include macropeloids, unusual stromatolite facies, barite crystals, and cylindrical tubes of carbonate (Kennedy, 1996; James et al., 2001; Xiao et al., 2004; Corsetti and Grotzinger, 2005; Jiang et al., 2006; Hoffman et al., 2007, 2017; Hoffman, 2011). The cap dolostones are commonly overlain by limestones rich in aragonite crystal fans (Fig. 18.3C) and/or by deep-water fine-grained siliciclastics (Hoffman et al., 2007; Hoffman, 2011). This suite of features permits most or all basal Ediacaran (post-Marinoan) cap dolostones to be readily distinguished from the dark, bituminous limestones that characterize older post-Sturtian caps (Kennedy et al., 1998) and from the light gray micritic (recrystallized to sparry calcite) limestone atop the younger (mid Ediacaran) Gaskiers diamictite (Fig. 18.3G) (Myrow and Kaufman, 1999). Interpretations of Neoproterozoic cap dolostones vary considerably, but most interpretations involve a perturbation in the saturation state of the oceans accompanying the rapid meltdown of continental ice sheets (Hoffman et al., 2017).

Although the Ediacaran GSSP in South Australia has not been dated, radioisotopic ages constrain the base of the Ediacaran System to be around 635 Ma. The

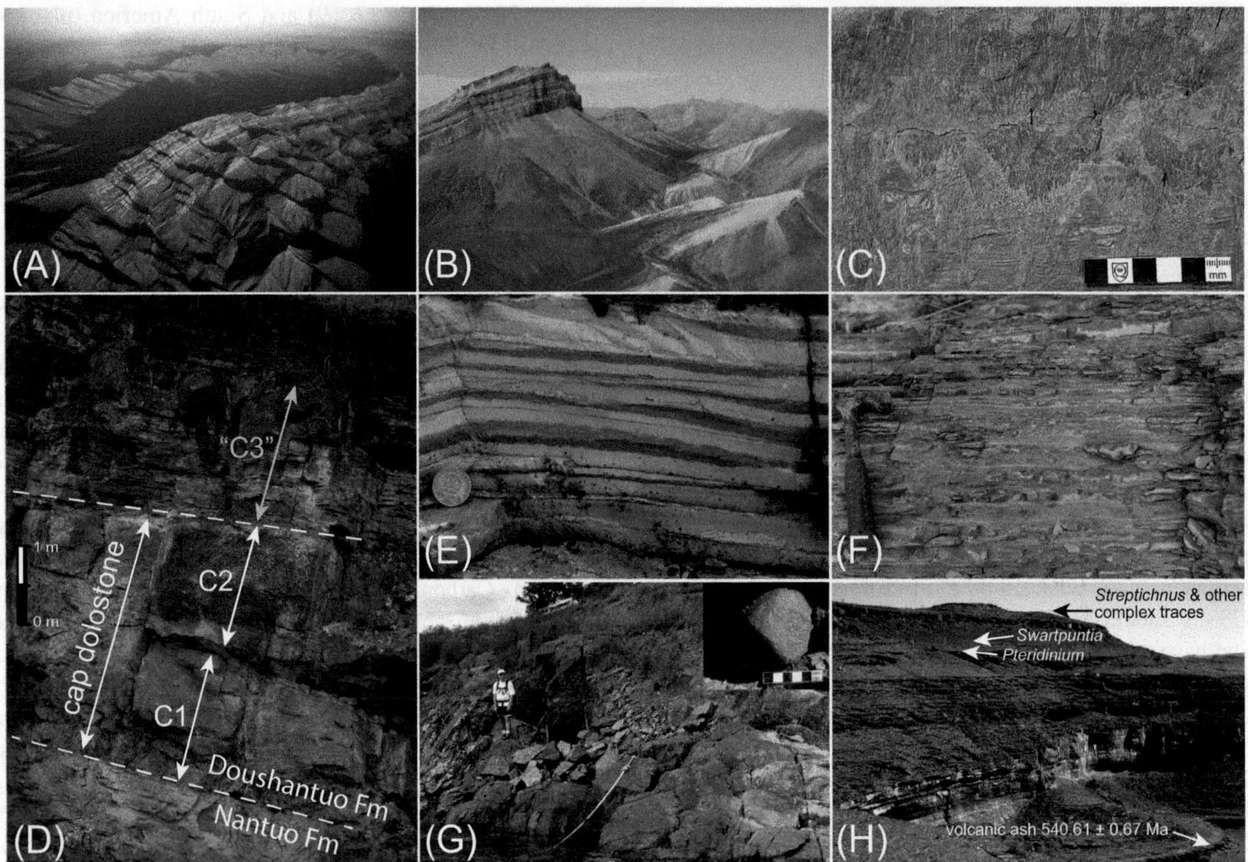

FIGURE 18.3 **Field photographs of Ediacaran outcrops:** (A) Overview of the Flinders Ranges succession at Wilpena Pound. The lip of the syncline marks the disconformable base of the Cambrian over shallow-water Ediacaran sandstones and shales. Ediacara-type fossil impressions occur in the banded sandstones below the massive quartzite ridge at the top of the bluff. (B) Overview of c. 1 km upper Cryogenian–basal Ediacaran strata near Shale Lake, NW Canada. The prominent light ridge and scree marks the basal Ediacaran cap dolostone (Ravensthroat Formation) overlying the terminal Cryogenian Ice Brook Formation (after Fig. 4A of James et al., 2001). (C) Aragonite crystal fans in the Hayhook Formation (limestone) overlying the Ravensthroat Formation (cap dolostone). (D) Basal Ediacaran cap dolostone (Doushantuo Formation) overlying the terminal Cryogenian Nantuo Formation at Huajipo, Yangtze Gorges area, South China. Unit "C3" was previously considered as part of the cap dolostone (Jiang et al., 2006) but is now excluded from the cap dolostone (Wang et al., 2017b). (E) Ribbon rocks (interbedded limestone and dolostone) in the upper Doushantuo Formation at Guancaiyao, Yangtze Gorges area, South China. This lithofacies records EN3, which is considered as an equivalent of the Shuram negative $\delta^{13}C$ excursion. Coin is ~20 mm in diameter. (F) Ribbon rocks of the Shuram Formation at Wadi Bani Awf, Jabal Akhdar, northeastern Oman, which records the Shuram negative $\delta^{13}C$ excursion. (G) Mid-Ediacaran (~580 Ma) Gaskiers Diamictite in Harbour Main, Newfoundland. Strata strongly dipping with stratigraphic top to the left of the photograph. Note abundant clasts and increasing red color upward through the Gaskiers Formation, white capping limestone (left of figure), and overlying thin turbidites of the Drook Formation. Inset shows a striated clast in the Gaskiers Formation. (H) Uppermost Ediacaran strata at Swartpunt, Namibia showing stratigraphic levels of key fossils and a dated volcanic ash bed (Grotzinger et al., 1995). The section is approximately 125 m thick. See Narbonne et al. (1997) for details. *(A) Photo by J.G. Gehling.*

Cryogenian–Ediacaran boundary is constrained to be $<636.41 \pm 0.45$ Ma in Kings Island of Tasmania, Australia (Calver et al., 2013), $<635.21 \pm 0.59$ Ma in northern Namibia (Prave et al., 2016), and $>632.3 \pm 5.9$ Ma in northwestern Canada (Rooney et al., 2015). Importantly, the Cryogenian–Ediacaran boundary is bracketed between a 634.57 ± 0.88 Ma age from the uppermost Nantuo Formation of terminal Cryogenian age (Zhou et al., 2019) and a 635.23 ± 0.57 Ma age from just above the basal Ediacaran cap dolostone (Condon et al., 2005). These two ages are indistinguishable within analytical errors, and together they suggest that the Cryogenian–Ediacaran boundary is at 635 Ma.

18.3 The biostratigraphic basis for the Ediacaran System

18.3.1 Ediacaran megafossils and trace fossils

Ediacara-type megafossils represent the first abundant, large, and architecturally complex organisms in the Earth evolution. Their impressions on the bases of event beds provide the most distinctive and readily recognizable character of the Ediacaran System and appear to be a reliable indicator of the upper part of this system worldwide (Figs. 18.4 and 18.5). The affinities of the Ediacara biota are contentious—some groups such as the rangeomorphs, arboreomorphs and erniettomorphs may not be ancestral to any Phanerozoic or living lifeforms (Dececchi et al., 2017, 2018), whereas other forms such as *Dickinsonia*, *Yorgia*, and *Kimberella* preserving evidence of locomotion and feeding arguably represent stem-group animals (Gehling et al., 2005, 2014; Ivantsov, 2013). The iconic Ediacara fossil *Dickinsonia* has highly regulated developmental patterns indicative of a eumetazoan or bilaterian affinity (Gold et al., 2015; Evans et al., 2017; Hoekzema et al., 2017; Dunn et al., 2018), an interpretation that has been independently confirmed by biomarker data (Bobrovskiy et al., 2018).

Ediacara-type fossils have been reported from more than 30 regions worldwide (Fedonkin et al., 2007; Laflamme et al., 2013). A few possible pre-Ediacaran precursors (Hofmann et al., 1990) and post-Ediacaran survivors are known (Jensen et al., 1998; Hagadorn et al., 2000; Hoyal Cuthill and Han, 2018), but in general, Ediacara-type fossils are strictly restricted to the upper half of the Ediacaran System. Some occurrences (e.g., Finnmark in northern Europe) are low in diversity and/or contain only simple disks such as *Aspidella*, *Nemiana* and *Hiemalora* that are of limited use in biostratigraphy

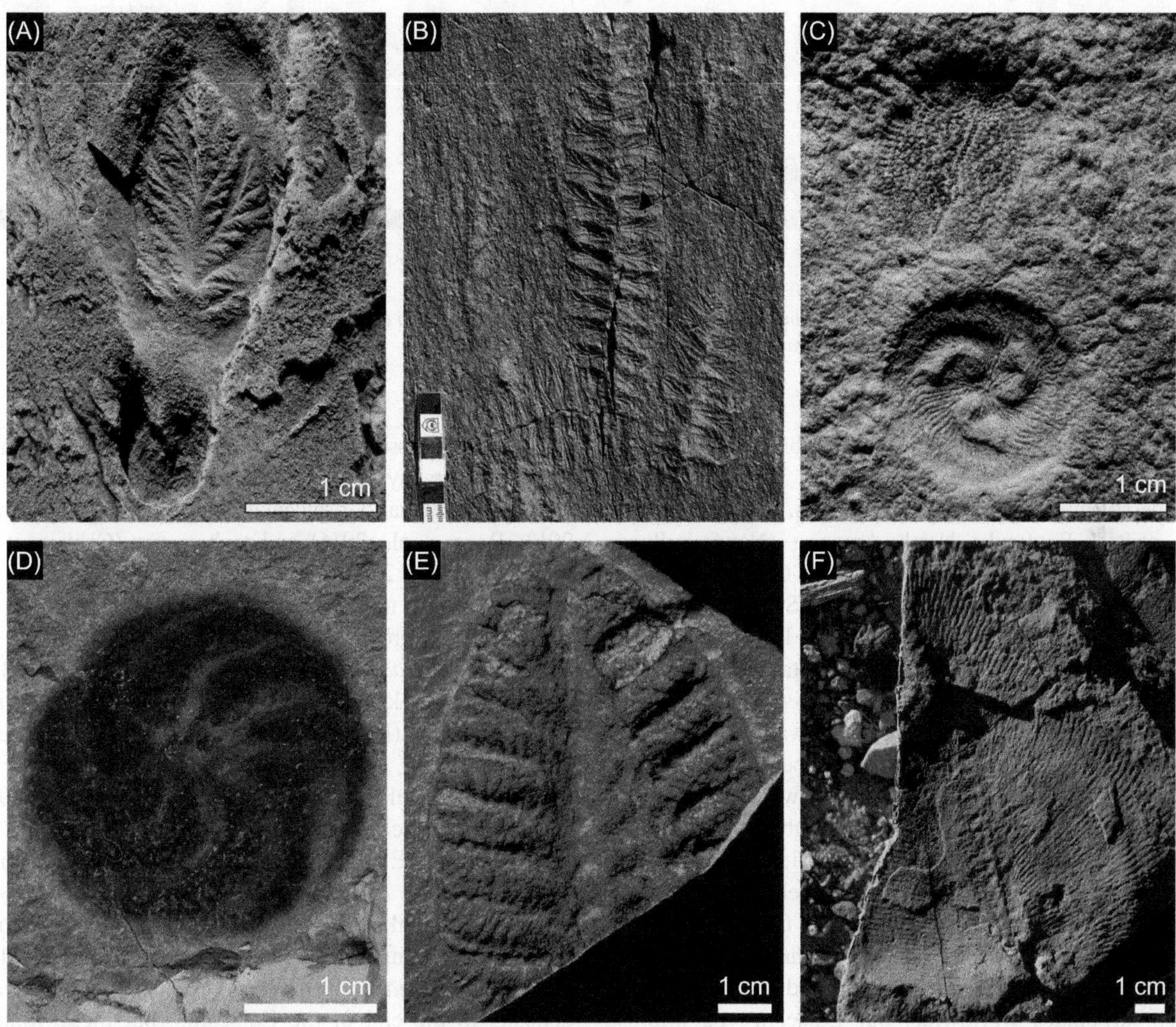

FIGURE 18.4 **Representative Ediacara-type megafossils.** Parts (A and B), (C and D), and (E and F) are examples from the Avalon, White Sea, and Nama assemblages, respectively. (A) Rangeomorph *Beothukis mistakensis* (NFM F-758), Trepassey Formation, Spaniard's Bay, Newfoundland (Narbonne et al., 2009). (B) Rangeomorph *Fractofusus misrai*, surface E, Mistaken Point, Newfoundland (Gehling and Narbonne, 2007). (C) *Tribrachidium heraldicum* (lower) and possibly *Solza margarita* (upper) from the Yorga Formation, Zimnie Gory, White Sea, Russia. (D) *Eoandromeda octobrachiata* from the upper Doushantuo Formation, northeastern Guizhou Province, South China. (E) *Rangea schneiderhoehoni* from the Nama Group, southern Namibia. Specimen reposited in Geological Survey of Namibia. (F) *Swartpuntia germsi* from the Spitskopf Member, Urusis Formation, Nama Group, Farm Swartpunt, southern Namibia. *(A and C) Courtesy Marc Laflamme.*

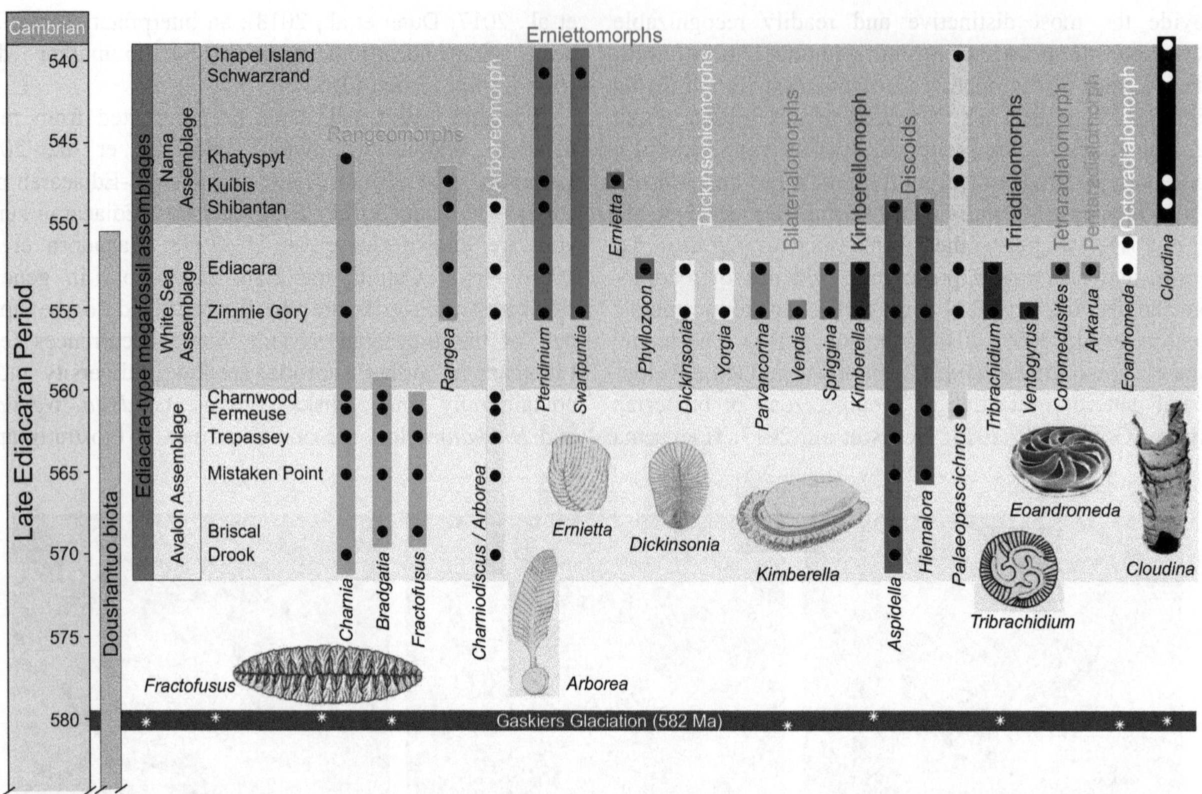

FIGURE 18.5 **Ediacara-type megafossil zonation of the upper Ediacaran System.** *After Xiao and Laflamme (2009), with updated age constraints from Schmitz (2012), Pu et al. (2016), and Linnemann et al. (2019).*

(Högström et al., 2013). Diverse assemblages suitable for biostratigraphy have been described from Australia (Flinders Ranges); Europe (White Sea, Urals, Ukraine, and central England); North America (Newfoundland, Mackenzie Mountains, Nevada, North Carolina); Africa (Namibia); and Asia (South China, Siberia). Possible Ediacara-type fossils described from India and South America require further study and substantiation. In general, Ediacara-type fossils and trace fossils are relatively common in both shallow- and deep-water siliciclastics (Narbonne et al., 2014) and have also been reported sporadically from shallow- and deep-water carbonates (Narbonne and Aitken, 1990; MacNaughton et al., 2000; Grazhdankin et al., 2008; Chen et al., 2014; Bykova et al., 2017), enhancing global correlation based on Ediacara-type megafossils and trace fossils. Calcified megafossils such as *Cloudina*, *Namacalathus* and *Sinotubulites* are common in latest Ediacaran shallow-water carbonates worldwide, but Ediacara-type impressions occur only rarely in these facies.

Available dates allow three broad assemblages to be recognized, including the Avalon, White Sea, and Nama assemblages (Fig. 18.5) (Waggoner, 2003). Each assemblage exhibits a major diversity change and evolutionary innovation in complex multicellularity, segmentation, mobility, or calcification (Droser et al., 2017). Use of these assemblages for biostratigraphy is complicated by obvious evidence for both environmental (Grazhdankin, 2004; Gehling and Droser, 2013; Boag et al., 2016) and taphonomic (Gehling et al., 2005; Narbonne, 2005) influences on their composition, but this problem is not unique to Ediacaran megafossils and affects all fossil groups of all ages to varying degrees.

The *Avalon assemblage* (~571–560 Ma; Figs. 18.4A and B, 18.5) is known only from deep-water deposits in Newfoundland (Misra, 1969; Narbonne and Gehling, 2003; Narbonne, 2004; Hofmann et al., 2008; Liu et al., 2014a,c; Mitchell et al., 2015), England (Ford, 1958; Brasier and Antcliffe, 2009; Wilby et al., 2011), and the June beds in SE Mackenzie Mountains of NW Canada (Narbonne and Aitken, 1990, 1995; Narbonne et al., 2014). Grazhdankin et al. (2008) showed that some long-ranging and cosmopolitan taxa of the Avalon assemblage (such as *Charnia* and *Hiemalora*) persist in deep-water deposits to the end of the Ediacaran, but these younger deep-water assemblages typically also contain Ediacaran fossils typical of younger Ediacaran assemblages (e.g., Hofmann and Mountjoy, 2010). The Avalon assemblage (s.s.) consists largely of rangeomorphs (Fig. 18.4A and B), fossils consisting of centimeter-scale elements exhibiting self-similar branching that were used as modules to build decimeter- to meter-scale constructions such as *Beothukis* (Fig. 18.4A), *Fractofusus* (Fig. 18.4B), *Charnia* and *Bradgatia* (Narbonne, 2004). The oldest Ediacara-type fossils are specimens of the conical fossil *Thectardis* that occur approximately 150 m below an ash dated at 570.94 ± 0.38 Ma (Pu et al., 2016) in the Drook Formation of eastern Newfoundland (Narbonne and Gehling, 2003), and a diverse assemblage of juvenile specimens of *Trepassia wardae*, *Charnia masoni* and other Ediacaran fronds directly underlies this ash and is directly dated by it (Liu et al., 2012). These fossils are <9.5 million years after the end of the 580 Ma Gaskiers glaciation, which also corresponds with geochemical evidence for a significant rise in deep-sea oxygen levels (Canfield et al., 2007), implying a causal relationship between Neoproterozoic glaciation, oxygenation, and the rise of complex eukaryotic life (Narbonne, 2010). Ediacaran fossils have not been found in age-equivalent shallow-water deposits, implying that these early experiments in complex megascopic life originated in deep-sea settings (Xiao, 2004b; Narbonne et al., 2014). Liu et al. (2010, 2014a), Menon et al. (2013), and Liu and McIlroy (2015) described biological features interpreted as trace fossils from the Avalon assemblage in Newfoundland, but the origin of these structures as trace fossils is uncertain (Buatois and Mángano, 2016) and trace fossils are not known from equivalent strata in NW Canada (Narbonne et al., 2014). In general, evidences of mobility are either absent from or exceedingly rare in the Avalon assemblage worldwide.

The *White Sea assemblage* (~560–550 Ma; Figs. 18.4C and D, 18.5) has the highest taxonomic diversity among the three assemblages of Ediacara-type fossils (Shen et al., 2008; Droser and Gehling, 2015; Droser et al., 2017). It is best known from shallow-water settings in the White Sea, Urals, and Ukraine in Eastern Europe (Fedonkin, 1981, 1990, 1992) and in the Flinders Ranges of Australia (Sprigg, 1947; Glaessner and Wade, 1966; Jenkins, 1992; Gehling et al., 2005; Droser and Gehling, 2015; Droser et al., 2018). The White Sea assemblage contains a depauperate assemblage of rangeomorph taxa, many of them holdovers from the preceding Avalon assemblage, along with other fronds such as *Arborea* and "*Charniodiscus*." New developmental plans include erniettomorphs (e.g., *Pteridinium* and *Phyllozoon*), which show a modular construction of soda straw–shaped elements. Segmented forms (e.g., *Dickinsonia*), some of which show polarity and possible cephalization (e.g., *Spriggina*, *Kimberella*), provide iconic images of the Ediacara biota. These segmented fossils are commonly regarded as metazoans and likely stem-group bilaterians (Gehling, 1991; Fedonkin and Waggoner, 1997; Sperling and Vinther, 2010; Gold et al., 2015; Evans et al., 2017; Hoekzema et al., 2017; Bobrovskiy et al., 2018). The diverse macroscopic algae and other carbonaceous compressions of the Miaohe assemblage from the Doushantuo Formation of China (Xiao et al., 2002; Ye et al., 2017) are also age-equivalent to the White Sea assemblage, a view supported by the presence of the Miaohe fossil *Eoandromeda* (Fig. 18.4D) and certain algal fossils in the White Sea assemblage (Xiao et al., 2013; Golubkova et al., 2018). The White Sea assemblage also witnessed the first appearance of abundant and reasonably unequivocal animal burrows (Gehling and Droser, 2018). Simple, unbranched, subhorizontal burrows such as *Planolites* and *Helminthoidichnites* dominate the assemblage, with some like *Torrowangea* showing beaded fills implying peristalsis and active backfill (Narbonne and Aitken, 1990; Jensen et al., 2006; Gehling and Droser, 2018). Most of these simple Ediacaran trace fossil genera also range into the Phanerozoic, but the appearance of abundant Ediacaran burrows may mark a significant evolutionary and biostratigraphic event (Jensen et al., 2006).

The *Nama assemblage* (~550–538 Ma; Figs. 18.4E and F, 18.5) may represent a declining phase of the Ediacara biota (Shen et al., 2008; Boag et al., 2016; Darroch et al., 2016, 2018a,b; Muscente et al., 2018), although new taxa and new ecology did evolve in this assemblage (Schiffbauer et al., 2016; Droser et al., 2017). The Nama assemblage includes Ediacara-type fossils and biomineralized tubular fossils that are best known from terminal Ediacaran siliciclastic successions in Namibia (Gürich, 1930; Germs, 1972; Narbonne et al., 1997; Grotzinger et al., 2000; Grazhdankin and Seilacher, 2002, 2005; Vickers-Rich et al., 2013; Darroch et al., 2016; Ivantsov et al., 2016); NW Canada (Carbone et al., 2015); Nevada (Smith et al., 2016, 2017); and Brazil (Babcock et al., 2005; Warren et al., 2012; Pacheco et al., 2015; Adôrno et al., 2017; Becker-Kerber et al., 2017), as well as carbonate successions in China (Sun, 1986; Xiao et al., 2005; Chen et al., 2008, 2014; Cai et al., 2015, 2017) and northern Siberia (Grazhdankin et al., 2008; Bykova et al., 2017). These contain depauperate assemblages of Ediacara-type fossil impressions, mainly rangeomorphs and erniettomorphs also known from the preceding assemblages (Xiao and Laflamme, 2009; Boag et al., 2016), but *Swartpuntia* (Narbonne et al., 1997; Hagadorn and Waggoner, 2000) and *Ernietta* (Ivantsov et al., 2016; Smith et al., 2017) first appear in the Nama assemblage of Namibia and western North America. Abundant and moderately complex trace fossils occur in the Nama assemblage (Jensen et al., 2000; Jensen and Runnegar, 2005; Chen et al., 2013, 2018, 2019; Meyer et al., 2014a, 2017; Buatois et al., 2018). U–Pb dates from Namibia (Grotzinger et al., 1995; Linnemann et al., 2019), Oman (Amthor et al., 2003; Bowring et al., 2007), South China (Condon et al., 2005; Yang et al., 2017a,b) and Brazil (Parry et al., 2017) constrain the Nama assemblage between c. 550 and 538 Ma (Table 18.1). The decline and eventual disappearance of the Nama assemblage at or near

TABLE 18.1 Key radioisotopic dates constraining the Ediacaran System and its correlation.

Region	Locality	Period	Unit	Age plotted in Fig. 18.10	Error plotted in Fig. 18.10	Reported age	Reported error	Recalculated age Schmitz (2012)	w/o λ error	w/λ error	Type of age	Reference
Australia	Kings Island of Tasmania, Australia Cryogenian	Cryogenian	Cottons Breccia	636.41	0.45	636.41	0.45				TIMS	Calver et al. (2013)
Namibia	northern Namibia Cryogenian	Cryogenian	Ghaub Diamictite	635.21	0.59	635.21	0.59				TIMS	Prave et al. (2016)
Namibia	northern Namibia Cryogenian	Cryogenian	Ghaub Diamictite	639.29	0.26	639.29	0.26				TIMS	Prave et al. (2016)
South China	Yunnan, South China Cryogenian	Cryogenian	Nantuo Formation	634.57	0.88	634.57	0.88				TIMS	Zhou et al. (2019)
Avalon	Avalon Peninsula, Newfoundland, Canada	Ediacaran	Drook Formation, 150 m above first appearance of Ediacara fossils	570.94	0.38	570.94	0.38				TIMS	Pu et al. (2016)
Avalon	Avalon Peninsula, Newfoundland, Canada	Ediacaran	Mistaken Point Formation	566.25	0.35	566.25	0.35				TIMS	Pu et al. (2016)
Avalon	Avalon Peninsula, Newfoundland, Canada	Ediacaran	Mall Bay, below Gaskiers	580.34	0.52	580.34	0.52				TIMS	Pu et al. (2016)
Avalon	Avalon Peninsula, Newfoundland, Canada	Ediacaran	Mall Bay, below Gaskiers	580.9	0.4	580.9	0.4				TIMS	Pu et al. (2016)
Avalon	Avalon Peninsula, Newfoundland, Canada	Ediacaran	Drook Formation, above Gaskiers	579.88	0.44	579.88	0.44				TIMS	Pu et al. (2016)
Avalon	Bonavista Peninsula, Newfoundland, Canada	Ediacaran	Rocky Harbour Formation, below Trinity Diamictite	579.63	0.15	579.63	0.15				TIMS	Pu et al. (2016)
Avalon	Bonavista Peninsula, Newfoundland, Canada	Ediacaran	Rocky Harbour Formation, within Trinity Diamictite	579.35	0.33	579.35	0.33				TIMS	Pu et al. (2016)
Avalon	Bonavista Peninsula, Newfoundland, Canada	Ediacaran	Rocky Harbour Formation, above Trinity Diamictite	579.24	0.17	579.24	0.17				TIMS	Pu et al. (2016)
Avalon	England	Ediacaran	Park Breccia Member	559.3	7.3	559.3	2	559.3	7.3	7.3	SHRIMP	Compston et al. (2002)

(Continued)

TABLE 18.1 (Continued)

Region	Locality	Period	Unit	Age plotted in Fig. 18.10	Error plotted in Fig. 18.10	Reported age	Reported error	Recalculated age Schmitz (2012)	w/o λ error	w/λ error	Type of age	Reference
Avalon	England	Ediacaran	Bardon Hill Complex	566.1	3.1	566.1	3.1				SHRIMP	Compston et al. (2002)
Avalon	England	Ediacaran	Stretton Shale Formation	566.6	2.9	566.6	2.9				SHRIMP	Compston et al. (2002)
Avalon	England	Ediacaran	Lightspout Formation	555.9	3.5	555.9	3.5				SHRIMP	Compston et al. (2002)
Avalon	Wales	Ediacaran	Padarn Tuff Formation	604.7	1.6	604.7	1.6				SHRIMP	Compston et al. (2002)
Avalon	Wales	Ediacaran	Padarn Tuff Formation	605.9	3.8	605.9	3.8				SHRIMP	Compston et al. (2002)
Avalon	Wales	Ediacaran	Fachwen Formation	574.3	2.7	574.3	2.7				SHRIMP	Compston et al. (2002)
Avalon	Wales	Ediacaran	Fachwen Formation	572.5	1.2	572.5	1.2				SHRIMP	Compston et al. (2002)
Avalon	England	Ediacaran	Hanging Rock Formation	556.6	6.4	556.6	6.4				LA-ICP-MS	Noble et al. (2015)
Avalon	England	Ediacaran	Bradgate Formation	561.85	0.66	561.85	0.66	561.85	0.66	0.89	TIMS	Noble et al. (2015)
Avalon	England	Ediacaran	Beacon Hill Formation	565.22	0.65	565.22	0.65	565.22	0.65	0.89	TIMS	Noble et al. (2015)
Avalon	England	Ediacaran	Benscliffe Breccia	569.08	0.73	569.08	0.73	569.08	0.73	0.94	TIMS	Noble et al. (2015)
Baltica	Russia	Ediacaran	Uppermost Ust-Pinega Formation	555.3	0.3	555.3	0.3	552.85	0.77	2.62	TIMS	Martin et al. (2000)
Brazil	Corumba, Mato Grosso do Sul State, Brazil	Ediacaran	Upper Tamengo Formation	541.85	0.77	541.85	0.75	541.85	0.77	0.97	TIMS	Parry et al. (2017)
Brazil	Corumba, Mato Grosso do Sul State, Brazil	Ediacaran	Upper Tamengo Formation	542.37	0.32	542.37	0.28	542.37	0.32	0.68	TIMS	Parry et al. (2017)
Brazil	Corumba, Mato Grosso do Sul State, Brazil	Ediacaran	Upper Bocaina Formation	555.18	0.34	555.18	0.3	555.18	0.34	0.7	TIMS	Parry et al. (2017)
Namibia	Namibia	Ediacaran	Urusis Formation, upper Spitskopf Member	540.61	0.67	543.3	1	540.61	0.67	0.88	TIMS	Grotzinger et al. (1995)
Namibia	Namibia	Ediacaran	Urusis Formation, upper Spitskopf Member	542.68	1.25	545.1	1	542.68	1.25	2.8	TIMS	Grotzinger et al. (1995)

(Continued)

TABLE 18.1 (Continued)

Region	Locality	Period	Unit	Age plotted in Fig. 18.10	Error plotted in Fig. 18.10	Reported age	Reported error	Recalculated age Schmitz (2012)	w/o λ error	w/λ error	Type of age	Reference
Namibia	Namibia	Ediacaran	Hoogland Formation, above Omkyk Shuram	547.32	0.31	548.8	1	547.32	0.31	0.65	TIMS	Grotzinger et al. (1995)
Namibia	Namibia	Ediacaran	Urusis Formation, upper Spitskopf Member	538.99	0.21	538.99	0.21				TIMS	Linnemann et al. (2019)
Namibia	Namibia	Ediacaran	Urusis Formation, Spitskopf Member	539.64	0.19	539.64	0.19				TIMS	Linnemann et al. (2019)
Namibia	Namibia	Ediacaran	Urusis Formation, Spitskopf Member	539.52	0.14	539.52	0.14				TIMS	Linnemann et al. (2019)
Namibia	Namibia	Ediacaran	Urusis Formation, Spitskopf Member	539.58	0.34	539.58	0.34				TIMS	Linnemann et al. (2019)
NW Canada	Mackenzie Mountains, northwestern Canada	Ediacaran	basal Sheepbed Formation	632.3	5.9	632.3	5.9				Re–Os	Rooney et al. (2015)
Oman	Oman Cambrian	Ediacaran	Ara Group, 1 m above A4 carbonate	541	0.29	541	0.21	541	0.29	0.63	TIMS	Bowring et al. (2007)
Oman	Oman	Ediacaran	Ara Group, 9 m below top of A3 carbonate	542.37	0.28	542.23	0.19	542.37	0.28	0.63	TIMS	Bowring et al. (2007)
Oman	Oman	Ediacaran	Ara Group, 3 m above base of A3 carbonate	542.9	0.29	542.9	0.2	542.9	0.29	0.63	TIMS	Bowring et al. (2007)
Oman	Oman	Ediacaran	Ara Group, A0 carbonate	546.72	0.34	546.72	0.29	546.72	0.34	0.66	TIMS	Bowring et al. (2007)
Oman	Oman	Ediacaran	Fara Formation	542.54	0.53	542.54	0.53				TIMS	Bowring et al. (2007)
Oman	Oman	Ediacaran	Fara Formation	547.23	0.36	547.23	0.36				TIMS	Bowring et al. (2007)
South China	Huajipo, Yangtze Gorges area, South China	Ediacaran	Atop Doushantuo cap dolostone	635.26	0.84	635.23	0.57	635.26	0.84	1.07	TIMS	Condon et al. (2005)
South China	Jiuqunao, Yangtze Gorges area, South China	Ediacaran	Doushantuo member II	632.48	0.84	632.5	0.48	632.48	0.84	1.02	TIMS	Condon et al. (2005)
South China	Jiuqunao, Yangtze Gorges area, South China	Ediacaran	Doushantuo member IV	551.09	0.84	551.07	0.61	551.09	0.84	1.02	TIMS	Condon et al. (2005)

(*Continued*)

TABLE 18.1 (Continued)

Region	Locality	Period	Unit	Age plotted in Fig. 18.10	Error plotted in Fig. 18.10	Reported age	Reported error	Recalculated age Schmitz (2012)	w/o λ error	w/λ error	Type of age	Reference
South China	Zhangcunping, South China	Ediacaran	Lower Doushantuo Formation, just above middle dolostone and middle phosphorite	609	5	609	5				SHRIMP	Zhou et al. (2017b)
South China	Zhangcunping, South China	Ediacaran	Lower Doushantuo Formation, just above lower phosphorite	614	9	614	7.6	614	9	9	SHRIMP	Liu et al. (2009)
South China	Weng'an, South China	Ediacaran	Doushantuo Formation, middle phosphorite	599	4	599	4				Pb–Pb	Barfod et al. (2002)
South China	Fanglong, Guizhou, South China	Ediacaran	Lower Dengying Formation	557	3	557	3				SHRIMP	Zhou et al. (2018)
South China	Fanglong, Guizhou, South China	Ediacaran	Lower Liuchapo Formation	550	3	550	3				SHRIMP	Zhou et al. (2018)
South China	Yunnan, South China	Ediacaran	Basal Jiucheng Member, Dengying Formation	553.6	3.8	553.6	2.7	553.6	3.8		SIMS	Yang et al. (2017b)
South China	Yunnan, South China	Ediacaran	Middle Jiucheng Member, Dengying Formation	546.3	3.8	546.3	2.7	546.3	3.8		SIMS	Yang et al. (2017b)
South China	Longbizui, Hunan, South China	Ediacaran	Lower Liuchapo Formation, Longbizui	545.76	0.66	545.76	0.66				SIMS	Yang et al. (2017a)
South China	Ganqiping, Hunan, South China	Ediacaran	Lower Liuchapo Formation, below *Palaeopascichnus* occurrence	542.1	5	542.1	5				SIMS	Chen et al. (2015)
South China	Bahuang, Guizhou, South China	Ediacaran	Upper Liuchapo Formation	542.6	3.7	542.6	3.7				SIMS	Chen et al. (2015)
Namibia	Namibia	Cambrian	Urusis Formation, Spitskopf Member	538.58	0.19	538.58	0.19				TIMS	Linnemann et al. (2019)
Namibia	Namibia Cambrian	Cambrian	Nomtsas Formation	538.18	1.11	539.4	1	538.18	1.11	1.24	TIMS	Grotzinger et al. (1995)
South China	Ganqiping, Hunan, South China	Cambrian	Upper Liuchapo Formation, above Palaeopascichnus occurrence	536.3	5.5	536.3	5.5				SIMS	Chen et al. (2009)

In "Type of age" column: *LA-ICP-MS*, laser ablation inductively coupled plasma mass spectrometer; *SHRIMP*, Sensitive High-Resolution Ion MicroProbe; *SIMS*, secondary ion mass spectrometery; *TIMS*, isotope dilution thermal ionization mass spectrometry.

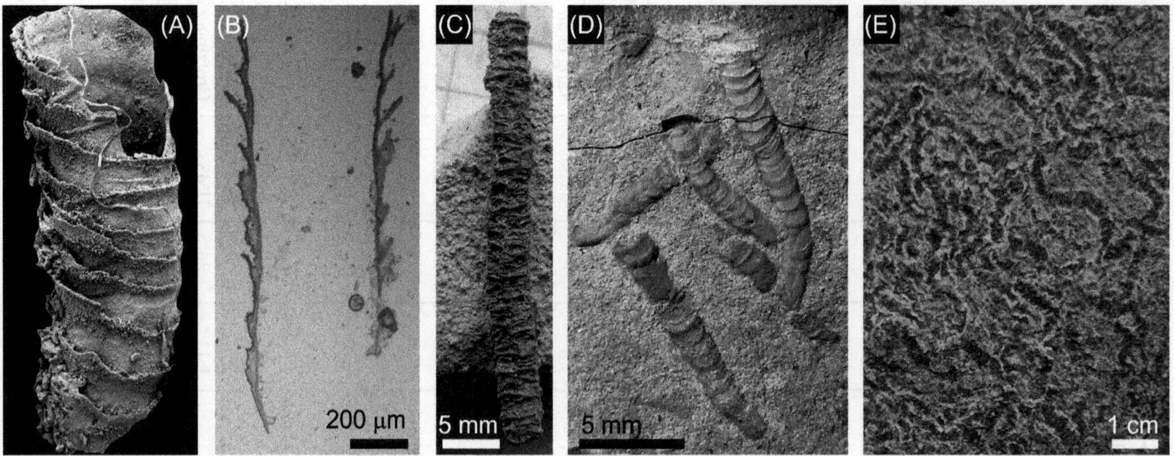

FIGURE 18.6 Representative tubular or ribbon-shaped fossils from the terminal Ediacaran stage. Parts (A–C) are biomineralized skeletal fossils and Parts (D–E) are nonbiomineralized fossils. (A and B) *Cloudina riemkeae*, (C) *Sinotubulites baimatuoensis*, and (D) *Conotubus hemiannulatus*, Dengying Formation, southern Shaanxi Province, South China. Part (B) is longitudinal cross section of (A), showing nested funnels (Hua et al., 2005). (E) *Shaanxilithes ningqiangensis*, Taozichong Formation, Guizhou Province, South China (Hua et al., 2004). *Modified from Xiao et al. (2016).*

the Ediacaran–Cambrian boundary represents an area of current research (Laflamme et al., 2013; Smith et al., 2016; Darroch et al., 2018b; Muscente et al., 2018; Tarhan et al., 2018; Linnemann et al., 2019).

The Nama assemblage witnessed the appearance of the earliest skeletal animal fossils, which represent an important evolutionary event of probable biostratigraphic significance. These include weakly biomineralized fossils such as *Cloudina* (Fig. 18.6A and B), *Sinotubulites* (Fig. 18.6C) and *Namacalathus*. Among these skeletal fossils, *Cloudina* was the first described (Germs, 1972) and is the most widespread, occurring in terminal Ediacaran successions in Namibia (Grant, 1990), Oman (Conway Morris et al., 1990), South China (Hua et al., 2005; Cai et al., 2013; Cortijo et al., 2015b), Spain (Cortijo et al., 2010, 2015a), Siberia (Kontorovich et al., 2008; Zhuravlev et al., 2012; Grazhdankin et al., 2015), Canada (Hofmann and Mountjoy, 2001), Mexico (Sour-Tovar et al., 2007), South America (Warren et al., 2017), and eastern California and Nevada where it was described as *Nevadatubulus dunfeei* by Signor et al. (1987) but considered as *Cloudina* by Grant (1990) and Zhuravlev et al. (2012). Although the stratigraphic range of *Cloudina* may extend into the basal Cambrian (Zhuravlev et al., 2012; Yang et al., 2016; Han et al., 2017; Zhu et al., 2017), it is clear that the first appearance of *Cloudina* is in the terminal Ediacaran Period. *Sinotubulites* also has a wide geographic distribution and has been recovered from terminal Ediacaran strata in South China (Cai et al., 2015), Mexico (McMenamin, 1985), eastern California and Nevada (Signor et al., 1987), and Spain (Cortijo et al., 2015a). *Namacalathus* was first described from the terminal Ediacaran Nama Group in Namibia (Grotzinger et al., 2000; Zhuravlev et al., 2015) and also occurs in terminal Ediacaran strata in western Canada (Hofmann and Mountjoy, 2001), Oman (Amthor et al., 2003), and Siberia (Kontorovich et al., 2008; Grazhdankin et al., 2015).

In addition, the Nama assemblage contains a number of nonbiomineralized ribbon-shaped or tubular fossils such as *Conotubus* (Fig. 18.6D), *Shaanxilithes* (Fig. 18.6E), *Wutubus*, *Sekwitubulus*, *Saarina* and *Sabellidites* (Selly et al., 2019). *Shaanxilithes* has been found in terminal Ediacaran rocks in South China (Meyer et al., 2012), North China and Chaidam Blocks (Shen et al., 2007), India (Tarhan et al., 2014), Siberia (Zhuravlev et al., 2009; Cai and Hua, 2011; Rogov et al., 2012), and possibly Namibia (Darroch et al., 2016). *Conotubus* is known from terminal Ediacaran successions in South China (Cai et al., 2011), and it has been regarded as an evolutionary precursor of *Cloudina* (Hua et al., 2007; Wood et al., 2017). *Sabellidites cambriensis* first appears in terminal Ediacaran rocks in the East European Platform (Moczydłowska et al., 2014), but it also extends into the basal Cambrian (Narbonne et al., 1987; Landing, 1994). These tubular fossils have the potential to improve the precision of biostratigraphic correlation of terminal Ediacaran strata.

One important but geochronologically poorly constrained assemblage is the Lantian biota in South China. The Lantian biota is loosely constrained somewhere between 635 and 551 Ma on the basis of correlation with the Doushantuo Formation in the Yangtze Gorges area. It consists of centimeter-scale carbonaceous compressions interpreted as fleshy algae along with problematic fossils informally compared with cnidarians and simple bilaterians (Yuan et al., 2011; Van Iten et al., 2013; Wan et al., 2014, 2016). Several Lantian taxa also range into the younger Miaohe biota of the Doushantuo Formation

(Xiao et al., 2002; Ye et al., 2017), which is capped by a 551 Ma ash bed (Condon et al., 2005) and contains a diverse flora of megascopic algae and problematica, including *Eoandromeda* (Fig. 18.4D) (Tang et al., 2008; Zhu et al., 2008; Xiao et al., 2013). These exceptional fossil assemblages are important in showing the level of macroscopic complexity achieved in Ediacaran soft-bodied algae and potentially even animals, but their limited geographic occurrence and loose age constraints limit their value in biostratigraphy.

18.3.2 Ediacaran microfossils

The lower part of the Ediacaran System is characterized by a group of relatively large acanthomorphic (spiny) acritarchs that are variously known as Doushantuo–Pertatataka acritarchs (Zhou et al., 2001, 2007), Ediacaran Complex-Acanthomorph-dominated Palynoflora (Grey et al., 2003), or large ornamented Ediacaran microfossils (Cohen et al., 2009a). These acritarchs are 50–1000 μm in diameter (Vorob'eva and Sergeev, 2018) and are ornamented with processes of different morphologies (Fig. 18.7). Although a number of Mesoproterozoic–Tonian acritarch species can develop processes (Tang et al., 2015) and a few can reach 400 μm in diameter (Agić et al., 2017), Ediacaran acanthomorphs are morphologically diverse and taxonomically distinct. There are more than 200 described species of Ediacaran acanthomorphs and the list keeps growing (Cohen and Macdonald, 2015). These taxonomically diverse and morphologically complex acanthomorphs are in sharp contrast to basal Cambrian acanthomorphs that are extremely small (typically <50 μm in diameter) (Moczydłowska, 1991, 1998; Yao et al., 2005; Dong et al., 2009; Ahn and Zhu, 2017).

Ediacaran acanthomorphs provide a useful biostratigraphic tool for Ediacaran subdivision and correlation. These acanthomorphs have been described from Ediacaran shales, cherts, and phosphorites in South China (Yuan and Hofmann, 1998; Zhang et al., 1998; Zhou et al., 2001; Xiao, 2004a; McFadden et al., 2009; Liu et al., 2014f; Xiao et al., 2014b; Ouyang et al., 2017; Liu and Moczydłowska, 2019; Ouyang et al., 2019); Australia (Zang and Walter, 1992; Grey, 2005; Willman et al., 2006; Willman and

FIGURE 18.7 **Representative acanthomorphic acritarchs from the Ediacaran System.** (A) *Tianzhushania spinosa* from lower Member II of the Doushantuo Formation in the Yangtze Gorges area, South China. (B) *Mengeosphaera reticulata* from the Doushantuo Formation at Weng'an, South China. (C–E) *Hocosphaeridium anozos* from Tanana Formation, Officer Basin, Australia (Willman and Moczydłowska, 2008); upper Doushantuo Formation (Member III) at Niuping, Yangtze Gorges area, South China (Liu et al., 2014f); and lower Doushantuo Formation (Member II) at Siduping, Hunan Province, South China (Hawkins et al., 2017). Parts (A), (D), and (E) are preserved in chert nodules, (B) in phosphorites, and (C) in shales. *(C) Courtesy Sebastian Willman and (D) Courtesy Pengju Liu.*

Moczydłowska, 2008, 2011); Siberia (Moczydłowska et al., 1993; Nagovitsyn et al., 2004; Moczydłowska, 2005; Vorob'eva et al., 2008; Golubkova et al., 2010; Sergeev et al., 2011; Moczydłowska and Nagovitsin, 2012); India (Tiwari and Azmi, 1992; Tiwari and Knoll, 1994; Shukla et al., 2008; Shukla and Tiwari, 2014; Joshi and Tiwari, 2016); Svalbard (Knoll, 1992); and Baltica (Vidal, 1990; Veis et al., 2006; Vorob'eva et al., 2006, 2009a,b). Globally, these acanthomorphs seem to be restricted in the lower Ediacaran System: in southern Norway, they occur below the Gaskiers age Moelv diamictite (Bingen et al., 2005), and in South China, South Australia and Siberia, they predate negative δ^{13}C excursions that are interpreted as equivalent to the Shuram Excursion. However, recent studies have shown that some species of Doushantuo–Pertatataka-type acanthomorphs may occur in terminal Ediacaran rocks (Golubkova et al., 2015; Anderson et al., 2017a, 2019) or postdate the Shuram Excursion (Ouyang et al., 2017).

In search for a biostratigraphic resolution, one is tempted to ask whether biozones of Ediacaran acanthomorphs can be recognized and used in biostratigraphic subdivision and correlation. Indeed, five Ediacaran acritarch assemblage zones have been distinguished in Australia and these can be correlated in the Adelaide Rift Complex, Officer sub-Basin, and Amadeus Basin (Grey, 2005). The biozones are in ascending order: (1) the *Leiosphaeridia jacutica–Leiosphaeridia crassa* Assemblage Zone; (2) the *Appendisphaera tabifica* (=*Appendisphaera barbata*)–*Alicesphaeridium medusoidum–Gyalosphaeridium pulchra* Assemblage Zone; (3) the *Tanarium conoideum–Schizofusa risoria–Variomargosphaeridium litoschum* Assemblage Zone; (4) *Tanarium irregulare–Ceratosphaeridium glaberosum–Multifronsphaeridium pelorium* Assemblage Zone; and (5) *Ceratosphaeridium mirabile–Distosphaera australica–Apodastoides verobturatus* Assemblage Zone. Except for the first assemblage zone, which is characterized by smooth-walled leiospheres, the other four zones are all characterized by large acanthomorphs. Although it is unclear whether these assemblage zones can be recognized outside Australia, there is some encouraging evidence that a moderate biostratigraphic resolution can be achieved in interregional correlation based on Ediacaran acanthomorphs. For example, Vorob'eva et al. (2009a,b) recognized three acritarch assemblages from the Vychedga Formation in the northeastern margin of Baltica. These authors interpreted the lower Vychedga assemblage as Tonian in age, but the middle and upper assemblages share some broad similarity with Grey's assemblage zone (1) and zones (2)–(5), respectively; their correlation predicts that the Cryogenian System, including the Sturtian and Marinoan glaciations, is represented by a cryptic unconformity between the lower and middle Vychedga assemblages. In South China, Ediacaran acanthomorphs are best known in the Doushantuo Formation of the Yangtze Gorges area. They first occur immediately after the basal Ediacaran cap dolostone and range upward to and perhaps above the upper Doushantuo negative δ^{13}C excursion EN3 that is believed to be equivalent to the Shuram negative δ^{13}C excursion (Zhou et al., 2007; Ouyang et al., 2017). Viewed at the broadest scale, there is seemingly a discrepancy between the Australia and South China record; in Australia, Ediacaran acritarchs began with leiospheres and it is not until after the Acraman Impact that the first acanthomorphs appear, whereas in South China acanthomorphs diversified almost immediately after the basal Ediacaran cap dolostone (Yin et al., 2007, 2009; Zhou et al., 2007). This discrepancy indicates that there are regional variations in Ediacaran acanthomorph diversification and/or preservation, which can hinder inter-regional biostratigraphic correlation using acanthomorph biozones.

In South China, *Tianzhushania spinosa* (Fig. 18.7A) is one of the first acanthomorph taxa to appear after the basal Ediacaran cap dolostone (Yin et al., 2007; Zhou et al., 2007; McFadden et al., 2009), in close proximity to an ash bed dated at 632.48 ± 1.02 Ma age (Schmitz, 2012). Liu et al. (2013, 2014e,f) recognized two lower Ediacaran acanthomorph biozones in the Yangtze Gorges area of South China, namely the *T. spinosa* biozone in Member II of the Doushantuo Formation (below EN2) followed by the *T. conoideum–Hocosphaeridium scaberfacium–Hocosphaeridium anozos* biozone in lower Member III (below EN3) of the Doushantuo Formation. They propose that the *T. spinosa* biozone only occurs in South China and northern India (Tiwari and Knoll, 1994; Joshi and Tiwari, 2016), but it is absent in Australia, Siberia, and Baltica. The *T. conoideum–H. scaberfacium–H. anozos* biozone may be correlated with Grey's (2005) assemblage zones (2)–(5) and Vorob'eva et al.'s (2009a) upper Vychedga assemblage zone. Several recent studies, however, call for a revision of the acanthomorph biozonation proposed by Liu et al. (2014f). For example, *H. anozos* (Fig. 18.7C–E) has been shown to occur in Member II of the Doushantuo Formation and its stratigraphic range may extend below the δ^{13}C feature EN2 (Hawkins et al., 2017; Liu and Moczydłowska, 2019), *T. spinosa* and *H. anozos* cooccur in the middle Doushantuo Formation at Weng'an (Xiao et al., 2014b), some acanthomorph taxa range above the δ^{13}C chemostratigraphic feature EN3 (Ouyang et al., 2017), and the taxonomic distinction between the *T. spinosa* biozone and the *T. conoideum–H. scaberfacium–H. anozos* biozone may have been more subtle than previously thought (Ouyang et al., 2019). Liu and Moczydłowska (2019), on the other hand, proposed four acanthomorphic biozones based on early Ediacaran material from the Yangtze Gorges area of South China: *Appendisphaera grandis–Weissiella grandistella–T. spinosa*, *Tanarium tuberosum–Schizofusa zangwenlongii*, *T. conoideum–Cavaspina basiconica*, and *Tanarium pycnacanthum–C. glaberosum* assemblage zones.

Although there are some promising data suggesting the biostratigraphic importance of Ediacaran acanthomorphs, there are several challenges limiting the full potential of these microfossils. First, Ediacaran acanthomorphic acritarchs are well known from continental shelf successions in Asia, Australia and Europe, but these successions typically do not contain Ediacara-type megafossils. This could be due to their differences in environmental, taphonomic or biostratigraphic ranges, which make it difficult to define the exact biostratigraphic relationships between Ediacaran acanthomorphs and Ediacara-type megafossils. Second, Ediacaran acritarchs can be preserved in cherts (Fig. 18.7A, D, and E), in phosphorites (Fig. 18.7B), or in shales (Fig. 18.7C). Thus different methods (e.g., acid maceration and thin sectioning) are used in the extraction and observation of these microfossils, resulting in different taxonomic practices (Xiao et al., 2014b). The situation has been exacerbated by taphonomic alteration that is common in Ediacaran acanthomorphs (Grey and Willman, 2009). As such, there have been some taxonomic inconsistencies between systematic treatments based on thin section and maceration materials. Also, environmental factors and preservational bias can lead to variation in the geographic and stratigraphic distribution of Ediacaran acanthomorphs (Zhou et al., 2007); this is especially evident in the smooth leiospheres, which characterize terminal Ediacaran strata worldwide but also occur as default taxa in some early Ediacaran microfossil assemblages where acanthomorphs may have been excluded by environmental or taphonomic variables. It should be noted, however, that these challenges are not unique to Ediacaran acanthomorphs; they are general problems that all biostratigraphers face. Careful taphonomical and paleoenvironmental analyses will help us to maximize the biostratigraphic potential of Ediacaran acanthomorphs.

Ediacaran successions also yield several other groups of microfossils, but these fossils have limited biostratigraphic significance, either because of their limited geographic distribution or because of their rather long stratigraphic ranges. Of the former category are animal embryo-like fossils, tubular microfossils, and multicellular algal fossils from the Doushantuo Formation at Weng'an of South China (Xiao et al., 2014c). Of the latter category are various coccoidal and filamentous cyanobacteria (Venkatachala et al., 1990; Tiwari and Azmi, 1992; Zhang et al., 1998; Shukla et al., 2005). Of potential but unproven biostratigraphic significance are *Salome hubeiensis*—a multisheathed filamentous cyanobacterium that has been found in several lower Ediacaran units, including the Doushantuo Formation in South China (Zhang et al., 1998), the lower Krol Group in northern India (Shukla et al., 2008) and the Shuurgat Formation in the Zavkhan Terrane of southwestern Mongolia (Anderson et al., 2017b). Similarly, *Vendotaenia antiqua* and related fossils have been found in upper Ediacaran (<555 Ma) successions in Russia, South China and Namibia (Zhao et al., 1988; Gnilovskaya, 1990; Cohen et al., 2009b), and they may also have biostratigraphic significance.

18.3.3 Ediacaran glaciations

In contrast with the Cryogenian, in which abundant evidence of continental glaciation dominates the sedimentary record despite largely equatorial positions for most of the continents, Ediacaran glacial deposits are rare and typically isolated despite their generally more polar positions. In their recent compilation, Hoffman and Li (2009) listed 13 probable Ediacaran glacial deposits located on eight paleocontinents (see also Li et al., 2013b). The best known Ediacaran glacial deposit is the Gaskiers Formation from Avalonian Newfoundland (Fig. 18.3G) (Eyles and Eyles, 1989; Myrow and Kaufman, 1999), which is constrained between 580.90 ± 0.40 and 579.88 ± 0.44 Ma in the Avalon Peninsula and between 579.63 ± 0.15 and 579.24 ± 0.17 Ma in the Bonavista Peninsula (Pu et al., 2016) (Table 18.1). The Gaskiers Formation is a 250-m thick, deep-water, glaciomarine deposit that is similar to Cryogenian glacial deposits in showing significant iron enrichment upward and in locally exhibiting a cap carbonate (0.5 m thick composed of light gray sparry calcite) in an otherwise completely carbonate-free succession. Sparse biostratigraphic, chemostratigraphic, and geochronological data imply that the Squantum Tillite in the Boston Basin (Thompson and Bowring, 2000), the Croles Hill diamictite in Tasmania (Calver et al., 2004), the Moelv diamictite in southern Norway (Bingen et al., 2005), the Serra Azul diamictite in the Paraguay belt of Brazil (de Alvarenga et al., 2007), possibly the Hankalchough diamictite in Tarim (Xiao et al., 2004), and perhaps the Mortensnes Formation of northern Norway (Rice et al., 2011) may be correlative with the Gaskiers. If true, then Doushantuo–Pertatataka-type acanthomorphs from the Biskopås Formation (Vidal, 1990), which is older than the Moelv Formation in southern Norway, can provide insights into the temporal relationship between Ediacaran acanthomorph biozonation and the Gaskiers glaciation: some if not most Doushantuo–Pertatataka-type acanthomorphs appeared before the Gaskiers glaciation.

18.3.4 Chemical evolution of Ediacaran oceans

18.3.4.1 Carbon isotopes

Basal Ediacaran "cap dolostones" are characterized by negative $\delta^{13}C_{carb}$ values (Knoll et al., 2006), representing a negative excursion designated as EN1 in South China (Zhou and Xiao, 2007) (Fig. 18.8). Although there are some facies-dependent regional variations in the magnitude of this negative excursion (Jiang et al., 2007; Sato et al., 2016; Lang et al., 2017) and there are localized microfabric-dependent occurrence of extremely negative

$\delta^{13}C_{carb}$ values (Jiang et al., 2003; Wang et al., 2008), bulk-sample $\delta^{13}C_{carb}$ values of the cap dolostone are about −5‰ (Hoffman et al., 2007), after which they return to near 0‰ within about 3 million years (Condon et al., 2005). A subsequent rise to highly positive $\delta^{13}C_{carb}$ values (+6‰ to 10‰) has been noted from many sections [e.g., NW Namibia (Cui et al., 2018), NE Svalbard (Halverson et al., 2005), Brazil (Sial et al., 2016), and South China (McFadden et al., 2008)]. In South China a regionally consistent negative excursion (EN2) in the middle Doushantuo Formation punctuated the highly positive $\delta^{13}C_{carb}$ values (Zhou and Xiao, 2007); additional negative excursions are documented in some sections (Sawaki et al., 2010; Zhu et al., 2013), but they are not regionally consistent and may represent diagenetic alterations.

The most prominent feature in the Ediacaran $\delta^{13}C$ record is an unusually negative $\delta^{13}C_{carb}$ excursion with values below −10‰, commonly referred to as the *Shuram* (or *Shuram–Wonoka*) Excursion or anomaly (Burns and Matter, 1993). Possible equivalents of the Shuram Excursion include the EN3 excursion in the upper Doushantuo Formation in South China, the Zhuya (=Nikol'skoe + Chencha) excursion in Siberia, the Wonoka excursion in South Australia, the Gametrail excursion in northwestern Canada, and the Kanies/Mara excursion in southern Namibia (Fig. 18.8 and references cited in figure caption). Additional correlatives include the Rainstorm Member in Death Valley (Kaufman et al., 2007; Bergmann et al., 2011; Verdel et al., 2011; Witkosky and Wernicke, 2018), the Member E of the Nyborg Formation in northern Norway (Halverson et al., 2005; Rice et al., 2011), and possibly the Shuiquan Formation in the Tarim block (Xiao et al., 2004), but these successions are dominated by siliciclastics and, as a result, their $\delta^{13}C$ records are stratigraphically sporadic and can be more disproportionately compromised by authigenic carbonates (Macdonald et al., 2013; Schrag et al., 2013; Cui et al., 2017). Current controversies surrounding the Shuram Excursion and its potential correlatives include (1) its origin: whether the Shuram Excursion represents a disturbance of the global ocean dissolved inorganic carbon (DIC) reservoir due to oxidation of organic carbon or methane (Rothman et al., 2003; Fike et al., 2006; Kaufman et al., 2007; McFadden et al., 2008; Bjerrum and Canfield, 2011), reflects conditions conducive to authigenic carbonate precipitation (Grotzinger et al., 2011; Macdonald et al., 2013; Schrag et al., 2013; Cui et al., 2017), or results from burial or meteoric diagenesis (Knauth and Kennedy, 2009; Derry, 2010); (2) its complexity: whether the Shuram Excursion consists of a simple negative anomaly (Fike et al., 2006; Le Guerroue et al., 2006; An et al., 2015) or a complex negative anomaly punctuated with one or more small-scale positive anomalies (Condon et al., 2005; Verdel et al., 2011; Lu et al., 2013; Xiao et al., 2017a; Zhou et al., 2017a); (3) its age and duration: whether it lasted a few million years or up to 50 million years (Le Guerroue et al., 2006); and (4) its stratigraphic relationship with the c. 580 Ma Gaskiers glaciation, Doushantuo–Pertatataka acanthomorphs, and Ediacara-type fossils.

In some regions a negative $\delta^{13}C$ excursion regarded as a Shuram equivalent sits stratigraphically below a glacial diamictite interpreted as a Gaskiers equivalent, suggesting that the Gaskiers glaciation may postdate the initiation or even the entirety of the Shuram Excursion. For example, on the basis of a basin subsidence rate model Witkosky and Wernicke (2018) estimated that the Shuram Excursion (as recorded in the Rainstorm Member) occurred 585–579 Ma, thus older than the c. 580 Ma Gaskiers glaciation (as represented by the incision of the Rainstorm Member shelf). Other possible examples of Shuram–Gaskiers relationships include the negative $\delta^{13}C$ excursion in Member E in the uppermost Nyborg Formation that underlies the Mortensnes diamictite in northern Norway (Halverson et al., 2005), the negative $\delta^{13}C$ excursion in the Shuiquan Formation that underlies the Hankalchough diamictite in the Tarim Block (Xiao et al., 2004), and the negative $\delta^{13}C$ excursion in the Hongzaoshan Formation that underlies the Hongtiegou Diamictite in the Chaidam Basin of northwestern China (Shen et al., 2010). These relationships would suggest that the Gaskiers glaciation postdated the initiation of the Shuram negative $\delta^{13}C$ excursion. However, whether these examples represent Shuram and Gaskiers equivalents has not been tested thoroughly. Indeed, there are some preliminary data implying that there may have been more than one glaciation in the Ediacaran Period. For example, the Hankalchough and Hongtiegou diamictites may represent a post–Shuram Excursion near the Ediacaran–Cambrian boundary rather than equivalents of the Gaskiers glaciation (Shen et al., 2010), and several authors have argued for the presence of glacial diamictites near the Ediacaran–Cambrian boundary in Kazakhstan, Kyrgyzstan and Siberia (Chumakov, 2009; Kaufman et al., 2009).

In other regions, there is evidence suggesting that the Gaskiers is older than the Shuram. For example, Prave et al. (2009) argued that the Inishowen–Loch na Cille–MacDuff ice-rafted debris beds in the Dalradian Supergroup represent the Gaskiers glaciation in Scotland and Ireland, and the overlaying Girlsta Limestone records a negative $\delta^{13}C$ excursion equivalent to the Shuram Excursion; if correct, then the Gaskiers glaciation would predate the Shuram Excursion. In Newfoundland a Shuram-like excursion has been reported from the upper Briscal and Mistaken Point Formations, and a possible equivalent of EN2 from the Mall Bay Formation, indicating that the Gaskiers Formation—which immediately overlies the Mall Bay Formation but predates the Briscal

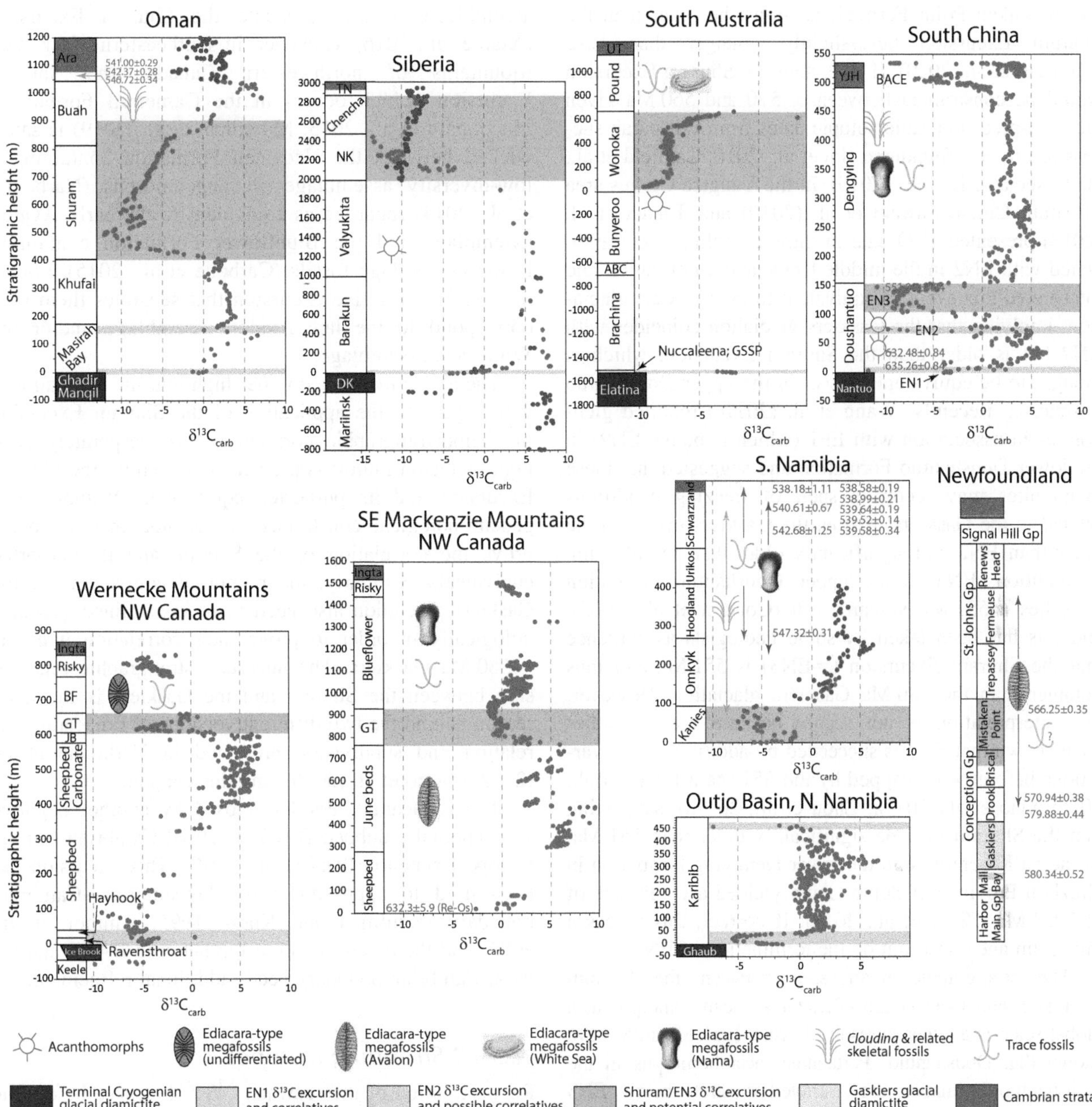

FIGURE 18.8 Representative $\delta^{13}C$ profiles with approximate horizons of fossil occurrences in Ediacaran successions, highlighting possible equivalents of the Shuram Excursion. *Oman*: $\delta^{13}C$ data shown in blue from Fike et al. (2006); $\delta^{13}C$ data shown in red from Amthor et al. (2003). *Siberia*: $\delta^{13}C$ data shown in blue from Ura Uplift Section and $\delta^{13}C$ data shown in red from Zhuya River section (Pokrovskii et al., 2006); biostratigraphic data from Sergeev et al. (2011) and Moczydłowska and Nagovitsin (2012). *South Australia*: $\delta^{13}C$ data of the Wonoka Formation from canyon shoulder section 1 in the Flinders Ranges (Husson et al., 2015) and $\delta^{13}C$ data of the Nuccaleena Formation from Calver (2000); biostratigraphic data from Jenkins (1995), Gehling (2000), and (Grey, 2005). *Wernecke and Mackenzie Mountains, Northwestern Canada*: $\delta^{13}C$ data from Macdonald et al. (2013); radiometric date from Rooney et al. (2015); biostratigraphic data from Macdonald et al. (2013), Narbonne et al. (2014), and Carbone and Narbonne (2014). *South China*: $\delta^{13}C$ data of the Doushantuo Formation from McFadden et al. (2008) and Li et al. (2010), $\delta^{13}C$ data of Dengying Formation from Wang et al. (2014), $\delta^{13}C$ data of Yanjiahe Formation from Ishikawa et al. (2008), Jiang et al. (2012), and Ishikawa et al. (2013); biostratigraphic data from Cai et al. (2010), Meyer et al. (2012), Chen et al. (2013), Chen et al. (2014), Cai et al. (2015), and Cortijo et al. (2015b). *Southern Namibia*: $\delta^{13}C$ data shown in blue from Brak section and $\delta^{13}C$ data shown in red from Zebra River section, both in Zaris Sub-basin (Wood et al., 2015); biostratigraphic data from Germs (1995), Grotzinger et al. (1995), Jensen et al. (2000), Jensen and Runnegar (2005), and Wood et al. (2015). *Northern Namibia*: $\delta^{13}C$ data from Halverson et al. (2005). *Newfoundland*: biostratigraphic data from Narbonne and Gehling (2003), and Liu et al. (2010, 2014b); radiometric dates from Pu et al. (2016); the potential occurrence of EN2 and Shuram Excursion from Canfield et al. (2020). All radiometric dates are cited from Schmitz (2012) unless otherwise noted. *ABC*, ABC Range Quartzite; *BF*, Blueflower Formation; *DK*, Dzhemkukan Formation; *GT*, Gametrail Formation; *JB*, June beds; *NK*, Nikol'skoe Formation; *TN*, Tinnaya Formation; *UT*, Uratanna Formation; *YJH*, Yanjiahe Formation. *Modified from Xiao et al. (2016).*

and Mistaken Point Formations—must be older than the Shuram Excursion but slightly younger than EN2 (Canfield et al., 2020). If true, then the Shuram Excursion would be constrained between c. 570 and 560 Ma given the high-precision radioisotopic dates from Ediacaran successions in Newfoundland (Pu et al., 2016; Canfield et al., 2020; see also Rooney, 2019). In the Yangtze Gorges area of South China, Sawaki et al. (2010) and Tahata et al. (2013) presented $\delta^{18}O$ data to show a cooling event associated with EN2 in the middle Doushantuo Formation and interpreted this event as equivalent to the Gaskiers glaciation, implying that the Gaskiers glaciation coincides with EN2 but is older than the Shuram Excursion, which is thought to be equivalent to EN3 in the upper Doushantuo Formation. Recently, Wang et al. (2017c) reported glendonites in association with EP1 (which is below EN2) in the lower Doushantuo Formation and suggested that these glendonites may record a spell of freezing conditions related to the Gaskiers; if true, the Gaskiers may even be older than EN2 and significantly older than the Shuram. In addition, EN3 in the upper Doushantuo Formation underlies a 551 Ma volcanic ash (Condon et al., 2005), and this has been taken by some geologists as evidence that the Shuram Excursion (=EN3) is 551 Ma and thus younger than the 580 Ma Gaskiers glaciation. However, this interpretation is not secure because recent studies have shown that EN3 is succeeded by additional $\delta^{13}C$ variations before being capped by the 551 Ma ash (An et al., 2015; Xiao et al., 2017a; Zhou et al., 2017a), suggesting that the Shuram may be significantly older than 551 Ma. In fact, a K-bentonite in the lower Dengying Formation in Guizhou Province of South China yielded a U–Pb age of 557 ± 3 Ma (Zhou et al., 2018); if correct, this places a minimum age constraint on the termination of EN3.

The stratigraphic relationship between the Shuram Excursion and Doushantuo–Pertatataka acanthomorphs at a global scale is another unresolved issue. Earlier studies have shown that Doushantuo–Pertatataka acanthomorphs in the Doushantuo Formation are restricted to strata below EN3 (McFadden et al., 2008; Liu et al., 2014f), but recent studies have shown that some elements of Doushantuo–Pertatataka-type acanthomorphs may postdate EN3 in South China (Ouyang et al., 2017) or may occur in terminal Ediacaran rocks in the East European Platform (Golubkova et al., 2015) and northern Mongolia (Anderson et al., 2017a, 2019), opening the possibility that the stratigraphic ranges of the Shuram Excursion, Doushantuo–Pertatataka-type acanthomorphs, and Ediacara-type megafossils may partially overlap.

The stratigraphic relationship between the Shuram Excursion and Ediacara-type megafossils at a global scale is not fully resolved. In South China, South Australia, and Namibia where both Ediacara-type megafossils and purported Shuram Excursion are recorded, Ediacara-type megafossils of the White Sea or Nama assemblages clearly postdate the Shuram Excursion (Xiao et al., 2016). However, in southeastern Mackenzie Mountains of northwestern Canada, the Shuram Excursion (which occurs in the Gametrail Formation; Macdonald et al., 2013; Moynihan et al., 2019) is sandwiched between the Nadaleen Formation containing a low-diversity assemblage of rangeomorphs (Narbonne et al., 2014) regarded as equivalent to the early Avalon assemblage and the Blueflower Formation containing Nama assemblage fossils (Carbone et al., 2015), implying that the negative excursion that separates them may correspond to the late Avalon assemblage and/or the White Sea assemblage.

The above mentioned issues highlight the uncertainties with regard to the application of the Shuram Excursion in chemostratigraphic correlation. We desperately need high-precision radioisotopic ages to constrain the Shuram Excursion and its purported equivalents. Without such geochronological constraints, we cannot unambiguously prove the correlation of the Shuram and its purported equivalents. Similarly, the purported equivalents of the Gaskiers glaciation also need to be constrained geochronologically in order to prove their correlation with the ~580 Ma Gaskiers. The uncertain stratigraphic relationship between the Shuram and the Gaskiers is the main reason behind the two different versions of Ediacaran correlation and subdivision presented in Narbonne et al. (2012a), Xiao et al. (2016), and this chapter.

The Ediacaran Period is closed by another negative $\delta^{13}C$ anomaly, dubbed BACE or Basal Cambrian Carbon Isotope Excursion (Zhu et al., 2006). This excursion has been used to approximate the Precambrian–Cambrian boundary (Kaufman and Knoll, 1995; Amthor et al., 2003), but the precise relationship between BACE and the basal Cambrian boundary needs additional refinement.

18.3.4.2 Strontium isotopes

Reconstruction of the seawater $^{87}Sr/^{86}Sr$ curve before the Ordovician Period suffers greatly from a lack of suitably well-preserved materials, which necessitates careful sample selection and preparation (Kaufman et al., 1993; Bailey et al., 2000; Liu et al., 2014d) (Fig. 18.9). Nevertheless, strontium isotope stratigraphy can potentially resolve stratigraphic conflicts caused by the ambiguity and circular reasoning inherent in matching otherwise identical $\delta^{13}C$ excursions because of the magnitude of the rise in seawater $^{87}Sr/^{86}Sr$ during the Ediacaran Period (from ~0.7071 to ~0.7087).

Basal Ediacaran cap dolostones tend to have highly variable and sometimes highly elevated $^{87}Sr/^{86}Sr$ ratios based on bulk samples (Yoshioka et al., 2003; Sawaki et al., 2010), probably due to variable diagenetic/hydrothermal alterations (Huang et al., 2011; Zhao et al., 2018) or mixing with glacial meltwaters carrying radiogenic signals derived from continental weathering (Liu et al., 2013a, 2014d, 2018b). Stepwise leaching technique can help to minimize the contamination of clay minerals, revealing end-member $^{87}Sr/^{86}Sr$ values from the cap dolostone in Australia and Mongolia, including high ratios reflecting glacial meltwaters as well as low ratios (0.7072–0.7073) interpreted as primary seawater signatures (Liu et al., 2013a, 2014d, 2018b). These low $^{87}Sr/^{86}Sr$ ratios from the cap dolostone in Australia and Mongolia are similar to $^{87}Sr/^{86}Sr$ values of laminated micrite and fibrous calcite seafloor cement in the Sete Lagoas cap dolostone in Brazil (Misi et al., 2007). After the deposition of the cap dolostone, limestone samples are readily available for $^{87}Sr/^{86}Sr$ analysis. For example, Sr-rich limestone of the Hayhook Formation (NW Canada) yielded $^{87}Sr/^{86}Sr$ ratios of 0.70714 ± 2 (James et al., 2001), which are consistent with data from postglacial limestones of Namibia (Halverson et al., 2007). In Namibia, least altered $^{87}Sr/^{86}Sr$ values subsequently rise to c. 0.7080 as $\delta^{13}C$ values recover from −4.4‰ to 0‰, and a rise of similar magnitude has been recorded in lower Ediacaran carbonate in the Doushantuo Formation of South China (Sawaki et al., 2010; Lv et al., 2018). High-Sr samples from NW Canada show an increase to 0.70753, while least altered $^{87}Sr/^{86}Sr$ data from South America trace a rise from c. 0.7074 to 0.70777 ± 2 during the $\delta^{13}C$ recovery (Nogueira et al., 2007; de Alvarenga et al., 2008). Nearly identical values (c. 0.7077–0.7078) have been reported for basal Ediacaran barite samples of NW Africa at a comparable point in the postglacial $\delta^{13}C$ curve (Shields et al., 2007). Taken together, these data indicate a rise in seawater $^{87}Sr/^{86}Sr$ from c. 0.7071 to c. 0.7077 or higher during the postglacial $\delta^{13}C$ recovery to positive values, which lasted <3 million years (Condon et al., 2005).

The most complete $^{87}Sr/^{86}Sr$ record derives from South China (Sawaki et al., 2010; Cui et al., 2015; Furuyama et al., 2016; Lv et al., 2018). This record indicates that, following the initial rise in $^{87}Sr/^{86}Sr$ ratios after the cap dolostone, $^{87}Sr/^{86}Sr$ ratios seem to stabilize at a plateau of 0.7080 that characterizes the lower Ediacaran System, then rise to a peak of ~0.7090 roughly concurrent with the Shuram Excursion, and finally fall back to values around 0.7085 in terminal Ediacaran (Fig. 18.9). A ~0.7085–0.7090 peak in association with purported Shuram Excursion has also been reported from Siberia (Pokrovskii et al., 2006; Melezhik et al., 2009), Oman (Burns et al., 1994), and Australia (Calver, 2000). Several $^{87}Sr/^{86}Sr$ studies span the Precambrian–Cambrian boundary, the most comprehensive being that of Brasier et al. (1996). That study and other work (Derry et al., 1994; Kaufman et al., 1996; Nicholas, 1996; Valladares et al., 2006) constrain latest Ediacaran and earliest Cambrian $^{87}Sr/^{86}Sr$ to c. 0.70845 ± 5. Least altered samples from Mongolia (Brasier et al., 1996), Siberia (Kaufman et al., 1996), and South China (Li et al., 2013a) indicate that seawater $^{87}Sr/^{86}Sr$ decreased through the Precambrian–Cambrian transition interval to reach a low of 0.70805 ± 5 during Cambrian Stage 2.

18.3.4.3 Sulfur isotopes

Evaporite sulfate deposits are scarce during the Ediacaran Period and so with few exceptions, knowledge of seawater $\delta^{34}S_{sulfate}$ through this interval derives mainly from carbonate-associated sulfate (CAS), trace sulfate in phosphorite, and barite. A high-resolution analysis of the cap dolostone in South China reveals high $\delta^{34}S_{CAS}$ values (25–40‰, mean 30‰) in intrashelf facies, low values (17–33‰, mean 26‰) in outer shelf facies, and still lower values (17–33‰, mean 22‰) in slope facies (Huang et al., 2013). $\delta^{34}S_{barite}$ data indicate that seawater $\delta^{34}S_{suphate}$ had reached values of 20–45‰ by the end of the cap dolostone (Shields et al., 2007). CAS data show predominantly high and variable $\delta^{34}S_{CAS}$ values (20–45‰) values in the Ediacaran Period (Fike et al., 2006; McFadden et al., 2008; Halverson et al., 2010). There is some evidence suggesting a decline in $\delta^{34}S_{CAS}$ values during the Shuram Excursion (Fike et al., 2006; McFadden et al., 2008; Li et al., 2017; Shi et al., 2018), but $\delta^{34}S_{CAS}$ rises again to high values (~40‰) in the terminal Ediacaran (Fike et al., 2006; Cui et al., 2016a,b; Tostevin et al., 2017). By the early Cambrian $\delta^{34}S_{sulfate}$, as measured in a variety of minerals, including evaporites, francolite, and carbonate, was also high (35‰–40‰) in most basins (Holser and Kaplan, 1966; Strauss, 1993; Shields et al., 1999; Kampschulte and Strauss, 2004; Schröder et al., 2004).

Pyrite sulfur isotope data ($\delta^{34}S_{pyrite}$) are available for many Ediacaran successions, including those in Oman (Fike et al., 2006), Australia (Gorjan et al., 2000), Namibia (Ries et al., 2009; Tostevin et al., 2017), South China (McFadden et al., 2008; Cui et al., 2015; Wang et al., 2017a), Newfoundland (Canfield et al., 2007), Eastern European Platform (Johnston et al., 2012), and Siberia (Cui et al., 2016a). There are significant stratigraphic and geographic variations in $\delta^{34}S_{pyrite}$, which can range from −30‰ to +40‰ (Tostevin et al., 2017). Given the many factors that can affect $\delta^{34}S_{pyrite}$ values, including primary production and availability of organic matter (Leavitt et al., 2013), marine sulfate concentration (Gomes and Hurtgen, 2015; Bradley et al., 2016), cell-specific sulfate reduction rate (Bradley et al., 2016), oxidative recycling of sulfide (Fike et al., 2015), and the location of pyrite formation (Gomes and Hurtgen, 2015), as well as the complex redox structure of Ediacaran oceans with generally low sulfate concentrations

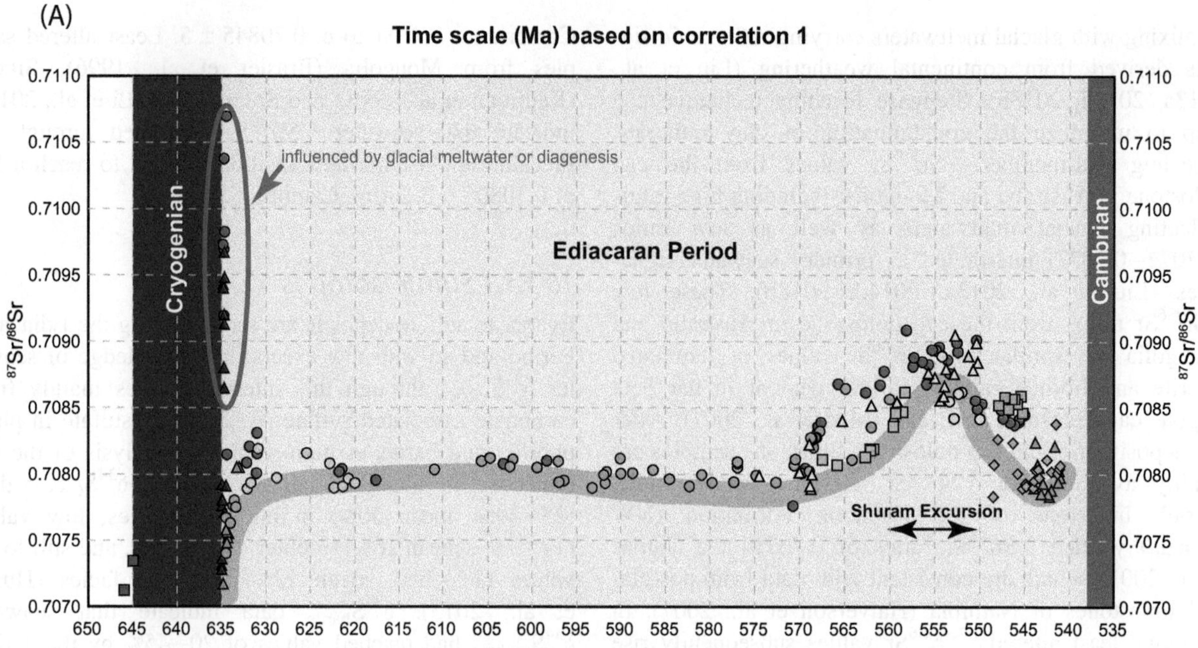

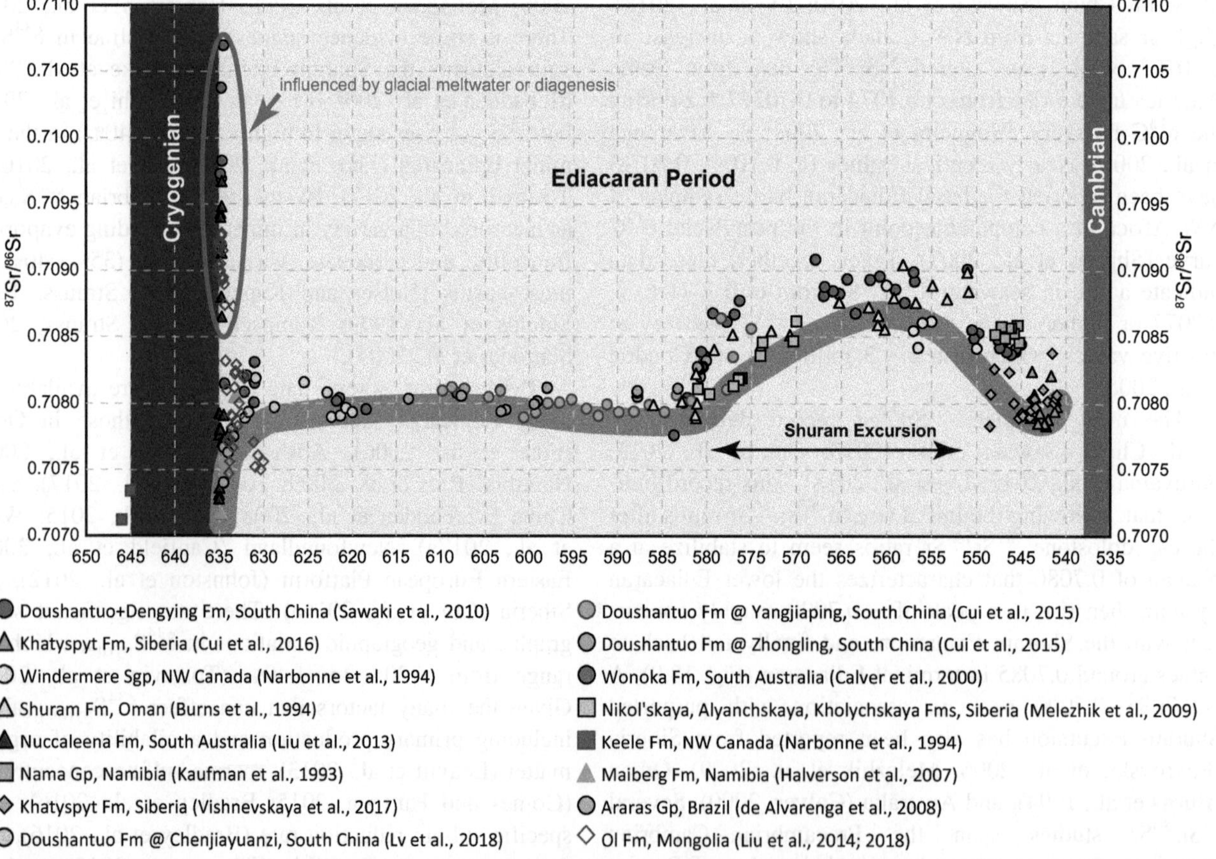

FIGURE 18.9 Compilation of Ediacaran $^{87}Sr/^{86}Sr$ data. Data are screened using the criteria of carbonate wt.% > 60% and Mn/Sr < 1, except those from the basal Ediacaran cap dolostone. High $^{87}Sr/^{86}Sr$ ratios of cap dolostones may have resulted from diagenetic alteration or influence of glacial meltwaters (Liu et al., 2013a, 2014d), thus not representing seawater signals. Most likely seawater $^{87}Sr/^{86}Sr$ ratios are marked by thick gray line. The approximate age of the Shuram Excursion is marked by a double-arrow-headed line. Age estimates are based on the two correlations shown in Fig. 18.10. *$^{87}Sr/^{86}Sr$ data from Kaufman et al. (1993), Narbonne et al. (1994), Burns et al. (1994), Calver (2000), Halverson et al. (2007), de Alvarenga et al. (2008), Melezhik et al. (2009), Sawaki et al. (2010), Liu et al. (2013a, 2014d), Cui et al. (2015, 2016a), Vishnevskaya et al. (2017), Liu et al. (2018b), and Lv et al. (2018).*

(Li et al., 2010), it is not surprising that Ediacaran $\delta^{34}S_{pyrite}$ data exhibit significant stratigraphic and geographic variations. Thus, compared with carbon and strontium isotopes, $\delta^{34}S_{pyrite}$ is perhaps inherently less useful in global chemostratigraphic correlation of Ediacaran successions. Nonetheless, the $\delta^{34}S_{pyrite}$ record from Oman (Fike et al., 2006) and South China (McFadden et al., 2008; Cui et al., 2015; Shi et al., 2018) shows a steady decline during the Shuram (and EN3) anomaly, but it remains to see whether this decline represents a global signature that overwhelms local and regional heterogeneities.

18.3.4.4 Redox proxies

The strong stratigraphic and geographic variations in Ediacaran $\delta^{34}S_{pyrite}$ and $\delta^{34}S_{sulfate}$ values are commonly interpreted in terms of a low-sulfate ocean (Halverson and Hurtgen, 2007). A low-sulfate ocean coupled with a low-oxygen atmosphere is prone to develop ferruginous deep waters. The prevalence of ferruginous deep waters in the Ediacaran Period has been borne out by Fe speciation data (Canfield et al., 2008). The combined use of Fe_{HR}/Fe_T (highly reactive iron vs total iron) and Fe_P/Fe_{HR} (pyrite iron vs highly reactive iron) ratios can help to distinguish sediments deposited under oxic, ferruginous, and euxinic water columns (Raiswell et al., 1988; Poulton and Canfield, 2005; Lyons and Severmann, 2006). A compilation of Fe speciation data shows that about half of Ediacaran samples from outer shelf and basinal environments are characterized by high Fe_{HR}/Fe_T ratios indicative of deposition in anoxic conditions, and the majority ($>90\%$) of these anoxic samples were deposited in ferruginous deep waters (Sperling et al., 2015). Because ferruginous conditions can only arise when the molar flux of Fe_{HR} to the deep ocean is greater than half the flux of sulfide, these Fe speciation data are consistent with a generally low-sulfate ocean reservoir in the Ediacaran Period.

Trace metal concentrations and isotopes, on the other hand, indicate that deep waters were not completely and continuously ferruginous throughout the entire Ediacaran Period. Instead, there were probably several episodes of deep-water oxygenation to various extent. The concentration of redox-sensitive trace metals (such as Mo, V, and U) in euxinic black shales can be used to track the oceanic reservoir size of these metals and to deduce the relative extent of deep-ocean oxygenation. Based on trace metal data from the Doushantuo Formation in South China, Sahoo et al. (2016) have identified three episodes of deep-ocean oxygenation events that punctuated more or less ferruginous conditions. These three events are recorded in black shales immediately above the basal Ediacaran cap dolostone, the middle Doushantuo Formation, and the uppermost Doushantuo Formation. Sahoo et al. (2016) proposed that these three oxygenation events occurred at ~632, ~580, and ~560–551 Ma, respectively (Fig. 18.10). Additional deep-water oxygenation events may have occurred during the Shuram Excursion (Fike et al., 2006; McFadden et al., 2008; Zhang et al., 2019) and following the Gaskiers glaciation (Canfield et al., 2007). The ~560–551 Ma oxygenation event is also supported by a global compilation of Mo concentration data (Scott et al., 2008) as well as $\delta^{238}U$ and $\delta^{98}Mo$ data (Kendall et al., 2015). After 551 Ma, the deep ocean returned to pervasive anoxia as inferred from exceptionally low $\delta^{238}U$ data from terminal Ediacaran carbonates (Tostevin et al., 2018; Wei et al., 2018; Zhang et al., 2018). If these episodic oxygenation events had a global impact, they can be used for global correlation of Ediacaran strata. In this respect, proxies for global redox conditions (such as $\delta^{238}U$ and $\delta^{98}Mo$) may prove to be useful.

Against the backdrop of ferruginous conditions in deep waters, Fe speciation data suggest that mid-depth and shallow waters experienced more complex and dynamic redox conditions. For instance, Li et al. (2010) have shown that euxinic or sulfidic conditions may have developed in mid-depth waters along distal continental margins of the Yangtze Platform. In shallow waters on continental shelves, local redox conditions may have been modulated by oceanic upwelling, sea-level change, temperature, and isolation from global ocean isolation—factors contributing to the temporally dynamic and spatially heterogeneous redox conditions that controlled the distribution of Ediacaran metazoan ecosystems (Wood et al., 2015; Bowyer et al., 2017). As such, geochemical proxies for local redox conditions such as Fe speciation data are less useful for the global correlation of Ediacaran strata (Xiao et al., 2017a).

18.3.5 Radioisotopic dating

Key U–Pb dates from the Ediacaran System and immediately adjacent Cryogenian and Cambrian strata are listed in Table 18.1, where recalculated ages are presented to take into consideration of tracer and decay constant uncertainties. The base of the Ediacaran is well constrained by U–Pb dates of: (1) 635.21 ± 0.59 Ma from the terminal Cryogenian Ghaub Formation in Oman (Hoffmann et al., 2004; Prave et al., 2016); (2) 634.57 ± 0.88 Ma from the terminal Cryogenian Nantuo Formation in South China (Zhou et al., 2019); (3) 636.41 ± 0.45 Ma from the terminal Cryogenian Cottons Breccia in King Island, Tasmania, Australia (Calver et al., 2013); (4) 635.2 ± 0.6 Ma atop the Doushantuo Formation in South China and 632.5 ± 0.5 Ma a few meters above its basal Ediacaran cap dolostone (Condon et al., 2005); and (5) a Re–Os date of 632.3 ± 5.9 Ma from the basal Sheepbed Formation of the lower Ediacaran System in northwest Canada (Rooney et al., 2015). The top of the Ediacaran in Namibia is constrained by dates of 540.61 ± 0.67 Ma immediately below and 538.18 ± 1.11 Ma immediately above the disconformable contact with the overlying Lower Cambrian (recalculated from Grotzinger et al., 1995). A recent study further constraint the Ediacaran–Cambrian boundary in Namibia between 538.58 ± 0.19 and 538.99 ± 0.21 Ma, with additional dates of 539.64 ± 0.19, 539.52 ± 0.14 and 539.58 ± 0.34 Ma from the terminal Ediacaran Spitskopf Member (Linnemann et al., 2019). In Oman the carbon isotope feature BACE and the last appearance of *Cloudina* were constrained by dates of 542.37 ± 0.28 Ma immediately below and 541.00 ± 0.29 Ma immediately above the BACE (recalculated from Bowring et al., 2007). However, given that BACE may slightly predate the Ediacaran–Cambrian boundary (Smith et al., 2016; Ahn and Zhu, 2017), and considering that the Ediacaran–Cambrian boundary in Namibia is constrained around 538 Ma (Linnemann et al., 2019), it is possible that the Ediacaran–Cambrian boundary in Oman is above the 541.00 ± 0.29 Ma ash.

Key U–Pb dates within the Ediacaran Period are available to constrain the beginning and end of the Gaskiers glaciation in Avalon, all three Ediacara-type megafossil assemblages, the beginning of the Ediacaran acanthomorphic acritarchs in South China, and the end of EN3—a purported equivalent of the Shuram Excursion in South China (Fig. 18.10; Table 18.1). These dates provide a geochronological framework for the subdivision and correlation of the Ediacaran System. However, the Shuram Excursion has not been tightly bracketed by radioisotopic dates, regional acanthomorph biozones have not been bracketed geochronologically, and there is a general scarcity of radioisotopic dates from lower Ediacaran successions. Clearly, more high-precision radioisotopic dates are needed to constrain the age of Ediacaran carbon isotope features, to test whether the purported equivalents of the Shuram Excursion can be correlated, and to resolve the stratigraphic relationship between the Shuram Excursion, the Gaskiers glaciation, and acanthomorph biozones.

18.4 Toward an Ediacaran chronostratigraphy

From the above, it is clear that the integration of acanthomorphic acritarchs, Ediacara-type megafossils, carbon and strontium isotopes, precise U–Pb dates, and climatic events has the potential to subdivide the Ediacaran into broad divisions. All of these indicators are strongly affected by facies and preservational factors (see the respective discussions previously), requiring the integration of multiple biological and geochemical proxies from multiple regions to provide a robust Ediacaran subdivision. The lower third of the Ediacaran System (~635–600 Ma) contains acanthomorphic acritarchs but apparently lacks Ediacara-type megafossils. In addition, it is characterized by relatively low $^{87}Sr/^{86}Sr$ ratios (0.7071–0.7080) and a significant rise in $\delta^{13}C_{carbonate}$ from c. −5‰ in cap dolostone to high values of c. 5‰ in the lower Ediacaran System. The uppermost part of the Ediacaran System (~550–538 Ma), or the TES, typically contains a leiosphere microfossil assemblage (but see Golubkova et al., 2015; Anderson et al., 2017a, 2019) and numerous Ediacaran megafossils. It is characterized by high $^{87}Sr/^{86}Sr$ ratios (>0.7080) and moderately positive $\delta^{13}C_{carbonate}$ values terminated by a negative excursion (BACE). It is also constrained by many high-precision radioisotopic dates and abundant fossils from the overlying Cambrian Strata.

Uncertainty in correlating siliciclastic and carbonate facies in the middle part of the Ediacaran (~600–560 Ma) hinders global correlation and our understanding of the transition between the basal and uppermost Ediacaran. Phosphatic carbonates, chert nodules, and fine siliciclastics of this age in central Asia contain diverse acanthomorphic acritarchs that are amenable to an array of chemostratigraphic techniques but apparently lack either radioisotopic age constraints or Ediacara-type megafossils. In contrast, deep-water siliciclastics in Newfoundland and England contain abundant Ediacara-type megafossils of the Avalon assemblage beneath volcanic ash beds suitable for radioisotopic dating, but carbonates suitable for chemostratigraphy are virtually absent and only nondiagnostic leiosphere microfossils are preserved in these thermally mature strata. The ~580 Ma Gaskiers glaciation marks a significant divide that at least regionally separates lower Ediacaran strata lacking Ediacaran megafossils from upper Ediacaran strata with abundant Ediacaran megafossils (Pu et al., 2016). However, the Gaskiers glaciation is known only from Avalonia and a few other continents, and its global correlation remains uncertain. Although there is strong evidence to suggest that all Ediacara-type megafossils postdate the ~580 Ma Gaskiers glaciation, the stratigraphic relationship among the Gaskiers glaciation, the Shuram Excursion, and Ediacaran acanthomorphic acritarchs is not resolved with confidence. To reflect these uncertainties, two distinct correlations consistent with all available radioisotopic dates and biostratigraphic and chemostratigraphic data are presented in Fig. 18.10. These two correlations are built upon the assumption that the negative C-isotope excursion marked by the Gaskiers cap carbonate is a global event (Myrow and Kaufman, 1999) and thus the short-lived Gaskiers glaciation ought to be temporally associated with a negative $\delta^{13}C$ excursion (but see Wang et al., 2017c and

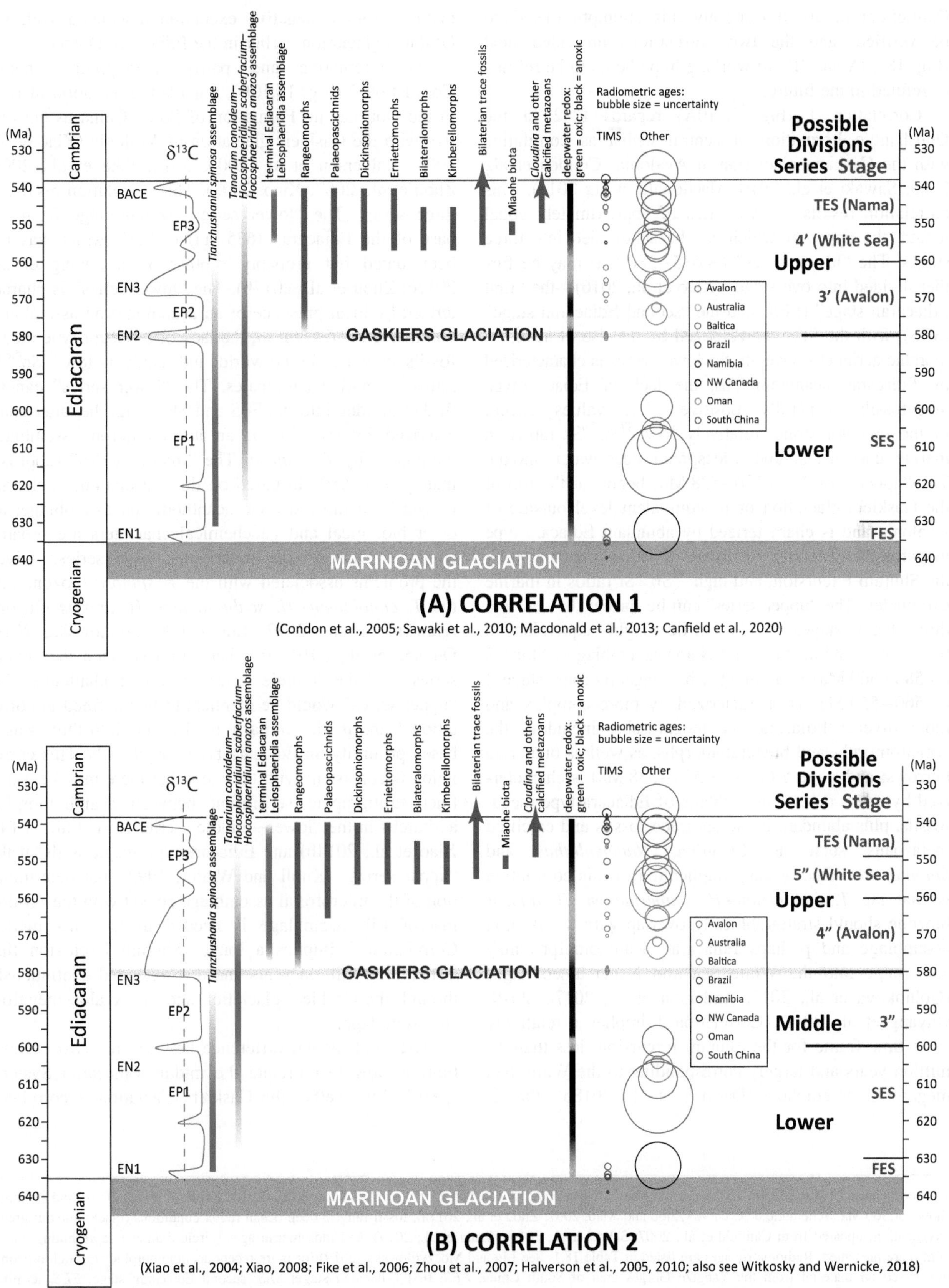

FIGURE 18.10 Correlation and internal subdivision of the Ediacaran System: (A) Correlation 1 and (B) Correlation 2. The key difference between these two correlations relates to how the Gaskiers glaciation is correlated with $\delta^{13}C$ excursions (EN2 vs EN3 = Shuram). Both correlations assume that the Gaskiers glaciation coincides with a negative $\delta^{13}C$ excursion, although this assumption remains to be tested (see Wang et al., 2017c; Canfield et al., 2020). Canfield et al. (2020) proposed a correlation similar to Correlation 1, but with EN2 slightly predating the Gaskiers glaciation.

Canfield et al., 2020). Certainly, this assumption needs to be verified, and the two correlations presented next (Fig. 18.10A and B) are working hypotheses to be refined or refuted in the future.

Correlation 1 (Fig. 18.10A) regards EN2 in the Doushantuo Formation of central China as correlative with the Gaskiers glaciation in Avalonia (Condon et al., 2005; Sawaki et al., 2010; Macdonald et al., 2013). This correlation results in two series of approximately equal length, the upper of which can be subdivided into three stages. The "lower series" ($\sim$635–580 Ma) may be further divided into two stages (Xiao et al., 2016)—the "first Ediacaran stage" (FES) and the "second Ediacaran stage" (SES), with the SES characterized by the rise of acanthomorphic acritarchs. Overall, the lower series is characterized by Ediacaran acanthomorphs, the lack of Ediacara-type megafossils, generally positive $\delta^{13}C$ values except in the cap dolostone, relatively low $^{87}Sr/^{86}Sr$ ratios in marine carbonates, and widespread deep-water anoxia. The "upper series" ($\sim$580–538 Ma) begins at the top of the Gaskiers glaciation or its equivalent level outside of Avalonia and is characterized by abundant Ediacara-type megafossils, generally positive $\delta^{13}C$ values punctuated by the Shuram Excursion, and high $^{87}Sr/^{86}Sr$ ratios in marine carbonates. The "upper series" can be further divided into three stages: stages 3–5 would be roughly equivalent to the Avalon, White Sea, and Nama assemblages. Stage 3 ($\sim$580–560 Ma) is dominated by rangeomorphs; stage 4 ($\sim$560–550 Ma) is characterized by more complex and more diverse Ediacara-type megafossils, including the erniettomorphs and bilateralomorphs, as well as bilaterian burrows; and stage 5 (TES; $\sim$550–538 Ma) is characterized by a less diverse assemblage of Ediacara-type megafossils, plus abundant bilaterian trace fossils and calcified metazoans such as *Cloudina*, *Namacalathus* and *Sinotubulites*. One testable implication of this correlation is that the *T. conoideum–H. scaberfacium–H. anozos* biozone should stratigraphically overlap with the Avalon assemblage and perhaps Ediacaran acanthomorphs may also range into the White Sea and Nama assemblages (Golubkova et al., 2015; Anderson et al., 2017a, 2019; Ouyang et al., 2017). Correlation 1 implies a relatively short time frame for the Shuram Excursion, less than 10 million years and largely corresponding to the White Sea megafossil assemblage (Darroch et al., 2018b), that is distinct from a negative excursion associated with the Gaskiers glaciation earlier in the Ediacaran Period.

An alternative and partly overlapping scheme, Correlation 2 (Fig. 18.10B), regards the initiation of EN3 in the Doushantuo Formation of South China as correlative with the Gaskiers glaciation in Avalonia (Xiao et al., 2004; Halverson et al., 2005, 2010; Fike et al., 2006; Zhou et al., 2007; Xiao, 2008). This correlation results in three series. The "lower series" would range from the base of the Ediacaran (635 Ma) to EN2, which has not been dated but probably $<609 \pm 5$ Ma (Wang et al., 2017c; Zhou et al., 2017b). The "lower series" is characterized by local presence of an acanthomorph assemblage dominated by *T. spinosa*, the lack of Ediacara-type megafossils anywhere in the world, and relatively low $^{87}Sr/^{86}Sr$ ratios in marine carbonates. The "lower series" can be further divided into the FES and SES, with the latter characterized by the rise of an acanthomorph assemblage dominated by *T. spinosa*. The "middle series" (approximately 600–580 Ma based on this correlation) is characterized by a more diverse acanthomorph assemblage; all other biological and geochemical characters are broadly similar to those of the underlying "lower series." Given the problems associated with the *T. spinosa* biozone and the *T. conoideum–H. scaberfacium–H. anozos* biozone (Hawkins et al., 2017; Liu and Moczydłowska, 2019; Ouyang et al., 2019), the distinction between the "lower series" and the "middle series" may be a challenge. The "upper series" would be identical to that defined in correlation 1 and might similarly be divisible into three stages based primarily on Ediacara-type megafossils. This correlation is consistent with the view that there may be a distinct stratigraphic separation between acanthomorphic acritarchs in the "lower–middle" series (Liu et al., 2014f; Xiao et al., 2014b) and Ediacara-type megafossils in the "upper series" (Knoll and Walter, 1992), but determination of the microfossil assemblage coeval with the Avalon macrofossil assemblage is needed to test this model. Correlation 2 implies a longer Shuram Excursion that lasted $\sim$20 million years and that extended continuously through the Gaskiers glaciation and the Avalon megafossil assemblage.

The fundamental difference between the two correlations is how to correlate the middle Ediacaran System, specifically whether the Gaskiers glaciation is correlated

The termination of the Shuram Excursion may be between 557 ± 3 and 566.25 ± 0.35 Ma (Zhou et al., 2018; Canfield et al., 2020) and is herein shown at 560 Ma. Schematic $\delta^{13}C$ curve (Zhou and Xiao, 2007; Zhou et al., 2017a), fossil ranges, deep-ocean redox conditions (black: anoxia; green: oxygenation; updated from Canfield et al., 2007; Sahoo et al., 2016; Zhang et al., 2019), and radiometric ages (circle diameter representing uncertainty) are presented. Radiometric ages are listed in Table 18.1. See Liu and Moczydłowska (2019) for more recent acanthomorphic acritarch biozonation based on material from the Yangtze Gorges area of South China. *FES*, first Ediacaran stage; *SES*, second Ediacaran stage; *TES*, terminal Ediacaran stage; *EN*, Ediacaran negative $\delta^{13}C$ excursions; *EP*, Ediacaran positive $\delta^{13}C$ excursions. *Modified from Narbonne et al. (2012a) and Xiao et al. (2016).*

with the $\delta^{13}C$ chemostratigraphic feature EN2, EN3, or neither. They make different predictions about the age of EN2 and EN3 (or Shuram Excursion), which have not been precisely bracketed by radioisotopic dates: correlation 1 predicts an EN2 at 580 Ma and a shorter EN3 at ~570–560 Ma, whereas correlation 2 predicts an EN2 at ~600 Ma and a longer EN3 at ~580–560 Ma. These predictions can be tested with precise age constraints on EN2 and EN3, as well as potential $\delta^{13}C$ chemostratigraphic data from well-dated siliciclastic sequences (e.g., Canfield et al., 2020).

Both correlations recognize a similar "upper series" rich in Ediacara-type megafossils and overlying the Gaskiers glacial deposits or its equivalents. This stratigraphic interval is remarkably similar to Sokolov's (1952) original concept of "Vendian Series" of western Russia, although Sokolov's elegant designation has regrettably been extended by others to include most of what is presently defined as the Ediacaran Period. This "upper series" is recognizable worldwide and could usefully be formalized. The main problem at present is the reliable correlation of its lower boundary between the siliciclastic strata of Europe and North America (rich in Ediacara-type megafossils) and the phosphatic carbonates of central Asia (rich in microfossils and amenable to a wide array of chemostratigraphic techniques). This resolution is likely to come from integrated macrofossil, microfossil, and chemostratigraphic studies of mixed siliciclastic–carbonate successions and the discovery of additional datable horizons.

Both correlations also agree on the recognition of the TES and the SES, where consensus is emerging with regard to stratigraphic markers of global significance (Xiao et al., 2016). The most important criterion for recognizing the basal boundary of the TES is the rise of skeletal animals such as *Cloudina*, *Sinotubulites* and *Namacalathus*, which are abundant and globally distributed. A few Cambrian-style skeletal fossils, such as *Cambrotubulus* and *Anabarites*, have also been reported from the terminal Ediacaran (Nagovitsin et al., 2015; Rogov et al., 2015; Zhu et al., 2017; Cai et al., 2019), but they are less abundant in the Ediacaran than in the Cambrian. Biostratigraphically, the TES is also characterized by numerous nonmineralized tubular or ribbon-shaped fossils [e.g., *Corumbella* (Babcock et al., 2005; Pacheco et al., 2015; Walde et al., 2015; Warren et al., 2017), *Conotubus* (Cai et al., 2011), *Wutubus* (Chen et al., 2014), *Sekwitubulus* (Carbone et al., 2015) and *Saarina* (Selly et al., 2019)], and these provide alternative biological criteria for correlation. Ediacara-type fossil impressions are low in diversity and dominated by long-ranging forms (Boag et al., 2016), with *Ernietta* being the only global taxon that is restricted to this stage (Ivantsov et al., 2016; Smith et al., 2017). Horizontal trace fossils of moderate complexity occur sporadically in this stage (Jensen et al., 2000; Jensen and Runnegar, 2005; Chen et al., 2013, 2018, 2019; Meyer et al., 2014b; Buatois and Mángano, 2016; Buatois et al., 2018). Chemostratigraphically, the TES is characterized by slightly to moderately positive $\delta^{13}C$ values (Wood et al., 2015; Cui et al., 2016b), sandwiched between the Shuram Excursion beneath and the BACE at its top (Fig. 18.10), significantly facilitating recognition of this stage using multiple criteria. TES sections that exhibit many or most of these criteria occur in Namibia, South China, Siberia, Spain, northern Norway, western North America and eastern South America. Sections in Namibia and South China are geochronologically well constrained between ~550 and ~538 Ma (Grotzinger et al., 1995; Condon et al., 2005; Chen et al., 2015; Yang et al., 2017a,b; Zhou et al., 2018; Linnemann et al., 2019).

Defining the base of the SES is more challenging because fewer stratigraphic markers are available in the lower Ediacaran. Xiao et al. (2016) listed several potential criteria, including $\delta^{13}C$ crossing over to positive values, $^{87}Sr/^{86}Sr$ ratios rising from ~0.7073 to 0.7080, and the first appearance of Doushantuo–Pertatataka-type acanthomorphs, all of which seem to occur near 632 Ma based on currently available evidence. These biostratigraphic and chemostratigraphic criteria need to be used in conjunction with geochronological data in order to test their potential to define the SES. We are optimistic that an integrative approach will eventually lead to a better stratigraphic framework to subdivide and correlate the Ediacaran Period, the most recently named period of the geologic time scale.

Acknowledgments

This chapter is an update of the Ediacaran chapter in the Geologic Time Scale 2012 (Narbonne et al., 2012a) and integrates discussion presented in Xiao et al. (2016). Thus we would like to thank all coauthors of Narbonne et al. (2012a) and (Xiao et al., 2016), including Jim Gehling, Graham Shields-Zhou, Chuanming Zhou, Marc Laflamme, Dmitriy V. Grazhdankin, Małgorzata Moczydłowska-Vidal and Huan Cui. We would also like to thank the entire Ediacaran community for sharing their knowledge about this critical geological time period. Xiao acknowledges financial support provided by National Science Foundation (EAR-1528553) and NASA Exobiology and Evolutionary Biology Program (80NSSC18K1086); Narbonne acknowledges financial support provided by a Natural Sciences and Engineering Research Council of Canada (NSERC) Discovery Grant (05561-2014) and a Queen's University Research Chair.

References

Adôrno, R.R., Do Carmo, D.A., Germs, G., Walde, D.H.G., Denezine, M., Boggiani, P.C., et al., 2017, *Cloudina lucianoi* (Beurlen & Sommer, 1957), Tamengo Formation, Ediacaran, Brazil: taxonomy, analysis of stratigraphic distribution and biostratigraphy.

Precambrian Research, **301**: 19–35, https://doi.org/10.1016/j.precamres.2017.08.023.

Agić, H., Moczydłowska, M., and Yin, L., 2017, Diversity of organic-walled microfossils from the early Mesoproterozoic Ruyang Group, North China Craton – a window into the early eukaryote evolution. *Precambrian Research*, **297**: 101–130, https://doi.org/10.1016/j.precamres.2017.04.042.

Ahn, S.Y., and Zhu, M., 2017, Lowermost Cambrian acritarchs from the Yanjiahe Formation, South China: implication for defining the base of the Cambrian in the Yangtze Platform. *Geological Magazine*, **154**: 1217–1231, https://doi.org/10.1017/S0016756816001369.

Amthor, J.E., Grotzinger, J.P., Schröder, S., Bowring, S.A., Ramezani, J., Martin, M.W., et al., 2003, Extinction of *Cloudina* and *Namacalathus* at the Precambrian–Cambrian boundary in Oman. *Geology*, **31**: 431–434.

An, Z., Jiang, G., Tong, J., Tian, L., Ye, Q., Song, H., et al., 2015, Stratigraphic position of the Ediacaran Miaohe biota and its constrains on the age of the upper Doushantuo $\delta^{13}C$ anomaly in the Yangtze Gorges area, South China. *Precambrian Research*, **271**: 243–253, https://doi.org/10.1016/j.precamres.2015.10.007.

Anderson, R.P., Macdonald, F.A., Jones, D.S., McMahon, S., and Briggs, D.E.G., 2017a, Doushantuo-type microfossils from latest Ediacaran phosphorites of northern Mongolia. *Geology*, **45**: 1079–1082, https://doi.org/10.1130/G39576.1.

Anderson, R.P., McMahon, S., Bold, U., Macdonald, F.A., and Briggs, D.E.G., 2017b, Palaeobiology of the early Ediacaran Shuurgat Formation, Zavkhan Terrane, south-western Mongolia. *Journal of Systematic Palaeontology*, 947–968, https://doi.org/10.1080/14772019.2016.1259272.

Anderson, R.P., McMahon, S., Macdonald, F.A., Jones, D.S., and Briggs, D.E.G., 2019, Palaeobiology of latest Ediacaran phosphorites from the upper Khesen Formation, Khuvsgul Group, northern Mongolia. *Journal of Systematic Palaeontology*, **17**: 501–532, https://doi.org/10.1080/14772019.2018.1443977.

Babcock, L.E., Grunow, A.M., Sadowski, G.R., and Leslie, S.A., 2005, *Corumbella*, an Ediacaran-grade organism from the Late Neoproterozoic of Brazil. *Palaeogeography, Palaeoclimatology, Palaeoecology*, **220**: 7–18.

Bailey, T.R., McArthur, J.M., Prince, H., and Thirlwall, M.F., 2000, Dissolution methods for strontium isotope stratigraphy: whole rock analysis. *Chemical Geology*, **167**: 313–319.

Barfod, G.H., Albaréde, F., Knoll, A.H., Xiao, S., Télouk, P., Frei, R., et al., 2002, New Lu-Hf and Pb-Pb age constraints on the earliest animal fossils. *Earth and Planetary Science Letters*, **201**: 203–212.

Becker-Kerber, B., Pacheco, M.L.A.F., Rudnitzki, I.D., Galante, D., Rodrigues, F., and Leme, Jd.M., 2017, Ecological interactions in *Cloudina* from the Ediacaran of Brazil: implications for the rise of animal biomineralization. *Scientific Reports*, **7**: 5482, https://doi.org/10.1038/s41598-017-05753-8.

Bergmann, K.D., Zentmyer, R.A., and Fischer, W.W., 2011, The stratigraphic expression of a large negative carbon isotope excursion from the Ediacaran Johnnie Formation, Death Valley. *Precambrian Research*, **188**: 45–56.

Billings, E., 1872, On some fossils from the Primordial rocks of Newfoundland. *The Canadian Naturalist and Geologist*, **6**: 465–479.

Bingen, B., Griffin, W.L., Torsvik, T.H., and Saeed, A., 2005, Timing of Late Neoproterozoic glaciation on Baltica constrained by detrital zircon geochronology in the Hedmark Group, south-east Norway. *Terra Nova*, **17**: 250–258.

Bjerrum, C.J., and Canfield, D.E., 2011, Towards a quantitative understanding of the late Neoproterozoic carbon cycle. *Proceedings of the National Academy of Sciences of the United States of America*, **108**: 5542–5547.

Boag, T., Darroch, S.A.F., and Laflamme, M., 2016, Ediacaran distributions in space and time: testing assemblage concepts of earliest macroscopic body fossils. *Paleobiology*, **42**: 574–594, https://doi.org/10.1017/pab.2016.20.

Bobrovskiy, I., Hope, J.M., Ivantsov, A., Nettersheim, B.J., Hallmann, C., and Brocks, J.J., 2018, Ancient steroids establish the Ediacaran fossil *Dickinsonia* as one of the earliest animals. *Science*, **361**: 1246–1249, https://doi.org/10.1126/science.aat7228.

Bowring, S.A., Grotzinger, J.P., Condon, D.J., Ramezani, J., Newall, M.J., and Allen, P.A., 2007, Geochronologic constraints on the chronostratigraphic framework of the Neoproterozoic Huqf Supergroup, Sultanate of Oman. *American Journal of Science*, **307**: 1097–1145.

Bowyer, F., Wood, R.A., and Poulton, S.W., 2017, Controls on the evolution of Ediacaran metazoan ecosystems: a redox perspective. *Geobiology*, **15**: 516–551, https://doi.org/10.1111/gbi.12232.

Bradley, A.S., Leavitt, W.D., Schmidt, M., Knoll, A.H., Girguis, P.R., and Johnston, D.T., 2016, Patterns of sulfur isotope fractionation during microbial sulfate reduction. *Geobiology*, **14**: 91–101, https://doi.org/10.1111/gbi.12149.

Brasier, M.D., and Antcliffe, J.B., 2009, Evolutionary relationships within the Avalonian Ediacara biota: new insights from laser analysis. *Journal of the Geological Society, London*, **166**: 363–384.

Brasier, M.D., Shields, G., Kuleshov, V.N., and Zhengallo, E.A., 1996, Integrated chemo- and biostratigraphic calibration of early animal evolution: Neoproterozoic-early Cambrian of southwestern Mongolia. *Geological Magazine*, **133**: 445–485.

Buatois, L.A., and Mángano, M.G., 2016, Ediacaran ecosystems and the dawn of animals. *In* Mángano, M.G., and Buatois, L.A. (eds), *The Trace Fossil Record of Major Evolutionary Events (Volume 1: Precambrian and Paleozoic)*. Springer, Dordrecht, 27–72.

Buatois, L.A., Almond, J., Mángano, M.G., Jensen, S., and Germs, G.J. B., 2018, Sediment disturbance by Ediacaran bulldozers and the roots of the Cambrian explosion. *Scientific Reports*, **8**: 4514, https://doi.org/10.1038/s41598-018-22859-9.

Burns, S.J., and Matter, A., 1993, Carbon isotope record of the latest Proterozoic from Oman. *Eclogae Geologicae Helvetiae*, **86**: 595–607.

Burns, S.J., Haudenschild, U., and Matter, A., 1994, The strontium isotopic composition of carbonates from the late Precambrian (~560-540 Ma) Huqf Group of Oman. *Chemical Geology*, **111**: 269–282, https://doi.org/10.1016/0009-2541(94)90094-9.

Bykova, N.V., Gill, B.C., Grazhdankin, D., Rogov, V., and Xiao, S., 2017, A geochemical study of the Ediacaran discoidal fossil *Aspidella* preserved in limestones: implications for its taphonomy and paleoecology. *Geobiology*, **15**: 572–587, https://doi.org/10.1111/gbi.12240.

Cai, Y., and Hua, H., 2011, Discussion of 'First finds of problematic Ediacaran fossil *Gaojiashania* in Siberia and its origin'. *Geological Magazine*, **148**: 329–333.

Cai, Y., Hua, H., Xiao, S., Schiffbauer, J.D., and Li, P., 2010, Biostratinomy of the late Ediacaran pyritized Gaojiashan Lagerstätte from southern Shaanxi, South China: importance of event deposits. *Palaios*, **25**: 487–506, https://doi.org/10.2110/palo.2009.p09-133r.

Cai, Y., Schiffbauer, J.D., Hua, H., and Xiao, S., 2011, Morphology and paleoecology of the late Ediacaran tubular fossil *Conotubus hemiannulatus* from the Gaojiashan Lagerstätte of southern Shaanxi Province, South China. *Precambrian Research*, **191**: 46–57.

Cai, Y., Hua, H., Schiffbauer, J.D., Sun, B., and Yuan, X., 2013, Tube growth patterns and microbial mat-related lifestyles in the Ediacaran fossil *Cloudina*, Gaojiashan Lagerstätte, South China. *Gondwana Research*, **25**: 1008–1018.

Cai, Y., Xiao, S., Hua, H., and Yuan, X., 2015, New material of the biomineralizing tubular fossil *Sinotubulites* from the late Ediacaran Dengying Formation, South China. *Precambrian Research*, **261**: 12–24, https://doi.org/10.1016/j.precamres.2015.02.002.

Cai, Y., Cortijo, I., Schiffbauer, J.D., and Hua, H., 2017, Taxonomy of the late Ediacaran index fossil *Cloudina* and a new similar taxon from South China. *Precambrian Research*, **298**: 146–156, https://doi.org/10.1016/j.precamres.2017.05.016.

Cai, Y., Xiao, S., Li, G., and Hua, H., 2019, Diverse biomineralizing animals in the terminal Ediacaran Period foreshadow the Cambrian Explosion. *Geology*, **47**: 380–384, https://doi.org/10.1130/G45949.1.

Calver, C.R., 2000, Isotope stratigraphy of the Ediacarian (Neoproterozoic III) of the Adelaide Rift Complex, Australia, and the overprint of water column stratification. *Precambrian Research*, **100**: 121–150.

Calver, C.R., Black, L.P., Everard, J.L., and Seymour, D.B., 2004, U-Pb zircon age constraints on late Neoproterozoic glaciation in Tasmania. *Geology*, **10**: 893–896, https://doi.org/10.1130/G20713.1.

Calver, C.R., Crowley, J.L., Wingate, M.T.D., Evans, D.A.D., Raub, T. D., and Schmitz, M.D., 2013, Globally synchronous Marinoan deglaciation indicated by U-Pb geochronology of the Cottons Breccia, Tasmania, Australia. *Geology*, **41**: 1127–1130, https://doi.org/10.1130/G34568.1.

Canfield, D.E., Poulton, S.W., and Narbonne, G.M., 2007, Late Neoproterozoic deep-ocean oxygenation and the rise of animal life. *Science*, **315**: 92–95.

Canfield, D.E., Poulton, S.W., Knoll, A.H., Narbonne, G.M., Ross, G., Goldberg, T., et al., 2008, Ferruginous conditions dominated later Neoproterozoic deep-water chemistry. *Science*, **321**: 949–952.

Canfield, D.E., Knoll, A.H., Poulton, S.W., Narbonne, G.M., and Dunning, G.R., 2020, Carbon isotopes in clastic rocks and the Neoproterozoic carbon cycle. *American Journal of Science*, https://doi.org/10.2475/02.2020.01.

Carbone, C., and Narbonne, G.M., 2014, When life got smart: the evolution of behavioral complexity through the Ediacaran and early Cambrian of NW Canada. *Journal of Paleontology*, **88**: 309–330.

Carbone, C.A., Narbonne, G.M., Macdonald, F.A., and Boag, T.H., 2015, New Ediacaran fossils from the uppermost Blueflower Formation, northwest Canada: disentangling biostratigraphy and paleoecology. *Journal of Paleontology*, **89**: 281–291, https://doi.org/10.1017/jpa.2014.25.

Chen, Z., Bengtson, S., Zhou, C., Hua, H., and Yue, Z., 2008, Tube structure and original composition of *Sinotubulites*: shelly fossils from the late Neoproterozoic in southern Shaanxi, China. *Lethaia*, **41**: 37–45, https://doi.org/10.1111/j.1502-3931.2007.00040.x.

Chen, D., Wang, J., Qing, H., Yan, D., and Li, R., 2009, Hydrothermal venting activities in the Early Cambrian, South China: petrological, geochronological and stable isotopic constraints. *Chemical Geology*, **258**: 168–181.

Chen, Z., Zhou, C., Meyer, M., Xiang, K., Schiffbauer, J.D., Yuan, X., et al., 2013, Trace fossil evidence for Ediacaran bilaterian animals with complex behaviors. *Precambrian Research*, **224**: 690–701, https://doi.org/10.1016/j.precamres.2012.11.004.

Chen, Z., Zhou, C., Xiao, S., Wang, W., Guan, C., Hua, H., et al., 2014, New Ediacara fossils preserved in marine limestone and their ecological implications. *Scientific Reports*, **4**: 4180, https://doi.org/10.1038/srep04180.

Chen, D., Zhou, X., Fu, Y., Wang, J., and Yan, D., 2015, New U-Pb zircon ages of the Ediacaran-Cambrian boundary strata in South China. *Terra Nova*, **27**: 62–68, https://doi.org/10.1111/ter.12134.

Chen, Z., Chen, X., Zhou, C., Yuan, X., and Xiao, S., 2018, Late Ediacaran trackways produced by bilaterian animals with paired appendages. *Science Advances*, **4**: eaao6691, https://doi.org/10.1126/sciadv.aao6691.

Chen, Z., Zhou, C., Yuan, X., and Xiao, S., 2019, Death march of a segmented and trilobate bilaterian elucidates early animal evolution. *Nature*, **573**: 412–415, https://doi.org/10.1038/s41586-019-1522-7.

Chumakov, N.M., 2009, The Baykonurian Glaciohorizon of the Late Vendian. *Stratigraphy and Geological Correlation*, **17**: 373–381.

Cloud, P., and Glaessner, M.F., 1982, The Ediacarian Period and System: metazoa inherit the Earth. *Science*, **217**: 783–792.

Cohen, P.A., and Macdonald, F.A., 2015, The Proterozoic record of eukaryotes. *Paleobiology*, **41**: 610–632, https://doi.org/10.1017/pab.2015.25.

Cohen, P.A., Knoll, A.H., and Kodner, R.B., 2009a, Large spinose microfossils in Ediacaran rocks as resting stages of early animals. *Proceedings of the National Academy of Sciences of the United States of America*, **106**: 6519–6524.

Cohen, P.A., Bradley, A., Knoll, A.H., Grotzinger, J.P., Jensen, S., Abelson, J., et al., 2009b, Tubular compression fossils from the Ediacaran Nama Group, Namibia. *Journal of Paleontology*, **83**: 110–122.

Compston, W., Wright, A.E., and Toghill, P., 2002, Dating the late Precambrian volcanicity of England and Wales. *Journal of the Geological Society, London*, **159**: 323–339.

Condon, D., Zhu, M., Bowring, S., Wang, W., Yang, A., and Jin, Y., 2005, U-Pb ages from the Neoproterozoic Doushantuo Formation, China. *Science*, **308**: 95–98.

Conway Morris, S., Mattes, B.W., and Chen, M., 1990, The early skeletal organism *Cloudina*: new occurrences from Oman and possibly China. *American Journal of Science*, **290-A**: 245–260.

Corsetti, F.A., and Grotzinger, J.P., 2005, Origin and significance of tube structures in Neoproterozoic post-glacial cap carbonates: example from Noonday Dolomite, Death Valley, United States. *Palaios*, **20**: 348–362.

Cortijo, I., Martí Mus, M., Jensen, S., and Palacios, T., 2010, A new species of *Cloudina* from the terminal Ediacaran of Spain. *Precambrian Research*, **176**: 1–10.

Cortijo, I., Mus, M.M., Jensen, S., and Palacios, T., 2015a, Late Ediacaran skeletal body fossil assemblage from the Navalpino anticline, central Spain. *Precambrian Research*, **267**: 186–195, https://doi.org/10.1016/j.precamres.2015.06.013.

Cortijo, I., Cai, Y., Hua, H., Schiffbauer, J.D., and Xiao, S., 2015b, Life history and autecology of an Ediacaran index fossil: development and dispersal of *Cloudina*. *Gondwana Research*, **28**: 419–424, https://doi.org/10.1016/j.gr.2014.05.001.

Cui, H., Kaufman, A.J., Xiao, S., Zhu, M., Zhou, C., and Liu, X.-M., 2015, Redox architecture of an Ediacaran ocean margin: integrated chemostratigraphic ($\delta^{13}C-\delta^{34}S-{}^{87}Sr/{}^{86}Sr-Ce/Ce^*$) correlation of the Doushantuo Formation. *Chemical Geology*, **405**: 48–62.

Cui, H., Grazhdankin, D.V., Xiao, S., Peek, S., Rogov, V.I., Bykova, N.V., et al., 2016a, Redox-dependent distribution of early macro-organisms: evidence from the terminal Ediacaran Khatyspyt Formation in Arctic

Siberia. *Palaeogeography, Palaeoclimatology, Palaeoecology*, **461**: 122–139, https://doi.org/10.1016/j.palaeo.2016.08.015.

Cui, H., Kaufman, A.J., Xiao, S., Peek, S., Cao, H., Min, X., et al., 2016b, Environmental context for the terminal Ediacaran biomineralization of animals. *Geobiology*, **14**: 344–363, https://doi.org/10.1111/gbi.12178.

Cui, H., Kaufman, A.J., Xiao, S., Zhou, C., and Liu, X., 2017, Was the Ediacaran Shuram Excursion a globally synchronized early diagenetic event? Insights from methane-derived authigenic carbonates in the uppermost Doushantuo Formation, South China. *Chemical Geology*, **450**: 59–80, https://doi.org/10.1016/j.chemgeo.2016.12.010.

Cui, H., Kaufman, A.J., Peng, Y., Liu, X.-M., Plummer, R.E., and Lee, E.I., 2018, The Neoproterozoic Huttenberg delta C-13 anomaly: genesis and global implications. *Precambrian Research*, **313**: 242–262, https://doi.org/10.1016/j.precamres.2018.05.024.

Darroch, S.A.F., Boag, T.H., Racicot, R.A., Tweedt, S., Mason, J., Erwin, S., et al., 2016, A mixed Ediacaran-metazoan assemblage from the Zaris Sub-basin, Namibia. *Palaeogeography, Palaeoclimatology, Palaeoecology*, **459**: 198–208, https://doi.org/10.1016/j.palaeo.2016.07.003.

Darroch, S.A.F., Laflamme, M., and Wagner, P.J., 2018a, High ecological complexity in benthic Ediacaran communities. *Nature Ecology and Evolution*, **2**: 1541–1547, https://doi.org/10.1038/s41559-018-0663-7.

Darroch, S.A.F., Smith, E.F., Laflamme, M., and Erwin, D.H., 2018b, Ediacaran extinction and Cambrian explosion. *Trends in Ecology & Evolution*, **33**: 653–663, https://doi.org/10.1016/j.tree.2018.06.003.

Darwin, C., 1859, *On the Origin of Species by Means of Natural Selection*. 490 pp. John Murray.

de Alvarenga, C.J.S., Figueiredo, M.F., Babinki, M., and Pinho, F.E.C., 2007, Glacial diamictites of Serra Azul Formation (Ediacaran, Paraguay belt): evidence of the Gaskiers glacial event in Brazil. *Journal of South American Earth Sciences*, **23**: 236–241, https://doi.org/10.1016/j.jsames.2006.09.015.

de Alvarenga, C.J.S., Dardenne, M.A., Santos, R.V., Brod, E.R., Gioia, S., Sial, A.N., et al., 2008, Isotope stratigraphy of Neoproterozoic cap carbonates in the Araras Group, Brazil. *Gondwana Research*, **13**: 469–479, https://doi.org/10.1016/j.gr.2007.05.004.

Dececchi, T.A., Narbonne, G.M., Greentree, C., and Laflamme, M., 2017, Relating Ediacaran fronds. *Paleobiology*, **43**: 171–180, https://doi.org/10.1017/pab.2016.54.

Dececchi, T.A., Narbonne, G.M., Greentree, C., and Laflamme, M., 2018, Phylogenetic relationships among the Rangeomorpha: the importance of outgroup selection and implications for their diversification1. *Canadian Journal of Earth Sciences*, https://doi.org/10.1139/cjes-2018-0022.

Derry, L.A., 2010, A burial diagenesis origin for the Ediacaran Shuram-Wonoka carbon isotope anomaly. *Earth and Planetary Science Letters*, **294**: 152–162, https://doi.org/10.1016/j.epsl.2010.03.022.

Derry, L.A., Brasier, M.D., Corfield, R.M., Rozanov, A.Y., and Zhuravlev, A.Y., 1994, Sr isotopes in Lower Cambrian carbonates from the Siberian Craton: a paleoenvironmental record during the "Cambrian explosion. *Earth and Planetary Science Letters*, **128**: 671–681.

Dong, L., Xiao, S., Shen, B., Zhou, C., Li, G., and Yao, J., 2009, Basal Cambrian microfossils from the Yangtze Gorges area (South China) and the Aksu area (Tarim Block, northwestern China). *Journal of Paleontology*, **83**: 30–44, https://doi.org/10.1017/S0022336000058108.

Droser, M.L., and Gehling, J.G., 2015, The advent of animals: the view from the Ediacaran. *Proceedings of the National Academy of Sciences of the United States of America*, **112**: 4865–4870, https://doi.org/10.1073/pnas.1403669112.

Droser, M.L., Tarhan, L.G., and Gehling, J.G., 2017, The rise of animals in a changing environment: global ecological innovation in the late Ediacaran. *Annual Review of Earth and Planetary Sciences*, **45**: 593–617, https://doi.org/10.1146/annurev-earth-063016-015645.

Droser, M.L., Gehling, J.G., Tarhan, L.G., Evans, S.D., Hall, C.M.S., Hughes, I.V., et al., 2018, Piecing together the puzzle of the Ediacara Biota: excavation and reconstruction at the Ediacara National Heritage site Nilpena (South Australia). *Palaeogeography, Palaeoclimatology, Palaeoecology*, https://doi.org/10.1016/j.palaeo.2017.09.007.

Dunn, F.S., Liu, A.G., and Donoghue, P.C.J., 2018, Ediacaran developmental biology. *Biological Reviews*, **93**: 914–932, https://doi.org/10.1111/brv.12379.

Evans, S.D., Droser, M.L., and Gehling, J.G., 2017, Highly regulated growth and development of the Ediacara macrofossil *Dickinsonia costata*. *PLoS One*, **12**: e0176874, https://doi.org/10.1371/journal.pone.0176874.

Eyles, N., and Eyles, C.H., 1989, Glacially-influenced deep-marine sedimentation of the late Precambrian Gaskiers Formation, Newfoundland, Canada. *Sedimentology*, **36**: 601–620.

Fedonkin, M.A., 1981, Belomorskaya biota venda. *Trudy Akademii Nauk SSSR*, **342**: 1–100.

Fedonkin, M.A., 1990, Systematic description of Vendian Metazoa. *In* Sokolov, B.S., and Iwanowski, A.B. (eds), *The Vendian System, Vol 1: Paleontology*. Springer-Verlag, Heidelberg, 71–120.

Fedonkin, M.A., 1992, Vendian faunas and the early evolution of Metazoa. *In* Lipps, J.H., and Signor, P.W. (eds), *Origin and Early Evolution of the Metazoa*. Plenum Press, New York, 87–129.

Fedonkin, M.A., and Waggoner, B.M., 1997, The late Precambrian fossil *Kimberella* is a mollusc-like bilaterian organism. *Nature*, **388**: 868–871.

Fedonkin, M.A., Gehling, J.G., Grey, K., Narbonne, G.M., and Vickers-Rich, P., 2007, *The Rise of Animals: Evolution and Diversification of the Kingdom Animalia*. 326 pp. Johns Hopkins University Press.

Fike, D.A., Grotzinger, J.P., Pratt, L.M., and Summons, R.E., 2006, Oxidation of the Ediacaran ocean. *Nature*, **444**: 744–747.

Fike, D.A., Bradley, A.S., and Rose, C.V., 2015, Rethinking the ancient sulfur cycle. *Annual Review of Earth and Planetary Sciences*, **43**: 593–622.

Ford, T.D., 1958, Precambrian fossils from Charnwood Forest. *Proceedings of the Yorkshire Geological Society*, **31**: 211–217.

Furuyama, S., Kano, A., Kunimitsu, Y., Ishikawa, T., and Wang, W., 2016, Diagenetic overprint to a negative carbon isotope anomaly associated with the Gaskiers glaciation of the Ediacaran Doushantuo Formationin South China. *Precambrian Research*, **276**: 110–122, https://doi.org/10.1016/j.precamres.2016.01.004.

Gehling, J.G., 1991, The case for Ediacaran fossil roots to the metazoan tree. *Memoirs—Geological Society of India*, **20**: 181–224.

Gehling, J.G., 2000, Environmental interpretation and a sequence stratigraphic framework for the terminal Proterozoic Ediacara Member within the Rawnsley Quartzite, South Australia. *Precambrian Research*, **100**: 65–95.

Gehling, J.G., and Narbonne, G.M., 2007, Spindle-shaped Ediacara fossils from the Mistaken Point assemblage, Avalon Zone, Newfoundland. *Canadian Journal of Earth Sciences*, **44**: 367–387.

Gehling, J.G., and Droser, M.L., 2012, Ediacaran stratigraphy and the biota of the Adelaide Geosyncline, South Australia. *Episodes*, **35**: 236–246.

Gehling, J.G., and Droser, M.L., 2013, How well do fossil assemblages of the Ediacara Biota tell time? *Geology*, **41**: 447–450.

Gehling, J.G., and Droser, M.L., 2018, Ediacaran scavenging as a prelude to predation. *Emerging Topics in Life Sciences*, **2**: 213–222, https://doi.org/10.1042/ETLS20170166.

Gehling, J.G., Droser, M.L., Jensen, S.R., and Runnegar, B.N., 2005, Ediacara organisms: relating form to function. *In* Briggs, D.E.G. (ed), *Evolving Form and Function: Fossils and Development*. Yale Peabody Museum Publications, New Haven, 43–66.

Gehling, J.G., Jago, J.B., and Paterson, J.R., 2012, Ediacaran-Cambrian of South Australia. *34th International Geological Congress (IGC) Field Trip Guide Book. pp. 1–36.*

Gehling, J.G., Runnegar, B.N., and Droser, M.L., 2014, Scratch traces of large Ediacara bilaterian animals. *Journal of Paleontology*, **88**: 284–298.

Germs, J.G.B., 1972, New shelly fossils from the Nama Group, South West Africa. *American Journal of Science*, **272**: 752–761.

Germs, G.J.B., 1995, The Neoproterozoic of southwestern Africa, with emphasis on platform stratigraphy and paleontology. *Precambrian Research*, **73**: 137–151.

Glaessner, M.F., 1959, Precambrian Coelenterata from Australia, Africa and England. *Nature*, **183**: 1472–1473.

Glaessner, M.F., and Wade, M., 1966, The late Precambrian fossils from Ediacara, South Australia. *Palaeontology*, **9**: 599–628.

Gnilovskaya, M.B., 1990, Vendotaenids—Vendian metaphytes. *In* Sokolov, B.S., and Iwanowski, A.B. (eds), *The Vendian System Vol 1, Paleontology*. Springer-Verlag, Berlin, 138–147.

Gold, D.A., Runnegar, B., Gehling, J.G., and Jacobs, D.K., 2015, Ancestral state reconstruction of ontogeny supports a bilaterian affinity for *Dickinsonia. Evolution & Development*, **17**: 315–324, https://doi.org/10.1111/ede.12168.

Golubkova, E.Y., Raevskaya, E.G., and Kuznetsov, A.B., 2010, Lower Vendian microfossil assemblages of East Siberia: significance for solving regional stratigraphic problems. *Stratigraphy and Geological Correlation*, **18**: 353–375.

Golubkova, Y.E., Zaitseva, T.S., Kuznetsov, A.B., Dovzhikova, E.G., and Maslov, A.V., 2015, Microfossils and Rb-Sr age of glauconite in the key section of the upper Proterozoic of the northeastern part of the Russian Plate (Keltmen-1 Borehole). *Doklady Earth Sciences*, **462**: 547–551, https://doi.org/10.1134/S1028334X15060045.

Golubkova, E.Y., Kushima, E.A., Kuznetsov, A.B., Yanovskii, A.S., Maslov, A.V., Shvedov, S.D., et al., 2018, Redkinian biota of macroscopic fossils from the northwestern East European Platform (South Ladoga Region). *Doklady Earth Sciences*, **479**: 300–304, https://doi.org/10.1134/S1028334X18030169.

Gomes, M.L., and Hurtgen, M.T., 2015, Sulfur isotope fractionation in modern euxinic systems: implications for paleoenvironmental reconstructions of paired sulfate-sulfide isotope records. *Geochimica et Cosmochimica Acta*, **157**: 39–55.

Gorjan, P., Veevers, J.J., and Walter, M.R., 2000, Neoproterozoic sulfur-isotope variation in Australia and global implications. *Precambrian Research*, **100**: 151–179.

Grabau, A.W., 1922, The Sinian System. *Bulletin of the Geological Society of China*, **1**: 1–4.

Grant, S.W.F., 1990, Shell structure and distribution of *Cloudina*, a potential index fossil for the terminal Proterozoic. *American Journal of Science*, **290-A**: 261–294.

Grazhdankin, D., 2004, Patterns of distribution in the Ediacaran biotas: facies versus biogeography and evolution. *Paleobiology*, **30**: 203–221.

Grazhdankin, D., and Seilacher, A., 2002, Underground Vendobionta from Namibia. *Palaeontology*, **45**: 57–78.

Grazhdankin, D., and Seilacher, A., 2005, A re-examination of the Nama-type Vendian organism *Rangea schneiderhoehni. Geological Magazine*, **142**: 571–582.

Grazhdankin, D.V., Balthasar, U., Nagovitsin, K.E., and Kochnev, B.B., 2008, Carbonate-hosted Avalon-type fossils in Arctic Siberia. *Geology*, **36**: 803–806.

Grazhdankin, D.V., Kontorovich, A.E., Kontorovich, V.A., Saraev, S.V., Filippov, F.Y., Efimov, A.S., et al., 2015, Vendian of the Fore-Yenisei sedimentary basin (southeastern West Siberia). *Russian Geology and Geophysics*, **56**: 560–572, https://doi.org/10.1016/j.rgg.2015.03.008.

Grey, K., 2005, Ediacaran palynology of Australia. *Memoirs of the Association of Australasian Palaeontologists*, **31**: 1–439.

Grey, K., and Willman, S., 2009, Taphonomy of Ediacaran acritarchs from Australia: significance for taxonomy and biostratigraphy. *Palaios*, **24**: 239–256.

Grey, K., Walter, M.R., and Calver, C.R., 2003, Neoproterozoic biotic diversification: Snowball Earth or aftermath of the Acraman impact? *Geology*, **31**: 459–462.

Grotzinger, J.P., Bowring, S.A., Saylor, B.Z., and Kaufman, A.J., 1995, Biostratigraphic and geochronologic constraints on early animal evolution. *Science*, **270**: 598–604.

Grotzinger, J.P., Watters, W.A., and Knoll, A.H., 2000, Calcified metazoans in thrombolite-stromatolite reefs of the terminal Proterozoic Nama Group, Namibia. *Paleobiology*, **26**: 334–359.

Grotzinger, J.P., Fike, D.A., and Fischer, W.W., 2011, Enigmatic origin of the largest-known carbon isotope excursion in Earth's history. *Nature Geoscience*, **4**: 285–292, https://doi.org/10.1038/NGEO1138.

Gürich, G., 1930, Die bislang ältesten Spuren von Organismen in Südafrika. *International Geological Congress, South Africa*, **2**: 670–680.

Gürich, G., 1933, Die Kuibis-Fossilien der Nama-Formation von Südwestafrika. *Paläontologische Zeitschrift*, **15**: 137–154.

Hagadorn, J.W., and Waggoner, B.M., 2000, Ediacaran fossils from the southwestern Great Basin, United States. *Journal of Paleontology*, **74**: 349–359.

Hagadorn, J.W., Fedo, C.M., and Waggoner, B.M., 2000, Early Cambrian Ediacaran-type fossils from California. *Journal of Paleontology*, **74**: 731–740.

Halverson, G.P., and Hurtgen, M.T., 2007, Ediacaran growth of the marine sulfate reservoir. *Earth and Planetary Science Letters*, **263**: 32–44.

Halverson, G.P., Hoffman, P.F., Schrag, D.P., Maloof, A.C., and Rice, A.H.N., 2005, Toward a Neoproterozoic composite carbon-isotope record. *Geological Society of America Bulletin*, **117**: 1181–1207, https://doi.org/10.1130/B25630.1.

Halverson, G.P., Dudás, F.Ö., Maloof, A.C., and Bowring, S.A., 2007, Evolution of the $^{87}Sr/^{86}Sr$ Composition of Neoproterozoic Seawater.

Palaeogeography, Palaeoclimatology, Palaeoecology, **256**: 103–129.

Halverson, G.P., Wade, B.P., Hurtgen, M.T., and Barovich, K.M., 2010, Neoproterozoic chemostratigraphy. *Precambrian Research*, **182**: 337–350.

Han, J., Cai, Y., Schiffbauer, J.D., Hua, H., Wang, X., Yang, X., et al., 2017, A *Cloudina*-like fossil with evidence of asexual reproduction from the earliest Cambrian, South China. *Geological Magazine*, **154**: 1294–1305, https://doi.org/10.1017/S0016756816001187.

Harland, W.B., and Rudwick, M.J.S., 1964, The great Infra-Cambrian ice age. *Scientific American*, **211** (2), 28–36.

Harland, W.B., and Herod, K.M., 1975, Glaciations through time. *Geological Journal Special Issues*, **6**: 189–216.

Harland, W.B., Cox, A.V., Llewellyn, P.G., Pickton, C.A.G., Smith, A. G., and Walters, R., 1982, *A Geologic Time Scale*. 131 pp. Cambridge University Press.

Harland, W.B., Armstrong, R.L., Cox, A.V., Craig, L.E., Smith, A.G., Smith, D.G., et al., 1990, *Geologic Time Scale*. 1989. 263 pp. Cambridge University Press.

Hawkins, A.D., Xiao, S., Jiang, G., Wang, X., and Shi, X., 2017, New biostratigraphic and chemostratigraphic data from the Ediacaran Doushantuo Formation in intra-shelf and upper slope facies of the Yangtze platform: implications for biozonation of acanthomorphic acritarchs in South China. *Precambrian Research*, **300**: 28–39, https://doi.org/10.1016/j.precamres.2017.08.004.

Hoekzema, R.S., Brasier, M.D., Dunn, F.S., and Liu, A.G., 2017, Quantitative study of developmental biology confirms *Dickinsonia* as a metazoan. *Proceedings of the Royal Society B: Biological Sciences*, **284**: 20171348, https://doi.org/10.1098/rspb.2017.1348.

Hoffman, P.F., 2011, Strange bedfellows: glacial diamictite and cap carbonate from the Marinoan (635 Ma) glaciation in Namibia. *Sedimentology*, **58**: 57–119, https://doi.org/10.1111/j.1365-3091.2010.01206.x.

Hoffman, P.F., and Li, Z.-X., 2009, A palaeogeographic context for Neoproterozoic glaciation. *Palaeogeography, Palaeoclimatology, Palaeoecology*, **277**: 158–172, https://doi.org/10.1016/j.palaeo.2009.03.013.

Hofmann, H.J., and Mountjoy, E.W., 2001, *Namacalathus-Cloudina* assemblage in Neoproterozoic Miette Group (Byng Formation), British Columbia: Canada's oldest shelly fossils. *Geology*, **29**: 1091–1094.

Hofmann, H.J., and Mountjoy, E.W., 2010, Ediacaran body and trace fossils in Miette Group (Windermere Supergroup) near Salient Mountain, British Columbia, Canada. *Canadian Journal of Earth Sciences*, **47**: 1305–1325, https://doi.org/10.1139/e10-070.

Hofmann, H.J., Narbonne, G.M., and Aitken, J.D., 1990, Ediacaran remains from intertillite beds in northwestern Canada. *Geology*, **18**: 1199–1202.

Hoffmann, K.-H., Condon, D.J., Bowring, S.A., and Crowley, J.L., 2004, U-Pb zircon date from the Neoproterozoic Ghaub Formation, Namibia: constraints on Marinoan glaciation. *Geology*, **32**: 817–820.

Hoffman, P.F., Halverson, G.P., Domack, E.W., Husson, J.M., Higgins, J.A., and Schrag, D.P., 2007, Are basal Ediacaran (635 Ma) post-glacial "cap dolostones" diachronous? *Earth and Planetary Science Letters*, **258**: 114–131.

Hofmann, H.J., O'Brien, S.J., and King, A.F., 2008, Ediacaran biota on Bonavista Peninsula, Newfoundland, Canada. *Journal of Paleontology*, **82**: 1–36.

Hoffman, P.F., Abbot, D.S., Ashkenazy, Y., Benn, D.I., Brocks, J.J., Cohen, P.A., et al., 2017, Snowball Earth climate dynamics and Cryogenian geology-geobiology. *Science Advances*, **3**: e1600983, https://doi.org/10.1126/sciadv.1600983.

Högström, A.E.S., Jensen, S., Palacios, T., and Ebbestad, J.O.R., 2013, New information on the Ediacaran–Cambrian transition in the Vestertana Group, Finnmark, northern Norway, from trace fossils and organic-walled microfossils. *Norwegian Journal of Geology*, **93**: 95–106.

Holser, W.T., and Kaplan, I.R., 1966, Isotope geochemistry of sedimentary sulfates. *Chemical Geology*, **1**: 93–135.

Hoyal Cuthill, J.F., and Han, J., 2018, Cambrian petalonamid Stromatoveris phylogenetically links Ediacaran biota to later animals. *Palaeontology*, **61**: 813–823, https://doi.org/10.1111/pala.12393.

Hua, H., Chen, Z., and Zhang, L., 2004, *Shaanxilithes* from lower Taozichong Formation, Guizhou Province and its geological and paleobiological significance. *Journal of Stratigraphy*, **28**: 265–269.

Hua, H., Chen, Z., Yuan, X., Zhang, L., and Xiao, S., 2005, Skeletogenesis and asexual reproduction in the earliest biomineralizing animal *Cloudina*. *Geology*, **33**: 277–280.

Hua, H., Chen, Z., and Yuan, X., 2007, The advent of mineralized skeletons in Neoproterozoic Metazoa: new fossil evidence from the Gaojiashan Fauna. *The Journal of Geology*, **42**: 263–279.

Huang, J., Chu, X., Jiang, G., Feng, L., and Chang, H., 2011, Hydrothermal origin of elevated iron, manganese and redox-sensitive trace elements in the c. 635 Ma Doushantuo cap carbonate. *Journal of the Geological Society, London*, **168**: 805–815, https://doi.org/10.1144/0016-76492010-132.

Huang, J., Chu, X., Lyons, T.W., Sun, T., Feng, L., Zhang, Q., et al., 2013, The sulfur isotope signatures of Marinoan deglaciation captured in Neoproterozoic shallow-to-deep cap carbonate from South China. *Precambrian Research*, **238**: 42–51, https://doi.org/10.1016/j.precamres.2013.09.002.

Husson, J.M., Maloof, A.C., Schoene, B., Chen, C.Y., and Higgins, J.A., 2015, Stratigraphic expression of Earth's deepest $\delta^{13}C$ excursion in the Wonoka Formation of South Australia. *American Journal of Science*, **315**: 1–45, https://doi.org/10.2475/01.2015.01.

Ishikawa, T., Ueno, Y., Komiya, T., Sawaki, Y., Han, J., Shu, D., et al., 2008, Carbon isotope chemostratigraphy of a Precambrian/Cambrian boundary section in the Three Gorge area, South China: prominent global-scale isotope excursions just before the Cambrian Explosion. *Gondwana Research*, **14**: 193–208.

Ishikawa, T., Ueno, Y., Shu, D., Li, Y., Han, J., Guo, J., et al., 2013, The $\delta^{13}C$ excursions spanning the Cambrian explosion to the Canglangpuian mass extinction in the Three Gorges area, South China. *Gondwana Research*, https://doi.org/10.1016/j.gr.2013.03.010.

Ivantsov, A.Y., 2013, Trace fossils of Precambrian metazoans "Vendobionta" and "mollusks". *Stratigraphy and Geological Correlation*, **21**: 252–264, https://doi.org/10.1134/S0869593813030039.

Ivantsov, A.Y., Narbonne, G.M., Trusler, P.W., Greentree, C., and Vickers-Rich, P., 2016, Elucidating *Ernietta*: new insights from exceptional specimens in the Ediacaran of Namibia. *Lethaia*, **49**: 540–554, https://doi.org/10.1111/let.12164.

James, N.P., Narbonne, G.M., and Kyser, T.K., 2001, Late Neoproterozoic cap carbonates, Mackenzie Mountains, northwestern Canada: precipitation and global glacial meltdown. *Canadian Journal of Earth Sciences*, **38**: 1229–1262.

Jankauskas, T.V., Mikhailova, N.S., and Hermann, T.N., 1989, *Mikrofossilii Dokembriya SSSR [Precambrian Microfossils of the USSR]*. 190 pp. Nauka.

Jenkins, R.J.F., 1981, The concept of an "Ediacaran Period" and its stratigraphic significance in Australia. *Transactions of the Royal Society of South Australia*, **105**: 179–194.

Jenkins, R.J.F., 1992, Functional and ecological aspects of Ediacaran assemblages. *In* Lipps, J.H., and Signor, P.W. (eds), *Origin and Early Evolution of Metazoa*. Plenum Press, New York, 131–176.

Jenkins, R.J.F., 1995, The problems and potential of using animal fossils and trace fossils in terminal Proterozoic biostratigraphy. *Precambrian Research*, **73**: 51–69.

Jensen, S., and Runnegar, B.N., 2005, A complex trace fossil from the Spitskop Member (terminal Ediacaran-? Lower Cambrian) of southern Namibia. *Geological Magazine*, **142**: 561–569.

Jensen, S., Gehling, J.G., and Droser, M.L., 1998, Ediacara-type fossils in Cambrian sediments. *Nature*, **393**: 567–569.

Jensen, S., Saylor, B.Z., Gehling, J.G., and Germs, G.J.B., 2000, Complex trace fossils from the terminal Proterozoic of Namibia. *Geology*, **28**: 143–146.

Jensen, S., Droser, M.L., and Gehling, J.G., 2006, A critical look at the Ediacaran trace fossil record. *In* Xiao, S., and Kaufman, A.J. (eds), *Neoproterozoic Geobiology*. Springer, Dordrecht, The Netherlands, 115–157.

Jiang, G., Kennedy, M.J., and Christie-Blick, N., 2003, Stable isotopic evidence for methane seeps in Neoproterozoic postglacial cap carbonates. *Nature*, **426**: 822–826.

Jiang, G., Kennedy, M., Christie-Blick, N., Wu, H., and Zhang, S., 2006, Stratigraphy, sedimentary structures, and textures of the late Neoproterozoic Doushantuo cap carbonate in South China. *Journal of Sedimentary Research*, **76**: 978–995.

Jiang, G., Kaufman, A.J., Christie-Blick, N., Zhang, S., and Wu, H., 2007, Carbon isotope variability across the Ediacaran Yangtze platform in South China: implications for a large surface-to-deep ocean $\delta^{13}C$ gradient. *Earth and Planetary Science Letters*, **261**: 303–320.

Jiang, G., Wang, X., Shi, X., Xiao, S., Zhang, S., and Dong, J., 2012, The origin of decoupled carbonate and organic carbon isotope signatures in the early Cambrian (ca. 542-520 Ma) Yangtze platform. *Earth and Planetary Science Letters*, **317**: 96–110, https://doi.org/10.1016/j.epsl.2011.11.018.

Johnston, D.T., Poulton, S.W., Goldberg, T., Sergeev, V.N., Podkovyrov, V., Vorob'eva, N.G., et al., 2012, Late Edicaran redox stability and metazoan evolution. *Earth and Planetary Science Letters*, **335-336**: 25–35.

Joshi, H., and Tiwari, M., 2016, *Tianzhushania spinosa* and other large acanthomorphic acritarchs of Ediacaran Period from the Infrakrol Formation, Lesser Himalaya, India. *Precambrian Research*, https://doi.org/10.1016/j.precamres.2016.09.024.

Kampschulte, A., and Strauss, H., 2004, The sulfur isotopic evolution of Phanerozoic seawater based on the analysis of structurally substituted sulfate in carbonates. *Chemical Geology*, **204**: 255–286.

Kaufman, A.J., and Knoll, A.H., 1995, Neoproterozoic variations in the C-isotope composition of sea water: stratigraphic and biogeochemical implications. *Precambrian Research*, **73**: 27–49.

Kaufman, A.J., Jacobsen, S.B., and Knoll, A.H., 1993, The Vendian record of Sr and C isotopic variations in seawater: implications for tectonics and paleoclimate. *Earth and Planetary Science Letters*, **120**: 409–430.

Kaufman, A.J., Knoll, A.H., Semikhatov, M.A., Grotzinger, J.P., Jacobsen, S.B., and Adams, W., 1996, Integrated chronostratigraphy of Proterozoic-Cambrian boundary beds in the western Anabar region, northern Siberia. *Geological Magazine*, **133**: 509–533.

Kaufman, A.J., Knoll, A.H., and Narbonne, G.M., 1997, Isotopes, ice ages, and terminal Proterozoic earth history. *Proceedings of the National Academy of Sciences of the United States of America*, **94**: 6600–6605.

Kaufman, A.J., Corsetti, F.A., and Varni, M.A., 2007, The effect of rising atmospheric oxygen on carbon and sulfur isotope anomalies in the Neoproterozoic Johnnie Formation, Death Valley, USA. *Chemical Geology*, **237**: 47–63.

Kaufman, A.J., Grazhdankin, D., Rogov, V., Peek, S., Kochnev, B., Nagovitsin, K., et al., 2009, A glacial divide between Ediacaran extinction and the Cambrian explosion of life. *Geological Society of America Abstracts with Programs*, **41**: 395.

Kaufman, A.J., Vickers-Rich, P., Walde, D., Gaucher, C., and Boggiani, P.C., 2014, Corumba Meeting 2013: the Neoproterozoic Paraguay Fold Belt (Brazil): glaciation, iron-manganese formation and biota, an IGCP workshop and field excursion on the Ediacaran System. *Episodes*, **37**: 71–73.

Kendall, B., Komiya, T., Lyons, T.W., Bates, S.M., Gordon, G.W., Romaniello, S., et al., 2015, Uranium and molybdenum isotope evidence for an episode of widespread ocean oxygenation during the late Ediacaran Period. *Geochimica et Cosmochimica Acta*, **156**: 173–193, https://doi.org/10.1016/j.gca.2015.02.025.

Kennedy, M.J., 1996, Stratigraphy, Sedimentology, and isotope geochemistry of Australian Neoproterozoic postglacial cap dolostone: deglaciation, 13C Excursions, and carbonate precipitation. *Journal of Sedimentary Research*, **66**: 1050–1064.

Kennedy, M.J., Runnegar, B., Prave, A.R., Hoffmann, K.H., and Arthur, M.A., 1998, Two or four Neoproterozoic glaciations? *Geology*, **26**: 1059–1063.

Knauth, L.P., and Kennedy, M.J., 2009, The late Precambrian greening of the Earth. *Nature*, **460**: 728–732.

Knoll, A.H., 1992, Microfossils in metasedimentary cherts of the Scotia Group, Prins Karls Forland, western Svalbard. *Palaeontology*, **35**: 751–774.

Knoll, A.H., and Walter, M.R., 1992, Latest Proterozoic stratigraphy and Earth history. *Nature*, **356**: 673–678.

Knoll, A.H., Hayes, J.M., Kaufman, A.J., Swett, K., and Lambert, I.B., 1986, Secular variation in carbon isotope ratios from Upper Proterozoic successions of Svalbard and East Greenland. *Nature*, **321**: 832–838.

Knoll, A.H., Grotzinger, J.P., Kaufman, A.J., and Kolosov, P., 1995, Integrated approaches to terminal Proterozoic stratigraphy: an example from the Olenek Uplift, northeastern Siberia. *Precambrian Research*, **73**: 251–270.

Knoll, A.H., Walter, M.R., Narbonne, G.M., and Christie-Blick, N., 2004, A new period for the geologic time scale. *Science*, **305**: 621–622.

Knoll, A.H., Walter, M.R., Narbonne, G.M., and Christie-Blick, N., 2006, The Ediacaran Period: a new addition to the geologic time scale. *Lethaia*, **39**: 13–30.

Kontorovich, A.E., Varlamov, A.I., Grazhdankin, D.V., Karlova, G.A., Klets, A.G., Kontorovich, V.A., et al., 2008, A section of Vendian in the east of West Siberian Plate (based on data from the Borehole Vostok 3). *Russian Geology and Geophysics*, **49**: 932–939.

Kumar, S., and Sharma, M., 2010, *Field Guide, Vindhyan Basin, Son Valley Area.* 107 pp. The Palaeontological Society of India.

Kumar, S., and Sharma, M., 2012, *Palaeontological Society of India Field Guide: Vindhyan Basin, Son Valley Area.* 145 pp. The Palaeontological Society of India.

Laflamme, M., Darroch, S.A.F., Tweedt, S.M., Peterson, K.J., and Erwin, D.H., 2013, The end of the Ediacara biota: extinction, biotic replacement, or Cheshire Cat? *Gondwana Research*, **23**: 558–573.

Landing, E., 1994, Precambrian-Cambrian boundary global stratotype ratified and a new perspective of Cambrian time. *Geology*, **22**: 179–182.

Lang, X., Shen, B., Peng, Y., Huang, K., Lv, J., and Ma, H., 2017, Ocean oxidation during the deposition of basal Ediacaran Doushantuo cap carbonates in the Yangtze Platform, South China. *Precambrian Research*, **281**: 253–268, https://doi.org/10.1016/j.precamres.2016.06.006.

Le Guerroue, E., Allen, P.A., Cozzi, A., Etienne, J.L., and Fanning, M., 2006, 50 Myr recovery from the largest negative $\delta^{13}C$ excursion in the Ediacaran ocean. *Terra Nova*, **18**: 147–153.

Leavitt, W.D., Halevy, I., Bradley, A.S., and Johnston, D.T., 2013, Influence of sulfate reduction rates on the Phanerozoic sulfur isotope record. *Proceedings of the National Academy of Sciences of the United States of America*, **110**: 11244–11249.

Lee, J.S., 1924, Geology of the Gorge District of the Yangtze (from Ichang to Tzekuei) with special reference to the development of the Gorges. *Bulletin of the Geological Society of China*, **3**: 351–392.

Li, C., Love, G.D., Lyons, T.W., Fike, D.A., Sessions, A.L., and Chu, X., 2010, A stratified redox model for the Ediacaran ocean. *Science*, **328**: 80–83, https://doi.org/10.1126/science.1182369.

Li, D., Ling, H.F., Shields-Zhou, G.A., Chen, X., Cremonese, L., Och, L., et al., 2013a, Carbon and strontium isotope evolution of seawater across the Ediacaran-Cambrian transition: evidence from the Xiaotan section, NE Yunnan, South China. *Precambrian Research*, **225**: 128–147, https://doi.org/10.1016/j.precamres.2012.01.002.

Li, Z.-X., Evans, D.A.D., and Halverson, G.P., 2013b, Neoproterozoic glaciations in a revised global palaeogeography from the breakup of Rodinia to the assembly of Gondwanaland. *Sedimentary Geology*, **294**: 219–232, https://doi.org/10.1016/j.sedgeo.2013.05.016.

Li, C., Hardisty, D.S., Luo, G., Huang, J., Algeo, T.J., Cheng, M., et al., 2017, Uncovering the spatial heterogeneity of Ediacaran carbon cycling. *Geobiology*, **15**: 211–224, https://doi.org/10.1111/gbi.12222.

Linnemann, U., Ovtcharova, M., Schaltegger, U., Gärtner, A., Hautmann, M., Geyer, G., et al., 2019, New high-resolution age data from the Ediacaran-Cambrian boundary indicate rapid, ecologically driven onset of the Cambrian explosion. *Terra Nova*, **31**: 49–58, https://doi.org/10.1111/ter.12368.

Liu, A.G., and McIlroy, D., 2015, Horizontal surface traces from the Fermeuse Formation, Ferryland (Newfoundland, Canada), and their place within the late Ediacaran ichnological revolution. *Geological Association of Canada Miscellaneous Publication (Papers from ICHNIA III)*, **9**: 141–156.

Liu, P., and Moczydłowska, M., 2019, Ediacaran microfossils from the Doushantuo Formation chert nodules in the Yangtze Gorges area, South China, and new biozones. *Fossils and Strata*, **65**: 1–172, https://doi.org/10.1002/9781119564195.

Liu, P., Yin, C., Gao, L., Tang, F., and Chen, S., 2009, New material of microfossils from the Ediacaran Doushantuo Formation in the Zhangcunping area, Yichang, Hubei Province and its zircon SHRIMP U-Pb age. *Chinese Science Bulletin*, **54**: 1058–1064, https://doi.org/10.1007/s11434-008-0589-6.

Liu, A.G., McIlroy, D., and Brasier, M.D., 2010, First evidence for locomotion in the Ediacara biota from the 565 Ma Mistaken Point Formation, Newfoundland. *Geology*, **38**: 123–126.

Liu, A.G., McIlroy, D., Matthews, J.J., and Brasier, M.D., 2012, A new assemblage of juvenile Ediacaran fronds from the Drook Formation, Newfoundland. *Journal of the Geological Society, London*, **169**: 395–403.

Liu, C., Wang, Z., and Raub, T.D., 2013a, Geochemical constraints on the origin of Marinoan cap dolostones from Nuccaleena Formation, South Australia. *Chemical Geology*, **351**: 95–104, https://doi.org/10.1016/j.chemgeo.2013.05.012.

Liu, P., Yin, C., Chen, S., Tang, F., and Gao, L., 2013b, The biostratigraphic succession of acanthomorphic acritarchs of the Ediacaran Doushantuo Formation in the Yangtze Gorges area, South China and its biostratigraphic correlation with Australia. *Precambrian Research*, **225**: 29–43, https://doi.org/10.1016/j.precamres.2011.07.009.

Liu, A.G., Kenchington, C.G., and Mitchell, E.G., 2014a, Remarkable insights into the paleoecology of the Avalonian Ediacaran macrobiota. *Gondwana Research*, **27**: 1355–1380, https://doi.org/10.1016/j.gr.2014.11.002.

Liu, A.G., McIlroy, D., Matthews, J.J., and Brasier, M.D., 2014b, Confirming the metazoan character of a 565 Ma trace-fossil assemblage from Mistaken Point, Newfoundland. *Palaios*, **29**: 420–430, https://doi.org/10.2110/palo.2014.011.

Liu, A.G., Matthews, J.J., Menon, L.R., McIlroy, D., and Brasier, M.D., 2014c, *Haootia quadriformis* n. gen., n. sp., interpreted as a muscular cnidarian impression from the Late Ediacaran period (approx. 560 Ma). *Proceedings of the Royal Society B: Biological Sciences*, 281, https://doi.org/10.1098/rspb.2014.1202.

Liu, C., Wang, Z., Raub, T.D., Macdonald, F.A., and Evans, D.A.D., 2014d, Neoproterozoic cap-dolostone deposition in stratified glacial meltwater plume. *Earth and Planetary Science Letters*, **404**: 22–32, https://doi.org/10.1016/j.epsl.2014.06.039.

Liu, P., Chen, S., Zhu, M., Li, M., Yin, C., and Shang, X., 2014e, High-resolution biostratigraphic and chemostratigraphic data fromthe Chenjiayuanzi section of the Doushantuo Formation in the Yangtze Gorges area, South China: implication for subdivision and global correlation of the Ediacaran System. *Precambrian Research*, **249**: 199–214, https://doi.org/10.1016/j.precamres.2014.05.014.

Liu, P., Xiao, S., Yin, C., Chen, S., Zhou, C., and Li, M., 2014f, Ediacaran acanthomorphic acritarchs and other microfossils from chert nodules of the upper Doushantuo Formation in the Yangtze Gorges area, South China. *Journal of Paleontology*, **88** (Suppl. 1), 1–139, https://doi.org/10.1666/13-009.

Liu, A.G., Matthews, J.J., McIlroy, D., Narbonne, G.M., Landing, E., Menon, L.R., et al., 2018a, International Symposium on the

Ediacaran–Cambrian Transition (ISECT) 2017. *Episodes*, **41**: 128–132.

Liu, C., Wang, Z., and Macdonald, F.A., 2018b, Sr and Mg isotope geochemistry of the basal Ediacaran cap limestone sequence of Mongolia: implications for carbonate diagenesis, mixing of glacial meltwaters, and seawater chemistry in the aftermath of Snowball Earth. *Chemical Geology*, **491**: 1–13, https://doi.org/10.1016/j.chemgeo.2018.05.008.

Lu, M., Zhu, M., Zhang, J., Shields-Zhou, G., Li, G., Zhao, F., et al., 2013, The DOUNCE event at the top of the Ediacaran Doushantuo Formation, South China: broad stratigraphic occurrence and non-diagenetic origin. *Precambrian Research*, **225**: 86–109.

Lv, Y.W., Liu, S.A., Wu, H.C., Hohl, S.V., Chen, S.M., and Li, S.G., 2018, Zn-Sr isotope records of the Ediacaran Doushantuo Formation in South China: diagenesis assessment and implications. *Geochimica et Cosmochimica Acta*, **239**: 330–345, https://doi.org/10.1016/j.gca.2018.08.003.

Lyons, T.W., and Severmann, S., 2006, A critical look at iron paleoredox proxies: new insights from modern euxinic marine basins. *Geochimica et Cosmochimica Acta*, **70**: 5698–5722, https://doi.org/10.1016/j.gca.2006.08.021.

Macdonald, F.A., Strauss, J.V., Sperling, E.A., Halverson, G.P., Narbonne, G.M., Johnston, D.T., et al., 2013, The stratigraphic relationship between the Shuram carbon isotope excursion, the oxygenation of Neoproterozoic oceans, and the first appearance of the Ediacara biota and bilaterian trace fossils in northwestern Canada. *Chemical Geology*, **362**: 250–272, https://doi.org/10.1016/j.chemgeo.2013.05.032.

MacNaughton, R.B., Narbonne, G.M., and Dalrymple, R.W., 2000, Neoproterozoic slope deposits, Mackenzie Mountains, northwestern Canada: implications for passive-margin development and Ediacaran faunal ecology. *Canadian Journal of Earth Sciences*, **37**: 997–1020.

Martin, M.W., Grazhdankin, D.V., Bowring, S.A., Evans, D.A.D., Fedonkin, M.A., and Kirschvink, J.L., 2000, Age of Neoproterozoic bilaterian body and trace fossils, White Sea, Russia: implications for metazoan evolution. *Science*, **288**: 841–845.

Mawson, D., and Sprigg, R.C., 1950, Subdivision of the Adelaide System. *The Australian Journal of Science*, **13**: 69–72.

McFadden, K.A., Huang, J., Chu, X., Jiang, G., Kaufman, A.J., Zhou, C., et al., 2008, Pulsed oxidation and biological evolution in the Ediacaran Doushantuo Formation. *Proceedings of the National Academy of Sciences*, **105**: 3197–3202, https://doi.org/10.1073/pnas.0708336105.

McFadden, K.A., Xiao, S., Zhou, C., and Kowalewski, M., 2009, Quantitative evaluation of the biostratigraphic distribution of acanthomorphic acritarchs in the Ediacaran Doushantuo Formation in the Yangtze Gorges area, South China. *Precambrian Research*, **173**: 170–190.

McMenamin, M.A.S., 1985, Basal Cambrian small shelly fossils from the La Ciénega Formation, northwestern Sonora, Mexico. *Journal of Paleontology*, **59**: 1414–1425.

Melezhik, V.A., Pokrovsky, B.G., Fallick, A.E., Kuznetsov, A.B., and Bujakaite, M.I., 2009, Constraints on $^{87}Sr/^{86}Sr$ of late Ediacaran seawater: insight from Siberian high-Sr limestones. *Journal of the Geological Society*, **166**: 183–191, https://doi.org/10.1144/0016-76492007-171.

Menon, L.R., McIlroy, D., and Brasier, M.D., 2013, Evidence for Cnidaria-like behavior in ca. 560 Ma Ediacaran *Aspidella*. *Geology*, **41**: 895–898.

Meyer, M., Schiffbauer, J.D., Xiao, S., Cai, Y., and Hua, H., 2012, Taphonomy of the upper Ediacaran enigmatic ribbon-like fossil *Shaanxilithes*. *Palaios*, **27**: 354–372.

Meyer, M., Xiao, S., Schiffbauer, J.D., Chen, Z., Zhou, C., and Yuan, X., 2014a, *Lamonte trevallis*, a new trace fossil from the Dengying Formation of South China: insights into late Ediacaran benthic ecology. *Geological Society of America Abstracts with Programs*, **46** (3), 86.

Meyer, M., Xiao, S., Gill, B.C., Schiffbauer, J.D., Chen, Z., Zhou, C., et al., 2014b, Interactions between Ediacaran animals and microbial mats: insights from *Lamonte trevallis*, a new trace fossil from the Dengying Formation of South China. *Palaeogeography, Palaeoclimatology, Palaeoecology*, **396**: 62–74, https://doi.org/10.1016/j.palaeo.2013.12.026.

Meyer, M., Polys, N., Yaqoob, H., Hinnov, L., and Xiao, S., 2017, Beyond the stony veil: reconstructing the Earth's earliest large animal traces via computed tomography X-ray imaging. *Precambrian Research*, **298**: 341–350, https://doi.org/10.1016/j.precamres.2017.05.010.

Misi, A., Kaufman, A.J., Veizer, J., Powis, K., Azmy, K., Boggiani, P. C., et al., 2007, Chemostratigraphic correlation of neoproterozoic successions in South America. *Chemical Geology*, **237**: 143–167, https://doi.org/10.1016/j.chemgeo.2006.06.019.

Misra, S.B., 1969, Late Precambrian (?) fossils from southeastern Newfoundland. *Geological Society of America Bulletin*, **80**: 2133–2140.

Mitchell, E.G., Kenchington, C.G., Liu, A.G., Matthews, J.J., and Butterfield, N.J., 2015, Reconstructing the reproductive mode of an Ediacaran macro-organism. *Nature*, **524**: 343–346, https://doi.org/10.1038/nature14646.

Moczydłowska, M., 1991, Acritarch biostratigraphy of the Lower Cambrian and the Precambrian–Cambrian boundary in southeastern Poland. *Fossils and Strata*, **29**: 1–127.

Moczydłowska, M., 1998, Cambrian acritarchs from Upper Silesia, Poland: biochronology and tectonic implications. *Fossils and Strata*, **46**: 1–121.

Moczydłowska, M., 2005, Taxonomic review of some Ediacaran acritarchs from the Siberian Platform. *Precambrian Research*, **136**: 283–307.

Moczydłowska, M., and Nagovitsin, K.E., 2012, Ediacaran radiation of organic-walled microbiota recorded in the Ura Formation, Patom Uplift, East Siberia. *Precambrian Research*, **198–199**: 1–24.

Moczydłowska, M., Vidal, G., and Rudavskaya, V.A., 1993, Neoproterozoic (Vendian) phytoplankton from the Siberian Platform, Yakutia. *Palaeontology*, **36**: 495–521.

Moczydłowska-Vidal, M., Grey, K., Xiao, S., and Willman, S., 2008, Swedish workshop on Ediacaran acritarch taxonomy (SWEATSHOP). *Episodes*, **31**: 442.

Moczydłowska, M., Westall, F., and Foucher, F., 2014, Microstructure and biogeochemistry of the organically preserved Ediacaran metazoan *Sabellidites*. *Journal of Paleontology*, **88**: 224–239.

Moynihan, D.P., Strauss, J.V., Nelson, L.L., and Padget, C.D., 2019, Upper Windermere Supergroup and the transition from rifting to continent margin sedimentation, Nadaleen River area, northern Canadian Cordillera. *Geological Society of America Bulletin*, **131**: 1673–1701, https://doi.org/10.1130/B32039.1.

Muscente, A.D., Boag, T.H., Bykova, N., and Schiffbauer, J.D., 2018, Environmental disturbance, resource availability, and biologic turnover at the dawn of animal life. *Earth-Science Reviews*, **177**: 248–264, https://doi.org/10.1016/j.earscirev.2017.11.019.

Myrow, P.M., and Kaufman, A.J., 1999, A newly discovered cap carbonate above Varanger-aged glacial deposits in Newfoundland, Canada. *Journal of Sedimentary Research*, **69**: 784–793.

Nagovitsin, K.E., Rogov, V.I., Marusin, V.V., Karlova, G.A., Kolesnikov, A.V., Bykova, N.V., et al., 2015, Revised Neoproterozoic and Terreneuvian stratigraphy of the Lena-Anabar Basin and north-western slope of the Olenek Uplift, Siberian Platform. *Precambrian Research*, **270**: 226–245, https://doi.org/10.1016/j.precamres.2015.09.012.

Nagovitsyn, K.E., Faizullin, M.S., and Yakshin, M.S., 2004, New forms of Baikalian acanthomorphytes from the Ura Formation of the Patom Uplift, East Siberia. *Geologiya e Geofisika*, **45**: 7–19.

Narbonne, G.M., 2004, Modular construction of early Ediacaran complex life forms. *Science*, **305**: 1141–1144.

Narbonne, G.M., 2005, The Ediacara Biota: Neoproterozoic origin of animals and their ecosystems. *Annual Review of Earth and Planetary Sciences*, **33**: 421–442, https://doi.org/10.1146/annurev.earth.33.092203.122519.

Narbonne, G.M., 2010, Neoproterozoic oceans and early animals. *Science*, **328**: 53–54.

Narbonne, G.M., and Aitken, J.D., 1990, Ediacaran fossils from the Sekwi Brook area, Mackenzie Mountains, northwestern Canada. *Palaeontology*, **33**: 945–980.

Narbonne, G.M., and Aitken, J.D., 1995, Neoproterozoic of the Mackenzie Mountains, northwestern Canada. *Precambrian Research*, **73**: 101–121.

Narbonne, G.M., and Gehling, J.G., 2003, Life after snowball: the oldest complex Ediacaran fossils. *Geology*, **31**: 27–30.

Narbonne, G.M., Myrow, P.M., Landing, E., and Anderson, M.M., 1987, A candidate stratotype for the Precambrian-Cambrian boundary, Fortune Head, Burin Peninsula, southeastern Newfoundland. *Canadian Journal of Earth Sciences*, **24**: 1277–1293.

Narbonne, G.M., Kaufman, A.J., and Knoll, A.H., 1994, Integrated chemostratigraphy and biostratigraphy of the Windermere Supergroup, northwestern Canada: implications for Neoproterozoic correlations and the early evolution of animals. *Geological Society of America Bulletin*, **106**: 1281–1292.

Narbonne, G.M., Saylor, B.Z., and Grotzinger, J.P., 1997, The youngest Ediacaran fossils from southern Africa. *Journal of Paleontology*, **71**: 953–967.

Narbonne, G.M., Laflamme, M., Greentree, C., and Trusler, P., 2009, Reconstructing a lost world: Ediacaran rangeomorphs from Spaniard's Bay, Newfoundland. *Journal of Paleontology*, **83**: 503–523.

Narbonne, G.M., Xiao, S., and Shields, G.A., 2012a, The Ediacaran Period. *In* Gradstein, F.M., Ogg, J.G., Schmitz, M., and Ogg, G. (eds), *Geologic Time Scale 2012*. Elsevier, Oxford, 413–435.

Narbonne, G.M., Laflamme, M., and Thomas, R., 2012b, When life got big: glaciation, oxidation, and the Mistaken Point biota of Newfoundland. *Geologic Association of Canada Field Trip Guides*, **B1**: 1–78.

Narbonne, G.M., Laflamme, M., Trusler, P.W., Dalrymple, R.W., and Greentree, C., 2014, Deep-water Ediacaran fossils from northwestern Canada: taphonomy, ecology, and evolution. *Journal of Paleontology*, **88**: 207–223, https://doi.org/10.1666/13-053.

Nicholas, C.J., 1996, The Sr isotopic evolution of the oceans during the 'Cambrian explosion'. *Journal of the Geological Society*, **153**: 243–254, https://doi.org/10.1144/gsjgs.153.2.0243.

Noble, S.R., Condon, D.J., Carney, J.N., Wilby, P.R., Pharaoh, T.C., and Ford, T.D., 2015, U-Pb geochronology and global context of the Charnian Supergroup, UK: constraints on the age of key Ediacaran fossil assemblages. *Geological Society of America Bulletin*, **127**: 250–265, https://doi.org/10.1130/b31013.1.

Nogueira, A.C.R., Riccomini, C., Sial, A.N., Moura, C.A.V., Trindade, R.I. F., and Fairchild, T.R., 2007, Carbon and strontium isotope fluctuations and paleoceanographic changes in the late Neoproterozoic Araras carbonate platform, southern Amazon craton, Brazil. *Chemical Geology*, **237**: 168–190, https://doi.org/10.1016/j.chemgeo.2006.06.016.

Ogg, J.G., Ogg, G.M., and Gradstein, F.M., 2016, *A Concise Geologic Time Scale 2016*. 240 pp. Elsevier.

Ouyang, Q., Guan, C., Zhou, C., and Xiao, S., 2017, Acanthomorphic acritarchs of the Doushantuo Formation from an upper slope section in northwestern Hunan Province, South China, with implications for early Ediacaran biostratigraphy. *Precambrian Research*, **298**: 512–529, https://doi.org/10.1016/j.precamres.2017.07.005.

Ouyang, Q., Zhou, C., Xiao, S., Chen, Z., and Shao, Y., 2019, Acanthomorphic acritarchs from the Ediacaran Doushantuo Formation at Zhangcunping in South China, with implications for the evolution of early Ediacaran eukaryotes. *Precambrian Research*, **320**: 171–192, https://doi.org/10.1016/j.precamres.2018.10.012.

Pacheco, M.L.A.F., Galante, D., Rodrigues, F., Leme, Jd.M., Bidola, P., Hagadorn, W., et al., 2015, Insights into the skeletonization, lifestyle, and affinity of the unusual Ediacaran fossil *Corumbella*. *PLoS One*, **10**: e0114219, https://doi.org/10.1371/journal.pone. 0114219.

Pandey, S.K., and Dimri, B., 2014, Field workshop on the Marwar Supergroup. *Current Science*, **107**: 169–170.

Parry, L., Boggiani, P.C., Condon, D., Garwood, R., Leme, J.M., McIlroy, D., et al., 2017, Ichnological evidence for meiofaunal bilaterians from the terminal Ediacaran and earliest Cambrian of Brazil. *Nature Ecology and Evolution*, **1**: 1455–1464, https://doi.org/10.1038/s41559-017-0301-9.

Pokrovskii, B.G., Melezhik, V.A., and Bujakaite, M.I., 2006, Carbon, oxygen, strontium, and sulfur isotopic compositions in late Precambrian rocks of the Patom Complex, central Siberia: communication 1. results, isotope stratigraphy, and dating problems. *Lithology and Mineral Resources*, **41**: 450–474.

Poulton, S.W., and Canfield, D.E., 2005, Development of a sequential extraction procedure for iron: implications for iron partitioning on contitentally derived particulates. *Chemical Geology*, **214**: 209–221, https://doi.org/10.1016/j/chemgeo.2004.09.003.

Prave, A.R., Fallick, A.E., Thomas, C.W., and Graham, C.M., 2009, A composite C-isotope profile for the Neoproterozoic Dalradian Supergroup of Scotland and Ireland. *Journal of the Geological Society, London*, **166**: 845–857.

Prave, A.R., Condon, D.J., Hoffmann, K.H., Tapster, S., and Fallick, A. E., 2016, Duration and nature of the end-Cryogenian (Marinoan) glaciation. *Geology*, **44**: 631–634, https://doi.org/10.1130/G38089.1.

Pu, J.P., Bowring, S.A., Ramezani, J., Myrow, P., Raub, T.D., Landing, E., et al., 2016, Dodging snowballs: geochronology of the Gaskiers glaciation and the first appearance of the Ediacaran biota. *Geology*, **44**: 955–958, https://doi.org/10.1130/G38284.1.

Raiswell, R., Buckley, F., Berner, R.A., and Anderson, T.F., 1988, Degree of pyritisation of iron as a paleoenvironmental indicator of bottom-water oxygenation. *Journal of Sedimentary Research*, **58**: 812–819.

Reusch, H., 1891, Skuringsmærker og morængrus eftervist i Finnmarken fra en periode meget ældre end 'istiden'. *Norges geologiske undersøkelse*, **1**: 78–85.

Rice, A.H.N., Edwards, M.B., Hansen, T.A., Arnaud, E., and Halverson, G.P., 2011, Glaciogenic rocks of the Neoproterozoic Smalfjord and Mortensnes formations, Vestertana Group, E. Finnmark, Norway. *In* Arnaud, E., Halverson, G.P., and Shields-Zhou, G. (eds), *The Geological Record of Neoproterozoic Glaciations*. Geological Society of London, London.

Ries, J.B., Fike, D.A., Pratt, L.M., Lyons, T.W., and Grotzinger, J.P., 2009, Superheavy pyrite ($\delta^{34}S_{pyr} > \delta^{34}S_{CAS}$) in the terminal Proterozoic Nama Group, southern Namibia: a consequence of low seawater sulfate at the dawn of animal life. *Geology*, **37**: 743–746.

Robb, L.J., Knoll, A.H., Plumb, K.A., Shields, G.A., Strauss, H., and Veizer, J., 2004, The Precambrian: the Archean and Proterozoic eons. *In* Gradstein, F.M., Ogg, J.G., and Smith, A.G. (eds), *A Geologic Time Scale 2004*. Cambridge University Press, Cambridge, 129–140.

Rogov, V., Marusin, V., Bykova, N., Goy, Y., Nagovitsin, K., Kochnev, B., et al., 2012, The oldest evidence of bioturbation on Earth. *Geology*, **40**: 395–398.

Rogov, V.I., Karlova, G.A., Marusin, V.V., Kochnev, B.B., Nagovitsin, K.E., and Grazhdankin, D.V., 2015, Duration of the first biozone in the Siberian hypostratotype of the Vendian. *Russian Geology and Geophysics*, **56**: 573–583, https://doi.org/10.1016/j.rgg.2015.03.016.

Rooney, A., 2019, New Re-Os ages and Os geochemistry from the Neoproterozoic: fresh insights into links between climate, animal evolution and biogeochemical cycles. *Geological Society of America Abstracts with Programs*, **51** (5), https://doi.org/10.1130/abs/2019AM-336265.

Rooney, A.D., Strauss, J.V., Brandon, A.D., and Macdonald, F.A., 2015, A Cryogenian chronology: two long-lasting synchronous Neoproterozoic glaciations. *Geology*, **43**: 459–462, https://doi.org/10.1130/G36511.1.

Rothman, D.H., Hayes, J.M., and Summons, R., 2003, Dynamics of the Neoproterozoic carbon cycle. *Proceedings of the National Academy of Sciences of the United States of America*, **100**: 8124–8129.

Sahoo, S.K., Planavsky, N.J., Jiang, G., Kendall, B., Owens, J.D., Wang, X., et al., 2016, Oceanic oxygenation events in the anoxic Ediacaran ocean. *Geobiology*, **14**: 457–468, https://doi.org/10.1111/gbi.12182.

Sato, H., Tahata, M., Sawaki, Y., Maruyama, S., Yoshida, N., Shu, D., et al., 2016, A high-resolution chemostratigraphy of post-Marinoan cap carbonate using drill core samples in the Three Gorges area, South China. *Geoscience Frontiers*, **7**: 663–671, https://doi.org/10.1016/j.gsf.2015.07.008.

Sawaki, Y., Ohno, T., Tahata, M., Komiya, T., Hirata, T., Maruyama, S., et al., 2010, The Ediacaran radiogenic Sr isotope excursion in the Doushantuo Formation in the Three Gorges area, South China. *Precambrian Research*, **176**: 46–64.

Schiffbauer, J.D., Huntley, J.W., O'Neil, G.R., Darroch, S.A.F., Laflamme, M., and Cai, Y., 2016, The latest Ediacaran wormworld fauna: setting the ecological stage for the Cambrian explosion. *GSA Today*, **26**: 4–11, https://doi.org/10.1130/GSATG265A.1.

Schmitz, M.D., 2012, Appendix 2—Radioisotopic ages used in GTS2012. *In* Gradstein, F., Ogg, J., Schmitz, M.D., and Ogg, G. (eds), *The Geologic Time Scale 2012*. Elsevier, Boston, MA, 1045–1082.

Schrag, D.P., Higgins, J.A., Macdonald, F.A., and Johnston, D.T., 2013, Authigenic carbonate and the history of the global carbon cycle. *Science*, **339**: 540–543, https://doi.org/10.1126/science.1229578.

Schröder, S., Schreiber, B.C., Amthor, J.E., and Matter, A., 2004, Stratigraphy and environmental conditions of the terminal Neoproterozoic-Cambrian period in Oman: evidence from sulphur isotopes. *Journal of the Geological Society*, **161**: 489–499, https://doi.org/10.1144/0016-764902-062.

Scott, C., Lyons, T.W., Bekker, A., Shen, Y., Poulton, S.W., Chu, X., et al., 2008, Tracing the stepwise oxygenation of the Proterozoic ocean. *Nature*, **452**: 456–459.

Selly, T., Schiffbauer, J.D., Jacquet, S.M., Smith, E.F., Nelson, L.L., Andreasen, B.D., et al., 2019, A new cloudinid fossil assemblage from the terminal Ediacaran of Nevada, USA. *Journal of Systematic Palaeontology*, https://doi.org/10.1080/14772019.2019.1623333.

Sergeev, V.N., Knoll, A.H., and Vorob'Eva, N.G., 2011, Ediacaran microfossils from the Ura Formation, Baikal-Patom Uplift, Siberia: taxonomy and biostratigraphic significance. *Journal of Paleontology*, **85**: 987–1011.

Shen, B., Xiao, S., Dong, L., Zhou, C., and Liu, J., 2007, Problematic macrofossils from Ediacaran successions in the North China and Chaidam blocks: implications for their evolutionary roots and biostratigraphic significance. *Journal of Paleontology*, **81**: 1396–1411.

Shen, B., Dong, L., Xiao, S., and Kowalewski, M., 2008, The Avalon explosion: evolution of Ediacara morphospace. *Science*, **319**: 81–84.

Shen, B., Xiao, S., Zhou, C., Kaufman, A.J., and Yuan, X., 2010, Carbon and sulfur isotope chemostratigraphy of the Neoproterozoic Quanji Group of the Chaidam Basin, NW China: basin stratification in the aftermath of an Ediacaran glaciation postdating the Shuram event? *Precambrian Research*, **177**: 241–252.

Shi, W., Li, C., Luo, G.M., Huang, J.H., Algeo, T.J., Jin, C.S., et al., 2018, Sulfur isotope evidence for transient marine-shelf oxidation during the Ediacaran Shuram Excursion. *Geology*, **46**: 267–270, https://doi.org/10.1130/g39663.1.

Shields, G.A., Strauss, H., Howe, S.S., and Siegmund, H., 1999, Sulphur isotope compositions of sedimentary phosphorites from the basal Cambrian of China: implications for Neoproterozoic-Cambrian biogeochemical cycling. *Journal of the Geological Society*, **156**: 943–955, https://doi.org/10.1144/gsjgs.156.5.0943.

Shields, G.A., Deynoux, M., Strauss, H., Paquet, H., and Nahon, D., 2007, Barite-bearing cap dolostones of the Taoudéni Basin, northwest Africa: sedimentary and isotopic evidence for methane seepage after a Neoproterozoic glaciation. *Precambrian Research*, **153**: 209–235.

Shukla, R., and Tiwari, M., 2014, Ediacaran acanthomorphic acritarchs from the Outer Krol Belt, Lesser Himalaya, India: their significance for global correlation. *Palaeoworld*, **23**: 209–224, https://doi.org/10.1016/j.palwor.2014.07.001.

Shukla, M., Babu, R., Mathur, V.K., and Srivastava, D.K., 2005, Additional terminal proterozoic organic-walled microfossils from the Infra-Krol Formation, Nainital Syncline, Lesser Himalaya, Uttaranchal. *Journal of the Geological Society, India*, **65**: 197–210.

Shukla, M., Mathur, V.K., Babu, R., and Srivastava, D.K., 2008, Ediacaran microbiota from the Baliana and Krol groups, Lesser Himalaya, India. *Palaeobotanist*, **57**: 359–378.

Sial, A.N., Gaucher, C., Misi, A., Boggiani, P.C., de Alvarenga, C.J.S., Ferreira, V.P., et al., 2016, Correlations of some Neoproterozoic carbonate-dominated successions in South America based on high-resolution chemostratigraphy. *The Brazilian Journal of Geology*, **46**: 439–488, https://doi.org/10.1590/2317-4889201620160079.

Signor, P.W., Mount, J.F., and Onken, B.R., 1987, A pre-trilobite shelly fauna from the White-Inyo region of eastern California and western Nevada. *Journal of Paleontology*, **61**: 425–438.

Singh, V.K., and Ansari, A.H., 2014, A report on the international field workshop on the Marwar Supergroup, Rajasthan, western India,

20th-28th January, 2014. *Journal of the Palaeontological Society of India*, **59**: 113–114.

Smith, E.F., Nelson, L.L., Strange, M.A., Eyster, A.E., Rowland, S.M., Schrag, D.P., et al., 2016, The end of the Ediacaran: two new exceptionally preserved body fossil assemblages from Mount Dunfee, Nevada, USA. *Geology*, **44**: 911–914, https://doi.org/10.1130/G38157.1.

Smith, E.F., Nelson, L.L., Tweedt, S.M., Zeng, H., and Workman, J.B., 2017, A cosmopolitan late Ediacaran biotic assemblage: new fossils from Nevada and Namibia support a global biostratigraphic link. *Proceedings of the Royal Society B: Biological Sciences*, **284**: 20170934, https://doi.org/10.1098/rspb.2017.0934.

Sokolov, B.S., 1952, On the age of the old sedimentary cover of the Russian Platform. *Izvestiya Akademii Nauk SSSR, Seriya geologicheskaya*, **5**: 21–31.

Sokolov, B.S., and Fedonkin, M.A., 1982, The Vendian as the terminal system of the Precambrian. *Episodes*, **7**: 12–19.

Sour-Tovar, F., Hagadorn, J.W., and Huitrón-Rubio, T., 2007, Ediacaran and Cambrian index fossils from Sonora, Mexico. *Palaeontology*, **50**: 169–175.

Sperling, E.A., and Vinther, J., 2010, A placozoan affinity for *Dickinsonia* and the evolution of late Proterozoic metazoan feeding modes. *Evolution & Development*, **12**: 201–209.

Sperling, E.A., Wolock, C.J., Morgan, A.S., Gill, B.C., Kunzmann, M., Halverson, G.P., et al., 2015, Statistical analysis of iron geochemical data suggests limited late Proterozoic oxygenation. *Nature*, **523**: 451–454, https://doi.org/10.1038/nature14589.

Sprigg, R.C., 1947, Early Cambrian (?) jellyfishes from the Flinders Ranges, South Australia. *Transactions of the Royal Society of South Australia*, **71**: 212–224.

Strauss, H., 1993, The sulfur isotopic record of Precambrian sulfates - new data and a critical-evaluation of the existing record. *Precambrian Research*, **63**: 225–246, https://doi.org/10.1016/0301-9268(93)90035-z.

Sun, W., 1986, Late Precambrian pennatulids (sea pens) from the eastern Yangtze Gorge, China: Paracharnia gen.nov. *Precambrian Research*, **31**: 361–375.

Tahata, M., Ueno, Y., Ishikawa, T., Sawaki, Y., Murakami, K., Han, J., et al., 2013, Carbon and oxygen isotope chemostratigraphies of the Yangtze platform, South China: decoding temperature and environmental changes through the Ediacaran. *Gondwana Research*, **23**: 333–353, https://doi.org/10.1016/j.gr.2012.04.005.

Tang, F., Yin, C., Bengtson, S., Liu, P., Wang, Z., and Gao, L., 2008, Octoradiate spiral organisms in the Ediacaran of South China. *Acta Geologica Sinica*, **82**: 27–34.

Tang, Q., Pang, K., Yuan, X., Wan, B., and Xiao, S., 2015, Organic-walled microfossils from the Tonian Gouhou Formation, Huaibei region, North China Craton, and their biostratigraphic implications. *Precambrian Research*, **266**: 296–318, https://doi.org/10.1016/j.precamres.2015.05.025.

Tarhan, L.G., Hughes, N.C., Myrow, P.M., Bhargava, O.N., Ahluwalia, A.D., and Kudryavtsev, A.B., 2014, Precambrian-Cambrian boundary interval occurrence and form of the enigmatic tubular body fossil *Shaanxilithes ningqiangensis* from the Lesser Himalaya of India. *Palaeontology*, **57**: 283–298.

Tarhan, L.G., Droser, M.L., Cole, D.B., and Gehling, J.G., 2018, Ecological expansion and extinction in the late Ediacaran: weighing the evidence for environmental and biotic drivers. *Integrative and Comparative Biology*, **58**: 688–702, https://doi.org/10.1093/icb/icy020/4989946.

Termier, H., and Termier, G., 1960, L'Ediacarien, premier etage paleontologique. *Revue génerale des sciences pures et appliquées et bulletin de l'Association Française pour l'Avancement des Sciences*, **67**: 79–87.

Thompson, M.D., and Bowring, S.A., 2000, Age of the Squantum "tillite", Boston Basin, Massachusetts: U-Pb zircon constraints on terminal Neoproterozoic glaciation. *American Journal of Science*, **300**: 630–655.

Thomson, J., 1871, *On the Stratified Rocks of Islay. Report of the 41st Meeting of the British Association for the Advancement of Science*. (pp. 110–111). John Murray.

Timofeev, B.V., 1966, *Mircropaleophytological Investigations of Ancient Formations*. 147 pp. Nauka.

Tiwari, M., and Azmi, R.J., 1992, Late Proterozoic organic-walled microfossils from the Infrakrol of Solan, Himchal Lesser Himalaya: an additional age constraint in the Krol Belt succession. *Palaeobotanist*, **39**: 387–394.

Tiwari, M., and Knoll, A.H., 1994, Large acanthomorphic acritarchs from the Infrakrol Formation of the Lesser Himalaya and their stratigraphic significance. *Journal of Himalayan Geology*, **5**: 193–201.

Tostevin, R., He, T.C., Turchyn, A.V., Wood, R.A., Penny, A.M., Bowyer, F., et al., 2017, Constraints on the late Ediacaran sulfur cycle from carbonate associated sulfate. *Precambrian Research*, **290**: 113–125, https://doi.org/10.1016/j.precamres.2017.01.004.

Tostevin, R., Clarkson, M.O., Gangl, S., Shields, G.A., Wood, R.A., Bowyer, F., et al., 2018, Uranium isotope evidence for an expansion of anoxia in terminal Ediacaran oceans. *Earth and Planetary Science Letters*, **506**: 104–112, https://doi.org/10.1016/j.epsl.2018.10.045.

Valladares, M.I., Ugidos, J.M., Barba, P., Fallick, A.E., and Ellam, R. M., 2006, Oxygen, carbon and strontium isotope records of Ediacaran carbonates in Central Iberia (Spain). *Precambrian Research*, **147**: 354–365, https://doi.org/10.1016/j.precamres.2006.01.021.

Van Iten, H., Leme, J.D.M., Marques, A.C., and Simões, M.G., 2013, Alternative interpretations of some earliest Ediacaran fossils from China. *Acta Palaeontologica Polonica*, **58**: 111–113, https://doi.org/10.4202/app.2011.0096.

Veis, A.F., Vorob'eva, N.G., and Golubkova, E.Y., 2006, The early Vendian microfossils first found in the Russian Plate: taxonomic composition and biostratigraphic significance. *Stratigraphy and Geological Correlation*, **14**: 368–385.

Venkatachala, B.S., Shukla, M., Bansal, R., and Acharyya, S.K., 1990, Upper Proterozoic microfossils from the Infra Krol sediments, Nainital synform, Kumaon Himalaya, India. *Palaeobotanist*, **38**: 29–38.

Verdel, C., Wernicke, B.P., and Bowring, S.A., 2011, The Shuram and subsequent Ediacaran carbon isotope excursions from southwest Laurentia, and implications for environmental stability during the metazoan radiation. *Geological Society of America Bulletin*, **123**: 1539–1559.

Vickers-Rich, P., Ivantsov, A.Y., Trusler, P.W., Narbonne, G.M., Hall, M., Wilson, S.A., et al., 2013, Reconstructing *Rangea*: new discoveries from the Ediacaran of southern Namibia. *Journal of Paleontology*, **87**: 1–15.

Vidal, G., 1990, Giant acanthomorph acritarchs from the upper Proterozoic in southern Norway. *Palaeontology*, **33**: 287–298.

Vishnevskaya, I.A., Letnikova, E.F., Vetrova, N.I., Kochnev, B.B., and Dril, S.I., 2017, Chemostratigraphy and detrital zircon geochronology of the Neoproterozoic Khorbusuonka Group, Olenek Uplift, Northeastern Siberian platform. *Gondwana Research*, **51**: 255–271, https://doi.org/10.1016/j.gr.2017.07.010.

Vorob'eva, N.G., and Sergeev, V.N., 2018, *Stellarossica* gen. nov. and the Infragroup Keltmiides infragroup. nov.: extremely Large Acanthomorph Acritarchs from the Vendian of Siberia and the East European Platform. *Paleontological Journal*, **52**: 563–573, https://doi.org/10.1134/S0031030118040147.

Vorob'eva, N.G., Sergeev, V.N., and Semikhatov, M.A., 2006, Unique lower Vendian Kel'tma microbiota, Timan ridge: new evidence for the paleontological essence and global significance of the Vendian System. *Doklady Earth Sciences*, **410**: 1038–1043.

Vorob'eva, N.G., Sergeev, V.N., and Chumakov, N.M., 2008, New finds of early Vendian microfossils in the Ura Formation: revision of the Patom Supergroup Age, middle Siberia. *Doklady Earth Sciences*, **419A**: 411–416.

Vorob'eva, N.G., Sergeev, V.N., and Knoll, A.H., 2009a, Neoproterozoic microfossils from the margin of the East European Platform and the search for a biostratigraphic model of lower Ediacaran rocks. *Precambrian Research*, **173**: 163–169.

Vorob'eva, N.G., Sergeev, V.N., and Knoll, A.H., 2009b, Neoproterozoic microfossils from the northeastern margin of the East European Platform. *Journal of Paleontology*, **83**: 161–196.

Waggoner, B., 2003, The Ediacaran biotas in space and time. *Integrative and Comparative Biology*, **43**: 104–113.

Walcott, C.D., 1914, Abrupt appearance of the Cambrian fauna on the North America continent. *Smithsonian Miscellaneous Collections*, **57**: 1–16.

Walde, D.H.G., do Carmo, D.A., Guimarães, E.M., Vieira, L.C., Erdtmann, B.-D., Sanchez, E.A.M., et al., 2015, New aspects of Neoproterozoic-Cambrian transition in the Corumbá region (state of Mato Grosso do Sul, Brazil). *Annales de Paléontologie*, **101**: 213–224, https://doi.org/10.1016/j.annpal.2015.07.002.

Wan, B., Xiao, S., Yuan, X., Chen, Z., Pang, K., Tang, Q., et al., 2014, *Orbisiana linearis* from the early Ediacaran Lantian Formation of South China and its taphonomic and ecological implications. *Precambrian Research*, **255**: 266–275, https://doi.org/10.1016/j.precamres.2014.09.028.

Wan, B., Yuan, X., Chen, Z., Guan, C., Pang, K., Tang, Q., et al., 2016, Systematic description of putative animal fossils from the early Ediacaran Lantian Formation of South China. *Palaeontology*, **59**: 515–532, https://doi.org/10.1111/pala.12242.

Wang, J., Jiang, G., Xiao, S., Li, Q., and Wei, Q., 2008, Carbon isotope evidence for widespread methane seeps in the ~635 Ma Doushantuo cap carbonate in South China. *Geology*, **36**: 347–350.

Wang, X.Q., Shi, X.Y., Jiang, G.Q., and Tang, D.J., 2014, Organic carbon isotope gradient and ocean stratification across the late Ediacaran-Early Cambrian Yangtze Platform. *Science China-Earth Sciences*, **57**: 919–929, https://doi.org/10.1007/s11430-013-4732-0.

Wang, W., Guan, C., Zhou, C., Peng, Y., Pratt, L.M., Chen, X., et al., 2017a, Integrated carbon, sulfur, and nitrogen isotope chemostratigraphy of the Ediacaran Lantian Formation in South China: spatial gradient, ocean redox oscillation, and fossil distribution. *Geobiology*, **15**: 552–571, https://doi.org/10.1111/gbi.12226.

Wang, Z., Wang, J., Kouketsu, Y., Bodnar, R.J., Gill, B.C., and Xiao, S., 2017b, Raman geothermometry of carbonaceous material in the basal Ediacaran Doushantuo cap dolostone: the thermal history of extremely negative $\delta^{13}C$ signatures in the aftermath of the terminal Cryogenian snowball Earth glaciation. *Precambrian Research*, **298**: 174–186, https://doi.org/10.1016/j.precamres.2017.06.013.

Wang, Z., Wang, J., Suess, E., Wang, G., Chen, C., and Xiao, S., 2017c, Silicified glendonites in the Ediacaran Doushantuo Formation (South China) and their potential paleoclimatic implications. *Geology*, **45**: 115–118, https://doi.org/10.1130/G38613.1.

Warren, L.V., Pacheco, M., Fairchild, T.R., Simoes, M.G., Riccomini, C., Boggiani, P.C., et al., 2012, The dawn of animal skeletogenesis: ultrastructural analysis of the Ediacaran metazoan Corumbella werneri. *Geology*, **40**: 691–694, https://doi.org/10.1130/g33005.1.

Warren, L.V., Quaglio, F., Simões, M.G., Gaucher, C., Riccomini, C., Poiré, D.G., et al., 2017, *Cloudina-Corumbella-Namacalathus* association from the Itapucumi Group, Paraguay: increasing ecosystem complexity and tiering at the end of the Ediacaran. *Precambrian Research*, **298**: 79–87, https://doi.org/10.1016/j.precamres.2017.05.003.

Wei, G.-Y., Planavsky, N.J., Tarhan, L.G., Chen, X., Wei, W., Li, D., et al., 2018, Marine redox fluctuation as a potential trigger for the Cambrian explosion. *Geology*, **46**: 587–590, https://doi.org/10.1130/G40150.1.

Wilby, P.R., Carney, J.N., and Howe, M.P.A., 2011, A rich Ediacaran assemblage from eastern Avalonia: evidence of early widespread diversity in the deep ocean. *Geology*, **39**: 655–658, https://doi.org/10.1130/g31890.1.

Willman, S., and Moczydłowska, M., 2008, Ediacaran acritarch biota from the Giles 1 drillhole, Officer Basin, Australia, and its potential for biostratigraphic correlation. *Precambrian Research*, **162**: 498–530.

Willman, S., and Moczydłowska, M., 2011, Acritarchs in the Ediacaran of Australia – local or global significance? Evidence from the Lake Maurice West 1 drillcore. *The Review of Palaeobotany and Palynology*, **166**: 12–28.

Willman, S., Moczydłowska, M., and Grey, K., 2006, Neoproterozoic (Ediacaran) diversification of acritarchs: a new record from the Murnaroo 1 drillcore, eastern Officer Basin, Australia. *The Review of Palaeobotany and Palynology*, **139**: 17–39.

Witkosky, R., and Wernicke, B.P., 2018, Subsidence history of the Ediacaran Johnnie Formation and related strata of southwest Laurentia: implications for the age and duration of the Shuram isotopic excursion and animal evolution. *Geosphere*, **14**: 2245–2276, https://doi.org/10.1130/GES01678.1.

Wood, R.A., Poulton, S.W., Prave, A.R., Hoffmann, K.H., Clarkson, M.O., Guilbaud, R., et al., 2015, Dynamic redox conditions control late Ediacaran metazoan ecosystems in the Nama Group, Namibia. *Precambrian Research*, **261**: 252–271, https://doi.org/10.1016/j.precamres.2015.02.004.

Wood, R., Ivantsov, A.Y., and Zhuravlev, A.Y., 2017, First macrobiota biomineralization was environmentally triggered. *Proceedings of the Royal Society B: Biological Sciences*, **284**: 20170059, https://doi.org/10.1098/rspb.2017.0059.

Xiao, S., 2004a, New multicellular algal fossils and acritarchs in Doushantuo chert nodules (Neoproterozoic, Yangtze Gorges, South China). *Journal of Paleontology*, **78**: 393–401.

Xiao, S., 2004b, Neoproterozoic glaciations and the fossil record. *In* Jenkins, G.S., McMenamin, M., Sohl, L.E., and McKay, C.P. (eds),

The Extreme Proterozoic: Geology, Geochemistry, and Climate. American Geophysical Union (AGU), Washington, DC, 199–214.

Xiao, S., 2008, Geobiological events in the Ediacaran Period. *In* Kelly, P.H., and Bambach, R.K. (eds), *From Evolution to Geobiology: Research Questions Driving Paleontology at the Start of a New Century*. The Paleontological Society, New Haven, CT, 85–104.

Xiao, S., and Laflamme, M., 2009, On the eve of animal radiation: phylogeny, ecology and evolution of the Ediacara biota. *Trends in Ecology & Evolution*, **24**: 31–40, https://doi.org/10.1016/j.tree.2008.07.015.

Xiao, S., and Sharma, M., 2014, International Field Workshop on the Marwar Supergroup, Rajasthan, India. *Episodes*, **37**: 74–75.

Xiao, S., Yuan, X., Steiner, M., and Knoll, A.H., 2002, Macroscopic carbonaceous compressions in a terminal Proterozoic shale: a systematic reassessment of the Miaohe biota, South China. *Journal of Paleontology*, **76**: 347–376.

Xiao, S., Bao, H., Wang, H., Kaufman, A.J., Zhou, C., Li, G., et al., 2004, The Neoproterozoic Quruqtagh Group in eastern Chinese Tianshan: evidence for a post-Marinoan glaciation. *Precambrian Research*, **130**: 1–26.

Xiao, S., Shen, B., Zhou, C., Xie, G., and Yuan, X., 2005, A uniquely preserved Ediacaran fossil with direct evidence for a quilted bodyplan. *Proceedings of the National Academy of Sciences of the United States of America*, **102**: 10227–10232.

Xiao, S., Grazhdankin, D.V., Sovetov, J.K., Kaufman, A.J., and Rich, P., 2011, International Conference on Neoproterozoic Sedimentary Basins, Neoproterozoic Subcommission Workshop on Ediacaran Paleobiology, and IGCP Field Excursion to the East Sayan Mountain Range. *Episodes*, **34**: 273–275.

Xiao, S., McFadden, K.A., Peek, S., Kaufman, A.J., Zhou, C., Jiang, G., et al., 2012, Integrated chemostratigraphy of the Doushantuo Formation at the northern Xiaofenghe section (Yangtze Gorges, South China) and its implication for Ediacaran stratigraphic correlation and ocean redox models. *Precambrian Research*, **192-95**: 125–141, https://doi.org/10.1016/j.precamres.2011.10.021.

Xiao, S., Droser, M., Gehling, J.G., Hughes, I.V., Wan, B., Chen, Z., et al., 2013, Affirming life aquatic for the Ediacara biota in China and Australia. *Geology*, **41**: 1095–1098, https://doi.org/10.1130/G34691.1.

Xiao, S., Zhou, C., and Zhu, M., 2014a, International Symposium and Field Workshop on Ediacaran and Cryogenian Stratigraphy. *Episodes*, **37**: 218–221.

Xiao, S., Zhou, C., Liu, P., Wang, D., and Yuan, X., 2014b, Phosphatized acanthomorphic acritarchs and related microfossils from the Ediacaran Doushantuo Formation at Weng'an (South China) and their implications for biostratigraphic correlation. *Journal of Paleontology*, **88**: 1–67, https://doi.org/10.1666/12-157R.

Xiao, S., Muscente, A.D., Chen, L., Zhou, C., Schiffbauer, J.D., Wood, A.D., et al., 2014c, The Weng'an biota and the Ediacaran radiation of multicellular eukaryotes. *National Science Review*, **1**: 498–520, https://doi.org/10.1093/nsr/nwu061.

Xiao, S., Narbonne, G.M., Zhou, C., Laflamme, M., Grazhdankin, D.V., Moczydłowska-Vidal, M., et al., 2016, Toward an Ediacaran Time Scale: problems, protocols, and prospects. *Episodes*, **39**: 540–555, https://doi.org/10.18814/epiiugs/2016/v39i4/103886.

Xiao, S., Bykova, N., Kovalick, A., and Gill, B.C., 2017a, Stable carbon isotopes of sedimentary kerogens and carbonaceous macrofossils from the Ediacaran Miaohe Member in South China: implications for stratigraphic correlation and sources of sedimentary organic carbon. *Precambrian Research*, **302**: 171–179, https://doi.org/10.1016/j.precamres.2017.10.006.

Xiao, S., Vickers-Rich, P., Narbonne, G.M., Laflamme, M., Darroch, S., Kaufman, A.J., et al., 2017b, Field Workshop on the Ediacaran Nama Group of southern Namibia. *Episodes*, **40**: 259–261.

Xiao, S., do Carmo, D., Walde, D., Silva, A.M., Denezine, M., and Silva, A., 2018, Field workshop on the Ediacaran Corumbá Group of southwestern Brazil. *Episodes*, **41**: 207–211.

Yang, B., Steiner, M., Zhu, M., Li, G., Liu, J., and Liu, P., 2016, Transitional Ediacaran-Cambrian small skeletal fossil assemblages from South China and Kazakhstan: implications for chronostratigraphy and metazoan evolution. *Precambrian Research*, **285**: 202–215, https://doi.org/10.1016/j.precamres.2016.09.016.

Yang, C., Zhu, M., Condon, D.J., and Li, X.-H., 2017a, Geochronological constraints on stratigraphic correlation and oceanic oxygenation in Ediacaran-Cambrian transition in South China. *Journal of Asian Earth Sciences*, **140**: 75–81, https://doi.org/10.1016/j.jseaes.2017.03.017.

Yang, C., Li, X.-H., Zhu, M., and Condon, D.J., 2017b, SIMS U-Pb zircon geochronological constraints on upper Ediacaran stratigraphic correlations, South China. *Geological Magazine*, **154**: 1202–1216, https://doi.org/10.1017/S0016756816001102.

Yao, J., Xiao, S., Yin, L., Li, G., and Yuan, X., 2005, Basal Cambrian microfossils from the Yurtus and Xishanblaq formations (Tarim, north-west China): systematic revision and biostratigraphic correlation of *Micrhystridium*-like acritarchs from China. *Palaeontology*, **48**: 687–708, https://doi.org/10.1111/j.1475-4983.2005.00484.x.

Ye, Q., Tong, J., An, Z., Hu, J., Tian, L., Guan, K., et al., 2017, A systematic description of new macrofossil material from the upper Ediacaran Miaohe Member in South China. *Journal of Systematic Palaeontology*, **17**: 183–238, https://doi.org/10.1080/14772019.14772017.11404499.

Yin, L., and Li, Z., 1978, Precambrian microfloras of southwest China with reference to their stratigraphic significance. *Memoirs of Nanjing Institute of Geology and Palaeontology, Academia Sinica*, **10**: 41–108.

Yin, L., Zhu, M., Knoll, A.H., Yuan, X., Zhang, J., and Hu, J., 2007, Doushantuo embryos preserved inside diapause egg cysts. *Nature*, **446**: 661–663.

Yin, C., Liu, P., Chen, S., Tang, F., Gao, L., and Wang, Z., 2009, Acritarch biostratigraphic succession of the Ediacaran Doushantuo Formation in the Yangtze Gorges. *Acta Palaeontologica Sinica*, **48**: 146–154.

Yoshioka, H., Asahara, Y., Tojo, B., and Kawakami, S., 2003, Systematic variations in C, O, and Sr isotopes and elemental concentrations in Neoproterozoic carbonates in Namibia: implications for glacial to interglacial transition. *Precambrian Research*, **124**: 69–85.

Yuan, X., and Hofmann, H.J., 1998, New microfossils from the Neoproterozoic (Sinian) Doushantuo Formation, Weng'an, Guizhou Province, southwestern China. *Alcheringa*, **22**: 189–222.

Yuan, X., Chen, Z., Xiao, S., Zhou, C., and Hua, H., 2011, An early Ediacaran assemblage of macroscopic and morphologically differentiated eukaryotes. *Nature*, **470**: 390–393, https://doi.org/10.1038/nature09810.

Zang, W., and Walter, M.R., 1992, Late Proterozoic and Cambrian microfossils and biostratigraphy, Amadeus Basin, central Australia. *Memoirs of the Association of Australasian Palaeontologists*, **12**: 1–132.

Zhang, Y., Yin, L., Xiao, S., and Knoll, A.H., 1998, Permineralized fossils from the terminal Proterozoic Doushantuo Formation, South China. *Journal of Paleontology*, **72** (Suppl. 4), 1–52.

Zhang, F., Xiao, S., Kendall, B., Romaniello, S.J., Cui, H., Meyer, M., et al., 2018, Extensive marine anoxia during the terminal Ediacaran Period. *Science Advances*, **4**: eaan8983, https://doi.org/10.1126/sciadv.aan8983.

Zhang, F., Xiao, S., Romaniello, S.J., Hardisty, D., Li, C., Melezhik, V., et al., 2019, Global marine redox changes drove the rise and fall of early animals. *Geobiology*, **17**: 594–610, https://doi.org/10.1111/gbi.12359.

Zhao, Z., Xing, Y., Ding, Q., Liu, G., Zhao, Y., Zhang, S., et al., 1988, *The Sinian System of Hubei*. 205 pp. China University of Geosciences Press.

Zhao, Y.-Y., Zhao, M.-Y., and Li, S.-Z., 2018, Evidences of hydrothermal fluids recorded in microfacies of the Ediacaran cap dolostone: geochemical implications in South China. *Precambrian Research*, **306**: 1–21, https://doi.org/10.1016/j.precamres.2017.12.028.

Zhou, C., and Xiao, S., 2007, Ediacaran $\delta^{13}C$ chemostratigraphy of South China. *Chemical Geology*, **237**: 89–108.

Zhou, C., Brasier, M.D., and Xue, Y., 2001, Three-dimensional phosphatic preservation of giant acritarchs from the terminal Proterozoic Doushantuo Formation in Guizhou and Hubei provinces, South China. *Palaeontology*, **44**: 1157–1178.

Zhou, C., Xie, G., McFadden, K., Xiao, S., and Yuan, X., 2007, The diversification and extinction of Doushantuo-Pertatataka acritarchs in South China: causes and biostratigraphic significance. *The Journal of Geology*, **42**: 229–262.

Zhou, C., Xiao, S., Wang, W., Guan, C., Ouyang, Q., and Chen, Z., 2017a, The stratigraphic complexity of the middle Ediacaran carbon isotopic record in the Yangtze Gorges area, South China, and its implications for the age and chemostratigraphic significance of the Shuram excursion. *Precambrian Research*, **288**: 23–38, https://doi.org/10.1016/j.precamres.2016.11.007.

Zhou, C., Li, X.-H., Xiao, S., Lan, Z., Ouyang, Q., Guan, C., et al., 2017b, A new SIMS zircon U-Pb date from the Ediacaran Doushantuo Formation: age constraint on the Weng'an biota. *Geological Magazine*, **154**: 1193–1201, https://doi.org/10.1017/S0016756816001175.

Zhou, M., Luo, T., Huff, W.D., Yang, Z., Zhou, G., Gan, T., et al., 2018, Timing the termination of the Doushantuo negative carbon isotope excursion: evidence from U-Pb ages from the Dengying and Liuchapo formations, South China. *Science Bulletin*, **63**: 1431–1438, https://doi.org/10.1016/j.scib.2018.10.002.

Zhou, C., Huyskens, M.H., Lang, X., Xiao, S., and Yin, Q.-Z., 2019, Calibrating the termination of Cryogenian global glaciations. *Geology*, **47**: 251–254, https://doi.org/10.1130/G45719.1.

Zhu, M.Y., Babcock, L.E., and Peng, S.C., 2006, Advances in Cambrian stratigraphy and paleontology: integrating correlation techniques, paleobiology, taphonomy and paleoenvironmental reconstruction. *Palaeoworld*, **15**: 217–222.

Zhu, M., Gehling, J.G., Xiao, S., Zhao, Y.-L., and Droser, M., 2008, Eight-armed Ediacara fossil preserved in contrasting taphonomic windows from China and Australia. *Geology*, **36**: 867–870, https://doi.org/10.1130/G25203A.1.

Zhu, M., Lu, M., Zhang, J., Zhao, F., Li, G., Yang, A., et al., 2013, Carbon isotope chemostratigraphy and sedimentary facies evolution of the Ediacaran Doushantuo Formation in western Hubei, South China. *Precambrian Research*, **225**: 7–28, https://doi.org/10.1016/j.precamres.2011.07.019.

Zhu, M., Zhuravlev, A.Y., Wood, R.A., Zhao, F., and Sukhov, S.S., 2017, A deep root for the Cambrian Explosion: implications of new bio- and chemostratigraphy from the Siberian Platform. *Geology*, **45**: 459–462, https://doi.org/10.1130/G38865.1.

Zhuravlev, A.Y., Gámez Vintaned, J.A., and Ivantsov, A.Y., 2009, First finds of problematic Ediacaran fossil *Gaojiashania* in Siberia and its origin. *Geological Magazine*, **146**: 775–780.

Zhuravlev, A.Y., Liñán, E., Vintaned, J.A.G., Debrenne, F., and Fedorov, A.B., 2012, New finds of skeletal fossils in the terminal Neoproterozoic of the Siberian Platform and Spain. *Acta Palaeontologica Polonica*, **57**: 205–224, https://doi.org/10.4202/app.2010.0074.

Zhuravlev, A.Y., Wood, R.A., and Penny, A.M., 2015, Ediacaran skeletal metazoan interpreted as a lophophorate. *Proceedings of the Royal Society B: Biological Sciences*, **282**: 20151860.